THE OXFORD ENCYCLOPEDIA OF
THE HISTORY OF AMERICAN SCIENCE, MEDICINE, AND TECHNOLOGY

THE OXFORD ENCYCLOPEDIA OF
THE HISTORY OF AMERICAN SCIENCE, MEDICINE, AND TECHNOLOGY

Hugh Richard Slotten

EDITOR IN CHIEF

VOLUME 2

MACHINERY AND MANUFACTURING—ZWORYKIN, VLADIMIR KOSMA

OXFORD
UNIVERSITY PRESS

OXFORD
UNIVERSITY PRESS

Oxford University Press is a department of the
University of Oxford. It furthers the University's objective
of excellence in research, scholarship, and education
by publishing worldwide.

Oxford   New York

Auckland   Cape Town   Dar es Salaam   Hong Kong   Karachi
Kuala Lumpur   Madrid   Melbourne   Mexico City   Nairobi
New Delhi   Shanghai   Taipei   Toronto

With offices in

Argentina   Austria   Brazil   Chile   Czech Republic   France   Greece
Guatemala   Hungary   Italy   Japan   Poland   Portugal   Singapore
South Korea   Switzerland   Thailand   Turkey   Ukraine   Vietnam

Oxford is a registered trade mark of Oxford University Press
in the UK and certain other countries.

Published in the United States of America by
Oxford University Press
198 Madison Avenue, New York, NY 10016
www.oup.com

The Library of Congress Cataloging-in-Publication Data
The Oxford encyclopedia of the history of American science,
medicine, and technology/Hugh Richard Slotten, editor in chief.
volumes   cm
ISBN 978-0-19-976666-6 (set: alk. paper)—
ISBN 978-0-19-020332-0 (vol. 1: alk. paper)—
ISBN 978-0-19-020333-7 (vol. 2: alk. paper)
1. Science—United States—History—Encyclopedias.   2. Medicine—United States—
History—Encyclopedias.   3. Technology—United States—History—Encyclopedias.
I. Slotten, Hugh Richard.   II. Title: Encyclopedia of the
history of American science, medicine, and technology.
Q127.U6O95   2014
509.7303—dc23   2014009198

9 8 7 6 5 4 3 2 1
Printed in the United States of America
on acid-free paper

COMMON ABBREVIATIONS USED IN THIS WORK

AD *anno Domini,* in the year of the Lord

AH *anno Hegirae,* in the year of the Hajj

b. born

BCE before the common era (= BC)

ca. *circa,* about, approximately

CE common era (= AD)

cf. *confer,* compare

d. died

diss. dissertation

ed. editor (pl., eds.), edition

f. and following (pl., ff.)

fl. *floruit,* flourished

l. line (pl., ll.)

n. note

n.d. no date

no. number

n.p. no place

n.s. new series

p. page (pl., pp.)

pt. part

rev. revised

ser. series

supp. supplement

USSR Union of Soviet Socialist Republics

Vol. Volume (pl., Vols.)

THE OXFORD ENCYCLOPEDIA OF
THE HISTORY OF AMERICAN SCIENCE, MEDICINE, AND TECHNOLOGY

M

MACHINERY AND MANUFACTURING

In one of the most fundamental feedbacks in the modern world, new technological knowledge had powerful economic outcomes that in turn fostered technological change. Whole economies changed in the process. Between 1790 and 1929, the largely agrarian economy of the United States evolved to become the world's leading industrial power. Manufacturing led the way, as the handicrafts employing a few percent of the labor force in 1790 gave way to a factory-dominated sector employing a quarter of the labor force and affecting the whole economy. Mechanization was central to the growth of manufacturing output and productivity. New machines emerged when new technological knowledge, generated from practitioners, from abroad, and from science, was embodied in equipment. Firms and occupations that made and used new machines formed networks that spread knowledge among practitioners through commodity sale, worker mobility, knowledge sharing, trade associations, and publications. Practitioners often improved the techniques and developed others. Mechanization came to form a self-reinforcing process that reshaped the U.S. economy.

Beginnings. By 1835 the United States developed thriving mechanized industries to spin and weave, print newspapers and books, power factories and boats, work wood, and make clocks and firearms. Mechanization began in an array of industry-specific processes that transferred European techniques and innovated domestically. Although distinct, each process spread knowledge in ways that led to ongoing innovation.

Cotton textiles. Just as in England, the most important factory development occurred in textiles. Although the British Industrial Revolution was well known, practical machines only came with the immigration of the superintendent of a British cotton-spinning factory, Samuel Slater.

Slater achieved success in Pawtucket, Rhode Island, in the early 1890s when he, as superintendent of the partnership Almy and Brown, employed local metal- and woodworkers to reproduce water-powered Arkwright spinning machines and carding engines he had used in England. Machine-makers built and maintained the machines using hand tools and primitive lathes. The technology diffused slowly, led initially by those who practiced it: Slater, Almy, Brown, and their machinists. As learning widened after 1810, the new techniques spread more rapidly, educating more machinists in the process. U.S. textile machinists migrated to build machines in textile factories and to form new firms. David Wilkinson, who had built machinery for Slater, led in forming the textile machinery industry around 1800; to turn machine parts, he patented a metalworking lathe in 1798 (Jeremy, 1981; Thomson, 2009).

The communications network connecting textile and textile machinery practitioners was central to developing and diffusing new techniques. Immigration brought the spinning mule and the power loom. Providence firms introduced and perfected a Scottish loom for weaving high-quality cloth. Wilkinson improved its design and diffused it through sale, and his workers and Rhode Island associates formed other machinery firms. After visiting British factories, the Boston merchant Francis Lowell formed a corporation to operate an integrated spinning and weaving factory and employed the mechanic Paul Moody to design a simple loom for coarse goods. Lowell's success led to the formation of the many Lowell, Massachusetts, textile firms and the leading machinery and waterpower firm, Locks and Canals. Important new techniques arose principally from skilled, industry practitioners. The card-makers Amos Whittemore and Pliny Earle developed methods to straighten cotton before spinning by, respectively, automating the production of hand cards and designing a machine to make card-clothing for carding machines. The textile machinist John Thorp invented a ring-spinning technique that later would gain worldwide usage. Among patentees with known occupations, machinists received 77 percent of textile patents; textile network members—mostly textile machinists but also mill owners and weavers—received 71 percent. Because networks expanded with machine usage, so did invention; annual patents grew from under one through 1805 to seventeen from 1826 through 1835 (Thomson, 2009, pp. 20–33).

Printing. The process of machine introduction, diffusion, learning by machinists and other practitioners, and ongoing innovation would be replicated in many industries. Printing presses spread when British immigrants brought wooden presses and when Americans copied early German–British cylinder presses. Urban printers improved the images on wooden presses by replacing screws with toggle joints, developed iron presses that could sustain the force of toggle joints, and invented more automated bed and platen presses.

Steam power. Powering mills and boats by steam was another amalgam of foreign and U.S. innovation, with domestic innovation playing a bigger role. Newcomen and Watt engines gained some use in America, but Americans undertook two key improvements. Oliver Evans, the greatest inventor of the early Republic who already had developed an automated flour mill, rejected Watt's low-pressure design and patented a high-pressure engine in 1804, apparently independently of Richard Trevithick's Cornish engine. Practical by about 1812, Evans's engine could generate the same power with smaller cylinders and placed fewer demands on America's modest metalworking capabilities. Robert Fulton, an American painter who immigrated to Britain and became a canal engineer, returned to the United States to develop and patent the first practical steamboat around 1810. Both Evans and Fulton learned through steam engineering networks, and their success greatly deepened these networks. Engines spread into many industries and regions; by 1838 firms used about 2,000 stationary engines and 850 boat engines, 98 percent of which were produced inside the country. Growing usage resulted in part from ongoing invention. Annual patents grew from under one before 1806 to ten in the 1826–1835 decade, led by engine makers. Horizontal engines replaced vertical ones on boats and in factories.

A few engines introduced cut-offs in which steam expansion completed the piston stroke. The horizontal, high-pressure engine became the dominant design for mills and Western steamboats (Hunter, 1949, 1985; Ferguson, 1980; Hindle, 1981; Pursell, 1969; Thomson, 2009, pp. 33–47).

Firearms. Other innovations were more distinctly American. Firearms constitute a classic case of government-led mechanization. Inspired by the French, the federal government sought to arm troops with firearms made with interchangeable parts and pursued this end in government armories at Springfield, Massachusetts, and Harpers Ferry, Virginia, and in contracts with private armorers concentrated in the Connecticut River valley. The government set standards, advanced capital, and required knowledge sharing among public and private armories. With long-term government orders at fixed prices, armories endeavored to standardize parts and reduce costs using jigs and fixtures and developing new equipment. The Springfield Armory adapted Wilkinson's lathe to turn gun barrels. Two basic innovations transformed production. In 1819, Thomas Blanchard patented a pattern lathe that turned wooden gunstocks by tracing the form of a master gunstock, which he used as a Springfield contractor. Around 1816 Simeon North invented the milling machine, a machine tool with a series of cutting edges on a rotating tool. By 1830, federal and private armories used systems of machines, gauges, fixtures, and skilled labor to make firearms with modest interchangeability obtained with hand filing (Smith, 1977; Cooper, 1991).

Clocks. Not all interchangeable production involved the government. Private clockmakers innovated to mass produce interchangeable-parts clocks. Eli Terry designed a simple, wooden shelf clock with movements that could be mass produced. He introduced jigs and gauges, adapted circular saws, and used lathes to cut stacks of gears. The roughly uniform parts could be assembled and adjusted to make cheap, functional clocks that spread widely. Ready communication in the Plymouth–Bristol area of Connecticut diffused the innovation (Hoke, 1990).

Woodworking. Gunstocks and clocks were parts of the far wider innovation in woodworking. In an age where wood was the chief building material, the dominant fuel, and essential for road and ship transportation, woodworking innovations were common and widely dispersed. Circular saws, invented largely in rural areas from the 1810s, began to enter sawmills by the 1830s, although reciprocating saws predominated. Urban woodworkers and machinists developed planing machines after 1825, led by William Woodworth's machine that also cut tongues and grooves. Wood-turning lathes became faster and more specialized. Mortising and tenoning invention accelerated after 1825, and two other wood-joining methods—nailing and screwing—spread with the invention of machines to make nails from the 1820s and wood screws from 1830.

These mechanization paths were largely independent, conducted by different people in distinct networks and different locations. Other paths had the same autonomy, including the cotton gin patented by Eli Whitney in 1794 and papermaking, which began to adopt the British–French Fourdrinier machine in the 1820s. Along each path, usage grew over time, networks of practitioners and capital-goods firms expanded, and patenting grew. But innovation faced limits. The near absence of machinists in the United States slowed initial mechanization; each path had to build its own mechanical skills. Limited metalworking capabilities also slowed innovation; with only primitive lathes and without planers, producing complex machinery such as steam engines with cut-offs and cylinder presses was virtually impossible.

Interlinked Mechanization. By the second third of the nineteenth century, common production methods and design principles interlinked early industrializing sectors. Mechanization benefited from technological convergence, to use Nathan Rosenberg's term, so that innovations in some industries spilled over to others (Rosenberg, 1976, pp. 9–31). Such convergence was not new; craft blacksmiths and woodworkers held knowledge pertinent to many industries. But machines—as systems of interrelated parts that effected a desired transformation of a material—

had distinct designs and production requirements, which earlier crafts could not easily meet.

Production Convergence. Machine-tool innovation typically affected many metal products. The most important machine tools for general usage were engine lathes, which utilized slide rests and change gears to cut rotating metal parts, and metal-planing machines, which chipped flat surfaces. Wilkinson's lathe gained some use in New England, but wider usage came when the British machinist Henry Maudslay's lathe spread to the United States around 1825. Many British machinists developed the metal planer; Joseph Whitworth's planer spread to the United States around 1838. The milling machine and other American innovations spread among industries. Annual machine-tool patents increased from 0.7 before 1846 to 8.0 in the following 20 years. The new machine tools greatly improved precision in a wide range of industries, making it possible for the first time to produce complex engines, printing presses, and, in a positive feedback, accurate machine tools. Convergent production innovations extended to methods of casting and forging metal and working wood; Blanchard's pattern lathe patent, for example, was widely assigned to turn gunstocks, shoe lasts, hat blocks, and oars (Roe, 1977; Cooper, 1991; Thomson, 2009, pp. 144–152).

Design Convergence. Machines also converged in design. Machines all had a power source (including the human hand), transmission mechanisms, and working tools that operated on the material. Water- and steam-power innovations applied quite generally, although in 1835 neither supplied the regularity of motion needed in certain operations. Transmitting power involved shafting, gearing, belting, clutches, and such generic principles as changing motion from reciprocating to rotary. The working tool varied greatly by task and material, but often shared principles with tools used in other industries. For example, Amos Whittemore arrayed a series of cams around a rotating shaft to complete a series of operations in making card clothing; this principle came to be used across the machinery sector. Aza Arnold developed a differential gear to vary the rotating speed of two textile machine parts; the same principle later enabled automobile wheels to rotate at different speeds when rounding curves. Many industries benefited from narrower convergences, such as when the thread-manipulating mechanisms of a loom were adapted to sewing.

The Machinery Sector. The machinery sector was organized in a way that realized these convergences. In a period when most machines were made individually or in small batches, machinists had knowledge of machine design. They visualized the relation of parts, depicted the parts geometrically using increasingly sophisticated drafting methods, forged or machined parts, and assembled, tested, and serviced the machines. Mechanical engineers, who originated in machine shops, had similar knowledge. Because their skills applied to machinery of every kind, machinists moved among all mechanized industries, spreading knowledge in the process. Midcentury machinery firms only exceptionally specialized on a single industry and often diversified into new machines. Machine-tool firms, initiated from 1850, sold to metalworking firms across the economy. As U.S. machinists grew from 45,000 in 1850 to 101,000 in 1880 and 479,000 in 1910, and as skilled machine-using workers also multiplied, so did the capabilities to design and produce machines (Meyer, 2006; Calvert, 1967; Thomson, 2010, pp. 7–8).

Inventions and Patents. Growing innovation was one outcome. Patents provide an indicator, although clearly imperfect. Annual patents in the decade surrounding 1820 averaged 200; this average grew to 960 in the decade around 1850, 16,200 around 1880, and 35,700 around 1910. Machinists often invented; under 1 percent of the labor force in 1860, they received 29 percent of patents (for inventors with known occupations) from 1836 through 1865. Invention was common for machinery firms; 44 percent of the principals of such firms received patents from 1836 through 1865, and their 4.5 average patents far exceeded the 1.7 of all patentees. Machinists and other occupations with cross-industry knowledge—engineers, patent agents, and related groups—received 40 percent of patents. These occupations were particularly adept at inventing in multiple industries, benefitting from convergent machine designs. Other manufacturing occupations received 41 percent. The increase of machinists and other manufacturing occupations expanded the knowledge base and hence the supply of inventions. Demand-side factors also mattered. The profitability of patenting grew as transportation improvements and market growth increased the usage of inventions, inducing greater inventive effort. The U.S. patent system contributed because patents were relatively inexpensive and, when federal agents examined patents for originality after 1836, relatively secure (Schmookler, 1996; Sokoloff, 1988; Khan, 2005; Thomson, 2009, pp. 109 and 141).

Inventions, of course, were only exceptionally great successes. But many incremental inventions gained usage. About one-fifth of 1836–1865 inventors were principals in firms that could use their own patents. Three-eighths of inventors assigned patents to others who expected to gain returns from them. Taken together, almost half of all inventors were positioned to gain usage, and the share rose to three-quarters for machinists. The pattern continued long after the Civil War; at the end of the 1920s, over half of the patents were assigned when issued, seven-eighths to firms. Many inventors gained usage by starting new firms. Machinery firms expanded from about 1,100 in 1850 to 5,000 in 1880 and 13,300 in 1910; new firms were vital to industry expansion. Because new firms often had patents—about half of the machinery firms did so between 1850 and 1860—invention was a means to become a proprietor. Successful new firms, in turn, educated future inventors (Thomson, 2009, pp. 119–121; Lamoreaux and Sokoloff, 1999; Lamoreaux et al., 2011; Thomson, 2010, p. 8).

Evolution of Industrial Revolution Sectors. Industries that began mechanizing by 1835 remained significant a century later; textiles, engines, printing, woodworking, clocks, and firearms still employed one-quarter of manufacturing workers in 1929. Each also continued to innovate.

Cotton textiles. Textile mechanization deepened after 1835. Immigrants, America's highly mobile skilled workers, and increasingly textile machinery firms and consulting engineers spread methods widely. The most important technique transferred from Britain was Richard Roberts' self-acting mule, which automated operations and reduced the need for skilled mule spinners. American machinery firms patented the machine in Roberts' name and licensed and manufactured it. New England firms adopted French water turbines to power mills; careful studies at Lowell increased their efficiency. Locks and Canals adopted British metal-planing machines, which enabled it to meet the precision requirements of faster machines.

U.S. inventors improved British methods and developed others. Network inventors received three-quarters of the textile patents from 1836 through 1865, four-fifths of which were issued to textile machinists. William Mason developed a more automated self-acting mule and set up a firm to sell it in Taunton, Massachusetts. Trained at Taunton, Charles Danforth invented the cap-spinner to overcome speed limits of the spindle flyer; he formed a major Paterson, New Jersey, firm to manufacture it. Thorp's ring spinner dispensed with the flyer; as improved and produced by Mason, the Lowell Machine Shop, and others, it spun coarse fabrics before 1860 and, led by George Draper, finer fabrics later in the century. Other Massachusetts workers addressed weaving. By 1860, William and George Crompton developed fancy looms, and Erastus Bigelow invented carpet-weaving looms. Ira and George Draper patented loom temples, cloth-holding devices that enabled an operative to run two looms. In the most significant postbellum invention, James Northrop invented and assigned to George Draper an automatic loom, which replaced the weft automatically without stopping the machine. This loom dominated American weaving by the 1920s (Gibb, 1950; Lozier, 1986; Mass, 1989).

Printing. Printing was revolutionized after 1835. Printers, press makers, and engravers received 72 percent of printing patents through 1865. Isaac and Seth Adams invented a steam-driven bed and platen press, which came to dominate the book trade. Richard Hoe's self-inking cylinder press, which used a cylinder to print on a flat bed, transformed newspaper production. Faster yet was Hoe's rotary press, in which a type-carrying cylinder made impressions on a series of rotating cylinders. Hoe became the dominant U.S. press maker. Others developed presses to print both sides of the page simultaneously. To make these fast, complex presses, press firms sought and by 1850 acquired precise machine tools. Lithography and, from the 1880s, half-tone photography conveyed pictures. Typesetting remained a slow hand operation until the instrument maker and inventor Ottmar Mergenthaler developed the linotype machine, which cast whole lines of type at one time.

Steam Power. The great expansion of the steam engine occurred after 1835; by 1870 the engine supplied over half of the horsepower used in manufacturing, and steamboat horsepower multiplied 10-fold. The steam engine has been called a general-purpose technology because it was used in many industries for purposes including power, pumping, and transportation and because improvements of the engine and of methods in the industries using it were mutually supporting. As such, its development had effects across the economy. As engines spread, patents for engines and steamboats rose from 9.4 annually from 1826 through 1845 to 44.1 annually from 1856 through 1865. Machinists, engineers, and inventive occupations dominated invention. Early engines were limited in fuel efficiency, the regularity of motion they provided, and their sluggish response to changes in load. George Corliss undertook the most significant innovation. He learned in a Providence engine firm that bought planers from Locks and Canals, sold them to Hoe, and trained a leading Philadelphia machine-tool maker. The Corliss engine employed a complex valve gear that quickly and precisely cut off the flow of steam into the cylinder, which saved fuel and supplied regular motion. To make sufficiently precise engines, Corliss employed a battery of machine tools, including a gear cutter he patented in 1849, the same year as his basic engine patent.

By 1900 Corliss-type engines generated three-quarters of the horsepower of large and medium stationary engines in the country (Hunter, 1949, 1985; Thomson, 2009, pp. 67, 79–87).

Steam boilers evolved partly to overcome the problem of explosions. More fuel-efficient fire-tube boilers replaced cylindrical boilers by the 1880s. The water-tube boiler, most prominently made by Babcock and Wilcox, offered greater safety, efficiency, and flexibility; by 1900 it was common in larger plants, often alongside steam turbines. By the 1880s, steel replaced wrought iron in boiler plates, and forging and drilling machines replaced hand work.

Steam applications multiplied. Steamboats grew larger, but retained their basic form. After 1870, Britain led in developing oceangoing iron steamships with screw propellers driven by compound engines. Locomotives spread steam transportation to land. Henry Worthington invented a direct-acting steam pump, in which the steam cylinder directly drove liquid-moving mechanisms, to feed water into boilers; by the 1880s it evolved to became the leading pump in urban waterworks, factories, drainage, and oil pipelines. For larger waterworks, Edwin Reynolds, once Corliss's superintendent who moved to the E. P. Allis Company (later Allis–Chalmers) in Milwaukee, designed highly efficient triple-expansion pumping engines. The steam hammer and steam pile-driver extended direct-acting machines to other fields.

Firearms. The path toward interchangeable-parts firearms in the Connecticut River valley deepened even as institutions, agents, and markets changed. The government contract system declined after 1840. New private firms such as Colt, Smith and Wesson, and Remington sold patented products to mostly civilian markets except in wartime. Yet interchangeability advanced. The Springfield Armory improved gauging methods, gunstocking lathes, milling machines, and drop forging; it approached machine-based interchangeability by 1860. Private firms had wide effects. From 1844 Robbins and Lawrence met civilian and government contracts by learning from Springfield Armory and by significant machine-tool innovation, including the development of turret lathes, in which tools held in a rotating turret made several successive cuts. Its interchangeable-parts firearms, demonstrated in 1851 at London's Crystal Palace Exhibition, brought a British Parliamentary Commission to the United States, which awarded the company extensive contracts. After Robbins and Lawrence failed, its workers moved to several other firearms firms. Samuel Colt studied methods at Springfield and private armories, negotiated an 1847 contract for his patented pistols, had pistols made at another contractor's armory, and kept patterns and machinery after the contract had been completed. Colt used the machines, patterns, and knowledge gained from the contract and the services of the drop-forging innovator Elisha Root as superintendent and two contractors trained at Robbins and Lawrence to open his leading Hartford armory in 1854. Capabilities so gained proved decisive in the Civil War, when the output of the Springfield Armory and private armories in the North dwarfed Southern output. Between the Civil War and World War I, private firms led in developing the breechloader, repeating rifle, machine gun, and metallic cartridges (Hounshell, 1984; Thomson, 2009).

Clocks and watches. Timekeeping evolved as mass-produced brass clocks displaced wooden clocks, led by three workers trained in Eli Terry's shop. Chauncey Jerome first succeeded in the early 1840s by applying gauging methods used in wooden clock manufacture to rolled brass, a recently imported British method used by Waterbury brass makers. Jerome failed in 1855, but other Waterbury clockmakers took up where he left off. In a distinct path, the Waltham Watch Company (also called the American Watch Company and American Waltham Watch Company) mass produced watches by 1860. Aaron Dennison, a watch repairer who studied interchangeable-parts methods at the Springfield Armory, was the key innovator. Two Armory workers brought basic insights into gauging, standardization, and machining, but the smaller size of watch parts required Dennison to design special metalworking machines. True interchangeability remained elusive, and highly skilled workers persisted through-

out the century. Emulators such as the Elgin National Watch Company succeeded only by hiring away Waltham workers (Moore, 1945).

Woodworking. The promise of woodworking mechanization in 1835 was realized in the following decades. Invention grew greatly; annual patents for lathes, planers, and mortising and tenoning machines grew from 0.7 from 1806 through 1825 to 16.3 from 1846 through 1865. By 1865, circular saws were common in sawmills, partly because metalworking improvements reduced blade wobbling at high speeds. Flooring shops widely adopted planers. Faster wood lathes and new special-purpose wood-cutting machines made dozens of products. That machinists increasingly produced, designed, and sold woodworking machines was one source of success. They also invented, receiving over half of the woodworking patents from 1836 through 1865, enabling woodworking to benefit from design improvements elsewhere (Thomson, 2009, pp. 69, 92–94).

Industries that began to mechanize before 1835 continued to do so along similar paths, structured by the same networks, commonly in the same locations. Invention grew in part because machine practitioners multiplied. But paths did change. Each industry depended more on purchased machinery. U.S. industries that had relied heavily on technology imports, including textiles and printing, generated more of their own methods and spread some abroad. As mechanics' associations and technical publications expanded after 1825, off-the-job learning shaped innovation, although it never replaced learning on the job. New European and domestic machine tools made a growing variety of complex machines. Inventors used design principles learned in some industries to transform others and to form entirely new industries.

New Machines and New Industries. Before 1860 the railroad, sewing machine, and reaper revolutionized transportation, garment making, and harvesting. Later mechanization reshaped shoemaking, office work, metallurgy, mining, road transportation, lighting, and power. Each of these changes generated new machine-making or machine-using industries; the new industries employed one-fifth of manufacturing workers in 1929. Each mechanization path built on knowledge and networks that came before it; some also relied on knowledge originating outside the economy.

Railroads. The railroad was one of the first new industries fostered by earlier mechanization. George and Robert Stephenson developed a practical railroad in Britain by the late 1820s. Americans introduced it so quickly that by 1840 U.S. mileage equaled that of Britain, and Americans produced over three-quarters of the country's locomotives. The quick adoption can be attributed to U.S. capabilities and institutions. Steam engines and textile machinery formed capabilities; one-time steam engine producers supplied seven-tenths of domestically built locomotives in 1838, led by Matthias Baldwin, and textile machinery firms manufactured another sixth, led by Locks and Canals. Locomotive and railroad firms purchased machine tools and hired machinists trained in other sectors. Similarly, civil engineers trained on canals, together with the U.S. Corps of Topographical Engineers, laid out tracks and built bridges. Interfirm mobility, extensive knowledge sharing, and publications including the *Journal of the Franklin Institute* and the *American Railroad Journal* spread knowledge among railroads and railroad equipment firms. Practitioners adapted British railroads to the steeper terrain and sharper curves of U.S. track. Most importantly, John Jervis's six-wheel locomotive design of 1831 enabled trains to negotiate sharp curves by letting a leading four-wheel truck turn independently of the back, power-supplying wheels. Unpatented, it spread quickly, championed by Baldwin.

Railroad networks and convergent technologies directed innovation in the surging industry, which expanded from 2,300 miles of track in 1839 to 28,800 in 1850, 199,000 in 1890, and 429,100 in 1929. Many entered the locomotive industry, including the engine-maker Holmes Hinkley and the textile machinery producers William Mason, Thomas Clark, and Charles Danforth. Railroad executives, master mechanics, and locomotive and other input makers advanced the mechanical aspects of railroads. To gain more power, Philadelphia locomotive producers added two power-supplying wheels and a stabilizing mechanism to create the dominant design of the nineteenth century. New forms of engine cut-offs, boilers, switches, brakes, cars, and couplings improved the performance and efficiency of the increasingly longer and heavier trains. Machinists received 46 percent of patents through 1865 and engineers and inventive occupations another 11 percent. Network inventors gained usage most readily, often by patent assignment. After 1870, railroads and input manufacturers employed educated engineers to conduct systematic tests of combustion, energy consumption, heating and ventilation, and the strength of steel, but these tests were designed to establish standards rather than to develop new techniques. Seeking to reduce repair costs, locomotive manufacturers such as Baldwin moved toward interchangeability. In the 1890s Baldwin introduced electrical power to move materials and power machines, leading the country in industrial electrification (Brown, 1995, pp. 29–31; Usselman, 2002; Thomson, 2009, pp. 232–248).

Key inventions also came from outside the domain of railroad knowledge. Steelmaking innovations by Henry Bessemer and, in the United States, Alexander Holley and Andrew Carnegie generated steel rails that replaced iron rails by the 1880s. The machinist George Westinghouse Jr. introduced an air brake in which the train engineer applied brakes in each car by pulling a lever that reduced the pressure of compressed air in a pipe running the length of the train. Railroads adopted the invention for passenger service in the 1870s but waited another two decades for freight. William Robinson brought electrical technology to the railroad with his automatic signal, invented in 1870 but not widely used until the early twentieth century, which prevented trains from entering a station before earlier trains had left.

Sewing machines. The sewing machine rested on technological convergence and machinists' mobility for its design and production. The principal early inventor, Elias Howe, a Lowell and Boston machinist, used knowledge of textile machine design to invent a machine in which a loom-like, thread-carrying shuttle and a recipro-cating eye-point needle formed a lockstitch. Others, mostly around Boston, improved Howe's machine, including John Bachelder, who intro-duced a continuous feeding mechanism. Early efforts at sale educated Isaac Singer. Allen Wilson developed his four-motion feed, the final element in a practical machine, to avoid infringing on an earlier patent. By 1856, when a patent pool formed based on the patents of Howe and three leading companies, diffusion was rapid. Sales surged from 3,700 machines in 1854 to 85,000 in 1865, peaked at 855,000 in 1872, and slowed to 803,000 in 1900. Patenting too surged, rising from 3 annually in the 1846–1850 period to 21 in 1851–1855 and 76 in 1856–1860, 184 in 1872–1874, and, after the patent pool expired, 192 in 1879–1882. Ma-chinists received two-thirds of the patents through 1865 (Thomson, 1989, pp. 72–155).

New England sewing machine firms benefited from interchangeable-parts firearms methods. Al-ready a leading precision firm, Brown and Sharpe contracted to make Willcox and Gibbs sewing machines in the late 1850s and utilized milling ma-chines, turret lathes, and measurement methods to do so. In part to make sewing machines, Joseph Brown invented two fundamental machine tools, the universal milling machine to cut complex shapes such as twist drills and grinding machines for basic metal cutting. Utilizing the knowledge of four veteran firearms producers, Wheeler and Wilson built an interchangeable-parts factory in 1863, although it still relied on hand filing. Inter-changeability was not easily attained; Singer's New Jersey plant only did so in the 1880s.

Shoe machinery. Shoemaking mechanized through design convergences with the sewing ma-chine. Network inventors led the way. Shoemak-ers modified the sewing machine to stitch light leathers. The machinist-inventor William Wicker-sham developed a hooked needle and a looper to sew uppers with waxed thread; his machine spread widely by 1860. Shoe bottoming was first mechanized when woodworking methods were adapted to make pegged shoes, the dominant form of cheaper shoes. Benjamin Sturtevant de-signed practical machines and a lathe to cut a strip of peg wood from the circumference of a log. In 1858, Lyman Blake, a shoemaker who distributed and used Singer machines, invented a machine to stitch uppers, soles, and welts through a horn in-serted inside the shoe. Gordon McKay, the super-intendent of a Massachusetts textile machinery firm, bought the patent and with Blake and others brought the machine to practicality, benefitting from Civil War army contracts; the machine dif-fused rapidly afterward. From 1860 through 1890, Charles Goodyear Jr. purchased and developed inventions to mechanize higher-quality hand-type shoes using one machine to unite uppers with welts and a second to sew welts to soles. Jan Matzeliger, a machinist who ran a McKay stitcher, received the key patent that mechanized the last major hand operation, lasting, by mechanically reproducing the laster's hand movements. After development by the United Shoe Machinery Co., the machine diffused in the early twentieth cen-tury. Before 1866, 59 percent of all shoemaking inventors learned in shoemaking networks, and they received 67 percent of patents. Machinists formed 28 percent of inventors, but their share rose to 56 percent in sewing and pegging ma-chines. Machinists formed about the same share of inventors through 1900, led by shoe machinists (Thomson, 1989, 2009, pp. 291–295).

Harvesting. Agricultural machinery did not have close proximity to machinists and developed more slowly as a consequence. Cyrus McCormick and Obed Hussey invented key elements of suc-cessful reapers to cut wheat and grass in the early 1830s, but a practical reaper only emerged in the late 1840s. McCormick invented on a Virginia farm in a county without a machine shop. He un-derstood problems of reaping and the limits of his father's reaper inventions, but little about machine design and production. He initially sold locally and licensed for others to sell at a distance. Al-though he improved his machine to enable work-ers to better rake cut grain, sales were small until he built his Chicago plant in 1850 and found methods to produce with sufficient quality. His plant relied essentially on filing and forging metal parts, techniques far behind those of firearms and sewing machines. Yet his output grew from 450 reapers in 1847 to 7,000 in 1865 and 55,000 harvesters of all types in 1884, and his numerous competitors grew faster yet. Diffusion spread knowledge and invention; annual patenting grew from 1.8 from 1846 through 1850 to 54.8 a decade later. Machinists received 45 percent of patents through 1865 and farmers 23 percent. Harvester patents accelerated after the war; machinery company owners, workers, or assignors received about half of the patents. Self-raking reapers reduced labor costs, harvesters lifted cut grain to be hand-bound, binders tied grain with wire or twine, and, after 1900, combines harvested, winnowed, and threshed grain. Mechanization complemented biological innovation in seed type and disease control, which, however, relied much more on government activity and publication than on private firms and patents (Hutchinson, 1930; Nader, 1994; David, 1975; Hounshell, 1984; Thomson, 2009, pp. 244–256).

Postbellum Mechanization. After the Civil War, mechanization continued where established and extended to many other industries. Inventors successfully targeted craft operations, including hatmaking, stoneworking, and many metalworking operations. Tobacco machines packed tobacco and rolled cigarettes. Canning machines preserved food. Rock-drilling machines changed construction and mining. Most were invented and developed by machinists, mechanical engineers, and others with mechanical knowledge.

Resource processing. As mineral and petroleum extraction skyrocketed after 1860, chemical and mechanical processes combined to transform materials into refined products. Holley and others adapted Bessemer's steelmaking invention, imported during the Civil War, to mass produce steel and steel products. Many mechanical innovations, including detachable converter bottoms, blowers, metal mixers, and rolling mill designs, enabled Carnegie to integrate blast furnaces, converters, and rolling mills. Mechanical innovation was needed to make armor plate for naval ships and continuous sheet steel for automobiles. New refining methods increased yields of gold, silver, and copper. Begun before the Civil War,

petroleum drilling and refining dramatically improved afterward when deep drilling methods and multistage, large-batch refineries developed in the nineteenth century and, as chemical engineering emerged, continuous-flow refineries began from the 1920s. Mechanical engineers and chemists were paramount in these innovations. New hoists and conveyance mechanisms moved material in metallurgy, mining, and transportation (Misa, 1995; Mowery and Rosenberg, 1998).

Business machines. Machines to count and type transformed business practices. William Burroughs invented an adding machine used initially by banks. Cash registers recorded transactions and later issued receipts. Herman Hollerith's tabulating machine, first used on the Census of 1890, marked a major advance in information-processing technology. Christopher Sholes developed a practical typewriter, and Remington applied design and metalworking capabilities learned making firearms to improve and produce it. Early problems with key jamming led to the QWERTY keyboard layout that may well be inferior but unchangeable (David, 1986).

Bicycles and automobiles. The high-wheel bicycle and the safety bicycle with its equal-size wheels connected by a chain emanated from France and Britain. Produced from the late 1870s, U.S. sales skyrocketed through the late 1890s. The Otto four-cycle engine and Benz automobile were continental innovations patented in the United States. U.S. inventors often aimed at mass markets. Ransom Olds' Oldsmobile, Henry Leland's Cadillac, Henry Ford's Model T, and later closed sedans of Chevrolet and Chrysler were practical and capable of mass production. Thousands of improvements in engines, steering, brakes, transmissions, bodies, ignition, and lighting contributed to speed, safety, and versatility. Knowledge was widely shared informally, and after George Selden's overly wide patent was circumscribed, cross-licensing provided firms access to the key technologies. As better cars developed and prices fell, U.S. auto registrations grew from 8,000 in 1900 to 458,000 in 1910 and 23,035,000 in 1930 (Flink, 1988; Mowery and Rosenberg, 1998, pp. 48–50).

Mass production. Mass production comprised America's greatest contribution to bicycle and automobile development. Albert Pope, the leading bicycle entrepreneur, contracted to have bicycles made by George Fairfield, a Hartford sewing machine producer who earlier had worked for Robbins and Lawrence and Colt. Fairfield and his successors mass produced the bicycle by adapting interchangeable-parts sewing machine methods. The Western Wheel Works of Chicago applied metal-stamping techniques to most bicycle parts. Production problems led to further innovations, including grinding ball bearings and the use of formed cutters and oil-tube drills.

The automobile industry developed mass production so quickly because it utilized convergent technologies. From their inception, auto firms bought machine tools, including mass-production turret lathes and milling machines. Workers trained in machine-tool firms organized production, including Henry Leland, who worked for the Springfield Armory, Colt, Brown and Sharpe, and his own machine-tool firm before making engines for Olds and becoming president of Cadillac and Lincoln. Similarly, Walter Flanders made sewing machines at Singer and machine tools at the Landis Tool Company before coming to Ford Motor Company, where he was vital to Ford's mass production. Because autos were much heavier than earlier interchangeable-parts products, machine-tool firms introduced heavier mass-production machine tools. Charles Norton developed heavy production grinders, and the Bullard Machine Tool Company developed a turret lathe that could drill, bore, and turn simultaneously. Stamping techniques spread, and steel firms supplied alloy steels, such as the vanadium steel used by Ford. Tire firms quickly adapted their product to the automobile. Automobile firms were fundamental innovators by designing machine tools and organizing the flow of work, most importantly through the moving assembly line (Rosenberg, 1976; Hounshell, 1984).

Changes in the automobile industry spilled over into other sectors. Heavy grinding, new machine tools, forced lubrication of machines, antifriction bearings, and the moving assembly line all spread widely through machinery sale, machinist mobility, and diversification such as General Motors' ownership of Frigidaire. Auto design also had wide-ranging effects, including trucks, tractors including Ford's Fordson, earth-moving equipment of Caterpillar Tractor, and airplane engines. To solve other technological problems, aircraft innovators relied on scientific and hobbyists' information outside existing industries, which enabled Wilbur and Orville Wright to greatly improve aircraft control. Although the federal government inadequately supported aircraft development in World War I, the U.S. Mail Service effectively supported aircraft innovation in the 1920s. Several later innovators, including Glenn Curtiss and Pratt and Whitney, applied knowledge from the automobile and machine-tool sectors to aircraft engines, and machine-tool expertise was indispensable in crafting accurate parts.

Machine tools. The machine-tool industry evolved through innovational complementarities characteristic of general-purpose technologies. Most machines were produced in small batches, and the planer, industrial lathe, and universal milling machine met their precision requirements. Turret lathes, milling machines, grinding machines, drop forging, and other mass-production metalworking methods spread among many industries. Machine-tool sale was one means. Brown and Sharpe sold 68 percent of its machine tools to firearms and sewing machine firms in the 1860s but only 18 percent in the 1900–1904 period, when it sold 13 percent to electrical machinery firms, 11 percent to business machine firms, and 4 percent to emerging automobile producers. Machinist mobility was another means. Brown and Sharpe workers are known to have moved to or formed 6 engine and boiler firms, 10 auto and auto-parts firms, 4 electrical equipment firms, 25 machine-tool firms, 11 other machinery firms, and 11 tool firms; the workers then invented in their new industries. Developments in automobile and other new application sectors induced machine-tool development, which altered techniques in existing application sectors and enabled other such sectors to emerge. At the same time, machine tools themselves evolved when their consumers developed products such as high-speed steel and unit electric drive (Scranton, 1997; Thomson, 2010, pp. 11–18).

Electrification. As important as automobiles had become by 1929, electrical machinery firms employed five-sixths as many workers and produced a much wider range of products. The telegraph was the major electrical technology until, from the late 1870s, the telephone transmitted voice, incandescent and arc lights illuminated spaces, generators supplied power, the electric railroad moved passengers, electric motors powered machines, and, early in the twentieth century, the radio communicated wirelessly. Always resting on mechanical technology, electrical machinery also advanced through physical science.

Telegraphs.   Samuel Morse invented the dominant U.S. telegraph. His science studies at Yale and his interaction with northeastern scientists proved decisive in forming his telegraph's electromagnets, circuitry, and sending and receiving mechanisms. He relied on machinists to perfect and produce his equipment. Aided by government funding, he succeeded in 1844, and telegraph messages transmitted by Western Union, the near-monopoly intercity provider, rose to 9.2 million in 1870 and 75.1 million in 1910. The telegraph's success nurtured three new occupations with electrical knowledge—telegraphers, electrical engineers, and electrical machinists—who became the industry's principal inventors. Annual patents grew from 2 in the 1846–1855 decade to 22 around 1870 and 47 around 1890, before falling to 42 around 1910, with a steady three-quarters issued to network inventors. Inventors including Thomas Edison developed repeaters to extend distance, ways to send multiple messages simultaneously, printing mechanisms, and fire-alarm and stock-price telegraphs. To provide precision equipment, Western Union helped form a machinery company, Western Electric (Israel, 1992; Thomson, 2011, pp. 3–7).

Electrical convergence.   The telegraph supplied convergent technology, personnel, and financing that sped broader electrification. Edison

exemplified the design spillovers. Telegraphs constituted 20 percent of his 743 electrical patents through 1929, largely issued by 1877. Widening his sights, he received 12 percent of his electrical patents for generic circuitry devices, 15 percent for batteries, 5 percent for telephones, 25 percent for lights, 15 percent for dynamos and motors, 3 percent for railroads, and 5 percent for other improvements. With his team of electricians and machinists formed to make telegraph inventions, Edison used generic circuitry and specific telegraph techniques in many telephone and lighting inventions. The sale of telegraph patents helped finance inventive efforts at his Menlo Park lab. Edison's experience was common; half of a sample of telegraph inventors had other electrical patents, and two-thirds of inventors in telegraph networks did so. Their other electrical patents—as numerous as their telegraph patents—spread widely over electrical operations (Israel, 1992; Thomson, 2011, pp. 7–22).

Communications.   The telegraph had its biggest effects early in the development of other electrical techniques; these techniques then formed their own knowledge base and networks. Alexander Graham Bell's critical telephone patent for "an improvement in telegraphy" developed through learning in Boston telegraph networks, collaboration with telegraph practitioners, and financing from telegraph entrepreneurs. Edison's carbon button transmitter was essential to its success. American Telephone and Telegraph's later efforts at coast-to-coast communication relied on scientists, increasingly with PhD's, culminating in its research and development department in 1911. The radio rested even more on advances in science and university-educated innovators. American inventors developed Guglielmo Marconi's wireless telegraph to transmit voice rather than code. Independent inventors such as Reginald Fessenden and Lee de Forest invented alternators and the triode amplifier and transmitter, which AT&T, GE, and, after its 1919 formation, RCA developed (Aitken, 1985).

Light, power, and railways.   Electric lighting, railroads, and motors involved different technological problems than the telegraph and required far more power. Telegraph technology, networks, and agents sped the inception of electric light and power, as Edison and others illustrate. But training in science and in lighting and power networks proved more important. Electric lighting formed a system requiring electrical generators and transmitters. Edison solved the interlinked problems and opened his first direct-current central power station in Manhattan in 1882. Frank Sprague, a former Edison worker, developed a direct-current electric motor, which transformed electrical into mechanical power. Elihu Thomson and Edwin Houston developed arc lights and much superior generators. George Westinghouse, who turned to electric power through his interest in railroad signaling, employed William Stanley and Nikola Tesla to develop such key alternating-current innovations as practical transformers and polyphase motors. Westinghouse also licensed and developed British steam turbine inventions to power the increasingly large generators of utility companies. Sprague went on to develop the first practical electric railroad. Soon after Edison and Thomson–Houston interests merged to form General Electric, the company formed a research and development lab, which conducted fundamental research leading to basic advances in ductile tungsten filaments, X-rays, and radios. By the 1920s, when the macroeconomic effects of electrification were just being felt, electric power formed a technological system in which large utilities used coal-driven steam turbines or water power to generate electricity that was transmitted hundreds of miles to factories, railroads, public facilities, and homes (Reich, 1985; Hughes, 1983, 1990; Carlson, 1991; Friedel and Israel, 1986; Noble, 1977).

Machinery production. Without convergent production techniques, electrification would have been long delayed. Edison relied on machinists to produce his experimental equipment and manufacture dynamos and other heavy machines. American Bell, which later became AT&T, acquired and greatly expanded Western Electric to design and produce its complex equipment, including amplifiers and switchboards. General

Electric and Westinghouse were among the largest machine-tool purchasers. Unlike automobile firms, they produced small batches of specially designed equipment; their generators weighing hundreds of tons, and turbines rotating at three thousand rpm required precise, heavy machine tools that could be brought to the work. Electrical machinery firms designed some of their own production equipment, including portable and electrically driven machine tools.

Electrical motors in turn transformed manufacturing production by developing unit drive, which linked motors to individual machines varying in size from sewing machines to subways. Machinery production itself was revolutionized; electrical power reduced costs and enabled greater precision, superior control, and quicker adjustment in redesigned factories liberated from shafting. In conjunction with high-speed steel, which greatly increased cutting speeds, electrification brought about a wholesale redesign of machine tools. By 1929 electricity supplied 78 percent of manufacturing power, and GE, Westinghouse, and Western Electric had joined Singer and International Harvester as the five largest machinery firms (Reich, 1985; Nye, 1992; Passer, 1953; Chandler, 1977; David, 1991).

Trajectory. Why did U.S. mechanization, which began so tentatively in the early nineteenth century, continue to develop into the twentieth? Incentives to make and use inventions remained high in an environment of large and rapidly growing markets, resource abundance, scarce labor, and a supportive patent system. Moreover, mechanization helped to generate inventive capabilities when machinists and machine users acquired technological knowledge. Access to knowledge was relatively easy in an economy of rapid mobility inside and into the country, particularly for those embedded in networks of mechanized firms, their capital goods suppliers, and relevant occupations. In this setting, invention was often undertaken by principals or employees in firms or in anticipation of forming firms, complemented by independent inventors who sold patents or gained shares in firm ownership but were not active in management. The networks were substantially independent; even late in the period telephones, electric power, and radios evolved along separate paths although firms had overlapping technology.

Convergent technologies accelerated movement along paths and helped start new ones, sustaining a profound technological momentum. Mass-production machine tools had wide effects from firearms through automobiles and electrical appliances, often leading to economics of scale and interchangeable parts. But machine-tool innovation also lent precision to batch production. Common machine designs spilled over, helping to explain how mechanization could develop in new industries, such as when textile inventors turned to sewing machines or telegraph inventors improved telephones and lighting. Technological convergence in the machinery sector widened over time, and nonmechanical technologies added to the convergence. Metallurgical technologies developed to make alloy steels used in automobiles and high-speed steel that increased machine-tool cutting speeds. Innovations in nonferrous abrasives, made by electrochemical methods, transformed the cutting edges of metal-grinding machines. Electrical innovations led to unit drive, one of the basic twentieth-century improvements in machinery.

Would this momentum persist beyond the 1920s? A number of factors suggest that it would not persist in the same form. Innovation had already led to large firms with extensive internal planning and economies of scale in railroads, sewing machines, agricultural machines, steel, petroleum, business machines, automobiles, and electrical machinery, although start-ups and small firms still flourished, particularly in the Midwest. Science-based industry had different knowledge sources. Although much learning occurred on the job, inventors increasingly were trained in universities; the traditional knowledge base of machinists was less relevant in this setting. Organized research and development within firms was in its infancy but clearly on the ascent. The federal government had taken a strong interest in radio technology and might do so with other techniques. And macroeconomic conditions of depression and war would

surely change incentives. In the radically different conditions of the 1930s and 1940s, a great deal changed; large firms, science, research and development, and the government came to play much larger roles. But that did not fundamentally alter the momentum of the turn of the century; nonelectrical machinery, electrical machinery, and motor vehicles were the largest industries in 1960, and manufacturing workers were four times as productive as those a half century earlier.

[*See also* **Agricultural Technology; Airplanes and Air Transport; American System of Manufactures; Bell, Alexander Graham; Bell Laboratories; Bicycles and Bicycling; Clocks and Clockmaking; Colt, Samuel; Cotton Gin; De Forest, Lee; Edison, Thomas; Electricity and Electrification; Engineering; Ford, Henry; Food Processing; Forestry Technology and Lumbering; Fulton, Robert; Gender and Technology; Goodyear, Charles; Hydroelectric Power; Illumination; Lowell Textile Mills; Maritime Transport; McCormick, Cyrus Hall; Morse, Samuel F. B.; Motor Vehicles; Petroleum and Petrochemicals; Photography; Printing and Publishing; Radio; Railroads; Science; Shipbuilding; Slater, Samuel; Springfield Armory; Steam Power; Technology; Telegraph; Telephone; Tesla, Nikola; Westinghouse, George; Whitney, Eli;** *and* **Wright, Wilbur and Orville.**]

BIBLIOGRAPHY

Aitken, Hugh G. J. *The Continuous Wave: Technology and the American Radio, 1900–1932.* Princeton, N.J.: Princeton University Press, 1985.

Brown, John K. *The Baldwin Locomotive Works, 1831–1915.* Baltimore: Johns Hopkins University Press, 1995.

Calvert, Monte A. *The Mechanical Engineer in America: 1830–1910.* Baltimore: Johns Hopkins University Press, 1967.

Carlson, W. Bernard. *Innovation as a Social Process: Elihu Thomson and the Rise of General Electric, 1870–1900.* Cambridge, U.K.: Cambridge University Press, 1991.

Chandler, Alfred D., Jr. *The Visible Hand: The Managerial Revolution in American Business.* Cambridge, Mass.: Belknap Press, 1977.

Cooper, Carolyn C. *Shaping Invention: Thomas Blanchard's Machinery and Patent Management in Nineteenth-Century America.* New York: Columbia University Press, 1991.

David, Paul A. "Computer and Dynamo: The Modern Productivity Paradox in a Not-too-distant Mirror." In *Technology and Productivity: The Challenge for Economic Policy.* Paris: OECD, 1991.

David, Paul A. *Technical Choice, Innovation, and Economic Growth: Essays on American and British Experience in the Nineteenth Century.* London: Cambridge University Press, 1975.

David, Paul A. "Understanding the Economics of QWERTY: The Necessity of History." In *Economic History and the Modern Economist*, edited by William N. Parker, pp. 30–49. New York: Basil Blackwell, 1986.

Ferguson, Eugene S. *Oliver Evans: Inventive Genius of the American Industrial Revolution.* Wilmington, Del.: Hagley Museum and Library, 1980.

Flink, James J. *The Automobile Age.* Cambridge, Mass.: MIT Press, 1988.

Friedel, Robert, and Paul Israel with Bernard S. Finn. *Edison's Electric Light: Biography of an Invention.* New Brunswick, N.J.: Rutgers University Press, 1986.

Gibb, George S. *The Saco-Lowell Shops: Textile Machinery Building in New England, 1813–1949.* Cambridge, Mass.: Harvard University Press, 1950.

Hindle, Brooke. *Emulation and Invention.* New York: New York University Press, 1981.

Hoke, Donald R. *Ingenious Yankees: The Rise of the American System of Manufactures in the Private Sector.* New York: Columbia University Press, 1990.

Hounshell, David A. *From the American System to Mass Production, 1800–1932.* Baltimore: Johns Hopkins University Press, 1984.

Hughes, Thomas P. *American Genesis: A Century of Invention and Technological Enthusiasm.* New York: Penguin, 1990.

Hughes, Thomas P. *Networks of Power: Electrification in Western Society, 1880–1930.* Baltimore: Johns Hopkins University Press, 1983.

Hunter, Louis C. *A History of Industrial Power in the United States, 1780–1930.* Vol. 2, *Steam Power.* Charlottesville: University Press of Virginia, 1985.

Hunter, Louis C. *Steamboats on the Western Rivers.* Cambridge, Mass.: Harvard University Press, 1949.

Hutchinson, William T. *Cyrus Hall McCormick: Harvest, 1856–1884.* New York: D. Appleton–Century Co., 1930.

Hutchinson, William T. *Cyrus Hall McCormick: Seed-Time, 1809–1856.* New York: D. Appleton–Century Co., 1930.

Israel, Paul. *From Machine Shop to Industrial Laboratory: Telegraphy and the Changing Context of American Invention, 1830–1920.* Baltimore: Johns Hopkins University Press, 1992.

Jeremy, David J. *Transatlantic Industrial Revolution: The Diffusion of Textile Technologies between Britain and America, 1790–1830s.* Cambridge, Mass.: MIT Press, 1981.

Khan, B. Zorina. *The Democratization of Invention: Patents and Copyrights in American Economic Development, 1790–1920.* Cambridge, U.K.: Cambridge University Press, 2005.

Lamoreaux, Naomi R., and Kenneth L. Sokoloff. "Inventors, Firms, and the Market for Technology in the Late Nineteenth and Early Twentieth Centuries." In *Learning by Doing in Markets, Firms, and Countries*, edited by Naomi Lamoreaux, Daniel M. G. Raff, and Peter Temin, pp. 19–57. Chicago: University of Chicago Press, 1999.

Lamoreaux, Naomi R., Kenneth L. Sokoloff, and Dhanoos Sutthiphisal. "The Reorganization of Inventive Activity in the United States in the Early Twentieth Century." In *Understanding Long-Run Economic Growth: Geography, Institutions, and the Knowledge Economy*, edited by Dora L. Costa and Naomi R. Lamoreaux, pp. 235–274. Chicago: University of Chicago Press, 2011.

Lozier, John W. *Taunton and Mason: Cotton Machinery and Locomotive Manufacture in Taunton, Massachusetts, 1811–1861.* New York: Garland, 1986.

Mass, William. "Developing and Utilizing Technological Leadership: Industrial Research, Vertical Integration, and Business Strategy at the Draper Company, 1816–1930." *Business and Economic History* 18 (1989): 129–139.

Meyer, David R. *Networked Machinists: High-Technology Industries in Antebellum America.* Baltimore: Johns Hopkins University Press, 2006.

Misa, Thomas J. *A Nation of Steel: The Making of Modern America, 1865–1925.* Baltimore: Johns Hopkins University Press, 1995.

Moore, Charles W. *Timing a Century: History of the Waltham Watch Company*. Cambridge, Mass.: Harvard University Press, 1945.

Mowery, David C., and Nathan Rosenberg. *Paths of Innovation: Technological Change in 20th-Century America*. Cambridge, U.K.: Cambridge University Press, 1998.

Nader, John. "The Rise of an Inventive Profession: Learning Effects in the Midwestern Harvester Industry, 1850–1890." *Journal of Economic History* 52 (June 1994): 397–408.

Noble, David F. *America by Design: Science, Technology, and the Rise of Corporate Capitalism*. New York: Alfred A. Knopf, 1977.

Nye, David E. *Electrifying America: Social Meanings of a New Technology*. Cambridge, Mass.: MIT Press, 1992.

Passer, Harold C. *The Electrical Manufacturers, 1875–1900*. Salem, N.H.: Ayers, 1953.

Pursell, Carroll W., Jr. *Early Stationary Steam Engines in America*. Washington, D.C.: Smithsonian Institution, 1969.

Reich, Leonard S. *The Making of American Industrial Research: Science and Business at GE and Bell, 1876–1926*. New York: Cambridge University Press, 1985.

Roe, Joseph W. *English and American Tool Builders*. New Haven, Conn.: Yale University Press, 1916.

Rosenberg, Nathan. *Perspectives on Technology*. Cambridge, U.K.: Cambridge University Press, 1976.

Schmookler, Jacob. *Invention and Economic Growth*. Cambridge, Mass.: Harvard University Press, 1966.

Scranton, Phillip. *Endless Novelty: Specialty Production and American Industrialization, 1865–1925*. Princeton, N.J.: Princeton University Press, 1997.

Smith, Merritt Roe. *Harpers Ferry Armory and the New Technology*. Ithaca, N.Y.: Cornell University Press, 1977.

Sokoloff, Kenneth L. "Inventive Activity in Early Industrial America: Evidence from Patent Records, 1790–1846." *Journal of Economic History* 48 (December 1988): 813–850.

Thomson, Ross. "Did the Telegraph Lead Electrification? Industry, Science, and Innovation in the United States." *Business and Economic History On-line* (Fall 2011).

Thomson, Ross. *The Path to Mechanized Shoe Production in the United States*. Chapel Hill: University of North Carolina Press, 1989.

Thomson, Ross. *Structures of Change in the Mechanical Age: Technological Innovation in the United States, 1790–1865*. Baltimore: Johns Hopkins University Press, 2009.

Thomson, Ross. "Understanding Machine Tool Development in the United States: Uniting Economic and Business History." *Business and Economic History On-line* (Fall 2010).

Usselman, Steven W. *Regulating Railroad Innovation: Business, Technology, and Politics in America, 1840–1920*. Cambridge, U.K.: Cambridge University Press, 2002.

Ross Thomson

MALARIA

Malaria is a group of diseases caused by parasites of the *plasmodium* genus, transmitted through the bites of *anopheles* mosquitoes. Once called intermittent fever for its patterns of intense fever and pains alternating with disease-free spells, its two most common forms in the United States were vivax and falciparum malaria. *Plasmodium vivax* is adapted to temperate zones; immigrants from the boggy areas of England, Holland, Spain, and Italy brought it to North America. Vivax causes miserable chills and fever, but is less likely than falciparum malaria to end in death. Falciparum, which demands a more tropical environment, traveled to the American colonies in the unwilling bodies of slaves from the west coast of Africa.

In the 1680s falciparum malaria exploded in South Carolina, where slave workers harvested rice from flooded fields that were ideal for breeding the anopheles species that carry the parasite from one person to another. From being a fairly healthy colony, the low-country areas of South Carolina became deadly for white people, especially their children. Two historians who studied South Carolina parish records for the eighteenth century found that 86 percent of white babies born in one of the colony's parishes died before the age of 20, an astounding outcome likely resulting in large measure from falciparum malaria (Merrens and Terry, 1984, p. 542). It was no accident that well into the nineteenth century

South Carolina had more black people than white and that planter rhetoric proclaimed that only black people were physically suited to plantation work.

Fortunately for white settlers in the lands that were to become the United States, falciparum did not tolerate the temperatures much further north than Tennessee and North Carolina. Vivax, on the other hand, was quite adapted to temperate climes and extended as far north as Ontario, Canada, and as far west as Iowa, Minnesota, and Nebraska. Malaria made life miserable on the American frontier because so much travel was by river and the earliest settlements were near those transportation waterways. Frontier housing was porous, and mill ponds (created to grind the ubiquitous corn that fed the pioneers and their animals) formed ideal nurseries for anopheles larvae. Malaria followed the frontier, wreaking havoc in the eighteenth-century Chesapeake and in the Connecticut River Valley, traveling by the mid-nineteenth century into the Midwest along the Ohio, Mississippi, and Missouri rivers. By the time of the Civil War, both vivax and falciparum malaria were well entrenched in the United States.

Conditions during the war vastly amplified malaria's spread among Americans. The occupation of the southern coastal low country and the lower Mississippi Valley all brought men, malaria parasites, and mosquitoes together in great numbers. And those men were living outdoors, with only the slight protection of a tent to ward off mosquitoes. Of the several million men who served as soldiers in the war, thousands on both sides sickened with malaria, making it the second most common camp disease in the war (Steiner, 1968, pp. 20–21). Although the disease rarely killed outright, it persistently weakened the troops and frequently disabled them from active service (Bell, 2010, pp. 21–31).

Fighting Back. In the mid-nineteenth century humans began to fight back against malaria with increasing success. In 1821 Parisian researchers Joseph Pelletier and Joseph Caventou isolated quinine from the bark of the cinchona tree, and by the 1840s quinine pills were widely available on the malarious American frontier. As that frontier became more prosperous, settlers built tighter houses and moved to higher ground, where mosquito pests were less abusive. Drainage to ready land for agriculture decreased breeding sites, and the cows imported to graze on those lands diverted mosquitoes from human skin. With the spread of railroads from the 1830s, settlers lost their dependence on waterways for transport. All of these actions began to cut malaria rates, especially in the more temperate northern tier of states. By 1900 malaria had become largely a disease of the South, with a few outposts on the West Coast and in the southernmost parts of the Midwest.

In contrast to earlier theorists, who had declared that malaria emerged from the stinky air of swampy lands, scientists working in the last two decades of the nineteenth century identified the *plasmodium* and demonstrated its carriage by the *anopheles* mosquito. These discoveries quickly generated new tools for fighting the disease. Local authorities spread oil on breeding grounds or sprinkled the water with toxic chemicals to kill mosquito larvae. Where possible, drainage removed the breeding sites altogether. Public-health officials also recognized that giving quinine to patients or even prophylactically to a whole community would reduce the parasite burden of individuals and decrease transmission. William Crawford Gorgas, U.S. Army physician and chief sanitary officer on the Panama Canal project, was able to control both malaria and yellow fever in the Panama Canal Zone, given the power and infusion of enough money to control mosquitoes and treat patients effectively.

The American military implemented these measures to protect American camps during World War I, and after the war the Rockefeller Foundation tested them in demonstration projects in the Mississippi Delta. The foundation sought to determine which method of malaria control was both cheapest and most effective. Their demonstration projects targeted this objective, judging the results by cost per case of malaria reduced. They supplied free quinine at one site, organized larvicidal measures at a second, and sponsored a screening campaign at a third. Every intervention they made worked well in the first year, reducing malaria cases by 90 percent or more. But then the programs began to fall apart. Physicians objected to the distribution of free medication as impinging on their right to practice. And the drug method failed to prevent recurrence in the longer term. The second year, when surveyors came back to the screened households, they found many of the screens in disrepair. Often the household occupants had changed because the sharecropping population was so migratory, leaving one farm at the end of a contract for another, hoping for a better deal. The new occupants, knowing nothing about the program, had failed to continue maintenance.

The larvicidal program seemed to work best. It did not depend on the cooperation of the larger population, but relied instead on the determination of the local authorities, who oiled standing water, sprinkled arsenical larvicides on stream and ponds, or diverted waterways into underground culverts. Such work proved especially popular in urban areas, where local officials reaped political acclaim by reducing both malaria and the presence of mosquito pests. Drained land had greater value in the urban setting as well. Although the disease spiked briefly in the counties affected by the 1927 Mississippi River flood, by the early 1930s malaria was at a low ebb in the United States and had largely disappeared from urban settings.

The Great Depression temporarily reversed this trend of malaria decline. Many of those who had worked in town returned to the rural countryside, where malaria still thrived. This last surge of the disease in the United States peaked between 1933 and 1935; it had largely ended by the early 1940s. The causes of its demise are hard to measure, for a variety of reasons. First, most of the statistics available concern malaria death rates, whereas the number of cases would be a much better metric for malaria prevalence. Physicians did not usually observe deaths among the rural southern poor, so the cause of death listed officially was only a guess generated by the family report and the public official creating the death certificate. When federal public-health officials began paying for documented cases (demonstrated by a positive microscopic blood smear examination) in the late 1940s, they found that counties thought to be persistently malarious actually had no cases at all.

By the early 1940s malaria was hard to find in the United States. At Charity Hospital in Louisiana, a malaria case was an exciting event by 1942. In the 1920s the U.S. Public Health Service had set up a field station to study malaria in Newton, Georgia, but in 1944, with the disappearance of malaria, it converted the mission to studying mosquitoes. The most likely cause of the decline of malaria in these years was an inadvertent by-product of New Deal legislation that sought to improve southern agriculture. Government programs paid farmers to take their land out of cultivation to prop up the prices of the crops that were produced. Federal loan programs supplied capital for farmers to buy machinery such as tractors and other mechanical devices. These measures in turn meant that the old system of sharecropping, in which poor blacks and whites lived in shacks on the land and cultivated it with a hand plow and mule, became less cost effective. A massive depopulation of the southern rural landscape followed, and even where planters hired day labor, that labor lived in town (where malaria had already been controlled). As a result, large populations were removed from the one-mile flight zone around many malaria breeding sites, breaking the chain of malaria transmission.

World War II and New Tools for the Malaria Wars. By the time the United States entered the world war late in 1941, malaria had disappeared as a major problem in the American South. Yet military and civilian public-health leaders feared an upsurge in the disease. They saw malaria as a disease of mysterious cycles, of peaks and troughs of unexplained pattern. With so many military camps in the South, troops from all over the country were at risk as the country mobilized for the war. The U.S. Public Health Service created a special agency to protect military sites from malaria, dubbing it the Malaria Control in War Areas (MCWA). The military authorities created malaria-control programs within military camps, and the MCWA's job was to create a malaria-free zone around camps and other war-related sites. They used familiar tools: larvicides, insecticides, screens, insect repellants, and oral medication. Because Japan had occupied Java, where almost all of the world's quinine-source trees now grew, the U.S. authorities substituted the drug atabrine. Atabrine was not particularly popular given its side-effect profile, but it kept men on their feet in malaria zones overseas and on American soil.

Two new weapons for the malaria wars emerged from American military research during World War II. The first was the synthesis of chloroquine, a new malaria drug that was far better tolerated than earlier malaria compounds. The second was dichlorodiphenyltrichloroethane (DDT), a near magical insecticide. It could be sprayed on a wall and continue killing mosquitoes that landed there for up to three months. It was equally effective as a larvicide and could be spread on lakes from airplanes or from boats with motorized sprayers. DDT had a major impact on the military control of malaria (and other insect-borne diseases) overseas, and in August 1945 it became available for purchase within the United States.

At the end of the war, the MCWA agency had more than four thousand employees, but no longer had a mandate to protect the war effort. Its leaders argued successfully that Congress should continue agency funding, which they used to launch a malaria eradication campaign in the United States, with DDT as their principal weapon. Changing the name of their agency to the Communicable Disease Center (CDC), officials with the MCWA agency oversaw the DDT spraying of millions of homes in the American South from 1945 to 1950. There was very little malaria to measure, so they instead counted the reduction in *anopheles* mosquitoes, which was significant. In 1951 they declared victory. After a three-century run malaria was no longer indigenous in the United States. It is likely that the CDC campaign eradicated a few remaining pockets of the disease and deserves some credit for that result. It is also likely that malaria had largely subsided by the time the campaign began, so that their victory was not a difficult one.

In 2012, there were still about 1,500 cases of malaria cases in the United States each year. During the previous 50 years, malaria had spread from imported cases to local inhabitants at least 63 times, although the outbreaks were quite limited (Filler, 2006). Experts predicted that

the diffusion of air conditioning and window screens made it unlikely that malaria would ever again become widespread in the United States.

[*See also* Biological Sciences; Centers for Disease Control and Prevention; Columbian Exchange; Disease; Entomology; Life Expectancy; Medicine; Pesticides; Public Health; Public Health Service, U.S.; Race and Medicine; Refrigeration and Air Conditioning; Rockefeller Institute, The; *and* War and Medicine.]

BIBLIOGRAPHY

Ackerknecht, Erwin H. *Malaria in the Upper Mississippi Valley, 1760–1900.* New York: Arno Press, 1977. First published in 1945. Classic detailed work on malaria in this geographic area, written by a historian in conversation with malariologists active in fighting the remnants of malaria in the U.S. South.

Bell, Andrew McIlwaine. *Mosquito Soldiers: Malaria, Yellow Fever, and the Course of the American Civil War.* Baton Rouge: Louisiana State University Press, 2010. Describes the importance and understanding of malaria in the war.

Centers for Disease Control. "Malaria." http://www.cdc.gov/malaria/ (accessed 17 October 2012). Modern understanding of malaria's parasite, vector, and life cycle.

Curtin, Philip. "Epidemiology and the Slave Trade." *Political Science Quarterly* 83 (1968): 191–216. Explains the role of the slave trade in bringing tropical diseases to the New World.

Etheridge, Elizabeth W. *Sentinel for Health: A History of the Centers for Disease Control.* Berkeley: University of California Press, 1992. Provides background on MCWA and World War II malaria efforts.

Filler, Scott, et al. "Locally Acquired Mosquito-Transmitted Malaria: A Guide for Investigations in the United States." *Morbidity and Mortality Weekly Report* 55, no. RR13 (8 September 2006): 1–9. http://www.cdc.gov/mmwr/PDF/rr/rr5513.pdf (accessed 17 October 2012). On recent malaria cases in the United States.

Humphreys, Margaret. *Malaria: Poverty, Race and Public Health in the United States.* Baltimore and London: Johns Hopkins University Press, 2001.

History of malaria in colonial America through the eradication campaign at the end of World War II.

Merrens, H. Roy, and George D. Terry. "Dying in Paradise: Malaria, Mortality, and the Perceptual Environment in Colonial South Carolina." *Journal of Southern History* 50 (November 1984): 533–550. Documents the arrival and deadliness of falciparum malaria in colonial South Carolina.

Packard, Randall M. *The Making of a Tropical Disease: A Short History of Malaria.* Baltimore and London: Johns Hopkins University Press, 2007. General history of malaria, including detailed discussion of twentieth-century global campaigns against the disease.

Slater, Leo B. *War and Disease: Biomedical Research on Malaria in the Twentieth Century.* New Brunswick, N.J.: Rutgers University Press, 2009. Solid account of research on antimalaria drugs, including the importance of wartime funding in supporting this research.

Steiner, Paul E. *Disease in the Civil War: Natural Biological Warfare in 1861–1865.* Springfield, Ill.: Charles C. Thomas, 1968. Summarizes the importance of disease for Civil War casualties.

Margaret Humphreys

MANHATTAN PROJECT

The Manhattan Project refers to the Army Corps of Engineers's "Manhattan Engineer District," the code name of the military project established in June 1942 for atomic-bomb research and development. In the years leading up to World War II, many scientists pondered building nuclear weapons, particularly after Lise Meitner's and Otto Frisch's startling interpretation in 1938 of earlier uranium and neutron bombardment experiments (by Enrico Fermi and others) as nuclear fission.

Albert Einstein's August 1939 letter to President Franklin Delano Roosevelt (actually written by the Hungarian-born emigré physicist Leo Szilard [1898–1964]) was one means by which the U.S. government became aware of the atomic potential. In late 1940, the British and American governments joined forces to establish an atomic-bomb project in the industrially stronger and more protected country. Vannevar Bush, director of the government's new Office of Scientific Research and Development, drafted plans for the Manhattan Project, whose urgency was underscored by Japan's attack on Pearl Harbor on 7 December 1941. On 2 December 1942, less than three months after the appointment of Colonel (later Brigadier General) Leslie Groves as director of the Manhattan Project, Fermi demonstrated the first chain reaction at the University of Chicago. The Manhattan Project eventually grew into a $3-billion conglomeration, which included the Chicago Metallurgical Laboratory; the Berkeley Radiation Laboratory; the Oak Ridge, Tennessee, and Hanford, Washington, materials-production facilities; and the Los Alamos, New Mexico, laboratory, where the first atomic bombs were built.

Centralizing the many separate research efforts devoted to atomic-bomb research was essential, both for efficiency and to maintain secrecy. J. Robert Oppenheimer, whom Groves appointed in 1942 to head the project, selected a site on a high mesa in New Mexico, the Los Alamos Ranch School. Here a large community of scientists, engineers, and military personnel worked behind a security fence in a town identified only by its post office box number (1663). Everyone at Los Alamos—even scientific luminaries, such as Fermi, Hans Bethe, Edward Teller, Richard Feynman, John von Neumann, George Kistiakowsky, Stanislav Ulam, and Niels Bohr—was assigned and reassigned as needed and required to work collaboratively in the mode later known as "big science."

The technical program, geared initially toward "gun-type" uranium and plutonium bombs (in which the fissionable material would be shot together), was abruptly realigned after the April 1944 discovery of a high level of spontaneous fission in reactor-made plutonium. Attention then turned to the more rapid, and technically complex, assembly known as implosion. Despite enormous hurdles, an implosion bomb was successfully detonated at the "Trinity" test at Alamogordo, New Mexico, on 16 July 1945.

Told of the successful test while at the Potsdam Conference, President Harry S. Truman authorized dropping the uranium bomb that fell on

Hiroshima on 6 August and the plutonium bomb dropped on Nagasaki on 9 August. These weapons, which killed more than 120,000 Japanese, are widely believed to have led directly to the Japanese surrender on 14 August. They marked the start of the nuclear age and touched off an arms race that persisted throughout the Cold War era.

[*See also* **Army Corps of Engineers, U.S.; Atomic Energy Commission; Bethe, Hans; Bush, Vannevar; Einstein, Albert; Fermi, Enrico; Feynman, Richard; Military, Science and Technology and the; Nuclear Power; Nuclear Weapons; Office of Scientific Research and Development; Oppenheimer, J. Robert; Physics; Science; Teller, Edward;** *and* **Von Neumann, John.**]

BIBLIOGRAPHY

Hoddeson, Lillian, Paul W. Henriksen, Roger A. Meade, and Catherine Westfall. *Critical Assembly: A Technical History of Los Alamos during the Oppenheimer Years, 1943–1945*. Cambridge, U.K.: Cambridge University Press, 1993.

Rhodes, Richard. *The Making of the Atomic Bomb*. New York: Simon and Schuster, 1986.

Rotter, Andrew J. *Hiroshima: The World's Bomb*. New York: Oxford University Press, 2008.

Lillian Hoddeson

MARGULIS, LYNN

(1938–2011), theoretical and experimental biologist who made fundamental contributions to cell biology and microbial evolution. The eldest of four daughters born to Leone and Morris Alexander, Margulis grew up on the South Side of Chicago and attended the University of Chicago, where she was profoundly influenced by a course of the common core, Natural Science 2. In 1966, while a young faculty member at Boston University, she was the first to provide substantial microbiological evidence for the endosymbiotic theory originally formulated by Konstantin Mereschcowsky

(1855–1921) in 1905 and later independently advanced by Umberto Pierantoni (1876–1959) in 1909 and by Ivan Wallin (1883–1969) in the 1920s. According to this theory, certain organelles composing eukaryotic cells, for example, mitochondria and chloroplasts, originated as free-living bacteria and were incorporated through endophagocytosis into a primitive cell, which eventually evolved, over millions of years, into the eukaryotic cell. Revolutionizing the study of the early history of eukaryotic evolution, Margulis questioned a central tenet of neo-Darwinism, challenging the significance of competition as a motor of evolution. Emphasizing cooperation instead of competition, she argued that inherited variation does not come primarily from random mutations and that symbiogenesis is a primary force behind evolution.

While studying at the University of Chicago, Margulis met Carl Sagan (1934–1996) and married him in 1957, immediately after graduating from college. The couple moved to Wisconsin, where Margulis obtained her M.Sc. in zoology and genetics in 1960 from the University of Wisconsin-Madison, and then relocated to Oakland, where she started a PhD in genetics at the University of California, Berkeley. In 1963, she was appointed research associate and lecturer in biology at Brandeis University; she divorced Sagan one year later. In 1965, she obtained her PhD from Berkeley and, in 1966, she joined the faculty of biology at Boston University, where she taught for 22 years. In 1967 she married X-ray crystallographer Thomas N. Margulis who she divorced in 1980. Her most influential paper, "On the Origin of Mitosing Cells," was rejected by about 15 scientific journals before being published in *the Journal of Theoretical Biology* in 1967. Margulis also made significant contributions to taxonomy and provided support for James E. Lovelock's (b. 1919) Gaia hypothesis, according to which the Earth is a living, self-regulating organism that maintains conditions suitable for life through complex interactions between its living and nonliving components. Elected to the National Academy of Sciences in 1983, Margulis joined the faculty of the University of Massachusetts, Amherst, in 1988. The author of more than

300 scientific publications, including articles, books, and book chapters, she was a member of the American Academy of Arts and Sciences, a member of the World Academy of Art and Science, an elected foreign member of the Russian Academy of Natural Sciences, and a fellow of the Massachusetts Academy of Sciences. In 1998, the Library of Congress announced its decision to permanently archive all of her papers. In 1999, she was awarded the William Procter Prize for Scientific Achievement and received the National Medal of Science from President Clinton. Margulis received the Alexander von Humboldt Prize (2002–2005) and the 2008 Darwin-Wallace Medal by the Linnean Society of London and in 2010 she was inducted into the Leonardo Da Vinci Society for the Study of Thinking.

[*See also* **Biological Sciences; Evolution, Theory of;** *and* **Genetics and Genetic Engineering.**]

BIBLIOGRAPHY

Di Properzio, J. "Full Speed Ahead." *University of Chicago Magazine* 96, no. 3 (2004): 28–33.
Lake, J. A. "Lynn Margulis (1938–2011)." *Nature* 480, no. 7378 (2011): 458.
Schaechter, M. "Lynn Margulis (1938–2011)." *Science* 335, no. 6066 (2012): 302.

Daniele Macuglia

MARITIME TRANSPORT

Water-borne transportation has played a central role in shaping American economies from pre-Columbian times to the present. Native Americans developed sophisticated vessels such as the birch-bark canoe and kayak to facilitate travel, trade, hunting, and fishing. In the continental United States, Native groups developed trade routes on inland waters that featured portages between bodies of water, whereas in Florida several canals attest to an actual infrastructure to support canoe traffic. In the Pacific, Polynesians who settled Hawaii developed advanced navigation techniques that permitted them to transit thousands of miles of ocean safely.

When Europeans came to North America, they did so by ship and initially clung to coastal areas and navigable rivers. Water routes, many of them based on Native American portages, were the primary means by which Europeans accessed the interior, whereas coastal routes connecting the various colonies bolstered a growing coastal trade. Although some European powers such as the French and Spanish attempted to control transatlantic trade, the English and Dutch permitted freer trade that rewarded initiative and competitive pricing. The English colony of Massachusetts Bay proved especially successful in pursuing maritime transport as an important part of its economy, and throughout the colonial period Boston dominated much of the coastal (including West Indian) trade.

After the United States became independent, Americans became much more involved in long-distance trading with China and other foreign nations. Increasingly, these blue-water trades became concentrated in a handful of large entrepôts, which were in turn fed commodities by coasting vessels arriving from smaller communities and the larger port's hinterland for transshipment. The nation's internal maritime trade was even more crucial to the development of the nation's economy. Improved steamboat designs unlocked the huge riverine system in the continent's center to rapid development after the Louisiana Purchase and the War of 1812. The Erie Canal and its competitors in turn linked ports like New York City to a vast hinterland that could now be said to stretch from New York Harbor to the western shores of Lake Superior, moving bulky goods such as Midwest grain to the coast on canal barges, while immigrants and settlers moved west.

By the end of the Civil War, railroads began to replace maritime transportation in inland waters, especially for passenger traffic. In the face of well-established, highly capitalized, and technologically advanced British competition, American blue-water trade shriveled. Increasingly, American overseas trade moved in British-flagged vessels. Nonetheless, maritime transport continued to play an enormous role in developing the industrializing American economy. For example, Great

Lakes ore boats provided iron ore to the nation's rapidly growing steel industry, and coasting schooners moved the coal and other materials that fueled industrialization and urban growth.

World War I marked massive federal intervention into the maritime industry. During the phase of American neutrality, the withdrawal of British-flagged shipping nearly caused the collapse of the American export economy. With American entry came an enormous shipbuilding effort and the nationalization of the merchant fleet, with industry, labor unions, and the federal government working in partnership under the Atlantic Agreement of 1917, the first time that government partnered with maritime labor unions or industry on such a massive scale. Now alerted to the strategic importance of a viable merchant marine, the Jones Act of 1920 marked the first time the national government clearly stated that fact, but also announced its dedication to a privately owned and operated merchant fleet and contained strict protectionist measures that preserved the coasting trade for American-flagged vessels. The government established mail subsidies on strategic routes to promote shipping in the 1920s, but American-flagged shipping cannot be said to have thrived in this period: the subsidies were often abused, and the maritime industry suffered from labor troubles and bad publicity such as when the cruise ship *Morro Castle* burned off the New Jersey coast.

The administration of President Franklin D. Roosevelt moved strongly to bolster American shipping. Investigations revealed the misuse of mail subsidies, and a new program of operational subsidies and a national maritime academy were established under the guidance of a new agency, the U.S. Maritime Commission. The approach of World War II added greater urgency to these measures and federal subsidies for government-designed cargo ships that could serve in both peace and war. These preparations proved their value when World War II broke out, and a massive federal shipbuilding program successfully supported Allied war goals. In fact, the United States emerged from the war as the world's dominant shipping power, both because of the building program and because of the destruction of a large part of other nations' fleets. Throughout the Cold War these World War II ships assisted American strategic goals in a variety of ways, and the federal government administered generous Operational Differential Subsidies (ODS) to vessels sailing on selected strategic routes.

American commercial shipping thrived in the 1940s and 1950s, but declined rapidly thereafter. The transatlantic jetliner quickly killed off ocean liners. Multinational firms increasingly utilized foreign-flagged ships that offered lower labor costs, less regulation, and lower taxes than American ships. The trend toward larger "super ships" and automation meant fewer ships and smaller crews, whereas containerization removed cargo operations to vast terminals far removed from the traditional urban docks. Shipping largely slipped from the public consciousness as American-flagged shipping all but disappeared, replaced by cheaper foreign competitors. The exception is when American ships appear in the news, such as when the *Exxon Valdez* caused a massive oil spill in Alaskan waters in 1989 or when Somali pirates temporarily seized the *Maersk Alabama* off Africa in 2009. Maritime transport moves massive amounts of goods from industrial powerhouses like China to the United States, but very little of this cargo is moved by American-flagged shipping.

Policy makers who are aware of the strategic importance of shipping have occasionally attempted to reverse this trend, most notably with President Nixon's Merchant Marine Act of 1970. In the 1980s President Reagan bolstered Military Sealift Command, a fleet of cargo vessels owned by the U.S. Navy but operated by civilian mariners. In response to strategic needs in the 1990s, the federal government created a new subsidy that supports companies that participate in the Maritime Security Program (MSP), paying a set amount annually for each ship. By the 1990s less than 5 percent of U.S. imports and exports were carried in American-flagged bottoms, and in the early twenty-first century that number had dropped to less than 3 percent (Roland et al., 2008, p. 415). As of 2012, the American merchant fleet is small and largely linked to the nation's strategic needs. Even the Jones Act, which has long preserved the coasting trade for U.S.-flagged ships, is under attack by free traders ideologically opposed to such protectionist measures.

In the early twenty-first century maritime transport remained vital for the nation's economic well-being. West Coast ports bustled with Chinese imports, liquefied natural gas and petroleum products arrived by tanker, and Florida-based cruise ships provided vacations for hundreds of thousands of passengers each year. But little was moved by American-flagged shipping except relief and military cargoes and the relatively small amount of Jones Act coastal shipping.

[*See also* Canals and Waterways; *Exxon Valdez* Oil Spill; Railroads; Shipbuilding; *and* Steam Power.]

BIBLIOGRAPHY

Gibson, Andrew, and Arthur Donovan. *The Abandoned Ocean: A History of U.S. Maritime Policy.* Columbia: University of South Carolina Press, 2000.
Kilmarx, Robert A., ed. *America's Maritime Legacy: A History of the U.S. Merchant Marine and Shipbuilding Industry since Colonial Times.* Boulder, Colo.: Westview Press, 1979.
Roland, Alex, W. Jeffrey Bolster, and Alexander Keyssar. *The Way of the Ship: America's Maritime History Reenvisioned, 1600–2000.* Hoboken, N.J.: John Wiley & Sons, 2008.

Joshua M. Smith

MARSH, OTHNIEL CHARLES

(1831–1899), among the most important American vertebrate paleontologists of the nineteenth century. Marsh was born in Lockport, New York. His mother Mary, younger sister of banker and philanthropist George Peabody, died in 1834. With his uncle's financial support, Marsh attended Yale College, graduating with a Bachelor of Arts in 1860. Marsh continued his graduate studies in geology, zoology, and paleontology at Yale and several German universities.

Marsh persuaded his uncle to establish Yale's Peabody Museum of Natural History in 1866, where he was named curator and professor of paleontology (the first in the United States). When Peabody died in 1869, Marsh inherited a sizable fortune, which he used to fund his research. He led four student expeditions (1870–1873) into the American West in pursuit of fossils. Thereafter, he paid local collectors to do his fieldwork.

Marsh was a controversial figure, respected by some for his dedication to science, but despised by many, including most of the next generation of American paleontologists, for his self-interestedness and dour personality. His monograph *Odontornithes*—hailed by Charles Darwin as "the best support to the theory of evolution"—was ridiculed in an 1892 congressional debate about wasteful government spending. As a result, Marsh lost his lucrative federal appropriation. Marsh feuded infamously with paleontologist Edward Drinker Cope over access to fossils and priority of publication. Exactly how and why their feud began is a mystery, but by the 1870s they were bitter rivals. Their private feud became a public scandal when they exchanged accusations of incompetence and dishonesty on the front page of the *New York Herald* in 1890. Both of their reputations were tarnished by the scandal.

Marsh published approximately three hundred papers and books and described some five hundred new species. He served as president of the National Academy of Sciences (1883–1895) and vertebrate paleontologist of the U.S. Geological Survey (1882–1892). He won France's prestigious Cuvier Prize in 1897. In 1898 he presented his renowned collections to Yale.

[*See also* Cope, Edward Drinker; Dinosaurs; Evolution, Theory of; Geological Surveys; Museums of Science and Natural History; National Academy of Sciences; Paleontology; Science; *and* Zoology.]

BIBLIOGRAPHY

McCarren, Mark J. *The Scientific Contributions of Othniel Charles Marsh: Birds, Bones, and Brontotheres.* Peabody Museum of Natural History Special Publication No. 15. New Haven, Conn.: Peabody Museum of Natural History, 1993. This is a useful contribution on Marsh's scientific achievements.

Schuchert, Charles, and Clara Mae LeVene. *O. C. Marsh: Pioneer in Paleontology*. New Haven, Conn.: Yale University Press, 1940. This is the best biography available on Marsh's life and career.

Paul D. Brinkman

MATHEMATICS AND STATISTICS

Mathematics has been part of American higher education since the founding of Harvard College in 1636, whereas mathematical statistics only evolved much later as an area of scholarly concentration. Until the latter part of the nineteenth century, "statistics" referred more to the gathering and compiling, often in tabular form, of numerical data about social and economic problems than to the mathematical analysis and development of statistical methods.

Mathematics in the Context of the General Structure Building of American Science.

In the seventeenth century, mathematics instruction was largely limited to arithmetic and the rudiments of Euclidean geometry, a level that reflected both the primitive state of elementary education and the colleges' underlying aim of preparing young men for the ministry. By 1800, however, new colleges had been founded that were less under the direct influence of particular religious denominations, and colleges as a whole focused more broadly on liberal education. The mathematics curriculum had grown accordingly—and in tandem with the needs of the natural philosophy curriculum—to include algebra, trigonometry, and sometimes even Newton's fluxional calculus. Colonial professors of mathematics had tended to draw, however, from Great Britain, a country that had fallen behind the continent—especially France—relative both to pedagogical innovations and to original research.

This had begun to change by the 1820s. Beginning in 1817, the U.S. Military Academy at West Point (opened in 1802) followed the example of France's state-of-the-art École polytechnique, incorporating into its curriculum not only the calculus in the form it had taken in the hands first of the seventeenth-century German mathematician, Gottfried Leibniz, and then of his eighteenth-century successors like Leonhard Euler, but also the descriptive geometry developed in the latter quarter of the eighteenth century by French *académicien*, Gaspard Monge. At midcentury Harvard, Benjamin Peirce crafted an even more advanced curriculum in the mathematical sciences for the new Lawrence Scientific School (founded in 1847) that included some of the latest foreign research, in particular the work of French mathematical scientists Augustin-Louis Cauchy, Joseph-Louis Lagrange, Pierre Simon de Laplace, and Siméon Denis Poisson, as well as that of the noted Germans Carl Friedrich Gauss and Wilhelm Bessel. Despite curricular advances like these at West Point and Harvard, America's colleges were almost exclusively undergraduate institutions prior to 1876. Research was not part of the faculty's mission, although some, like Benjamin Peirce with his abstract theory of algebras (1870), pursued research anyway (Cajori, 1890; Smith and Ginsburg, 1934; Parshall and Rowe, 1994).

The colleges were not the sole loci of mathematical activity during the first three-quarters of the century, however. Some worked individually: mathematics instructor Robert Adrain discovered the law of least squares in 1809 independently of Gauss, whereas Nathaniel Bowditch, the president of the Essex Fire and Marine Insurance Company in Salem, Massachusetts, translated and wrote penetrating mathematical commentary on Laplace's challenging *Méchanique céleste* (Celestial Mechanics; 1828–1839). The federal government also supported mathematical activity in its U.S. Coast Survey and in its U.S. Nautical Almanac Office, where George William Hill did groundbreaking work on the three-body problem (1877). Examples of original research are, however, isolated prior to the century's closing quarter.

The relative absence of a research ethos manifested itself in what was a 100 percent mortality rate in the United States for specialized mathematics journals prior to 1878. When they did communicate the fruits of their labors in print, mathematicians instead utilized the publications of the general scientific societies that had arisen, such as the American Philosophical Society founded in Philadelphia in 1743 or the American Academy of Arts and Sciences begun in Boston in 1780 and, later, the National Academy of Sciences established in 1863. After its founding in 1848, mathematicians also used the podium at meetings of the American Association for the Advancement of Science to present their ideas directly to their fellow scientists. The United States in the first three-quarters of the nineteenth century did not have the critical mass in mathematics to sustain specialized scientific societies or journals. During the nation's first century from 1776 to 1876, the field evolved not so much as a separate discipline but rather within the broader context of the structure building of American science (Parshall and Rowe, 1994).

The Emergence and Consolidation of Research-level Mathematics.

After 1870, new research-oriented universities were founded, and many extant colleges subsequently reoriented their missions. In mathematics, the first program created to foster research and to offer research-level training opened in 1876 under the British algebraist James Joseph Sylvester at the newly founded Johns Hopkins University. Hopkins president Daniel Coit Gilman had taken a gamble on the 61-year-old Sylvester. One of the most preeminent research mathematicians in Great Britain, Sylvester nevertheless had had mixed experiences in the classroom and had never taught at the graduate level. Prior to his departure to assume the Savilian Professorship of Geometry at Oxford in December of 1883, however, Sylvester and his American colleagues, William Story and Charles S. Peirce, had exposed dozens of students to the latest work in mathematical logic, invariant theory, geometry, partition theory, and the theory of numbers. Those students published primarily in the pages of the *American Journal of Mathematics*, a research-level journal founded by Sylvester in 1878 with Gilman's blessing and encouragement and with the university's financial support. The *American Journal* remains the longest-lived, continuously published

mathematical research journal in the United States (Parshall and Rowe, 1994; Parshall, 2006).

Following Sylvester's return to England, the United States could no longer boast a true graduate-level program in mathematics. Story and his new Hopkins colleague, astronomer Simon Newcomb, tried but failed to maintain the momentum of the Hopkins program, a situation made worse by Story's departure in 1889 to head up the mathematics department at Clark University in Worcester, Massachusetts, a new experiment in purely graduate education. Americans turned instead primarily to the trendsetting German scene and particularly to Felix Klein, first at the University of Leipzig and then at Göttingen University beginning in 1886. Klein, widely recognized in the early 1880s as one of the most talented mathematicians on the continent, embraced graduate teaching and opened his lecture halls and seminars to promising students from Germany as well as abroad. In particular, students in the so-called "American colony" that emerged in Göttingen absorbed from Klein the latest mathematics as well as the notion that teaching and research defined the dual mission of the academic mathematician.

Klein's students returned home to American institutions newly receptive to the educational ideals he had instilled in them. For example, the American Henry Seely White joined his German academic "brother" Oskar Bolza at Clark. There, together with their colleagues Story, Henry Taber, and Joseph de Perott, they crafted a curriculum that encompassed much of nineteenth-century mathematics, including courses in geometry, invariant theory, the calculus of variations, the theory of elliptic functions, algebra, and number theory. This vibrant program suffered a major blow in 1892 when William Rainey Harper stole Bolza away for the University of Chicago, which opened its doors in 1892 and of which he was the first president. Headed by American-trained Eliakim Hastings Moore, the Chicago department soon also included another of Klein's German students, Heinrich Maschke, as well as Moore's student, Leonard Eugene Dickson. These four men guided a generation of American mathematicians into the fields of algebra, the calculus of variations, and functional analysis. Moore and Dickson, in particular, also introduced them to the postulate-theoretic work of Göttingen powerhouse David Hilbert.

Meanwhile, on the East Coast, William Fogg Osgood and Maxime Bôcher brought their German training and research ethos to Harvard University, which, under president Charles Eliot, transformed itself into a major research university over the course of Eliot's 40-year term from 1869 to 1909. The story at Princeton was in some ways similar. Klein's student, Henry Burchard Fine, served as dean there and worked with Princeton president Woodrow Wilson to effect the same kind of transformation. In mathematics, they had assembled a group of researchers, both American and foreign trained, that, by the start of World War I, included Oswald Veblen in topology and the foundations of geometry, Joseph H. M. Wedderburn in algebra, and Luther Pfahler Eisenhart in differential geometry. Klein's students, together with a slowly growing cadre of home-grown talent, also helped to animate programs at Cornell University; the Massachusetts Institute of Technology; the University of California, Berkeley; Johns Hopkins University; and others, literally from coast to coast (Duren et al., 1988–1989; Parshall and Rowe, 1994).

The attainment of a certain critical mass that these developments suggest is further reflected in the creation of at least two key professional accoutrements: a national specialized society and specialized research journals. Begun as the New York Mathematical Society with a mere six members in 1888, the American Mathematical Society (AMS) had evolved by 1894 and had grown to a membership of well over two hundred strong. Mathematicians used the regular meetings of the AMS in New York City—as well as the meetings of its officially sanctioned "sections" in Chicago beginning in 1896, in San Francisco starting in 1902, and in the "southwest," convening first in Columbia, Missouri, in 1906—to communicate their evolving mathematical ideas. At the same time, they filled the pages of new research journals like the *Annals of Mathematics* (1884 to the present) and the *Bulletin* (1891 to the present) and the *Transactions of the American Mathematical Society* (1900 to the present). By 1900, then, the United States

boasted a self-sustaining professional community of mathematicians characterized by active research programs across the country and the regular communication of new results, both face to face at meetings and in print in high-quality technical journals (Archibald, 1938; Parshall and Rowe, 1994).

This community consolidated and grew from 1900 to World War II. Although Americans embraced much of pure mathematics, certain areas became recognized American strengths. Leonard Eugene Dickson and his student, A. Adrian Albert, established a center for algebra at the University of Chicago (Parshall, 2004). Princeton, with Oswald Veblen, Luther Pfahler Eisenhart, James Alexander, and Solomon Lefschetz, became known for geometry and topology. Robert L. Moore engendered a school of point-set topology at the University of Texas at Austin. Harvard built on its strength in analysis with George David Birkhoff, Joseph Walsh, and Marshall Stone (Duren et al., 1988–1989; Parshall and Rowe, 1994).

The Evolution of a Statistical Community. Many of the same factors that contributed to the emergence of research-level mathematics in the United States in the last quarter of the nineteenth century—the founding of new colleges and universities, the rise of a research ethos within higher education, the establishment of general scientific societies and publications, the creation within the federal government of loci of support for scientific inquiry—also affected the development of a statistical community, especially in the opening decades of the twentieth century. Although 5 men—a printer and social reformer, a minister, 2 lawyers, and a doctor—joined in 1839 to form the American Statistical Association (ASA), this group never had more than 75 members or more than 10 in attendance at any of its meetings prior to the 1880s and, not surprisingly, was unable to sustain a publication. Its members, moreover, viewed their association as an agent for the gathering of statistical data for the betterment of society; theirs was not a mathematical concept of statistics. By midcentury, however, the launching of numerous geographic surveys aimed at better understanding the vast territory that was by then the United States, the founding of observatories that focused both on basic research and on the generation of precise astronomical observations applicable to navigation, and the establishment of an American insurance industry all influenced the development of mathematical statistics (Stigler, 1980; Hunter, 1996).

Interestingly, two of the contributors to the emergence of research-level mathematics were also two of the early developers of statistical thought in the United States, Benjamin Peirce and his son, Charles Sanders Peirce. As Harvard's Perkins Professor of Mathematics and Astronomy, Benjamin Peirce was also involved in questions concerning observational astronomy and worked closely with the U.S. Coast Survey, first as its director of longitude determinations and then as its superintendent. This astronomical work prompted him to consider the question of when an observational outlier should be rejected and to develop, in a paper published in 1852, the first significance test for use in answering it. Peirce's son, Charles, worked for the Coast Survey but had interests that ranged widely, from mathematics to experimental psychology to mathematical logic to philosophy. Particularly in the 1870s and 1880s, C. S. Peirce made novel contributions to the design of experiments as well as to the theory of errors of observations. Other key nineteenth-century American contributors to mathematical statistics were Simon Newcomb, the same astronomer who had replaced Sylvester at the Johns Hopkins University, and Yale-trained Erastus DeForest, whose work in mathematical statistics on issues such as test of fit stemmed from his analysis of the actuarial problem of smoothing mortality tables (Stigler, 1980).

These men, however, pursued their statistical research largely in isolation from the activities of the ASA, which continued to emphasize statistics as the collection of data for the study of social issues and not statistics of a more mathematical or theoretical cast. This is perhaps not surprising in light of the fact that in the last 20 years of the nineteenth century and through the opening two decades of the twentieth, the limited statistics instruction available in the United States took place in courses in the social sciences and not in departments of mathematics. Starting in the 1920s, however, academic centers in mathematical statistics coalesced at the University of Iowa under Henry Rietz, at Columbia University, and then at the University of North Carolina at Chapel Hill under Harold Hotelling and elsewhere. One unintended consequence of this growth was the increasing tension between those engaged in social science statistics and those with more sophisticated mathematical training interested in grounding statistical methods in rigorous mathematical theory. A rift between these two constituencies ultimately resulted in the formation of two largely separate communities of statistical practitioners.

The break first manifested itself in the formation of the *Annals of Mathematical Statistics* in 1929 by Harry Carver, a professor of mathematics at the University of Michigan. Although he initially chose to work within and to cooperate with the ASA in founding and running his new journal, by 1933 the interests of the social scientists in the ASA and those of the more mathematically oriented statisticians, who contributed to and supported the *Annals of Mathematical Statistics* through the ASA, had significantly diverged. In 1935, Carver and others formed the Institute of Mathematical Statistics (IMS) and adopted the *Annals* as the Institute's publication. That year thus marks, at least symbolically, the coming of age of a new discipline—mathematical statistics—in the United States (Hunter, 1996). The mathematical divide that gave birth to the IMS and to a separate field of mathematical statistics in the 1930s would largely be closed—at least institutionally—after World War II, with the American Statistical Society reclaiming its dominant position within the statistical profession.

The Impact of Geopolitics in the 1930s and 1940s. The so-called "big migration" of European scholars displaced by the rise of national socialism in Germany in the 1930s ultimately resulted in an influx of more than 120 European-trained mathematical scientists primarily into America's colleges and universities. These scientists, including many world leaders in their fields, stepped into the high-level mathematical and intellectual environment that had evolved in the United States as a result of the developments sketched above. Although they worked in many of the areas that had come to characterize American mathematics, some of them brought new areas of expertise to American shores. For example, algebraists Emil Artin, Richard Brauer, and Emmy Noether were well known and established themselves quickly within what was already a vibrant American algebraic community, whereas mathematical statisticians Jerzy Neyman and Abraham Wald took up positions at the University of California, Berkeley and Columbia, respectively, and helped to further the development of the community of mathematical statisticians as reflected in the IMS. Somewhat in a class by himself, the German algebraist and mathematical physicist Hermann Weyl accepted, as did Albert Einstein, a position at the Institute for Advanced Study, a privately funded, elite research institution founded in Princeton in 1930. On the other hand, Richard von Mises at Harvard, Mark Kac at Cornell, and William Feller at Princeton established mathematical probability as a new area of strength in American mathematics following their immigration. Applied mathematics likewise profited from the European influx—German émigré Richard Courant established a major center in the field at New York University—as well as from the formation of industrial research facilities like Bell Telephone Laboratories (founded in 1925) and from the actual war effort (Duren et al., 1988–1989). Primarily through the Applied Mathematics Panel, a unit within the federal government's Office of Scientific Research and Development (established by executive order in 1941), mathematicians and statisticians of all stripes contributed to the solution of a host of war-related questions involved in fire control, bombing, and statistical analysis, among others (Owens, 1989).

The Mathematical Sciences in the Postwar Era.

Partly as a result of wartime successes, the postwar period witnessed a dramatic increase in federal support for the mathematical sciences. The establishment of the National Science Foundation in 1950 led to an institutionalization of academic grants that has contributed to the explosive growth of American mathematical

and statistical research from the 1960s to the present. For example, American mathematicians have solved such noted problems as the Bieberbach conjecture, the classification of finite simple groups, the four-color problem, and Fermat's last theorem. The immigration of mathematical scientists from China, the former Soviet bloc, and elsewhere has also contributed to the country's strength in mathematics and statistics, although it has taxed resources dependent on the nation's overall financial health. Whereas Germany had dominated the mathematical sciences on the international scene from the late nineteenth century up to the outbreak of World War II, the United States assumed that leadership role in the postwar era (Parshall, 2009).

[See also American Association for the Advancement of Science; American Philosophical Society; Astronomy and Astrophysics; Bell Laboratories; Bowditch, Nathaniel; Einstein, Albert; National Academy of Sciences; National Science Foundation; Newcomb, Simon; and Office of Scientific Research and Development.]

BIBLIOGRAPHY

Archibald, Raymond C. *A Semicentennial History of the American Mathematical Society.* New York: American Mathematical Society, 1938; reprint ed., New York: Arno Press, 1980. A history of the first 50 years of the American Mathematical Society drawn largely from its archives and published records.

Cajori, Florian. *The Teaching and History of Mathematics in the United States.* Washington, D.C.: U.S. Government Printing Office, 1890. A rare glimpse of program histories, mathematical curricula, and educational practice based on data gathered from institutions of higher education extant in 1888.

Duren, Peter L., Richard A. Askey, Harold M. Edwards, and Uta C. Merzbach, eds. *A Century of Mathematics in America. Parts I–III.* Providence, R.I.: American Mathematical Society, 1988–1989. Three volumes of historical articles, both reprinted and specially commissioned, compiled on the occasion of the hundredth anniversary of the American Mathematical Society and documenting many aspects of the technical and institutional history of mathematics in the United States.

Hunter, Patti Wilger. "Drawing the Boundaries: Mathematical Statistics in 20th-Century America." *Historia Mathematica* 23 (1996): 7–30. An astute analysis of the formation of mathematical statistics as a subdiscipline, distinct from statistics as routine data gathering.

Owens, Larry. "Mathematicians at War: Warren Weaver and the Applied Mathematics Panel, 1942–1945." In *The History of Modern Mathematics*, edited by David E. Rowe and John McCleary, Vol. 2, pp. 287–305. Boston: Academic Press, 1989. A valuable study of the efforts to integrate and use America's mathematical talent during World War II.

Parshall, Karen Hunger. "Defining a Mathematical Research School: The Case of Algebra at the University of Chicago, 1892–1945." *Historia Mathematica* 31 (2004): 263–278. A case study on the emergence of the United States as an international leader in algebra in the twentieth century.

Parshall, Karen Hunger. *James Joseph Sylvester: Jewish Mathematician in a Victorian World*. Baltimore: Johns Hopkins University Press, 2006. A biography of Sylvester that details, among the other aspects of his life, his role in bringing research-level mathematics to the United States via his professorship at the Johns Hopkins University.

Parshall, Karen Hunger. "Marshall Stone and the Internationalization of the American Mathematical Research Community." *Bulletin of the American Mathematical Society* 46 (2009): 459–483. A study of the self-conscious efforts of American mathematicians, and especially Marshall Stone, to exert a leadership role within the international mathematical community.

Parshall, Karen Hunger, and David E. Rowe. *The Emergence of the American Mathematical Research Community, 1876–1900: James Joseph Sylvester, Felix Klein, and Eliakim Hastings Moore*. Providence, R.I.: American Mathematical Society, 1994. The first, and still the definitive, book-length study of the institutional and technical mathematical developments that shaped a professional community of mathematicians in the United States.

Smith, David Eugene, and Jekuthiel Ginsburg. *A History of Mathematics in America before 1900*. Chicago: Mathematical Association of America, 1934; reprint ed., New York: Arno Press, 1980. An early historical study of mathematics in America that provides fact-filled overviews of seventeenth-, eighteenth-, and nineteenth-century developments.

Stigler, Stephen M., ed. *American Contributions to Mathematical Statistics in the Nineteenth Century*. 2 vols. New York: Arno Press, 1980. A collection of reprints of the principal research works in statistics published by nineteenth-century Americans, together with several historical articles, among them Stigler's introduction on "Mathematical Statistics in the Early States" reprinted from the *Annals of Statistics*.

Karen Hunger Parshall

MAURY, MATTHEW FONTAINE

(1806–1873), naval oceanographer. Born near Fredericksburg, Virginia, Matthew Fontaine Maury grew up in Tennessee. His formal education was limited. After graduating from Harpeth Academy in 1825 at the age of 19, he joined the U.S. Navy as a midshipman and participated in international naval cruises, including a circumnavigation of the world between 1826 and 1830. Maury decided to collect the necessary data for a practical navigational textbook for young naval officers, which he published in 1836. After his appointment as lieutenant in 1836, he accepted an invitation to serve as astronomer for the U.S. Exploring Expedition to the Pacific Ocean and nearby regions (known as the Wilkes Expedition). Although he decided to withdraw after a change in the leadership of the expedition, preparation for the assignment gave him an opportunity to work with experts at an observatory in Philadelphia.

Maury was badly injured in a stagecoach accident in 1839, and the Navy decided to limit his duties to shore assignments. In 1842, the Secretary of the Navy placed him in charge of the Depot of Charts and Instruments, which had been acquiring scientific instruments since its establishment in 1830. The Depot sought to advance navigation through the application of hydrography, meteorology, the study of magnetism, and especially astronomy. Congress agreed to fund an astronomical observatory building, and when it was finished in 1844, the Secretary of the Navy also appointed Maury to head the new "National Observatory."

Although Maury's contributions to astronomy were limited, he did make major contributions to navigation by collecting information on winds and currents from old ships' logs and publishing useful charts based on these data. He also organized a cooperative effort involving over one thousand mariners who sent him standardized reports about winds and currents, which he used to construct navigational charts with accompanying instructions as well as charts of useful physical and biological information. By reducing sailing times and minimizing dangers, the charts saved money and lives. Maury also played a key role in organizing an international congress in Brussels, Belgium, in 1853 that sought to develop an international system of standardized weather observations by trained weather observers. And he used naval resources to map out and investigate the bottom composition of the undersea plateau that would provide the best location for the laying of the first transatlantic undersea telegraph cable.

Maury became especially well known for his 1855 book, *The Physical Geography of the Sea*. Although often seen as an important early effort in the science of oceanography, the book was criticized by contemporaries for relying on speculative theories. Alexander Dallas Bache, the head of the U.S. Coast Survey and the central leader of a group of elite men of science in the United States during the 1840s and 1850s, was particularly critical of Maury, not only for being overly speculative but also for not having the proper educational qualifications and expertise to pursue investigations in specialized fields such as astronomy. Bache and Joseph Henry, the secretary of the Smithsonian Institution, also headed rival institutions pursuing similar scientific activities.

During the Civil War, Maury joined the confederate navy. He taught at the Virginia Military Academy from 1868 until his death in 1873.

[*See also* **Astronomy and Astrophysics; Geophysics; Maritime Transport; Meteorology and Climatology; Oceanography;** *and* **Science.**]

BIBLIOGRAPHY

Burstyn, Harold L. "Matthew Fontaine Maury." In *Complete Dictionary of Scientific Biography*, Vol. 9. Detroit: Charles Scribner's Sons, 2008.

Williams, Frances Leigh. *Matthew Fontaine Maury, Scientist of the Sea*. New Brunswick, N.J.: Rutgers University Press, 1963.

Hugh Richard Slotten

MAYER, MARIA GOEPPERT

(1906–1972), theoretical physicist, Nobel laureate. She received the Nobel Prize in Physics in 1963 for a theoretical model for the structure of the atomic nucleus. She is the only woman other than Marie Curie to receive this prize.

Maria Goeppert was born in Kattowitz, Germany (now Poland), and studied theoretical physics and quantum mechanics at the University of Göttingen under Max Born. In 1930 she received her PhD and married the American chemist Joseph E. Mayer. The couple moved to Baltimore, Maryland, where Joe had an appointment at the Johns Hopkins University. Maria became an American citizen in 1933. For the next 15 years, despite having no paid position, Goeppert Mayer remained scientifically active by collaborating with both chemists and physicists at Hopkins and then at Columbia University after her husband joined the faculty there in 1939. During World War II she worked part time with a branch of the Manhattan Project, investigating the separation of uranium isotopes.

After the war, the University of Chicago attracted both Mayers to its new Institute for Nuclear Studies. Goeppert Mayer worked as a voluntary associate professor at the institute and took a part-time (paid) position as a research physicist at the new Argonne National Laboratory. While working on a theory of the origin of the chemical elements, Goeppert Mayer discovered that nuclei with certain specific numbers of protons or neutrons—2, 8, 20, 28, 50, 82, or 126—were unusually stable. She called these "magic numbers"; they suggested that nuclei have quantized energy levels, or "shells." However, she was unable to explain why it was that protons and neutrons occupy shells in a different order than electrons do until she recognized that the phenomenon of "spin-orbit coupling" could account for the observed shells in nuclei. This was the basis of her spin-orbit coupling shell model of the nucleus.

A team of scientists in Germany including Hans D. Jensen at the University of Heidelberg reached this same model simultaneously and independently. Mayer and Jensen collaborated on the development of their model of the nucleus and coauthored the book *Elementary Theory of Nuclear Shell Structure*. They shared the Nobel Prize in 1963.

Goeppert Mayer moved to California in 1960 after both she and her husband were offered full (paid) professorships at the University of California at San Diego. She taught there until her death in 1972.

[*See also* **Gender and Science; Manhattan Project; Nobel Prize in Biomedical Research; Physics;** *and* **Quantum Theory.**]

BIBLIOGRAPHY

Johnson, Karen E. "Maria Goeppert Mayer." In *Dictionary of Scientific Biography, Supplement II.* New York: Charles Scribner's Sons, 1990. The most comprehensive survey of Goeppert Mayer's scientific career.
Mayer, Maria Goeppert, and J. Hans D. Jensen. *Elementary Theory of Nuclear Shell Structure.* New York: John Wiley & Sons, 1955. The most complete treatment of Goeppert Mayer's nuclear model.

Karen E. Johnson

MAYO CLINIC

Innovative medical center in Rochester, Minnesota. In 1863, an English-born, nomadic country doctor, William Worrall Mayo, moved his wife, three daughters, and infant son, William James Mayo, to the frontier town of Rochester (population three thousand), where a second son, Charles Horace Mayo, was born in 1865. The unwillingness of W. W. Mayo's wife to move again compelled the restless doctor to remain in Rochester.

When a tornado devastated the town in 1883, the local sisters of the Order of St. Francis offered to build a hospital there if Dr. Mayo and his two physician sons, affectionately known as Drs. Will and Charlie, would staff it. Saint Mary's, the first general hospital in southeastern Minnesota, opened in 1889. Drs. Will and Charlie tirelessly traveled throughout Europe and the United States to learn the newest surgical techniques, and soon their reputation for expert diagnoses and safe surgery lured physicians from around the world to Rochester to watch the brothers perform. In 1892, the Mayos began inviting other doctors to join their practice. Among the first was Dr. Henry Plummer, whose vision of a private, coordinated, multispecialty group practice of medicine dedicated to patient care became the core of the Mayo Clinic philosophy. The Mayo Graduate School of Medicine, the world's first formal program to train medical specialists, opened in 1915 with an endowment from the Mayo brothers. In 1919, the Mayos turned over their personal assets to form what is now the Mayo Foundation; the partnerships were dissolved and the entire staff became salaried. The Mayo Medical School was started in 1972. The Mayo Foundation opened its first "satellite" Mayo Clinic in Jacksonville, Florida, in 1986 and its second in Scottsdale, Arizona, in 1987.

Mayo milestones include sharing the Nobel Prize for the discovery of cortisone, creation of a system to grade different types of cancer, development of the first effective tuberculosis treatment, performing the first hip replacement, pioneering open-heart surgery, and pivotal work in the development of successful organ transplantation.

[*See also* **Cardiology; Group Practice; Health and Fitness; Health Insurance; Health Maintenance Organizations; Hospitals; Medical Education; Medical Specialization; Medicine; Nobel Prize in Biomedical Research; Organ Transplantation;** *and* **Surgery.**]

BIBLIOGRAPHY

Clapesattle, Helen. *The Doctors Mayo.* Rochester, Minn.: Mayo Foundation for Medical Education and Research, 1990.

Fye, W. Bruce. "The Origins and Evolution of the Mayo Clinic from 1864 to 1939: A Minnesota Family Practice Becomes an International 'Medical Mecca.'" *Bulletin of the History of Medicine* 84 (Fall 2010): 323–357.

C. D. B. Bryan

MAYR, ERNST

(1905–2005), ornithologist and evolutionary biologist. Mayr's long life included successes in the diverse fields of ornithology (avian systematics and biogeography), evolution, history, and philosophy of science. After training in Berlin, Germany, under Erwin Stresemann and receiving a PhD in 1926, Mayr undertook a tripartite expedition to New Guinea and the Solomon Islands (1928–1930), returning to Berlin in May 1930. Shortly thereafter, he received an invitation as a temporary curator at the American Museum of Natural History to work on the large Whitney collection of South Sea birds beginning in January 1931. The museum had also just obtained the huge bird collection of Lord Rothschild. In 1932 Mayr was appointed the Whitney-Rothschild curator and remained there until 1953, publishing over two hundred papers and describing 26 new species and 445 new subspecies. His work on species systematics and geographic variation laid the foundation for his book *Systematics and the Origin of Species*—based on his 1941 Jesup lectures at Columbia University and considered the second volume of the evolutionary synthesis (1937–1948) that established the foundation of modern evolutionary theory. Mayr was one of the founders of the Society for the Study of Evolution (secretary, 1946, and president, 1950) and the first editor (1947–1949) of its journal, *Evolution*. Based on his systematic work, Mayr clarified the concept of the species and the evolutionary process of speciation and analyzed the mechanisms of animal distribution (including island biogeography, 1933) and the patterns of historical biogeography.

In 1953, Mayr accepted a position as an Alexander Agassiz Professor (1953–1975 and Emeritus until his death in January 2005) at the Museum of Comparative Zoology, Harvard University, serving as director of the museum (1961–1970). He continued his ornithological work as the main editor and organizer for the completion of the multivolumed (vol. 8–15) *Peters' Check-list of the Birds of the World* and served as president of the American Ornithologists' Union (1956–1959) and of the International Ornithological Congress (Ithaca, N.Y., 1961). But with his move to Harvard, Mayr's scholarly work changed from largely avian systematics to mainly evolutionary theory (*Animal Species and Evolution*, 1963), history (*The Growth of Biological Thought*, 1982), and philosophy of biology (*Toward a New Philosophy of Biology*, 1988). He advocated the basic idea of dual causation (functional and evolutionary), which is unique to biology and is central for the autonomy of biology from the physical sciences.

Of the many honorary degrees and awards received by Mayr during his life, he was most proud that the library of the Museum of Comparative Zoology was named for him in 1994 in recognition of his ninetieth birthday.

[*See also* Biological Sciences; Evolution, Theory of; Museums of Science and Natural History; Science: From 1914 to 1945; Science: Since 1945; Social Sciences: Before 1945; Social Sciences: Post–World War II; *and* Zoology.]

BIBLIOGRAPHY

Bock, W. J., and M. R. Lein, eds. "Ernst Mayr at 100." *Ornithological Monographs* 58 (2005): vii + 109. Includes a DVD, "A Taped Interview with Ernst Mayr."

Haffer, J. *Ornithology, Evolution and Philosophy, the Life and Science of Ernst Mayr (1904–2005)*. Berlin: Springer Verlag, 2007.

Walter J. Bock

McCLINTOCK, BARBARA

(1902–1992), biologist and Nobel laureate. Born in Hartford, Barbara McClintock was educated at

Cornell, from which she received a BS in 1923, an MA in 1925, and a PhD in botany in 1927. She taught at Cornell and the University of Missouri before joining the Department of Genetics at the Carnegie-funded research center at Cold Spring Harbor, Long Island, in 1941, where she remained for the rest of her career.

McClintock's place in the history of biology is guaranteed by a lifelong career of pathbreaking research in genetics and cytology. The year of her birth coincided with the rediscovery of Gregor Mendel's work and her coming of age with that of genetics. Her early work on maize at Cornell University in the 1920s and 1930s, combining microscopic studies of chromosome structure with the new science of genetics, provided crucial evidence for the chromosomal basis of genetic crossover and made her reputation among geneticists. Her 1931 paper, "A Correlation of Cytological and Genetical Crossing-Over in *Zea mays*," co-written with graduate student Harriet Creighton, confirmed the correlation between cytological crossing over, in which two chromosome arms physically cross each other and exchange segments, and genetic crossover, where alleles change linkage groups.

McClintock's pioneering work on the transposition of genes in the 1940s and 1950s is that for which she is best known. This work, performed after she moved to Cold Spring Harbor, started with a cross of two strains of maize in an attempt to complete a normal gene-mapping exercise. Instead, the cross produced a number of surprising mutations. Her study of this phenomenon demonstrated that chromosomes are dynamic structures, but it went against the prevailing view of the time that the position of genes on the chromosome was fixed. As a result, her findings seemed incomprehensible to many scientists and went largely unheeded for years. In the 1970s, however, with the identification of "jumping genes" in the bacteria *Escherichia coli*, McClintock's much earlier work with maize was recalled and granted new recognition. In 1983, she was awarded the Nobel Prize, 32 years after her first definitive paper on the subject.

McClintock particularly interests historians of biology for her success in breaking with tradition on a number of fronts: as a geneticist whose understanding of genes was shaped by her interests in development, as a woman who refused to be constrained by conventional notions of gender, and as a scientist who dared to affirm the necessity of a "feeling for the organism" in the rational construction of knowledge.

[*See also* **Biological Sciences; Botany; Gender and Science; Genetics and Genetic Engineering; Nobel Prize in Biomedical Research;** *and* **Science.**]

BIBLIOGRAPHY

Comfort, Nathaniel C. "McClintock, Barbara." *Complete Dictionary of Scientific Biography*, Vol. 23, pp. 67–72. Detroit: Charles Scribner's Sons, 2008.

Comfort, Nathaniel C. *The Tangled Field: Barbara McClintock's Search for the Patterns of Genetic Control.* Cambridge, Mass.: Harvard University Press, 2001.

Federoff, Nina, and David Botstein, eds. *The Dynamic Genome: Barbara McClintock's Ideas in the Century of Genetics.* Cold Spring Harbor, N.Y.: Cold Spring Harbor Laboratory Press, 1992.

Keller, Evelyn Fox. *A Feeling for the Organism: The Life and Work of Barbara McClintock.* San Francisco: W. H. Freeman, 1983.

Evelyn Fox Keller;
updated by Elspeth Knewstubb

McCORMICK, CYRUS HALL

(1809–1884), inventor and manufacturer. Cyrus Hall McCormick was born on a farm in Rockbridge County, Virginia, the eldest of eight children. His father, Robert, was a farmer and inventor, interested especially in developing labor-saving innovations for farming. In 1831, McCormick took up a project his father had pursued unsuccessfully for 20 years: building a reaper to speed the harvesting of small grains. In July 1831, he gave a public demonstration of his new design, mowing a field of wheat on John Steele's farm in

Rockbridge. This prototype reaper included key innovations common to every subsequent reaper. Other inventors were also working on creating reaping machinery, so in 1834 McCormick secured a 14-year patent for his invention. Although he was not the first person to receive a patent for a reaper (Obed Hussey had obtained one a year earlier), McCormick's skill at marketing his invention made his reaper the foremost machine used. He showed that his machine was faster than Hussey's and designed a seat that allowed the farmer to sit on the reaper rather than walk alongside. In 1847 McCormick moved to Chicago, where he established a manufacturing business for his new invention. Relocating to Chicago was an advantage because it was closer to the agricultural heartland, with excellent transportation access. His company soon became the leading manufacturer, a position it held until the Civil War.

During the war, while McCormick lived in London and sought to promote his machine in Europe, his company lost its leadership as a manufacturer of farm machinery, although it remained important. After the war, McCormick left the company management to his brother Leander. When the devastating Chicago fire destroyed his factory in 1871, McCormick considered abandoning the business, but his wife, Nettie Fowler (whom he married in 1858), intervened, urging reconstruction of the factory. Thereafter she played a central role in the management of the McCormick Company and its successor, the International Harvester Corporation.

From 1857 until his death, McCormick was deeply involved in Democratic Party politics. He was also a committed Presbyterian layman. In 1859, he endowed four professorships at the Presbyterian Theological Seminary of the Northwest (renamed McCormick Theological Seminary in 1886). McCormick's inventive genius transformed grain harvesting and agricultural practices, yet the success of his company (and, perhaps, his reputation) resulted primarily from the business acumen of his wife and, subsequently, his eldest son, Cyrus Jr.

[See also **Agricultural Technology**; *and* **Machinery and Manufacturing.**]

BIBLIOGRAPHY

"Cyrus Hall McCormick." In *Movers & Shakers: The 100 Most Influential Figures in Modern Business*, pp. 256–259. Cambridge, Mass.: Basic Books, 2003.

Hurt, R. Douglas. *American Farm Tools: From Hand-Power to Steam-Power*. Manhattan, Kan.: Sunflower University Press, 1982.

Hutchinson, William T. *Cyrus Hall McCormick*. 2 vols. New York: The Century Co., 1930, 1935. With a foreword by William E. Dodd.

Rikoon, J. Sanford. *Threshing in the Midwest, 1820–1940: A Study of Traditional Culture and Technological Change*. Bloomington: Indiana University Press, 1989.

Fred V. Carstensen; updated by Elspeth Knewstubb and Hugh Richard Slotten

MEAD, MARGARET

(1901–1978), anthropologist and social reformer. Margaret Mead was born in Philadelphia to Emily Fogg, a sociologist, feminist, and suffragist, and Edward Sherwood Mead, professor of economics at the University of Pennsylvania. She graduated from Barnard College with a bachelor's degree in 1923 and in 1929 received a PhD in anthropology from Columbia University, where she was trained by Franz Boas, a pioneer in cultural anthropology. In 1926, she took up employment in the American Museum of Natural History's anthropology department, staying in this position until her death.

Initially specializing in children and women, Mead later extended her interests to psychological and applied anthropology, gender and cultural change, human settlements, and diet and nutrition. Her *Coming of Age in Samoa: A Psychological Study of Primitive Youth for Western Civilization* (1928) established her reputation as a field researcher and writer. Mead proposed that cultural conditioning shaped human behavior, an anthropological theory that came to be known as cultural determinism. The book was also one of the first major anthropological works read widely by a general audience. With hindsight, later critics would note that in this and later works, such as *Sex and Temperament in Three Primitive Societies*

(1935), she neglected the biological determinants of human behavior. In *Margaret Mead and Samoa: The Making and Unmaking of an Anthropological Myth* (1983), anthropologist Derek Freeman criticized her research methodology and suggested that her idyllic picture of polymorphous, guilt-free sexual activity among adolescent Samoans was intended primarily as a critique of Western sexual repressiveness. Still, these and other works by Mead remain acknowledged classics. As a field-worker, she encouraged the use of photography, film, and tape recorders.

Mead believed that science could and should promote human betterment. Appalled by America's atomic bombing of Hiroshima and Nagasaki in 1945, she sought to ameliorate social problems through anthropological understanding. During the 1950s and 1960s she became a media celebrity, projecting the image of a wise, advice-giving grandmother commenting on a wide range of issues. She testified at congressional hearings and spoke in public forums on U.S. foreign policy, family and child-rearing issues, drug laws, and nuclear-power regulation; participated in international and United Nations conferences concerning population control, food supply, and health; and served as president of the Scientists' Institute for Public Information (1972), the World Federation of Mental Health (1956–1957), and the American Association for the Advancement of Science (1975). A prolific writer, Mead published some 35 books and hundreds of articles, both scholarly and popular.

[*See also* **American Association for the Advancement of Science; American Museum of Natural History; Anthropology; Boas, Franz; Film Technology; Food and Diet; Gender and Science; Museums of Science and Natural History; Nuclear Power; Nuclear Regulatory Commission; Photography; Sex and Sexuality; Sex Education; Social Sciences;** *and* **Sound Technology, Recorded.**]

BIBLIOGRAPHY

Batesone, Mary Catherine. *With a Daughter's Eye: A Memoir of Margaret Mead and Gregory Bateson.* New York: W. Morrow, 1984.

Duncan, Joyce. "Margaret Mead (1901–1979)." In *Ahead of Their Time: A Biographical Dictionary of Risk-Taking Women,* pp. 217–221. Westport, Conn.: Greenwood Press, 2002.

Mead, Margaret. *Blackberry Winter: My Earlier Years.* New York: W. Morrow, 1972.

Molloy, Maureen A. *On Creating a Usable Culture: Margaret Mead and the Emergence of American Cosmopolitanism.* Honolulu: University of Hawai'i Press, 2008.

Virginia Yans;
updated by Elspeth Knewstubb

MEDICAL EDUCATION

Until well into the nineteenth century most American physicians, when trained at all, learned to heal by serving apprenticeships. Nevertheless, they commonly appropriated the academic title "doctor." In one contract, drawn up in 1736, an experienced "Practitioner in Physick [Medicine] & Surgery" in Boston pledged to instruct a young man in "the Arts, Mysterys and Businesses of Physick & Surgery" for two years and to provide room and board in return for a payment of two hundred pounds. Although estimates in the historical literature for the length of an apprenticeship vary greatly, the only quantitative study, for colonial Massachusetts, shows that the average apprenticeship lasted only a little over a year. Only a handful of trained physicians moved to the colonies, and not many aspiring physicians from the American colonies traveled abroad for MDs. During the last half of the eighteenth century the medical school at the University of Edinburgh, then the most popular European destination, attracted a little more than a hundred American students (Christianson, 1987, pp. 117–126).

Because of the indelicacy of dissecting former patients for educational purposes, few preceptors gave their apprentices hands-on instruction in human anatomy. This deficiency gave rise, about 1730, to short anatomical courses in urban areas. The first extant announcement dates from 1752, when a New Jersey surgeon advertised a course of anatomical lectures, justifying his venture by claiming that "anatomy is allowed on all hands, to be the foundation both of physick [that is, medicine] and surgery." William Shippen, who had studied in London, established the first regularly delivered lectures on anatomy, in Philadelphia in 1762. He also offered a pioneering course on midwifery or obstetrics (Blake, 1980, pp. 29–31).

In 1765 the trustees of the College of Philadelphia created the first medical professorship in British North America and appointed the Edinburgh-trained John Morgan to fill it. The purpose of the new medical school was to provide training in the medical sciences, not to offer clinical training, which was still to be acquired by apprenticeship. In sharing his vision of medical education, Morgan emphasized the importance of "medical science," which comprised such disciplines as anatomy, materia medica, botany, and chemistry. He urged that "medical researches and careful experiments" be undertaken in the field of natural history, "as natural history is one of the most essential studies to prepare a person for prosecuting medicine with success, and one of the most distinguished ornaments of a physician and man of letters" (Bell, 1965). Despite such good intentions, it would be over a century before American medical schools invested seriously in research.

One of the primary reasons for the miniscule record of research was that American medical schools, like many in Great Britain, derived their income almost solely from student fees, which the professors divided among themselves. This scheme fostered mediocrity because high standards would almost inevitably have reduced the number of fee-paying students. Because some medical schools required less of their matriculants than did the best liberal arts colleges, they sometimes enrolled what one observer called "*the leavings of all the other professions.*" Most medical students never attended college, and some barely knew how to read and write. The college boys who did go into medicine, complained one educator, were often those "who, from various causes—ill-health, poor scholarship, bad conduct and general discouragement—fall by the wayside and after one or two years of study, leave college without a diploma." In view of such conditions, it is not surprising that contemporary critics frequently identified inadequate preliminary education as the highest barrier to the cultivation of medical sci-

ence in America. "Our physicians and other professional men have genius enough," observed a Boston medical journal in 1833; "their defect is in mental discipline, which was not acquired during their preparatory studies in such a degree as to make the daily acquisition of knowledge, and the habitual exercise of the mental powers, become a primary object of pursuit, and a principal source of their highest enjoyment" (Bonner, 1995; Numbers, 1988, pp. 52–53; Numbers and Warner, 1987, p. 194).

American students not only entered medical school ill prepared for a scientific career, but also frequently left in the same condition. In contrast to the leading continental schools, which at midcentury required attendance for four years and devoted nine or ten months each year to lectures, the medical school of the University of Pennsylvania, one of American's finest, required only 25 weeks a year for two years, and most American schools offered annual terms of fewer than four months. To make matters worse, American medical students until the last quarter of the century customarily repeated the very same courses during their second "year" that they had taken during their first. Because of the brevity and nature of the medical curriculum, it was no wonder, commented one medical reformer in 1845, that 99 of every one hundred American physicians were poorly educated:

> With no *practical* knowledge of chemistry and botany; with but a smattering of anatomy and physiology, hastily caught during a sixteen weeks' attendance on the anatomical theater of a medical college; with still less of real pathology; they enter the profession having mastered just enough of the details of practice to give them the requisite *self-assurance* for commanding the confidence of the public.

Such practitioners, charged another reformer, tended to pursue "medicine as a trade instead of a profession, [and to] study the science of patient-getting to the neglect of the science of patient-curing." Yet no occupational group contributed more to the advancement of science in America

(Numbers and Warner, 1987, pp. 194–95; Numbers, 1988, p. 53).

By 1800 four medical schools were operating in the United States: at the University of Pennsylvania (formerly the College of Philadelphia), Harvard University, Columbia College in New York City, and Dartmouth College. During the following half century the number of medical schools grew rapidly; by the outbreak of the Civil War some 85 had appeared—and a few had already folded (Flexner, 1910; Norwood, 1944). Beginning in 1812, when the state of Maryland granted a charter to what Abraham Flexner memorably described as "the so-called medical department of the so-called University of Maryland" (Flexner, 1910, p. 5), most of the new schools operated on a proprietary basis; that is, they were commercial businesses owned by the medical faculty, typically five to seven local physicians who aspired to make a profit from students fees: $3–5 to matriculate, $15 per ticket for specific courses, $5–10 to attend a dissection, and $15–20 to graduate. Although the proprietary schools sometimes obtained their charters from existing colleges and universities, they had no real academic or financial connection to the "parent" institution. Occasionally, a medical society or a hospital would launch a medicine school, and in 1825 the University of Virginia opened a medical department as an integral part of the university with a full-time professor on salary (Norwood, 1944, pp. 381–384, 392–395, 396).

Unlike most European governments on the continent, which regulated and supported medical education, the state legislatures in America granted charters virtually on request—an estimated 457 by 1910—and allowed schools to set their own standards. During roughly the middle third of the nineteenth century the states also repealed licensing laws for physicians, making it possible, wrote an alarmed doctor, for "any one, male or female, learned or ignorant, an honest man or a knave" to "assume the name of a physician, and 'practice' upon any one, to cure or to kill, as either may happen, without accountability. It's a free country!" (Numbers, 1988, p. 51).

State legislators behaved much more stingily when it came to providing medical schools with

the cadavers they needed to teach anatomy. The quest for reliable information about the human frame led medical educators in the early nineteenth century to engage in what one disgustedly called "a traffic of dead bodies." To stem the illegal activities of grave-robbing "resurrectionists" and provide medical schools with needed cadavers, some state legislatures legalized the practice, but many did not. One legislative opponent of human dissection reminded his colleagues that "Holy Writ" declared that "God made man in his own image." "We may pass a bill to permit the immolation of this sacred image upon the altar of science," he argued, "yet…a higher law…will hold us responsible for granting so questionably a license to a class of men…who laugh at the jest and top off the bowl, while before them quivers the flesh of inanimate humanity" (Sappol, 2002, pp. 99, 131).

Between 1815 and 1861 over a thousand American physicians and medical students sailed to Paris, then the leading medical center in the world, to seek advanced training. Few of these medical pilgrims returned to replicate what they had seen, although William Wood Gerhard in the 1830s successfully employed Parisian methods at the "little hospital" in Philadelphia to confirm the alleged distinction between typhoid and typhus fever. The exhilarating experience abroad, however, often left an indelible impression. "Merely to have breathed a concentrated scientific atmosphere like that of Paris," gushed young Oliver Wendell Holmes during his 1833 sojourn, "must have an effect on anyone who has lived where stupidity is tolerated, where mediocrity is applauded, and where excellence is defied" (Warner, 1998, pp. 3, 38, 250, 279).

In a country plagued by a surplus of low-quality proprietary medical schools, which lacked a single laboratory until 1871, the outlook for medical science looked bleak indeed. Writing home from Paris in 1869, where he was attending Claude Bernard's lectures, the aspiring physiologist Henry P. Bowditch confessed to wanting to devote himself "entirely to the science of the profession." He worried that America was "in danger of being left very far in the rear" if it did not encourage more young people to take up "medical science," adding that he did not see why Americans were "not as capable of doing good work in a scientific way as any other people." Two years later Bowditch, with the assistance of his family, established the first physiological laboratory in the United States, at the Harvard Medical School. At the same time a senior colleague, Henry J. Bigelow, complained of too much science in the curriculum. "In an age of science, like the present, there is more danger that the average medical student will be drawn from what is practical, useful, and even essential, by the well-meant enthusiasm of the votaries of less applicable science, than that he will suffer from want of knowledge of these," declared the distinguished surgeon. In his opinion, no medical student should "while away his time in the labyrinths of Chemistry and Physiology, when he ought to be learning the difference between hernia and hydrocele" (Warner and Tighe, 2001, p. 198; Numbers, 2011, p. 210; Fye, 1987, pp. 107–108).

During the decades between about 1870 and 1910, medical education in America began slowly to improve. Premedical education got better with the rise of the public high school and the expansion of collegiate education. By early in the twentieth century, at a time when many medical schools required no more than a high-school diploma, the American Medical Association (AMA) was recommending that they require a minimum of one year of college. Medical schools increasingly adopted a graded curriculum (instead of simply requiring students to take the same courses twice), expanded the "year" to nine months, and required four years of instruction. As more and more medical schools affiliated with hospitals and dispensaries, clinical training shifted from the apprenticeship to the years of medical school. The best schools instituted laboratory training as well (Hudson, 1972).

During this same time an estimated 15 thousand American physicians traveled across the Atlantic to study in German-speaking countries, which had replaced France in the medical pecking order. When these doctors first began returning from German laboratories and clinics in the 1870s, they experienced difficulty finding employment as medical scientists. On returning to the United States in 1878, the pathologist William H. Welch told his sister that he "was often asked in

Germany how it is that no scientific work in medicine is done in this country, how it is that many good men who do well in Germany and show evident talent there are never heard of and never do any good work when they come back here." The explanation, he continued was simple. Unlike Germans, Americans gave no encouragement to scientific work—and "the condition of medical education here is simply horrible." The only remedy, concluded a like-minded New York colleague, was to turn American medical schools into "workshops of scientific medicine" (Flexner and Flexner, 1941, pp. 112–13; Bonner, 1963).

The German model may have inspired reform in the United States, but, as the late historian Thomas N. Bonner pointed out, the German model "was transformed in important ways as it made its way across the Atlantic." Instead of postponing clinical training until after graduation from medical school, American educators incorporated it into the medical curriculum. "They ignored altogether the popular didactic lecture before hundreds of students that had become the staple of German medical teaching"; instead they gave every student "the kind of attention reserved for advanced students and graduates in Germany" (Bonner, 1995, pp. 292–294).

The opening of the Johns Hopkins School of Medicine in 1893 under the leadership of Welch launched a new era in American medical education. Blessed with a large endowment, Johns Hopkins became the first real center for medical science in the country. In addition to creating chairs in anatomy, physiology, pathology, and pharmacology, it provided their occupants—recruited nationally—with well-equipped laboratories and salaries sufficient to free them from the burdens of practice. Before long Hopkins students were spreading across the land, similarly transforming other medical schools. By the turn of the century the medical schools at Harvard, Pennsylvania, Chicago, and Michigan had joined Hopkins as important medical research centers (Numbers and Warner, 1987).

Although the AMA had been formed in 1847 in part to reform medical education, it accomplished little of importance before the early twentieth century. (Partially to fill the vacuum, medical educators in 1876 formed the Association of American Medical Colleges.) In 1906 the AMA belatedly joined the movement to elevate American medical education when its Council on Medical Education began grading medical schools. Within four years 29 inferior schools had closed or merged.

In 1910 Abraham Flexner published a muckraking exposé of the continuing horrors of medical education in North America. Sponsored by the Carnegie Foundation for the Advancement of Teaching, the little-known Kentucky schoolmaster, who possessed no medical training, personally visited all 155 extant medical schools: 147 in the United States and 8 in Canada. Flexner reported that only Johns Hopkins required a college degree for admission. Not surprisingly, Johns Hopkins served as Flexner's model for reform, embracing, as it did, a full-time teaching staff, "unexcelled" laboratories, and a hospital and dispensary that provided "practically ideal opportunities." Only 15 additional schools required even two years of preliminary college work. All of these, like Hopkins, were "organic parts of full-fledged universities," not proprietary institutions, where a high-school diploma or its "equivalent" was commonly listed as a requirement (Flexner, 1910, pp. 28, 71, 234–235).

Among the worst schools was the California Medical College, a tiny eclectic school in Oakland, which had previously "led a roving and precarious existence." It boasted 26 "professors" but a mere nine students. Flexner spared no scorn:

The school occupies a few neglected rooms on the second floor of a fifty-foot frame building. Its so-called equipment is dirty and disorderly beyond description. Its outfit in anatomy consists of a small box of bones and the dried-up filthy fragments of a single cadaver. A few bottles of reagents constitute the chemical laboratory. A cold and rusty incubator, a single microscope, and a few unlabeled wet specimens, etc., for the so-called "equipment" for pathology and bacteriology.

The judgment: "The school is a disgrace to the state whose laws permit its existence" (Flexner, 1910, p. 190).

Flexner's solution was to cut the number of medical schools from 155 down to 31, eliminating all of the sectarian schools. This draconian reduction, he argued, would readily produce the requisite number of new physicians. He pinned his hopes largely on state licensing boards, which had reappeared during the last quarter of the nineteenth century. He believed that they would be "the instruments through which the reconstruction of medical education will be largely effected": by imposing preliminary educational requirements, by insisting on adequate facilities for training physicians, and by strictly examining medical-school graduates before granting them a license to practice. The activities of the boards varied greatly from state to state, but overall they failed to live up to Flexner's high expectations for them (Flexner, 1910, pp. 154, 167; Ludmerer, 1985, p. 73).

For more than a century scholars have hotly debated the significance of Flexner's 1910 report. In the years after his report appeared, the number of medical schools in the United States declined from 131 in 1910 (the year after Flexner actually conducted his survey) to a low of 79 in 1924, but, as we have seen, in the four years between 1906 and 1910 the number had already declined from a peak of 162. Meanwhile, the number of medical-school graduates dipped from a high of 5,747 in 1904 to a low of 2,520 in 1922 (U.S. Bureau of the Census, 1975, p. 76). Flexner may have contributed to these declines, but more important was the discovery among medical educators that commercialism had "ceased to pay." Proprietary schools simply could not afford the expensive laboratories and clinical facilities required for modern medical education (Flexner, 1910, p. 11; Kohler, 1982, pp. 121–122).

According to Robert P. Hudson (1972), Flexner's historical significance stems less from his report than from his subsequent use of Rockefeller Foundation funds to upgrade medical education to the standards of the report: "His enduring legacy derived from what he accomplished quietly after the sensation created by his report had subsided. Largely due to Flexner's efforts John D. Rockefeller donated almost $50 million to improve the nation's medical schools through the ministrations of the General Education Board," a Rockefeller philanthropy, which Flexner formally joined in 1912 (Bonner, 2002). He used his position—and money—there to promote full-time medical-school faculties, teaching hospitals controlled by the medical schools, and organic connections with universities.

Unable, even with Rockefeller's fortune, to bring every surviving medical school up to Hopkins's standards, Flexner adopted a regional strategy, investing primarily in some of the best private schools in the country: Johns Hopkins, Yale, Chicago, Columbia, Washington (in St. Louis), and Vanderbilt universities. In the upper Midwest he selected the public University of Iowa, correctly believing that neighboring states would prove sufficiently competitive to underwrite their own upgrading. By the late 1920s Flexner had used Rockefeller funds to improve 25 of the surviving 66 medical schools (Bonner, 2002). Within a decade or so, argues Kenneth M. Ludmerer, American medical schools "had become the best in the world, and American physicians, the best prepared" (Ludmerer, 1999, p. 122).

Flexner's connection with the Carnegie and Rockefeller foundations has prompted some scholars to portray him as a tool of capitalism. The sociologist E. Richard Brown (1979), for example, has alleged that "the Flexner report united the interests of elite practitioners, scientific medical faculty, and the wealthy capitalist class"—while ignoring the needs of the working class. The reliance on foundation funding in the decades after 1910, he argues, showed that "medical education could be guided by whoever footed the bill." This, however, flies in the face of Flexner's (and Rockefeller's) failure, despite pouring tens of millions of dollars into the effort, to impose the full-time plan on clinical faculty. It also ignores the primary motivation of the reformers: to create an institutional setting where they could pursue science, not to make practice more lucrative. As Ludmerer (1985, p. 129) has described their goals, "they sought glory, not gold."

As medicine grew more and more complex in the twentieth century, medical educators found it increasingly difficult to squeeze into four years all the scientific and clinical training that a physician or surgeon would need to practice medicine effectively. Thus, in the 1910s medical schools and state licensing boards began requiring an additional year of internship in a hospital. But even this proved insufficient training for some specialties, and by the 1920s and 1930s a number of physicians were continuing to train for several years after the internship in postgraduate residency programs, specializing in fields such as ophthalmology, obstetrics, and orthopedic surgery. After World War II it became customary for all but general practitioners to study medicine for about eight years before engaging in independent practice (Ludmerer, 1999, pp. 79–101; Rothstein, 1987, pp. 134–138, 214–216, 314–324).

During the two decades following World War II, during which federal funds for biomedical research became available in unprecedented amounts, scientific research began to eclipse the teaching mission of American schools. However, this emphasis on research began to shrink in the late 1960s with the coming of Medicare and Medicaid, which pushed scientific research to the periphery in favor of cash-generating clinical service (Ludmerer, 1999, pp. 139–161). "The behavior of medical faculties no longer so clearly demonstrated a commitment to advancing the public good," claims Ludmerer in a stinging—and somewhat hyperbolic—indictment of his medical-school colleagues. "Their gaze turned inward, as they increasingly focused on their own rights and entitlements and spoke less of the ways they could continue to act as guardians of the nation's health. In addition, medical schools seemed to fall prey to unprecedented levels of greed, commercialism and intellectual dishonesty. In the post-Medicare era, as medical schools lost touch with their intellectual roots in the university, they also lost touch with their moral roots as a public trust" (Ludmerer, 1999, p. 337).

In the century following Flexner's 1910 report a significant percentage of American physicians received their medical education abroad, a phenomenon still inadequately explored. In the 1930s, at a time when American medical schools overtly discriminated against Jewish students, more than five thousand immigrant practitioners, primarily Jews, arrived from Europe (Stevens et al., 1978, p. 33; Halperin, 2001). The Immigration Act of 1965, which abolished existing quotas, opened the door to throngs of foreign-trained physicians, including some 75 thousand in the first decade alone. "By the mid-1970s foreign medical graduates (FMGs) comprised one-fifth of physicians in the United States and one-third of physicians in graduate training as interns or residents" (Stevens et al., 1978, p. 1; Mick, 1975). The Health Professions Educational Assistance Act of 1976 reduced the influx of FMGs somewhat (Mick and Worobey, 1984); however, by 2010 international medical graduates (IMGs), as they were now called, constituted approximately a quarter of the physicians practicing in America. More than a quarter of these emigrated from India and Pakistan; the Philippines contributed over 8 percent of the total. Mexico and the Caribbean (the Dominican Republic, Grenada, and Dominica) trained just over 10 percent (*International Medical Graduates*, 2010).

Until shortly before the Civil War, American medical schools admitted only white males, but this barrier fell under the influence of the antebellum abolitionist and feminist movements. Elizabeth Blackwell in 1849 became the first American woman to earn a medical degree. Women made rapid strides in separate as well as coeducational (especially sectarian) medical schools during the late nineteenth century. Between 1848, when the New England Female Medical College in Boston opened its doors, and the end of the nineteenth century at least 17 women's medical schools were launched. By the turn of the century roughly a third of regular medical schools admitted women. In 1903, seven years before the appearance of Flexner's report, only three remained. Nevertheless, the United States led the world in the number of female medical students and practicing physicians. In Boston, an atypical example, nearly one of every five physicians (18.2 percent) was a woman; over the next two decades the percentage plummeted to 9.7 percent (with 5.0 percent becoming the national average). Between 1910 and 1960, few American medical schools had a student population of more than 5 percent female (Walsh, 1977, pp. 179–185; see also Morantz-Sanchez, 1985;

Peitzman, 2000; Tuchman, 2006; Bonner, 1992; Barzansky and Gevitz, 1992, pp. 51–64). Over the years some observers have unfairly blamed Flexner for the decline in female medical students and practitioners. Although he denounced the separate medical schools for women as unworthy of saving, he applauded the presence of nearly a hundred coeducational medical schools (Flexner, 1910, pp. 178–179). As late as 1960 American medical schools graduated only 405 women, a mere 5.7 percent of the total. By 1997, largely as a result of the "equal opportunity" amendments to the Civil Rights Act of 1964, the number had zoomed to 6,614 graduates, or 40.0 percent of the graduating classes (More, 1999, pp. 216–221).

Although African Americans, like women, had long served as healers in America, the first one to earn an MD, James McCune Smith, was forced to obtain it from the University of Glasgow in 1837, having been denied admission by American medical schools. It was not until 1847 that Rush Medical College in Chicago became the first American institution to award an MD degree to an African American (Byrd and Clayton, 2000, pp. 304–307). Between the end of the Civil War and 1900 some 14 predominantly black medical schools appeared in the United States (Savitt, 2007, pp. 122–125, 256; see also Barzansky and Gevitz, 1992, pp. 65–82). By the time Flexner conducted his survey, only seven black medical schools remained, five of which he deemed virtually worthless. They not only wasted money but also sent out "undisciplined men, whose lack of real training is covered up by the imposing MD degree." The only two he thought worth saving were Meharry Medical College in Nashville and the Howard University Medical Department in Washington, D.C.—the only two to survive past 1925 (Flexner, 1910, pp. 180–181; Savitt, 2007, pp. 252–266). At midcentury Meharry and Howard trained nearly all of the 133 blacks who graduated from medical school in 1950. The social ferment of the 1960s and 1970s led to the founding of two new primarily African American medical schools: the Charles Drew Postgraduate Medical School in Los Angeles, affiliated with the University of California at Los

Angeles, which opened in 1966 and later took the name Charles Drew University of Medicine and Science; and the Morehouse Medical School in Atlanta, which began in 1978. The civil rights movement led to widespread affirmative action, boosting the number of black graduates to 571 in 1974, by which time almost one fourth of entering students represented various minority groups: African American, Hispanic Americans, and Native American. Black applications to medical school reached a peak of 3,524 in 1996 but then nosedived by more than 20 percent in the next eight years ("JBHE Check-up," 2005).

In 2011 there were 136 accredited MD-granting programs in the United States, plus an additional 26 colleges of osteopathic medicine, which awarded D.O. degrees. A dozen or more new medical schools were in the planning stages.

[*See also* **American Association for the History of Medicine; American Medical Association; Anatomy and Human Dissection; Biological Sciences; Blackwell, Elizabeth; Botany; Chemistry; Flexner Report; Forensic Pathology and Death Investigation; Gender and Science; Higher Education and Science; High Schools, Science Education in; Hospitals; Medicare and Medicaid; Medicine; National Medical Association; Pharmacology and Drug Therapy; Physiology; Race and Medicine; Rockefeller Institute, The; Science; Societies and Associations, Science; Surgery; Welch, William H.;** *and* **Zakrzewska, Marie**]

BIBLIOGRAPHY

Barzansky, Barbara, and Norman Gevitz, eds. *Beyond Flexner: Medical Education in the Twentieth Century*. New York: Greenwood Press, 1992.

Bell, Whitfield J., Jr. *John Morgan: Continental Doctor*. Philadelphia: University of Pennsylvania Press, 1965.

Blake, John. "Anatomy." In *The Education of American Physicians, Historical Essays*, edited by Ronald L. Numbers, pp. 29–47. Berkeley and Los Angeles: University of California Press, 1980.

Bonner, Thomas Neville. *American Doctors and German Universities: A Chapter in International Intellectual Relations, 1870–1914*. Lincoln: University of Nebraska Press, 1963.

Bonner, Thomas Neville. *Becoming a Physician: Medical Education in Great Britain, France, Germany, and the United States, 1750–1945*. New York: Oxford University Press, 1995.

Bonner, Thomas Neville. *Iconoclast: Abraham Flexner and a Life in Learning*. Baltimore: Johns Hopkins University Press, 2002.

Bonner, Thomas Neville. *To the Ends of the Earth: Women's Search for Education in Medicine*. Cambridge, Mass.: Harvard University Press, 1992.

Brown, E. Richard. "He Who Pays the Piper: Foundations, the Medical Profession, and Medical Education." In *Health Care in America: Essays in Social History*, edited by Susan Reverby and David Rosner, pp. 132–154. Philadelphia: Temple University Press, 1979.

Byrd, W. Michael, and Linda A. Clayton. *An American Health Dilemma*, Vol. 1. *A Medical History of African Americans and the Problem of Race: Beginnings to 1900*. New York: Routledge, 2000.

Christianson, Eric H. "New England." In *Medicine in the New World: New Spain, New France, and New England*, edited by Ronald L. Numbers, pp. 101–153. Knoxville: University of Tennessee Press, 1987.

Flexner, Abraham. *Medical Education in the United States and Canada: A Report to the Carnegie Institution for the Advancement of Teaching*. New York: Carnegie Institution for the Advancement of Teaching, 1910.

Flexner, Simon, and James T. Flexner. *William Henry Welch and the Heroic Age of American Medicine*. New York: Viking, 1941.

Fye, W. Bruce. *The Development of American Physiology: Scientific Medicine in the Nineteenth Century*. Baltimore: Johns Hopkins University Press, 1987.

Halperin, Edward C. "The Jewish Problem in U.S. Medical Education, 1920–1955." *Journal of the History of Medicine and Allied Sciences* 56 (2001): 140–167.

Hudson, Robert P. "Abraham Flexner in Perspective: American Medical Education, 1865–1910." *Bulletin of the History of Medicine* 56 (1972): 545–561.

International Medical Graduates in American Medicine: Contemporary Challenges and Opportunities. Chicago: American Medical Association, 2010.

"A JBHE Check-up on Blacks in U.S. Medical Schools." *Journal of Blacks in Higher Education* 47 (Spring 2005): 76–81.

Kohler, Robert E. *From Medical Chemistry to Biochemistry: The Making of a Biomedical Discipline.* Cambridge, U.K.: Cambridge University Press, 1982.

Ludmerer, Kenneth M. *Learning to Heal: The Development of American Medical Education.* New York: Oxford University Press, 1985.

Ludmerer, Kenneth M. *Time to Heal: American Medical Education from the Turn of the Century to the Era of Managed Care.* New York: Oxford University Press, 1999.

Mick, Stephen S. "The Foreign Medical Graduate." *Scientific American* 232 (February 1975): 4–21.

Mick, Stephen S., and Jacqueline Lowe Worobey. "Foreign Medical Graduates in the 1980s: Trends in Specialization." *American Journal of Public Health* 74 (1984): 698–703.

Morantz-Sanchez, Regina Markell. *Sympathy and Science: Women Physicians in American Medicine.* New York: Oxford University Press, 1985.

More, Ellen S. *Restoring the Balance: Women Physicians and the Profession of Medicine, 1850–1995.* Cambridge, Mass.: Harvard University Press, 1999.

Norwood, William Frederick. *Medical Education in the United States before the Civil War.* Philadelphia: University of Pennsylvania Press, 1944.

Numbers, Ronald L., ed. *The Education of American Physicians: Historical Essays.* Berkeley and Los Angeles: University of California Press, 1980.

Numbers, Ronald L. "The Fall and Rise of the American Medical Profession." In *The Professions in American History*, edited by Nathan O. Hatch, pp. 51–72. Notre Dame, Ind.: University of Notre Dame Press, 1988.

Numbers, Ronald L. "Science and Medicine." In *Wrestling with Nature: From Omens to Science*, edited by Peter Harrison, Ronald L. Numbers, and Michael H. Shank, pp. 201–224. Chicago: University of Chicago Press, 2011.

Numbers, Ronald L., and John Harley Warner. "The Maturation of American Medical Science." In *Scientific Colonialism, 1800–1930: A Cross-Cultural Comparison*, edited by Nathan Reingold and Marc Rothenberg, pp. 191–214. Washington, D.C.: Smithsonian Institution Press, 1987.

Peitzman, Steve J. *A New and Untried Course: Women's Medical College and Medical College of Pennsylvania, 1850–1998.* New Brunswick, N.J.: Rutgers University Press, 2000.

Rothstein, William G. *American Medical Schools and the Practice of Medicine: A History.* New York: Oxford University Press, 1987.

Sappol, Michael. *A Traffic of Dead Bodies: Anatomy and Embodied Social Identity in Nineteenth-Century America.* Princeton, N.J.: Princeton University Press, 2002.

Savitt, Todd L. *Race and Medicine in Nineteenth- and Early-Twentieth-Century America.* Kent, Ohio: Kent State University Press, 2007.

Stevens, Rosemary, Louis Wolf Goodman, and Stephen S. Mick. *The Alien Doctors: Foreign Medical Graduates in American Hospitals.* New York: John Wiley & Sons, 1978.

Tuchman, Arleen Marcia. *Science Has No Sex: The Life of Marie Zakrzewska, MD* Chapel Hill: University of North Carolina Press, 2006.

U.S. Bureau of the Census. *Historical Statistics of the United States: Colonial Times to 1970*, Part 1. Washington, D.C.: U.S. Government Printing Office, 1975.

Walsh, Mary Roth. *"Doctors Wanted: No Women Need Apply": Sexual Barriers in the Medical Profession, 1835–1975.* New Haven, Conn.: Yale University Press, 1977.

Warner, John Harley. *Against the Spirit of System: The French Impulse in Nineteenth-Century American Medicine.* Princeton, N.J.: Princeton University Press, 1998.

Warner, John Harley, and Janet A. Tighe, eds. *Major Problems in the History of American Medicine and Public Health.* Boston: Houghton Mifflin, 2001.
Ronald L. Numbers

MEDICAL MALPRACTICE

Medical malpractice—the process by which society holds medical practitioners legally and financially responsible for wrongful or substandard care—has been one of the most complicated and contentious issues in U.S. public life. The medical malpractice phenomenon is frequently viewed only as a product of the mid- to late twentieth century, but physicians protested what they viewed as a malpractice "crisis" as early as the 1830s. Since then, they and other observers have identified successive periods of intensified litigation in the 1890s, 1930s, 1970s, 1980s, and, more recently, in the early twenty-first century. Contemporary observers in each respective historic period have identified and focused primarily on short-term causes of the suits, but have been unable to identify the underlying and ongoing origins of the litigation. Medical malpractice, however, has always been a multifaceted phenomenon and its history is a chronicle of the overlapping influences of medicine, technology, politics, culture, economics, and law. Its development serves also as an imperfect reflection of society's continually evolving view of what constitutes medical error and culpable error. Widespread malpractice suits in the 1830s, as in the 2000s, were the result of a variety of multiple short-term topical causes and long-term cultural preconditions, but the development and use of new medical technologies and procedures has played a consistent and central role throughout the history of the litigation.

The Law of Medical Malpractice.

Medical malpractice suits occur in a social, cultural, and medical context that fundamentally influences the way in which they arise and are resolved. Medical malpractice is first and foremost a legal action designed to compensate individuals for the harms that they have suffered as a result of medical negligence or other wrongdoing in the medical setting. It also serves a deterrence function by prompting physicians to alter their behavior before harm to individuals occurs. Although legal doctrine has evolved in important ways, the basic required elements of a medical malpractice action have remained essentially stable for over 150 years. Medical malpractice is based on the tort theory of professional negligence. Patients are plaintiffs in this context; physicians are defendants. To construct a successful malpractice action, a plaintiff must demonstrate, by a "preponderance of the evidence" (more likely than not), four "elements": (1) the defendant had a duty toward the plaintiff; (2) that duty or "standard of care" was breached; (3) the plaintiff suffered harm or damage; and (4) the breach was the proximate cause of the harm the plaintiff suffered. There is no single proscribed standard of care for any particular procedure, illness, or injury that applies in all cases, for all patients. Instead, the standard of care requires

that a physician possess and exercise the skill, knowledge, learning, and care that a reasonable prudent physician would possess and exercise in the same or similar circumstances. Experts for both the plaintiff and the defendant are required to offer opinions to aid the jury on whether the defendant-physician met the standard of care in the treatment of the plaintiff-patient. Although the wording of the physician's legal duty has not changed significantly, technological development and advancements in medical sciences dramatically altered the essential *content* of that standard over time.

The Nineteenth-Century Background: 1830–1850.

Although malpractice suits in the early republic were not unheard of, before the 1830s suits in the United States were rare. Medical journals rarely mentioned suits except to comment on their infrequency. All that changed by midcentury. In 1844 the *Boston Medical and Surgical Journal* lamented that physicians were "constantly liable to vexatious suits instituted by ignorant and unprincipled persons." By 1860 John Elwell, a physician-lawyer who authored a book on malpractice, claimed, "There can hardly be found a place in the country where the oldest physicians in it have not been actually sued or annoyingly threatened." This period, from 1830 to 1860, represents a critical threshold—many of the factors that underlie the first perceived malpractice "crisis" in the United States persisted through subsequent cyclical outbursts of increased litigation (Burns, 1969; DeVille, 1990).

The short-term topical causes for this apparent sudden outburst of litigation were accurately identified by contemporary observers. For example, physicians had suffered a clear loss of status since the latter half of the eighteenth century, in part attributable to the antielitism that is said to characterize the Jacksonian period. Leaders of the profession speculated that this decline in status contributed to the unprecedented wave of suits. Patients often had little respect for physicians, who could claim few genuine cures. Moreover, the tradition of domestic and alternative medicine in the United States undermined physicians' reputations. Some of the problem lay in the educational system. After 1800, medical schools proliferated and the competition for students frequently led to degraded educational standards and debased the profession in the eyes of the public. The increased number of schools also produced a flood of physicians. When physicians were rare, suits were unlikely. Defense attorneys sometimes asked juries to weigh the value of an accused physician to the community against the injury suffered by the plaintiff. By 1850, such a tactic was much less likely to be successful because when one physician left the city or town, another was waiting to take his place. Finally, the burgeoning number of physicians often led to bitter competition. Malpractice accusations were occasionally used as competitive weapons against professional enemies. The lack of medical licensure control and professional discipline at midcentury may have encouraged the individuals to rely on litigation to attack what they viewed as deficient practitioners and medical error (DeVille, 1990; Mohr, 2000).

Although these short-term topical factors are an important part of the causal explanation of the mid-nineteenth-century malpractice phenomenon, two long-term cultural developments also played a central and important role in the litigation. The first of these developments was a transformation in Americans' belief in divine providence. Much of America in the eighteenth century believed that physical misfortune was an explicit expression of divine will. This belief held that physical misfortune was inflicted upon humans to either test or punish them. To those who held such beliefs, to sue for misfortune would have been to question God's judgment. This attitude may have affected both potential plaintiffs and the juries who would judge their claims. Although these attitudes had been evolving for at least two centuries, the first half of the nineteenth century was marked by a period of especially dramatic and rapid religious transformation. A greater portion of society began to believe that God observed but did not intrude on ordinary affairs of day-to-day life. Scientific and social progress strengthened the growing belief that physical ills could and should be changed on earth. These developments allowed and even led individuals to look for earthly reasons and human culpability for human suffering. Without

this large-scale religious transformation, widespread suits for malpractice would have been unimaginable (DeVille, 1990).

The second cultural transformation that allowed medical malpractice suits to flourish for the first time in the mid-nineteenth century was the dissipation of a community ethos that tended to suppress lawsuits. Legal anthropologists have suggested that the "relational distance" between members of a community influences their willingness to rely on legal remedies. In communities characterized by face-to-face relationships and populated by economically self-sufficient farmers and merchants—typical of eighteenth-century life in the United States—lawsuits were viewed as an inappropriate response to personal injuries, regardless of culpability. Litigation disturbed the peace of the community, violated religious-based community strictures against suing for misfortune, and threatened to rob the community of a valuable social resource, its physician. This species of communal structure changed only slowly but profound changes to old ways of thinking took place in the early to middle nineteenth century, the same time that the first malpractice crisis arose. There was a clear movement from the communal mentality in colonial America to the more anonymous individualism of the nineteenth- and twentieth-century United States. As the notion of community evolved, individualism became a greater feature in American life and community stigma against suits had less influence. Without this change, individuals would not have felt free to sue on a wide scale (DeVille, 1990). Indeed, social distance may still influence what is considered legitimate litigation. An important empirical study of malpractice in the late twentieth century contends that "urbanization is the single most powerful predictor of both frequency and severity of [malpractice] claims" (Danzon, 1985).

The vast majority of malpractice suits in the mid-nineteenth century resulted from fracture and dislocation cases. Orthopedic treatments played only an inconsequential role in the few publicized suits prior to the 1830–1850 period. The explanation is revealing. In 1800, the standard of care for severe fractures and dislocations was amputation. Amputations, however, did not generate a large number of suits. Claimants typically had no limb left to present as evidence to experts and the jury but, most significantly, public and professional expectations were low for severe orthopedic injuries. Amputations and/or death were the norm. By the late 1830s, however, the profession had developed a series of dramatic new orthopedic techniques that allowed physicians to save rather than amputate limbs. Accordingly, saving, rather than amputating, limbs in severe orthopedic injuries had become the standard of care by 1850. This orthopedic revolution fostered excitement and inflated expectations in both the profession and the lay public. Medical treatises referred to fracture treatment as a relatively mechanical procedure in which physicians and patients could expect perfect cures. Orthopedic care, however, was far from mechanical or predictable. The new technologies and treatment methods were complex and, in many ways, required more skill, knowledge, and care than did amputations. During the long recovery period associated with orthopedic treatment, physicians were faced with a host of new concerns and complications. Moreover, although physicians could now more frequently save limbs, fractures and dislocations usually yielded permanent injuries: shortened or deformed limbs, frozen joints, and complications associated with the long periods of convalescence. Dissatisfied patients were now provided clear manifestations of their alleged injury to show jurors. As a result, less-than-perfect results following orthopedic injuries constituted the most common type of malpractice suits well into the twentieth century (DeVille, 1990; Smith, 1941).

Clarifying the contribution of technology and medical advancement to mid-nineteenth-century litigation is central for understanding the first malpractice crisis and the subsequent waves of suits to follow. Physicians' experience with orthopedic treatment in the mid-nineteenth century illustrates a phenomenon that would recur as medicine advanced in other areas of practice. Dramatic and genuine medical advancements are invariably followed by heightened, and frequently excessive, professional and lay expectations. As Mark Grady (1988) has explained, improved procedures more often than not require greater learning, skill, and

care. Consequently, technological advancement carries with it a greater opportunity for what is now perceived as error or accident. Moreover, the cost of that error is greater because the potential benefit of the improved treatment is higher than the treatment that it replaced. As a result, in the words of Grady, medical innovation and advancement "captures" what was previously "natural risk" and transforms it into "medical risk" providing the precipitating cause of malpractice suits.

Medical Malpractice: 1850–1900. In the late nineteenth century and beyond, there was a clear decline of many of the inciting factors of the 1830s–1850s. Antiprofessionalism weakened. Medical education improved by 1900 and even more dramatically during the first half of the twentieth century. By 1900, the status of physicians had improved; later it skyrocketed. But despite the disappearance of most of the topical causes of the litigation in the first half of the nineteenth century, suits continued. New inciting factors arose to take the place of the old. The status-based resentment of the Jacksonian period, for example, was gradually replaced by a species of class-based resentment as physicians' income slowly increased. A growing population of lawyers and more frequent use of contingency fees in the late nineteenth and early twentieth centuries provided legal services to a wider range of the population. As importantly, whereas the law of malpractice in the early century was undeveloped, by 1900 case law and legal treatises provided important and heretofore unavailable guidance to potential malpractice attorneys. Medical licensure had been largely reinstituted by 1900, but professional discipline was rarely vigorously pursued. Thus, as the nineteenth century progressed, physicians increasingly recognized the existence of more exacting profession-wide standards, but only modestly enforced those norms on their membership. The absence of a robust, formal professional response to medical error and deficient practitioners left the resolutions of those questions by default to the anarchic medical malpractice litigation system (Mohr, 2000; Hogan, 2003).

At the same time, the cultural preconditions for suits did not abate, they matured. The trend toward urbanism steadily continued and community cohesion dissipated further. Religious fatalism decreased further and individuals increasingly came to believe that human ills and suffering had an early cause and remedy. Medical progress, too, played an ongoing and central role in malpractice litigation in the second half of the nineteenth century. Technological advancement in the late nineteenth and early twentieth centuries helped raise the overall status of the profession and eliminated one of the early causes of suits. However, specific improvements in medical treatment, like the orthopedic revolution of the 1830s, incited cycles of heightened expectations, greater clinical demands, unforeseen complications, and resultant disappointments when expectations were unmet. For example, in the 1870s the Plaster-of-Paris "revolution" and innovations related to aseptic practice again transformed orthopedic care and again generated unfounded expectations of near-flawless cures. According to some physicians, the treatment of compound fractures had been brought to a "state of perfection." A new spate of orthopedic suits arose in the 1890s. Thus, as in the early part of the century, large numbers of suits followed periods of successful and dramatic improvement in a particular treatment modality (DeVille, 1990; Grady, 1988). X-rays, developed in 1895, followed a similar course. By early 1896, physicians were predicting that their use was a foolproof protection against suits for medical malpractice. The X-ray indeed had jurisprudential significance, but not that anticipated by the medical profession. By the end of 1896, physicians were being sued for failing to take X-rays, and radiological evidence was being employed against physicians in court to demonstrate negligent care. By 1900, physicians had been sued for iatrogenic injuries (burns) caused by the technology. Like fracture treatment a half century before, the X-ray generated expectations that it could not meet. Moreover, it created a record of ambiguous evidence, a record that did not previously exist. This record, susceptible to subjective interpretations, could and would be used against defendant-physicians (Hogan, 2003).

Medical Malpractice: 1900–1950. Medical malpractice suits continued a "slow, but steady,

rise" in the first half of the twentieth century, slowing during the war years. Medical societies began to play a greater role in the development of defense strategies for their members and malpractice insurance became a prevalent feature of a physician's professional life. Professional consciousness of suits was said to result in the so-called "conspiracy of silence" in which physicians refused to testify as experts against their colleagues. At the same time, physicians continued to believe that careless comments from colleagues were frequently responsible for sparking suits about another's care. The new availability of insurance protected physician-litigants individually, but it may have played a role in increasing the rate and size of damage awards. The number of attorneys in the United States increased by as much as 50 percent between 1900 and the 1930s and these attorneys developed new theories and a new sophistication for pursuing medical negligence cases. For example, suits for insufficient informed consent appeared. Courts began to accept the doctrine of *res ipsa loquitur,* which allowed attorneys and their clients to pursue cases without expert witnesses when the situation was such that the jury could infer negligence from the facts. The use of *res ipsa loquitur* expanded the range of cases for which patients could seek remedies (Mohr, 2000; Hogan, 2003).

Although the rate of suits was affected by these readily identifiable early twentieth-century topical factors, long-term causes of the litigation persisted as well. Public acceptance of litigation and the cultural proclivity to sue grew in part because overall a greater number of communities became more heterogenous, individualism flourished, and communal restraints against suing weakened as the twentieth century progressed. Also continuing early nineteenth-century trends, Americans became even more secularized and more convinced that humans could improve their lives. Partly as a result, some commentators have suggested that individuals in the twentieth century became ever more concerned about their physical condition, a tendency historian T. J. Jackson Lears has described as a "fretful preoccupation with secular well-being" (*No Place of Grace: Antimodernism and the Transformation of American*

Culture, 1880–1920, Pantheon, 1975). Accordingly, Americans became more convinced that there must be a remedy or a solution when something went wrong.

Despite the importance of these cultural factors in inciting or providing the social context for suits, technological and medical advancement continued to play a central role in litigation between 1900 and 1950. Continuing the trend originating in the previous century, suits resulting from the use or nonuse of X-rays multiplied (Hogan, 2003). Suits spread to new procedures as well. Before the 1880s, operative surgery was limited and, not surprisingly, generated few suits. By the turn of the twentieth century, however, the prevalence of surgical procedures had increased. Consistent success was hampered by factors such as surgical shock, infection, inadequate training, and primitive instruments. Despite the growing number of surgical procedures, including experimentation and uneven results, suits related to surgical practice did not increase dramatically in the first two decades of the twentieth century. It was not until the advent of sulfa drugs to fight deadly infections, transfusions to assuage the effects of surgical shock, the development of residency programs to train surgeons, the refinement of aseptic practices, and the development of more reliable and appropriate instruments that surgeons were able to boast noteworthy and more numerous successes. After that time, suits involving surgical treatments increased precipitously, overtaking orthopedics as the most common source of medical malpractice suits by the 1940s (DeVille, 1998).

Body-cavity surgery was performed with some regularity for over 40 years before it generated large numbers of malpractice suits. As with orthopedic care, surgical procedures, even in the face of failure, did not incite suits until the treatment modality reached a threshold of lay and professional expectation. It was not until the end of the 1920s that surgical intervention could be championed by the profession and viewed by the public as a predictable and reliable solution for injury and disease, sparking the demand for accountability and compensation. In addition, surgeons of the post-1930s medical world had to monitor and manage shock, bleeding, and vital signs while they were performing complex and new procedures, demands unheard of in previous medical care. As the Grady thesis (1988) suggests, when surgeon performance fell short or inflated expectations were not met, suits followed. This consequence is consistent as well with human performance research that demonstrates that complex medical technological environments typically increase the likelihood of knowledge-based, skill-based, and attention-based mistakes.

Medical Malpractice: 1950–2000. The most visible increase in the incidence of malpractice suits in U.S. history occurred in the last 30 years of the twentieth century, increasing by some accounts from approximately one claim per one hundred physicians in the late 1950s to ten claims per one hundred physicians in the mid-1980s (DeVille, 1998). Physicians self-identified successive malpractice "crises" in the early 1970s, in the 1980s, and in the first decade of the twenty-first century (Sage, 2003). Unlike previous periods, the perception of "crisis" now extended not only to the number and costs of the suits, but also to the increasing expense and decreasing availability of physician medical malpractice insurance coverage (Hogan, 2003).

The rate of malpractice claims increased so dramatically after 1950 because of particular and identifiable topical factors specific to the historic period. The gradual decline of the "locality rule" meant that physicians might be held to a national, instead of a merely local, standard of care and in theory increased the availability of expert witnesses for patient-plaintiffs. Attorney advertising, which appeared only in the late 1970s, gave guidance and options to patients who believed they had been wrongfully injured by physicians. Increasingly specialized and organized plaintiff's attorneys increased further the sophistication and expertise of lawyers who would pursue complicated medical malpractice cases. Expansive media coverage of both medical issues and adverse events likely affected the public's consciousness as well. The spectacular medical promise of the second half century was paradoxically juxtaposed with multiplying stories of medical error. Physicians, for the first time, began to suggest that limits in doctor–patient communication played an important part in inciting malpractice litigation (Hogan, 2003). In a society like the United States, with no universal insurance coverage, crushing medical expenses frequently associated with medically related injuries undoubtedly played a role in encouraging reliance on litigation as a means to satisfy medical expenses.

By all accounts, health-care delivery in the late twentieth century became increasingly complicated, fragmented, and diffuse. Medical care at the beginning of the millennium inescapably involved the interaction of multiple providers, institutions, and modalities ordinarily without the benefit of a coordinated, overarching organization structure. Physician–patient communication and patient understanding in this setting are likely to be undermined, providing a source of dissatisfaction that has been linked to litigiousness. In addition, the role and importance of complex systems are also nearly an article of faith among those who think and write about error in medicine. These complex health-delivery environments are replete with error traps that are difficult, if not impossible, for individuals to identify. Increased errors in such a context are inevitable. Thus, although individuals frequently spark error, mistake also often has its genesis in interactions among various critical actors and in organizational structures and distribution of tasks and work responsibilities. Thus, the endemic and increasing complexity of medical care has itself likely played a contributing role in increasing mistakes and, as a consequence, increasing litigation. Finally, in the late twentieth century, physician and public policy discourse focused nearly as heavily on the cost and availability of medical malpractice insurance as it did on the number and the cost and justice of the lawsuits themselves. Concern over insurance premiums had remained muted for much of the century, in part because physicians frequently had been able to pass the costs on to patients and third-party payers. As health-care cost containment became a central feature of medical life as the century closed, however, it became progressively more difficult to transfer premium-rate increases, and as a consequence physicians began to feel rate increases more acutely (Sage, 2003).

Despite these important causal explanations, the increase in suits in this period, as in previous ones, should be traced to the dazzling number of medical technologies that were developed and reached widespread use in the last half of the twentieth century. These technologies, available for use because of the advent of widespread health-care insurance coverage, generated both a public and a professional belief in predictable results and substantial benefit. For example, obstetrical care generated relatively few medical malpractice claims until the 1970s. Maternal and fetal risk remained considerably high at midcentury, but improved rapidly thereafter. By the 1970s, new drugs, medical regimens, and technologies provided obstetricians with a broad range of exciting and valuable diagnostic and clinical options. Although beneficial, in some respects these advancements have complicated treatment decisions by placing greater demands on clinicians. Dramatic improvement in the safety of pregnancy, labor, and delivery has also increased expectations and contributed to resentment over tragic outcomes. By 1985, obstetric claims had increased precipitously, representing perhaps 10 percent of all malpractice suits (DeVille, 1998).

Similarly, diagnostic advancements of the last half of the twentieth century have revolutionized the practice of medicine. These technologies, as did the X-ray before them, improved care but stimulated malpractice litigation by engendering the expectation that life-threatening and debilitating illnesses can be foreseen and thwarted by early intervention. Some of this enthusiasm was well founded, but some was not. Patients, and even frontline physicians, are often insufficiently aware of the workings and limitations of the new diagnostic techniques. As a result, both are sometimes disappointed by the results. Some diagnostic technologies posed iatrogenic dangers to patients. Finally, diagnostic technology, when used, may leave a record to be used against the physician. Consider the example of electronic fetal monitors (EFMs), used to monitor fetal heart rates and to identify fetal distress. Like X-rays, EFM was seen not only as an improvement in care, but also as a prophylaxis for the growing number of obstetric malpractice suits.

However, EFM proved a mixed legal blessing. EFM may be indicated in some cases, but it simultaneously increased the risk of suit following the birth of an injured infant by providing a retrospective record of the fetal heart rate that was sometimes susceptible to ambiguous interpretations. Similar conclusions might be drawn about the use and implications of such diagnostic technologies as ultrasound, bronchoscopy, endoscopy, magnetic resonance imaging, computed tomography, sophisticated laboratory tests, genetic screening, and even the modern medical record itself, all diagnostic innovations that were refined in the last half of the twentieth century. All may sometimes represent the required standard of care, and each, in the event of an untoward outcome, can provide often ambiguous evidence of oversight or negligence. Significantly, the fastest growing medical malpractice allegation in the closing decades of the twentieth century was the failure to diagnose an existing illness or injury (DeVille, 1998; Jacobson, 2006).

The heightened, and sometimes ill-informed, expectations inspired by diagnostic advances of the second half of the twentieth century are analogous to those generated by innovations in fracture treatment in the mid-nineteenth century and surgery in the first third of the twentieth century. Other medical innovations, too, have proceeded through similar "life cycles" of introduction, proliferation, inflated expectations, and lawsuits when expectations were not met and unforeseen complications and limitations led to injury or less-than-perfect results. Suits related to pharmaceutical therapies, for example, increased in the decades after 1950, a period during which drug treatments became both more sophisticated and more complex. After a technological innovation is initially widely used, the medical profession cannot fully realize its potential limits, risks, or side effects; the precise degree of skill, care, or knowledge required to employ it; the patient populations on which it is most and least effective and dangerous; and the clinicians most qualified to offer it. When the new drug, device, or procedure is used on a larger and broader scale, the limitations and peculiarities of the innovations become apparent as injuries and less-than-perfect results

surface. As the profession uncovers the hidden limitations and dangers of the medical innovation, physicians institute precautions to resolve them, outcomes improve, and adverse outcomes and perceived errors decline. It is likely, however, that in many cases the number of suits generated by the new procedure will still be higher than before the advancement was introduced, in part because the new procedure frequently generates higher expectations, requires greater care and skill, and provides more opportunity for oversight and accident. This analysis suggests that although the legal standard for negligence has not changed, the real-world content and requirements have burgeoned (Grady, 1988; DeVille, 1998). Using this model, Peter Jacobson analyzed the medical malpractice claims associated with laparoscopic cholecystectomy, neonatology, diagnosis of breast cancer, and anesthesiology from 2001 to 2003. Jacobson concluded that the data are "consistent with the view that claims increase upon the introduction of a new technology, but then level off over time, in part because a new procedure is typically more complex and exacting than previous treatment methods" (Jacobson, 2006).

Although physician calls for reform of the medical malpractice litigation system surfaced in the late nineteenth century and became progressively more strident, they did not yield significant changes until much later. Successive spikes in physician concern regarding premium rates and malpractice suits in the mid-1970s, 1980s, and the early twenty-first century inspired a wave of legislative reforms to decrease the frequency and costs of the litigation. Legislative reform of medical malpractice posed a complicated challenge for policy makers. Public debate was dominated by factions of physicians, attorneys, and various public advocacy groups; the range of complaints varied, depending on the interest group evaluating the issue. As the twentieth century closed, although nearly all groups agreed that the current system of reimbursing those who are injured by medical negligence could be improved, there was little agreement on the best remedies. Empirical data on medical malpractice, made increasingly available near the end of the century, did not definitively resolve many of the key questions regarding the nature, magnitude, and source of the problem (Studdert et al., 2004). In a review of arguments for and against medical malpractice reform, Bovbjerg and Berenson (2005) concluded that many of the most strident claims of both proponents and opponents of fundamental malpractice reform were misguided. Instead, they argued that the "top five real problems" in medical malpractice litigation included the following: (1) too many patients suffer preventable injuries; (2) compensation of injuries is very poor because few patients make claims and fewer still collect; (3) claims resolution is inefficient: too slow and costly; (4) liability fears hamper physician-patient communication and disclosure of injuries; and (5) determinations of negligent medical injury are inherently subjective. Similarly, Tom Baker (2005), in an analysis of available empirical data titled *The Medical Malpractice Myth*, concluded that despite a high rate of medical error, relatively few patients file medical malpractice suits and that, despite public perception, the rate of litigation actually declined at the end of the twentieth century. Baker contended as well that medical malpractice suits had "little or nothing" to do with insurance rates and that medical malpractice had only a small impact on health-care costs in general. Such studies do not demonstrate that medical malpractice litigation poses no problem to the medical profession and society. Instead, as through the history of the litigation, these empirical refinements of phenomenon confirm that reality rarely conforms to the beliefs and observations of contemporary observers.

Legacy. Overall, the incidence of malpractice suits increases because a greater number of individual patients sue physicians for the use of, or failure to use, a particular technology, procedure, or therapeutic approach. Paradoxically, malpractice suits have appeared to increase in the face of what appears to be extraordinary and unceasing medical progress. And the cultural origins and the continuing foundations for the suits—individuals' growing concern for their bodies and their increasing acceptance of litigation as a remedy for misfortune—suggest that medical malpractice suits are as much a social–cultural phenomenon as a legal one. These observations have ambivalent implications for those who wish to reform the medical malpractice liability system.

[*See also* **Forensic Pathology and Death Investigation; Health Insurance; Journals in Science, Medicine, and Engineering; Law and Science; Medicine; Public Health; Religion and Science;** *and* **Technology.**]

BIBLIOGRAPHY

Baker, Tom. *The Medical Malpractice Myth.* Chicago: University of Chicago Press, 2005. Baker synthesizes the scholarly and empirical evidence on medical malpractice and makes a special attempt to test and dispel popular and professional misconceptions regarding suits.

Bovbjerg, Randall R., and Robert A. Berenson. "Surmounting Myths and Mindsets in Medical Malpractice." *Urban Policy Briefs.* Urban Institute, 2005. http://www.urban.org/uploadedPDF/411227_ medical_malpractice.pdf (accessed 17 October 2012). This study weighs the available empirical evidence in an attempt to blunt the rampant misinformation and misunderstanding that dominate policy debates on medical malpractice.

Burns, Chester R. "Malpractice Suits in American Medicine before the Civil War." *Bulletin of the History of Medicine* 43 (1969): 41–56. A pioneering work on the history of medical malpractice in antebellum America that discusses the nature of early suits and the medical profession's response.

Danzon, Patricia. *Medical Malpractice: Theory, Evidence and Public Policy.* Cambridge, Mass.: Harvard University Press, 1985. An important early empirical work that analyzes the workings of the medical malpractice system in the second half of the twentieth century. Danzon considers the efficiency of the system in compensating victims and engendering deterrence, analyzes the medical malpractice insurance system, and provides guidance on potential reforms.

DeVille, Kenneth A. *Medical Malpractice in Nineteenth Century America: Origins and Legacy.* New York: New York University Press, 1990. Analyzes the emergence of malpractice litigation in antebellum life, tracing its origins to changing attitudes about the physical body, the role of providence, and the changing nature of community. It also explores how the first malpractice "crisis" is integrally connected to specific advances in treatment.

DeVille, Kenneth A. "Medical Malpractice in Twentieth Century United States: The Interactions of Technology, Law and Culture." *International Journal of Technology Assessment in Health Care* 14, no. 2 (1998): 197–211. Examines how nineteenth-century antecedents of the litigation carry over into the next century. Provides extended illustrated discussion of role of medical advancement in the suits.

Grady, Mark F. "Why Are People Negligent? Technology, Nondurable Precautions, and the Medical Malpractice Explosion." *Northwestern University Law Review* 82 (1988): 293–334. The seminal work explicating the role that technology plays in medical malpractice litigation and the development of the litigation over time.

Hogan, Neal C. *Unhealed Wounds: Medical Malpractice in the Twentieth Century*. New York: LFB Scholarly Publishing, 2003. Hogan explores the malpractice phenomenon in the first two-thirds of the twentieth century. He focuses on legal changes, the role of medical societies, public awareness of the litigation, malpractice insurance, and the growing role of hospitals.

Jacobson, Peter D. "Medical Liability and the Culture of Technology." In *Medical Malpractice and the U.S. Health Care System*, edited by William M. Sage and Rogan Kersh, pp. 115–136. Cambridge, U.K.: Cambridge University Press, 2006. A systematic analysis and empirical confirmation of the thesis that the advancement of medical technology and practice has played and the pivotal role in the history and continuing development of medical malpractice litigation. Jacobson considers the implications of this analysis for reform.

Jost, Kenneth. "Medical Malpractice." *CQ Researcher* 13, no. 2 (2003): 129–152. Drawing on a wide range of scholarship and guidance, Jost focuses on late twentieth-century suits and prospects for reform, but connects this discussion to the historical origins of the suits.

Mohr, James C. "American Medical Malpractice Litigation in Historical Perspective." *JAMA* 283 (2000): 1731–1737. Mohr provides an overview of the historical origins of medical malpractice, focusing on the recurring influences of the phenomenon. Mohr pays special attention to the role of medical professionalism and its interaction with the legal community.

Sage, William C. "Understanding the First Malpractice Crisis of the 21st Century." In *Health Law Handbook*, edited by Alice C. Gosfield, pp. 1–31. St. Paul, Minn.: West Publishing, 2003. Sage discusses the first malpractice "crisis" of the twenty-first century and explains how it differs from later twentieth-century concerns.

Smith, Hubert Winston. "Legal Responsibility for Medical Malpractice." *JAMA* 116, no. 24 (1941): 2670–2679. Smith's article represents an early attempt to understand the malpractice phenomenon in a systematic way and provides a window into the first half of the twentieth century.

Studdert, David M., Michelle M. Mello, and Troyen A. Brennan. "Medical Malpractice." *New England Journal of Medicine* 350, no. 3 (2004): 283–292. This article provides an overview and discussion of the functioning and efficiency of the medical malpractice system in the last third of the twentieth century. Drawing from the best available empirical data, the authors also critique various medical malpractice reforms.

Kenneth Allen DeVille

MEDICAL SPECIALIZATION

Specialization gained its initial and primary justification in the nineteenth century as a form of knowledge production and dissemination rather than as a type of skill or form of practice. Medical specialties developed in the United States several decades after they appeared in Europe. With few of the conditions that fostered specialization across the ocean—large medical schools with traditions of research, municipal hospital bureaucracies—there were only sporadic instances of specialization among American doctors before 1855. However, in the years that followed, specialization spread swiftly, facilitated by a competitive environment fostered by large numbers of private medical schools and hospitals.

Specialties in the United States, as elsewhere, based their claims to acceptance on the need to advance medical science and invent new procedures that could then be incorporated into general medical practice. But there also existed a stronger practical and utilitarian orientation among American specialists than was the case in Europe. Supervisors of lunatic asylums in 1844 created the first specialty society in America, the Association of Medical Superintendents of American Institutions for the Insane (which evolved into the American Psychiatric Association), and the same year launched the *American Journal of Insanity*. Other early specialties included the much larger practices of surgery and obstetrics; these had always been viewed as distinct from medicine (if not separate professions) but now came to be redefined as specialties of medicine. They were followed by gynecology and ophthalmology. The roughly one thousand American students and physicians who visited Paris in the 1840s and 1850s followed private courses in the specialties and were the first large cohort of Americans to embrace and proselytize for specialism as an appropriate professional model for medicine. In subsequent decades, some 15 thousand Americans seeking postdoctoral training went to Vienna and other German-language universities, largely because of the perceived excellence of practical clinical instruction in the specialties. These set the tone for aspirants to elite medical status who could not afford travel to Europe.

Specialties were first accepted in American urban hospitals in the 1860s in the form of outpatient departments that had low status. An alternative was the establishment of small specialist hospitals that did not compete directly against general hospitals. By the 1880s, however, specialists were ensconced in hospital wards and medical-school professorships. The latter development reflected the determination of American medical elites to enter the world of international medical research that had become synonymous with specialization. The American educational context thus combined profound dissatisfaction with existing medical teaching, deference to European (increasingly German) academic models of medical and higher education that prioritized research, and uniquely decentralized and privatized management of competing institutions that were still small enough to expand with relative ease.

This situation was not without its problems. General practitioners (GPs) were critical of specialists, whom they viewed as professional competitors. The American Medical Association (AMA) complained that academic specialists were fragmenting the profession because they frequently ignored its annual meetings, where the quality of papers was low, and instead frequented the proliferating specialty societies that restricted memberships. But following a brief period of intense conflict in the 1880s and 1890s, these issues were largely resolved with the specialist sections of the AMA also becoming significant foci of specialist organizational activity.

Regulating Specialties in the Twentieth Century. From the last two decades of the nineteenth century to the years before and after World War II, specialization continued to provide a significant framework for research and general medical education, but it simultaneously became the dominant form of medical practice, as more and more physicians began calling themselves specialists. They did so because private specialist practice seemed by now to offer substantially greater economic rewards and professional status than general practice. Anyone could call himself or herself a specialist in the early twentieth century. Poorly trained or even untrained specialists discredited the profession and threatened the livelihoods of both general practitioners and well-trained specialists. This created pressure to develop structures to train and certify specialists and set jurisdictional boundaries among them.

In the United States (as in Germany at roughly the same time) physicians opted for a system of specialist training and certification controlled by organizations representing the medical profession (as opposed to state agencies). The process was very gradual, taking over two decades to complete. It began with surgery, a field that had changed radically during the previous half century and that was itself competing against emerging surgical specialties. In 1913 a group of prominent surgeons established the American College of Surgeons, which granted membership to those with appropriate skills. Because it proved highly inclusive, it was a great success and eventually introduced training requirements followed by examinations as criteria for membership. In 1915, internists followed this model by creating the American College of Physicians but without trying to control training and entry to the specialty.

A year later, three ophthalmological associations set up a joint certification board that recognized specialists on the basis of credentials, experience, and in some cases examinations. Although the AMA initially supported a system of postgraduate education controlled by university medical schools that it authorized, it began in 1924 to also authorize hospital residency programs that eventually became the dominant training locations for specialists. Meanwhile, more and more specialist groups, including otolaryngologists (1928) and obstetrician-gynecologists (1930), created boards of certification to control education standards. In 1934 several professional leaders, with some input from the AMA, set up the Advisory Board for Medical Specialists to coordinate the process of board formation. By 1940, 14 specialty boards were in existence and had certified about 40 percent of all self-declared specialists.

This American system of certification by specialty boards has remained substantially unchanged since the middle of the twentieth century except for the regular addition of new specialties and subspecialties and the introduction of periodic recertification. The result is that specialties now dominate the medical landscape. The number of general practitioners has fallen continuously and precipitously as American medical students have chosen en masse to enter specialties and earn higher incomes. In 1963, general practitioners made up 28 percent of the active physician population; by 1977 the figure was 13 percent. A uniquely American response to the disappearance of the general practitioner was the creation of a new specialty to take its place. (Since then, European nations have been gradually moving in a similar direction.) The creation of the American Board of Family Medicine was formally approved in 1969. It offered certification in the field after a residency of three years. Not to be left behind, the American Boards of Internal Medicine established a special certificate in general internal medicine, which occupied much the same structural terrain and could also be obtained after three years of training. The two groups, along with pediatricians, now provide a significant portion of primary care to Americans. But despite continually intensifying pressure to curb its dominance, spe-

cialization continues to play a preponderant role in American medicine.

[*See also* **American Medical Association; Higher Education and Science; Hospitals; Medical Education; Medicine; Ophthalmology; Pediatrics; Psychiatry; Research and Development; Science;** *and* **Surgery.**]

BIBLIOGRAPHY

Stevens, Rosemary. 1998. *American Medicine and the Public Interest.* Updated ed. Berkeley: University of California Press. (Originally published New Haven, Conn.: Yale University Press, 1971.)

Weisz, George. 2006. *Divide and Conquer: A Comparative History of Medical Specialization.* New York and Oxford: Oxford University Press.

George Weisz

MEDICARE AND MEDICAID

On 30 July 1965, President Lyndon B. Johnson signed the Medicare and Medicaid Bill into law at the Truman Library in Independence, Missouri. The site of the bill signing was chosen to honor the former president Harry S. Truman, who had supported an earlier version of national health care. Also of significance, the date of the signing was only two weeks shy of the thirtieth anniversary of the 1935 Social Security Act to which Medicare was attached.

The law that President Johnson signed in 1965 contained three parts that were put together a year earlier by the House Ways and Means chairman Wilbur Mills (D-Arkansas). The first part, Medicare, was an expansion of the Social Security Old Age Pension program. Through wage deductions, employees would contribute to a trust fund that was separate from the Social Security trust fund. At retirement those eligible to receive Social Security benefits would also receive hospital care, some surgical care, and nursing-home reimbursements. The original law specified 120 days of hospital benefits and 120 days of nursing-home follow-up benefits. The Medicare program also included general revenue funds for hospital construction, diagnostic equipment purchase, and grants to teaching hospitals for medical education.

A second part of the 1965 law, called Part B, covered physician's office visits. This part was optional and had to be selected by an eligible individual upon retirement. If chosen, deductions were made from monthly Social Security checks. This optional part originated from the American Medical Association's alternative to Medicare. Called Eldercare in 1964, Wilbur Mills streamlined the proposal and made it into an optional addition to Medicare.

Medicaid was the third part of the 1965 bill. This program, funded from general tax revenue, provided health care for needy poor. Because it was given to the states to administer, Medicaid could reimburse for a broad number of people, such as welfare recipients, persons who were blind or disabled, and low-income elderly who did not qualify for Social Security or whose Medicare benefits ran out. The Medicaid program originated in the early 1960s as the Republican alternative to the Johnson administration's push for a compulsory health insurance plan, such as Medicare.

The wish to provide health-care insurance began as part of an early-twentieth-century reform movement called the Progressive Era. I. M. Rubinow, I. S. Falk, and other reformers worked with state legislatures to discuss using a social insurance method to ameliorate causes of poverty, such as old age, unemployment, and ill health. These discussions became the basis for the 1935 Social Security Act, signed into law by Franklin Roosevelt in 1935. A plan for health insurance was left out of the 1935 act because of objections raised by members of Congress and medical associations. However, as early as 1943, a health insurance bill known as the Wagner-Murray-Dingell Bill was introduced and reintroduced over the next several years. Opponents galvanized around two main features of the legislative proposal: the compulsory inclusion and the role played by the federal government. What Congress passed instead was the Hill-Burton Act, which reimbursed for hospital construction, and a Kerr-Mills program, which gave grants to the states for health care for the poor.

By 1957, advocates of a more comprehensive health insurance bill for the elderly, including Wilbur Cohen, Nelson Cruikshank, and Robert Ball, enlisted the support of Representative Aime Forand (D-Rhode Island). The Forand bill was the direct ancestor of Medicare. In 1960, President John Kennedy made Medicare part of his national agenda. This time Representative Cecil King (D-California) and Senator Clinton Anderson (D-New Mexico) sponsored the bill. In 1965, after a number of hearings in the House and the Senate, and following the 1964 Democratic election landslide, Medicare became a top priority for President Lyndon Johnson.

Congress has modified Medicare and Medicaid periodically in an effort to control escalating costs and increase coverage. Changes in 1971 and 1974 dealt with a review of standards and costs as well as the elimination of equipment and hospital construction duplication. Changes in 1983 standardized illness charges. Although President Bill Clinton was successful in introducing an expanded Medicaid program for uninsured children in 1993 he lost a bid to overhaul the nation's health-care system. Known as the Health Security Act and written by a large committee of experts chaired by Hillary Clinton, the act was defeated in Congress after a well-funded campaign by lobbyists to associate the plan with a loss of "individual choice."

President George W. Bush had better luck focusing on a narrower goal. Medicare was expanded in 2003 to include a Part D, a prescription drug benefit that included general drug coverage, and a second provision for those seniors in need of more expensive coverage. Private companies were asked to compete for the coverage of seniors, who were in turn offered a choice of plans and encouraged to pick one based on their individual pharmaceutical needs.

With an eye toward expanding Medicare coverage and controlling costs, in 2010 President Barack Obama signed into law the Patient Protection and Affordable Care Act (also referred to as the Affordable Care Act). The new program provided coverage to several million Americans with income 400 percent above the poverty level minimum for Medicaid. However, the coverage depended on state cooperation, and many states resisted. The Affordable Care Act also influenced Medicare in several ways. One part of the program urged hospitals to carefully monitor Medicare patients' readmissions within 30 days of treatment. Financial penalties encouraged hospitals to look toward less expensive ways to assist patients after discharging them. The act also expected hospitals to use money saved through other parts of the Affordable Care Act to benefit charges to the Medicare system. Both state and federal agencies wage a continual battle to control fraud and abuse of the system. The debate over the future of Medicare as well as the larger debate over health-care policy has focused on controlling costs, especially in anticipation of the health-care demands of the large Baby Boomer cohort of the population becoming eligible for coverage.

Perhaps the biggest change to Medicare in the early twenty-first century has been the growth of health maintenance organizations. Introduced by the private sector as a way to control rising costs, health maintenance organizations were included as a choice for Medicare and Medicaid recipients. Many viewed an expansion of the private sector using government-issued vouchers as a way to cut skyrocketing costs. Others looked to an income test, where wealthier seniors paid higher deductibles. Overall, Medicare has become an integral part of retirement expectations as well as a major part of the health-care industry. Medicaid, too, has filled a gap in providing health care for low-income families. Discussion of health-care policy in the early twenty-first century focused on the need to expand or modify Medicare and Medicaid, looking for ways to control costs while also retaining access and choice.

[*See also* **Health Insurance;** *and* **Health Maintenance Organizations.**]

BIBLIOGRAPHY

Berkowitz, Edward. *America's Welfare State; From Roosevelt to Reagan.* Baltimore: Johns Hopkins University Press, 1991. In Part 3 of Berkowitz's book, there is an excellent analysis of problems the program encountered in the 1980s.

David, Sheri I. *With Dignity: The Search for Medicare and Medicaid.* Westport, Conn.: Greenwood Press, 1985. David's book is an insightful legislative history of the Medicare and Medicaid program.

Dean, Howard. *Howard Dean's Prescription for Real Healthcare Reform.* White River Junction, Vt.: Chelsea Green Publishing, 2009. Dean's book is especially useful for identifying the challenges facing Medicare and Medicaid in the twenty-first century—especially the challenges of costs.

Harris, Richard. *A Sacred Trust.* New York: New American Library Publishing, 1966. Harris offers the reader an excellent account of what the American Medical Association was doing to shape the Medicare legislation as it made its way through Congress.

Marmor, Theodore. *The Politics of Medicare.* 2d ed. Hawthorne, N.Y.: Aldine de Gruyter, 2000. Marmor puts the Medicare and Medicaid program into the larger context of the politics of the 1960s.

Stevens, Robert, and Rosemary Stevens. *Welfare Medicine in America: A Case Study of Medicaid.* 2d ed. New Brunswick, N.J.: Transaction Publishers, 2003. Stevens' work focuses on the Medicaid program—and is helpful in understanding the challenges of having a program run by states.

Sheri I. David

MEDICINE

This entry contains six subentries: Overview; Colonial Era; From 1776 to the 1870s; From the 1870s to 1945; Since 1945; *and* Alternative Medicine.

OVERVIEW

For centuries, sick and injured Americans typically received their medical care at home, either from family members or from informally trained healers. The first permanent hospital did not open until 1751 and the first medical school in 1765. The medical profession remained weak and divided; even the creation of the American Medical Association in 1847 did little to help. The half century spanning the years 1875 to 1925 brought revolutionary changes to American medicine. The germ theory of disease led to the availability of new diagnostic and therapeutic procedures, such as diphtheria antitoxin (1894). The locus of practice shifted from home to hospital as the number of general hospitals mushroomed from no more than 150 in 1875 to nearly 7,000 fifty years later. Medical practice, heretofore virtually unregulated, became subject to licensing laws. With the new Johns Hopkins Medical School (1893) leading the way, medical education improved dramatically.

In one of the most significant developments in all of American history, life expectancy at birth increased from under 30 years at the time of the Revolutionary War to about 77 years in 2000. Surprisingly, before the mid-twentieth century, when antibiotics became available, therapeutic medicine contributed little to this improvement. The great killers of nineteenth-century Americans—infectious diseases such as tuberculosis, influenza, and pneumonia—were declining for decades before physicians discovered effective ways to treat or prevent them. Of greater importance were public-health measures such as improved sanitation, purified water, and compulsory smallpox vaccinations for children. Better food, housing, and personal hygiene also helped reduce mortality rates.

[*See also* **American Medical Association; Disease; Germ Theory of Disease; Hospitals; Hygiene, Personal; Life Expectancy; Medical Education;** *and* **Public Health.**]

Ronald L. Numbers

COLONIAL ERA

For all the grievances against Great Britain enumerated in the Declaration of Independence, the American revolutionaries offered no evidence that imperial regulations had inhibited colonial medical practice. This simple fact of noninterference is important for a general understanding of health care in colonial America. Indeed, during the Colonial Era, perhaps fewer than 20 percent of all identified medical practitioners were immigrants. Of these, most came from provincial England, where the regulatory powers of London's medical guilds, such as the Royal College of Physicians, were relatively weak. Few were college or medical-school graduates, although many had gained experience by serving apprenticeships or working as surgeons in the military or on passenger and cargo vessels. Of the vast majority of colonial medical practitioners who were native born, most had no formal training; those who did typically served an apprenticeship, averaging little more than a year, with an established doctor. The first American medical school did not open its doors until 1765 in Philadelphia.

A diversity of Old World medical practices and healing traditions, including self-medication, formed an important part of the cultural baggage colonists brought to America. The absence of effective regulation assured the continuation of such diversity. As in provincial England, the American landscape abounded in general practitioners, herbalists, minister-physicians, and innumerable self-taught itinerants who offered their services as dentists, bonesetters, and fever doctors. Given the high colonial birthrate, female midwives modestly prospered until the eighteenth century, when male physicians became competitors in larger communities. Medical services were usually delivered at the patient's residence rather than in an office or hospital. Although poorhouses and workhouses occasionally cared for the sick, the first permanent hospital did not open until 1751, again in Philadelphia. The evidence suggests that these colonial healers exercised considerable independent judgment and avoided dogmatic adherence to such practices as vigorous bloodletting, purging, or the administration of highly active drugs. Healers included some Native American herbal remedies among their generally imported armamentarium.

With the notable exceptions of African American slaves and the very poor, colonial Americans generally enjoyed better health and greater longevity than their English counterparts. Their most common complaints included injuries, dysentery, common colds, and ague or malaria. Periodic epidemics of measles, diphtheria, and smallpox afflicted European and Native Americans alike.

The most important public-health development of the Colonial Era occurred in connection with a smallpox epidemic that struck New England in 1721. To combat the epidemic in Boston, the Reverend Cotton Mather enlisted Dr. Zabdiel Boylston in a pioneering effort to inoculate volunteers with the live smallpox virum. Despite considerable medical opposition, led by the town's only school-trained physician, William Douglass, the risky experiment saved many lives. Douglass himself became a convert and in 1730 helped to organize the first colonial medical guild, the Boston Medical Society, which collectively endorsed smallpox inoculation. During the Revolutionary War this practice was employed successfully by the medical corps of the Continental Army.

Efforts by colonial legislatures to regulate medical practice began as early as the 1640s in Massachusetts. In the later Colonial Era, one finds in the larger colonial cities a growing professionalism, manifested especially in the formation of medical societies. Perhaps the epitome of the colonial surgeon was Dr. Silvester Gardiner (1708–1786) of Boston. A colonial-trained apprentice, Gardiner studied with surgical luminaries in Paris and London, and in Boston he compiled an impressive record in lithotomy (removal of stones, or urinary calculi, in the bladder) and in general surgery. In 1741, before the Boston Medical Society, Gardiner successfully removed a large stone from a six-year-old boy. To combat the improper dispensing of drugs, Gardiner also established apothecary shops in Boston as well as in Meriden and Hartford, Connecticut.

In general, however, licensing laws and the move toward professionalization had little effect on the practice of medicine throughout the colonial period. Local medical societies, although more numerous than in provincial England, proved ineffective as regulatory agencies. The experience of medical practitioners in the Revolutionary War would inspire the creation of various state medical societies, but on the eve of independence, the estimated 3,500 medical practitioners in the American colonies were little regulated and enjoyed few legal protections against the encroachment of ill-trained interlopers or quacks. More than a century would pass before these problems were solved. Nevertheless, Dr. Benjamin Rush of Philadelphia, a signer of the Declaration of Independence, saw the Revolution as a foundational event in the exuberant, patriotic process of creating an American medical profession.

[*See also* **Demography; Dentistry; Diphtheria; Disease; Gender and Science; Health and Fitness; Life Expectancy; Malaria; Medical Education; Midwifery; Native American Healers; Pharmacology and Drug Therapy; Religion and Science; Rush, Benjamin; Smallpox; Societies and Associations, Science; Surgery;** *and* **War and Medicine.**]

BIBLIOGRAPHY

Bell, Whitfield J., Jr. *The Colonial Physician and Other Essays*. New York: Science History Publications, 1975.

Cash, Philip. *Medical Men at the Siege of Boston, April 1775–April 1776*. Philadelphia: American Philosophical Society, 1973.

Christianson, Eric H. "Medicine in New England." In *Medicine in the New World: New Spain, New France, and New England*, edited by Ronald L. Numbers, pp. 102–153. Knoxville: University of Tennessee Press, 1987.

Donegan, Jane B. *Women & Men Midwives: Medicine, Morality and Misogyny in Early America*. Westport, Conn.: Greenwood Press, 1978.

Duffy, John. *Epidemics in Colonial America*. Baton Rouge: Louisiana State University Press, 1953.

Estes, J. Worth. "Therapeutic Practice in Colonial New England." In *Medicine in Colonial Massachusetts, 1620–1820*, edited by Philip Cash, Eric H. Christianson, and J. Worth Estes, pp. 289–383. Boston: The Society, 1980.

Ulrich, Laurel Thatcher. *A Midwife's Tale: The Life of Martha Ballard, Based on Her Diary, 1785–1812*. New York: Alfred A. Knopf, 1990.

Eric Howard Christianson

FROM 1776 TO THE 1870s

Of about 3,500 physicians in America at the time of the Revolutionary War, only one in ten held an MD degree. The establishment during the 1760s of the first medical schools, societies, and licensing laws had encouraged a growing sense of corporate identity. Yet male physicians played a modest role in the medical care of sick Americans, who more frequently turned to midwives and other women healers and to herbalists, bonesetters, nostrum vendors, and domestic medical guidebooks.

During the early decades of the republic, expanding medical institutions sustained a new, confident professionalism. The organization of local and state medical societies—which adopted ethical codes and fixed fee scales—helped regularly trained physicians distinguish themselves from other healers, a move state legislatures reinforced by placing licensing power in the hands of the societies. Apprenticeship, sometimes supplemented by lectures, remained the core of medical education. Harvard (1783) and Dartmouth (1798) joined existing medical schools in Philadelphia and New York City, and an elite group continued to study in London and Edinburgh. Starting in the 1810s, medical schools proliferated rapidly—26 were founded between 1810 and 1840 and another 47 by 1877. Most were proprietary ventures, run by the professors for profit. Typically the student attended lectures for four months, duplicating in the second year the courses attended during the first. Keen competition for paying pupils kept requirements low.

Although Americans insisted that European precepts were often unsuited to New World practice, their understanding of disease was strongly informed by the theoretically elaborate, rationalistic systems of eighteenth-century British medicine. University of Pennsylvania professor Benjamin Rush, who received his MD in Edinburgh, was in the late eighteenth century the most influential medical teacher in America, and his theories promoted the so-called "heroic" therapeutics that dominated American practice through the 1830s. Disease in Rush's scheme was essentially an overexcited condition remedied by aggressively depleting the body by blood-letting and mineral purgatives such as calomel (mercurous chloride). If depletion was sometimes practiced by rote, physicians nonetheless argued that treatment should be individuated to patients and environments, an attitude that promoted investigations of the relationships among topography, climate, and disease.

From the 1820s through the 1860s, Americans who traveled to Europe for medical study favored the hospitals of Paris, which offered unrivaled access to the body, living and dead. These physicians returned committed to grounding medicine on empirical observation and symptom–lesion correlation—that is, tracing the symptoms of disease viewed in the living patient to their underlying pathological lesions in the body's tissues revealed at autopsy. They denounced rationalistic systems, like that of Rush, and challenged heroic drugging while calling for greater trust in nature's healing powers. By midcentury, supportive and stimulative treatment was supplanting depletion.

The ideas, practices, and social pretensions of the regular profession also came under assaults from antiorthodox healers. Samuel Thomson's botanic system of domestic practice, consolidated by his *New Guide to Health* (1822), gained a large following. Thomsonians attacked heroic medicine and tapped into the Jacksonian Era's egalitarian distrust of claims to privilege based on special learning. Eclecticism (a parallel botanical healing system in which professional practitioners supplanted self-help), hydropathy (water cure), and a wider health-reform movement flourished in the 1840s and 1850s. During the same decades homeopathy, introduced to America in 1825, became the most powerful challenge to the regular profession, boasting institutions such as the Homoeopathic Medical College of Pennsylvania (1848) and the first national medical association, the American Institute of Homoeopathy (1844). During this period the states revoked virtually all medical licensing laws, leaving American medicine the freest from regulation in the Western world.

It was in this laissez-faire context that a movement toward orthodoxy arose. In 1847 the American Medical Association (AMA) was founded, partly to promote educational reforms but chiefly to establish a unified front and demarcate the orthodox faithful. The association initially exerted little political influence, but its code of ethics was a culturally powerful device to enforce orthodoxy by forbidding members to associate professionally with practitioners the AMA derisively called "sectarians."

The absence of state regulation facilitated women's access to MD degrees earlier than in any other nation. When in 1849 Elizabeth Blackwell received an MD from Geneva College in upstate New York, she became the first woman anywhere to win that degree. Male opposition kept most schools closed to women. In 1850, however, the Female Medical College of Pennsylvania opened as the world's first MD-granting medical school entirely for women. Over the next several decades a number of other women's medical colleges (orthodox and homeopathic) opened, as did women's dispensaries and hospitals.

Hospitals in antebellum America remained chiefly charitable asylums for the sick poor. Elite physicians sought hospital appointments for access to clinical teaching, experience, and investigation; thus, at the Pennsylvania Hospital in Philadelphia, William Gerhard used his Parisian experiences as the model for the clinical instruction he offered starting in the 1830s and for research that differentiated typhoid fever from typhus (1843). Although some institutions for the mentally ill dated from the Colonial Era, the emergence of moral treatment and the campaign that Dorothea Dix launched in 1841 to reform the care of the insane poor fostered a host of state insane asylums created before the Civil War.

American innovations, chiefly in surgery, won international attention. Ephraim McDowell's 1809 operation in Kentucky for an ovarian cyst and J. Marion Sim's operation for vesicovaginal fistula, developed on slave women during the 1840s, were celebrated as exemplifying native mechanical ingenuity. William Beaumont's experiments on the physiology of digestion—performed during the 1820s and 1830s on a patient with a gastric fistula that provided a direct opening to the stomach—also drew European notice. The most celebrated American achievement, although clouded by priority disputes, was the first public operation on a patient anesthetized with ether, an 1846 performance at the Massachusetts General Hospital in Boston during which William T. G. Morton administered the anesthetic and John Collins Warren performed the surgery.

The state, little involved in regulating the medical profession, also had meager involvement in public health. Cholera and yellow fever epidemics prompted the creation of municipal boards of health to orchestrate sanitation (based on the belief that miasms or emanations from filth produced disease) and quarantine. But through the mid-nineteenth century, such activities were temporary. The Civil War did not transform medicine, but the organizational skills and commitments on display in the U.S. Sanitary Commission (1861) raised expectations of state responsibility for public health. In 1869 Massachusetts established the first state board of health; by 1880, 20 such boards existed. In 1879 Congress created the National Board of Health, a short-lived but important precedent for federal involvement in public medicine.

After the war in 1868, Howard University in Washington, D.C., established the first medical school for African Americans. In 1871, Harvard adopted a three-year graded medical curriculum, but with diploma mills still flourishing, few other schools followed this lead. In 1873 New York's Bellevue Hospital established a nursing school modeled after Florence Nightingale's plan, and over a dozen such institutions appeared before the end of the decade. Reflecting the elevated status of expert knowledge in Gilded-Age American culture, by the 1870s some states reinstituted medical licensing laws, usually broad enough to encompass homeopathic, eclectic, and orthodox physicians.

Although few important new therapies had arisen by the 1870s, some doctors were looking to the experimental laboratory as the wellspring of therapeutic progress. Americans studying abroad shifted to German laboratories and clinics, and in 1871 Henry Pickering Bowditch returned from Leipzig to set up at Harvard the nation's first laboratory for experimental physiology and to occupy the first full-time post in physiology. The most dramatic early post–Civil War change in American medical practice was the rise of specialization, patterned after German models. Ophthalmologists formed their own society in 1864 and otologists (who specialized in diseases of the ear) in 1868. During the 1870s such specialty societies proliferated, testimony both to social reality and to the public's esteem for specialization as a hallmark of the emerging medical order.

[*See also* American Medical Association; Beaumont, William; Blackwell, Elizabeth; Botany; Cholera; Disease; Ethics and Medicine; Gender and Science; Hospitals; Hygiene, Personal; Medical Education; Medical Specialization; Mental Health Institutions; Mental Illness; Midwifery; Nursing; Ophthalmology; Physiology; Public Health; Race and Medicine; Rush, Benjamin; Societies and Associations, Science; Surgery; Typhoid Fever; Typhus; War and Medicine; *and* Yellow Fever.]

BIBLIOGRAPHY

D'Antonio, Patricia. *American Nursing: A History of Knowledge, Authority, and the Meaning of Work.* Baltimore: Johns Hopkins University Press, 2010.

Duffy, John. *The Sanitarians: A History of American Public Health.* Urbana: University of Illinois Press, 1990.

Grob, Gerald N. *The Mad among Us: A History of the Care of America's Mentally Ill.* New York: Free Press, 1994.

Leavitt, Judith Walzer, and Ronald L. Numbers, eds. *Sickness and Health in America: Readings in the History of Medicine and Public Health.* 3d ed. Madison: University of Wisconsin Press, 1997.

Morantz-Sanchez, Regina Markell. *Sympathy and Science: Women Physicians in American Medicine.* New York: Oxford University Press, 1985.

Rosenberg, Charles E. *The Care of Strangers: The Rise of America's Hospital System.* New York: Basic Books, 1987. Reprint, 1995.

Rothstein, William G. *American Physicians in the Nineteenth Century.* Baltimore: Johns Hopkins University Press, 1972. Reprint, 1992.

Starr, Paul. *The Social Transformation of American Medicine.* New York: Basic Books, 1982.

Warner, John Harley. *Against the Spirit of Systems: The French Impulse in Nineteenth-Century American Medicine.* Princeton, N.J.: Princeton University Press, 1998.

Warner, John Harley. *The Therapeutic Perspective: Medical Practice, Knowledge, and Identity in America, 1820–1885.* Cambridge, Mass.: Cambridge University Press, 1986. Reprint, 1997.

John Harley Warner

FROM THE 1870s TO 1945

In 1876, American physicians gathered in Philadelphia to survey the nation's first hundred years of medical progress. A parade of speakers celebrated the introduction of anesthesia and antisepsis in surgery, the use of new chemical discoveries to treat fever, and the profession's growing knowledge of disease, grounded in the pathological and microscopic research of the previous 50 years. America's special genius, they suggested, lay in applying these European accomplishments. Laboratory studies shed new light on the workings of blood and bodily chemistry, while American sanitary institutions contained the once dreaded cholera when it had last arrived in 1866 and 1873. At the same time, speakers warned, American medical education remained in a parlous state, and sanitary reform lacked the public support it deserved. Nor, they might have added, did physicians get the material rewards and respect they sought.

The next 70 years witnessed unprecedented improvements in the social and economic status of U.S. physicians, in medical knowledge about the causes of specific diseases, and in life expectancy. Hospitals were transformed from refuges for the urban poor to surgeons' workshops patronized by the middle and working classes. Bacteriologists identified the causes of the major infectious diseases, although control over viral diseases eluded them. But if physicians gained new frameworks for understanding disease from the laboratory, they clung to their caste's prejudices in making sense of their society: categories of race and gender figured prominently in medical thought and action. Meanwhile, both professional and social progress were unevenly distributed. Specialists and urban practitioners earned far more than their rural counterparts, and sanitary improvements only slowly reached working-class, rural, immigrant, and African American citizens. Nonetheless, medicine's scientific and institutional accomplishments engendered a belief in progress that neither social inequality nor injustice could refute.

Science, Disease, and Public Health. In 1882, the German physician Robert Koch

(1843–1910) demonstrated that tuberculosis, probably the leading cause of death in Western Europe and the United States, was caused by a living micro-organism, the tubercle bacillus. More important, he laid down a set of procedures (Koch's postulates) for researchers to follow in determining the bacterial causes of specific diseases. By 1906, European researchers had identified the micro-organisms responsible for typhoid fever (1880–1884), diphtheria (1883), cholera (1884), gonorrhea (1885), pneumonia (1886), tetanus (1889), plague (1894), dysentery (1898), and syphilis (1905). American doctors like William H. Welch and Frederick Novy (1864–1957) traveled to Europe to train in the new bacteriological techniques. American companies, quick to realize the commercial potential of the new "germ" theories, marketed disinfectants like Listerine and Radam's Microbe Killer. Bacteriological concepts held less appeal for medical practitioners, who continued to view disease as a complex interaction among the "constitution" of individual patients, the susceptibility of particular "racial" groups, and exposure to specific bacteria.

Although physicians who were trained after 1890 increasingly viewed infectious diseases as caused by specific micro-organisms, the new science failed to fulfill its early therapeutic promise. Although diphtheria antitoxin (1894) rescued thousands from a disease that had routinely killed a quarter of those infected, subsequent vaccines and antisera proved far less effective, as did chemical anti-infectives prior to the introduction of sulfa drugs in the 1930s. Many practitioners avoided innovative treatments with dangerous side effects, such as pneumonia serum or Paul Ehrlich's salvarsan, a celebrated antisyphilis drug. Nowhere was medicine's therapeutic impotence more vividly demonstrated than in the viral epidemics of poliomyelitis, which in 1916 killed 2,400 children in New York City alone, and influenza, which killed more than 315,000 Americans in 1918–1919, many of them young adults.

In contrast to medical practitioners, public-health departments readily embraced the new bacteriological science. New York City's public-health laboratory, opened in 1892, was but the first to adopt routine bacteriological testing. By 1906, health officer Charles V. Chapin of Providence, Rhode Island, could write disparagingly of the "fetich [sic] of disinfection" that had led earlier sanitarians to emphasize the removal of offensive but innocuous urban nuisances. Stop worrying about rotting vegetables and "sewer gas," Chapin advocated, and instead block the specific infection path of each disease-causing organism: for yellow fever, kill the mosquito; for typhoid, purify water, milk, and food.

Chapin's advice fit well with the Progressive Era's "social-engineering" ethos, which sought to put all social reforms on a "scientific" basis. By World War I, Chapin and others increasingly emphasized the importance of personal habits in stopping infectious disease. Scientific policing of water and food supplies could do little, they argued, if housewives did not wash their hands and refrigerate their milk. Sanitary fairs, public-health "propaganda," and school-hygiene campaigns joined other contemporary efforts aimed at the "Americanization" of immigrants and the "modernization" of the poor. Forced testing of prostitutes for venereal disease marked another area where new science sanctioned existing middle-class mores.

Long before the germ theory's triumph, urban reformers had championed purified water systems and underground sewers for waste disposal. In the closing decades of the nineteenth century, death rates for waterborne diseases like typhoid fever plummeted in cities adopting these reforms. Not everyone benefited: residents of Pittsburgh's low-lying, working-class districts experienced five to six times the typhoid mortality of middle-class districts. African Americans living in Kansas City, Cincinnati, and Indianapolis between 1910 and 1920 had typhoid mortality rates two to four times those of whites in the same cities.

Regional variations compounded those of race and class. Despite northern-led campaigns against hookworm and pellagra, most rural counties in the South remained without full-time health officers until Franklin Delano Roosevelt's New Deal. As late as 1940, the heavily rural and African American states of South Carolina, Georgia, and Alabama reported some of the nation's highest rates of typhoid and enteritis mortality. Local initiatives sometimes countered the effects of regional poverty and prejudice. African American women in Atlanta, Georgia, and Salisbury, North Carolina, for example, launched antituberculosis campaigns that reached across racial lines, as did North Carolina's dynamic public-health department, led by Watson S. Rankin (1879–1970).

Between 1900 and 1930, American life expectancy at birth climbed from 47.3 to 59.7 years. Many observers concluded that infectious diseases were "conquered," despite continued deaths from tuberculosis, pneumonia, and syphilis. By 1920, medical researchers were turning their attention to the detailed workings of the body's "chemical machinery," the chemical reactions that regulate nutrition and excretion, growth and reproduction, activity and rest. Biochemists like the University of Wisconsin's Conrad A. Elvehjem (1901–1962) and Johns Hopkins University's Elmer V. McCollum (1879–1967) discovered numerous vitamins, whereas other researchers studied "metabolic pathways," the chemical reactions that govern the body's use of carbohydrates, proteins, and electrolytes. Apart from the discovery of insulin in 1922, however, this added knowledge had little impact on everyday medical practice. Vitamins nonetheless became the best-selling drug products of the 1930s, whereas numerous urban practitioners measured the "basic metabolic rate" of middle-class women to identify the causes of their irritability, anxiety, and fatigue. Here again, new science underwrote existing social beliefs.

Political Economy of Medical Practice.

In 1870, some 64 thousand physicians were practicing in the United States. For the majority, economic security was uncertain at best. Much illness was self-treated; for the rest, physicians faced competition from midwives, lay healers, and patent-medicine vendors. In rural Wisconsin, for example, three-quarters of all physicians had to supplement their medical earnings by farming, teaching, or operating small businesses. In metropolitan centers such as New York or Philadelphia, a handful of physicians succeeded by offering postgraduate hospital training that gave them opportunities both to teach and to cultivate the socially prominent benefactors of the city's charitable hospitals. Yet even well-connected young physicians could fail. John Sedgwick Billings, son of one of the country's most prominent physicians, ended his career where it began, as an employee of New York City's health department, after several unsuccessful efforts to build a private practice.

Most physicians in 1870 had been trained through an apprenticeship, supplemented by up to two years of study at a medical college. Virtually any group of physicians could start a medical college. From midcentury, medical leaders sought to raise standards of medical training and, with it, practitioners' social and economic status. Success came in the early twentieth century, when Abraham Flexner's *Medical Education in the United States and Canada: A Report to the Carnegie Foundation for the Advancement of Teaching* (1910) capped educational reforms begun by the American Medical Association. Flexner (1866–1959), a lay educator, called for the closure of 124 of the country's 155 medical schools as redundant, inadequately staffed and equipped, or lax in their entrance requirements. By 1920 only 85 schools remained. (Of these, only 2 were dedicated to training African American physicians and 1 to training women.)

After 1900, new physicians increasingly opted to practice in larger cities, especially in the newly emerging downtown business districts. Doctors' preferences for urban, wealthy communities paid off. By 1928, physicians' mean annual income ($9,000) put them above all but 1 percent of the population. Doctors were overwhelmingly white, native-born males at a time when 11 percent of the population were immigrants, nearly 10 percent were African Americans, and 49 percent were women. Sharing the prejudices of their class and gender, physicians endorsed public-health policies that held immigrants and African Americans responsible for spreading infectious disease and attempted to regulate sexual and reproductive behavior through educational campaigns and, at times, the active sterilization of poor women.

Most physicians worked in solo "private" practice. Like other small business owners, they fared badly in the Great Depression of the 1930s, with average net annual incomes declining nearly

$2,000. Specialty practice was one means to make good: from 1930 on, a majority of medical-school graduates eventually became specialists. Surgery was among the first of the full-time specialties. The advent of antiseptic and then aseptic surgery in the late nineteenth century enabled surgeons safely to perform intra-abdominal surgery on a routine basis. Operations like appendectomies flourished as hospitals became the preferred surgical sites for surgeons and middle-class patients alike. By 1928, 74 percent of admissions to Philadelphia's hospitals were surgical or obstetrical.

Social as well as technical innovations engendered the modern hospital. Religious groups—Protestant, Catholic, and Jewish—founded hospitals, as did small-town doctors who saw the advantages in hospitalizing patients. Hospitals provided surgeons not only with operating rooms, X-ray equipment, and diagnostic laboratories, but also with nurses to care for patients. By 1939, more than half of the nation's babies were being delivered in hospitals, as obstetricians (and their patients) followed surgeons into the hospital.

As with sanitary reforms, use of the new hospitals varied by class, race, and place. Only one-quarter of African American women gave birth in hospital in 1939; a decade earlier, families earning over $5,000 had more than twice the number of tonsillectomies per capita as families with incomes under $1,200, whereas rural families of all incomes had surgery at rates well below those of city dwellers.

Much health care remained outside the orbit of the new, "scientific" medicine. In the 1930s, roughly 20 percent of "medical-care" expenditures went for patent medicines and medical supplies, whereas another 8 to 10 percent went to midwives, chiropractors, and other practitioners condemned by orthodox physicians. In most years, Americans spent at least as much on funeral expenses as on hospitals.

From many perspectives, American medicine in 1945 had little in common with that of 1870. Discoveries in bacteriology, the reform of medical education, the rise of medical specialization, advances in surgery and public health, and the emergence of the modern hospital all contributed to the transformation. Yet the rewards of modernity were distributed along well-established lines of place, race, class, and gender.

[*See also* **American Medical Association; Biological Sciences; Chemistry; Childbirth; Cholera; Death and Dying; Diabetes; Diphtheria; Disease; Ethics and Medicine; Eugenics; Flexner Report; Food Processing; Foundations and Health; Gender and Science; Germ Theory of Disease; Health and Fitness; Hospitals; Hygiene, Personal; Influenza; Life Expectancy; Medical Education; Medical Malpractice; Medical Specialization; Midwifery; Nobel Prize in Biomedical Research; Nursing; Pesticides; Poliomyelitis; Public Health; Race and Medicine; Religion and Science; Sewage Treatment and System; Sexually Transmitted Diseases; Surgery; Tuberculosis; Typhoid Fever; War and Medicine;** *and* **Yellow Fever.**]

BIBLIOGRAPHY

Beardsley, Edward H. *A History of Neglect: Health Care for Blacks and Mill Workers in the Twentieth-Century South.* Knoxville: University of Tennessee Press, 1987.

Brandt, Allan M. *No Magic Bullet: A Social History of Venereal Disease in the United States since 1880.* Expanded ed. New York: Oxford University Press, 1987.

Dowling, Harry F. *Fighting Infection: Conquests of the Twentieth Century.* Cambridge, Mass.: Harvard University Press, 1977.

Morantz-Sanchez, Regina Markell. *Sympathy and Science: Women Physicians in American Medicine.* New York: Oxford University Press, 1985.

Rosen, George. *Preventive Medicine in the United States, 1900–1975: Trends and Interpretations.* New York: Science History Publications, 1975.

Rosenkrantz, Barbara Gutman. *Public Health and the State: Changing Views in Massachusetts, 1842–1936.* Cambridge, Mass.: Harvard University Press, 1972.

Rothstein, William G. *American Medical Schools and the Practice of Medicine: A History.* New York: Oxford University Press, 1987.

Starr, Paul. *The Social Transformation of American Medicine.* New York: Basic Books, 1982.

Stevens, Rosemary. *In Sickness and in Wealth: American Hospitals in the Twentieth Century*. New York: Basic Books, 1989.

Warner, John Harley. *The Therapeutic Perspective: Medical Practice, Knowledge, and Identity in America, 1820–1885*. Cambridge, Mass.: Harvard University Press, 1986.

Harry M. Marks

SINCE 1945

In the second half of the twentieth century, American medicine was characterized by unprecedented technological progress and profound social disagreements over how medical care should be organized, financed, and regulated. In the years from World War II through the mid-1960s, widely publicized technological developments encouraged expansive optimism about what science and technology could ultimately do for the health of Americans. After the later 1960s, skepticism about the fruits of medical science and technology dominated public discussions, just as researchers finally began to realize their ambitions of reengineering the human machine.

A similar chronological divide marks contrasting approaches to financing medical services. Between 1945 and 1965, middle- and working-class Americans looked to employment-based, private health insurance to secure access to medical care, whereas the federal government's role was largely restricted to infrastructural investments in hospital facilities and medical research. After 1965, Washington's role in financing health-care markets expanded 11-fold, from three cents of every dollar spent in 1965 to 33 cents in 1995. The ensuing ideological debates over the government's regulatory and budgetary role in health care largely eclipsed the more basic question of whether any one party could or should control the nation's highly decentralized $879 billion health economy.

The Early Postwar Era. In the immediate aftermath of World War II, American physicians attempted to assimilate the legacy of war medicine. For some, the war experience offered new models of medical care and research. In July 1945,

more than one in four American physicians was serving in the military. War medicine encouraged specialization, the delegation of tasks to nurses and technicians, and a hierarchical model of medical organization, with academic consultants and hospitals at the pinnacle. Such a system, postwar planners argued, had delivered wartime medical innovations in an efficient, organized way. Rather than returning to the isolated conditions of individual general practice, planners insisted, physicians should work in groups, supported by modern, well-equipped hospitals.

Although prewar trends toward specialization continued (three fourths of 1945 medical graduates entered specialty practices), the lucrative private-practice model remained strong. In 1965, only 10 percent of U.S. physicians worked in group practices.

Development of the regional medical centers envisioned by postwar planners proved similarly slow. Although the number of cottage hospitals (under 25 beds) declined after the war, the supply of small community hospitals of between 25 and 100 beds increased, abetted by federal subsidies designed to distribute hospitals more widely. Overall per-capita use of hospitals doubled between 1945 and 1975. By 1960, nearly all (white) women delivered their babies in hospitals.

Patients financed their increased use of hospital and medical services through private health insurance, with medical opposition having defeated successive initiatives for publicly financed insurance. Court rulings in 1949 making health insurance benefits a legitimate subject for collective bargaining accelerated the growth of private, employment-linked health insurance. Middle-class and unionized workers especially benefited from this development. By 1956, more than 116 million Americans had some health insurance, but the private, job-based system meant that rural, poor, and black citizens were less likely to be insured, and thus they saw doctors and stayed in hospitals less often.

A series of innovations making surgery easier and safer fueled increased hospital use. Intravenously administered fluids that mimicked the blood's chemical makeup and volume minimized postsurgical shock. Penicillin, the product of a publicly financed World War II crash program, was the first of many new antibiotics for controlling postsurgical infection. Intensive-care units, the symbol of high-technology medicine, were standard features of U.S. hospitals by 1970. Publicists promoting magazine sales, drugs, and medical charities spread awareness of these life-saving innovations, ushering in what historian John Burnham has termed the "golden age" of American medicine.

Penicillin aside, the best-known medical triumph of this era was Jonas Salk's poliomyelitis vaccine, publicized in a 1954 field test involving nearly two million schoolchildren. Although the media hailed Salk, his scientific colleagues, although acknowledging his technical skill and dedication, deemed his contribution less significant than that of John Enders, Thomas Weller, and Frederick Robbins, who received the 1954 Nobel Prize in Medicine for developing the underlying technique of cultivating poliovirus in tissue culture. The Salk episode points to a divide between medical scientists and the lay public regarding the means, if not the aims, of medical research. The most significant research in the biological sciences in the 1950s and 1960s, which studied the structure and operations of the cell, was remote from "practical" results and everyday medical concerns. Those who sought immediate relief from suffering emphasized organized research programs targeting specific diseases. In their quest for new antibiotic and anticancer therapies, researchers built on the wartime model of screening for antimalarial drugs. Laboratory researchers following standardized protocols systematically tested thousands of substances to see what micro-organisms they killed or which tumors they might inhibit.

Methodic and resource intensive, such research helped produce the antibiotics streptomycin (1944), chloramphenicol (1947), aureomycin (1948), neomycin (1949), and terramycin (1950). The National Cancer Institute's (NCI) search for anticancer drugs adopted a similar screening model but produced fewer tangible results. University scientists argued that such narrowly targeted research lacked imagination and could not produce the deeper understanding of disease essential to its eventual control. American Cancer Society publicists drew a different lesson: the NCI program was not practical enough. New drugs needed to be tested in human beings, not test tubes.

Until the late 1960s, Congress generally sided with basic science, allowing university scientists to determine where federal funds should be spent, while rejecting proposals that medical research dollars be distributed broadly, like agricultural research support or highway construction funds. Between 1945 and 1960, as annual congressional funding for the National Institutes of Health (NIH) increased from $2.8 million to $300 million, NIH's administrators convinced Congress that long-term investment in basic research would ultimately bring better health.

To demographers, who measure improvements in health by increases in life expectancy, progress after midcentury seemed almost imperceptible. But most citizens, and many physicians, measured postwar medical progress by its more tangible technological accomplishments: the penicillin shot that saved an elderly person from death by pneumonia or painlessly cured syphilis; the polio vaccine that allowed children to swim in the community pool without fear of paralysis or death. In the 1950s, only a few medical specialists gave much attention to the fact that the widespread use of antibiotics gave rise to antibiotic-resistant pathogens, that the sexual behaviors that transmitted syphilis remained unaltered by penicillin, or that the risks of death from polio were small compared with other childhood hazards. Even the rising mortality rates from heart disease and cancer seemed a problem that more science and improved medical-care delivery arrangements would resolve.

Government and Markets since 1965. Following the defeat of national health-insurance proposals in the 1940s, congressional Democratic leaders adopted a new strategy, seeking government subsidies for groups excluded from the private insurance system. Building on New Deal–era and wartime programs, such legislation extended federal support to state governments that would provide health insurance to welfare clients and other medically needy groups. This supplementation strategy culminated with the 1965 passage of Medicare, which provided health insurance for all Americans over the age of 65, and Medicaid, a cost-sharing program with the states to pay for the medical care of the poor. These two laws extended medical-care coverage to millions of underserved Americans.

To ensure the participation of doctors, hospitals, and state governments in the new programs, federal officials promised to pay for any medical care provided. They even offered special inducements, such as a 2 percent premium to participating hospitals beyond their direct operating costs. Participation mushroomed, but so did program costs. By 1975, the two programs served 47 million people at a cost of $28 billion, nearly a quarter of the nation's total health-care expenditures.

Health care remained a national problem for the rest of the century. Federal programs created new political interests in health policy. No longer solely a concern of physicians and labor unions, health-care policies affected hospitals, nursing homes, the pharmaceutical industry, home health-care vendors, and state governments. New fault lines appeared in the political landscape: medical specialists versus primary-care physicians, teaching versus community hospitals, home care versus nursing homes, Medicare versus Medicaid recipients. The proliferation of interest groups led to a new kind of health politics, in which conventional partisan differences over such issues as "competition versus regulation" or "market versus government" were replaced by a managerial politics that emphasized administrative innovations and technocratic expertise.

By the early 1970s, policy debates focused on the explosive growth in health-care costs, from 10 to 13 percent annually and growing. President Jimmy Carter promoted regional health planning under which community groups would assess medical needs and limit new hospital construction. President Richard M. Nixon first imposed wage and price controls and then supported legislation providing federal subsidies for health maintenance organizations (HMOs) to compete with traditional fee-for-service medicine. President Ronald Reagan attempted to limit the federal share

of Medicaid expenses by administrative changes in cost-sharing formulas and eligibility rules. Following the advice of Harvard economists, President George Bush's administration redesigned Medicare fee schedules to favor primary-care physicians over more costly specialists.

But the federal government refrained from imposing direct limits on health expenditures. Although Washington's share of total health-care costs rose to 28 percent by 1990, only the Medicare program was fully controlled by the federal government. Most federal initiatives in the 1970s and 1980s were indirect efforts to steer the health-care system away from hospital-based, specialty-oriented care (health planning and fee-schedule reform) and toward more cost-conscious organizations (such as HMOs), with the overall aim of lowering costs without compromising access to medical care. These government efforts to influence decentralized, largely private health-care markets had limited, even perverse effects. The shift from hospital and nursing-home care, for example, fueled explosive growth in the harder-to-regulate home health-care industry. During the early twenty-first century the number of uninsured Americans rose to approximately 55 million. As a partial solution to the problem, President Barack Obama in 2010 won congressional approval of his Patient Protection and Affordable Care Act, known popularly as Obamacare. By means of individual mandates and the expansion of Medicaid, his plan extended coverage to some 30 million uninsured Americans, leaving roughly 25 million still without coverage. Two years later the U.S. Supreme Court ruled positively on the constitutionality of the most comprehensive extension of health insurance since 1965.

Beginning in the 1980s, public debates over soaring health-care costs became private contests over who should pay for these costs. Businesses saddled with expensive employee-benefit programs sought to shift a greater share of the premiums to employees while reducing coverage for retirees and dependents. The growing ranks of part-time workers and employees of small firms often found themselves without insurance entirely. After the defeat of President Bill Clinton's proposal for national health insurance in 1993, owing largely to the opposition of political conservatives and the powerful health-insurance industry, cutbacks in coverage reached previously protected employees in large manufacturing firms. The greatest gaps in coverage, however, remained among the poor, African Americans, Hispanic Americans, and citizens of rural states such as Arkansas, Mississippi, and Texas, where one in four adults lacked health insurance at the end of the twentieth century.

The postwar social contract, which had offered employers labor peace in exchange for generous benefits, eroded in the 1980s. Simultaneously, the working conditions of America's physicians changed radically. As the pattern of independent practice faded at the end of the twentieth century, roughly two in five physicians engaged in patient care were employed by a hospital or other health-care organization, and the remainder received about 40 percent of their income from managed-care organizations that oversaw the amount and kind of treatment provided. Although medicine remained among the highest paid occupations, these changes caused great anxiety among physicians.

Medical Progress and Medical Care since 1960.   The details of health-care policy concerned most Americans less than what happened when they got sick. In this realm, the changing treatment of heart disease offers a window on medical progress. In 1960, doctors could offer relatively little for the heart-attack patient who survived long enough to reach the hospital: anticoagulants to thin blood clots and diuretics to reduce the work of the damaged heart. Coronary-artery bypass surgery became widely available by the late 1960s, accompanied by specialized wards for monitoring the recovering patient. New therapies emerged at the end of the 1970s to dissolve or remove clots in the coronary arteries, allowing many patients to avoid open-heart surgery. By the late 1980s, a broad array of drugs was available for treating the underlying conditions that bring on heart attacks, including drugs to lower cholesterol and regulate the heartbeat.

Although the gains in treating heart disease were exceptional, there are few cases where medical researchers cannot point to substantial differences between the "dark ages" of the 1960s and the ever-emerging present. The return of infectious diseases in the 1980s, including new infections such as acquired immunodeficiency syndrome (AIDS) and older infections in newer, drug-resistant forms, such as tuberculosis and pneumonia, suggested the limits of technological progress. Although the emergence of new infections was rooted in social behaviors, including sexual practices, drug use, and the medical and commercial abuse of antibiotics, the preferred solution for medical researchers and the general public alike remained technological.

Beginning in the late 1960s, a disparate group of economists, philosophers, and public-health advocates vocally challenged contemporary medicine's technological orientation as intrusive, financially ruinous, and ultimately counterproductive. The trajectory of the women's health movement was instructive. In the 1970s, feminist activists, defending women's autonomy against medical domination, challenged existing obstetrical practices and explored alternatives to technologically oriented hospital births; popularized surgical alternatives to radical mastectomy for breast cancer; and identified the risks of technologically defined birth control, such as oral contraceptive hormones. Yet the autonomy of the 1970s became the consumer activism of the 1990s as activists lobbied to ensure that women's diseases would be researched and treated as aggressively as those of men. AIDS activists similarly demanded quicker access to experimental drugs. Autonomy was redefined as the right to pursue nontraditional treatments alongside the latest NIH innovations in cancer therapy. As with the politics of health care, the nation's social arrangements for ensuring medical progress were embroiled in struggles among groups of consumers over who would win the most favorable position at the medical table and who would be left waiting.

[*See also* **Biological Sciences; Birth Control and Family Planning; Cancer; Cardiology; Childbirth; Demography; Disease; Ethics and Medicine; Foundations and Health; Gender and Science; Group Practice; Health and Fitness; Health Insurance; Health Maintenance Organizations; HIV/AIDS; Hospitals;**

Instruments of Science; Life Expectancy; Malaria; Medical Education; Medical Specialization; Medicare and Medicaid; Medicine and Technology; National Institutes of Health; Nobel Prize in Biomedical Research; Nursing; Penicillin; Pharmacology and Drug Therapy; Poliomyelitis; Race and Medicine; Research and Development; Salk, Jonas; Science; Sexually Transmitted Diseases; Technology; *and* War and Medicine.]

BIBLIOGRAPHY

Derickson, Alan. *Health Security for All: Dreams of Universal Health Care in America.* Baltimore: Johns Hopkins University Press, 2005.

Fox, Daniel M. *Health Policies, Health Politics: The British and American Experience, 1911–1965.* Princeton, N.J.: Princeton University Press, 1986.

Marks, Harry M. *The Progress of Experiment: Science and Therapeutic Reform in the United States, 1900–1990.* Cambridge, U.K.: Cambridge University Press, 1997.

Rothman, David J. *Beginnings Count: The Technological Imperative in American Health Care.* New York: Oxford University Press, 1997.

Starr, Paul. *The Social Transformation of American Medicine.* New York: Basic Books, 1982.

Stevens, Rosemary. *American Medicine and the Public Interest: A History of Specialization.* Berkeley: University of California Press, 1998.

Stevens, Rosemary. *In Sickness and in Wealth: American Hospitals in the Twentieth Century.* New York: Basic Books, 1989.

Strickland, Stephen. *Politics, Science and Dread Disease: A Short History of United States Medical Research Policy.* Cambridge, Mass.: Harvard University Press, 1972.

Harry M. Marks

ALTERNATIVE MEDICINE

Although the cast of healers has changed dramatically, the medical marketplace in America has always been diverse and competitive. In the Colonial Era, patients sought out bonesetters, midwives, preacher-healers, and root-and-herb doctors, as well as a broad range of school-trained and apprentice-trained physicians, known as regular, orthodox, or, in the nineteenth century, allopathic practitioners. At a time when many regular physicians bled, blistered, puked, and purged their patients—and when the population was largely rural and scattered—Americans often treated themselves and their families, relying on domestic recipes, almanacs, or, by the later eighteenth century, medical manuals.

Thomsonianism, Physiomedicalism, Eclecticism, Homeopathy, Hydropathy. Some medical entrepreneurs offered patients distinctive forms of treatment. In the 1790s, for example, the Connecticut physician Elisha Perkins began treating pain and disease with metal rods, or "tractors." The state medical society expelled him, but he obtained a patent for his device and built up a considerable practice. In 1806, the New Hampshire farmer turned healer Samuel Thomson (1769–1843) began selling "family rights" to his system of botanical medicine, which relied heavily on the emetic *lobelia*, steam baths, and hot pepper. Proclaiming "Every Man His Own Physician," he attacked not only physicians but also priests and lawyers. In the 1830s, Thomson's supporters pressured state legislatures to repeal licensing laws, which in any event had had little effect on medical practice. At the height of his popularity, Thomson (generously) estimated that 3 million Americans were using his system, but by the late 1830s his movement was in sharp decline.

With the demise of Thomsonianism, two other botanic groups arose to fill the vacuum. The first, physiomedicalism, was formed by restless Thomsonians who wanted trained botanical physicians. The second, eclecticism, was started in the 1830s by a regularly trained physician, Wooster Beach. Like their physiomedical competitors, the eclectics established medical schools and societies. Their largest institution, the Eclectic Medical Institute in Cincinnati, Ohio, ranked among America's largest medical schools at midcentury. Eclecticism flourished well into the twentieth century.

Even more successful were the homeopaths, followers of a system developed by the German physician Samuel Hahnemann in the early nineteenth century and brought to the United States around 1825 by German-speaking immigrants. Rejecting orthodox drugs and doses, homeopathic practitioners relied on the law of similars (like cures like) and the law of infinitesimals (the smaller the dose, the more potent). During the second half of the nineteenth century, homeopathy became the most significant professional and economic rival to orthodox medicine. By the 1880s homeopathic medical colleges and hospitals existed in most major cities, including women's homeopathic schools in Cleveland, Ohio, and New York City.

A much smaller medical movement, hydropathy, or the water cure, appeared in the mid-1840s. Relying on various water therapies developed by a Silesian peasant, Vincent Priessnitz, American hydropaths set up coeducational schools to train hydropathic physicians, established scores of water-cure institutions, and published the popular *Water-Cure Journal*, which claimed 100,000 subscribers. Many water-cure enthusiasts also embraced the health-reform movement launched in the 1830s by the Massachusetts temperance lecturer and sex reformer Sylvester Graham (1794–1851), who preached the virtues of a twice-a-day diet devoid of meat, rich foods, tea, coffee, spices, and commercially made bread.

The growing popularity of alternative-healing movements spurred the founding in 1847 of the American Medical Association (AMA). Its code of ethics, made compulsory for member societies in 1855, barred consultation with anyone "whose practice is based on exclusive dogma," an obvious reference to eclectics, homeopaths, hydropaths, and other sectarians. Enforcement of the code frequently created awkward moments, as when in 1878 a county medical society in Connecticut expelled Moses Pardee, a regular physician, for consulting with his wife, Emily, a homeopathic practitioner. In 1884 the New York State Medical Society split, with rural general practitioners upholding the AMA code, whereas urban specialists, often German trained, claimed that truly scientific physicians could recognize legitimate expertise regardless of creed. A revision of the code in 1903 recognized this latter view. Henceforth, homeo-

paths and eclectics who embraced "scientific medicine" and abandoned their sectarian identities were welcomed as members.

Christian Science, Osteopathy, and Chiropractic.

In the late nineteenth century, as the practices of allopaths, homeopaths, and eclectics increasingly converged under the banner of science, three new alternative-healing movements, all offshoots of mesmerism or animal magnetism, rose to prominence: Christian Science, osteopathy, and chiropractic. Christian Science, a religion founded by Mary Baker Eddy in the 1860s, taught that disease and death do not exist physically but only mentally; thus treatment consists of helping the sick alter their state of mind. Osteopathy, originated by a magnetic healer and bonesetter, Andrew Taylor Still, focused on removing obstructions to the flow of body fluids by manipulating out-of-place bones, particularly vertebrae. In 1892, Still opened the American School of Osteopathy in Kirksville, Missouri. Daniel David Palmer, a magnetic healer from Davenport, Iowa, started the chiropractic movement in 1895, initially as a spiritual healing sect employing spinal adjustments to relieve pinched nerves that impeded the flow of "Innate Intelligence." Despite the return of medical licensing laws in the later nineteenth century, by the early 1930s roughly 20 percent of all healers in the United States were unorthodox. Some 46 states legally recognized osteopathy, and 39 permitted chiropractic practice. After many legal battles, Christian Science practitioners, too, had won the right to pursue their activities.

When Abraham Flexner issued his muckraking survey *Medical Education in the United States and Canada* (1910), he excoriated the homeopathic, eclectic, and osteopathic schools he had visited and dismissed chiropractors as "unconscionable quacks" unworthy of "serious notice in an education discussion." The Flexner Report and Flexner's unwillingness to "compromise between science and revelation" profoundly shaped elite attitudes toward alternative medicine in America. But the public's increasing reliance on hospitals and medical specialists did not necessarily undermine support for medical alternatives. And the often racist and anti-Semitic admissions policies of many orthodox medical schools led many African Americans and Jews to study osteopathy and chiropractic (as well as dentistry and optometry) instead of medicine. Throughout the twentieth century, ethnic and racially segregated communities commonly used herbalists, midwives, medical advisers, and spiritual healers—often for complementary rather than alternative care.

Alternative Medicine in the Later Twentieth Century. By the 1960s and 1970s, American physicians faced increasing criticism as elitist, overly interventionist, and too Eurocentric. Critics compared Western scientific medicine with the allegedly gentler, more humane, and more natural health practices of other cultures, such as those of Native Americans, Asians, and Hispanics. Communes and some college campuses welcomed alternative medicine. In 1969, Michigan State University established the first university-affiliated osteopathic school, followed in the 1970s by state universities in Texas, West Virginia, Oklahoma, Ohio, New Jersey, New York, and Maine. In 1966 the U.S. Department of Defense accepted osteopaths as military physicians and surgeons, and soon thereafter osteopaths gained admission to hospital residency and fellowship programs. In 1972, Congress mandated Medicare coverage of chiropractic, but, facing continuing discrimination, American chiropractors in 1976 sued the AMA for violating antitrust laws. Although the AMA revised its code of ethics to allow physicians the freedom "to choose whom to serve, with whom to associate, and the environment in which to provide medical services," it eventually lost the suit.

During the 1980s and 1990s, growing public fascination with so-called New Age healing (a mixture of naturopathy, homeopathy, Ayurvedic healing, and other Eastern vitalist systems) gave rise to various alternative schools and numerous health-food stores and magazines. The growing incidence of chronic diseases for which orthodox medicine offered no cure—especially cancer, rheumatoid arthritis, persistent fatigue, and ac-

quired immunodeficiency syndrome (AIDS)—spurred interest in unorthodox treatments. Recognizing the public's growing interest in alternative healing, Congress in 1991 created an Office of Alternative Medicine in the National Institutes of Health.

Meanwhile, the practice of alternative healing flourished. In 1993 the prestigious *New England Journal of Medicine* published news of a recent survey in which over a third of the respondents "reported using at least one unconventional therapy in the past year, and a third of these saw providers for unconventional therapy." This report also revealed that Americans annually paid more visits (425 million) to alternative practitioners than to "all U.S. primary care physicians" combined and spent more money on alternative healers ($13.7 billion) than on out-of-pocket expenditures for hospitalization. A follow-up survey seven years later reported a 47.3 percent increase in visits to alternative healers. Among the fastest-growing unconventional therapies were "herbal medicine, massage, megavitamins, self-help groups, folk remedies, energy healing, and homeopathy." So popular had alternative medicine become that by the year 2000 well over half of American medical schools were offering courses on the subject.

[*See also* **American Medical Association; Botany; Cancer; Childbirth; Dentistry; Ethics and Medicine; Flexner Report; Food and Diet; Graham, Sylvester; HIV/AIDS; Hospitals; Medical Education; Medicare and Medicaid; Medicine and Technology; Midwifery; National Institutes of Health; Native American Healers; Optometry; Race and Medicine;** *and* **War and Medicine.**]

BIBLIOGRAPHY

Baker, Robert B., et al., eds. *The American Medical Ethics Revolution: How the AMA's Code of Ethics Has Transformed Physicians' Relationships to Patients, Professionals, and Society.* Baltimore: Johns Hopkins University Press, 1999.
Barzansky, Barbara, and Norman Gevitz, eds. *Beyond Flexner: Medical Education in the Twentieth Century.* New York: Greenwood Press, 1992.

Gevitz, Norman, ed. *Other Healers: Unorthodox Medicine in America.* Baltimore: Johns Hopkins University Press, 1988.

Haller, John S., Jr. *Medical Protestants: The Eclectics in American Medicine, 1825–1939.* Carbondale, Ill.: Southern Illinois University Press, 1994.

Numbers, Ronald L., and Darrel Amundson, eds. *Caring and Curing: Health and Medicine in the Western Religious Traditions.* Baltimore: Johns Hopkins University Press, 1998.

Risse, Guenter, Ronald L. Numbers, and Judith W. Leavitt, eds. *Medicine without Doctors: Home Health Care in American History.* New York: Science History Publications, 1977.

Rogers, Naomi. *The Making and Remaking of Hahnemann Medical College and Hospital of Philadelphia.* New Brunswick, N.J.: Rutgers University Press, 1998.

Naomi Rogers

MEDICINE AND TECHNOLOGY

Since 1800, technology has played a significant role in medicine by providing improved methods of diagnosis, enhanced therapeutics for patients, and greater understandings of disease and the body. Medical technologies altered the practice of medicine, including how the medical community approached and treated illness as well as the ways in which physicians and patients related to one another. It was also not without controversy because the adoption and use of specific devices and drugs sparked debate relating to issues of professionalization, economics, access, risk, and more.

Medical technology, broadly defined, encompasses the instruments, devices, machines, drugs, and systems developed for medical research and/or clinical practice. The development, diffusion, adoption of, or sometimes resistance to new technologies is historically contingent, neither inevitable nor necessarily linear. Traditional scholarship presented technological developments as a one-way progression from invention through innovation to diffusion, starting with laboratory research and moving out through clinical applications in medicine. In the early twenty-first century, most historians agreed that the process of technological innovation and application in medicine is multidirectional and often incremental, serendipitous, and even circular. New medical technologies were not adopted simply because they were superior. Few scholars support technological determinism (a reductionist theory that suggests that technology shapes a society's structure and cultural values) and instead study the political, economic, and sociocultural meanings of technology that are attributed to, not inherent in, technologies.

Extending the Physician's Senses. Medical technology in the nineteenth century extended the physician's senses, notably to see and to hear internal lesions of the body, and improved their ability to offer a diagnosis (cause of illness) and even a prognosis (probable outcome) for their patients with greater proficiency and objectivity. New diagnostic instruments empowered the medical practitioner to connect internal anatomic lesions to specific diseases within the living patient rather than at autopsy. Earlier seventeenth- and eighteenth-century scientific inventions, such as the Italian physician Santorio Santorio's (1561–1636) crude clinical thermometer or the Dutch tradesman Anton van Leeuwenhoek's (1632–1723) improved microscope, were not adopted into the day-to-day medical practice of physicians. Conversely, the medical community embraced several key nineteenth-century diagnostic instruments, including the stethoscope (1819), the laryngoscope (1829), and the ophthalmoscope (1851).

Invented by the French physician René Laennec (1781–1826), the stethoscope mediated the technique of auscultation (listening to internal body sounds), allowing the physician to correlate sounds heard from within the patient's chest to specific lung diseases, such as bronchitis and tuberculosis, based on their anatomical lesions. The stethoscope changed in form from Laennec's cylinder shape (1819) to a flexible monaural (one earpiece) stethoscope in 1843 and then to a binaural (two earpieces) instrument in 1852.

The British physician Benjamin Babington (1794–1866) invented the laryngoscope (1829), a tubular instrument that was inserted into the patient's mouth; it combined a retractor with a mirror and allowed physicians to see past the patient's tongue to examine the larynx (or voice box) and other epiglottis structures. Medical practitioners used this tool to assist in the diagnosis and treatment of various head and neck disorders. Physicians experimented with different mirrors and improved their techniques, and indirect viewing eventually gave way to direct viewing of this area with the addition of lights and cameras, but the fundamental form of Babington's instrument remain unchanged. By the early twentieth century, physicians began using laryngoscopes (without mirrors) as a means to intubate the trachea.

Particular specialties formed around certain instruments such as the case of ophthalmology and the ophthalmoscope (1851), an instrument containing a perforated mirror and lenses used to examine the interior of the eye. Invented by the German physician-scientist Hermann von Helmholtz (1821–1894), the ophthalmoscope was the most powerful of the early viewing devices, partly because it allowed its operator to treat as well as diagnose. With this tool, physicians were able not only to see the interior of the eye, but also later to operate on the iris and correct strabismus (cross-eye or deviating eye).

Additional useful instruments that were introduced into medical practice at this time included the endoscope (1807), a rigid or flexible instrument to allow a lit view of the inside of the body; the pleximeter (1826), used in the percussion of a patient; the clinical thermometer (1867), a smaller and now portable version (typically six inches in length), which was either straight or curved; and the sphygmomanometer (1881), which consisted of a pressure gauge and rubber cuff to measure a patient's blood pressure. The syringe dates back to the Greeks and had many uses—to drain abscesses, to administer enemas, and more; however, the invention of the hypodermic syringe in 1853, independently by the French surgeon Charles Gabriel Pravaz (1791–1853) and the Scottish physician Alexander Wood (1817–1884), allowed physicians to inject medicines under the skin through a hollow needle attached to the barrel of the syringe.

Technology in the Hospital. In contrast to the nineteenth-century tools of the individual

medical practitioner, medical technology in the twentieth century involved large, expensive equipment purchased by hospitals and was used by teams of technicians and medical professionals. Such technology included the electrocardiogram, which outlines the heart's movement, the ventilator, which assists with breathing, and medical imaging technologies, especially the X-ray and magnetic resonance imaging (MRI) machines, which depict the interior of the body. This technological change in medicine was significant, contributing substantially to the rise of the hospital as the doctor's workshop and the preferred place of treatment, to the systematization of health care, and to the emergence of medical technology specialists. These new and improved medical technologies expanded the ability of physicians to diagnose and treat disease and also shaped the ways in which physicians and patients related to one another.

The X-ray, more than any other technology, played the greatest influential role in the practice of medicine. In 1895, the German physicist Wilhelm Röntgen (1845–1923) used electromagnetic radiation to produce inner images of the body; an X-ray of his wife's hand, complete with her wedding ring, generated enormous publicity and excitement. Thereafter, X-rays and associated technologies allowed physicians to visualize and treat the body in ways never before possible. The early history of X-ray technology illustrates that technology was central to the rise of the specialization and the hospital. As X-ray apparatus grew more complex and expensive, physicians looked to hospitals to share the capital and operating costs. But as the historians Bettyann Kevles, Joel Howell, and Stuart Blume have argued, the adoption of X-ray technology in hospitals necessitated a social reorganization of hospital work in terms of reporting, record keeping, payment, and professionalizing of X-ray technicians and other hospital staff (Kevles, 1997; Howell, 1996; Blume, 2010). By the late 1920s, medical doctors, now called radiologists, were in charge of ray technology in the hospitals; this development was partly in response to the requirements of the accreditation system established in 1918 by the American College of Surgeons. Physicians and hospital administrators who had been reluctant to adopt X-ray technology changed their views as more paying patients demanded access to the newest medical technology.

The twentieth-century patient record compiled the data generated from the new medical technologies and represented the collective actions taken by physicians in their care of patients. With the introduction of the computer into medicine in the 1960s, the electronic patient record emerged within a larger information system that sought to integrate clinical information with administrative, financial, and related services. The electronic record promised to be a more complete and accessible record for multiple practitioners, allowing greater efficiency and effectiveness in medicine; however, its cost remains a challenge in the implementation of electronic records systems in many places.

From Diagnostic to Therapeutic Use.

Before 1900, American pharmaceutical companies were small and dealt primarily in natural product extracts such as codeine, quinine, and morphine, as well as a narrow range of ointments and pain medicines. By the turn of the twentieth century, technical changes in pharmaceutical discovery, development, and manufacturing, such as improved chemical separation and novel methods of compound synthesis, contributed to the explosion of new drugs by midcentury. The discovery of insulin in Toronto (1921–1922) and its production and distribution by Eli Lilly and Company of Indianapolis boosted American pharmaceutical research and development programs to counter European manufacturers. The discovery and production of sulfa drugs and antibiotics in the 1930s and 1940s led to an explosion of synthetic drugs such as improved analgesics, anti-inflammatories, antihistamines, diuretics, and more. The number of useful drugs rose from about a dozen in 1930 to more than two thousand in 1960. Starting with the sulfa drugs that were developed in the 1930s, many of the chemical drugs were products of scientific method combined with accident. One such potent and serendipitous addition to *material medica* was chlorpromazine, the first drug that mitigated the dreadful effects of schizophrenia. This drug spurred a reorientation to mental illness as an organic, biological condition rather than a social or emotional disorder (and supplanted such surgical interventions as lobotomy). Other influential drugs of this period included the birth control pill for women, released commercially as Enovid in 1960, and tranquilizers like Valium, available in 1963. As the historians Elizabeth Watkins and Andrea Tone argue, these drugs demonstrate the golden age of pharmaceutical science as well as the shifting political, social, and medical ideas surrounding reproduction, women's bodies, anxiety, drug use, and more (Watkins, 1998; Tone, 2001, 2009).

Diagnostic imaging continued to be the site of dramatic developments in the three decades following World War II. In the 1960s, the first computed tomographic scanner combined X-ray with computer technology. MRI was first attempted in the 1970s; it became a versatile tool for diagnosis of diseases and conditions in most tissues and for examining the flow of blood. Technological innovations in medicine continued to offer what would have been unimaginable to physicians and patients at the beginning of the century. The Zeiss operating microscope, invented in the 1950s, transformed surgery and expanded the possibilities of neurosurgery and transplantation in the 1960s. Lasers also arrived in the 1960s and were quickly taken up by ophthalmologists and later by other surgeons. One of the most famous medical technological developments of the twentieth century was the invention of the artificial heart. The Dutch physician Willem Kolff (1911–2009), inventor of the artificial kidney machine (1943), led an ambitious research program on artificial organs in the United States, and in 1982, the Jarvik-7 artificial heart became the first mechanical heart implanted in a patient as a permanent therapy. Less spectacular, but appreciated by hundreds of thousands, was the development of small hearing aids during the 1950s made possible by the invention of the transistor in the late 1940s. Early attempts at cochlear implants during the 1950s, viewed as a fundamental advance over conventional hearing aids, promised to cure deafness, although it was contested by the deaf community.

Twentieth-century optimism in medicine and technology rose precipitously, and in response, some scholars and medical professionals began to question its emerging dominant role. The 1940s were the beginning of randomized clinical trials and other aspects of what would become evidence-based medicine. This new technology—broadening to include knowledge and practice related therein—was changing the structure of medicine and the relative prestige of its specialties, as had the development of laboratory science and early diagnostic tools 50 years before.

Debates and Concerns. By the last third of the twentieth century, there was less enthusiasm about scientific medicine and its technological orientation. In the pharmaceutical industry, great hopes for more "magic bullets" had given way to disappointment, even public anger, over the failure of medical technology and its professional and government watchdogs to protect patients from iatrogenic or physician-caused illness. One of the most publicized disasters was thalidomide, a drug prescribed for nausea in pregnancy, which caused severe, nonreversible birth defects in thousands of babies in the late 1950s. The overuse of antibiotics fed the rise of antibiotic-resistant "superbugs," including a form of multi-drug-resistant tuberculosis. During the early and mid-1970s, public outrage over American deaths and injuries from defective heart valves, pacemakers, and intrauterine devices (the Dalkon Shield controversy) led to accusations that such devices had not been adequately tested and helped rally support for the passage of medical device legislation. The Medical Device Amendments of 1976, which awarded the U.S. Food and Drug Administration greater regulatory powers over medical devices from development through clinical use, aimed to safeguard the health of Americans but without denying them the benefits of new technologies. Further monitoring of devices by the Food and Drug Administration went into effect with the Safe Medical Devices Act of 1990 and the Medical Devices Amendments of 1992.

Emerging in the 1970s, the new social history of medicine engendered ambivalent theoretical perspectives on technology; technology was seen as a tool that worsened race, class, and gender barriers and inequalities and also promoted the power of doctors at the expense of patients. The cultural role of technology, or the questions of race, class, gender, and professional status raised by certain devices and techniques, contributed to the identity of certain diseases and caregivers. As argued by the historian Keith Wailoo, the technologies of blood analysis—such as the diagnostic blood tests, iron and liver pills, hemacytometers, electrophoresis, and others—sometimes reinforced existing social biases and other times challenged medical orthodoxy and patient identities, as in the case of sickle-cell anemia as a disease of Negro blood (Wailoo, 1999). The historian Margarete Sandelowski has highlighted the role of gender in her study of how nurses' interaction with technology both improved and limited their professional status and ability to care for the patient (Sandelowski, 2001). Of course the role of technology in shaping professional identity and practice extended beyond the nurse.

The historian Stanley Reiser has argued that technology separated, physically and emotionally, the doctor and the patient, a process that began early in the twentieth century (Reiser, 1978, 2009). The adoption of blood tests, urinalysis, and X-rays resulted in less time spent by physicians with their patients. Technology overshadowed the social and humanistic side of medical practice, according to Reiser, and reinforced the prevailing anatomical thinking by physicians with their focus on the disease and its lesions rather than the person. The diagnostic "objective" measurements of the machine appeared to dominate over the "subjective" accounts of the patient, resulting in an ever-widening distance emerging between doctors and patients. Arguably both groups became dissatisfied by the deterioration of the doctor-patient relationship, but neither thought abandoning technology was the answer.

Legacy. The scope and meaning of medical technology shifted over time, notably from nineteenth-century medical instruments and the clinical art of the individual practitioner to the twentieth-century "science" of medical machines, procedures, and equipment that necessitated an integrated team of health-care professionals. In this transitional period, the function of medical technology expanded from diagnostic tools to therapeutic devices, contributing to the growing optimism in technological solutions and the emergence of the technological imperative (or the inevitability of its dominant role) in medicine. Better technology did translate into better outcomes for patients fighting disease, but not always, and certainly not without debate. By the early twenty-first century, the place of diagnostic technologies in medicine was almost certainly fixed, and despite challenges of false positives and human errors, it remained much less controversial than the place of many therapeutic technologies in medicine.

Life-saving medical technologies, such as the dialysis machine to ward off kidney failure or the artificial ventilator to breathe mechanically for the patient who cannot, may prevent death but also have raised a variety of medical, socioeconomic, and ethical questions. Historically, the iron lung or negative pressure mechanical ventilator, developed by the Harvard engineer Philip Drinker (1894–1972) in 1928, was both hailed as a life-saving machine for children suffering from bulbar polio and criticized as a kind of "halfway medical technology" (Maxwell, 1986). Medical technologies that are not either preventative or curative of disease, but rather prolong life as temporary fixes, such as dialysis machines or artificial ventilators, have raised issues of cost, access, quality of life, and more. The escalating cost of medicine and technology has disturbed governments, citizen groups, and others; however, American citizens have continued to expect, daresay demand, the use of medical technologies in addressing their health-care issues. In the early twenty-first century, the allure of medical technology and its role in the health-care system, although at times challenged, have remained strong in American medicine and culture.

[See also **Biotechnology; Birth Control and Family Planning; Cardiology; Cloning; Deafness; Dentistry; DNA Sequencing; Genetics and Genetic Engineering; Medical Specialization; Medicine: Overview; Ophthalmology; Penicillin; Pharmacology and Drug Therapy; Psychopharmaceutical Drugs; Radiology; Research and Development; Stem-Cell Research; Surgery;** *and* **Technology.**]

BIBLIOGRAPHY

Atwater, Edward C. "Internal Medicine." In *The Education of American Physicians: Historical Essays*, edited by Ronald L. Numbers, pp. 143–174. Berkeley: University of California Press, 1980. In this essay, the author describes how the creation of internal medicine as a specialty can be linked to the new technology of the nineteenth century, such as the stethoscope, the ophthalmoscope, the sphygmomanometer, the percussion hammer, and the spirometer, as well as microscopic and chemical tests on blood and urine, which required specialized training.

Bliss, Michael. *The Discovery of Insulin.* Toronto: McClelland and Stewart, 1982. 25th anniversary ed. Toronto: University of Toronto Press, 2007. The definitive history that argues that the discovery of insulin was the result of a four-man team—F. G. Banting, J. J. R. Macleod, C. H. Best, and J. B. Collip—in Toronto, Canada.

Blume, Stuart S. *The Artificial Ear: Cochlear Implants and the Culture of Deafness.* Piscataway, N.J.: Rutgers University Press, 2010. An in-depth analysis of the early development and implementation of cochlear implants from the 1930s to early twenty-first century, highlighting the various medical, political, economic, and cultural factors that shaped its divergent course. The author laments how the experience of deaf people and the arguments of Deaf advocates played little or no role in shaping the development and use of cochlear implants.

Edmonson, James M. *American Surgical Instruments: The History of Their Manufacture and a Directory of Instrument Makers to 1900.* San Francisco: Norman Publishing, 1997. A study of the American surgical instrument trade, detailing how instrument makers collaborated with physicians and medical schools to manufacture and distribute their tools and including an extensive listing of nineteenth-century surgical instrument companies.

Howell, Joel D. *Technology and the Hospital: Transforming Patient Care in the Early Twentieth Century.* Baltimore: Johns Hopkins University Press, 1996. A study of the adoption of technology in two hospitals—the Pennsylvania Hospital, Philadelphia, and the New York Hospital, New York City—from roughly the 1900s to the late 1920s, focusing on the use of X-ray imaging, blood tests, urinalysis, and administration systems including the management of patient records.

Kevles, Bettyann Holzmann. *Naked to the Bone: Medical Imaging in the Twentieth Century.* New York: Basic Books, 1997. A history of X-rays, fluoroscopy, ultrasound, computed tomography, MRI, and positron emission tomography scans and the impact of these technologies on the practice of medicine, as well as its effects on American social attitudes and adoption into popular culture.

Maxwell, James H. "The Iron Lung: Halfway Technology or Necessary Step?" *The Milbank Quarterly* 64, no. 1 (1986): 3–29. Challenging Lewis Thomas's position of the iron lung as a halfway technology, James H. Maxwell argues that this machine saved lives and stimulated developments for new respiratory technologies. In addition to basic science, Maxwell points to the value of technology, not only as "the handmaiden of science" but also as a source of knowledge and discovery in its own right.

Reiser, Stanley Joel. *Medicine and the Reign of Technology.* Cambridge, U.K., and New York: Cambridge University Press, 1978. Rev. ed. 1981. Pathbreaking and seminal work in the field of medical technology. Reiser was among the first to reflect on the use of technology in medicine concluding that technology's dominant role in the practice of medicine contributed to the change in the doctor-patient relationship. Discussing instruments such as the stethoscope, the X-ray, and the microscope, Reiser argues how doctors' understanding of disease emerged less from the "subjective" history of the patient and more from the "objective" measurements of medical technology.

Reiser, Stanley Joel. *Technological Medicine: The Changing World of Doctors and Patients.* Cambridge, U.K., and New York: Cambridge University Press, 2009. After 30 years studying the socioeconomic impact of technology on health-care delivery, Reiser argues that technology overshadows the social and humanistic side of medical practice. He pleads for stronger patient-physician relationships, more effective social policies, and a less dominant role of technology in medicine. The book includes an examination of the artificial kidney machine, the artificial ventilator, and debates on resource allocation.

Sandelowski, Margarete. *Devices and Desires: Gender, Technology, and American Nursing.* Chapel Hill: University of North Carolina Press, 2001. The author raises the dilemmas posed by technology for nurses since the 1870s in America, highlighting the role of gender and power in the use of medical technology by health-care professionals.

Tone, Andrea. *The Age of Anxiety: A History of America's Turbulent Affair with Tranquilizers.* New York: Basic Books, 2009. A history of tranquilizers in American culture and the role played by medicine, the pharmaceutical industry, the media, and society in embracing drugs such as Valium, Ativan, and Miltown.

Tone, Andrea. *Devices and Desires: A History of Contraceptives in America.* New York: Hill and Wang, 2001. A well-researched medical and social history of contraception, beginning with the 1873 Comstock Law banning contraceptives and tracing the illicit trade in birth control through to its legitimate business success with the availability of the Pill and the Dalkon Shield.

Wailoo, Keith. *Drawing Blood: Technology and Disease Identity in Twentieth-Century America.* Baltimore: Johns Hopkins University Press, 1999. This is a medical and cultural study of blood diseases that explores the rise of technology as a contributing force in defining disease. The author studies chlorosis, splenic anemia, aplastic anemia, and sickle-cell anemia and how technology, race, and science interacted to shape the meaning of these diseases.

Watkins, Elizabeth. *On the Pill: A Social History of Oral Contraceptives, 1950–1970.* Baltimore: Johns Hopkins University Press, 1998. This is a medical and cultural history of the Pill, focusing on its development and the shifting attitudes of scientists, women, and society regarding its use in America in the 1950s and 1960s. Watkins argues that the Pill as a medical technology ushered in a contraceptive revolution (distinct from a sexual revolution) and contributed to contested authority battles among physicians, scientists, the pharmaceutical industry, journalists, and women.

Shelley McKellar

MENARD, HENRY WILLIAM

(1920–1986), marine geologist whose research focused on the morphology of the ocean floor and deep-sea sedimentation. Best known for his contributions to the systematic mapping of large portions of the Pacific Ocean floor after World War II, he collected data on several research cruises conducted between 1950 and 1965, which were subsequently used in developing the idea of sea-floor spreading. Using bathymetric, geological, and magnetic data, Menard also discovered the Mendocino fracture zone and the Mid-Pacific Mountains, along with many other fracture zones and oceanic rises in the Pacific Ocean. His research spanned various disciplines such as geomorphology, geophysics, and sedimentology and contributed to the observational basis of plate tectonics theory. Menard was also a respected historian and sociologist of geology, as well as an educator and science popularizer.

Raised in Los Angeles, Menard joined the U.S. Navy in 1941. He earned his BS in geology from Caltech in 1942 and then served in the South Pacific as a staff intelligence officer and photo interpreter during the war. After marrying Gifford Merrill in 1946 (the couple had three children), he earned his MS from Caltech in 1947. He received his doctorate in marine biology from Harvard University in 1949, studying under the supervision of Henry Crosby Stetson (1900–1955). His experimental dissertation focused on sediment transport in a flume at the Woods Hole Oceanographic Institution. In 1949, he joined the Sea Floor Studies Section of the U.S. Navy Electronics Laboratory in San Diego and focused on the cutting-edge research programs involving bathymetry and studies on marine sedimentation.

After consulting for the AT&T Company, in 1951 he moved to the Scripps Institution of Oceanography, where he was appointed to the faculty of geology in 1955 and where he spent the rest of his career. In 1965–1966, he served as a technical advisor in the Office of Science and Technology in the White House and was elected to the National Academy of Sciences in 1968. He served as director of the U.S. Geological Survey from 1978 through 1981. In 1985, he received the William Bowie Award. His 1955 paper, "Deformation of the Northeastern Pacific Basin and the West Coast of North America," provided the first description of oceanic features later termed *trans-*

form faults by John Tuzo Wilson (1908–1993). The author of seven books and over one hundred papers in both geology and the history of science, Menard was a fellow of the American Academy of Arts and Sciences, the American Association for the Advancement of Science, the American Geophysical Union, the California Academy of Sciences, the Geological Society of America, and the American Association of Petroleum Geologists.

[*See also* **American Association for the Advancement of Science; Geological Surveys; Geology; National Academy of Sciences; Oceanography; Popularization of Science;** *and* **Scripps Institution of Oceanography.**]

BIBLIOGRAPHY

Agnew, Duncan Carr. "Menard, Henry William." *Complete Dictionary of Scientific Biography*, Vol. 23, pp. 96–97. Detroit: Charles Scribner's Sons, 2008.

Fisher, Robert L., and Edward D. Goldberg. "Henry William Menard." *Biographical Memoirs of the National Academy of Sciences* 64 (1988): 267–276.

Daniele Macuglia

MENNINGER, KARL AND WILLIAM

(1893–1990) and (1899–1966), respectively, psychiatrists, founders of the Menninger Foundation. Karl Menninger was the eldest of three brothers. He studied at the University of Wisconsin and the Harvard Medical School. Karl developed an interest in neurological cases while serving as an intern at the Kansas City General Hospital. This led him to take up a residency at the Boston Psychopathic Hospital, where he worked with Elmer Southard and became a follower of neuropsychiatry and mental hygiene. In 1919, with his homeopathic physician father, Charles Frederick Menninger, Karl established the Menninger Clinic in Topeka, Kansas. The clinic began as a small psychiatric facility in a renovated farmhouse.

Karl's younger brother, William Menninger, joined the clinic in 1925 after studying at Washburn

University and the Cornell University College of Medicine. A few years later the clinic became a full-scale psychiatric hospital named the Menninger Sanitarium. William became director of the sanitarium in 1930. Influenced by the innovative work of Southard, Adolf Meyer, and William Alonson White, the Menningers developed a comprehensive practice based on psychoanalytic therapy and a nineteenth-century tradition of moral treatment. In 1941, the hospital became part of the newly incorporated Menninger Foundation. Five years later, Karl Menninger founded the Menninger School of Psychiatry, which soon emerged as one of the nation's largest and most respected training facilities for psychiatrists, clinical psychologists, and psychiatric social workers.

In addition to his work for the Menninger Foundation, Karl Menninger helped popularize Sigmund Freud's psychoanalytic theories among American psychiatrists as well as the general public. He discussed Freud's ideas in several influential books, including *The Human Mind* (1930), *Man against Himself* (1938), *Love against Hate* (1942), and *The Vital Balance* (1963). He became especially well known for his espousal of Freud's dual-drive theory, which postulates that there are basic types of instincts—those that serve life (Eros) and those that serve death (Thanatos). In 1942, he organized the Topeka Institute for Psychoanalysis, which helped train new psychoanalysts along Freudian lines.

William Menninger, too, had a career outside the Menninger Foundation as a leader in the psychiatric treatment of American soldiers. Beginning his World War II military career as a neuropsychiatric consultant, by 1944 he was head of the army's psychiatric programs and held the rank of brigadier general. In 1945 he invented a system of psychiatric classification for the army, which became the foundation for the 1952 Diagnostic Statistical Manual (DSM-1) of the American Psychiatric Association.

[*See also* **Foundations and Health; Mental Health Institutions; Mental Illness; Military, Science and Technology and the; Psychiatry; Psychology; Psychotherapy;** *and* **War and Medicine.**]

BIBLIOGRAPHY

Friedman, Lawrence J. *Menninger: The Family and the Clinic*. New York: Alfred A. Knopf, 1990.
Shamdasani, Sonu. "Menninger, Karl." In *Dictionary of Medical Biography,* edited by W. F. Bynum and Helen Bynum, Vol. 4, pp. 867–869. Westport, Conn., and London: Greenwood University Press, 2007.

Mark I. West;
updated by Elspeth Knewstubb and
Hugh Richard Slotten

MENTAL HEALTH INSTITUTIONS

Before the Revolutionary War, most mentally ill persons in the colonies lived either with their families or in local almshouses. With urbanization, specialized institutions emerged to care for the dependent and ill. In 1752, the Pennsylvania Hospital in Philadelphia, the colonies' first general hospital, accepted insane patients. In 1773, the Virginia House of Burgesses established a free-standing "madhouse" in Williamsburg, modeled on London's Bethlem Royal Hospital (from whence the word "bedlam" derives). When the New York Hospital opened in 1791, it too made provision for "maniacs," along with medical and surgical cases. Charity hospitals' decision to include lunatics manifested the Enlightenment view of insanity as a treatable affliction. Among the best-known advocates of more active therapeutics was Benjamin Rush, a physician who developed a "tranquilizing chair" to soothe the agitated. Nonetheless, care generally remained harsh; hospitals relied on bleedings, purgings, and emetics to calm the disturbed and often locked those considered dangerous in basement cells.

In the 1820s, a very different regimen, known as "moral therapy," appeared, first at private nonprofit institutions like the Friends' Asylum at Frankford, Pennsylvania (1817), and the McLean Asylum outside Boston (1818), and then at state-funded institutions, like Massachusetts's Worcester State Hospital (1833). Inspired by the work of Philippe Pinel in France and William Tuke in England, advocates of moral therapy supported treatment of the insane by psychological methods, in particular a carefully constructed round of activities designed to stimulate patients' latent reason and capacity for self-control. Specialized lunatic asylums in peaceful, rural areas became the preferred therapeutic setting. By the second half of the nineteenth century, most states and many major cities had at least one public psychiatric institution, whereas corporate and proprietary hospitals continued to serve the wealthy. As the number and size of state hospitals increased, however, overcrowded wards housed chronic cases: long-term schizophrenics, the senile, paralytics, and epileptics. As a result, both the internal environment and the external image of the state asylums began to deteriorate. By 1900, hospital superintendents found themselves under bitter attack from other medical professionals (especially neurologists), ex-patients, and state legislators.

By the early twentieth century, the most innovative psychiatric research was taking place in research institutes, laboratories, and private practice. Psychopathic hospitals, intended to provide acute care, opened in a number of major cities. A mental-hygiene movement, aimed at promoting general mental health, emerged. Yet, in part because many psychiatrists were uninterested in the severely and chronically mentally ill, state hospital populations continued to grow. Underfunded and desperate for treatments that would control if not cure their patients, hospitals experimented with somatic therapies, including insulin shock, malarial fever, and lobotomies (surgical removal of part of the brain).

Staffing shortages during World War II further exacerbated this situation. During the 1940s and 1950s, however, new drug therapies and the increasing involvement of the federal government began to reshape mental health institutions. Two federal laws of 1946—the Mental Health Act and the Hill-Burton Act—helped to fund the rebuilding of the public hospital system, the expansion of general hospitals (including psychiatric units), and the development of community services. The hope that antipsychotic drugs, like chlorpromazine, and antidepressants, like reserpine, would enable the long-term mentally ill to return to their communities prompted state legislatures and mental health advocates to press for the downsizing of large psychiatric facilities. Mary Jane Ward's 1946 novel *The Snake Pit*, exposing the dreadful conditions in state mental institutions (made into a successful movie in 1948), intensified the pressures for reform.

During the 1950s and 1960s, as enthusiasm for community mental health centers swept the nation, new groups of mental health care consumers began to use them. Public institutions, however, continued to provide most of the inpatient care, especially for the severely impaired, although the average length of stay decreased. Some patients seemed caught in a "revolving door" syndrome, moving in and out of psychiatric facilities to little long-term effect. Others, particularly those with a dual diagnosis of mental illness and substance abuse, lived marginal but highly visible lives in shelters and on city streets. During the 1970s and 1980s, a loose coalition of politicians, advocacy groups like the National Alliance for the Mentally Ill, and health-care professionals pressured community mental health centers to refocus on the severely ill. The managed care movement of the 1990s increased the proliferation of halfway houses, supported-care facilities, and other quasi-independent residential facilities. As a result, the institutional landscape was highly diverse at the turn of the century, although the challenge of chronic mental illness remained.

[*See also* **Disabilities, Intellectual and Developmental; Medical Specialization; Medicine; Menninger, Karl and William; Mental Illness; Psychiatry; Psychology; Psychopharmaceutical Drugs;** *and* **Psychotherapy.**]

BIBLIOGRAPHY

Braslow, Joel. *Mental Ills and Bodily Cures: Psychiatric Treatment in the First Half of the Twentieth Century.* Berkeley, and Los Angeles: University of California Press, 1997.

Dowdall, George. *The Eclipse of the State Mental Hospital: Policy, Stigma, and Organization.* Albany: State University of New York Press, 1996.

Dwyer, Ellen. *Homes for the Mad: Life inside Two Nineteenth-Century Asylums.* Ann Arbor: University of Michigan Press, 1987.

Grob, Gerald N. *The Mad among Us: A History of the Care of America's Mentally Ill.* New York: Free Press, 1994.

Grob, Gerald N., and Howard H. Goldman. *The Dilemma of Federal Mental Health Policy: Radical Reform or Incremental Change?* New Brunswick, N.J.: Rutgers University Press, 2006.

McCandless, Peter. *Moonlight, Magnolias and Madness: Insanity in South Carolina from the Colonial Period to the Progressive Era.* Chapel Hill: University of North Carolina Press, 1996.

Rothman, David. *The Discovery of the Asylum: Social Order and Disorder in the New Republic.* Boston: Little, Brown, 1971.

Scull, Andrew. *Social Order/Mental Disorder: Anglo-American Psychiatry in Historical Perspective.* Berkeley, and Los Angeles: University of California Press, 1989.

Tomes, Nancy. *A Generous Confidence: Thomas Story Kirkbride and the Art of Asylum Keeping, 1840–1883.* New York: Cambridge University Press, 1984.

Ellen Dwyer

MENTAL ILLNESS

Physicians, popular writers, and laypeople employed a wide and changing vocabulary to describe mental distress in the past two centuries. Serious mental illness was generally referred to as insanity until the early twentieth century, and late-nineteenth- and early-twentieth-century psychiatrists described conditions they labeled as manic-depressive psychosis, dementia praecox (or schizophrenia), and involutional melancholia within hospital settings. Medical writers outside of institutions often used terms such as nervous disease and neurasthenia to describe nervous complaints in the nineteenth and early twentieth centuries, whereas lay writers used the concept of nervous breakdown through much of the twentieth century. In the heyday of psychoanalysis, many practitioners and laypeople used the term neurosis or reaction, even for illnesses identified with labels such as schizophrenia. In the era of the Cold War, writers engaged the idea of anxiety to capture both individual distress and social fears within the nation. By the 1960s and 1970s, biologically minded psychiatric researchers began to use specific labels for types of mental illness, including depression, bipolar disorder, and schizophrenia. Professional and popular authors created and transformed concepts and terminology for emotional disorder in dynamic with one another. In addition, assumptions about race and gender in American society reflected and reinforced changes in popular and professional explanations of nervous problems.

Nineteenth-Century Illness. In the Colonial Era, persons with disruptions in their thoughts or behaviors were cared for within their communities and treated with remedies common to other medical ailments, including bleeding and purging. By the middle of the nineteenth century, physicians and laypersons increasingly focused on insanity, or serious problems in behavior and relationship to the world, that reformers argued required special institutions for care. During this time period, psychiatry emerged as a specialty with the formation in 1844 of the Association of Medical Superintendents of American Institutions for the Insane (later renamed the American Psychiatric Association). Nascent psychiatrists extolled the virtues of asylums to care for seriously mentally disordered individuals in which patients would experience the benefits of a moral environment. Psychiatrists of the time focused attention on physical conditions within their buildings and the roles of the staff members at the hospital.

At the same time that psychiatrists were building a profession around institutions, other physicians struggled to compete in a crowded medical marketplace to develop new practice niches. A group of doctors who had seen unusual cases of physical and emotional injuries during the Civil War identified themselves as neurologists and began to seek out patients with nervous ailments. One of the most well known of these was the early neurologist George M. Beard, who helped to popularize the term neurasthenia in medical practice and lay discussions of nervous problems. Self-styled neurologists understood the nervous system in terms of circuits of energy and explained that nervous problems resulted from an impairment of energy flow. Practitioners used a variety of treatments, including rest (such as Silas Weir Mitchell's rest cure) or stimulation of the nervous system through mild electrical currents.

Neurologists (and other medical professionals) did not create the concept of nervous disease in a vacuum, nor did they promote the illness onto a blindly accepting public. Instead, a variety of individuals found the concept of nervous disease (including neurasthenia) helpful in framing their experiences of rapid social changes, especially after the Civil War. Medical writers produced materials intended for public audiences, whereas popular writers used medical concepts shaped for their own purposes that in turn influenced medical treatises on this subject. Patients flocked to see physicians for treatment of vague complaints of headaches, digestive upset, and fatigue. Those afflicted, including well-known figures such as the philosopher William James and the social reformer Jane Addams, often wrote about their experiences in books, popular magazine articles, and letters to family.

Descriptions and experiences of mental illness and nervous complaints depended on race and gender. Whereas asylums were idealized as beautiful environments for treatment, African Americans were institutionalized under much poorer conditions within racist assumptions about the origins of their illness and requirements for treatment. Women such as Elizabeth Packard found that they did not have control over their entrance to (or egress from) mental institutions. For individuals with nervous symptoms, physicians and lay writers projected assumptions about gender and society onto explanations for their illness. Some physicians argued that women experienced nervous illness when they overstrained their systems by engaging in intellectual work or activities beyond the domestic sphere, whereas cultural critics charged that women's increasing role in reform movements, as well as professions such as medicine, was a threat to American society and possibly the human race. Men, too, struggled with nervous disease during this time period, often related to shifts in their work environment. Medical and lay authors assumed that gender, race, and class defined Americans and that individuals were vulnerable to a breakdown of their nervous systems if they attempted work outside their proper place.

First Half of the Twentieth Century.

In the early twentieth century, psychiatrists and neurologists both competed and cooperated as their professional purviews expanded. Psychiatrists slowly began to look beyond institutions for patients, and some neurologists became interested in what they argued were early precursors to insanity. Within mental hospitals, American psychiatrists—influenced by German thinkers such as Emil Kraepelin—began to suggest that insanity could be divided into different types, including manic-depressive insanity and dementia praecox. Practitioners in the first half of the century also began to develop physical treatments for mental illness, including fever therapy, hydrotherapy, insulin coma, and shock (both metrazol and electroconvulsive).

Although psychiatrists stressed that they were trying aggressively to treat patients to improve American society, mental institutions reflected racist assumptions in both diagnosis and treatment of groups such as African Americans. Not only did nonwhite patients experience inferior care, but also mental health professionals projected fears about racial degeneration and decay onto the patients they believed were of a lower race. At the same time, gender shaped how medical professionals applied diagnostic concepts and treatments to patients. Psychiatrists selected more women than men for treatment with somatic therapies, reflecting patriarchal assumptions about interventions on women's bodies, as well as their desire to treat patients they thought might respond well. Further, class differences were heightened because poorer patients were likely to be sent to increasingly crowded state hospitals in which conditions deteriorated over time with more and more chronic patient populations.

Meanwhile, although some neurologists abandoned work with emotional ailments as they shifted from mechanistic interpretations of the nervous system to anatomical ones, other neurologists joined with psychiatrists to explore new ideas about the mind's function proposed by Sigmund Freud. As the specific concept of neurasthenia faded, physicians increasingly described nervous disease and neurosis as functional complaints—that is, diseases for which no anatomical lesion could be located. Even before psychoanalysis became dominant in American psychiatry, the language of conflict, repression, and neurotic symptoms helped many physicians frame their interactions with patients. Some physicians attempted to treat symptoms of fatigue and digestive disturbance through the use of sedative medications or informal talk methods, whereas others began to focus on uncovering the unconscious conflicts that presumably led to the symptoms.

In the expanding mass culture of the early twentieth century, nervous illness appeared to be everywhere. Early journalists explained both nervous problems and their treatments, and writers who identified themselves as nervous sufferers described their experiences both positive and negative with medical professionals. During this time period, physician authority was not necessarily any better than anyone else's, particularly since the problem of nervousness seemed to be a by-product of American ingenuity and increased industrialization. Popular writers often employed the term nervous breakdown to capture the idea that the stresses and strains of life had overwhelmed the human organism. Like the other modern devices that were overused and subject to mechanical failure (such as the automobile), Americans could also experience wear and tear. The stress of war, economic depression, and social upheaval naturally seemed to result in breakdown.

As in the nineteenth century, nervous disease and breakdown for both men and women in the first half of the century were connected to their intense emotions regarding changes in American life. But the implications were clearly different for the sexes. Women who overindulged in feelings ran the risk of becoming incapacitated by their emotions. Further, women's increased public roles, through suffrage and public participation in economic depression and two world wars, led to social and individual worries about whether women would break under the strain. Men faced mounting pressures as they were expected to provide for their families' increasing consumer needs in large, bureaucratic workplaces. Social and economic upheavals also took their toll on men, who, especially in the case of war, experienced multiple physical and emotional symptoms.

Second Half of the Twentieth Century.
During World War II, more Americans encoun-
tered mental health professionals than ever before through military screening and treatment for emotional disorders connected to the war. Psychiatrists greatly expanded their professional scope after the war, and with the increasing popularization of Freudian concepts more Americans used the language of mental conflict to describe their experiences in a rapidly changing world. By this time period, neurologists had retreated from the area of emotional illness and psychiatrists and general physicians had the most medical influence.

Even before the war, many psychiatrists had begun to shift their focus from patients in hospitals to those who could be treated in outpatient settings. After the war, this process accelerated as leaders within the profession increasingly distanced themselves from the mental hospitals that were overcrowded and in poor repair. Desperate physicians attempted more aggressive treatments such as intense courses of electroconvulsive therapy and lobotomy. But beginning at midcentury, waves of criticism both inside and outside psychiatry brought into question the hospital as a treatment setting. By the 1960s and 1970s, critics were derisive of psychiatric treatment in hospitals and even the diagnosis of mental illness itself. The century-old system of state-run psychiatric hospitals was gradually dismantled.

Meanwhile, the language of psychoanalysis fully permeated American society. Films portrayed individuals going through psychoanalytic treatment with wise and kind psychiatrists. Popular writers explained their experiences uncovering unconscious conflicts, and popular culture references about the ego, the superego, and the id were widely understood. Everyone seemed to be at least a little neurotic, although some worked with professionals to become better adjusted. Within a psychoanalytic framework, there were no major distinctions between serious mental illness and mild problems with feelings or relationships—all physical and emotional experience could be understood and improved with the insights of psychoanalytic conversations.

Although many psychiatrists embraced psychoanalysis in the middle decades of the century, some within the profession began to express concern that psychiatry was not employing new scientific tools or participating in the waves of discovery and treatment innovation that characterized the rest of medicine by the 1960s and 1970s. These biologically minded psychiatrists began to dominate mental illness discussions by the 1970s and 1980s. Researchers expunged psychoanalytic language, which they thought had become too popularized (and therefore meaningless), from new explanations of psychiatric theory and treatment. Instead of highly individualized accounts of patients with neurotic illnesses, research psychiatrists shifted the language of mental illness to concrete symptoms such as disturbed sleep or appetite and depressed mood. Further, changes in psychiatric nosology took place in the context of development of pharmaceuticals, and physicians paired specific diagnoses with specific medications. The use of psychoactive medications became one of the most common ways in which Americans experienced treatment of mental complaints.

But the focus of psychiatry shifted with both the turn toward the psychoanalytic during and after World War II and the rise of biological psychiatry in the 1970s. Criticism of psychiatric hospital settings, as well as the availability of biological interventions, helped close a large number of hospitals. This process, identified as deinstitutionalization, did help with the perceived problem of controlling institutions but it left many patients without adequate care. Although psychiatrists had traditionally taken care of seriously mentally ill individuals within psychiatric hospitals, those individuals were increasingly on the margins of psychiatric attention by the 1980s. With the closure of psychiatric institutions during the 1960s and 1970s, seriously mentally ill persons increasingly occupied the streets and homeless shelters. Meanwhile, treatment innovations with medication were often targeted as much for the worried well as for those with chronic and persistent mental illnesses.

With shifts in mental professionals' diagnostic categories and increasing presence of medications, a vocabulary of anxiety and depression widely circulated in the broader culture, and the concept of schizophrenia captured the social and cultural divides of the 1960s and 1970s. In the era of increasing mass-market products, some formal and informal sales strategies used popular depictions of mental distress—including anxiety and depression—to push a consumer approach toward treatment. Indeed, the concept of happiness itself became a commodity to be purchased through consumption of new pills such as tranquilizers and antidepressants.

Although research psychiatrists had intended diagnostic categories, as initially codified in the watershed third edition of the *Diagnostic and Statistical Manual* (*DSM-III*, 1980), to be free of bias, the categories were created in a context of gender and racial difference. Researchers who were influenced by their own historical contexts applied different standards of pathology based on social and cultural norms. Schizophrenia was a disease label more often applied to African American men, whereas white women were more often diagnosed with depression. Some diagnoses such as borderline personality disorder or the research diagnosis of premenstrual dysphoric disorder appeared to be based on assumptions of women's expected behavior and experiences.

Into the Future. Although psychiatrists claimed with the *DSM* to have delineated specific definitions of mental disease, the myriad number of ways to describe mental problems has not decreased. Instead, several stakeholders have continued to expand the ways in which Americans can be mentally disturbed. Since 1997, pharmaceutical companies have advertised directly to the public to generate consumer awareness of both mental distress and its treatment. In addition, the ever-expanding psychiatric manual of mental disorders continues to include more and more people within its pages. And despite critics' concerns about the potential problems of encoding racist or sexist assumptions within diagnostic categories, American psychiatrists have continued to pursue a policy of expansion in diagnostic labels. Finally, American society has continued to promote the use of consumer commodities in the ever-elusive pursuit of happiness. It is likely that the number of terms used to describe mental illness and breakdown will continue to increase in the future.

[*See also* Disabilities, Intellectual and Developmental; Disease; Medicine; Mental Health Institutions; Psychiatry; Psychology; Psychopharmaceutical Drugs; *and* Psychotherapy.]

BIBLIOGRAPHY

Abbott, Andrew. *The System of Professions: An Essay on the Division of Expert Labor.* Chicago: University of Chicago Press, 1988. Abbott's final chapter illuminates the relationship between neurology and psychiatry in the late nineteenth and early twentieth centuries, particularly through the construction of complaints that required medical intervention.

Barke, Megan, Rebecca Fribush, and Peter N. Stearns. "Nervous Breakdown in 20th-Century American Culture." *Journal of Social History* 33 (2000): 565–584.

Braslow, Joel T. *Mental Ills and Bodily Cures: Psychiatric Treatment in the First Half of the Twentieth Century.* Berkeley: University of California Press, 1997.

Dwyer, Ellen. *Homes for the Mad: Life inside Two Nineteenth-Century Asylums.* New Brunswick, N.J.: Rutgers University Press, 1987. Dwyer contrasts the environments for African American and white inmates of asylums.

Eldridge, Larry D. " 'Crazy Brained': Mental Illness in Colonial America." *Bulletin of the History of Medicine* 70 (1996): 361–386.

Gambino, Matthew. " 'These Strangers within Our Gates': Race, Psychiatry and Mental Illness among Black Americans at St Elizabeths Hospital in Washington, DC, 1900–40." *History of Psychiatry* 19 (2008): 387–408.

Gilman, Sander L. "Constructing Schizophrenia as a Category of Mental Illness." In *History of Psychiatry and Medical Psychology*, edited by Edwin R. Wallace IV and John Gach, pp. 461–483. New York: Springer, 2008.

Grob, Gerald N. *The Mad among Us: A History of the Care of America's Mentally Ill.* Cambridge, Mass.: Harvard University Press, 1994. Grob's volume provides an outstanding overview of treatment of mental illness over the past three centuries.

Herzberg, David. *Happy Pills in America: From Miltown to Prozac.* Baltimore: Johns Hopkins University Press, 2009. Herzberg looks at the interaction of psychiatric medications with American consumer culture in the second half of the twentieth century.

Horwitz, Allan V., and Jerome C. Wakefield. *The Loss of Sadness: How Psychiatry Transformed Normal Sorrow into Depressive Disorder.* New York: Oxford University Press, 2007.

Schuster, David G. *Neurasthenic Nation: America's Search for Health, Happiness, and Comfort, 1869–1920.* New Brunswick, N.J.: Rutgers University Press, 2011. Schuster explores the multiple ways in which practitioners and patients shaped concepts of nervous disease and the pursuit of happiness in the late nineteenth and early twentieth centuries.

Laura D. Hirshbein

MENTAL RETARDATION

See Disabilities, Intellectual and Developmental.

METEOROLOGY AND CLIMATOLOGY

Meteorology and climatology got off to a relatively slow disciplinary start in the nineteenth-century United States when compared with Western European nations. The country's size militated against a national network of observation stations, educational institutions lacked strong science staffs, and meteorologists and climatologists—theoretical and applied—were in short supply. Agricultural needs in the late nineteenth century finally spurred the development of the U.S. Weather Bureau, which would remain under the Department of Agriculture's umbrella until the growth of aeronautics and the need for accurate aviation forecasts influenced its move to the Department of Commerce in the early 1940s. Throughout most of the twentieth century, military needs provided the greatest boost to both disciplines' professionalization as atmospheric knowledge became critical for the successful prosecution of wars, hot and cold—not only with forecasts for operational forces on and under the ocean, on land, and in the air, but also with attempts at controlling the weather. Late in the twentieth century and continuing into the twenty-first, a warming global climate spurred research and policy interest, calling upon meteorologists and climatologists to forecast future climates, their impacts on the natural and built worlds, and possible ways to ameliorate them.

An Emerging Discipline. Along with the other earth sciences that now fall under the umbrella of geophysics, such as oceanography and terrestrial magnetism, meteorology emerged from natural history as an independent discipline in the early nineteenth century. Although it gained some measure of academic respectability in the United Kingdom and Western Europe, the scientific stature of U.S. meteorology lagged behind despite its role as an international leader in theoretical development. Starting early in the century, several institutions (including the U.S. Army Medical Department) collaborated in gathering observational weather data, and the resulting networks were expanded in the 1830s and 1840s to include storm and wind data. While Joseph Henry, director of the Smithsonian Institution, was creating the nation's first large-scale research-based meteorology project in 1849, combining smaller observing networks primarily located in the Northeast, James Pollard Espy of Philadelphia's Franklin Institute and the U.S. Army Signal Service's William Ferrel were gaining international reputations for their work on the convective theory of cyclones.

As the nation expanded westward and telegraph lines followed, additional observation stations joined the network. In 1870 the first national weather service was established under the auspices of the U.S. Army Signal Service—by mid-1891 becoming the U.S. Weather Bureau under the U.S. Department of Agriculture. Throughout this period and into the twentieth century, meteorologist Cleveland Abbe not only shepherded the development of the national weather service, but also developed synoptic weather maps and weather "probabilities" to provide the nation with information that improved safety, commerce, and agricultural undertakings while also conducting meteorological research and establishing the nation's first meteorological journal, *Monthly Weather Review*. As had Espy and Ferrel, Abbe received international recognition for his efforts to organize international meteorological networks.

Despite lacking an academic home for meteorology, the United States—through a variety of institutions and government agencies—managed to produce a small, internationally renowned community of scholars that was advancing the discipline. However, Henry, Espy, Ferrel, and Abbe left no academic progeny, and as they died, so did research meteorology in the United States. At the same time, demand for applied meteorological services increased and the Weather Bureau's focus turned to instrument development. In short order, the primary purpose of meteorology within the Weather Bureau was to produce daily forecasts of high and low temperatures and the occasional warning—not a fruitful path to disciplinary advances.

Much of meteorology's marginal status (compared with other sciences) in the United States stemmed from its lack of theoretical "rigor," nearly absent academic presence, and limited patronage. It also faced a public perception that meteorological information was "free." Despite a small boost triggered by the needs of World War I, such as forecasts for gas attacks and the targeting of large, long-range guns, these factors created a tremendous hurdle to disciplinary advancement that would not be overcome until World War II created an almost unimaginable opportunity for the rapid expansion and professionalization of meteorology and (later) climatology.

Before World War I. A meteorological renaissance spread throughout Europe in the early twentieth century spurred by Norwegian physicist Vilhelm Bjerknes's now-famous 1904 paper that served as a scientific appeal to transform meteorology into a theory-based geophysical science grounded in physics, mathematics, and atmospheric research. Although his appeal to advance meteorology through a symbiotic combination of forecasting and research fell on fertile ground in Europe—by the 1920s, Bjerknes's program would spread as he played an important role in creating the University of Leipzig's Geophysics Institute, returned to Norway to the new Norwegian Geophysics Institute (later known as the

Bergen School), and sent his acolytes all across Europe to spread his message and techniques— the rocky patch that was U.S. meteorology was not so hospitable.

Established by an act of Congress, the U.S. Weather Bureau's mission was to provide meteorological services to commercial and agricultural customers. Indeed, unique among other U.S. scientific bureaus and agencies, the Weather Bureau had no research component. Its personnel conducted "investigations" in their "spare" time in the Bureau's headquarters "Study Room," but these were not theoretical—either in question or in answer. Most focused on agricultural concerns. Unlike in Norway, where Bjerknes was able to set up and obtain data from a dense network of observation stations with the help of the government, sailors, and farmers, which were then analyzed by his team of university-trained meteorologists, the Weather Bureau was unable to fund such a network over the entire continent and had very few college-trained employees, much less ones with physics and mathematics backgrounds. After all, how many men with those kinds of credentials wanted to be part of a "guessing science," as Hungarian-born physicist and hydrodynamicist Theodore von Kármán would later call it (Koelsch, 1996)?

The Weather Bureau's employees were largely trained on the job—with most rising up through the ranks after starting as observers in their teens. Even if they had been able to attend college, they would not have found a program that offered an education in meteorology. Part of the lack of academic presence in U.S. higher education was certainly caused by the lack of rigor, but there were other more important considerations. As Harvard climatologist Robert DeCourcy Ward noted in 1918, because all people spend a lifetime keeping track of the weather around them, they were, in essence, all meteorologists. Who studies a subject they already "know"?

World War I—A Meteorological Opportunity. With about 90 percent of the country's meteorologists working for the U.S. Weather Bureau, World War I presented the century's first opportunity to train a larger cadre of meteorologists. Weather predictions for military forces had

not become more important because of better forecasts or a sudden realization that weather conditions could affect military operations, but because new weapons required meteorological support. The new, larger guns had ranges of 10 miles or more, and targeting decisions depended upon wind conditions. The widespread use of poison gas meant keeping track of favorable and unfavorable wind conditions—too little wind and the enemy could take evasive measures; too much wind and the gas would disperse too quickly; a shift in the wind could bring gas back over friendly forces. And, of course, the introduction of planes built out of fabric, wood, and wire required aviation forecasts to keep them out of high winds, turbulence, and hailstorms that could send them hurtling to the ground. A special program at Texas A&M prepared hundreds of Army Signal Corps meteorologists for service in France, but with no demand for their services after the war, they turned to better career prospects and an opportunity for meteorology to grow was lost.

After the war, the number of graduate-trained meteorologists remained extremely small and it was difficult to find qualified faculty. Harvard's Ward had hoped that faculty members in physics, geography, geology, or even more marginally related scientific departments might study meteorology on their own and offer at least a basic course to stir some interest, but that turned out to be a very slow process. Occasionally addressed as part of atmospheric electricity in physics courses, meteorology was often lumped in with natural history and taught empirically in geology or geography departments. Lacking physics and mathematics, it looked a lot more like descriptive climatology with discussions of average temperatures, rainfall, and other weather phenomena. With rare exceptions, meteorology began disappearing from geography courses, and even climatology became a bit player in economic and regional geography courses.

When meteorology was explicitly present in the curriculum, it was more likely attached to agriculture—much as the Weather Bureau's mission was tied to agriculture. As the years passed, it was also found as part of the curriculum in normal schools so that schoolteachers could present basic ideas about the atmosphere to their students.

The situation in the United States might have remained stagnant had it not been for the arrival of one of Vilhelm Bjerknes's Bergen School acolytes—Carl-Gustav Rossby—in the mid-1920s. The recipient of an American–Scandinavian Foundation fellowship to study in the United States, Rossby joined the Weather Bureau staff in Washington, D.C., only to find that the only meteorologist receptive to Bergen School methods was Navy officer Francis W. Reichelderfer, later the chief of the Weather Bureau. With frustration building on both sides, Rossby was lured away to the West Coast to organize weather services for the "airway" between Los Angeles and San Francisco being funded by the Guggenheim Fund. Once the project was finished, Rossby would establish the first U.S. graduate meteorology program at the Massachusetts Institute of Technology (MIT) and with it a toehold for theoretical meteorology.

World War II—Game Changer.
With World War II on the horizon, academic meteorology in the United States had certainly advanced since the beginning of the century—a more rigorous theoretical base was in place, and a handful of universities offered graduate programs courtesy of Bergen School acolytes—but most meteorologists still worked for the Weather Bureau, still forecasting by thumb rules assembled at the turn of the twentieth century. As university programs became more theoretical, the gap widened between the physics- and mathematics-based academics and their on-the-job-trained Weather Bureau brethren who were more likely to "feel" the atmosphere than to calculate it. Much to the chagrin of Weather Bureau leaders, many physical scientists continued to think of meteorology as an "art" rather than a science.

Once again, war placed great demands on—and provided a great opportunity for—meteorology and climatology. Aviation, which had been of relatively small import during World War I, would play a major role because of a worldwide theater of operations. When President Franklin D. Roosevelt ordered the building of 50 thousand military aircraft in May 1940, the need for meteorological manpower, climatological studies, and surface- and upper-air observational data became obvious. At four hundred, the number of professional meteorologists in the country was not enough to get the job done.

In response to the need, Carl-Gustav Rossby—by now one of the world's most prominent meteorologists—organized the University Meteorology Committee, which undertook the training of thousands of navy and army air corps officers in graduate-level meteorology at one of the "Big Five" (MIT, New York University, California Institute of Technology, University of Chicago, and University of California, Los Angeles). When insufficient mathematics and physics majors and graduates were available, they expanded the program to other universities that prepared young men to enter the one-year crash course. (Women entering the program had to have master's degrees in hand before acceptance.) Over seven thousand men completed the program and were assigned as meteorological officers to airfields, aircraft carriers, and staff headquarters to provide operational predictions. Another 20 thousand men were trained as observers and technicians. Although not all of them remained in meteorology after the war, most of the discipline's postwar leaders—including chaos theory creator Edward Lorenz, general atmospheric circulation theorist Norman Phillips, numerical weather prediction leader Jule Charney, and tropical storm expert and the first U.S. woman to earn a PhD in meteorology, Joanne Simpson—entered the field because of the wartime need for meteorologists and stayed because they foresaw limitless interesting problems to solve.

Postwar Advances.
Wartime meteorologists needed more than just more colleagues—they needed more data, particularly from surface- and upper-air stations, to fill in gaps in the tropics and high northern latitudes. Not only were the data critical for day-to-day operations, but also they would become even more important for theoretical advances in the postwar years. Those theoretical advances would also depend on electronic digital computers. The promise of gaining atmospheric knowledge via computer models would

lead to two disparate meteorological undertakings: numerical weather prediction and weather control.

The problems surrounding Earth's complex atmospheric system are unsolvable by analytical methods. Before the computer age, basic questions could only be addressed by months of painstaking calculations using numerical analysis techniques. Electronic digital computers were originally created to produce large ordnance targeting solutions during the war, but when Hungarian-born mathematician and computer architect John von Neumann sought a suitably complex problem to solve on his planned postwar computer, he settled on weather forecasting. And he thought that if he could create the atmosphere in a computer, it would be possible to control it—hence the attraction for military leaders.

His decision was good news for both applied and theoretical meteorologists. The equations defining atmospheric motion had been known since the nineteenth century. But because they took months to solve, they were impractical for everyday forecasting—as British meteorologist Lewis Fry Richardson had discovered during the hand-calculated trial run that he conducted between emergency runs for a Friends' Ambulance Unit during World War I—and made theoretical work extremely slow. Von Neumann's proposed computer held the promise of being able to describe the atmosphere theoretically, the theory being testable (or capable of verification) by making daily forecasts based on raw data.

With initial funding from the Office of Naval Research (the Air Force joined later), in 1946 von Neumann commenced work on his computer at the Institute for Advanced Studies in Princeton alongside the Meteorology Project—guided by the resourceful Rossby and for the most part directed by Jule Charney—which developed the first numerical weather prediction models. A little less than 10 years later, as a result of the efforts of U.S. and Scandinavian meteorologists, the Weather Bureau–Navy–Air Force Joint Numerical Weather Prediction Unit started producing operational forecasts for civilian and military customers. The early computer-generated prognostic maps were less accurate than hand-drawn maps produced by longtime synoptic meteorologists, but with feedback from field users and improvements in computing power, numerical models were soon producing most operational weather maps and by the 1970s very few hand-drawn maps remained on the weather facsimile broadcast.

During this same period, the almost all-pervasive idea that it was possible to cure any naturally occurring or manmade problem through science and technology led some people (including von Neumann and Nobel Prize–winning chemist Irving Langmuir) to think that weather control was on the not-so-distant horizon. With funding from the U.S. military, Langmuir explored the use of silver iodide "seeds" to clear fog and low-lying clouds that could be troublesome to aviators, cause thunderstorms to collapse before loosing damaging hail, and produce rain or snow on demand from available clouds. During the Eisenhower administration, the Advisory Committee on Weather Control—composed primarily of meteorologists—began reviewing the results of weather control efforts taking place in the civilian sector and ultimately recommended that the National Science Foundation oversee weather control research. By the 1960s, in addition to the commercial applications of the 1950s (e.g., producing water for farmers and ranchers), unclassified weather control efforts were underway by the Bureau of Reclamation (Project Skywater), the U.S. Forest Service (Project Skyfire), and the military (including Project Stormfury to snuff out hurricanes). However, there were classified attempts to control the weather as well, which led President Lyndon B. Johnson to use it as a weapon in Laos and Vietnam (dubbed COMPATRIOT) and as a diplomatic tool in India during the Bihar drought in 1967 (dubbed GROMET). Tens of millions of dollars were funneled into weather-control research by the U.S. government through the 1970s, only to die out in the 1980s as a lack of success coupled with ethical misgivings led the funding to dry up. However, the commercial version of weather control, which generally involves cloud seeding, continues today because states such as Utah have made it part of their water resources management strategy.

Determining Earth's Climate Future.
Until the mid-twentieth century, climatology remained a geography-driven descriptive study of atmospheric averages and extremes and their relationship to vegetation, latitude, and altitude. Based on observational data collected over many years, the resulting classification schemes and climatological studies provided useful information to any profession at the mercy of the elements (e.g., architects and engineers, farmers, and water managers). Regional climatological studies were also important to political empires that controlled far-flung territories and needed to consider the health implications of local climates on their governmental representatives. Early climatology, however, relied on the idea that climate was static. But by the late 1940s, climate specialists, including Helmut Landsberg (who was tracking warming trends on both sides of the Atlantic) and Swedish glaciologist Hans Ahlmann (who was studying retreating glaciers), were coming to the conclusion that the climate was not as static as they had thought. And if climate was changing, why?

As meteorologists developed weather forecasting models in the late 1940s and early 1950s, they were primarily concerned with producing accurate 24- to 48-hour forecasts. But others, including Norman Phillips and Joseph Smagorinsky, were working on modeling the global circulation of the atmosphere, a much tougher problem involving even more data and requiring even larger, faster computers. Although early global circulation models were marginal at best, they gradually became more sophisticated, incorporating not only routinely available data, but also data increasingly available from meteorological satellites' remote sensors. As they ran these global circulation models for longer periods of time, atmospheric scientists sensed they would be useful for carrying out computer-based experiments that would produce knowledge on the kinds of factors influencing climate. The global circulation models would become climate models—allowing climatology to become less descriptive and more physics based.

The lack of computing power combined with the problems inherent with model development had meant that atmospheric modelers in the 1940s and 1950s could only include a small number of atmospheric layers in their calculations. They could not include oceans—a major influence on changing atmospheric composition—or mountains. Essentially they were modeling climate on a flat Earth with no water. By the 1960s meteorologists were including several atmospheric layers, and climate scientists started to include heat-related processes such as radiation, condensation, and heat transfer. As computing power increased, they were able to include the effects of carbon dioxide, water vapor, and ozone concentrations on the absorption of solar radiation. With each addition to the models, atmospheric scientists tried to determine how air at different temperatures became distributed throughout the atmosphere—an important step in determining the climatic factors. They ran their models for longer periods so that changes in climate could be seen over centuries. Climate scientists tweaked initial conditions and modified atmospheric chemistry, cloud cover, solar radiation, and other possible atmospheric changes over time to develop virtual atmospheres for the future.

Advances in satellite remote sensors also aided climate models by providing data from remote land and sea areas where observational data were (and are) scarce and from the upper atmosphere. The first operational weather satellite, TIROS-1, only sent back blurry photos in April 1960, but by the 1970s the first operational GOES satellite transmitted clear photographs of Earth that aided hurricane forecasting in particular. In addition to photographs, sensors also measured a variety of atmospheric variables including temperature, moisture content, and components of atmospheric chemistry. In the early twenty-first century plans were made to launch new satellites, including NASA's *Aura* and *ICESat*, to measure ozone concentrations, and ice, clouds, and landforms, respectively, providing real-time data about changes in atmospheric chemistry and Earth's atmospheric, oceanic, vegetative, and geologic features. All of these data would be processed by supercomputers, allowing atmospheric scientists to run even more complex climate models to gain insight on climate states centuries from now. They would also help atmospheric scientists to determine connections among global climate change, extreme weather fluctuations, and severe weather that could bring untold harm to both the natural and the built world. Computer modeling has provided atmospheric scientists with a method of running experiments that would not be possible any other way.

Assessment. Since 1800, meteorology and climatology have been transformed from descriptive disciplines to physics- and mathematics-based physical sciences. Rigorous theory development, aided by sensitive instruments, rapidly increasing amounts of data, and massive computing power, will continue as atmospheric scientists work to gain a fuller understanding of atmospheric processes and how human activity influences, and is influenced by, those same processes.

[*See also* **Agricultural Technology; Agriculture, U.S. Department of; Airplanes and Air Transport; Computer Science; Computers, Mainframe, Mini, and Micro; Forest Service, U.S.; Geography; Geology; Geophysics; Global Warming; Henry, Joseph; Higher Education and Science; Instruments of Science; Kármán, Theodore von; Langmuir, Irving; Mathematics and Statistics; Military, Science and Technology and the; National Science Foundation; Nobel Prize in Biomedical Research; Oceanography; Physics; Satellites, Communications; Smithsonian Institution; Telegraph;** *and* **Von Neumann, John.**]

BIBLIOGRAPHY

Bates, Charles F., and John F. Fuller. *America's Weather Warriors: 1814–1985.* College Station: Texas A&M University Press, 1986. A readable account discussing military meteorologists and how they supported evolving warfare styles from the early nineteenth through the late twentieth centuries.

Doel, Ronald E., and Kristine C. Harper. "Prometheus Unleashed: Science as a Diplomatic Weapon in the Lyndon B. Johnson Administration." *Osiris* 21 (2006): 66–85. An analysis of Johnson's use of science as a tool in foreign and domestic policy, including the use of weather as a diplomatic tool

during the Bihar, India, drought of 1967 and as a weapon during the Vietnam War.

Dupree, A. Hunter. *Science in the Federal Government: A History of Policies and Activities,* revised ed. Baltimore: Johns Hopkins University Press, 1986. A classic overview of U.S. governmental activities relating to science from the beginning of the nation, including the formation of weather service activities.

Edwards, Paul N. *A Vast Machine: Computer Models, Climate Data, and the Politics of Global Warming.* Cambridge, Mass.: MIT Press, 2010. A historical analysis of the interconnection between computer models and atmospheric data as they relate to the development of climate knowledge and how these issues have influenced political discussions and action on global warming.

Fleming, James Rodger, ed. *Historical Essays on Meteorology, 1919–1995. The Diamond Anniversary History Volume of the American Meteorological Society.* Boston: American Meteorological Society, 1996. Twenty-one articles written by prominent scientists in their area of expertise covering the historical development of meteorology, climatology, and hydrology during the first 75 years of the American Meteorological Society.

Fleming, James Rodger. *Meteorology in America, 1800–1870.* Baltimore: Johns Hopkins University Press, 1990. Still the definitive work on meteorology in the nineteenth-century United States.

Friedman, Robert Marc. *Appropriating the Weather: Vilhelm Bjerknes and the Construction of Modern Meteorology.* Ithaca, N.Y.: Cornell University Press, 1989. An analysis of the development of the Bergen School, the research school created and promoted by Vilhelm Bjerknes, and its influence on twentieth-century meteorology.

Good, Gregory A., ed. *Sciences of the Earth: An Encyclopedia of Events, People, and Phenomena.* 2 vols. New York and London: Garland, 1998. Historical background on meteorology, climatology, and a wide variety of earth science disciplines and topics, arranged alphabetically. Short articles provide basic introductions to the topics and lists of additional sources.

Harper, Kristine C. "Climate Control: United States Weather Modification in the Cold War and Beyond." *Endeavour* 32, no. 1 (2008): 20–26. The development of weather control techniques in the United States in the immediate post–World War II years and how they came to be used as a tool of the state.

Harper, Kristine C. *Weather by the Numbers: The Genesis of Modern Meteorology.* Cambridge, Mass.: MIT Press, 2008. A history of the profession of meteorology as a discipline in the United States in the twentieth century and how the development of numerical weather prediction after World War II radically changed meteorological practice.

Koelsch, William A. "From Geo- to Physical Science: Meteorology and the American University, 1919–1945." In *Historical Essays on Meteorology, 1919–1995: The Diamond Anniversary Volume of the American Meteorological Society*, edited by James Rodger Fleming. Boston: American Meteorological Society, 1996. A short discussion on the changes in meteorological education as a result of World War II.

Kutzbach, Gisela. *The Thermal Theory of Cyclones: A History of Meteorological Thought in the Nineteenth Century.* Boston: American Meteorological Society, 1979. How meteorological ideas on the structure of cyclonic circulations and associated weather systems evolved during the nineteenth century and influenced meteorological theory in the twentieth.

Livingstone, David N. *The Geographical Tradition: Episodes in the History of a Contested Enterprise.* Oxford: Wiley–Blackwell, 1993. A survey of the practice of geography, especially in the nineteenth and twentieth centuries.

Richardson, Lewis Fry. *Weather Prediction by Numerical Process.* New York: Dover, 1965. This reprint of Richardson's 1922 groundbreaking book describes his failed experiment in forecasting the weather using the hydrodynamic equations defining the atmospheric motion.

Weart, Spencer R. *The Discovery of Global Warming.* 2d ed. Cambridge, Mass.: Harvard University Press, 2008. Background and current status of the global warming debate; the companion website, *The Discovery of Global Warming*, Center for History of Physics, American Institute of Physics contains additional, up-to-date information. http://www.aip.org/history/climate/index.htm (accessed 22 October 2012).

Kristine C. Harper

MICHELSON, ALBERT ABRAHAM

(1852–1931), physicist and a master of precision optical measurement, was the first American to be awarded a Nobel Prize in the sciences (1907). Michelson's attempts to detect the motion of the Earth through the ether, the hypothetical medium of light, set the stage for Albert Einstein's theory of relativity.

Michelson was born 19 December 1852 in Strelno, Prussia (now Poland), but his family soon immigrated and he grew up in gold rush towns in California and Nevada. After entering the Naval Academy at Annapolis in 1869, he began teaching physics there in 1875. Taking up optics, he measured the speed of light with unprecedented precision and began to ponder how it might be affected by motion. Physicists believed that as the Earth moved through the ether, it was swept by an "ether wind" blowing at about 18 miles per second (30 kilometers per second). This wind should speed up or slow down light waves moving with or against it, and in 1880, while studying in Europe, Michelson hit on a way to measure this small effect. Split a beam of light, he said, and send its two parts off at right angles; when these are reflected back and recombined, shifts in the resulting interference fringes will reveal any changes in the speeds or path lengths of the beams. Michelson first tried his "interferometer" at Potsdam in 1881, but found no shift of the fringes and no sign of the expected ether wind. The result was inconclusive, however, because the predicted effect lay at the limit of the sensitivity of his apparatus.

Michelson left the navy in 1881 and moved to the Case School of Applied Science in Cleveland, where in 1887 he and E. W. Morley of Western Reserve University performed their famous repetition of Michelson's Potsdam experiment. Using a more sensitive interferometer, set on a large block of sandstone, they again found no evidence of motion through the ether.

Michelson and Morley's result seemed impossible to square with the known facts of optics until G. F. FitzGerald in 1889 and H. A. Lorentz in 1892 independently proposed a striking hypothesis: perhaps motion through the ether affects the forces between molecules, causing the sandstone block to shrink by just enough to mask the expected effect. The "FitzGerald–Lorentz contraction" later became an important part of Einstein's relativity theory.

In 1889 Michelson left Case for Clark University in Massachusetts. He soon turned his interferometer to new uses, traveling to Paris in 1892 to measure the standard meter in terms of light waves. In 1893 he moved to the University of Chicago, where he headed the physics department until 1929.

Michelson spent much of the 1920s at Mt. Wilson Observatory in California, applying interferometric methods to astronomical problems and refining his measurements of the speed of light. In 1926 he bounced light between mountain peaks twenty miles apart, determining the speed of light to within less than three miles per second. He also performed an improved version of his ether-wind experiment, but again found no shift of the fringes. Michelson died in Pasadena on 9 May 1931.

[*See also* **Astronomy and Astrophysics; Einstein, Albert; Instruments of Science; Nobel Prize in Biomedical Research;** *and* **Physics.**]

BIBLIOGRAPHY

Livingston, Dorothy Michelson. *The Master of Light: A Biography of Albert A. Michelson.* Chicago: University of Chicago Press, 1973.

Swenson, Loyd S. *The Ethereal Aether: A History of the Michelson–Morley–Miller Aether–Drift Experiments, 1880–1930.* Austin: University of Texas Press, 1972.

Bruce J. Hunt

MICROPROCESSOR

See **Solid-State Electronics.**

MIDWIFERY

Until the twentieth century, midwives delivered most of America's babies. Self-trained neighbor women, who assisted family members or nearby friends, were the most common, but increasingly aspiring midwives served apprenticeships with older, more experienced practitioners. A few, especially in urban areas, built up large practices, but the average midwife probably delivered no more than a dozen babies a year. Martha Ballard, who began practicing midwifery in the late eighteenth century in the village of Augusta, Maine, delivered well over eight hundred babies in 35 years of practice (Ulrich, 1990, p. 373). Like other midwives of her time, she not only delivered babies but also performed a wide range of medical services for her patients and their families. In rural areas especially, busy physicians often relied on midwives to attend time-consuming births, preferring to be called only in cases of emergency.

The typical midwife was a middle-aged, married, immigrant woman from the working class. Delivering babies, like taking in boarders and lodgers, allowed her to contribute to the domestic economy and still take care of her family's needs. By the late nineteenth century a few schools for midwives had appeared, most of them controlled by physicians. Indeed, an Illinois law, passed in 1896, required that only "legally qualified" physicians could teach in state-recognized midwifery schools. Although some midwifery schools were little more than diploma mills, others tried to provide an education comparable to that offered in Europe. The municipally controlled Bellevue Hospital School for Midwives in New York City, founded in 1911, was reputed to be exemplary. Unlike nurses and teachers, midwives seldom aspired to professional status. They claimed neither a distinct body of knowledge nor control over the training and licensing of practitioners. Although some states regulated the practice of midwifery, Massachusetts banned midwifery in the 1890s and many southern states left midwifery free of control.

As late as 1900, about half of all the children born in the United States were delivered by midwives; by 1930 midwife-attended births had dropped to less than 15 percent of all births in the United States, and most of these were among African Americans in the South (Borst, 1995, p. 1). Although obstetrics was the worst taught clinical specialty in American medical schools in the early twentieth century and the safety record of midwives generally equaled that of physicians, parturient women increasingly opted for hospital-based, physician-assisted, pain-free birthing experiences. General practitioners and, increasingly after 1950, obstetricians attended most parturient women. Because midwives traditionally served their own ethnic communities, the decline in the number of immigrant families sharply reduced the practice of midwifery. By 1950, with the federal government picking up much of the cost of building new hospitals, 93 percent of births to white mothers were taking place in hospitals; 10 years later the figure had risen to virtually 100 percent. Midwives, however, still attended 28 percent of all minority women and 50 percent of rural nonwhite Americans in 1950 (Borst, 1995, pp. 156–157).

By this time, however, some women were beginning to question the desirability of a fully drugged, physician-controlled delivery and to protest what they regarded as inhumane and insensitive hospital care. Women in the feminist and countercultural movements helped to kindle a reexamination of physician-dominated obstetrics and to launch an alternative birthing movement. The movement did not survive the 1980s, but it did encourage the revival of midwifery in two forms: nurse-midwives, who worked primarily in hospitals under the aegis of physicians, and lay midwives, who worked independently and often extralegally. At the end of the century, midwives were attending less than 8 percent of the nation's births (Ventura, 2001, p. 14).

[*See also* American Medical Association; Birth Control and Family Planning; Childbirth; Ethics and Medicine; Gender and Science; Hospitals; Medical Education; Medical Specialization; Medicine; Nursing; Public Health; Public Health Service, U.S.; *and* Race and Medicine.]

BIBLIOGRAPHY

Borst, Charlotte G. *Catching Babies: The Professionalization of Childbirth, 1870–1920*. Cambridge, Mass.: Harvard University Press, 1995.

Donegan, Jane. *Women & Men Midwives: Medicine, Mortality, and Misogyny in Early America*. Westport, Conn.: Greenwood Press, 1978.

Ettinger, Laura E. *Nurse Midwifery: The Birth of a New American Profession*. Columbus: Ohio State University Press, 2006.

Fraser, Gertrude, Jacinta. *African American Midwifery in the South: Dialogues of Birth, Race, and Memory*. Cambridge, Mass.: Harvard University Press, 1998.

Ulrich, Laurel Thatcher. *A Midwife's Tale: The Life of Martha Ballard, Based on Her Diary, 1785–1812*. New York: Vintage Books, 1990.

Ventura, Stephanie J., et al. "Births: Final Data for 1999." *National Vital Statistics Reports* 49, no. 1 (2001): 14. http://www.cdc.gov/nchs/data/nvsr/nvsr49/nvsr49_01.pdf (accessed 31 October 2012).

Charlotte G. Borst

MILITARY, SCIENCE AND TECHNOLOGY AND THE

The American military's reliance upon science and technology for the development of new weapons in the early twenty-first century is at one with the military's role as the foremost patron of academic research in the science, engineering, and social science disciplines. World War II represented a watershed in relations among sectors of the American polity that had heretofore little sustained interaction. Simple narratives cannot capture the complexity of the transformation that took place during and after the war. Although the atomic bomb was certainly an important part of this story, the bomb's well-known history is neither identical nor necessary to understanding the changes wrought by the war. Instead, we can tell a new set of stories in which scientists, engineers, military officers, and others worked together to produce a new political economy of science in which federal, especially military, patronage would become a dominant factor favoring some areas of research over others, but also profoundly affecting the modes of inquiry as well as the organization of research. This new political economy replaced one in which private philanthropies and corporations had been the leading patrons of academic science, engineering, and social science. The federal government and the military's attitudes toward scientific research also changed. From the nation's founding until World War II, the dominant role for the military's involvement with scientific research lay in the exploitation of the nation's natural resources. Only with the war did the armed services, as well as the federal government, recognize that science, social science, and technology were national resources worthy of funding, cultivation, and exploitation for national security, economic power, and global prestige (Dupree, 1957; Kohler, 1991).

What follows maps this transformation. The military's main form of interaction with science in the nineteenth century lay in the expeditions that successfully mapped and explored the continent. Army armories were the site of a most important nineteenth-century military innovation—interchangeable parts—arguably one of the most important economic innovations as well as one demonstrating the military's central role in American economic development. World War I brought limited relations between researchers and the armed services, but save for the establishment of the Naval Research Laboratory in Washington, D.C., these relations ended with the armistice. World War II and the long Cold War saw the emergence of a new political economy of knowledge as well as a military and nation-state dependent upon the products of the laboratory for both military might and economic survival.

The Nineteenth Century—Exploration, Armories, and Invention. Expeditions and armories were the primary means of interaction among science, technology, and the military in the antebellum period. Beginning with the Lewis and Clark Expedition (1804–1806), exploring the new continent provided scientists and military men a common institution through which to pursue their own interests. For natural historians, the Corps of Discovery, the expedition's official name, inventoried the abundant wildlife and plants populating the newly acquired Louisiana Purchase. Charting the

new region's economic potential was among the mission's primary goals, as was the more mundane, but equally important task of mapping the new territory and learning the extent of the Missouri River and whether it led to a fabled Northwest Passage. Cartography served both commercial and military interests, but the expedition also demanded inquiry about the native peoples of the region. Benjamin Rush, a Philadelphia physician and among Meriwether Lewis's tutors in natural history, provided the explorers with a questionnaire to use when meeting indigenous peoples. In particular, he sought to discover whether native religious practices resembled Jewish practices on the chance that some native peoples might be from the Lost Tribe of Israel (Ambrose, 1997). Other military officers, including Captain Zebulon Pike from whom Colorado's Pikes Peak derives its name, played important roles in exploring the American West (Goetzmann, 1993).

After the Corps of Discovery mission, the most important undertaking was the U.S. Exploring Expedition (1838–1842). Also known as the Wilkes Expedition for its leader, Lieutenant Charles Wilkes, this enterprise consisted of six naval vessels that circumnavigated the globe while gathering data that would prove valuable well into the twentieth century. Staffed by an array of investigators, including naturalist Charles Pickering, geologist James Dwight Dana, and philologist Horatio Hale, the officers and scientists engaged in a comprehensive program of mapping and investigating the coasts of North and South America as well as a vast number of islands and atolls in the Pacific. Maps from the expedition were used as late as the invasion of Tarawa during World War II. Anthropological and linguistic investigations also filled the daily logs expedition members were required to keep. The materials gathered during the expedition filled an expensive, federally funded series of 24 planned volumes, of which 19 saw actual publication. Physical specimens of plants, animals, and artifacts representing indigenous peoples' cultural heritage acquired during the expedition became the foundation of the nascent Smithsonian Institution's collections (Stanton, 1975; Joyce, 2001).

Army Ordnance armories in Springfield, Massachusetts, and Harpers Ferry, West Virginia, were the site of a great nineteenth-century transformation in manufacturing—the rise of uniformity, also known as interchangeable parts. Often attributed to inventors such as Eli Whitney, the so-called American system of manufacture was a goal of the Ordnance Department from 1815 onward; it took at least 40 years to reach maturity. In the armories, military superintendents transformed artisanal practices that produced unique, functional weapons into a system of production that would allow parts from one weapon to function in another. The new system required a fundamental reorganization of the workplace and the replacement of individual judgment about parts and adjustment with metal gauges that adjudicated fit and precision. Artisans became workers and guns became commodities. Workers trained in the new methods left the armories and took the new practices to other industries. The military's role in creating the modern industrial economy is as undeniable as it is forgotten (Smith, 1985; Hounshell, 1984).

Science and technology played an important, but not a revolutionary role in the Civil War. Existing technologies, such as the railway, the telegraph, and the steamboat, found military applications, but attempts to harness science and technology for the conflict met with little immediate success. The establishment of the National Academy of Sciences as the official science advisor to the federal government created a new institution, but it did little to affect the conflict. Nor was the Navy's Permanent Commission either permanent or effective. Iron-clad ships such as the *Merrimac* and *Monitor* foreshadowed a future of warfare between such vessels (Mindell, 2000). Individual inventors, some within the services, such as John Dahlgren in the Union's navy, made important contributions, but this work was not organized as it would become in the future (Bruce, 1989). Perhaps the most important event with respect to science and technology took place during the Civil War with the passage of the Morrill Land Grant Act of 1862. This law established a land-grant institution in each state and set the stage for future scientific and technological developments. After all, it was agricultural research that

dominated the political economy of American science in the late nineteenth century.

The Twentieth Century—War and the State. Poison gas, tanks, submarines, and airplanes were among the military novelties unleashed in World War I. Each was the product of a network of relations among industry and the armed services. Save for poison gas, there was little connection to academic science and technology, but the war prompted American university researchers, as well as those in industry, to forge relationships with the armed services. Although these relations would not survive the war, several institutions created during the war, such as the National Advisory Committee for Aeronautics (NACA) and the National Research Council of the National Academy of Sciences, would play important roles in the war and interwar era. Others, such as the short-lived Naval Consulting Board, would have unexpected importance as progenitors of important military institutions.

The 1915 establishment of NACA represented a direct effort by the government and the armed services to play a role in the development of aviation technology, but like many early efforts it was greatly affected by lack of funds, receiving an annual budget of $5,000 from Congress. NACA's wartime role was as limited as that of the airplane itself, a technology that had more promise than usefulness in actual combat despite the enthusiasm of the technology's proponents. During the interwar era, NACA would have a profound effect upon the aviation industry. Performing research in its own government-funded laboratories and wind tunnels, NACA provided aircraft manufacturers with much of the fundamental knowledge from which they could construct new, more efficient, and powerful flying machines. NACA innovations moved into the marketplace through the efforts of private manufacturers, affording industry and the armed services a model of a public–private partnership (Roland, 1985).

Individual inventors were the major source of military innovation before World War I. Elmer Sperry famously designed gyroscopic stabilizers and gyrocompasses for the new steel ships that made up the modern navy and his technologies also found their way into military aircraft (Hughes, 1971). With the sinking of the *Lusitania*, America's most famous inventor, Thomas Edison, declared that American inventiveness could easily construct an antidote to the German submarine menace. Seizing upon the inventor's popularity, navy secretary Josephus Daniels summoned the inventor to Washington to organize what became known as the Naval Consulting Board. Despite its illustrious members, including Sperry, electric trolley developer Frank Sprague, and Willis Whitney of General Electric, the members were largely engineers interested in problems of manufacturing and standardization. Edison's desire for practical men who did things rather than individuals who talked about them made for good newspaper copy, but did little to create a defense against the submarine. The public submitted potential inventions to the Board as well, but despite constant admonition that it was impossible to electrify the ocean, poorly educated self-proclaimed inventors submitted schemes to do just that. Ironically, the Board's most lasting accomplishment was the construction of the Naval Research Laboratory (NRL), which because of its hiring of both scientists and engineers became the nation's most important developer of radar between the world wars (Kevles, 1995; Van Keuren, 1992).

Edison's dismissal of academics prompted a response from believers in both talk and action; George Ellery Hale, the pioneering astrophysicist and director of the Mount Wilson Observatory, condemned the inactivity of the National Academy of Sciences, ostensibly the federal government's science advisor. Hale took the Naval Consulting Board's membership as an affront to organized research. A proponent of interdisciplinary work, exemplified in his astrophysical work with the spectroheliograph, as well as an academic entrepreneur who had convinced steel magnate Andrew Carnegie to fund the building of a massive telescope beneath California's clear Western skies, Hale saw the war as an opportunity to reform the moribund National Academy while persuading the government of the role science might play in preparedness. Establishing the National Research Council (NRC) of the National Academy was Hale's great organizational reform;

making the NRC the government's primary science advisor for the conflict was his great political victory. The NRC did not see its mission as developing new weapons so much as taking existing technologies and improving them, if such devices existed. For example, Max Mason, a University of Wisconsin physicist, took an existing French submarine detection technology, the Walzer apparatus, and transformed it into a workable prototype that was easily modified into a powerful demonstration of the power of academic science to produce useful military technologies (Yerkes, 1920).

In conjunction with the army's Chemical Warfare Service, the NRC Subcommittee on Noxious Gases played a role in the development of the American response to the German use of chemical weapons. Initial work on the subject began in the Bureau of Mines where investigators had experience with breathing apparatus, hazardous fumes, and explosives. Early American research focused upon defensive technologies, especially the development of gas masks, but research on offensive agents quickly came to dominate the program, which took place in an array of laboratories in Washington, D.C., on the campus of American University. Among the most famous projects was the development of lewisite, a powerful poison that never saw use in combat, but which represented a nexus of academic, industrial, and military research and planning. By war's end, the chemical warfare program employed over 5,500 university-trained chemists and chemical engineers and exposed academic chemists to the problems and rewards of taking laboratory compounds and making mass-produced industrial chemicals. The academic organizer of the lewisite project, Harvard organic chemist James Bryant Conant, would serve as one of the architects of the Manhattan Project during World War II (Hershberg, 1993; Fitzgerald, 2008).

Most surprisingly, the technologies that outlived their wartime origins were the intelligence (IQ) tests developed by Yale psychologist Robert M. Yerkes and his colleagues as part of the NRC Committee on Psychology. For the army, the tests solved a fundamental problem. Before the war, the army had been a small organization in which officers knew each other as well as their enlisted men and had an understanding of each individual's strengths and weakness. With the war, the army needed a mechanism to sort and assess the vast influx of recruits in the absence of detailed knowledge of each individual. IQ tests were as much a managerial technology as a means of assessing intellectual ability. In turn, IQ became a proxy for habits and practices that officers wanted and needed. Developed to solve a pressing wartime personnel problem, the tests quickly became part of the American social landscape, as would the template of standardized testing for which they were the origins (Carson, 1993, 2006).

The Armistice halted the wartime research programs of the NRC and the Naval Consulting Board; Conant's lewisite, in transit at war's end, found a permanent home in the Atlantic Ocean. American chemists were among the most ardent advocates of the Geneva protocols banning chemical warfare. Still, what is striking is how quickly the wartime research became history and the political economy of American science returned to its prewar state in which private foundations and industrial corporations retained their role as the dominant patrons of the natural and social sciences. Even as the economy soured and the Great Depression took hold, American researchers found it nearly impossible to accept government monies. Individual researchers might work with the armed services; several researchers, including Edward Bowles and Charles Stark Draper, both at MIT, found it possible to work with the military during the interwar period. Nonetheless, efforts to forge relations among academic researchers and the federal government encountered an array of problems, not the least of which was who would own the fruits of government-sponsored research. Once again, it would take a war to move academic researchers and the armed services into a mutual embrace, one from which neither would emerge unchanged (Owens, 1990; Pang, 1990).

World War II. In December 1939 at the Washington Conference on Theoretical Physics, Danish physicist Niels Bohr announced that German physicists Otto Hahn and Lise Meitner had observed the heretofore unseen process of nuclear fission in uranium. Physicists greeted the news with excitement mixed with trepidation. For some researchers, fission cast a dark shadow across the future. Leo Szilard, a refugee from Nazi Germany, had long believed that nuclear fission made weapons of untold destructive power possible. Worse, the discovery of fission in Germany implied that Nazi researchers might develop such weapons long before their Allied counterparts. American researchers made several attempts to interest the army and the navy in fission's potential, with little luck. Although the navy expressed interest in fission as a future source of power, neither service believed it might yield a weapon. Einstein's famous August 1939 letter to President Roosevelt politely noted that fission might make a new source of power as well as bombs capable of destroying a port. Written by Szilard, the letter concluded on an ominous note—Germany had stopped the sale of uranium from recently acquired mines in Czechoslovakia. Szilard's prose and Einstein's signature prompted the establishment of the Uranium Committee under the laconic direction of Lyman Briggs, head of the National Bureau of Standards.

The Uranium Committee made little progress until June 1940 when FDR established the National Defense Research Committee (NDRC) under the chairmanship of Vannevar Bush, the recently appointed head of the Carnegie Institution of Washington and the National Advisory Committee for Aeronautics. As an MIT electrical engineering professor, Bush was famous for the development of sophisticated analog computers during the 1920s and 1930s; he had also served as MIT's first dean of engineering during physicist Karl T. Compton's reformation of the Institute during the Great Depression. When it became clear that Compton would not retire in the near future, Bush moved to Washington, D.C., to expand his administrative portfolio and prepare for the coming conflict. The NDRC also included Compton, James B. Conant, then Harvard University president; Caltech dean Richard Tolman; Frank Jewett, AT&T vice president and president of the National Academy of Sciences; Conway P. Coe, the commissioner of patents; and representatives from the army and navy. Immediately the group began preparing lists of researchers to solve problems in an array of areas from antiaircraft defense and armor to chemistry and explosives. Within a year, it became clear that the NDRC was inadequate to the task of organizing American science for the war because it lacked the ability to develop prototypes that industry might mass produce. Nor did the NDRC have any authority over medical research, another vital aspect of military preparedness. Bush pushed for the creation of the Office of Scientific Research and Development, the OSRD, in June 1941; the new agency received its own budget and incorporated both the NDRC and the nascent Committee on Medical Research. The *New York Times* hailed Bush as a "czar of research." It was to prove an apt appellation (Zachary, 1997).

Among the NDRC's administrative acquisitions was the Uranium Committee, to which Bush turned his attention. American physicists remained unsure whether they could produce enough of the uranium isotope, U235, which underwent fission; nor were they entirely clear on the amount of material needed for a weapon. As Stanley Goldberg (1992) persuasively argued, Bush pushed to have the National Academy of Sciences review the uranium situation with three different committees in the late spring and summer of 1941. With the third committee report, as well as data from the British MAUD Committee, which made it clear that a critical mass of U235 would weigh less than 30 kilograms, Bush secured FDR's consent to begin work on what would become the Manhattan Project in October 1941. Compelled to act because of a fear that German physicists might win the race for a weapon, it was no small irony that the United States made a decision to pursue an atomic bomb at roughly the same time the Germans decided that such a weapon would prove impossible to build for the current war. What distinguished the last committee's report from the previous two was that it emphasized the possibility of developing a weapon that an aircraft might deliver to its target.

Unlike World War I, where the airplane played a minor, supporting role, World War II saw the plane turned into an instrument of unparalleled destruction. Between the wars the doctrine of strategic bombing took hold throughout the air services of the future Allied and Axis powers.

Stanley Baldwin, a conservative British MP, neatly summarized strategic bombing with his declaration "that the bomber always gets through." Following the Italian military theorist, Guilio Douhet, whose 1921 work *The Command of the Air* was the original strategic bombing text, proponents of the new doctrine argued that the long-range bomber made another long, grinding ground war impossible. Instead, the nation that struck first would quickly achieve victory as the population of a bombed nation forced their leaders to sue for peace as they reverted to a form of industrial savagery amid the wasteland produced by a successful bombing campaign (Biddle, 2002). Strategic bombing meant that a defense against the bomber was an absolute necessity. Much of the wartime research focused upon solving this problem at three distinct levels. First, radar was a technology developed for detecting aircraft at a distance so that fighter aircraft might attack them, while providing adequate warning so civilian populations might take shelter. Second, improved fire-control systems connecting radar to gunsights provided soldiers and sailors with new methods for downing attacking aircraft. Fire control is the military term for the ability to coordinate antiaircraft artillery. Finally, the proximity fuse made shells "intelligent" and capable of detonating themselves when they were within a certain distance of a moving target. All three technologies were among the OSRD's greatest research efforts.

The MIT Radiation Laboratory was the preeminent American radar research facility. Although the Naval Research Laboratory had done pioneering work on long-wave radar, the Rad Lab was the site for the development of microwave radar (Allison, 1981). Unlike long-wave radar, microwave radar worked using smaller antennas, provided better discrimination among many targets, and worked better at detecting planes flying at low altitudes. The only problem was that no American-made vacuum tube could generate microwaves at the requisite intensities. During the summer of 1940, the British revealed that they had developed such a tube, the resonant cavity magnetron, and it fell to the physicists at the Rad Lab under the leadership of Lee DuBridge to learn how the magnetron worked, how to mass produce the device, and how to incorporate the new technology into radar sets that might work in aircraft to detect submarines when they surfaced to recharge their batteries and to detect ground targets through overcast. By August 1941 Rad Lab microwave sets could detect capital ships at a distance of twenty miles and surfaced submarines two to five miles from a moving aircraft. Such technology provided the Americans with a distinct advantage as they battled the U-boats sinking merchant ships at an unprecedented rate. By 1942, the Rad Lab employed roughly two thousand individuals with a monthly budget of $1.15 million. As the war continued, the laboratory opened a branch in Great Britain to assist with the Normandy invasion and the Allied bombing campaign against Germany. The laboratory cooperated with industry to ensure that the technologies working on a lab test bench might lend themselves to the vastly different forms of industrial mass production. Equally important was the Harvard Radio Research Laboratory under the direction of Frederick Terman of Stanford. Researchers at the Harvard lab had access to all that was done at the Rad Lab to design countermeasures against German and Japanese radar developments. Among their many technological achievements was chaff, tiny strips of foil that, when dropped from a plane, appeared on enemy radar screens as thousands of aircraft (Buderi, 1997).

Improved fire-control systems were another technological development of the Rad Lab as well as researchers working directly with the navy. At MIT, Charles Stark Draper, a professor in the Aeronautical Engineering Department, developed the Mark 14 lead computing gunsight. Unlike existing sights, the device used a custom gyroscopic arrangement to aim a gun at the appropriate distance ahead of a moving target so that the shell would hit the target. Sperry Gyroscope, the Navy's preferred source of such technology, saw the sight as a laboratory curiosity that would never survive the translation to mass production. Draper and his students produced the first quantity themselves; the navy persuaded Sperry to learn Draper's techniques. By war's end the navy had purchased over 85 thousand Mark 14 gunsights and several thousand of its successors.

Furthermore, Draper worked with the Rad Lab to integrate the sight with ship-based radar systems to provide a complete fire control solution (Mindell, 2002).

Finally, the proximity fuse transformed the very ammunition used to shoot down enemy aircraft. Rather than rely upon a direct hit or timing the shell to explode a certain number of seconds after leaving the gun, the proximity fuse worked by detonating the shell at a predetermined distance from the aircraft. Explosions at close range might damage or even destroy an aircraft. After the war, Vannevar Bush declared the fuse might have been more technologically difficult than the atomic bomb because it required not only scientific innovation but also mass production. Under the direction of Merle Tuve at the Johns Hopkins University Applied Physics Laboratory (APL), researchers developed a miniature radio set that fit inside an artillery shell and withstood the massive acceleration present within a moving shell. Using specially designed rugged miniature vacuum tubes, the fuse listened for reflections from a target. When the reflections reached a specific intensity, indicating a predetermined distance, the shell detonated. Mass production of the proximity fuse required an unprecedented level of integration among researchers and their corporate partners. At times, APL physicists worked in the factories, teaching assemblers the secrets of building working fuses; on more than one occasion industrialists wondered just who was in charge of production—the corporations or APL. Initially, the navy wanted the fuse only used over the ocean so that duds might fall harmlessly into the sea. By 1944, the army insisted that the fuse be used during the Battle of the Bulge to repel the German counterattack, with deadly results. The fuse also performed well against the German cruise missile, the V-1. By war's end, the fuse project employed much of the nation's vacuum tube production capacity and produced roughly 22 million fuses. Unlike radar sets that were produced by the thousands, the fuses were more like bullets, goods that were consumed each time they were used. The Manhattan Project's total yield was one U235 bomb (Hiroshima), one plutonium test device (the Trinity gadget), and one Pu239 implosion bomb (Nagasaki) plus the infrastructure to produce both enriched uranium and plutonium. Compare that almost artisanal output with the mass-produced character of the fuse program.

Another example of the centrality of mass production for the war lay in the massive effort to industrialize penicillin production. At the beginning of the war, penicillin was the product of painstaking laboratory work that failed as often as it succeeded. Although the new compound worked in killing microbes in the laboratory, there existed no large-scale clinical trials. Initial laboratory work could produce two units per centimeter of surface area; one thousand units was roughly one milligram. Early laboratory production went straight to clinical tests, which determined that a standard course of treatment would involve approximately 1 million units. After much experimentation, OSRD and Department of Agriculture researchers were able to isolate strains that might grow in more industrial conditions—eight-thousand-gallon vats with electrical stirring apparatus. By 1943, the War Production Board authorized the construction of 19 fermentation plants at a cost of $20 million. Production proceeded with great alacrity; by December 1944 fermentation plants yielded over 290,000 million units and by June 1945 over 600,000 million units. Costs fell as well. One hundred thousand units initially cost $20; by war's end the price had fallen to less than a dollar. Penicillin proved effective in treating a host of ailments and preventing infection, but its greatest success lay in treating venereal diseases acquired by Allied troops. The army had 127,345 new cases of syphilis between January 1942 and August 1945. Initial treatment consisted of repeated hospital stays and injections of arsenic and bismuth over several weeks. By 1944 the standard treatment was 2.4 million units of penicillin injected over eight days. Given the success of the production program, penicillin quickly entered the civilian world as well, becoming one of the first wartime advances to transform the home front (Bud, 2007; Neushul, 1993; Swann, 1983; Baxter, 1946).

Another prominent wartime development was the emergence of operations research (OR), a field populated by physicists, mathematicians, and economists in which mathematical techniques were applied to tactical matters. Initially used in the battle against the submarine, proponents hailed OR as a way to make warfare scientific by maximizing the use of scarce resources to solve specific problems. OR's history suffers from a basic problem—we do not know to what extent OR workers used, either with or without direct knowledge, the data revealed from the massive code-breaking enterprise underway at Bletchley Park in the United Kingdom. In other words, OR's success in the field may have been a product of successful intelligence as well as mathematics. OR put scientists in a position to suggest to military officers how to use their resources to ensure the best possible outcomes. For some officers, this was a threat to their authority, but Bush's negotiating skills had OR scientists working closely with the Tenth Fleet (Fortun and Schweber, 1993; Mirowski, 2002). At the Rad Lab, APL, and other wartime research institutions, scientists often went into the field to sell their new technologies to military users, but academics recognized the cardinal truth that the military ran the war. Nowhere was this lesson learned with greater pathos than in the Manhattan Project. Having spent four years developing the new weapon, some researchers believed themselves responsible for its use. At the Chicago Metallurgical Laboratory, Szilard, Eugene Wigner, James Franck, and others attempted to persuade the U.S. government that failing to inform the Soviet Union of the bomb's existence, let alone using it without warning, would only provoke a catastrophic arms race that might end the world. These scientists learned one of the war's most important lessons—they were no longer independent researchers with complete freedom of action, but employees whose advice might be disregarded as easily as that of any other employee (Sherwin, 1987; Price, 1995).

Long before Japan surrendered on the deck of USS *Missouri*, American researchers actively worked with their military partners to plan for their joint future. There would be no repeat of the disengagement that followed World War I. Military officers and researchers were eager to maintain their wartime relations after the cessation of hostilities. Equally important, researchers found in military problems technical work of great intellectual sophistication and personal fulfillment. Technical knowledge was a resource worth military cultivation. In September 1944, Vannevar Bush declared that OSRD would begin demobilizing once the war in Europe ended. Research would only continue on those projects essential for the prosecution of the war against Japan. Bush's decision served as an opportunity for researchers to craft their own contracts to work directly for the military, rather than work through the OSRD. At the APL, Merle Tuve and his colleagues quickly became the Navy Bureau of Ordnance's center for guided missile research. Their research program, Project Bumblebee, was to design and build a ram-jet, or supersonic, antiaircraft missile that might help the navy solve the kamikaze problem during the projected invasion of the Japanese home islands. Other laboratories, such as the MIT Rad Lab, made a deliberate decision to go out of business with the termination of hostilities, but MIT tempered this decision by creating the postwar Research Laboratory for Electronics on the Rad Lab's wartime foundations. Plans for the continuation of wartime relationships were widespread by late 1944, as were plans for something entirely different.

In November 1944 President Roosevelt asked Bush how the federal government might support science and technology during the postwar era. The letter elicited the very famous Bush Report of July 1945, *Science—The Endless Frontier*. Long seen as the blueprint for the postwar National Science Foundation, the report was nothing of the sort. Instead, it was part and parcel of the political battles taking place over the organization of research and development at war's end. In particular, Bush crafted his report to avoid a takeover of American science and technology by the armed services. To that end Bush created a new category of knowledge, basic research. Analogous to the prewar category of pure science, but lacking the moral connotations of that phrase, basic research was research done without thought of its usefulness in solving specific problems. According to Bush, the United States had been a net importer of such knowledge before World War II; now with Europe in ruins, the United States would have to

regenerate the body of basic research upon which it had drawn so freely during the war. There were problems with the new category, not the least of which was that basic research was only known through its application. Still, the idea that the government should pay for this research in public and private universities was novel. Also much discussed was the institution that Bush designed to implement the new federal role in funding science and technology—a National Research Foundation that would coordinate federal patronage of research with respect to military research and development, medical science, and the physical and biological sciences. Conspicuous through their absence were the social sciences, which, despite their contribution to the wartime effort, Bush believed unworthy of federal support because they were simply academic versions of mostly liberal political platforms. Bush's National Research Foundation would have provided one-stop shopping for research support in a vast array of disciplines, but like so many plans it existed only on paper. Bush's National Research Foundation failed to achieve the support of President Truman, and the legislation establishing the modern National Science Foundation (NSF) did not win congressional and presidential approval until 1952. The NSF controlled funds to support research in the biological and physical sciences, but there was no place or budget for military research and development or medical research in this more modest institution (Kleinman and Solovey, 1995; Dennis, 2004).

The armed services became the dominant patrons of the sciences in the postwar era. Often attention is paid to the Office of Naval Research and its seemingly liberal policies of funding basic research, but it is important to remember that for the U.S. military, technical knowledge in all forms might prove beneficial as the military prepared to wage global war against the Soviet Union. Research on topics as apparently benign as the deep ocean or the upper atmosphere became essential because these new domains became arenas of potential conflict for submarines and guided missiles. Disciplinary ends and military means converged as new technologies opened up new domains (DeVorkin, 1992). Bush did not simply abandon his quest to preserve American science and technology from military control. When it became clear that his National Research Foundation would not come into being, he became chair of the first Joint Research and Development Board within the National Military Establishment and, later, the Department of Defense. The Board's mission was to coordinate military research and development, but it lacked the authority and the budget to do anything more than advise the secretary of defense, and even that proved of little value when the advice went against the wishes of a particular service. Instead, the Board became a vast domestic information-gathering effort in which each research and development project funded by the military acquired a file and a set of computer punch cards. Academics, industrial researchers, and military officers served on the Board's numerous technical panels and subject-matter committees. The minutes of their meetings and their reports of visits to particular research facilities and project evaluations provide a fascinating window into the period's norms and practices. Without budgetary power, the Board still wielded influence by adjudicating technical disputes and standardizing the vocabulary in new fields of study, such as guided missiles. In turn, the Board inadvertently created a vast, machine-readable database of postwar research and development. A 1953 Pentagon overhaul replaced the Board with an assistant secretary of defense for research and development; it was an organizational recognition that research and development was now a constitutive element of U.S. national defense policy.

Four areas of research interest dominated postwar American science and technology with respect to the military: guided missiles, continental defense, mechanisms for gaining access to the Soviet Union, and the technologies to manage these vast technical projects. Ballistic missiles were among the technologies that the military wanted, but which the United States did not develop during World War II. Despite capturing a sizeable number of V-2 rockets as well as the lead designers, building a U.S. ballistic missile became one of the great Cold War technological projects requiring work in an array of disciplines from aeronautical engineering and chemistry to metallurgy and radio physics. Transistors, semiconductors, and the process of miniaturization, the now ubiquitous feature of modern electronics, were among the ballistic missile's many legacies. The sheer difficulty of building these complex technological systems demanded not only advances in the physical sciences and engineering disciplines but also advances in management. TRW, among the most famous of the Cold War industrial giants, had its origins in integrating the various technical components of the U.S. ballistic missile program; the firm worked so closely with the Air Force that it was often difficult for outsiders to determine just who worked for whom. Ballistic missiles required sophisticated guidance technologies to reach their targets deep in the Soviet Union. Given that the USSR might jam any technology requiring radio communication, Stark Draper and his students at MIT developed self-contained and incredibly expensive inertial technologies for U.S. missiles and ballistic missile submarines. Unjammable and self-contained, inertial technologies made ballistic missiles truly independent deterrents. Once launched, they would make their way to their target unaffected by enemy countermeasures (Braun and Macdonald, 1982; Dyer, 1998; MacKenzie, 1990; Sheehan, 2009).

Continental defense became a research program of newfound relevance with the Soviet detonation of Joe-1 in August 1949. The end of the U.S. atomic monopoly sparked fears of Soviet Bear bombers flying over the North Pole to deliver atomic munitions on unprepared U.S. cities. Developments in over-the-horizon radar and sophisticated communications gear became critical as the nation developed an array of ground-based interceptor missiles under computer control. Under Jay Forrester, Project Whirlwind, an MIT project to develop a digital flight simulator, quickly became part of Project SAGE (Semi-automated Ground Environment), the leading U.S. defense program linking radar stations in the Canadian Arctic (the Defense Early Warning [DEW] Line) to a network of command and control centers in the continental United States. SAGE provided IBM with the experience to design computers for commercial as well as government and military uses. SABRE, the first airline reservations system, was a direct descendant of SAGE. Instead of matching fighters and interceptors to attacking Soviet aircraft, SABRE (Semi-Automatic Business Research Environment) matched ticket buyers to flights (Redmond and Smith, 2000).

Intelligence technologies and the social sciences were the two other major areas of military interest. The Soviet Union was a closed society and access to any information about the disposition of its military forces or its technological innovations proved difficult to acquire. Although the United States clearly engaged in traditional espionage against the USSR, the true revolution in intelligence lay in technologies. Lockheed's U-2 spy plane was a technological marvel with cameras of unprecedented capacity capable of flying above Soviet air defenses until the infamous shoot-down of Francis Gary Powers' U-2 in 1960. In its short history the U2 effectively destroyed the so-called bomber gap, revealing that the USSR did not possess a lead in the number of long-range bombers. Supersonic spy craft such as the U2 and SR-71 were predecessors to the satellite revolution in intelligence. The Corona Program occupied researchers in industry, academia, and the military as they sought to develop a satellite-based system using polyester-based photographic film that Air Force planes picked up as film canisters descended from orbit on parachutes. Corona and its successors were the technical means that allowed the United States and USSR to enter into arms control agreements. The satellites also played a profound role in transforming American cartography and geodesy by providing data of unprecedented precision and accuracy (Cloud, 2001, 2002; Day, 1998).

Unlike Bush and the early NSF, the national security establishment made great use of the social sciences during the Cold War. Institutions such as the Harvard Russian Research Center, the MIT Center for International Studies, and the entire field of Area Studies were supported by the military, the intelligence services, and private philanthropies, such as the Ford Foundation. MIT's Center for International Studies was a follow-on from Project TROY, an MIT summer study that brought academics, military, and government officials together to determine the best means of overcoming Soviet jamming of Voice of America broadcasts. The project entailed not only a technological component, but also an earnest attempt to explicate just what kind of propaganda might prove effective for broadcast. A Cold War waged in areas where Americans had little experience, from Korea and Southeast Asia to South America and Africa, generated a demand for knowledge that American academics readily produced. Qualitative studies of foreign culture and political life were staples of area studies, as were studies using newly developed quantitative techniques (Simpson, 1998; Isaac, 2007). Finally, the postwar business school became a source for the new managerial technologies that the armed services deployed to manage the increasingly complex weapons programs of the Cold War.

Cold War military patronage profoundly affected existing institutions, especially the research universities. Having found new problems of significant intellectual interest, researchers took their wartime work back to their home institutions. As Paul Forman (1995) convincingly demonstrated, much of the postwar American physics interest in various forms of nuclear and molecular resonance was the upshot of the vast growth in the power and capacity of microwave-generating equipment achieved in wartime and postwar radar research. Such work had been impossible before the war and physicists rapidly used the new technologies to produce a vast array of novel effects, including the maser and the laser (Forman, 1992). Universities such as Stanford, MIT, and Johns Hopkins reoriented much of their technical research around the new interests of the armed services as they expanded their research capabilities with military patronage. The Office of Naval Research funded a particle accelerator at Cornell, and the Atomic Energy Commission funded accelerators and reactors at new facilities such as Brookhaven. Universities also became sites for the training of officers in the new technical areas of interest. MIT's Department of Aeronautical Engineering established a Weapons Systems Program for military officers to pursue advanced work in the growing field of guided missiles. At Stanford, Dean of Engineering Frederick Terman used military monies to fund research, build departments, and create the foundations for what would become Silicon Valley (Leslie, 1993; Lowen, 1997; Dennis, 1994). The Cold War was very good for American universities; the development of indirect overheads allowed for military patronage to pay for the expansion of facilities and resources outside the particular projects under contract.

American researchers accepted the new order although there were significant costs to personal freedom and political autonomy. As Jessica Wang (1999) demonstrated, scientists were the largest single group investigated for charges of disloyalty under the new loyalty and security legislation passed during the Truman administration. Even the Manhattan Project's otherworldly, charismatic leader, J. Robert Oppenheimer, fell afoul of McCarthy-era hysteria and institutional conflict over the development of the hydrogen bomb (Bird and Sherwin, 2005). Despite protestations that the loss of Oppenheimer's security clearance would alienate American scientists from defense work, nothing happened. Only with the student protests of the 1960s did a powerful language criticizing the military's role on U.S. campuses develop. Despite the protests, there was little substantive change in the military's role as the foundational patron of American science and technology, although the seeds were sown for changes in the authority of science in American culture (Moore, 2008).

New organizations as well as new types of researchers were the other products of this new political economy of technical knowledge. The RAND Corporation, originally designed to serve as a brain trust for the Air Force in the nuclear age, quickly became a new kind of organization: RAND researchers played a prominent role in shaping American nuclear strategy while developing a suite of intellectual methods, especially systems analysis and game theory, that allowed policy makers and politicians to believe that strategic decision making might have a rational and objective basis. When RAND arrived in Washington, D.C., with the Kennedy administration and Robert S. McNamara as secretary of defense, the methods of systems analysis quickly spread from the Pentagon to flourish within the rest of the government, especially as the Johnson administration embraced the

many programs of the Great Society (McDougall, 1985; Collins, 2002). Other new organizations, such as the JASONS, worked to make sure that the armed services would always have access to the best and brightest of the nation's technical talent (Aaserud, 1995). New institutions also produced new kinds of people—RAND's most famous employee was the defense intellectual, Herman Kahn, who appeared on television to discuss whether the survivors of a thermonuclear war might not envy the dead (Ghamari-Tabrizi, 2005). Others among this new cadre were not as popular, but capable of working in military institutions, universities, and corporations. Lloyd Berkner, a research physicist, did pioneering interwar work in ionospheric physics and went on to build a career moving among a diverse set of institutions ranging from the navy to Associated Universities, Inc., a group of nine universities that managed the Brookhaven laboratories and Texas Instruments. Along the way he supervised the 1950 National Academy report, "Science and Foreign Relations," and played a major role in planning and organizing the 1957 International Geophysical Year (Needell, 2000). Berkner was not alone; after *Sputnik*, the Advanced Research Projects Agency (ARPA) cultivated individuals who could work across disciplinary and institutional boundaries. It was no small irony that ARPA's greatest innovation, the ARPANET, was a technology that allowed for the interconnection of vastly different computer networks through a common communications standard.

Military patronage facilitated new fields, new institutions, and new kinds of people, but did it produce a new kind of knowledge? This is among the most contested of issues in studies of Cold War science, technology, and social science. For Paul Forman (1987), physics clearly became more instrumental and far more interested in technological development than it had been during the interwar period. Others, including Dan Kevles (1990), argued that such claims failed to address the problem that physics had always been shaped by its patrons, whether they were in private foundations, corporations, or the military. Some support for Forman is found in David Kaiser's (2011) recent work on Cold War quantum theory. For Kaiser, it was the downturn in defense funding after Vietnam that saw a growth in interest among physicists for aspects of quantum theory that were not reducible to technology or weapons. Certainly, the military's funding affected what could be imagined. The United States did little research on alternative energy sources during the long Cold War; cheap oil was an unspoken assumption, even after the 1970s Arab oil embargoes. Military monies had a profound effect on the production of knowledge, but they were not completely deterministic. Even in the social sciences, the new quantitative methods favored by the new patrons did not eliminate the older qualitative forms of social analysis. Also, large, industrial-scale research, what physicist Alvin Weinberg named "Big Science," was another consequence of the new patronage. What remains unclear is whether this team-oriented, instrument-focused research was more than a change in the scale and scope of knowledge production (Galison and Hevly, 1992).

What is most striking about the Cold War political economy of technical knowledge is its resilience. Although the Cold War has been over for two decades, the institutions and practices developed during that era show no signs of going away. Although there has been some change in funding patterns, the military remains a major patron of American science, technology, and social science. It is inconceivable for either the military or the scientific and technological establishment to imagine a world in which they are not partners in the production of knowledge. Although the war on terror in the wake of the 9/11 attacks has generated new areas of interest (e.g., drones, cyberwarfare, and counterinsurgency), it remains unclear how twenty-first-century relations among science, technology, and the military will differ from those of the late twentieth century.

[See also Agricultural Technology; Agriculture, U.S. Department of; Airplanes and Air Transport; American System of Manufactures; Anthropology; Army Corps of Engineers, U.S.; Astronomy and Astrophysics; Atomic Energy Commission; Berkner, Lloyd; Bush, Vannevar; Cartography; Chemistry; Compton, Karl Taylor; Computer Science; Computers, Mainframe, Mini, and Micro; Conant, James B.; Dana, James Dwight; Defense Advanced Research Projects Agency; Diplomacy (post-1945), Science and Technology and; Edison, Thomas; Einstein, Albert; Engineering; Hale, George Ellery; International Geophysical Year; Lewis and Clark Expedition; Machinery and Manufacturing; Manhattan Project; Mathematics and Statistics; Meteorology and Climatology; Missiles and Rockets; Morrill Land Grant Act; National Academy of Sciences; National Laboratories; Nuclear Weapons; Office of Scientific Research and Development; Oppenheimer, J. Robert; Penicillin; Pickering, Edward Charles; Physics; Psychological and Intelligence Testing; Quantum Theory; Railroads; Research and Development; Rush, Benjamin; Satellites, Communications; Science; Sexually Transmitted Diseases; Shipbuilding; Smithsonian Institution; Social Sciences; Space Science; Springfield Armory; Steam Power; Strategic Defense Initiative; Technology; Telegraph; Terman, Frederick E.; War and Medicine; Whitney, Eli; and Wilkes Expedition.]

BIBLIOGRAPHY

Aaserud, Finn. "Sputnik and the 'Princeton Three': The National Security Laboratory That Was Not to Be." Historical Studies in the Physical and Biological Sciences 25, no. 2 (1995): 185–240.

Allison, David K. New Eye for the Navy: The Origin of Radar at the Naval Research Laboratory. Washington, D.C.: U.S. Government Printing Office, 1981.

Ambrose, Stephen E. Undaunted Courage: Meriwether Lewis, Thomas Jefferson, and the Opening of the American West. New York: Simon and Schuster, 1997.

Baxter, James Phinney. Scientists against Time. Boston: Little, Brown, 1946.

Biddle, Tami Davis. Rhetoric and Reality in Air Warfare: The Evolution of British and American Ideas about Strategic Bombing, 1914–1945. Princeton, N.J.: Princeton University Press, 2002.

Bird, Kai, and Martin J. Sherwin. American Prometheus: The Triumph and Tragedy of J. Robert Oppenheimer. New York: Alfred A. Knopf, 2005.

Braun, Ernst, and Stuart Macdonald. *Revolution in Miniature: The History and Impact of Semiconductor Electronics*. New York: Cambridge University Press, 1982.

Bruce, Robert V. *Lincoln and the Tools of War*. Urbana and Chicago: University of Illinois Press, 1989.

Bud, Robert. *Penicillin: Triumph and Tragedy*. New York: Oxford University Press, 2007.

Buderi, Robert. *The Invention That Changed the World: The Story of Radar from War to Peace*. Boston: Little, Brown, 1997.

Carson, John S. "Army Alpha, Army Brass, and the Search for Army Intelligence." *Isis* 84 (1993): 278–309.

Carson, John S. *The Measure of Merit: Talents, Intelligence, and Inequality in the French and American Republics, 1750–1940*. Princeton, N.J.: Princeton University Press, 2006.

Cloud, John. "American Cartographic Transformations during the Cold War." *Cartography and Geographic Information Science* 29, no. 3 (2002): 261–282.

Cloud, John. "Imaging the World in a Barrel: Corona and the Clandestine Convergence of the Earth Sciences." *Social Studies of Science* 31, no. 2 (2001): 231–251.

Collins, Martin J. *Cold War Laboratory: RAND, the Air Force, and the American State, 1945–1950*. Washington, D.C.: Smithsonian Institution Press, 2002.

Day, Dwayne A., John M. Logsdon, and Brian Latell, eds. *Eye in the Sky: The Story of the Corona Spy Satellites*. Washington, D.C.: Smithsonian Institution Press, 1998.

Dennis, Michael Aaron. "'Our First Line of Defense': Two University Laboratories in the Postwar American State." *Isis* 85, no. 3 (1994): 427–455.

Dennis, Michael Aaron. "Reconstructing Sociotechnical Order: Vannevar Bush and US Science Policy." In *States of Knowledge: The Co-Production of Science and Social Order*, edited by Sheila Jasanoff, pp. 225–253. New York: Routledge, 2004.

DeVorkin, David. *Science with a Vengeance: How the Military Created the US Space Sciences after World War II*. New York: Springer-Verlag, 1992.

Dupree, A. Hunter. *Science in the Federal Government: A History of Policies and Activities to 1940*. Cambridge, Mass.: Belknap Press of Harvard University Press, 1957.

Dyer, Davis. *TRW: Pioneering Technology and Innovation since 1900*. Boston, Mass.: Harvard Business School Press, 1998.

Fitzgerald, Gerard J. "Chemical Warfare and Medical Response during World War I." *American Journal of Public Health* 98, no. 4 (2008): 611–625.

Forman, Paul. "Behind Quantum Electronics: National Security as Basis for Physical Research in the United States, 1940–1960." *Historical Studies in the Physical Sciences* 18 (1987): 149–229.

Forman, Paul. "Inventing the Maser in Postwar America." *Osiris (2nd ser.)* 7 (1992): 105–134.

Forman, Paul. "'Swords in Ploughshares': Breaking New Ground with Radar Hardware and Technique in Physical Research after World War II." *Reviews of Modern Physics* 67, no. 2 (1995): 397–455.

Fortun, Michael, and Silvan S. Schweber. "Scientists and the Legacy of World War II: The Case of Operations Research (OR)." *Social Studies of Science* 23, no. 4 (1993): 595–642.

Galison, Peter, and Bruce Hevly, eds. *Big Science: The Growth of Large Scale Research*. Stanford, Calif.: Stanford University Press, 1992.

Ghamari-Tabrizi, Sharon. *The Worlds of Herman Kahn: The Intuitive Science of Thermonuclear War*. Cambridge, Mass.: Harvard University Press, 2005.

Goetzmann, William H. *Exploration and Empire: The Explorer and the Scientist in the Winning of the American West*. Austin: Texas State Historical Association, 1993.

Goldberg, Stanley. "Inventing a Climate of Opinion: Vannevar Bush and the Decision to Build the Atomic Bomb." *Isis* 83 (1992): 429–452.

Hershberg, James G. *James B. Conant: Harvard to Hiroshima and the Making of the Nuclear Age*. New York: Alfred A. Knopf, 1993.

Hounshell, David. *From the American System to Mass Production, 1800–1932: The Development of Manufacturing Technology in the United States*. Baltimore: Johns Hopkins University Press, 1984.

Hughes, Thomas P. *Elmer Sperry: Inventor and Engineer*. Baltimore: Johns Hopkins University Press, 1971.

Isaac, Joel. "The Human Sciences in Cold War America." *The Historical Journal* 50, no. 3 (2007): 725–746.

Joyce, Barry Alan. *The Shaping of American Ethnography: The Wilkes Exploring Expedition, 1838–1842*. Lincoln: University of Nebraska Press, 2001.

Kaiser, David. *How the Hippies Saved Physics: Science, Counterculture, and the Quantum Revival*. New York: W. W. Norton, 2011.

Kevles, Dan. "Cold War and Hot Physics: Science, Security and the American State, 1945–1956." *Historical Studies in the Physical and Biological Sciences* 20, no. 2 (1990): 239–264.

Kevles, Daniel J. *The Physicists: The History of a Scientific Community in Modern America.* Cambridge, Mass.: Harvard University Press, 1995.

Kleinman, Daniel Lee, and Mark Solovey. "Hot Science/Cold War: The National Science Foundation after World War II." *Radical History Review* 63 (1995): 110–139.

Kohler, Robert E. *Partners in Science: Foundations and Natural Scientists, 1900–1945.* Chicago: University of Chicago Press, 1991.

Leslie, Stuart W. *The Cold War and American Science: The Military–Industrial–Academic Complex at MIT and Stanford.* New York: Columbia University Press, 1993.

Lowen, Rebecca S. *Creating the Cold War University: The Transformation of Stanford.* Berkeley: University of California Press, 1997.

MacKenzie, Donald. *Inventing Accuracy: A Historical Sociology of Nuclear Missile Guidance.* Cambridge, Mass.: MIT Press, 1990.

McDougall, Walter. *The Heavens and the Earth: A Political History of the Space Age.* New York: Basic Books, 1985.

Mindell, David A. *Between Human and Machine: Feedback, Control, and Computing before Cybernetics.* Baltimore: Johns Hopkins University Press, 2002.

Mindell, David A. *War, Technology, and Experience aboard the USS Monitor.* Baltimore: Johns Hopkins University Press, 2000.

Mirowski, Philip. *Machine Dreams: Economics Becomes a Cyborg Science.* New York: Cambridge University Press, 2002.

Moore, Kelly. *Disrupting Science: Social Movements, American Scientists, and the Politics of the Military, 1945–1975.* Princeton, N.J.: Princeton University Press, 2008.

Needell, Allan A. *Science, Cold War and the American State: Lloyd V. Berkner and the Balance of Professional Ideals.* London: Harwood Academic Publishers, 2000.

Neushul, Peter. "Science, Government, and the Mass Production of Penicillin." *The Journal of the History of Medicine and Allied Sciences* 48, no. 4 (1993): 371–395.

Owens, Larry. "MIT and the Federal 'Angel': Academic R&D and Federal–Private Cooperation before WWII." *Isis* 81 (1990): 188–213.

Pang, Alex Soojung-Kim. "Edward Bowles and Radio Engineering at MIT, 1920–1940." *Historical Studies in the Physical and Biological Sciences* 20, no. 2 (1990): 313–337.

Price, Matt. "Roots of Dissent: The Chicago Met Lab and the Origins of the Franck Report." *Isis* 86, no. 2 (1995): 222–244.

Redmond, Kent C., and Thomas M. Smith. *From Whirlwind to MITRE: The R&D Story of the SAGE Air Defense Computer.* Cambridge, Mass.: MIT Press, 2000.

Roland, Alex. *Model Research: The National Advisory Committee for Aeronautics 1915–1958.* 2 vols. Washington, D.C.: National Aeronautics and Space Administration, 1985.

Sheehan, Neil. *A Fiery Peace in a Cold War: Bernard Schriever and the Ultimate Weapon.* New York: Random House, 2009.

Sherwin, Martin J. *A World Destroyed: Hiroshima and the Origins of the Arms Race.* New York: Vintage, 1975; 1987.

Simpson, Christopher, ed. *Universities and Empire: Money and Politics in the Social Sciences during the Cold War.* New York: New Press, 1998.

Smith, Merritt Roe. "Army Ordnance and the 'American System' of Manufacturing, 1815–1861." In *Military Enterprise and Technological Change: Perspectives on the American Experience,* edited by Merritt Roe Smith, pp. 39–86. Cambridge, Mass.: MIT Press, 1985.

Stanton, William R. *The Great United States Exploring Expedition of 1838–1842.* Berkeley: University of California Press, 1975.

Swann, John Patrick. "The Search for Synthetic Penicillin during World War II." *The British Journal for the History of Science* 16, no. 2 (1983): 154–190.

Van Keuren, David K. "Science, Progressivism, and Military Preparedness: The Case of the Naval Research Laboratory, 1915–1923." *Technology and Culture* 33, no. 4 (1992): 710–736.

Wang, Jessica. *American Science in an Age of Anxiety: Scientists, Anticommunism, and the Cold War.* Chapel Hill; London: University of North Carolina Press, 1999.

Yerkes, Robert M., ed. *The New World of Science: Its Development during the War.* New York: Century Company, 1920.

Zachary, G. Pascal. *Endless Frontier: Vannevar Bush, Engineer of the American Century.* New York: Free Press, 1997.

Michael Aaron Dennis

MILLIKAN, ROBERT A.

(1868–1953), physicist and Nobel laureate. Robert A. Millikan was born in Morrison, Illinois, the son of a Congregational minister. In 1875, the family moved to Maquoketa, Iowa. He entered Oberlin College in 1886, intending to study Greek and Latin, but found physics more interesting. After receiving his AB (1891) and MA (1893) from Oberlin, Millikan enrolled as a graduate student at Columbia University, earning his PhD in physics in 1895. In 1896, after a year at the universities of Berlin and Göttingen, he joined the University of Chicago physics department. As a young faculty member at Chicago, he was committed to teaching and became well known as a contributor to physics textbooks. Millikan married Greta Blanchard in 1902; they had three sons.

Millikan's scientific reputation rests on his measurement of the charge on the electron (1907–1917), his verification of Albert Einstein's quantum equation for the photoelectric effect (1916), and his numerical determination of Max Planck's constant. The success of these experiments made him one of America's best known and most distinguished physicists well before he won the Nobel Prize for Physics in 1923.

Actively involved in the organization of American science, Millikan during World War I headed the science and research division of the Army Signal Corps. He also organized the physics work of the new National Research Council, where he conducted war-related research including methods for detecting submarines.

Moving to the California Institute of Technology in 1921, Millikan, as director of the Norman Bridge physics laboratory, began research on cosmic rays, a term he coined. As chair of the Institute's executive council he functioned as its de facto president and played a major role in its early development until his retirement in 1945. Millikan served as president of the American Physical Society and vice president of the American Association for the Advancement of Science. He became a major public figure not only because of his educational and organizational work for science but also for his lectures and writings promoting the reconciliation of science with religion.

[*See also* American Association for the Advancement of Science; Einstein, Albert; Higher Education and Science; Military, Science and Technology and the; Nobel Prize in Biomedical Research; Physics; Quantum Theory; Religion and Science; Research and Development; *and* Science.]

BIBLIOGRAPHY

Goodstein, Judith R. *Millikan's School: A History of the California Institute of Technology.* New York: W. W. Norton, 1991.
Kargon, Robert A. *The Rise of Robert Millikan: Portrait of a Life in American Science.* Ithaca, N.Y.: Cornell University Press, 1982.

Judith R. Goodstein

MINING TECHNOLOGY

Mining has played a central role in American economic development. Coal, petroleum, natural gas, and uranium helped fuel industrialization. Iron, cement, copper, and other mine products were transformed into manufactured goods and buildings. Gold and silver have at times served as official bases for the money supply. Mining contributed to the accumulation of numerous family fortunes, including those of the Guggenheims, the Rockefellers, and the Mellons. Until recently, the growth of mining and the growth of the economy have been strongly intertwined. Between 1880 and 1970 mining output was cyclical and the trend rate of growth for mining and real gross domestic product was similar. Since 1970, however, mining output has fluctuated around a flat trend.

Iron, copper, and coal were originally mined from outcroppings at or near the Earth's surface, and gold was panned in streams. As the demand for mine products increased, miners searched farther afield, dug deeper, and drilled in the ocean. The increased difficulty of tapping the resource led to increased capital investment and dramatic changes in mine technologies. Through the early 1920s, many mines depended on workers using hand tools and rule-of-thumb techniques, and mules and steam-run hoists or pumps were used to move the materials to the surface. Increases in mine output required more mine workers, although technological changes in blasting and machinery fueled by steam, compressed air, and then electricity contributed to steady growth in output per miner. After the 1920s the pace of technological change increased dramatically. New machinery dug, drilled, pumped, and clawed underground, and many mines began using large-scale earth movers to strip the hillsides above the mine seams. Consequently, mine output rose nearly eightfold from the mid-1920s to 2010 despite a 40 percent reduction in the number of miners. The improvements in mining technology also cut accident rates in half.

Mining was often the leading edge of development in many isolated areas. Gold and silver rushes opened up California, Nevada, Arizona, and the Black Hills. When coal and copper mines opened, employers attracted workers from outside the region by establishing company towns where there had been little agricultural settlement or prior infrastructure. As the number of mines increased or other industries developed, company towns gave way to independent towns and cities. In some isolated regions, however, the population left when the resource was depleted, leaving ghost towns behind.

During the employment booms in the early 1900s, competition among mine owners for labor was fierce. In consequence, miners were often highly mobile, they earned high hourly earnings to compensate for the dangers of mining, and employers hired an ethnically diverse work force. Competition among numerous mines in combination with the miners' use of collective action limited the employer's ability to exploit monopoly power in company towns. Miners struck more frequently than other workers, and several famous violent episodes occurred in the mine fields. Mine workers often were leaders in the major union movements. Miner Big Bill Haywood led the radical Industrial Workers of the World. The United Mine Workers of America, including long-time president John L. Lewis, played leading roles in the American Federation of Labor, the Congress of Industrial Organization, and the later merger of the two organizations.

[*See also* Electricity and Electrification; Machinery and Manufacturing; Petroleum and Petrochemicals; Steam Power; *and* Technology.]

BIBLIOGRAPHY

Freese, Barbara. *Coal: A Human History*. New York: Arrow Books, 2006.
Lynch, Martin. *Mining in World History*. London: Reaktion Books, 2002.

Price V. Fishback

MISSILES AND ROCKETS

Missiles as defined in this essay are weapons consisting of four major subsystems: a propulsion unit or units; a fuselage, case, or airframe; one of many types of guidance and control mechanisms, some of which may be external to the missile itself, as in sighting devices for aiming a launch tube on shoulder-fired rocket launchers; and one or more destructive devices or charges as in warheads using conventional explosives or nuclear warheads. There are far too many individual missiles as well as rockets and types of missiles/rockets for any generalizations about them to be absolutely certain, but the essay that follows will necessarily generalize. Where such generalizations are not qualified, the reader should assume that there may well be and probably are exceptions.

The two broadest categories of missiles are tactical and strategic, with "tactical" referring generally to a smaller, shorter-range weapon with a conventional warhead and "strategic" indicating larger, longer-range missiles with mass-destructive capabilities, usually by way of a nuclear warhead. Strategic missiles normally have potential enemy bases, missile sites, or cities as targets, whereas tactical missiles usually have various battlefield targets. However, there are short-range, tactical ballistic missiles (missiles that follow high, arching, suborbital trajectories and fall freely toward the target) that are used on a battlefield. There are other intermediate types of missiles.

Within these categories, there are subcategories such as intermediate-range and intercontinental ballistic missiles, which together make up the class of strategic missiles. Submarine-launched ballistic missiles are, in recent years, intercontinental in range, this being the case with the Trident II, the only missile in this category still in service. Most previous submarine-launched ballistic missiles (except the Trident I) were of intermediate range. In the tactical category, the types are greater in number, including surface-to-surface, surface-to-air, air-to-air, air-to-ground, sea-to-land, antitank, antipersonnel, antiship, and antiballistic missiles. Most missiles use rocket propulsion, but one major exception to this rule consists of cruise missiles, which typically use jet propulsion, meaning that to permit the burning of the fuel that creates their thrust, they use oxygen in the atmosphere rather than an oxidizer carried onboard the missile to supply the wherewithal for combustion.

Unlike jet engines, most rockets carry both fuel and oxidizer as propellants. (This is not true of ion thrusters, used in some space applications; see below.) Basically, like a missile, a full-fledged rocket (as distinguished from a component rocket serving as a subsystem thereof) consists of a propulsion element; a fuselage, case, or airframe; and guidance-and-control devices, but rockets that are not missiles do not have warheads. Their payloads may be types of instrumentation or spacecraft, including satellites. Nonmissile types of rockets include sounding rockets that carry scientific instruments into space; space-launch vehicles that carry satellites or other spacecraft beyond the Earth's atmosphere; vernier rockets used to make small adjustments in a spacecraft's trajectory or velocity; ullage motors for providing forward thrust to force propellants to the backs of tanks before firing the main engines; satellite apogee and perigee kick motors for circularizing a satellite's orbit from its furthest or nearest point above the Earth; stage-separation motors for separating a spent stage from other stages in a multistage rocket; and other auxiliary rockets. (Usually, the term rocket motor means that the rocket uses solid propellants, whereas rocket engine refers to liquid-propellant propulsion devices.) Many larger rockets and missiles have more than one stage, each with its own propulsion. As one stage uses up its propellant, it drops away, reducing the weight of the remaining stages, which accelerate the vehicle to higher velocities.

Tactical Missiles. The multiple types and examples of tactical missiles differ enough from one another that comprehensive statements about them are especially problematic. Illustrative examples will help to supplement the generalizations that can be made. Rockets using black powder consisting of saltpeter, sulfur, and charcoal have been around for centuries and were used to propel primitive missiles by the mid-twelfth century. But until World War II (1939–1945) more sophisticated missiles did not exist. The American rocket pioneer Robert H. Goddard worked during World War I (1914–1918) with his graduate student Clarence N. Hickman on the basic idea for one of the earliest truly useful missiles known popularly as the bazooka. The two men demonstrated the basic concept just before the armistice in 1918. In 1941, before U.S. entry into World War II, (now) Dr. Hickman worked with the U.S. Army to develop the idea into the M1 rocket-propelled antitank weapon featuring a shaped-charge warhead and fired from a tube on a soldier's shoulder. (A shaped charge is an explosive in a case with a hollow cavity in front that causes the force of the explosion to concentrate in the direction of the target, in this case so that it will penetrate the tank's armor.) It began to be deployed soon after the beginning of U.S. involvement in the war and proved to be highly effective against not only tanks but also other targets such as bunkers. With improvements over time, this became the grandfather of antitank missiles (Hunley, *Preludes*, 2008).

Hickman became the head of a section of the National Defense Research Committee on the East Coast that developed a small aircraft rocket with double-base (nitrocellulose and nitroglycerine) solid propellant used by the U.S. Army during World War II. Its West Coast counterpart, headed by physics professor Charles Lauritsen of the California Institute of Technology (Caltech), developed a number of missiles for the U.S. Navy, including antisubmarine rockets and aircraft rockets. These were small and primitive by later standards, but double-base propellants had higher performance (hence velocity) than black powder. Later developments included casting (allowing the propellant to be poured into a case and hardened), internal burning cavities to protect the case from heat and prevent unstable burning, and additives to the double-base propellants (which were now called composite modified double-base), permitting larger rockets with more propellant and higher performance. An alternative form of solid propellant was the castable composite propellant with different oxidizers, fuels, and additives than double-base propellants. This type of propellant often had lower performance than comparable double-base propellants but was less likely to detonate (explode) and hence safer (Hunley, *Preludes*, 2008; Moore, 2011).

There were also advances in case materials (including aluminum, hardened steel, and composites consisting of a fiber and a resin) and in guidance/control mechanisms. Examples of the latter included laser guidance on the Hellfire missile fired from helicopters at tanks and other hardened surface targets (in use since 1985) and infrared homing on many generations of the Sidewinder missile fired from one aircraft against another, in which the homing device seeks the source of heat from the target aircraft's engine (in use in various, increasingly improved versions since 1956). Other missiles used radar guidance (*The Modern US War Machine*, 1987).

Strategic Missiles. Strategic missiles evolved in a complicated process from much shorter-range ballistic missiles. After World War II, the Jet Propulsion Laboratory (JPL), associated with Caltech, which had developed castable composite propellants, began work on a short-lived, liquid-propellant ballistic missile named the Corporal and a solid-propellant replacement, the Sergeant, under contract with the U.S. Army. Meanwhile, a group including Germans who had helped develop the V-2 ballistic missile in Germany was working at the Army's Redstone Arsenal in Alabama to develop the liquid-propellant Redstone missile, which was longer and more powerful

than the Corporal or Sergeant, with an engine built by what became North American Aviation's Rocketdyne Division. All three were influenced by V-2 technologies but included many U.S. innovations as well.

All three of these shorter-range missiles contributed to the fund of knowledge necessary for engineers to develop the first intercontinental ballistic missile, the Atlas. Developed under the auspices of the Air Force's Western Development Division (later the Air Force Ballistic Missile Division) in Inglewood, California, the Atlas was built by the Consolidated Vultee Aircraft Corporation (Convair), with the engine contracted to Rocketdyne. Atlas underwent a difficult development process, but the first operational missile, the Atlas D, was completed in 1959, followed by Atlas E's and F's in 1961. All were phased out as missiles in 1965 but became important first stages for space-launch vehicles. While Atlas was still in development, the Air Force began development of the Thor and the Army began to develop the Jupiter, both liquid-propellant, intermediate-range ballistic missiles. Developed in competition but with both engines built by Rocketdyne, the two missiles became operational in 1959–1960.

By then, the navy's solid-propellant, submarine-launched ballistic missile, the Polaris, had demonstrated the future of long-range ballistic missiles in the United States, which lay with solid propellants. Liquid propellants have higher performance, but their complicated plumbing and their propellant tanks made fitting them in silos, let alone aboard submarines, impractical. Because liquid-propellant engines can be throttled as well as shut down and then reignited, they have important advantages in space-launch applications, but these factors were not operative for missiles. A key to the development of Polaris was Atlantic Research Corporation's discovery that the addition of aluminum to solid propellants greatly improved performance. With this discovery and many others, the navy was able to deploy Polaris on 15 November 1960.

Influenced by Polaris, the Air Force developed the three-stage Minuteman I land-based, solid-propellant missile with a different propellant that also included aluminum. It became operational in

October 1962. Polaris was succeeded by a series of submarine-launched ballistic missiles, all solid-propellant, culminating in the Trident II. Minuteman II and III followed Minuteman I, with the Minuteman III and the Trident II constituting the only two strategic missiles still in the U.S. inventory in 2011. Meanwhile, the Air Force had been developing the Titan I and II. It deployed Titan I in 1962 and deactivated it in 1965 after Titan II became fully operational at the very end of 1963. Titan IIs then went out of the inventory of strategic deterrents between 1984 and 1987. During its period of activation, Titan II had the greatest throw weight (amount of payload that could be carried) and the longest period of activation of any liquid-propellant missile. All of these missiles exhibited advances in rocket and other technologies and most became stages of space-launch vehicles. All contributed in one way or another to launch-vehicle technology (Hunley, *Preludes*, 2008).

Space-Launch Vehicles. The first successful American space-launch vehicle, Juno I, was actually an elongated Redstone missile with small-scale models of the Sergeant missile used in three upper stages. Launched on 31 January 1958, it placed the first U.S. satellite, Explorer I, in orbit. Developed by a joint Redstone Arsenal–JPL team, the Juno I beat the Naval Research Laboratory–Glenn L. Martin Company team to a successful launch of the Vanguard launch vehicle, which occurred on 17 March 1958 and did place its first satellite (of three) into orbit (of nine attempts). Other early launch vehicles were a modified Redstone called the Jupiter C, a modified Atlas, and a modified Titan II, used in the National Aeronautics and Space Administration (NASA) program to place astronauts in space and then in orbit (under projects Mercury and Gemini) in preparation for landing astronauts on the moon. The Atlas was also used in Project Gemini to launch an Agena upper stage for missions to practice docking one spacecraft with another.

The Thor missile became the basis for the first stage of a series of highly successful, multistage launch vehicles designated Thor-Delta and then just Delta before Delta IV introduced a totally new first stage. Delta IV had a successful first launch on 20 November 2002. Nine years later, it was still in use in various configurations as part of the Air Force's Evolved Expendable Launch Vehicle (EELV) program. Greatly improved over the years, Delta had begun as early as 1963 to use "strap-on" (attached) solid-propellant boosters to increase the thrust of the first stage, a practice continued with the Delta IV.

In December 1958 an Atlas missile served as a launch vehicle when it carried a repeater satellite into orbit. With an Agena upper stage, Atlas became a successful two-stage launch vehicle from 26 February 1960 to 27 June 1978. Development of the Centaur upper stage burning the high-performance combination of liquid hydrogen and liquid oxygen as propellants enabled Atlas to launch much heavier payloads starting on 30 May 1966. In various configurations, with as many as five optional strap-on solid-propellant boosters, the Atlas V—the most recent, improved Atlas-Centaur—was the second part of the Air Force's EELV program.

There is room only for a bare mention of the small, all-solid-propellant launch vehicle, the Scout, and the huge Saturn V that carried American astronauts to the vicinity of the moon for landing and return to the Earth in the spacecraft. Both derived much technology from missiles but not as much as the Titan III and IV space-launch vehicles, which consisted of upgraded Titan II missiles as a core with upper stages and two huge segmented, solid-propellant motors "strapped" to the core to add to the overall thrust. Titan IIIA successfully launched its first satellite to orbit on 6 May 1965. The last Titan IV successfully launched a satellite on 7 February 1994. Meanwhile, the highly sophisticated Space Shuttle (featuring even larger solid-rocket boosters; an enormously advanced space shuttle main engine; and the first reusable, orbiting, winged spacecraft carrying astronauts, one of whom landed it back on the earth) came into being after a difficult development period. It carried astronauts and spacecraft plus experiments into space from 1981 to its last flight on 21 July 2011. These and other launch vehicles built upon missile technology and developed many new technologies, including various sophisticated guidance-and-control systems different from those used on missiles (Hunley, both volumes, 2008; Vandenberg Air Force Base; NASA).

Spacecraft Propulsion. Most spacecraft have used chemical rocket propulsion for a variety of purposes. Highly efficient but low-thrust ion engines that use electric power to create thrust by accelerating ions were more recently used with photovoltaic power sources on U.S. spacecraft. Because of their low thrust, ion engines are not useful on launch vehicles, which must overcome the Earth's gravity, but in the microgravity of space, the high speeds of the ions emitted over a much longer period than chemical rockets can burn permit much higher velocities for spacecraft that can be small and light compared with chemically propelled counterparts, reducing launch costs (University of Michigan).

Significance. Missiles have significantly changed the nature of war, for better or worse. Satellites, placed into orbit by launch vehicles, have done the same. Global Positioning System satellites provide navigational information for ships at sea and for land forces crossing deserts. Weather satellites help in planning military operations as well as in predicting natural disasters. Other satellites provide targeting information for many missiles as well as intelligence about enemies. Global Positioning System satellites also provide directions to civilian drivers of automobiles, and communication satellites transmit meteorological data and images from around the world to television audiences. In these and other ways, missiles and satellites have enormously changed the nature of our world.

[*See also* **Atomic Energy Commission; Goddard, Robert H.; Instruments of Science; Military, Science and Technology and the; National Aeronautics and Space Administration; Nuclear Weapons; Satellites, Communications; Science; Space Program; Space Science; Technology; Television;** *and* **War and Medicine.**]

BIBLIOGRAPHY

Aerospaceweb.org "Strategic and Tactical Missiles". http://www.aerospaceweb.org/question/weapons/q0223.shtml, no pagination (accessed 20 March 2012). A highly useful article written by aerospace engineer Jeff Scott on 10 April 2005 about Russian and American missiles.

Friedman, Norman. *Seapower and Space: From the Dawn of the Missile Age to Net-Centric Warfare.* Annapolis, Md.: Naval Institute Press, 2000. Highly technical and useful source for the discussion of the significance of missiles and rockets.

Hunley, J. D. *Preludes to U.S. Space-Launch Vehicle Technology: Goddard Rockets to Minuteman III* and *U.S. Space-Launch Vehicle Technology: Viking to Space Shuttle.* Gainesville: University Press of Florida, 2008. These two separate books, essentially a set, provide recent, extensive treatment of major missiles and space-launch vehicles in considerable but not forbidding technical detail; large bibliography. They are the most comprehensive sources on the topic.

Lang, Walter N. *The Modern US War Machine: An Encyclopedia of American Military Equipment and Strategy.* London: Salamander Books, 1987. On pp. 214–237, this source provides reliable descriptions of a large number of U.S. missiles in use in 2011, including synopses of their histories.

Moore, Thomas L. "Solid Propulsion Enabling Technologies and Milestones for Navy Air-launched Tactical Missiles." AIAA-2011-6941. Paper presented at the AIAA Aviation Technology, Integration, and Operations (ATIO) Conference, Centennial of Naval Aviation Forum, 20–22 September 2011, Virginia Beach, Virginia.

NASA, Space Shuttle. "Space Shuttle Program: Spanning 30 Years of Discovery." http://www.nasa.gov/mission_pages/shuttle/main/index.html, no pagination (accessed 20 March 2012). A competent, up-to-date summary of the Space Shuttle program's history.

Sutton, George P., and Oscar Biblarz. *Rocket Propulsion Elements.* 8th ed. Hoboken, N.J.: John Wiley & Sons, 2010. The most recent edition of a classic account of rocket propulsion; highly useful on that subject but very technical.

The University of Michigan. "The Past and Future of Rocket Engine Propulsion, Part II: Electrostatic Systems." http://www.fathom.com/course/21701743/session6.html (accessed 20 March 2012). A good source for the nature of ion propulsion and its first use in space; needs to be supplemented by other sources for further uses, such as that on the *Dawn* spacecraft.

Vandenberg Air Force Base. "Evolved Expendable Launch Vehicle (EELV)." http://www.vandenberg.af.mil/library/factsheets/factsheet.asp?id=5207, no pagination (accessed 20 March 2012). Current as of November 2010, a recent assessment of this important program.

J. D. Hunley

MISSIONARIES AND SCIENCE AND MEDICINE

Science, Medicine, and American Christian Missions have been entangled since the seventeenth century. Understanding the numerous, important, and enduring interconnections among them requires questioning ways of thinking about the past that are widely entrenched in the modern West. We can only understand missionary science and medicine by setting aside the idea that science and religion comprehensively parted company in the modern world.

Holy Alliance. In early modern Europe, science flourished partly by strengthening existing links with organized Christianity. Counterreformation Catholic missionaries in Asia and the Americas, with Jesuits leading the way, deployed their scientific and medical training to win interest, patronage, and converts and brought back to the West new knowledge of the wider world. Hoping to guide future missionaries, the French Jesuit missionary-explorer Jacques Marquette (1637–1675) mapped the Mississippi river almost to the Gulf of Mexico.

Until the nineteenth century (and, for Roman Catholics, much later), North America was primarily a missionary-receiving region. To work effectively, missionaries had to acquire local knowledge. Learning the local vernacular to communicate, missionaries and their native teachers produced word lists, vocabularies, grammars, and dictionaries to aid language-learning and translation projects. Joining the Puritan exodus to New England in

1631, John Eliot (1603–1690), determined to preach in the vernacular, studied Massachusett with a Long Island Indian teacher. Noting many grammatical differences with English, Eliot and his teacher translated into Massachusett the Lord's Prayer, the Ten Commandments, and, by 1663, the whole Bible, the first complete translation in America. Eliot's *The Indian Grammar Begun* (1666) identified characteristics that distinguished Massachusett from English, Latin, Greek, and Hebrew, notably the frequency of compounding words. Moravian missionaries David Zeisberger (1721–1808) and John Heckewelder (1743–1823) produced a Delaware grammar.

Such linguistic tools, once written down in lasting form, circulated in transnational knowledge webs that, spanning time as well as space, proved indispensable to later scholars. Nineteenth-century philologists such as Peter Duponceau of the American Philosophical Society hailed Eliot's grammar and Bible, preserving dozens of Massachusett idioms and figures of speech, as a major contribution to comparative linguistics. Catholic and Protestant missionaries produced around 90 percent of the material available on American Indian languages before 1900. Although they aimed to expedite evangelism more than to advance knowledge for its own sake, they helped create the "science of language."

As native teachers taught the meanings of words in contexts of use, missionaries acquired new insights into indigenous cultures. Transnational anthropological webs owed much to missionaries and their indigenous informants. Lewis Grout (1815–1905), a New England Congregationalist, recorded Zulu songs, stories, and narratives told him by the natives themselves in *The Isizulu* (1859), an early Zulu grammar and ethnography. The writings of Robert Hamill Nassau (1835–1921), a Presbyterian who worked in equatorial West Africa from 1861 to 1906, owed their ethnographic value mainly to a key African informant, Anyentyuwe, governess to Nassau's daughter. Home missionaries often provided ethnographic as well as linguistic information for the federal government. Stephen R. Riggs (1812–1883), a Presbyterian missionary in Minnesota from 1837 until his death, forged links with the

Smithsonian Institution and, after 1878, with John Wesley Powell at the Bureau of American Ethnology. Committed to assimilating Indians, these institutions published Riggs's linguistic and ethnographic studies of the Dakota Sioux. Once such knowledge circulated in written form, its native and missionary originators lost control over the ways others read and used it.

As the activities of Grout and Nassau illustrate, Protestants from the mainline denominations launched overseas missions early in the nineteenth century. Most carried to the field the Scottish Common Sense realism, Newtonian cosmology, and Baconian induction they learned in college— a fertile matrix for cultivating and spreading science. Many of the New England missionaries arriving in Hawai'i from 1820 had studied natural history in college and continued collecting and classifying in the field. Sarah Lyman (1805–1885) arrived in Honolulu with her husband David, a graduate of Williams College and Andover Seminary, in 1831. From 1833, she systematically recorded detailed observations of earthquakes and volcanic eruptions in a diary continued by family members after her death, which modern seismologists have found invaluable. The Hawaiian mission hosted the U.S. Exploring Expedition of 1840–1841 (the "Wilkes Expedition").

When working in areas new to Western science, foreign missionaries were well placed to forge links with metropolitan experts. Between 1840 and 1881, the Reverend Titus Coan, leader of the Hawaiian mission at Hilo, sent dozens of specimens and descriptions of eruptions of Mauna Loa and Kilauea to Wilkes Expedition geologist J. D. Dana, who in 1850 became professor of natural history and geology at Yale. Able to observe lava flows close up and repeatedly for over 40 years, Coan turned out to be correct on most of the issues on which they disagreed, as Dana eventually acknowledged. Between the 1820s and 1920s, Hawaiian missionaries published at least 264 works on natural history, mostly on volcanoes, earthquakes, fossils, plants, animals, weather, and geography. Many reinterpreted Genesis to accommodate deep time.

The activities of Samuel Wells Williams (1812–1884) illustrate the close links that some mainline missionaries forged with metropolitan naturalists, big business, and the federal government. In 1832 his college friend Asa Gray, a botanist, asked Williams, bound for Canton, to collect plants. Gray used East Asian specimens sent by Williams (among others) to win a chair in botany at Harvard and, after 1859, defend Darwin against detractors. In 1848, Williams published *The Middle Kingdom*, a two-volume work on China's natural history, geography, demography, and politics that the British used for training diplomats. Between 1848 and 1851 he edited *The Chinese Repository*, a missionary-originated journal that disseminated Western science and medicine to China and Chinese languages, literature, natural history, geography, and medicine to the West. Williams became secretary of the U.S. Legation to China in 1855 and, from 1860, chargé d'affaires in Beijing. During the Second Opium War (1858–1860), he helped negotiate the Treaty of Tianjin, which forced the Qing dynasty to tolerate foreign and Chinese Christians and open up to Western legations, trade (including opium from the British East India Company), and missionaries. Returning to the United States, Williams won a chair in Chinese language and literature at Yale in 1877, becoming the first professor of sinology in the United States.

If missionaries often served as fieldworkers and research assistants for metropolitan experts, a gifted few made important theoretical contributions. Born into a large missionary family on Kaua'i Island in Hawai'i, John Thomas Gulick (1832–1923), fascinated by natural history as a boy, collected Achatinella land snails from Hawai'i's lush volcanic valleys during the 1850s. After studying at Williams College and Union Theological Seminary, he embraced evolution on reading Darwin's *Origin* in 1859. Carrying his shell collection to South America in 1861 and then to Japan and north China in 1862, he published papers in *Nature* and other learned journals arguing that natural selection could not adequately explain why snails living in almost identical environments in isolated valleys developed shells with distinctive shapes and colors. Highlighting isolation as an *essential* factor in evolution, Gulick became one of the most influential evolutionary theorists in the world by the 1890s.

Host Cultures Convert Missionaries. The rising profile of science and medicine in American missions during the nineteenth century cannot, however, be understood by focusing solely on the missionaries. Host cultures mattered. Interested in useful knowledge for self-strengthening, their hosts turned many missionaries into conduits of Western science and medicine.

This dynamic flourished especially in literate, self-confident Asian and Islamic cultures, where missionary preaching and Bible translation aroused hostility or indifference. Pragmatic Americans adapted by seeking common ground in science, medicine, and natural theology. In early-nineteenth-century Ceylon (modern Sri Lanka), for example, the Reverend Daniel Poor, a Massachusetts Presbyterian, decided that, since debating Scripture with learned brahmins often broke down in rancor, astronomy offered a way forward. As the principal of Batticotta Seminary at Jaffna from 1823, Poor aimed to spread Newtonian astronomy to sustain dialog and eventually, he hoped, debunk the "superstitious" cosmology of the masses (based partly on Hindu sacred texts). In 1829, after spotting inaccuracies in a local almanac, Poor used a portable telescope to show that he could predict the timing of a lunar eclipse more accurately than the local brahmin.

Similarly, in China, pioneer missionary-physician Peter Parker (1804–1888) aimed to spread Western science by founding the Medical Missionary Society in 1838 to enhance friendly engagement and undermine the "pitiable superstitions" of the Chinese. Women missionaries in Burma bought animal organs at the local market to dissect in classroom demonstrations, hoping to show the Burmese that natural laws and processes, not mysterious nonnatural forces, governed the workings of the human body. By facilitating dialog and exposing "heathen superstition," Western science and medicine would clear the way for Christianity.

When local people decided that missionary science worked, they often responded enthusiastically. In Ceylon, brahmins took astronomical information from American missionary almanacs to improve their own, almost driving the Christian almanacs to the wall. Chinese flocked to Parker's hospital, run like an assembly line, once they decided that it treated eye diseases and tumors effectively.

Local interest in Western science and medicine also tended to rise when famine, military defeat, economic distress, or political instability troubled the established order. Such crises spurred indigenous reformers, impressed by Western knowledge, wealth, and power, to modernize and strengthen their community, nation, and religion by embracing useful Western knowledge. Missionaries fluent in the vernacular, in touch with indigenous reformers, and frustrated by the ineffectiveness of traditional evangelism sought to capitalize on local interest in Western science and medicine.

They built institutions such as schools, colleges, hospitals, dispensaries, museums, laboratories, medical schools, leprosaria, and sanatoria. American Board missionaries founded the Syrian Protestant College (from 1920, American University) in Beirut in 1863, offering an excellent scientific and medical education to all. American and British missionaries cooperated with the Chinese government to found Peking Union Medical College in 1906, which has remained one of China's leading medical schools. They translated Western scientific and medical texts into local vernaculars. Young J. Allen (1836–1907), a southern Methodist, founded and edited the influential Chinese language monthly, *Wan Guo Gong Bao* (*Review of the Times*), between 1868 and 1907, whose articles on Western science, medicine, and technology inspired Chinese reformers. All these projects depended on local interest and cooperation.

Yet the "holy alliance" between Christianity and science seldom worked the way missionaries hoped. Local people decided when, how, why, and what they would take, if anything, from the package. In China, missionary medicine did not comprehensively discredit its indigenous rivals, eradicate local "superstition," or win many converts. Most Chinese operated as medical pluralists, adding Western medicine to existing therapies. In Meiji Japan, John Thomas Gulick and Japanese Christians presented evolution as God's method of creation in an effort to convince the Japanese that cooperation among individuals, races, and nations advanced human evolution better than unrestricted competition. Unconvinced, Japanese nationalists and the American agnostic Edward Morse, professor of zoology at Tokyo Imperial University, emphasized competitive struggle as the engine of social evolutionary progress. Despite missionary enthusiasm for scientific medicine as the "Golden Key to the Muslim World," almost every Muslim patient left Borden Memorial Hospital in North China, founded by the China Inland Mission in 1915, once they got the medicine or surgery they wanted—without converting. In the Arabian Gulf, Shaikh Abdulaziz Al Saud (1879–1953) patronized American medical missions from 1913 until the 1950s, when oil companies and government hospitals sprang up and the Gulf's Muslim rulers ejected the missionaries. Robust Asian and Islamic cultures seeking to enhance the health, wealth, knowledge, and power of their local community, caste, clan, religion, or nation "converted" missionaries into spreaders of Western science and medicine.

Professionalizing the Sciences: Missionaries Marginalized?

If missionaries generally fitted smoothly into transnational science webs before the 1870s, tensions increased during the next 60 years. American colleges, increasingly modeled on German research universities, secularized. Historians such as Andrew Dickson White, criticized by clergy for turning Cornell into a secular institution, hit back in a two-volume work of 1896 depicting science and "dogmatic theology" as perennial enemies. Professionalizing scientists, determined to enhance their discipline's autonomy, authority, and funding, began excluding nonprofessionals. Émigré Jewish professionalizers such as the anthropologist Franz Boas and his students Leonard Bloomfield and Edward Sapir, having suffered discrimination at the hands of European Christians, began marginalizing missionaries from the Amerindian linguistics establishment they took over from the 1890s. "[U]ntrained in the recognition of foreign speech sounds," claimed Bloomfield (*Language*, New York: H. Holt and Co., 1933), missionaries during the "era of exploration" after 1492 could "make no accurate record, and knowing only the terminology of Latin grammar, distorted their exposition by fitting it into this frame."

Images of missionaries as too prejudiced to obtain reliable knowledge flourished, especially in disciplines such as linguistics and anthropology. Popular twentieth-century novels and films depicted missionaries as ignorant fanatics destroying native cultures. Were such pictures historically reliable? Was missionary science an oxymoron?

Theological assumptions about the universality of sin often shaped and colored missionary writings about native languages, cultures, and religions, which could be arrogant and indiscriminately critical, as critics charged. Yet because they relied on native informants, even the most critical texts usually conveyed some, often substantial, information about indigenous realities. Recent research has acknowledged, *pace* Bloomfield, that missionaries produced the single largest body of knowledge about linguistic diversity around the world (Errington, 2008, p. viii). Professionalizing scientists' accounts of their discipline's dubious religious-and-missionary past should not uncritically be read as reliable, nonpartisan history.

If professionalizing and de-Christianizing currents might make the sciences and medicine less hospitable for evangelicals at home, foreign mission fields sometimes benefited. Some saw medical missions as a useful if not providential "safety valve" for surplus medical school graduates. Female missionary physicians or nurses became increasingly common by the end of the nineteenth century because many came to believe that penetrating literate, robust Islamic and Asian cultures required women to reach out to indigenous women, especially purdah (secluded high-caste) women.

Missionary Science Diversifies.

During the first half of the twentieth century, the United States began to lead the world in scientific and medical research and teaching, thanks partly to the arrival of gifted Jews from Europe. It also took over from Britain as the world's leading missionary-sending country. Meanwhile, debate over evolution and biblical criticism splintered evangelicalism, galvanizing the emergence of new varieties, ranging from fundamentalist to modernist. Missionary engagements with science diversified.

At the science-skeptical end of the spectrum, early American Pentecostals believed that the Holy Spirit equipped missionaries to speak foreign languages directly, without study. Alfred and Lillian Garr, baptized in the Spirit during Los Angeles' Azusa Street revival, arrived in Calcutta in 1906 confident that they had miraculously received "the language of India and dialects." But their "Bengali" befuddled locals. Soon, pragmatic Pentecostal leaders abandoned "missionary tongues" for regular language learning.

At the opposite, science-revering end of the spectrum, mainline missionaries invested in science and medicine more heavily than ever. By the 1930s, the typical mainline missionary, a female teacher or nurse, offered medical care or schooling without much attempt to evangelize. Ida Scudder (1870–1960) illustrates the feminizing, professionalizing, institution-building, and ecumenical dynamics transforming mainline missions. Born in India into a second-generation missionary family from the Reformed Church, she studied medicine at Cornell before opening a new hospital for women and children at Vellore in India. There she developed a new surgical technique for repairing vesicovaginal fistulae later known as the "Ida Scudder operation." The Christian Medical College and Hospital she founded at Vellore in 1918 trained over 1,200 Indian men and women.

By the early twentieth century, almost every American mission offered some form of medicine. The Seventh-Day Adventists, founded by prophetess and health reformer Ellen White during the 1840s, founded a Medical Missionary College in 1895. By the mid-1980s, Adventist medical institutions—165 hospitals and sanitariums, 246 clinics and dispensaries, 47 nursing schools, and 26 health food companies—girdled the globe. Harry Willis Miller, an Adventist missionary troubled by high infant mortality in East Asia, used his training in vegetarianism, dietetics, and food processing to develop, after years of experiments, palatable soy milk for infants and adults allergic to human and cow's milk. Once Soyalac proved its worth, global demand soared.

Missionary scientific and medical institutions opened up new opportunities for local people, especially women. In China, Shi Meiyu (Mary Stone, 1873–1954) and Kang Cheng (Ida Kahn, 1873–1930), after graduating from mission schools, studied medicine at the University of Michigan before returning to China in 1896 to establish successful medical practices. Maui Pomare, a Maori leader in New Zealand, used the Adventist medical training he received in the United States during the late 1890s to revitalize indigenous health and welfare, especially as the minister of health in New Zealand from 1923 to 1926 and minister for the Cook Islands from 1916 to 1928 (a New Zealand territory at the time).

Some missionary groups worked hard to adapt to the new professional standards. American Jesuits set up a chain of seismological stations across the United States and Canada during the early twentieth century to show that the Roman Catholic Church, contrary to critics' claims, supported science. Launched by Frederick Odenbach S. J. (1857–1933), Jesuit seismology flourished under the leadership of James B. Macelwane S. J. (1883–1956), a Berkeley-trained professor of geophysics at St. Louis University from 1925. Capitalizing on public concern sparked by big shakes in Montana and California in 1925, Macelwane made the Jesuit Seismological Service, staffed by Jesuits with PhDs in geophysics, a major center of seismological research. In 1944 Macelwane became the first Jesuit elected to the National Academy of Sciences.

Conservative evangelicals, growing in numbers and influence as mainline missions liberalized, founded the Summer Institute of Linguistics (SIL) during the 1930s. Evolving out of faith missions, the institute presented itself as a nonprofit scientific research organization to work in Mexico, governed by anticlerical socialists. SIL's goal of studying Indian languages to produce vernacular bibles and Protestant Christians overlapped with the government's aim of turning isolated Indians into literate modern Mexicans. Determined to emulate professional academic standards, SIL leaders sought advice and training from Bloomfield and Sapir and raised training and research standards at SIL. Linked from 1942 with the Wycliffe Bible Translators, SIL expanded into South America, Southeast Asia, Africa, and the Pacific Islands during the following decades. Shuttling between the academy and the mission field,

SIL leaders such as Kenneth Pike and Eugene Nida injected insights from structural linguistics and functionalist anthropology into missionary thinking and practice. As the Cold War heated up during the 1960s, younger left-leaning anthropologists, linguists, and activists within and beyond the churches attacked the institute as a pseudo-scientific organization linked with the Central Intelligence Agency. From the right, fundamentalists condemned its cultural relativism. Although hostility constrained SIL operations in Latin America, it continued to dominate research on endangered and minority languages during the late twentieth and early twenty-first centuries. Regularly updated editions of *Ethnologue*, the largest repository of knowledge about linguistic diversity in the world, has made this SIL publication an indispensable source for all students of language.

The spread of communism after 1945 saw missionaries ejected from countries such as Mao's China. Decolonization inspired nationalists in Africa, Asia, and elsewhere to criticize missionaries as destructive cultural imperialists, a view that remains popular among some post-colonial scholars. Historians such as Lamin Sanneh, by contrast, depicted vernacular Bible translation as revitalizing indigenous cultures. While declining in its old European heartlands, Christianity burgeoned in the southern hemisphere to become, once again, non-Western. African, Asian, Latin American, and Pacific Island Christians launched missions to the West.

[*See also* **Anthropology; Astronomy and Astrophysics; Biological Sciences; Botany; Creationism; Diplomacy (post-1945), Science and Technology and; Evolution, Theory of; Food and Diet; Geography; Geology; Geophysics; Linguistics; Medical Education; Medicine; Public Health; Religion and Science; Science; Surgery; Wilkes Expedition;** *and* **Zoology.**]

BIBLIOGRAPHY

Anderson, Allan. *Spreading Fires: The Missionary Nature of Early Pentecostalism*. Maryknoll, N.Y.: Orbis Books, 2007.

Armerding, Paul L. *Doctors for the Kingdom: The Work of the American Mission Hospitals in the Kingdom of Saudi Arabia 1913–1955*. Grand Rapids, Mich.: William B. Eerdmans, 2003.

Buck, Peter. *American Science and Modern China, 1876–1936*. New York: Cambridge University Press, 1980.

Cinnamon, John M. "Missionary Expertise, Social Science, and the Uses of Ethnographic Knowledge in Colonial Gabon." *History in Africa* 33 (2006): 413–432.

Errington, Joseph. *Linguistics in a Colonial World: A Story of Language, Meaning and Power*. Oxford: Blackwell, 2008.

Gilmour, Rachel. "A Nice Derangement of Epitaphs: Missionary Language-Learning in Mid-Nineteenth Century Natal." *Journal of Southern African Studies* 33 (2007): 521–538.

Gulick, Edward V. *Peter Parker and the Opening of China*. Cambridge, Mass.: Harvard University Press, 1973.

Hartch, Todd. *Missionaries of the State: The Summer Institute of Linguistics, State Formation, and Indigenous Mexico, 1935–1985*. Tuscaloosa: University of Alabama Press, 2006.

Hollinger, David A. *Science, Jews and Secular Culture: Studies in Mid-Twentieth-Century American Cultural History*. Princeton, N.J.: Princeton University Press, 1996.

Livingstone, David N., D. G. Hart, and Mark A. Noll, eds. *Evangelicals and Science in Historical Perspective*. New York: Oxford University Press, 1999.

Numbers, Ronald L., and Darrel W. Amundsen. *Caring and Curing: Health and Medicine in the Western Religious Traditions*. New York: Macmillan, 1986.

Reardon-Anderson, James. *The Study of Change: Chemistry in China, 1840–1949*. New York: Cambridge University Press, 1991.

Roeber, A. G., ed. *Ethnographies and Exchanges: Native Americans, Moravians and Catholics in Early North America*. University Park: Pennsylvania State University Press, 2008.

John Stenhouse

MITCHELL, MARIA

(1818–1889), astronomer. Born on Massachusetts' Nantucket Island, Mitchell was the daughter of a Quaker schoolmaster who also checked the accuracy of the chronometers of Nantucket's whaling fleet, a task in which Maria assisted. As librarian of the Nantucket Atheneum from 1836 to 1857, she had ample leisure time to pursue her astronomical studies. The precision of her observations attracted the notice of leading scientists, including William C. Bond, director of the Harvard Observatory, and Alexander Dallas Bache, head of the U.S. Coast Survey. Her discovery of a new comet in October 1847 and the plotting of its orbit gave her an international reputation in astronomy. She was awarded a gold medal by the king of Denmark for the discovery, the comet was named for her, and she was the first woman elected to the American Academy of Arts and Sciences in 1848. She was also admitted to the American Association for the Advancement of Science in 1850.

Leading scientists at Harvard, including George and William Bond of the Harvard College Observatory, helped introduce Mitchell to an international network of astronomers. Mitchell formed friendships with leading scientists in Europe, including a number of important women scientists, such as Mary Somerville. In 1865, although lacking a college degree herself, she joined the faculty of the newly opened Vassar Female College in Poughkeepsie, New York, where the founder, brewer Matthew Vassar, built her an observatory with a 12-inch telescope, the third largest in America at the time. Although refusing to give grades or take attendance, she won recognition as an inspiring teacher. Several of her students pursued careers in science or other disciplines. Although her true research interest was in comprehensively plotting the orbit of specific asteroids, Mitchell's research at Vassar was restricted by teaching and the scarcity of research funding. She consequently chose to research numerous small projects. She photographed solar phenomena daily and published on solar eclipses and surface changes of the planets.

Mitchell helped found the Association for the Advancement of Women in 1873 and was its president from 1875 to 1876. She was particularly interested in furthering the cause of women in science. "Nature made woman an observer," she observed; "the natural sciences are well fitted for woman's power of minute observation." In this statement and throughout her career, she argued against restricting women to a domestic role, believing them suited to the painstaking and detailed work of astronomical observation. Several of Mitchell's female students achieved prominence in scientific fields in the nineteenth century.

[*See also* **American Association for the Advancement of Science; Astronomy and Astrophysics; Bache, Alexander Dallas; Gender and Science; Higher Education and Science; Physics; Research and Development;** *and* **Science.**]

BIBLIOGRAPHY

Albers, Henry. *Maria Mitchell: A Life in Journals and Letters.* Clinton Corners, N.Y.: College Avenue Press, 2001.

Bergland, Renee. *Maria Mitchell and the Sexing of Science: An Astronomer among the American Romantics.* Boston: Beacon Press, 2008.

Coryell, Janet L. "Mitchell, Maria (1818–1889)." In *The History of Science in the United States: An Encyclopedia,* edited by Marc Rothenberg, pp. 355–356. New York and London: Garland Publishing, 2001.

Paul S. Boyer; updated by
Elspeth Knewstubb and
Hugh Richard Slotten

MOLECULAR BIOLOGY

What molecular biology is and what falls under its heading have been hotly disputed. Scientists and historians have argued that it is a set of tools or an umbrella term rather than a discipline in the narrow sense. Some place its beginnings in the 1930s and more specifically in the Rockefeller Foundation program promoting physical and chemical approaches in the life sciences. Others celebrate the elucidation of the double helical structure of DNA in 1953 by James Watson (1928–), an American postdoc, and the British researcher Francis Crick (1916–2004) as the origin of the new science. Molecular biology is sometimes taken to be synonymous with molecular genetics; other times it is understood in much broader terms, including all biological approaches on the molecular level and thus encompassing much of biochemistry. Biochemists have countered by exposing molecular biologists as biochemists practicing without a license. To complicate matters, historians have sometimes insisted on the existence of local traditions and national schools, while other times highlighting the international and collaborative space that was constitutive for the formation of the new biological science. These debates are part of the history of the field, although they complicate any straightforward account. Some people, tools, institutions, and scientific developments are nonetheless cited in most encompassing histories and the important contribution of American researchers, including initially several émigré scientists, is undisputed.

Model Systems and Technologies.

The introduction of phage as a model system for the study of genes, mutation, and biological replication by Max Delbrück (1906–1981), a German physicist who settled in America in 1937, and Linus Pauling's (1901–1994) physicochemical and model-building approach to the structure of biological macromolecules gave decisive impetus to the later development of molecular biology. Both researchers developed large research groups at Caltech that became magnets for researchers in the field. Delbrück, together with Italian émigré physicist Salvador Luria (1912–1991) from Indiana University, also founded the phage courses that were held annually at Cold Spring Harbor Laboratory from 1945 and attracted many researchers, including several physicists, who became leaders of the new biology. Further important contributions came from the genetic study of bacteria, including Joshua Lederberg's (1925–2008) and Edward Tatum's (1909–1975) discovery of bacterial conjugation in 1946, and from the study of viruses that became the model systems of choice for the investigation of molecular structure and function, while at the same time responding to medical and agricultural interests. Tatum, together with George Beadle (1903–1989), also formulated the one-gene, one-enzyme

hypothesis in 1951, building on large-scale genetic experiments with the fungus *Neurospora*.

Government funding for these projects, as well as a host of research falling under the broad heading of biophysics that included molecular investigations, increased dramatically during and after the war. This period also saw the introduction of new technologies such as electron microscopes, ultracentrifuges, electrophoretical apparatuses, radioisotopes, scintillation counters, and computers to the armamentarium of biologists. Prototypes of some of these instruments were developed before World War II, yet after the war they became standardized and commercialized. With new funds flowing into biological research, many laboratories were fitted out with the new equipment, which allowed researchers to probe molecular systems at the subcellular level.

DNA and Proteins.

The elucidation of the double helical structure of DNA spurred the search for the genetic code that linked the genetic information stored in the nucleic acids to the amino acid sequence of proteins. Russian émigré physicist and cosmologist George Gamow (1904–1968), then based at George Washington University, formed the RNA-Tie Club, which approached the question as a theoretical problem and used high-speed military computers for simulations. In the end the code was deciphered through the painstaking work of biochemists, including Marshall Nirenberg's (1927–2010) group at the National Institutes of Health (NIH), Har Gobind Khorana's (1922–2011) group at the University of Wisconsin–Madison, and Severo Ochoa's (1905–1993) group at New York University Medical School. Other relevant research areas included the crystallographic study of proteins, which was pursued at such institutions as Brookhaven National Laboratory, and the molecular study of muscle and nerve function. Dedicated departments of molecular biology started to be created in the early 1960s, as, for instance, the Department of Molecular Biology at Berkeley, which incorporated Wendell Stanley's (1904–1971) Virus Laboratory, founded a decade earlier. At other institutions where molecular biology was introduced as "new biology" in mainstream biological departments, such as in the newly founded Department of Biology at MIT, the term "molecular" did not necessarily appear in the title.

After the full determination of the genetic code and the demonstration of its universality, molecular biologists expanded their field of enquiry, taking up more complex problems like development and the nervous system, and correspondingly adopting eukaryotic model systems like drosophila, the mouse, or the round worm *Caenorhabditis elegans*. As part of Nixon's National Cancer Act of 1971, millions of dollars were injected into cancer virus research and the effects on mammalian cells, fueling the promise of medical breakthroughs built on molecular biology.

Genetic Engineering and Biotechnology.

With the isolation and characterization of a series of restriction enzymes to which American scientists contributed greatly, molecular biologists acquired new tools to cut and splice DNA from different organisms. When Paul Berg (1926–), a biochemist at the University of Stanford, together with his colleagues first managed to insert a piece of DNA from a tumor virus into the DNA of a phage containing bacterial genes, scientists raised concerns about the safety implications of such experiments. A letter published in the *Proceedings of the National Academy of Sciences* as well as in *Science* and *Nature* and signed by leading molecular biologists, including Paul Berg himself, called for a voluntary moratorium of splicing experiments and an international meeting to discuss the implications of such experiments (Paul Berg et al., *Proceedings of the National Academy of Sciences, USA* 71 [1974]: 2593–2594). This important meeting, held at Asilomar, California, in 1975 set out a series of guidelines, including physical and biological containments, under which recombinant DNA experiments could be resumed. The guidelines were adopted by the NIH and became the model for regulatory policies in other countries, although public concern initially remained high.

The first patents on the new technologies were granted in 1980. A large influx of venture capital led to the creation of a booming biotechnology industry, with the United States becoming a leader in the field. The automation of nucleic-acid sequencing, the development of polymerase chain reaction (PCR), which allowed the rapid and exponential amplification of specific sequences of DNA, developed by Kary Mullis (1944–) at Cetus Corporation in 1983, and new powerful computing technologies gave molecular biologists further decisive tools for work with DNA. In the late 1980s large government appropriations in the United States, together with funding from other countries, launched the collaborative project to sequence the full human genome. The same aim was pursued by Celera Genomics, a private company in Rockville, Maryland, created by Craig Venter (1946–). The full human genome sequence was announced in a common press conference hosted by President Bill Clinton in 2003. Since then, the focus on DNA as the "master molecule" as well as more generally the reductionist program of molecular biology have been challenged from various sides and developmental, evolutionary, and systems biological approaches are claiming their rights. Defenders argue that molecular biology was never just about molecular genetics and that molecular biological techniques are used in all biological fields and are here to stay.

[*See also* **Agricultural Technology; Biochemistry; Biological Sciences; Biotechnology; Cancer; Chemistry; Computer Science; Delbrück, Max; DNA Sequencing; Ethics and Medicine; Genetics and Genetic Engineering; Germ Theory of Disease; Human Genome Project; Instruments of Science; Lederberg, Joshua; Medicine; Medicine and Technology; National Institutes of Health; Pauling, Linus; Physics; Research and Development; Rockefeller Institute, The; Science; Stanley, Wendell Meredith; Technology;** *and* **Watson, James D.**]

BIBLIOGRAPHY

Cairns, John, Gunther S. Stent, and James D. Watson. *Phage and the Origins of Molecular Biology*. Cold Spring Harbor, N.Y.: Cold Spring Harbor Laboratory Press, 1966. This book, reissued in 2007 in a centennial edition, started the debate on the origins of molecular biology.

Kay, Lily E. *The Molecular Vision of Life: Caltech, the Rockefeller Foundation, and the Rise of the New Biology*. New York: Oxford University Press, 1993. Examines the role of the Rockefeller Foundation, Caltech, and the cultural climate of the time in the formation of molecular biology.

Kevles, Daniel J., and Leroy Hood, eds. *The Code of Codes: Scientific and Social Issues in the Human Genome Project*. Cambridge, Mass.: Harvard University Press, 1992. This is a useful starting point for the exploration of the early history of the human genome project. Contains vision statements by various major players in the genomic field as well as essays on ethical, legal, and societal issues.

Morange, Michel. *A History of Molecular Biology*. Cambridge, Mass.: Harvard University Press, 1998. An overview of the main developments of the field, aimed at a general readership.

Soraya de Chadarevian

MORGAN, LEWIS HENRY

(1818–1881), anthropologist. Lewis Henry Morgan played a leading role in establishing anthropology in the United States and gained worldwide influence through his writings. Born near Aurora, New York, Morgan attended Cayuga Academy and Union College. He read law and was admitted to the bar. In 1844, he moved to practice in Rochester, New York. In 1862, his investment in railroads, mining, and iron smelting enabled him to give up his practice in favor of devoting his time to scientific pursuits.

Interested in the Indians of his area, Morgan became an honorary Seneca in 1847. Morgan chiefly studied kinship, one of the two central topics around which anthropology arose (the other being "primitive" religion). Indeed, he largely invented kinship as an anthropological subject, making it the focus of his three major books. *The League of the Iroquois* (1851) documented the matrilineal family relationships underlying the Iroquois's political structure. Despite considerable research done since the publication of Morgan's work, it remained, in the early twenty-first century, arguably the best single ethnographic account of the Iroquois people.

In 1855 Morgan first visited Marquette, Michigan, on business and subsequently developed an interest in the behavior of the beaver. He published *The American Beaver and His Works* in 1868, the result of several years' study. For decades, this remained the most important book on beavers. While Morgan was researching beavers, he also began work on a comparative study of kinship that resulted in his major contribution to anthropology, the massive *Systems of Consanguinity and Affinity of the Human Family* (1871), published by the Smithsonian Institution. In this book Morgan compared kinship systems around the world, arguing that American Indian systems were similar not only among themselves but also to kinship systems in Asia. He argued that this proved the Asian origins of North American Indians. In this work, Morgan created most of the basic analytic tools used in kinship analysis and he is generally credited with establishing this area of anthropological inquiry. *Ancient Society* (1877) integrated Morgan's kinship studies into an evolutionary framework, drawing all societies into a single story of progress.

Writing at a time when the great antiquity of human history had suddenly become evident, Morgan theorized a progressive series of kinship stages, from "primitive promiscuity" through matriarchy and patriarchy to monogamy, thus thoroughly historicizing contemporary marriage norms. This work appealed to a diverse range of groups and individuals, including feminists; the evolutionary theorist Charles Darwin; the conservative English legal historian Sir Henry Maine; and Karl Marx and Friedrich Engels, who believed that Morgan's evolutionary kinship model strengthened their materialist view of history. Engels's widely read *The Origin of the Family, Private Property, and the State* (1884) owed much to *Ancient Society* and added to the fame of Morgan's work.

[*See also* **Anthropology; Evolution, Theory of; Smithsonian Institution;** *and* **Social Sciences.**]

BIBLIOGRAPHY

Tooker, Elizabeth. "The Structure of the Iroquois League: Lewis H. Morgan's Research and

Observations." *Ethnohistory* 30, no. 3 (1983): 141–154. Examines Morgan's collected papers to understand how he came to collect the ethnographic data for and write several key chapters in *The League of the Iroquois.*

Tooker, Elizabeth. "Morgan, Lewis Henry (1818–1881)." In *The History of Science in the United States: An Encyclopedia,* edited by Marc Rothenberg, p. 357. New York and London: Garland Publishing, 2001.

Trautmann, Thomas R. *Lewis Henry Morgan and the Invention of Kinship.* 2d ed. Lincoln: University of Nebraska Press, 2008. First published in 1987. This edition has a new introduction and appendices by the author.

Thomas Trautmann; updated by
Elspeth Knewstubb and
Hugh Richard Slotten

MORGAN, THOMAS HUNT

(1866–1945), zoologist, embryologist, geneticist, and Nobel laureate; received the Nobel Prize in Medicine or Physiology in 1933. Morgan grew up in Lexington, Kentucky, in a distinguished southern family. After undergraduate studies in zoology at the State College of Kentucky, he obtained a PhD at Johns Hopkins in 1890 for work on the development of sea spiders. Morgan's first job was at Bryn Mawr College (1891–1904), where he taught and supported the work of Nettie M. Stevens on chromosomal sex determination. He spent the rest of his academic career at Columbia University (1904–1928) and the California Institute of Technology (1928–1945). During the summers he conducted research at the Marine Biological Laboratory at Woods Hole, Massachusetts. In 1904 Morgan married Lilian Vaughan Sampson, a cytologist and embryologist he met while she studied at Bryn Mawr.

A champion of the experimental approach to biological research, Morgan first worked on differentiation in embryos (*The Development of the Frog's Egg: An Introduction to Experimental Embryology,* 1897). He also published on regeneration and evolution. But he is best known for work on variation and inheritance in the fruit fly

(*Drosophila melanogaster*) that he carried out at Columbia University in collaboration with A. H. Sturtevant, C. B. Bridges, and H. J. Muller, students and members of the famous "Fly Room."

Hoping to study sudden changes in body form that had recently been named "mutations" to research evolutionary change, Morgan started breeding fruit flies and examining changes in their appearance. He discovered that certain characteristics appeared only in one sex. He argued that this pattern could be explained by postulating that chromosomes carried certain factors or genes that influenced those characteristics and these factors separated in Mendelian fashion.

By analyzing the patterns of inheritance of additional visible traits and postulating the underlying chromosomal mechanisms that could account for those patterns, Morgan and his research group developed the chromosomal theory of Mendelian inheritance. This theory stated that the patterns of inheritance of the traits they analyzed in the fruit fly could be explained by the hypothesis that chromosomes are the physical basis of inheritance and postulating that the genes are aligned in a linear fashion in each chromosome. Morgan, Sturtevant, Bridges, and Muller put forward this theory in *The Mechanism of Mendelian Heredity* (1915). Morgan presented further developments in *The Physical Basis of Heredity* (1919) and *The Theory of the Gene* (1926). Morgan remained aware that a full explanation of variation and inheritance, as well as central issues in evolution, would require better understanding of development and thus continued to work on fundamental problems of embryology (*Experimental Embryology,* 1927; *Embryology and Genetics,* 1934).

A central figure in the establishment of experimental genetics and embryology in the early twentieth century, Morgan published over 20 books and about 370 research articles. He received numerous honors and became the president of several professional scientific societies, including the National Academy of Sciences (1927–1931) and the American Association for the Advancement of Science (1930).

[*See also* **American Association for the Advancement of Science; Biological Sciences;**

Evolution, Theory of; Genetics and Genetic Engineering; National Academy of Sciences; Nobel Prize in Biomedical Research; *and* Zoology.]

BIBLIOGRAPHY

Allen, Garland. *Thomas Hunt Morgan: The Man and His Science.* Princeton, N.J.: Princeton University Press, 1978.

Kohler, Robert. *Lords of the Fly: Drosophila Genetics and the Experimental Life.* Chicago: University of Chicago Press, 1994.

Maienschein, Jane. *Transforming Traditions in American Biology, 1880–1915.* Baltimore: Johns Hopkins University Press, 1991.

Marga Vicedo

MORRILL LAND GRANT ACT

This law, which provided land grants to the states for the founding of colleges to teach "agriculture and the mechanic arts," was first introduced in Congress in 1857 by Representative Justin Morrill, a Vermont Whig (later Republican). Morrill was convinced that existing colleges were failing to provide practical education for the nation's farmers and workers, whose productivity might be greatly improved through the diffusion of "useful knowledge." Although Morrill's first bill encountered strong Southern opposition and was ultimately vetoed by President James Buchanan, a similar bill was passed in 1862 after Southern secession and was signed into law by President Abraham Lincoln.

The Morrill Act entitled each state to a grant of 30 thousand acres of federal land for each member of Congress. Funds from the sale of these lands were to be used as a permanent endowment for "at least one college where the leading object shall be, without excluding other scientific and classical studies, to teach such branches of learning as are related to agriculture and the mechanic arts." The states themselves had authority to choose their parcels of federal land, arrange for their sales, and designate the re-cipients of the income. States chose existing universities (as in Wisconsin), founded new flagship universities (California), or named special agricultural and mechanical colleges (Indiana). Some Southern states (which received grants after the Civil War) split the funds among separate agricultural and mechanical (A&M) colleges for whites and blacks.

Most land-grant colleges struggled at first, lacking both students and a body of useful scientific knowledge to teach. Rising demand for engineering education and a surge in high-school graduates, however, eventually caused these institutions to prosper. They were assisted materially by two subsequent acts passed in part because of lobbying efforts by the colleges themselves. The Hatch Act (1887) provided federal funds for agricultural experiment stations, which considerably furthered agricultural science, and the Second Morrill Act (1890) legislated annual federal appropriations.

The Morrill Act shaped American higher education in important respects. It promoted the equal standing of practical and liberal studies; encouraged publicly supported higher education by inducing states to found universities and materially assist their development; and fostered a system of agricultural education, research, and dissemination that ultimately brought useful knowledge to the farmers Justin Morrill had originally sought to help.

[*See also* Agricultural Education and Extension; Agricultural Experiment Stations; Agricultural Technology; Agriculture, U.S. Department of; Engineering; High Schools, Science Education in; Higher Education and Science; *and* Research and Development.]

BIBLIOGRAPHY

Eddy, Edward D., Jr. *Colleges for Our Land and Time: The Land-Grant Idea in American Education.* New York: Harper, 1957.

Geiger, Roger L., ed. *The Land-Grant Act and American Higher Education, History of Higher Education Annual.* Piscataway, N.J.: Transaction Publishers, 1998.

Williams, Roger L. *The Origins of Federal Support for Higher Education: George W. Atherton and the Land-Grant College Movement.* University Park: Pennsylvania State University Press, 1991.

Roger L. Geiger

MORSE, SAMUEL F. B.

(1791–1872), artist and inventor. Samuel Finley Breese Morse was born in Charlestown, Massachusetts, the son of Jedediah Morse, a Congregational pastor and author of the first book on geography printed in the United States, *Geography Made Easy* (1784). Morse was educated at Yale University from 1808 to 1810. As well as studying art, he attended lectures on electricity and spent one vacation assisting with electrical experiments. After Yale, Morse began his career as an artist, studying painting at London's Royal Academy (1811–1815), but returning home when his father was no longer able to support him abroad. Morse is, however, best known for his work in telegraphy.

After settling in New York City in 1823, Morse helped to found the National Academy of Design, serving as its first president from its foundation in 1826 until 1845. In 1832 he became professor of painting and sculpture at the University of the City of New York. In the same year he drafted his first ideas for an electric telegraph. He worked alone on his system for several years, constructing his first electrical writing telegraph in 1835 in his classroom. He showed this to friends, including Leonard Gale, a professor of chemistry and geology. Gale suggested several improvements to the design and Morse continued his experiments. On 4 September 1837, Morse, with Gale's assistance, demonstrated the sending of messages over a wire of 1800 feet.

Congressional interest in establishing a semaphore telegraphy system led Morse to propose his electrical system as a superior alternative. In 1837, as a result of his successful experiment with Gale, Morse acquired the assistance of a former student, Alfred Vail (1807–1859), a member of the Mechanics Institute whose father, Judge Stephen Vail, supported their work at his Speedwell Iron Works in Morristown, New Jersey. Alfred Vail, who converted Morse's crude instrument designs into commercially practical devices, deserves credit as a coinventor of the American telegraph. He may also have revised the telegraph code, named for Morse, into its common form. With additional help from chemist Gale and physicist Joseph Henry—and $30,000 from Congress—Morse and Vail built the first telegraph line, between Washington, D.C., and Baltimore. After its completion in 1844, Congress refused to purchase Morse's patents or pay for additional lines. Morse and his associates, who included former Postmaster General Amos Kendall, subsequently sold the patent rights to private companies. Morse played only a small role in the subsequent development of the telegraph business, although he continued to defend his patents against legal challenge.

[*See also* **Electricity and Electrification; Geography; Henry, Joseph;** *and* **Telegraph.**]

BIBLIOGRAPHY

Huurdeman, Anton A. *The Worldwide History of Telecommunications.* Hoboken, N.J.: John Wiley & Sons, 2003.

Mabee, Carleton. *The American Leonardo: A Life of Samuel F. B. Morse.* New York: Alfred A. Knopf, 1943.

Silverman, Kenneth. *Lightning Man: The Accursed Life of Samuel F. B. Morse.* New York: Alfred A. Knopf, 2003.

Staiti, Paul J. *Samuel F. B. Morse.* Cambridge, U.K., and New York: Cambridge University Press, 1989.

Paul Israel;
updated by Elspeth Knewstubb

MOTOR VEHICLES

The pioneer mechanical engineer Oliver Evans built a steam-powered amphibious dredge in 1805, but the first significant American experiments with mechanized vehicles came in the 1820s. These heavy, smoky, and unreliable steam-driven vehicles ran on rails, which were smoother than any pavement and guided the vehicles through turns, but sharply limited their utility.

Other inventors, notably J. K. Fisher and Richard Dudgeon, built smaller, more reliable steam-powered vehicles around 1860, potential replacements for horses for at least some transportation functions, especially in cities where paved streets provided good surfaces. When lighter, higher-pressure steam engines first appeared in the 1870s, the rate of experimentation increased, although urban residents in particular worried about accidents, smoke, and boiler explosions and secured regulations that slowed development. Popular resistance, marked by occasional riots, led to outright prohibitions on steamers in some cities.

In the 1880s European inventors such as Karl Benz, Gottlieb Daimler, and Jean-Joseph Lenoir built the first gasoline-powered vehicles with internal combustion engines, which a few wealthy Americans imported. The *Chicago Times-Herald* organized a race in 1895 that generated enormous publicity for the new internal combustion technology. It inspired Charles and Frank Duryea, Elwood Haynes, Ransom E. Olds, and others to become the first American manufacturers of gasoline-powered vehicles.

Despite the growing popularity of the internal combustion engine, electric and steam alternatives remained the more popular options before 1903. In 1897, for example, the Pope Manufacturing Company—the nation's largest manufacturer of bicycles—led the nation in sales with its new Columbia electric vehicle, which had the distinction of being the first stock-model motor vehicle in an era otherwise devoted to made-to-order sales. Then, in 1900, sales of steam-powered vehicles moved into the lead, claiming 1,681 sales versus 1,575 for electric and 936 for gasoline. Only in 1903, when the Olds Motor Vehicle Company claimed the sales lead with its famous curved-dash Oldsmobile, did gasoline-powered vehicles gain the upper hand over steam and electric alternatives—a lead they never relinquished.

Regardless of engine type, nearly all early automakers merely strapped engines on carriages originally designed for horses. From a dizzying variety of body types through the 1890s, including hansoms, runabouts, stanhopes, phaetons, surreys, and victorias, by the turn of the century the industry had finally settled on a surrey-style, tiller-guided vehicle widely known as the "horseless carriage." The industry changed again after the introduction of the 1901 Mercedes, which combined a variety of advances—including a front-mounted motor, improved gearbox, and pressed-steel chassis, among others—into the first recognizably modern example of automotive design.

Most Mercedes-style automobiles were prohibitively expensive, however, leaving those at the lower end of the market to choose from among various types of underpowered (and cheaply built) "high-wheelers" and runabouts. Then, in late 1908 Henry Ford introduced the Model T, a durable Mercedes-style car that was reliable enough for poor rural roads. As the price of the Model T fell, it slowly and almost single-handedly changed the luxury status of cars. After experimenting with various high-volume production methods through the early 1910s, Ford's company introduced its first moving assembly lines in 1913 in its Highland Park, Michigan, factory, an innovation that, combined with other already established practices, exponentially improved labor productivity. As a result of these improvements, which Ford described as "mass production," Ford was able to cut Model T prices from $850 in 1908 to just $265 in 1922 (under $4,000 in 2014 dollars)—despite a high rate of inflation after World War I. Ford sold over 15 million Model T's before 1927, doing as much as all other automakers combined to put America on wheels. By 1925, for the first time, a majority of American families possessed cars, nearly half of which were Model T's.

Beginning in the mid-1920s, the Ford Motor Company fell from dominance in the face of competition from the General Motors Corporation (GM), founded in 1908 through the consolidation of several independent auto companies. Alfred P. Sloan, who became GM's president in 1923, turned to aggressive marketing after he realized that GM could not compete in price. His company extended customer credit through the GM Acceptance Corporation (1919) and, under the marketing slogan "A car for every purse and purpose," offered a variety of brands marketed for different audiences, from the plebeian Chevrolet to the patrician Cadillac. Brand marketing and annual model changes—another Sloan innovation—relied on the styling genius of one-time Hollywood car customizer Harley Earl, GM's head designer. (Earl would later introduce the ubiquitous tailfins that characterized 1950s cars.) The stodgy Model T, whose design failed to keep pace with GM's emphasis on attractive styling, could not compete with such marketing. Worse, Ford failed to adapt the Model T either to the rapid spread of smooth roads in rural America or to the new "closed car" era. Rather than following the lead of his competitors and redesigning the Model T as a closed car that capitalized on the performance improvements that smooth roads allowed, Ford responded to demand for enclosed cabins by adding a heavy, boxy cabin to an unmodified Model T chassis. The results left much to be desired from both performance and stylistic angles.

The Model T's successor, the Model A, initially fared much better, helping Ford reclaim—for a few years—its sales lead over GM. Where Ford held the Model A's design static, however, GM continued to introduce stylistic and technological improvements to the Chevrolet, helping it reclaim the sales lead in 1931. Eventually, Ford and the other major car company, Chrysler (founded in 1924 by Walter P. Chrysler [1875–1940]), adopted GM-style marketing.

The automobile contributed to massive social changes between the two world wars. The 1920s saw a boom in suburban and resort housing, as cars made outlying areas near big cities more accessible. They helped end the isolation of rural Americans, allowing farmers access to markets and facilitating rural–urban migration, including the well-known movement of Dust Bowl farmers to California during the Great Depression. They allowed poor blacks and whites from impoverished rural areas to move to booming northern industrial cities. Providing private space, cars encouraged personal freedom. Blacks could escape the stigma of racial segregation enforced on southern railroads and buses—although Jim Crow practices continued in roadside accommodations and restaurants. Court-ing adolescents could evade the social oversight of family and neighbors. Workers in milltowns could choose from workplaces spread over wider areas.

The auto increased access to consumer goods at, for example, the first self-service grocery store, Piggly-Wiggly (Memphis, 1916), and the first mall, Country Club Plaza (Kansas City, 1923). The drive-in culture extended to movies (Camden, New Jersey, 1933), restaurants (Dallas, 1921), and banks (Ventura, California, 1931). The first "motel" (motor hotel) opened in San Luis Obispo, California, in 1926. The Reverend Robert Schuller even opened a drive-in church in Garden Grove, California, in 1954, which he described as "a shopping center for Jesus Christ." The first restaurant chains (White Tower and A&W Root Beer, 1924) catered to a motoring public looking for predictability in food and speed in service. The new roadside businesses borrowed plastic architecture from amusement parks and ignored regional vernaculars. Shell-shape gas stations, milk bottle–shape ice cream stands, and duck-shape restaurants proliferated in the 1920s and 1930s.

The automobile also introduced traffic problems and hazards. By 1926 cars had become the fifth leading cause of fatalities, with most victims pedestrians or children. By the end of the twentieth century, cars had killed more than 2 million Americans. The big-city traffic jam emerged by 1914. Cities lost one-third of their street space to parked cars and by the 1930s were razing low-occupancy downtown buildings for the reliable revenue that parking lots generated. In 1914 Cleveland introduced the first traffic light and Detroit police sergeant Harry Jackson built the first octagonal stop sign. Using stop signs to create high-speed boulevards and adding progressively timed lights briefly improved urban traffic flow. When traffic jams worsened in the 1920s, cities turned to street widening and arterial highway construction. When those improvements failed to solve their problems, cities began in the second half of the 1930s to make tentative plans for limited-access "expressway" systems. Rural interests initially dominated road policy, however. At both the federal and the state levels, governments funded farm-to-market roads that rarely served cities or suburbs. The federal highway system, which grew rapidly in the 1920s, had by the late 1930s become choked with traffic generated by uncontrolled roadside businesses.

In this context, highway planners turned to the limited-access highway as a better long-term solution to traffic-flow problems. Well before the advent of the automobile, Frederick Law Olmsted had pioneered the grade separation of cross traffic in New York's Central Park (1857) and limited access to high-speed carriage arteries such as Brooklyn's Eastern Parkway (1868). At the end of the nineteenth century, Boston's Charles River Speedway built slowdown exit lanes for speedy carriage drivers. The Bronx River Parkway (1922), a toll route, adapted these high-speed design elements to automobile travel. New York highway builder Robert Moses (1888–1981) created a massive commuting road system on Long Island in the 1920s. New York City's West Side Highway, built in 1927, was the first elevated urban road. New Jersey added another element, constructing the first cloverleaf interchange (Woodbridge, 1929). Massachusetts engineer Franklin Pillsbury designed the first beltway (Route 128 outside Boston, planned in 1930, finished in 1949). Using Works Progress Administration funds, Connecticut built the first intercity parkway in 1937. Pennsylvania borrowed parkway techniques for its 1940 turnpike, the prototype for the state toll roads of the 1950s and for the interstate highway system begun in 1956.

As the automobile transformed American life, other motorized vehicles had profound effects as well. By 1940 growing fleets of buses were carrying passengers within cities and on longer trips, 4.1 million trucks were vying with the railroads for transporting freight, and the nation's 1.5 million tractors were revolutionizing U.S. agriculture. Motorcycles, although never a major form of motorized transport, proved popular with police and open-air enthusiasts.

Although World War II halted the production of automobiles for civilian use, the production of motor vehicles for the military surged. Major Detroit firms produced 49,000 tanks, 126,000 armored cars, and 2,600,000 trucks (as well as 27,000 airplanes and nearly 6 million guns) during the war. Moreover, confiscated Ford and GM overseas factories produced more than 70 percent of Germany's trucks. Ford faltered badly at wartime production, however, leading the U.S. government to force Henry Ford out in favor of his grandson, Henry Ford II.

By war's end the big-three auto firms, GM, Ford, and Chrysler, had become an oligopoly because most smaller firms had failed in the Depression of the 1930s. Henry Kaiser, Preston Tucker, and other independent producers tried but failed to introduce new automobile brands after the war. The oligopoly concentrated on marketing and increasing engine power in the postwar decades, choking off European innovations like front-wheel drive, radial tires, and disk brakes. Consumers could buy cars with 42-inch tailfins, 58 pounds of chrome, and more than five hundred horsepower. Germany began to export Volkswagens to the United States in 1958, controlling 8 percent of the American market with a compact car of the kind that Detroit refused to make. New (but short-lived) compacts, like the Ford Falcon, blunted the Volkswagen threat.

The antiauthority movements that characterized the 1960s affected the nation's car culture. Urban activists blocked the completion of many inner-city interstate highways, just as the economic center of American metropolises was shifting from downtown to the beltway. Muckraking attorney Ralph Nader, noting how fatalities to automobile occupants had soared in the postwar decades, attacked the auto industry on safety grounds. Detroit was slow to install brakes adequate for high horsepower and resisted seat belts and air bags for nearly 40 years. Quality control faltered and hazardous design became all too common. As American cars guzzled more gasoline, smog became an urban health problem. Los Angeles biochemist Arie Haagen-Smit demonstrated the relationship between auto emissions and smog in 1950. After much lobbying by environmentalists, Congress passed the Clean Air Act (1970), which banned leaded gasoline and required catalytic converters, significantly reducing some pollutants.

In the 1970s, the Detroit oligopoly faced the challenge of Japanese car makers, which began to export highly reliable, fuel-efficient models to the

United States in large numbers, capturing up to a third of the American market. In a decade of oil shortages, Detroit could not match the Japanese in cost, quality, or fuel efficiency. Chrysler escaped bankruptcy only by a government bailout and president Lee Iacocca's success at marketing.

Import taxes and quotas somewhat protected the battered domestic auto industry, and the 1980s brought a revival. Ford responded first, marketing the German-designed, Japanese-engineered Escort and Taurus (also German-engineered) in the mid-1980s. Chrysler also rebounded in the 1980s, adopting Japanese design and production techniques. GM continued to falter through the 1980s, however, losing 25 percent of its domestic market and laying off 74 thousand workers. Even when successful, the domestic industry's response to the Japanese import boom took its toll. Imported cars, Japanese-style "lean production" techniques, and the outsourcing of work, especially to Mexico, turned much of the Middle West into a "rust belt."

As the twentieth century ended, the United States remained the most auto- (and petroleum-) dependent nation in the world. The economy was increasingly centered in auto-dependent "edge cities." By 1990 the two-car family was the norm and annual mileage per car was up, increasing gasoline imports. The 1950s love of heavy cars returned, with four-wheel-drive cars, pickup trucks, and vans becoming popular. Traffic jams and air pollution worsened in major cities. In 1994, Seattle planners reported a 120 percent increase in traffic and Los Angeles commuters reported a doubling of travel time over the previous 10 years. The statistics did reveal one bright spot, however: as auto safety standards grew more rigorous, seat belt use and airbags became more common, drunken drivers faced increasing social stigma, and the grim annual toll of traffic fatalities decreased.

[*See also* **Agricultural Technology; Bicycles and Bicycling; Dust Bowl; Electricity and Electrification; Environmentalism; Environmental Protection Agency; Ford, Henry; Global Warming; Highway System; Internal Combustion Engine; Machinery and Manufacturing; Military, Science and Technology and the; Petroleum and Petrochemicals; Public Health; Railroads; Roads and Turnpikes, Early;** *and* **Steam Power.**]

BIBLIOGRAPHY

Bardou, Pierre, Jean-Jacques Chinaron, Patrick M. Fridenson, and James M. Laux. *The Automobile Revolution: The Impact of an Industry.* Chapel Hill: University of North Carolina Press, 1982.

Berger, Michael. *The Devil Wagon in God's Country.* Hamden, Conn.: Archon Books, 1979.

Caro, Robert A. *The Power Broker: Robert Moses and the Fall of New York.* New York: Vintage Books, 1975.

Gutfreund, Owen D. *Twentieth-Century Sprawl: Highways and the Reshaping of the American Landscape.* Oxford: Oxford University Press, 2004.

Halberstam, David. *The Reckoning.* New York: William Morrow, 1986.

Jennings, Jan, ed. *Roadside America: The Automobile in Design and Culture.* Ames: Iowa State University Press, 1990.

Ladd, Brian. *Autophobia: Love and Hate in the Automobile Age.* Chicago: University of Chicago Press, 2008.

McCarthy, Tom. *Auto Mania: Cars, Consumers, and the Environment.* New Haven, Conn.: Yale University Press, 2007.

McShane, Clay. *Down the Asphalt Path: American Cities and the Automobile.* New York: Columbia University Press, 1995.

National Automobile Chamber of Commerce. *Automobile Facts and Figures.* Detroit: Author, 1921–present.

Scharff, Virginia. *Taking the Wheel: Women and the Coming of the Motor Age.* New York: Free Press, 1991.

U.S. Department of Transportation. *Personal Travel in the U.S.* Washington, D.C.: Author, 1986.

Volti, Rudi. *Cars and Culture: The Life Story of a Technology.* Westport, Conn.: Greenwood Press, 2004.

Clay McShane and
Christopher W. Wells

MUIR, JOHN

(1838–1914), naturalist and a founder of the environmental movement. John Muir was born near

Edinburgh, Scotland. His family immigrated to America in 1849, settling on a farm in southeastern Wisconsin. After a grim childhood and adolescence, Muir in 1861 escaped to the state university at Madison, where he studied botany and geology. Years of travel through Canada and the United States followed. On a long hike in 1867 he intuited the central insight of his life: the need for human forbearance toward nature.

His initial encounter with California's Yosemite Valley, in 1869, moved him profoundly; he was thereafter identified with Yosemite and the Sierra Nevada Mountains. Independent geological work on the valley's glacial origins led to his first published articles in the 1870s. He kept detailed notebooks recording plants, birds, geological formations, and other aspects of the natural environment. After a hiatus for family and farming, he resumed writing and conservation work in 1889. Muir cofounded the Sierra Club in 1892 and served as its president until his death.

In the intramural battles of the nascent conservation movement, Muir led the amateur, preservationist wing, which fought both with and against the professional, utilitarian faction under Gifford Pinchot. Possessed of sparkling if verbose charm, Muir formed friendships with powerful men (such as Theodore Roosevelt and the financier E. H. Harriman), which proved useful to his causes. His passionate nature writings—in the tradition of Henry David Thoreau and implicitly pantheistic—gained him wide attention and support. Muir's protracted final battle, to forestall the Hetch Hetchy reservoir within Yosemite National Park, ended in a loss for the preservationists.

[*See also* Audubon, John James; Botany; Carson, Rachel; Conservation Movement; Ecology; Environmentalism; Environmental Protection Agency; Forestry Technology and Lumbering; Forest Service, U.S.; Geology; National Park System; *and* Sierra Club.]

BIBLIOGRAPHY

Cohen, Michael P. *The Pathless Way: John Muir and American Wilderness.* Madison: University of Wisconsin Press, 1984.

Fox, Stephen. *The American Conservation Movement: John Muir and His Legacy.* Madison: University of Wisconsin Press, 1985.

Worster, Donald. *A Passion for Nature: The Life of John Muir.* New York: Oxford University Press, 2008.

Stephen Fox

MULLER, HERMANN J.

(1890–1967), geneticist and Nobel laureate. Known especially for his contributions to Drosophila genetics and his activism on the hazards of radiation, Hermann Joseph Muller received the Nobel Prize in 1946 for his discovery that X-rays cause genetic mutations.

Muller began his career in Thomas Hunt Morgan's fruit fly laboratory at Columbia University in New York, contributing to its early work on gene mapping in *Drosophila melanogaster*. After receiving his PhD in 1916, he moved to the Rice Institute in Texas and then the University of Texas, where he carried out foundational research on genes, their function, and modification. Muller's work on gene crossovers, modifier genes, and especially X-ray radiation had profound implications for theories of genetics. His findings were made possible by his technical innovations, including new and complex Drosophila crossing schemes, and combinations of mutants that allowed researchers to study gene function.

Muller's interest in problems of modifying and controlling heredity was abundantly reflected in his concern with eugenics, specifically a socialist eugenics that, he argued, would produce more efficient means for controlling human evolution. The backdrop to his genetics and its politics was a restless trajectory across institutions in the United States, Europe, and the Soviet Union, propelled partly by several difficult personal relationships and his political radicalism. As an outspoken socialist he was unable to stay longer than a few years at the University of Texas, and in 1932 he moved first to Berlin and then to Leningrad. The imprisonment and execution of several colleagues soon embittered his admiration for Communism, and

Muller left the Soviet Union—first for the Spanish Civil War and then for a research job in Edinburgh. At the outbreak of World War II, Muller moved once again back to the United States, where, helped by the Rockefeller Foundation and many eminent and sympathetic colleagues, he finally joined the staff of Indiana University, where he remained for the rest of his career.

The atomic age brought new attention to Muller's genetic research and political activism. Although embroiled in Cold War politics—on one hand an outspoken critic of Stalin and on the other frequently mistrusted as a Communist sympathizer—he was also now a Nobel laureate and scientist of considerable status. Alongside his continued work on Drosophila genetics, he engaged in public debates over the deployment of atomic energy and the effects of radiation on humans. In the last years of his life he remained a controversial voice on issues of the control of reproduction and gene manipulation.

[*See also* **Biological Sciences; Eugenics; Genetics and Genetic Engineering; Nobel Prize in Biomedical Research; Nuclear Power; Science: 1914 to 1945;** *and* **Science: Since 1945.**]

BIBLIOGRAPHY

Carlson, E. A. *Genes, Radiation, and Society: The Life and Work of H.J. Muller.* Ithaca, N.Y.: Cornell University Press, 1981.

Paul, Diane B. "H. J. Muller, Communism, and the Cold War." *Genetics* 119 (1988): 223–225.

Jenny Bangham

MULLIKEN, ROBERT S.

(1896–1986), chemist and Nobel laureate. Robert Sanderson Mulliken received an undergraduate degree in chemistry from the Massachusetts Institute of Technology (MIT) in 1917 and earned a PhD in chemistry working under the supervision of the physical chemist William Draper Harkins at the University of Chicago in 1921. After appoint-

ments at Harvard University and New York University, he returned to the University of Chicago as associate professor in 1928. He became full professor in 1931, was elected to the National Academy of Sciences in 1936, collaborated during World War II in the Manhattan Project as director of the Information Division, and was scientific attaché of the U.S. Embassy in London during 1955.

Mulliken's recognition came late in life. In the 1960s he received five awards from the American Chemical Society and was awarded the Nobel Prize in Chemistry in 1966 for his "fundamental work concerning chemical bonds and the electronic structure of molecules by the molecular orbital method."

Together with Linus Pauling, Mulliken was one of the founders of quantum chemistry in the United States. Appropriating proposals of German physicist Friedrich Hund, he was instrumental in the definition of basic concepts and methods to study molecular structure and spectra, as well as in shaping its language and nomenclature.

Contrary to Pauling's valence bond approach, which was built on the chemical notion of bonds uniting atoms in molecules and which extended the classical structural theory to the quantum mechanical realm, based on notions introduced by the German physicists Walter Heitler and Fritz London, Mulliken's molecular orbital approach gave prominence to the role of electrons, to which were assigned individual quantum numbers and which encircled more than one atom in what were called molecular orbitals, in accounting for the structure and stability of molecules. Contrary to Pauling's approach, which followed "the ideology of chemistry," Mulliken's followed "the ideology of physics," to borrow Mulliken's own words.

Although the reaction of the chemical community was initially in favor of the valence bond approach, the molecular orbital approach proved better adapted to computer programs and the move from semiempirical toward wholly theoretical (ab initio) calculations. In fact, the contributions of Mulliken's group were essential to bringing mathematics and computers into the realm of quantum chemical practice. They also played a central role in the internationalization of quantum chemistry, a discipline that was neither physics nor chemistry, but which developed at the borderline of these two disciplines, with chief incursions into mathematics and biology.

[*See also* Biological Sciences; Chemistry; Computer Science; Manhattan Project; Mathematics and Statistics; Molecular Biology; National Academy of Sciences; Nobel Prize in Biomedical Research; Pauling, Linus; Physics; *and* Quantum Theory.]

BIBLIOGRAPHY

Gavroglu, Kostas, and Ana Simões. *Neither Physics nor Chemistry. A History of Quantum Chemistry.* Cambridge, Mass.: MIT Press, 2012.

Ransil, Bernard J. *Robert S. Mulliken: Life of a Scientist: An Autobiographical Account of the Development of Molecular Orbital Theory with an Introductory Memoir by Friedrich Hund.* Berlin: Springer-Verlag, 1989.

Simões, Ana. "Mulliken, Robert Sanderson." *New Dictionary of Scientific Biography* 23 (2008): 209–214.

Ana Simões

MUMFORD, LEWIS

(1895–1990), social philosopher, architectural critic, and moral reformer. Mumford was born in New York City and educated in its public schools. As a high school student, he intended to become an engineer. Although he made a different career choice and became a writer, he always maintained his interest in technology, invention, and science. In a succession of bold and brilliant books, beginning with *The Story of Utopias* (1922), and in his *Sky Line* column for the *New Yorker* magazine, he did more than any other American writer to heighten awareness of the role of architecture, cities, and technology in history and everyday life.

One of Mumford's most important early publications in the history of technology was a 1930 article titled "The Drama of Machines" in *Scribner's Magazine*. In 1934 he published a landmark examination of the relationship between western civilization and machinery, *Technics and Civilization*. This work grew out of contemporary debates surrounding the use of technology in World War I and the role of machinery in society. Mumford was fascinated with such recent inventions as the radio and airplane. But he also worried about the dehumanizing impact of automation. *Technics and Civilization* questioned conventional assumptions about the relationship between social progress and science and technology.

In addition to his work on machines, Mumford's two groundbreaking books on urban civilization, *The Culture of Cities* (1938) and *The City in History* (1961), helped alert researchers to the city as a subject of complex scholarly concern. Mumford wrote from a social and moral perspective in all his works. He analyzed technology within a "social ecology," as both a material and a mental construction. Mumford's two-volume *The Myth of the Machine* (1967–1970) returned to the themes of his earlier work by critically examining the forces shaping the history of technology. The second volume of this work, *The Pentagon of Power* (1970), reflected Mumford's revulsion with the uses to which technology had been put in the Vietnam War and showed his distrust of the computer, which he viewed as intrusive.

An activist as well as an intellectual, Mumford played a central role in some of the leading public-policy debates of the later twentieth century, including those on highways and urban renewal, nuclear weapons, and the problems and promise of technology. As a founder of the Regional Planning Association of America in 1924, he fashioned a program of regional development that resulted in the building of two model communities: Radburn, New Jersey, and Sunnyside Gardens, Queens. One of the outstanding public intellectuals of his era, Mumford produced a body of writing unmatched in modern American letters for its range and richness.

[*See also* Airplanes and Air Transport; Automation and Computerization; Building Technology; Highway System; Machinery and Manufacturing; Military, Science and Technology and the; Nuclear Weapons; Radio; Science; Social Sciences; Society for the History of Technology; *and* Technology.]

BIBLIOGRAPHY

Miller, Donald L. *Lewis Mumford, a Life*. Pittsburgh, Penn.: University of Pittsburgh Press, 1992.

Miller, Donald L., ed. *The Lewis Mumford Reader*. Athens, Ga.: University of Georgia Press, 1995.

Molella, Arthur P. "Mumford, Lewis (1895–1990)." In *The History of Science in the United States: An Encyclopedia,* edited by Marc Rothenberg, pp. 363–364. New York and London: Garland Publishing, 2001.

Donald L. Miller; updated by
Elspeth Knewstubb and
Hugh Richard Slotten

MUSEUMS OF SCIENCE AND NATURAL HISTORY

By the end of the first decade of the twenty-first century, the United States boasted nearly four hundred museums of natural history and science; combined annual attendance at these institutions stood at upward of 70 million visitors and continued to rise every year. Such institutional success was not a foregone conclusion, but rather the product of two centuries of negotiation between scientists and their publics about what would define museums and their role in American culture. The resulting heterogeneous science and natural history museum landscape drew from, as well as contributed to, the broader museum movement in the United States, especially during the twentieth century.

Colonial Period through Reconstruction.
The impulse to develop museums of natural history came from America's colonial rulers. The collection of local flora and fauna became the basis for assessing regional resources and educating transplanted colonists to aid in their survival, as well as a currency for international exchange. Colonial museums, like the Charleston Museum (1773) in South Carolina and the Academy of Natural Sciences (1812) in Philadelphia, highlighted the possession of exotic specimens and support from prominent men of science. In this way, American natural history practitioners gained prestige by underscoring their contribution to the international network of science in which they hoped to continue to participate. Philadelphia's Charles Willson Peale opened a museum in Philadelphia in 1812 in which he displayed portraits of famous Americans alongside collections of insects, plants, and mammals that he prepared himself; in the early 1800s Peale received and displayed specimens from the Lewis and Clark expedition, such as the California condor, and developed a "Mammoth Room" to display a mastodon skeleton he helped to excavate near Newburgh, New York. Later, Harvard's Asa Gray, Charles Darwin's chief American scientific correspondent and supporter, taught botany at Harvard and founded the Harvard Herbarium (1842).

The period from the middle to the second half of the nineteenth century saw an explosion of new museums of science and natural history, a trend that drew strength from the American museum movement as well as from the expansion of U.S. institutions of higher learning in which science and technology gained a prominent place. The Franklin Institute of Philadelphia opened in 1824 as a place "for the promotion of the Mechanical Arts"; by 1887, it played host to the International Electrical Exhibition. The U.S. Congress became aware of the Briton James Smithson's bequest to develop an institution dedicated "to the advancement and diffusion of knowledge" in 1835, and the Smithsonian Institution opened its first building to the public in 1846.

Other public natural history museums soon followed suit, in large cities—such as the American Museum of Natural History (1869) in New York—as well as later in smaller towns—such as the Davenport Museum of Natural History in Iowa (1867), the North Carolina Natural History Museum (1887) in Raleigh, and the Denver Natural History Museum (1900). Wards' Natural Scientific Establishment, purveyor of natural history specimens, trained a generation of taxidermists and museum exhibit makers to value the art and science of display. Many colleges, large and small, also opened university natural history museums based on the collections of their science faculty and used them for student nature studies. Spencer Baird, for instance, curated his personal specimens, which became the basis of the Dickinson College Museum starting in 1845; they remained there until he was made the first curator of the National Museum at the Smithsonian in 1850. Harvard's Museum of Comparative Zoology, spearheaded by Louis Agassiz, opened in 1859, only five years before Boston's Society of Natural History (1864) opened its own public museum in the same city.

In the antebellum United States and beyond, cultural battles raged openly over the content and shape of the young nation's museums. These clashes, occasioned by a dramatic proliferation of diverse public and private money-making institutions calling themselves museums, including P. T. Barnum's American Museum (1842), reflected growing tensions between competing ideas of the role that museums could and should play in American life—should museums be closed ceremonial shrines to scientific research, authority, and knowledge, or should they be open places for public education, confrontation, and debates about that same knowledge?

The 1880s through the Mid-Twentieth Century.

From the late 1880s onward, leaders of the nation's public natural history museums came to advocate a kind of détente between these extremes, a set of ideals and practices that they dubbed "the New Museum Idea." The New Museum Idea, especially as it was interpreted by the Smithsonian director George Brown Goode, called for museums to have a tripartite mission: to collect, to do research, and to educate the public through displays. Progressive-Era reformers' embrace of the New Museum Idea would ultimately inspire a century-long renegotiation of the relationship among exhibits, research, and education in American museums of nature and science. Conflicts over what museums should do and be continued unabated, and museum workers' struggle to balance multiple missions would profoundly alter institutions' appearances and functions.

Indeed, exhibits' transformation in the name of the New Museum Idea produced dramatic organizational innovation in older institutions and eventually led to the establishment of new types of museums—museums of science and industry—that eschewed collecting and research in the name

of science education and displaying America's Gilded Age industrial successes. The Columbian Museum of Chicago (est. 1983) changed its name to the Field Museum of Natural History in 1905 to reflect the support of a new major benefactor, the department store magnate Marshall Field, and to better reflect its focus on the natural sciences. Taking cues from popular World's Fairs as well as from early hands-on museums like the Deutsches Museum in Germany, the American industrialist Julius Rosenwald, head of the Sears Roebuck Corporation, endowed the Chicago Museum of Science and Industry (1933). Likewise, the Rockefeller family funded the development of early interactive exhibits and educational studies at the New York Museum of Science and Industry (1930). Around the same time, the Boston Museum of Natural History closed its doors, and under the influence of its new director, the explorer and businessman Bradford Washburn, it soon reopened as the Boston Museum of Science.

Existing museums of natural history responded to the popularity of these new and modernizing institutions by transforming their display and educational strategies, helped in part by the Works Progress Administration, which financed the increased presence of artists on museum payrolls. The American Museum of Natural History introduced some of the earliest and most dramatic habitat dioramas in the interwar period, and newly opened museums like the Natural History Museum of Los Angeles (1913) and the Buffalo Museum of Natural History (1933) planned large diorama halls. Buffalo, under the leadership of Carlos Cummings, took inspiration for new exhibits from a wide range of sources, including World's Fairs and commercial displays. Education departments in these institutions also grew larger and, through the development of films as well as traveling exhibits and classroom materials, soon came to dominate the public image of most science and natural history museums.

World War II and Beyond.

During World War II, both natural history and science museums contributed to the war effort by offering scientific expertise of foreign territories and education to troops and citizens. Both science and natural history museum leaders envisioned an expanded role for their institutions in postwar education, but in the decades after the war, this shared vision soon gave way to differentiated institutional missions. Science museums—a broad category that now encompassed museums of science and industry—used corporate-sponsored interactive exhibits and live animal displays to teach Americans about the applications of biology and medicine, but the institutions did not fully realize the dramatic changes in pedagogy and content that their earlier display reformers had envisioned. Natural history museums reinvigorated their research programs instead, as new federal funding for systematics became available in the early 1950s, and came to rely heavily on straightforward object-based displays and dioramas with only minimal updates.

Teachers, science policy makers, and scientists argued broadly over the relative merits of discipline-based science pedagogy and science literacy in the late 1950s, and these conflicts found their way into museums. In 1969, the physicist Frank Oppenheimer founded the Exploratorium, a new institution he aimed at democratizing the museum experience and making science accessible to broader publics through low-tech exhibits that put visitors in the place of scientific experimenter. Oppenheimer's novel take on museum-based science education became the hallmark of the science center movement that swept the United States through the 1980s. Informal learning and hands-on experiences became the foundation on which museums like the Pacific Science Center (1962), the Columbus (Ohio) Center of Science and Industry (1964), and New Jersey's Liberty Science Center (1993) built new relationships among content, pedagogy, and display and with them, brought museums new audiences.

From the 1980s onward, federal budget cuts and the ongoing professionalization of museum education combined to encourage natural history museums, science museums, and science centers to share shows, sources of funding, and pedagogical expertise. Increasingly more of the nation's varied institutions remade themselves into sites with common features: blockbuster exhibits, like the King Tut show (1971–1979) and the T. rex "Sue" display (2000–2002), and varied forms of family "edutainment," a term contemporaries now used to describe a commercially motivated blend of education and entertainment. Although tensions between museums' publics and scientific missions persisted, at the outset of the twenty-first century the displays of American natural history and science museums no longer functioned as active battlegrounds for competing ideas about what defined a museum and its work. These institutions had become culturally important sites for informal science, and as such, they collectively embodied museum professionals' vision of effective public science, as well as their shared goal of defending it.

[See also **Academy of Natural Sciences of Philadelphia; American Museum of Natural History; Higher Education and Science; Lewis and Clark Expedition; Popularization of Science; Science; Smithsonian Institution;** and **Wilkes Expedition.**]

BIBLIOGRAPHY

Association of Science-Technology Centers. *Statistics Analysis Package and Report.* Washington, D.C.: Author, 2012.

Barrow, Mark V., Jr. "The Specimen Dealer: Entrepreneurial; Natural History in American's Gilded Age." *Journal of the History of Biology* 33, no. 3 (2000): 493–534.

Cole, K. C. *Something Incredibly Wonderful Happens: Frank Oppenheimer and His Astonishing Exploratorium.* New York: Houghton Mifflin Harcourt Trade, 2009.

Coleman, Lawrence Vail. *The Museum in America: A Critical Study,* Vol. 1. Washington, D.C.: American Association of Museums, 1939.

Danilov, Victor. *Science and Technology Centers.* Cambridge, Mass.: MIT Press, 1982.

Goodyear, George. *Society and Museum: A History of the Buffalo Society of Natural Sciences, 1861–1993 and the Buffalo Museum of Science, 1928–1993.* Buffalo, N.Y.: The Society, 1994.

Kohlstedt, Sally Gregory. "Curiosities and Cabinets: Natural History Museums and Education on the Antebellum Campus." *Isis* 79, no. 3 (1988): 405–426.

Kohlstedt, Sally Gregory, ed. *The Origins of Natural Science in America: Essays of George Brown Goode.* Washington, D.C.: Smithsonian Institution Press, 1991.

Kohlstedt, Sally Gregory. *Teaching Children Science: Hands-On Nature Study in North America, 1890–1930.* Chicago: University of Chicago Press, 2011.

Koster, Emlyn H. "In Search of Relevance: Science Centers as Innovators in the Evolution of Museums." *Daedalus* 128, no. 3 (1999): 277–296.

Mitman, Gregg. "Cinematic Nature: Hollywood Technology, Popular Culture, and the American Museum of Natural History." *Isis* 84, no. 4 (1993): 637–661.

Quinn, Stephen Christopher. *Windows on Nature: The Great Habitat Dioramas of the American Museum of Natural History.* New York: American Museum of Natural History/Harry N. Adams, 2006.

Rader, Karen A., and Victoria E. M. Cain. *Life on Display: Revolutionizing U.S. Museums of Science and Natural History in the Twentieth Century.* Chicago: University of Chicago Press, 2014.

Sellers, Charles Coleman. *Mr. Peale's Museum: Charles Willson Peale and the First Popular Museum of Natural Science and Art.* New York: Barra Foundation, 1980.

Winsor, Mary P. *Reading the Shape of Nature: Comparative Zoology at the Agassiz Museum.* Chicago: University of Chicago Press, 1990.

Karen A. Rader

N

NANOTECHNOLOGY

Nanotechnology is the art and science of making useful things that have at least one dimension between one and approximately one hundred nanometers (billionths of a meter). That definition encompasses much of chemistry, physics, and engineering going back centuries. For example, Benjamin Franklin (in the eighteenth century) and Irving Langmuir and Katherine Blodgett (in the early twentieth century) created monolayer films that could be construed as protonanotechnology. However, "nanotechnology" was only coined (by a Japanese precision engineer) in 1974 and was not popularized until the publication of Eric Drexler's 1986 futurist manifesto, *Engines of Creation*. The demarcation of a distinct field of nanotechnology research, incorporating elements of many disciplines and bridging university, industry, and government, occurred in the 1990s. That process was driven by a coalition of federal grant officers, Clinton administration officials,

and high-profile corporate and academic scientists and research managers. Their efforts led to the creation of a National Nanotechnology Initiative in 2001, which (as of 2011) coordinates 25 federal agencies spending about $2 billion annually on nanotechnology research. The U.S. initiative was inspired by, and inspired, similar initiatives in other nations, which, with partners in industry, spent an estimated $20 billion on nanotechnology research in 2010.

The "standard story" (Baird and Shew, 2004) of nanotechnology's origins, frequently deployed in popular magazines, policy documents, and scientific journal articles, begins with a 1959 after-dinner speech by Nobel laureate physicist Richard Feynman. Feynman's "There's Plenty of Room at the Bottom" speech amalgamated (without acknowledgment) Robert Heinlein's fictional depiction of tools controlling smaller tools controlling even smaller tools (*ad infinitum*) with MIT materials scientist Arthur von Hippel's program for "molecular engineering" (Regis, 1995) to accurately predict the advent of microelectromechanical systems and ultra-high-density data storage. Feynman's speech also called for physicists to radically improve electron microscopy to aid biologists' studies of subcellular processes. Nanotechnology's proponents often claim Feynman's admonition was answered by the invention of the scanning tunneling microscope in 1981 at IBM's research laboratory in Zurich, Switzerland. Indeed, in many accounts (by scientists, social scientists, policy makers, and journalists), nanotechnology would be impossible but for the ability of the tunneling microscope (and close variants such as the atomic force microscope—known collectively as probe microscopes) to image and even manipulate matter at the nanoscale.

This "standard story" is accurate in some respects. Many prominent nanoscientists describe their dawning understanding of probe microscopy's capabilities in the late 1980s and early 1990s as the event that transformed them into nanotechnology enthusiasts. In the late 1990s, nanotechnology proponents praised probe microscopy's movement from corporate research to academic laboratories, especially from academic laboratories to university-affiliated start-up companies, as a model of university–industry partnership to be adopted in all areas of nanotechnology research. At the same time, the probe microscopy community's rapid disciplinary expansion from condensed-matter physics to electrical engineering, materials science, molecular biology, geology, and other fields made it a useful ally (and organizational template) for federal grant officers and institution-building scientists hoping to use nanotechnology as a framework for greater interdisciplinary collaboration among academic and government researchers (Mody, 2011).

However, the standard story obscures nanotechnology's historical context. For instance, Feynman's call for physicists to improve biological microscopy was probably not meant literally; more likely, it was intended as a cudgel against those who believed biologists could only advance by mimicking physicists' reliance on computers. Moreover, probe microscopy's inventors and early developers were utterly unaware of Feynman's speech. Ironically, the technical improvements to traditional electron microscopy that Feynman

foresaw contributed as much to nanotechnology as probe microscopy did, yet popular, scientific, and social scientific accounts of nanotechnology's origins often neglect electron microscopy's role and accentuate probe microscopy's, possibly because the latter's novelty reinforces nanotechnology's image as a revolutionary break with the past.

Feynman's speech was largely forgotten for 30 years and was only resurrected after 1990, partly so supporters of a National Nanotechnology Initiative could give nanotechnology a Nobel laureate pedigree. Curiously, the few who were aware of the "Room at the Bottom" speech in the 1970s and 1980s played important parts in nanotechnology's institutionalization, yet are mostly absent from the field's official histories. One such group included specialists in "microfabrication" who used electron, ion, and photon beams to carve small features in crystalline materials. Japanese competition in microelectronics in the mid-1970s stimulated American corporate and federal funding to build a series of academic microfabrication facilities. In the early 1980s, researchers from the two leading microfabrication facilities at Cornell and Stanford raced to claim a prize offered in Feynman's speech for miniaturizing a written page by 25 thousand times. In 1994, the Cornell and Stanford facilities allied to lead a National Nanofabrication Users Network, which in 2004 became the National Nanotechnology Infrastructure Network. This network (and its peers, such as the Nanoscale Science and Engineering Centers program) embodies the institutional strategy of American nanotechnology leaders: the construction of networked, academic (and some government) centers that, by sharing equipment and lightly coordinating research, foster commercialization of basic research and cooperation among engineering and biomedical disciplines.

The other group that initially popularized Feynman's speech was Eric Drexler's Foresight Institute, founded in 1986 near Stanford. Drexler's vision of programmable, self-replicating "molecular assemblers" capable of reconstructing matter (even human bodies) in any form imaginable caught fire in the late 1980s, thanks partly to Drexler's ties to software tycoons and prominent space colonization promoters such as Gerard O'Neill and Stewart Brand (McCray, 2013). Drexler's ideas were taken up by newspapers, science fiction novels, television series, and national leaders such as the vice president Al Gore and the admiral David Jeremiah, who lent their weight to the formation of a National Nanotechnology Initiative. Scientists such as the Nobel laureate chemist Richard Smalley (codiscoverer of the "buckyball") even used Drexler's book to recruit resources for early academic nanotechnology centers. Yet by the early 2000s, Smalley and other National Nanotechnology Initiative supporters attacked Drexler's vivid speculations—especially that self-replicating assemblers could inundate the globe in "gray goo"—as unscientific and unsettling enough to turn public opinion against nanotechnology.

Nanotechnology in America, therefore, has a long but occluded history. That occlusion arises partly because the institutions of nanotechnology occupy the interstices between research fields that often existed *avant la lettre*. But the occlusion also stems from deliberate attempts to foreshorten nanotechnology's official history to make the field seem novel and revolutionary but also tame and nonthreatening.

[*See also* Biological Sciences; Chemistry; Engineering; Feynman, Richard; Franklin, Benjamin; Geology; Journals in Science, Medicine, and Engineering; Langmuir, Irving; Molecular Biology; Physics; Science; Social Sciences; *and* Technology.]

BIBLIOGRAPHY

Baird, Davis, and Ashley Shew. "Probing the History of Scanning Tunneling Microscopy." In *Discovering the Nanoscale*, edited by Davis Baird, Alfred Nordmann, and Joachim Schummer, pp. 145–156. Amsterdam: IOS Press, 2004.

McCray, W. Patrick. *The Visioneers: How a Group of Elite Scientists Pursued Space Colonies, Nanotechnologies, and a Limitless Future*. Princeton, N.J.: Princeton University Press, 2013.

Mody, Cyrus C. M. *Instrumental Community: Probe Microscopy and the Path to Nanotechnology*. Cambridge, Mass.: MIT Press, 2011.

Regis, Edward. *Nano: The Emerging Science of Nanotechnology*. Boston: Little, Brown, 1995.

Cyrus C. M. Mody

NASA

See National Aeronautics and Space Administration.

NATIONAL ACADEMY OF SCIENCES

The National Academy of Sciences (NAS) was the brainchild of three nineteenth-century figures prominent in the American scientific community: Joseph Henry; Alexander Dallas Bache, superintendent of the U.S. Coast Survey; and Charles Henry Davis, a naval officer and scientist. These men hoped to create a body analogous to Great Britain's Royal Society and the French Academy. In 1863 they obtained a government charter for this organization, which they hoped would centralize control over American science, recognize the achievements of the scientific community, and serve as an agency for advising the federal government on scientific matters. Passage of legislation creating the academy in March 1863 depended on skillful use of legislative procedure by Republican Senator Henry Wilson of Massachusetts.

During the National Academy of Sciences' first half century, the federal government rarely sought its advice. Its impact on federal policy, however, increased markedly when it established the National Research Council (NRC)—a collaboration of academic and industrial scientific elites—at the onset of World War I. On behalf of the government, the National Research Council helped achieve large-scale production of optical glass, nitrates, and poison gas, among other materials. Toward the end of the war, President Woodrow Wilson issued an executive order requesting the Academy to continue the National Research Council. The National Academy of Sciences did not play as prominent a role in organizing science during World War II, although it did advise committees connected with the wartime Office of Scientific Research and Development, which also administered the work of the National Research Council. The National Research Council gradually combined with the National Academy of Sciences after the war. During the Cold War, the academy and the affiliated National Research Council received many contracts to provide advice to the government and thereafter continued to produce reports on a wide range of subjects. For example, from 1947 to 1973, the academy helped direct the work of the Atomic Bomb Casualty Commission in Japan, which conducted research on the impact of the atomic bomb on Japanese citizens.

The National Academy of Sciences established the National Academy of Engineering in 1964 and the Institute of Medicine six years later. The National Academy of Engineering and the National Academy of Sciences oversee the work of the National Research Council. Together, the four institutions are known as "the National Academies." The National Research Council conducts most studies dealing with technical issues and science and engineering policy. The Institute of Medicine conducts separate studies dealing with medicine and health and issues its own reports. In 2010, more than six thousand members of the National Academies served on hundreds of committees with the National Research Council and the Institute of Medicine. The National Academies Press (NAP) publishes the reports sponsored by the four institutions. In 2010, the press published over two hundred books dealing with science, engineering, and health policy. The institution also offered free versions online. The National Academy of Sciences has published a scholarly journal, *The Proceedings of the National Academy of Sciences*, since 1915. It also publishes the National Academy of Engineering's quarterly policy journal *Issues in Science and Technology*.

Election to the National Academies is considered a high honor among American scientists, engineers, and health professionals. Reflecting the general trend in American science, medicine, and engineering, the National Academies has been dominated by white males throughout its history. The first woman was elected to academy membership in 1925.

[*See also* Bache, Alexander Dallas; Engineering; Gender and Science; Henry, Joseph; Journals in Science, Medicine, and Engineering; Medicine; Military, Science and Technology and the; Office of Scientific Research and Development; Science; *and* Societies and Associations, Science.]

BIBLIOGRAPHY

Dupree, A. Hunter. *Science in the Federal Government: A History of Policies and Activities.* Baltimore: Johns Hopkins University Press, 1986.
Kevles, Daniel J. *The Physicists: The History of a Scientific Community in Modern America.* Cambridge, Mass.: Harvard University Press, 1995.
National Academy of Sciences. "About NAS: History." http://www.nasonline.org/about-nas/history/ (accessed 29 October 2012).

Daniel Lee Kleinman;
updated by Hugh Richard Slotten

NATIONAL AERONAUTICS AND SPACE ADMINISTRATION

The National Aeronautics and Space Administration (NASA) emerged in 1958 at the height of the Cold War rivalry between the United States and the Soviet Union. In the field of space exploration, the Soviets scored a dramatic coup on 4 October 1957, when they launched *Sputnik 1*, the first artificial satellite to orbit the Earth, as part of a larger scientific effort associated with the International Geophysical Year. Concerned about the perception that the United States had fallen behind the Soviet Union in technology and science, Congress established NASA to explore and use space for the benefit "of all mankind."

The new agency's space missions began with Project Mercury to study the possibilities of human space flight. The efforts expanded significantly in

1961 when President John F. Kennedy, responding to perceived challenges to U.S. leadership in science and technology, announced Project Apollo, whose goal was to place an American on the moon by 1970. For the next 11 years this project consumed NASA's energies. Between 1969 and 1972 NASA landed six teams of astronauts on the moon. The first landing mission, *Apollo 2*, achieved success on 20 July 1969, when astronaut Neil Armstrong (1930–2012) first set foot on the lunar surface, proclaiming to millions of listeners: "That's one small step for [a] man—one giant leap for mankind." Subsequent landings, coming at approximately six-month intervals thereafter, spent more time on the moon and conducted more sophisticated experiments.

NASA went into a holding pattern after Project Apollo. The reusable space shuttle, its major program of the 1970s, first flew in 1981 and by the end of 1985 had made 24 flights. During the launch of *Challenger* on 28 January 1986, however, a leak in the joints of a solid rocket booster detonated the main fuel tank. Six astronauts and high-school social studies teacher Christa McAuliffe died in this accident, the worst in NASA's history. Following the *Challenger* disaster, the shuttle program experienced a two-year hiatus, while NASA redesigned the system and revamped its management structure. Space shuttle flights resumed on 29 September 1988. In November 1998, 77-year-old John H. Glenn Jr. returned to space for a 10-day mission in the shuttle *Discovery*, 36 years after he flew a mission in Project Mercury in 1962.

In 1998 an international consortium of 16 nations began building the International Space Station (ISS) in the Earth's orbit. The first two station components, the Zarya and Unity modules, were launched and joined together in orbit in late 1998. Several other components were at that time nearing completion in the United States and elsewhere. Orbital assembly of the ISS began a new era of hands-on work in space, involving more spacewalks and new space robotics. The Space Shuttle and two types of Russian launch vehicles were intended to launch components of the station for orbital assembly. The ISS, like all space stations before it, must be supported with supplies from earth, and refuse must be loaded onto spacecraft to return to the Earth or burn up in the atmosphere. By the early twenty-first century the ISS had some capabilities to recycle air and water. The first crew of three occupied the station on 31 October 2000.

In the midst of the orbital construction effort, NASA lost the *Columbia* orbiter and its crew, including an Israeli astronaut, during a reentry from space on 1 February 2003. This effectively ended shuttle support to the ISS by the United States, and the crew had to be reduced to two members to conserve the meager resources that could be brought to it by smaller Russian vehicles. In the meantime, NASA worked to correct the causes of the *Columbia* accident. In January 2004 President George W. Bush announced a "Vision for Space Exploration" that refocused NASA on a return to the moon. It required the retirement of the Space Shuttle by 2010, the investment of funding for that program in the development of a new space capsule and launch vehicle, known as the Constellation program, and the phasing out of the ISS as a major U.S. program after 2015. In August 2005 the shuttle returned to flight, and thereafter ISS construction resumed.

Even as the Space Shuttle program pressed toward retirement, cost and schedule problems plagued the replacement Constellation effort. President Barak Obama, therefore, canceled that program in 2010, extended the Space Shuttle program for a year, and moved toward a commercial follow-on for American access to space.

In addition to the human space-flight programs, scientific probes were sent to the moon and planets, particularly Mars. The space vehicle *Viking* landed on Mars in 1976, the Mars Pathfinder in 1997, and then the Mars Exploration Rovers, and a host of follow-on missions transformed knowledge about the red planet. Now, it seems that Mars was once a watery planet with abundant life, and some scientists are convinced that micro-organisms might still be present under the surface. The *Voyager* mission to the outer solar system in the 1970s and early 1980s provided stunning images and data about distant planets and their moons. In the 1990s the Hubble space telescope, initially impaired, began returning exceptional scientific data about the origins and development of the universe; the Magellan mission radar-imaged Venus; and the Galileo probe to Jupiter and the Cassini missions to Saturn generated important scientific data. All pointed to a much more complex solar system than envisioned previously. At the same time, the high cost of space exploration dampened the enthusiasm of some members of Congress, which provided the funding. From the beginning, some critics had argued that NASA's budget might be better spent on social needs at home, but this remained a minority view because the romance of space continued to exert its allure.

[*See also* Challenger **Disaster; Hubble, Edwin Powell; Hubble Space Telescope; International Geophysical Year; Military, Science and Technology and the; Missiles and Rockets; Satellites, Communications; Science; Space Program; Space Science;** *and* **Technology.**]

BIBLIOGRAPHY

Launius, Roger D. *Frontiers of Space Exploration.* Westport, Conn.: Greenwood Press, 2004.

McCurdy, Howard E. *Inside NASA: High Technology and Organizational Change in the U.S. Space Program.* Baltimore: Johns Hopkins University Press, 1993.

McDougall, Walter A. *The Heavens and the Earth: A Political History of the Space Age.* New York: Basic Books, 1985.

Roger D. Launius

NATIONAL BUREAU OF STANDARDS

See Research and Development (R&D).

NATIONAL INSTITUTE OF STANDARDS AND TECHNOLOGY

See Research and Development (R&D).

NATIONAL INSTITUTES OF HEALTH

The National Institutes of Health (NIH)—a component of the U.S. Public Health Service, a division of the Department of Health and Human Services—is the United States's principal federal agency for medical research. The NIH funds basic and clinical research across the United States and in some foreign countries. By the end of the twentieth century its annual budget exceeded $17 billion, 80 percent of which was distributed as research grants to investigators at universities and other institutions. The NIH also maintained laboratories staffed by government scientists at its main campus in Bethesda, Maryland, and other locations.

What is now known as the NIH began in 1887 as a one-room hygienic laboratory at the Marine Hospital on Staten Island, New York. The hospital was operated by the Marine Hospital Service, which was established in 1798 to offer medical assistance for merchant seamen. To prevent epidemics, during the 1880s, Congress directed the Marine Hospital Service to check newly arrived passengers on ships for evidence of infectious diseases, especially cholera and yellow fever. In 1887, officials with the Marine Hospital Service asked one of their physicians trained in the new science of bacteriology, Joseph J. Kinyoun, to apply bacteriological methods to federal quarantine work at the small laboratory in the Staten Island Marine Hospital. Kinyoun modeled the laboratory on German developments and used the phrase "laboratory of hygiene" to signify that the institution was supporting public-health interests.

In 1891 the "Hygiene Laboratory" moved to Washington, D.C. In 1902 the laboratory established a formal research program on infectious diseases and assumed regulatory responsibility for licensing vaccines and antitoxins. In 1912, the research scope was broadened to include noninfectious diseases. In 1930 Congress changed the laboratory's name to the National Institute of Health and in 1937 created a National Cancer Institute, the first of more than 20 NIH institutes focusing on specific disease categories. The

1944 Public Health Service Act authorized the NIH to award grants and fellowships. In 1948, as more specialized institutes were created, the name of the umbrella agency became plural: the National Institutes of Health.

The NIH budget and staff expanded rapidly from 1955 through 1968 and more slowly thereafter. Among the thousands of discoveries made by NIH investigators are the cause and cure of pellagra; a vaccine against Rocky Mountain spotted fever; a typhus vaccine and confirmation of plasma's lifesaving value during World War II; and, in the 1990s, breaking the genetic code and developing therapies for acquired immunodeficiency syndrome (AIDS). NIH-funded research has resulted in over 80 Nobel prizes.

[*See also* Biological Sciences; Cancer; Disease; Genetics and Genetic Engineering; Germ Theory of Disease; HIV/AIDS; Medicine; Nobel Prize in Biomedical Research; Public Health; Public Health Service, U.S.; Research and Development; *and* Typhus.]

BIBLIOGRAPHY

Harden, Victoria A. *Inventing the NIH: Federal Biomedical Research Policy, 1887–1937*. Baltimore: Johns Hopkins University Press, 1986.
Kastor, John A. *The National Institutes of Health, 1991–2008*. New York: Oxford University Press, 2010.
Office of History, National Institutes of Health. "A Short History of the National Institutes of Health." history.nih.gov/exhibits/history/ (accessed 23 January 2012).

Victoria A. Harden;
updated by Hugh Richard Slotten

NATIONAL LABORATORIES

The Department of Energy's national laboratory system is the most prestigious federally funded, contractor-operated laboratory enterprise to appear since World War II. In 2010, the department operated 16 laboratories across the country.

These laboratories originated in the Radiation Laboratory of the University of California, Berkeley, during the 1930s. Ernest Lawrence created a center of nuclear physics research at Berkeley using the cyclotron. In the late 1930s, the laboratory expanded to nuclear chemistry and nuclear medicine. After Lawrence won the Nobel Prize in 1939, the Rockefeller Foundation endowed the construction of the world's largest cyclotron. World War II intervened and, at the request of the National Defense Research Committee, Lawrence committed his laboratory to the Manhattan Project.

The Postwar Research Era. The diaspora of physicists from the Radiation Laboratory to a number of other institutions—including its namesake at the Massachusetts Institute of Technology (MIT, which developed microwave radar), the Naval Underwater Sound Laboratory in San Diego, the Metallurgical Laboratory at the University of Chicago, and, most importantly, the Los Alamos Scientific Laboratory in New Mexico—created the basis for the postwar institutionalization of research in many fields. Los Alamos Scientific Laboratory, which the University of California had originally agreed to operate "for the duration" of the war, was rebuilt as a permanent facility. After the engineering aspects of nuclear-weapon development were separated to create Sandia Laboratories, operated by AT&T's Bell Laboratories, the University of California agreed to continue as the contractor for the facility.

Manhattan Project Commander Leslie Groves created a new facility, the Argonne National Laboratory, at the University of Chicago after the war. This followed Enrico Fermi's famous work there on the first successful nuclear reactor. At the request of prominent eastern scientists, Associated Universities, Inc., organized the Brookhaven National Laboratory in New York State and operated it under contract with the Manhattan Engineer District and its successor, the Atomic Energy Commission (AEC). The creation of the Oak Ridge National Laboratory supplemented the Manhattan Engineer District facilities at Oak Ridge, Tennessee, which included the uranium isotope separation facilities designed at the Berkeley

Radiation Laboratory and the K-2 gaseous diffusion facility, designed at Columbia.

Research and Development. The original purpose of the national laboratories was to carry forward the research and development (R&D) priorities of Groves and leading scientists of the Manhattan Engineer District after World War II. The Tolman Report, commissioned in 1944 by Groves, concluded that because much of that R&D would be classified, scientists could not conduct this research in university laboratories. Although the report recommended a single, centralized laboratory, the postwar system was regional. This followed in part the distribution of Manhattan Engineer District laboratories, but the interests of scientists in the Northeast to have such facilities also played a role. The national laboratories at Argonne, Brookhaven, and Oak Ridge offered exclusive access to nuclear reactors for research. Lawrence persuaded the AEC to allocate $9 million for accelerator R&D in 1947, for particle accelerators too large for universities to afford. These large accelerators included the Bevatron and Cosmotron, the first multibillion electron volt proton accelerators.

With the development of nuclear submarines and the passage of the Atomic Energy Act of 1954, the national laboratories lost their monopoly on reactor development. In the 1960s, the Congressional Overseer of the AEC questioned the roles of AEC multipurpose laboratories, including the Stanford Linear Accelerator Center established in 1962. The Congressional Joint Committee on Atomic Energy directed that the labs diversify their activities to be of use to other federal agencies. Laboratory scientists objected to conceiving their laboratories as "job shops." Meanwhile, high-energy physics, in which many of them worked, found a new home at the Stanford Center and at Brookhaven, and Berkeley decided to build the next generation of proton synchrotrons. At Argonne, competition with the Soviet Union in the field had already spurred construction of a 12.5-Gev zero-gradient synchrotron (ZGS) to beat out the 10-Gev machine unveiled at Dubna in 1956, but the machine had only slightly more utility than its inspiration. After Brookhaven completed

a strong-focusing 25-Gev proton synchrotron, Berkeley expected the next prize in the machine-building realm, especially because former Berkeley nuclear chemist Glenn Seaborg was appointed chairman of the AEC in 1961.

Agitation for a "truly national laboratory" arose in the Midwest, where the Midwest University Research Association sought to build a new design that used colliding beams to double the energy available in proton–proton interactions. Frustrated by Argonne's more conventional ZGS design and the creation of the Stanford Linear Accelerator Center instead of a new laboratory for their machine, scientists in the Midwest argued that Brookhaven and Berkeley should not retain their quasimonopoly of machines in high-energy physics. When Berkeley designed a 200-Gev proton synchrotron during the early 1960s, almost every state proposed a site for the machine. It ended up in the prairies west of Chicago rather than in California. When the machine's Berkeley designers declined to go to the new site, a leading critic of the Berkeley design, Robert R. Wilson, was persuaded to leave Cornell in 1967 to direct the new facility, which became the Fermi National Accelerator Laboratory.

The Oak Ridge director from 1955 to 1973, Alvin Weinberg, criticized the growth of high-energy physics at about the same time. Weinberg's laboratory had not been blessed with high-energy machines and had seen its mission of reactor development diminished after the Atomic Energy Act of 1954 opened the field to private enterprise. Weinberg questioned the favoring of high-energy physics in the other national laboratories and the loss of resources in other fields. Whereas Oak Ridge had been reduced to soliciting "work for others" to survive, Argonne, Berkeley, Brookhaven, Stanford, and Fermi reaped the rewards of the international accelerator race with the Soviet Union and the European Center for Nuclear Research (CERN, established in 1954). Beginning in the mid-1960s, this accelerator race was slowed by the need to fund the Vietnam War and President Lyndon Johnson's "Great Society" programs. Opposition to work on nuclear weapons, the other cash cow of the national laboratory system, also limited growth. This opposition was particularly important at the University of California, which operated the Los Alamos Scientific Laboratory and the Livermore Branch of the Lawrence Radiation Laboratory.

Role of the Department of Energy.

Although Berkeley had resisted the "national laboratory" role for the laboratories it operated, attempts by faculty committees to inject a measure of autonomy in their management during the 1970s produced the opposite effect. In 1980, the Department of Energy, which had succeeded the AEC and the short-lived Energy Research and Development Administration, asserted ownership rights in these facilities by renaming them the Lawrence Berkeley National Laboratory, the Lawrence Livermore National Laboratory, and the Los Alamos National Laboratory. During President Ronald Reagan's administration, Los Alamos and Lawrence Livermore received increased support with the reconstruction of the nuclear arsenal and the advent of the Strategic Defense Initiative (SDI), which sought to develop anti–ballistic missile technologies of radical designs.

As their missions and patrons diversified, the Department of Energy national laboratories became "multipurpose" national laboratories. The Department of Defense, Homeland Security, and the National Institutes of Health sponsored laboratory work related to strategic and tactical warfare, antiterrorism, and genetic engineering, whereas the Department of Transportation sponsored research into automotive design.

The national laboratories of the Department of Energy swelled in the wake of the decision to nationalize the University of California–managed facilities. What had been the Sandia Laboratories, operated by AT&T after the University of California rejected the weaponization of nuclear devices in 1948, became Sandia National Laboratories in 1979. The Hanford Works of the AEC, which had conducted research at the Pacific Northwest Laboratory from 1965, was renamed the Pacific Northwest National Laboratory in 1995. The National Reactor Test Station had been renamed the Idaho National Engineering Laboratory in 1977 with the creation of the Department of Energy. The department also added laboratories from other agencies folded into it alongside the AEC. New national laboratories were subsequently added, as when the Continuous Electron Beam Accelerator Facility, founded in the early 1980s and located in Newport News, Virginia, changed its name to the Thomas Jefferson National Accelerator Facility on 24 May 1996. In 2008, the Stanford Linear Accelerator Center (SLAC) became the SLAC National Accelerator Laboratory.

The nuclear-weapons laboratories were reorganized in the wake of a series of investigations of safety and security in the 1990s and made part of the new National Nuclear Security Administration in 2000 (located within the Department of Energy). This agency incorporated the weapons production facilities, Los Alamos National Laboratory, Stanford National Laboratory, and the Lawrence Livermore National Laboratory and reoriented them to their original national defense mission. However, during the early twenty-first century, the new agency mainly focused on decommissioning, rather than designing, nuclear weapons and working toward the environmental remediation of production facilities.

[*See also* **Atomic Energy Commission; Bell Laboratories; Chemistry; Fermi, Enrico; Higher Education and Science; Lawrence, Ernest O.; Manhattan Project; Medicine; Military, Science and Technology and the; National Institutes of Health; Nobel Prize in Biomedical Research; Nuclear Power; Nuclear Regulatory Commission; Nuclear Weapons; Physics; Research and Development; Rockefeller Institute, The; Science; Seaborg, Glenn T.;** *and* **Strategic Defense Initiative**]

BIBLIOGRAPHY

Crease, Robert. *Making Physics: A Biography of Brookhaven National Laboratory, 1946–1972.* Chicago: University of Chicago Press, 1999.

Furman, Necah. *Sandia National Laboratories: The Postwar Decade.* Albuquerque: University of New Mexico Press, 1990.

Galison, Peter Louis, and Bruce W. Hevley. *Big Science: The Growth of Large-Scale Research*. Stanford, Calif.: Stanford University Press, 1992.

Heilbron, John, and Robert W. Seidel. *Lawrence and His Laboratory*. Berkeley: University of California Press, 1989.

Hoddeson, Lillian, et al. *Critical Assembly: A Technical History of Los Alamos during the Oppenheimer Years, 1943–1945*. New York: Cambridge University Press, 1993.

Hoddeson, Lillian, et al. *Fermilab: Physics, the Frontier, and Megascience*. Chicago: University of Chicago Press, 2008.

Holl, Jack M., et al. *Argonne National Laboratory, 1946–96*. Urbana: University of Illinois Press, 1997.

Westwick, Peter. *The National Labs: Science in an American System, 1947–1974*. Cambridge, Mass.: Harvard University Press, 2003.

Robert W. Seidel

NATIONAL MEDICAL ASSOCIATION

Following Emancipation in 1865, opportunities for African Americans to gain an education and enter professions suddenly swelled. Northern white missionary groups and individual African American physicians founded medical schools in the latter part of the nineteenth century, greatly increasing the number of black physicians in the United States. Southern white doctors barred these physicians of color from joining state and local medical societies where doctors socialized, learned the latest information from colleagues, shared medical stories, and developed collegial relations. Some Northern medical societies admitted small numbers of African Americans to their ranks. The American Medical Association, founded in 1847, refused membership to physicians who were not members of local medical societies. Isolated, excluded from reaping the benefits of organized societies, and unable to admit patients to local hospitals, black doctors felt the need to join together. They formed statewide organizations such as the Medico-Chirurgical Society of the District of Columbia (1884); the Lone Star State Medical, Dental, and Pharmaceutical Society (Texas, 1886); and the Old North State Medical Society (North Carolina, 1887).

In 1892, Miles Vandahurst Lynk, editor and publisher of the first black medical journal, the *Medical and Surgical Observer*, issued a call for a national association of African American physicians. Three years later, on Doctors' Day (18 November 1895) at the Atlanta Cotton States and International Exposition, in the First Congregational Church, several physicians formed the American Association of Colored Physicians and Surgeons (changed to the National Medical Association in 1903). The group met sporadically at first, but then regularized annual conventions held around the country. In 1909 it authorized the publication of a quarterly, the *Journal of the National Medical Association (JNMA)*, which quickly became the voice of the organization. From the start, the National Medical Association (NMA), and shortly thereafter the *JNMA*, nurtured the development of a black medical profession and faced a racist society and medical world that disparaged and segregated black physicians.

Among its strongest leaders and most vocal early spokesmen were Charles Victor Roman (1864–1934) of Nashville, Tennessee, and John A. Kenney (1874–1950) of Tuskegee, Alabama, the first *JNMA* editor in chief and managing editor, respectively; Robert Fulton Boyd (1858–1912) of Nashville, the first president; and nationally respected surgeon and first vice president of the NMA, Daniel Hale Williams (1858–1931), founder of a large black hospital and nurse training school in Chicago.

Over its hundred-plus-year history, the NMA has faced many challenges, including battles to support financially starved black hospitals, to integrate all hospitals, to end the exclusionary practices of the AMA and state medical societies, to reform health care, and to improve the health of African Americans. One of its most visible NMA leaders during the era of segregation was W. Montague Cobb (1904–1990), who used his editorship of the *JNMA* to advocate for change. During the early twenty-first century, two of the NMA's major efforts has been to end health and health-care disparities and to promote the training of larger numbers of

African American physicians. Its membership- and health improvement–advocacy policies have always been inclusive of citizens of all backgrounds, socioeconomic status, and genders.

[*See also* **American Medical Association; Journals in Science, Medicine, and Engineering; Medical Education; Medicine; Race and Medicine; Societies and Associations, Science;** *and* **Williams, Daniel Hale.**]

BIBLIOGRAPHY

Byrd, W. Michael, and Linda A. Clayton. *An American Health Dilemma: A Medical History of African Americans and the Problem of Race.* Vols. 1 and 2. New York: Routledge, 2000 and 2002.

Savitt, Todd L. "The *Journal of the National Medical Association* 100 Years Ago: A New Voice of and for African American Physicians." *Journal of the National Medical Association* 102 (August 2010): 734–744.

Savitt, Todd L. *Race and Medicine in Nineteenth- and Early-Twentieth-Century America.* Kent, Oh.: Kent State University Press, 2007.

Todd L. Savitt

NATIONAL OCEANIC AND ATMOSPHERIC ADMINISTRATION

See Meteorology and Climatology; Oceanography.

NATIONAL PARK SYSTEM

In 1872, President Ulysses S. Grant designated 4.2 million acres of public land in Wyoming as Yellowstone National Park. Thus began a vast park system eventually administered by the National Park Service, established in 1916 within the Department of the Interior. By the 1990s, the National Park System oversaw 54 national parks and 112 national historic sites and historical parks, along with an array of national memorials, monuments, battlefields, seashores, parkways, scenic trails, and recreation areas.

The origins of the national park idea go back to the earlier growth of urban parks. Starting with New York City's Central Park in 1857, many cities created parks to provide healthful recreation for their residents. This goal, in turn, influenced the wilderness-preservation movement. The first legislation aimed at preserving a wilderness area, California's Yosemite Grant of 1864 setting aside the Yosemite Valley, was explicitly intended to provide healthful leisure for Californians. The valley was protected on the condition that it be kept open to the public. This goal of promoting public relaxation and enjoyment was reflected in the subsequent management of the valley and of Yosemite National Park (1890). The commissioners thinned trees and dredged lakes, for example, to make the valley more "park-like."

From the first, changes in technology profoundly affected the National Park System. Transcontinental railroads allowed easier access to parks, and the dry-printing process made possible the mass production of photographs that enhanced park publicity. As the parks became democratized, urban, middle-class tourists arrived in growing numbers. The rise of the automobile and a national highway system brought still more visitors. Managers at Yellowstone, Yosemite, and other parks responded by building more roads, hotels, and tourist facilities.

With more tourists came congestion and many of the problems associated with urbanization. By the 1950s, visitors were voicing unhappiness with park management because of overcrowding. By the 1990s, the parks and sites administered by the National Park System were attracting upward of 250 million visitors annually, creating profound tensions between the dual goals of public access and wilderness preservation. However, the founders of the National Park System had from the first encouraged citizens to enjoy recreation in a newly "civilized" wilderness. The problems confronting America's National Park System at the beginning of the twenty-first century were thus rooted, ironically, in the overwhelming success of the system's original goal: to provide outdoor recreation on a large scale to the American people.

[*See also* Audubon, John James; Carson, Rachel; Conservation Movement; Ecology; Environmentalism; Environmental Protection Agency; Fish and Wildlife Service, U.S.; Forest Service, U.S.; Health and Fitness; Highway System; Motor Vehicles; Muir, John; Photography; Railroads; *and* Sierra Club.]

BIBLIOGRAPHY

Hays, Samuel P. *Conservation and the Gospel of Efficiency: The Progressive Conservation Movement, 1890–1920.* Cambridge, Mass.: Harvard University Press, 1959.

Runte, Alfred. *National Parks: The American Experience.* Lincoln: University of Nebraska Press, 1979.

Michelle Lee Park

NATIONAL SCIENCE ADVISOR OFFICE

See Ethics and Professionalism in Engineering.

NATIONAL SCIENCE FOUNDATION

An independent agency within the executive branch of the federal government. Created in 1950, the National Science Foundation (NSF) awards grants and fellowships to institutions and individuals to support scientific research and science education. Policy is set by a 25-member board named by the president and approved by Congress. Although the NSF does not itself conduct research, it does maintain several research centers, such as the Kitt Peak National Observatory in Arizona.

The foundation's origins are rooted in two contrasting visions, one articulated by Democratic Senator Harley Kilgore of West Virginia and the other by the scientist Vannevar Bush. Kilgore's proposals, dating from the early 1940s and reflecting his populist belief in broad-based democratic participation in, and government coordination

of, science for public purposes envisioned a central science agency to set research priorities and to support research that would promote economic growth. Bush, head of the World War II Office of Scientific Research and Development, proposed in *Science—The Endless Frontier* (1945) an agency controlled by scientists and dedicated to the support of "basic" science.

By the time President Harry S. Truman signed legislation creating the NSF in 1950, many of the functions envisioned by Kilgore had been assumed by other agencies, such as the Atomic Energy Commission and the National Institutes of Health. In its early years, therefore, the NSF largely confined its grants to basic research. From the first, however, it had to justify its funding policies to a utilitarian-oriented public and Congress.

The Soviets' launch of the *Sputnik* satellite in 1957 led to a substantial boost in the NSF's budget and made it a serious player in research funding, responsible for some 13 percent of all federally supported academic research. But the upheavals of the 1960s prompted President Lyndon B. Johnson in 1968 to sign legislation proposed by Congressman Emilio Daddario (D-CT) that fundamentally altered the agency's mission in the direction of "applied" research. This set a pattern by which the NSF's funding priorities reflected current congressional and public concerns. During the oil crises of the 1970s, high priority went to developing alternative energy technologies. In the 1980s, worried that the United States was losing economic competitiveness, Congress pushed the NSF to support economically relevant research. In the 1980s, too, engineering, which had remained precarious within the NSF's priorities because of its image as a vocational field rather than a basic research field, gained greater representation and status within the foundation.

[*See also* Agricultural Education and Extension; Atomic Energy Commission; Bush, Vannevar; Engineering; High Schools, Science Education in; Higher Education and Science; Medical Education; National Aeronautics and Space Administration; National Institutes of Health; Office of Scientific Research and Development; Research and

Development; Science; Space Program; *and* Space Science.]

BIBLIOGRAPHY

Appel, Toby A. *Shaping Biology: The National Science Foundation and American Biological Research, 1945–1975*. Baltimore: Johns Hopkins University Press, 2000.

Kevles, Daniel J. *The Physicists: The History of a Scientific Community in Modern America*. New York: Random House, 1987.

Kleinman, Daniel Lee. *Politics on the Endless Frontier: Postwar Research Policy in the United States*. Durham, N.C.: Duke University Press, 1995.

Daniel Lee Kleinman

NATIONAL WEATHER SERVICE

See Meteorology and Climatology.

NATIVE AMERICAN HEALERS

Native American healing is based within indigenous science and practice. Health and medicine are intricately embedded in tribal language, culture, religion and spiritual beliefs, and tribal origin stories outlining teachings for a good life. There are inextricable ties to life ways, homeland, and seasonal cycles. Native healing existed well before European contact, documented by Native oral tradition and anthropologic findings such as trephination and orthopedic treatment. Curing ceremonies and efficacious therapies were detailed in journals and drawings of postcontact explorers.

Colonization had a devastating impact on indigenous healing practices, forcing some underground for survival. Some tribes lost healers and ceremonial details. Laws like the 1883 Code of Indian Offenses banned medicine persons to promote assimilation. In 1978, the Indian Religious Freedom Act decriminalized traditional medicine nationally, yet some communities did not recover from this trauma. Fortunately, in the early twenty-first century diverse healing practices and worldviews remained in many of the 565 federally recognized tribes.

Some healing principles and practices have been shared intertribally. Disease can be caused by imbalance in mind, body, or spirit; wellness is the harmony of these three elements. Human health is interconnected with the natural and spiritual world. Prayer and humility directed toward a Creator are powerful acts. Disease causality may differ from that of medical biopsychosocial models. For example, violation of tribal teachings about proper conduct during pregnancy or handling of the deceased can lead to minor or major illness. Healing typically extends beyond individuals to include families and entire communities and may influence past and future generations. Healers facilitate the restoration of harmony, but individuals must ultimately assure their ongoing well-being.

In the early twenty-first century, some tribes had a single healer, whereas others had a multitude involved in diagnosis, treatment, and prevention work. Titles may include medicine man/woman, elder, tribal doctor, or seer. They have been typically sanctioned and regulated by their tribal community, not by educational institutions or government entities. A person's family lineage or life experiences may result in selection for training. Apprenticeship can take years and involves tests to earn the right to use sacred knowledge. Most Native people have viewed traditional healers with respect for their vital community role and access them using tribal-specific protocols.

Medicine persons can be highly specialized. Examples include diagnosticians (Navajo hand tremblers or crystal gazers), singers (*hataalii* in Navajo), and midwives. In the early twenty-first century, dream interpreters existed among the Haudenosaunee (Six Nations), and healing-hands practitioners assisted Inuit villages. Others conducted specific ceremonies such as Sun Dance among the Blackfeet or girls' puberty rites among the Apache. Some tribes retained distinct medicine societies, like the Anishinaabeg (Ojibwe). Prayer and herbal medicine use were widespread in Native communities during the early twenty-first century. Sacred plants such as tobacco or corn pollen may be used for prayer offerings. Remedies like bitterroot for sore throat and raspberry leaf to improve lactation have been common intertribal knowledge. Ointments containing stinkweed or greasewood have been used for eczema treatment by Alaska Natives and Sonoran Desert tribes, respectively. Understandably, both healers and Western health professionals have been concerned for potential herb-drug interactions, particularly for their patients with chronic conditions. For diabetics, plants such as devil's club mixed with insulin or diabetes pills can lead to marked glucose reductions.

Native healing practices have included a diverse spectrum of activities beyond herbs and prayer. Examples include community dance (e.g., Yurok Brush Dance), sweatlodge purification, sings, and fasting. Sacred object use (e.g., eagle feathers) has been prevalent, as has smudging. Storytelling and counseling by elders may include tribal humor to relieve stress and reinforce appropriate behavior and attitudes. Hunting and harvesting of traditional foods such as *cous* root (Yakama) have provided vital medicines for ceremonies and for disease prevention. Some groups have preserved other unique treatments, including Kiowa horn healing to remove intrusions, and Hawaiian *ho'oponopono* (conflict resolution).

In the early twenty-first century, combined use of Native healing with Western medicine was well documented in urban and reservation health-care settings. Usage rates among urban Natives approached 40 percent, with estimates over 60 percent on reservations. Research studies supported its effectiveness beyond standard care for chemical dependency, youth suicide prevention, and depression. Collaboration between medicine people and Western-trained physicians was increasing. The Indian Health Service and the Association of American Indian Physicians had policies supporting traditional medicine and sponsored seminars to promote understanding. The Veterans Administration health system acknowledged select Navajo ceremonies to treat veterans.

Complex and sensitive issues have surrounded Native healing. Traumatic loss of culture and land has caused some tribes to question its effectiveness because access to spiritual connection is strongly linked to place of origin and indigenous language. In the early twenty-first century, elders were concerned about training the next generation of traditional healers. Tribes like the Lakota struggled to exert their treaty rights to access and protect sacred sites like the Black Hills and Bear Butte. Private insurance payment for ceremony was another challenge, as was the role of research for clinical outcomes and who should conduct studies. In 2014, the extent to which traditional practices could coexist with modern Western health-care systems remained uncertain. However, it is vital for Native communities to retain control and decide this for themselves.

[*See also* **Indian Health Service** *and* **Medicine.**]

BIBLIOGRAPHY

Beck, Peggy V., Anna Lee Walters, and Nia Francisco. *The Sacred: Ways of Knowledge, Sources of Life.* Flagstaff, Ariz.: Northland Publishing Company and Navajo Community College Press, 1990. Written by multiple Native contributors, this volume describes the complex connection of Indigenous worldviews to human healing and the sacred. Multiple references and film resources are listed for certain tribal practices.

Hill, Dawn Martin. "Traditional Medicine in Contemporary Contexts: Protecting and Respecting Indigenous Knowledge and Medicine." *National Aboriginal Health Organization.* 19 March 2003. http://www.naho.ca/documents/naho/english/pdf/research_tradition.pdf. This reference eloquently outlines controversies inherent in collaborations between Western medical practice and Indigenous healing from a First Nations (Canadian) perspective, paralleling issues in the United States.

National Library of Medicine. "Native Voices: Native Peoples' Concepts of Health and Illness." http://www.nlm.nih.gov/nativevoices/exhibition/index.html and http://americanindianhealth.nlm.nih.gov/trad-healing.html. Launched in October 2011, Native Voices explores the interconnectedness of wellness, illness, and cultural life for Native Americans, Alaska Natives, and Native Hawaiians through first-person interviews with Native healers. The traditional healing section of the American Indian Health site cites useful resources.

Swinomish Tribal Mental Health Project. *A Gathering of Wisdoms: Tribal Mental Health: A Cultural Perspective.* 2d ed. LaConner, Wash.: Swinomish Tribal Community, 2002. This collaboration between Native American tribal elders and mental health workers with non-Indian health professionals provides practical guidance for counselors, educators, and clinic administrators. It addresses major current health disparities by clarifying cultural considerations in treatment.

Theresa M. Maresca

NEWCOMB, SIMON

(1835–1909), mathematical astronomer, political economist, science commentator. Born in Wallace, Nova Scotia, Simon Newcomb showed exceptional intellectual promise under the tutelage of his schoolteacher father. For two years from 1854 he taught in a series of positions in rural Maryland, using his proximity to Washington and the Smithsonian Library to develop his knowledge of mathematics and astronomy. In 1856, taking advantage of his Smithsonian connections, Newcomb found a position as a computational assistant at the U.S. Navy's Nautical Almanac Office in Cambridge, Massachusetts, where he supervised publication of the *American Ephemeris*. He also studied mathematics at Harvard, which awarded him a B.S. degree in 1858. He advanced to professor of mathematics at the Naval Observatory in Washington, D.C., in 1861 and three years later became a naturalized U.S. citizen. Gaining an international reputation among astronomers for both observational and calculative skills, he served as superintendent of the Nautical Almanac Office, now located in Washington, from 1877 to 1897.

Newcomb excelled in mathematical analyses of the orbital motions of the moon and planets in relation to one another and to the sun. He helped bring international uniformity to classical, positional astronomy by overseeing an ambitious program of recasting computational methods, reevaluating astronomical constants, rectifying old observational data, recalculating commonly accepted orbits, and refining the positional tables for the planets and the moon. By the time of his death, he ranked among the era's most acclaimed American scientists. He received several important awards during his career, starting with the gold medal from the Royal Astronomical Society of London in 1874. He later became a Foreign Associate of the Paris Academy of Sciences, one of only eight. He was also awarded the Copley medal from the Royal Society of London.

Newcomb's work as a political economist further enhanced his reputation. Building on John Stuart Mill's classical liberalism, Newcomb published in 1885 a mathematically rigorous textbook on labor, currency, taxation, trade, and finance. Sensitive to other social and cultural issues, he criticized Christian natural theology, psychical research, and the nation's meager support for science. He underpinned his commentaries with appeals to a positivistic conception of the scientific method, aligning himself with the budding American movement later labeled pragmatism. Also adept at writing scientific popularizations and textbooks, and even science fiction, he published in all over five hundred technical, popular, and pedagogic books and articles.

[*See also* **Astronomy and Astrophysics; Mathematics and Statistics; Science; Science Fiction;** *and* **Smithsonian Institution.**]

BIBLIOGRAPHY

Kennedy, David M. *Freedom from Fear: The American People in Depression and War, 1929–1945.* New York: Oxford University Press, 1999.

Moyer, Albert E. "Newcomb, Simon (1835–1909)." In *The History of Science in the United States: An Encyclopedia,* edited by Marc Rothenberg, pp. 395–397. New York and London: Garland Publishing, 2001.

Moyer, Albert E. *A Scientist's Voice in American Culture: Simon Newcomb and the Rhetoric of Scientific Method.* Berkeley: University of California Press, 1992.

Albert E. Moyer;
updated by Elspeth Knewstubb and
Hugh Richard Slotten

NOBEL PRIZE IN BIOMEDICAL RESEARCH

This entry is about Nobel Prizes for biomedical research conducted wholly or partly in the United States, including all Nobel Prizes in Physiology or Medicine, as well as Nobel Prizes in Chemistry for research with bearing on biomedical problems. The main concern is with the types and characteristics of the organizations at which those awarded biomedical Nobel Prizes did their research.

Between 1901 and 2012, 149 scientists received the Nobel Prize for biomedical research work done partly or wholly in the United States (one hundred for physiology or medicine and 49 for chemistry with high relevance for biomedical research) (see Table 1). One hundred nine other scientists received Nobel Prizes for research in the United States in physics and types of chemistry with very little relevance to biomedical research. Of those awarded Nobel Prizes for doing all or some of their research in the United States, the vast majority received prizes after 1945. Before 1945, 9 scientists received Nobel Prizes in Physiology or Medicine for research in the United States, and 91 received Nobel Prizes after World War II. Before World War II, Theodore Richards ($C\,14$), Theodor Svedberg ($C\,26$), and Harold Urey ($C\,34$) received Nobel Prizes in Chemistry for their work in the United States (with high relevance for biomedical research); 46 individuals were so recognized after 1945. (In this entry M represents the Nobel Prize in Physiology or Medicine, C represents the Nobel Prize in Chemistry, and P represents the Nobel Prize in Physics.)

Of those who received Nobel Prizes, 37 percent had already received the Albert Lasker Basic Medical Research Award between 1945 and 2003 (Lasker Awards are the second most prestigious awards in biomedical science). Scientists who conducted their research in the United States received approximately 50 percent of the prizes in physiology or medicine and 40 percent of those in chemistry. Nobel Prizes have usually been awarded for discoveries leading to new ways of thinking about fundamental problems in the biological sciences, rather than for clinical research (although a few exceptions exist). Historically, prizes have recognized radical or new ideas, development of new methodologies, and new instruments or inventions. The annual awarding of the Nobel Prizes follows procedures slightly modified from those listed in the will of Alfred Nobel and prizes are awarded for no more than three living scientists in each field. The Karolinska Institute (Stockholm) awards prizes for physiology or medicine and the Royal Swedish Academy of Science awards those for chemistry and physics. Generally more than a decade elapses between the research work and the prize award, although Andrew Fire ($M\,2006$) and Craig Mello ($M\,2006$) were honored after relatively few years. In contrast, Peyton Rous ($M\,66$) was not recognized for more than 50 years, when he was 87. Barbara McClintock ($M\,83$) was recognized 30 years after her research, when she was 81. Since 1960, six laureates in medicine have been over the age of 80 at the time of their award, and the average age was 59 (Norrby, 2010).

Many deserving basic biomedical scientists have not been recipients of Nobel Prizes (e.g., Erwin Chargaff, the Columbia University biochemist whose work on DNA bases was vital to Watson and Crick; Oswald Avery of the Rockefeller Institute; and graduate student Albert Schatz in the lab of his professor, Selman Waksman [$M\,52$]). Peter Medawar ($M\,60$) argued that Avery's work was the most important in the biological sciences of the twentieth century, and Joshua Lederberg ($M\,58$) and others have suggested that more than 25 subsequent Nobel Prizes were dependent on it (Hollingsworth, 2004, p. 39; Pringle, 2012).

Some scholars have argued that Nobel awards are not awarded so much because of the intrinsic merit of the scientists, but more because of political considerations or "the luck of the draw" (Friedman, 2001). Yet, most of the scientific community believes Nobel Prizes are awarded on the basis of merit, and much of their behavior is influenced by this belief. There are occasionally vigorous campaigns by previous recipients to promote scientists for the Nobel Prizes. One of the more intense lobbying campaigns was that of Lawrence Bragg (*P 15*) and Linus Pauling (*C 54*) in 1960 and 1961 for Nobel Prizes for John Kendrew (*C 62*), Max Perutz (*C 62*), James Watson (*M 62*), Francis Crick (*M 62*), Maurice Wilkins (*M 62*), and Pauling's close colleague Robert Corey (Hunter, 2004).

Some Nobelists who did prize research in the United States also conducted part of their prize research outside the United States. For example, Derek Barton's was in the United States and the United Kingdom (*C 69*), Gobind Khorana's in Canada and the United States (*M 68*), Alexis Carrel's in France and the United States (*M 12*), and Karl Landsteiner's in Austria, the Netherlands, and the United States (*M 30*). Numerous laureates were foreign born but conducted all of their research in the United States, such as Severo Ochoa (*M 59*), Konrad Bloch (*M 64*), Salvador Luria (*M 69*), Baruj Benacerraf (*M 80*), Torsten Wiesel (*M 81*), David Hubel (*M 81*), Rita Levi-Montalcini (*M 86*), Mario Capecchi (*M 2007*), and Elizabeth Blackburn (*M 2009*).

There are several cases in which two or three scientists worked closely together over long periods, maximizing their scientific contributions through their association. When two such individuals had frequent and intense interaction over prolonged periods, they were able to "get inside one another's mind" to solve complex problems and increase the probability of finding a fundamental new way to solve an important problem. François Jacob (*M 65*) suggested that in contrast to the solo scientist—making all decisions about a research problem—those working in pairs often made a discovery as a result of arguing and criticizing one another or of confronting two different ways of looking at the world. Joseph Goldstein (*M 85*) referred to such relationships as scientific duopolies. Scientists working closely together over prolonged periods eventually had a kind of intuitive understanding of each others' scientific thinking. Examples of such Nobelist "twins" include Max Delbrück and Salvador Luria, Dan Nathans and Hamilton Smith, Gerty and Carl Cori (husband and wife), George Beadle and Edward Tatum, and Joseph Goldstein and Michael Brown. Occasionally, discoveries involved "triplets" (e.g.,

Frederick Robbins, Thomas Weller, and John Enders for research on the polio virus).

All 149 Nobel laureates in basic biomedical science are listed in Table 1.

The Research Environment of the Biomedical Sciences. Some universities claim "credit" for all Nobelists ever associated with them, including students, faculty, and visitors. An accurate way to assess the contribution of an organization to Nobel Prize research is to determine exactly where and when the research occurred. Determining the time and site of Nobel Prize scientific research requires extensive and painstaking archival work, as well as hundreds of interviews. Because of collaborative research, there were more Nobelists than discoveries (149 Nobelists; 125 discoveries). Only eight of the biomedical recipients were women—Gerty Cori (*M 47*), Rosalyn Yalow (*M 77*), Barbara McClintock (*M 83*), Rita Levi-Montalcini (*M 86*), Gertrude Elion (*M 88*), Linda Buck (*M 2004*), Carol Greider (*M 2009*), and Elizabeth Blackburn (*M 2009*). Among scientists who received Nobel Prizes for research in the United States, only Gertrude Elion had no degree beyond the undergraduate level.

Over time, the 149 Nobel Prize scientists did research at 78 different U.S. organizations (see Table 2). Some scientists did their Nobel Prize research at more than one organization or more than one type of organization (e.g., a university, a medical school, a research institute). Although many medical centers are in universities, they are presented here as a different type of organization. Because of their large budgets, different standards for appointments, and specific sources of funding, medical schools functioned like separate organizations, with great autonomy within universities of the same name.

Because their Nobel research was conducted over an extended time, some scientists were at different organizations during that period. Examples are Joshua Lederberg (*M 58*), who conducted his research at Columbia University, Yale University, and the University of Wisconsin; Konrad Bloch (*M 64*), who conducted his research at the University of Chicago, Columbia University College

Table 1. Scientists Recognized with Nobel Prizes in Basic Biomedical Science in U.S. Research Organizations 1901–2012*

Name	Year	Field	Name	Year	Field	Name	Year	Field
Agre, Peter	2003	Chemistry	Cori, Carl	1947	Medicine	Hartline, Halden	1967	Medicine
Altman, Sidney	1989	Chemistry	Cori, Gerti	1947	Medicine	Hartwell, Leland	2001	Medicine
Anfinsen, Christian	1972	Chemistry	Cormack, Alan	1979	Medicine	Hauptmann, Herbert	1985	Chemistry
Axel, Richard	2004	Medicine	Cournand, Andre	1956	Medicine	Heck, Richard	2010	Chemistry
Axelrod, Julius	1970	Medicine	Cram, Donald	1987	Chemistry	Hench, Philip	1950	Medicine
Baltimore, David	1975	Medicine	de Duve, Christian	1974	Medicine	Hershey, Alfred	1969	Medicine
Barton, Derek	1969	Chemistry	Delbrück, Max	1969	Medicine	Hershko, Avram	2004	Chemistry
Beadle, George	1958	Medicine	Doisy, Edward	1943	Medicine	Hitchings, George	1988	Medicine
Benacerraf, Baruj	1980	Medicine	Dulbecco, Renato	1975	Medicine	Holley, Robert	1968	Medicine
Berg, Paul	1980	Chemistry	Du Vigneaud, Vincent	1955	Chemistry	Horvitz, H. Robert	2002	Medicine
Beutler, Bruce A.	2011	Medicine				Hubel, David	1981	Medicine
Bishop, J. Michael	1989	Medicine	Edelman, Gerald	1972	Medicine	Huggins, Charles	1966	Medicine
Blackburn, Elizabeth	2009	Medicine	Elion, Gertrude	1988	Medicine	Ignarro, Louis	1998	Medicine
Blobel, Günter	1999	Medicine	Enders, John Franklin	1954	Medicine	Kandel, Eric	2000	Medicine
Bloch, Konrad	1964	Medicine	Erlanger, Joseph	1944	Medicine	Karle, Jerome	1985	Chemistry
Blumberg, Baruch	1976	Medicine	Evans, Martin	2007	Medicine	Kendall, Edward	1950	Medicine
Boyer, Paul	1997	Chemistry	Fenn, John	2002	Chemistry	Khorana, Gobind	1968	Medicine
Brown, Michael	1985	Medicine	Fire, Andrew	2006	Medicine	Knowles, William	2001	Chemistry
Buck, Linda	2004	Medicine	Fischer, Edmond	1992	Medicine	Kobilka, Brian K.	2012	Chemistry
Calvin, Melvin	1961	Chemistry	Furchgott, Robert	1998	Medicine	Kohn, Walter	1998	Chemistry
Capecchi, Mario	2007	Medicine	Gajdusek, D. Carleton	1976	Medicine	Kornberg, Arthur	1959	Medicine
Carrel, Alexis	1912	Medicine	Gasser, Herbert	1944	Medicine	Kornberg, Roger	2006	Chemistry
Cech, Thomas	1989	Chemistry	Gilbert, Walter	1980	Chemistry	Krebs, Edwin	1992	Medicine
Chalfie, Martin	2008	Chemistry	Gilman, Alfred	1994	Medicine	Landsteiner, Karl	1930	Medicine
Ciechanover, Aaron	2004	Chemistry	Goldstein, Joseph	1985	Medicine	Lauterbur, Paul	2003	Medicine
Claude, Albert	1974	Medicine	Greengard, Paul	2000	Medicine	Lederberg, Joshua	1958	Medicine
Cohen, Stanley	1986	Medicine	Greider, Carol	2009	Medicine	Lefkowitz, Robert J.	2012	Chemistry
Corey, Elias	1990	Chemistry	Guillemin, Roger	1977	Medicine	Levi-Montalcini, Rita	1986	Medicine

Name	Field	Year	Name	Field	Year	Name	Field	Year
Lewis, Edward	Medicine	1995	Pauling, Linus	Chemistry	1954	Steinman, Ralph	Medicine	2011
Lipmann, Fritz	Medicine	1953	Pedersen, Charles	Chemistry	1987	Steitz, Thomas	Chemistry	2009
Lipscomb, William	Chemistry	1976	Pople, John A.	Chemistry	1998	Sumner, James B.	Chemistry	1946
Luria, Salvador	Medicine	1969	Prusiner, Stanley	Medicine	1997	Sutherland, Earl W.	Medicine	1971
MacKinnon, Rod	Chemistry	2003	Ramakrishnan, V.	Chemistry	2009	Svedberg, Theodor	Chemistry	1926
McClintock, Barbara	Medicine	1983	Richards, Dickinson	Medicine	1956	Szostak, Jack W.	Medicine	2009
Mello, Craig	Medicine	2006	Richards, Theodore	Chemistry	1914	Tatum, Edward L.	Medicine	1958
Merrifield, R. Bruce	Chemistry	1984	Robbins, Frederick	Medicine	1954	Temin, Howard M.	Medicine	1975
Minot, George	Medicine	1934	Roberts, Richard	Medicine	1993	Theiler, Max	Medicine	1951
Moore, Stanford	Chemistry	1972	Rodbell, Martin	Medicine	1994	Thomas, E. Donnall	Medicine	1990
Morgan, Thomas H.	Medicine	1933	Rose, Irwin A.	Chemistry	2004	Tsien, Roger	Chemistry	2008
Muller, Hermann J.	Medicine	1946	Rous, Peyton	Medicine	1966	Urey, Harold	Chemistry	1932
Mullis, Kary	Chemistry	1993	Schally, Andrew V.	Medicine	1977	Varmus, Harold E.	Medicine	1989
Murad, Ferid	Medicine	1998	Sharp, Phillip A.	Chemistry	2001	von Békésy, Georg	Medicine	1961
Murphy, William P.	Medicine	1934	Sharpless, K. Barry	Chemistry	2001	Waksman, Selman	Medicine	1952
Murray, Joseph E.	Medicine	1990	Shimomura, Osamu	Chemistry	2008	Wald, George	Medicine	1967
Nathans, Daniel	Medicine	1978	Smith, Hamilton O.	Medicine	1978	Weller, Thomas H.	Medicine	1954
Negishi, Ei-ichi	Chemistry	2010	Smithies, Oliver	Medicine	2007	Whipple, George H.	Medicine	1934
Nirenberg, Marshall W.	Medicine	1968	Snell, George D.	Medicine	1980	Wiesel, Torsten	Medicine	1981
Northrop, John	Chemistry	1946	Sperry, Roger W.	Medicine	1981	Woodward, Robert	Chemistry	1965
Ochoa, Severo	Medicine	1959	Stanley, Wendell M.	Chemistry	1946	Yalow, Rosalyn	Medicine	1977
Palade, George	Medicine	1974	Stein, William H.	Chemistry	1972	Zewail, Ahmed H.	Chemistry	1999

*Recipients of the Nobel Prize in Chemistry are included only when their work had high relevance to biomedical science. Of the 149 Nobel laureates listed, 100 (67%) received the Nobel Prize in Physiology or Medicine and 49 (33%) received the Nobel Prize in Chemistry.

Table 2. Organizations at which 149 Biomedical Nobelists Conducted Their Nobel Prize Research in the United States

Type of organization	Number and percentage of biomedical Nobelists who worked in each type of organization		Number and percentage of organizations of each type	
University	68	46%	31	41%
Medical center or medical school	62	42%	27	34%
Research institute	47	32%	15	18%
For-profit firm	6	4%	5	7%
Total			78 Organizations	100%

of Physicians and Surgeons, and Harvard University; Linda Buck (*M 2004*), who conducted research at Columbia University College of Physicians and Surgeons and Harvard School of Medicine; and Louis Ignarro (*M 98*), who conducted research at Tulane and the UCLA Medical School.

What are the organizations that stand out in terms of prize research? More scientists were recognized with a Nobel Prize for research at Rockefeller Institute/University (eighteen) than anywhere else, followed distantly by Harvard Medical School with ten, Harvard College of Arts and Sciences and the California Institute of Technology (Caltech) with eight each, and Washington University Medical School with seven. Columbia University College of Physicians and Surgeons and Johns Hopkins Medical School each had six scientists who did Nobel Prize research. Three other organizations were home to Nobel research performed by five scientists (Yale, Cold Spring Harbor, and Stanford). The seven organizations at which four biomedical scientists awarded Nobel Prizes did research were Columbia University, Fox Chase Cancer Center, the Massachusetts Institute of Technology (MIT), the National Institute of Arthritis and Metabolic Diseases, the Salk Institute, University of Texas Southwestern Medical Center, and the University of Wisconsin (Madison). Thus, at least four biomedical Nobel Prize winners did research at 17 organizations, which indicates considerable concentration. In terms of Nobel Prize research, the distribution of organizations resembles a power-law, with a few organizations having several bodies of research, many

organizations having only one or two bodies of prize research, and most organizations never having research for which a basic biomedical Nobel Prize was awarded.

Characteristics of Environments for Nobel Prize Research. At multiple levels numerous factors influence the making of major discoveries. There is the national institutional level, and within the society there are organizations, most having departments/institutes, laboratories, and, of course, scientists. Each of these different levels interacts continuously with the others. Major discoveries do not randomly occur in any environment. There are certain environments in which they are most likely to occur, as well as those in which they are not likely to occur. Much of this essay attempts to explain the environments where major discoveries are likely to occur.

Institutional environments. National institutional environments consist of norms, habits, and rules that influence the behavior of research organizations, laboratories, and individual scientists. The institutional environment facilitating Nobel Prizes in the United States was one with weak central control over (1) funding for scientific research, (2) appointment of scientific personnel, (3) the existence and substance of scientific disciplines, and (4) the degree to which organizations and scientists were likely to engage in high-risk research. Historically, there tended to be a high degree of collinearity among these variables.

The more decentralized the control of a system of science, the greater the likelihood of radical discoveries and of Nobel Prizes. Across the twentieth century, the United States had a weak institutional environment, resulting in universities and research institutes with a high degree of autonomy. Partly because academic disciplines are less rigid in the United States and because universities and research institutes have considerable independence from academic disciplines and the state, Americans have had greater capacity to create new academic disciplines, institutes, and departments. In America a senior professor has the opportunity to move from one organization to another or to change research fields, and this mobility facilitates radical innovations. This is a consequence of both the weak institutional environment of American research organizations and the large number of research organizations. For example, the career path of Harvard Nobel laureate Walter Gilbert (C 80) is hardly imaginable in Europe. Gilbert, with a doctorate in physics, began teaching in the physics department at Harvard, but eventually became a professor of biology and received a Nobel Prize in Chemistry. Another case was Max Delbrück (M 69), who received a PhD in physics in Germany, but after his habilitation was rejected, he was unlikely to become a professor. In the more flexible U.S. system, he became a professor of biology at Caltech, although he had never had any formal training in biology. Essentially a self-trained biologist, he was the recipient of a Nobel Prize in Physiology or Medicine. Another unusual case was that of Gerald Edelman (M 72), who originally had a medical degree, but then worked in the physical chemistry of macromolecules. He moved from chemistry to genetics and back to chemistry and stereochemistry. Later, he made an important discovery in cell biology and ended his career with significant advances in neuroscience. Linus Pauling was probably the most extreme case of the twentieth century. Pauling defined himself as a physicist with an interest in chemistry. His scientific range included X-ray crystallography, mineralogy, biochemistry, nuclear science, genetics, molecular biology, and various areas of medicine (e.g., serology and immunology). He was the realization of the dream that leaders at the Rockefeller,

Caltech, and Hopkins had for researchers who would be at the frontiers of science.

Funding mechanisms are important means by which institutional environments influence the performance of research organizations. In the United States, there have been many different sources for financing biomedical research—major governmental organizations and literally thousands of private foundations. This diverse pool of funding has meant that American scientists have had the opportunity to pursue funding from numerous sources, some willing to support radical research agendas. Yet, over time research scientists in the United States became more dependent on the National Science Foundation and the National Institutes of Health (NIH) for funding. With competition for funding increasing, scientists became discouraged with pursuing high-risk research. However, by the end of the twentieth century, the Howard Hughes Medical Institute funded a great deal of high-risk research and a significant number of Hughes investigators have received Nobel Prizes for biomedical research.

Research organizations. Previous studies have identified several characteristics of research organizations facilitating the kind of major discoveries that often result in Nobel Prizes. These characteristics were identified through another, larger study of more than three hundred major discoveries (Hollingsworth, 2004; Hollingsworth and Hollingsworth, 2011). The characteristics are (1) moderately high scientific diversity—a variety of biological disciplines and medical specialties and subspecialties; (2) high degree of communication and integration among personnel and units, through joint publications, journal clubs and seminars, meals, and other informal activities; (3) high autonomy and flexibility—ability to shift rapidly from one area of science to another; (4) relatively small numbers of scientists; and (5) leadership with (a) strategic vision for integrating diverse areas and providing focused research, (b) ability to secure funding, (c) recruitment of scientists with moderately high scientific diversity to confront important scientific problems, and (d) provision of rigorous criticism in a nurturing manner. The more these characteristics cohere, the more likely it is there will be Nobel Prizes in an organization; little complementarity among these concepts makes Nobel Prizes less likely. These patterns will be illustrated in the case studies below. These characteristics suggest which organizations are more likely to have prize-winning research and which are unlikely to have such research. However, these characteristics do not permit any kind of prediction.

The Rockefeller Institute/University.

The Rockefeller had more scientists who received Nobel Prizes in the biomedical sciences than any other research organization in the world. In its early years, the Rockefeller established a culture of excellence and a structure that facilitated Nobel Prizes again and again. With the passage of time there have been modifications in the Rockefeller, but its underlying structure and culture of excellence have enabled it to continue to excel in research leading to radical discoveries in basic biomedical science.

From the beginning the Rockefeller emphasized scientific diversity and communication among its scientists. The first director (Simon Flexner) placed considerable emphasis on recruiting scientists whose origins were in different cultural areas and who worked in different scientific areas (e.g., Alexis Carrel [M 12] from France; Karl Landsteiner [M 30] from Austria; Hideyo Noguchi from Japan; Phoebus Levene and Samuel Meltzer from Russia; and Jacques Loeb, Leonor Michaelis, and Max Bergmann from Germany). Several were of Jewish origin in an era of strong anti-Semitism. Almost every one of these scientists internalized cultural diversity in his cognitive makeup, which increased the potential for crossing scientific disciplines.

Historically, the Rockefeller did not organize around academic disciplines, as has usually been the case in universities; rather, it has been organized around laboratories. The Rockefeller's recruitment of scientists socialized in different cultures, disciplines, and working environments has meant more potential to acquire new styles of thought. From the outset it was a place where researchers lived in multiple scientific worlds simultaneously. Primarily a research institute, the Rockefeller had

the luxury of being able to recruit scientists of excellence even if some lacked the ability to speak English well.

One of the most important reasons why the Rockefeller was able to excel in Nobel Prizes has been the quality of its leadership. Over the years nearly every Rockefeller director or president has been capable of interacting in a meaningful way with its scientists and has known personally the leading biomedical scientists of the world. Of the ten directors or presidents since its founding, five were Nobel laureates (Herbert Gasser, Joshua Lederberg, David Baltimore, Torsten Wiesel, and Paul Nurse) and two were former presidents of the U.S. National Academy of Sciences when they were appointed.

Early on, the intellectual tone at Rockefeller was one of sharing with each other the latest findings in multiple areas of biomedical science. Communication within a well-integrated research organization has the potential to change the way people view problems. The more scientists work within an integrated organizational context with a high degree of diversity, the greater the likelihood they will not stray into unproductive areas.

The environment of New York historically has been a great asset for the Rockefeller. Before jet aircraft, most distinguished foreign scientists traveling to America arrived in New York and invariably visited the Rockefeller. Certainly no other biomedical research organization in America has been so favored with visitors who discussed the latest work taking place in foreign laboratories. If a small organization could not have all the diverse ways of approaching biomedical science on its permanent staff, it nevertheless had the opportunity to have some of the world's leading scientists passing through. Moreover, it has been located in a magnificent part of New York City, with neighbors like the Cornell University Medical College and the Sloan Kettering Institute for Cancer Research. It has been at the core of one of the world's great centers of biomedical science.

Beginning around 1960, not long after Rockefeller became a small university, the relationship between the Rockefeller and other biomedical research organizations began to change. Jet aircraft had an extraordinary effect in shifting the locations of excellence in biomedical science. Distinguished scientists were increasingly willing to live in Southern California, Palo Alto, San Francisco, Seattle, Dallas, Houston, and other centers of research. Moreover, as scientific research became more complex and expensive, the NIH began to fund biomedical research on a grand scale, and the Rockefeller organization no longer had such distinctive financial advantages. The Rockefeller also became dependent on the NIH for its funding and therefore began to lose some of its autonomy. With new modes of transportation and new sources of funding, Rockefeller was no longer so able to dominate the world of biomedical science. The recipients of Nobel Prizes were no longer so concentrated in the eastern United States. Another consequence of the increasing complexity of science was that laboratories became larger, resulting in less communication among labs and scientists. Even so, the Rockefeller remained one of the world's great centers for biomedical research.

As more U.S. centers of science emerged, the Rockefeller found it necessary to appoint somewhat younger scientists to head labs. The number of laboratories there also increased. Unlike other universities structured around academic departments and disciplines, in the early twenty-first century the Rockefeller continued to be structured around labs headed by individual scientists. This structure of highly autonomous laboratories embodies a distinctive Rockefeller philosophy of basic research, built on laboratories in which individual researchers are the creative force in scientific discovery.

Throughout America, increases in knowledge place pressures on research organizations to become more internally differentiated. Even in universities that attempt to remain small, like the Rockefeller, there have been forces tending to increase the size of the organization. By the end of the twentieth century there were more than 750 scientists (postdocs, etc.) affiliated with Rockefeller, but there had never been more than 80 faculty.

If the Rockefeller became much larger and more fragmented in the early twenty-first century than it had been 40 years earlier, it still remained much less differentiated internally than every other American university. The fact that it has not had departments and that a lab closes when the head of the lab departs means that the organization has had an extraordinary amount of flexibility to adapt to the fast pace of change in science. This flexibility and adaptiveness help to explain why the Rockefeller, despite its small size, has towered over all other research organizations in America. It has had a higher proportion of its faculty as members of the U.S. National Academy of Sciences and as Howard Hughes investigators than any other biomedical research organization in America. Between 1999 and 2011, the following Rockefeller scientists received Nobel Prizes for research done at the Rockefeller: Günter Blobel (M 99), Paul Greengard (M 2000), Roderick MacKinnon (C 2003), and Ralph Steinman (M 2011). No other American university had ever received four Nobel Prizes in the biomedical sciences in a 12-year period. Even that did not equal the earlier three-year period (1972–1974), when six Rockefeller scientists received Nobel Prizes (Stanford Moore [C 72], William Stein [C 72], Gerald Edelman [M 72], Albert Claude [M 74], Christian de Duve [M 74], and George Palade [M 74]). In short, over time there is excellent evidence that Rockefeller has been one of the world's premier biomedical research organizations.

California Institute of Technology (Caltech).

Caltech has had the third largest number of Nobel Prizes in basic biomedical sciences in the United States. Some of its characteristics were similar to those of the Rockefeller; it did not have departments (rather, it had divisions of chemistry and biology). As well, it had a culture of excellence based on communication and collaboration among scientists across divisions.

Caltech differed significantly from most American universities in that it (1) was small, designed to have fewer undergraduates than faculty, postdocs, and academic visitors; (2) did not embrace all fields of knowledge, although it cultivated humanities (English, history, and economics); and (3) not only was a technical school, but also emphasized the development of fundamental basic knowledge that could be applied to practical problems. Caltech, unlike the Rockefeller and Johns Hopkins Universities, had no major philanthropic backing.

It began literally in the desert, an unlikely environment for an eminent research organization.

Caltech's structure was unique among American institutions of higher learning. Instead of a president, there was an executive council of four trustees and four senior members of the faculty. Caltech's executive council facilitated a broad and deep understanding of research throughout the institution, and the distinguished scientists on the executive committee communicated with all faculty and staff. The communication across the institute facilitated a learning environment supportive of Nobel-quality research. Only in the 1940s was the office of president created.

From the beginning, the leadership of both the Rockefeller and Caltech established a culture of excellence, prerequisite for Nobel Prizes. At the Rockefeller, this culture of excellence was developed by the president of its board, William Welch, dean of the Johns Hopkins Medical School, and Rockefeller's first director, Simon Flexner, both biomedical scientists. At Caltech the lead was taken by George Ellery Hale, an astronomer. The backgrounds of these three made for profound differences in the development of these organizations—from the outset, Welch and Flexner were bent on creating an organization emphasizing basic biomedical science. At Caltech, the early emphasis was the physical sciences.

Hale's key appointment was Arthur Noyes, one of the most distinguished U.S. chemists (trained partly by future Nobel laureate Wilhelm Ostwald, a German physical chemist). Noyes was interim president at MIT, and Hale, who had been his student, was determined to lure him to Caltech. Amazingly, he succeeded. Throughout his career, Noyes had an extraordinary ability to recruit high-quality scientists. Noyes and Hale then turned to recruiting Robert A. Millikan (P 23), a distinguished physicist at the University of Chicago who had studied with two Nobel laureates, Max Planck (P 19) and Walther Nernst (C 21). By the early 1920s, Caltech was led by a triumvirate of excellent scientists: Hale, Noyes, and Millikan. Each was an excellent scientist, administrator, and fundraiser.

To build the physics division, Millikan initiated a visiting scholar program that included A. A. Michelson, Niels Bohr, Max Born, Paul Dirac, Peter Debye, James Franck, Max von Laue, Erwin Schrödinger, Werner Heisenberg, and Albert Einstein, all leading physicists and Nobel laureates. It was quite impressive that this small university near the desert became so famous so quickly.

Caltech also trained graduate students in the physical science division. One of the first was Linus Pauling (C 54), whose subsequent research became important in transforming the basic biomedical sciences. Max Perutz (C 62) later described Pauling as the greatest chemist of the twentieth century. After his PhD, Pauling had gone to Europe as quantum mechanics was emerging and had an opportunity to learn about the new physics from Arnold Sommerfeld in Munich, Max Planck (P 19) in Berlin, and Erwin Schrödinger (P 33) in Zurich. When he returned to the United States, Pauling was one of the few chemists in the world with a good understanding of quantum mechanics, and his research at Caltech laid the foundation on which a number of Nobel Prizes in the United States and Europe were based. Amazingly, Caltech by the 1930s had become one of the world's leading centers for physicochemical research. This was in no small part because of Noyes's determination that engineering at Caltech would be subordinate to the basic sciences (Servos, 1990, p. 264).

To establish biology at Caltech, Hale, Noyes, and Millikan recruited in 1928 the best-known biologist in the United States, T. H. Morgan (M 33) of Columbia University. At that time, Morgan was becoming interested in incorporating chemistry and physics into his biology program, an approach that fit nicely with the strategy of the Caltech leaders. Within a few years of becoming head of the biology division, he was awarded the Nobel Prize in Physiology or Medicine for his work on *Drosophila*. Caltech's entry into biology with a firm foundation in genetics was a fortuitous choice. No one would have guessed that by the late 1950s the biological sciences would be firmly grounded in molecular genetics, for which numerous Nobel Prizes were awarded at Caltech and elsewhere.

Ever willing to cross fields, Linus Pauling wanted to merge his chemistry program with his increasing interest in biology. Like Rockefeller, Caltech had a dining room facilitating the coming together of scientists to promote a rich learning environment—the Athenaeum. At the lunch room Pauling's conversations with biology colleagues piqued his curiosity about biology. He mounted an effort to recruit George Beadle (*M 58*) to assist in the marriage of the two fields. Beadle moved to Caltech in 1946 as chairperson of the biology division and began working with Pauling to bring about the integration of physics, chemistry, and various aspects of biology. Beadle brought into his program emphasis on enzymology and microbiology, which included research on virology. At roughly the same time Pauling began to expand his chemistry program into studying nucleic acids and nucleoproteins. Beadle and Pauling emphasized the importance of X-ray studies of proteins, chromatography, electron microscopy, protein chemistry, chemical genetics, and biophysics, which required new instrumentation and collaboration across fields—a cross-disciplinary research program that would lead to recognition with several Nobel Prizes.

One of their first tasks was to appoint new biology staff members, one of whom was Ed Lewis (*M 95*), who over time began to work on bridging the huge gap between classical *Drosophila* genetics and a molecular approach to the early development of embryos—research resulting in his Nobel Prize. Perhaps the most impressive faculty member whom Beadle recruited during his first years was Max Delbrück (*M 69*), whose work was on bacterial viruses (phages). Delbrück's research on genetics was very different, concentrating on the replication of genetic information, whereas Beadle was primarily concerned with how genetic information was actually used.

Delbrück, Pauling, and Beadle shared several traits. They were scientific entrepreneurs, somewhat intuitive, who studied things in great depth but also had great breadth. Each had the ability to inspire others, was a visionary, and was able to recruit scientists with extraordinary talent. They also shared one other trait that facilitated their greatness. Each had such an unhappy childhood with such insecurity that he attempted to overcompensate for it by working ever harder, trying to be larger than life, often at great sacrifice, to gain greatness and recognition to compensate for dep-

rivation experienced as an adolescent. Similar traits were shared by numerous other Nobel laureates on both sides of the Atlantic (Hargittai 2002).

Delbrück's scientific biography is a key to Caltech's scientific program in an important respect. He was one of a number of physicists to move into biology about this time. Others included Salvador Luria (*M 69*), Francis Crick (*M 62*), and Seymour Benzer. In many respects, it was Delbrück's interaction with physicists and Linus Pauling (a physical chemist) that facilitated his becoming a leading figure in biology.

Beadle employed other strategies to strengthen the biology program, somewhat independent of the chemistry and physics program that he and Pauling had developed. Caltech's physics and chemistry environments were always pre-eminent over biology, but the biology program developed in its own direction. For example, Beadle took the lead in appointing as professor of psychobiology Roger Sperry (*M 81*) of the University of Chicago. Sperry worked on the specific programming of neural connections and relations between the hemispheres of the human brain, substantially advancing the understanding of consciousness, a body of research for which he was awarded a Nobel Prize.

In 1946, Caltech appointed Lee DuBridge as president, and Caltech began to be organized more like other U.S. universities. But consistent with seeds planted in its early history, it has retained frequent communication among its diverse faculty. As with Rockefeller, there has been considerable growth in its infrastructure, with large numbers of research associates, postdocs, technicians, and other support staff. Although the faculty size is small compared to most research universities, Caltech still has the capacity to be one of the most creative centers of the world in biomedical sciences. In recent years Ahmed Zewail (*C 99*) was the recipient of the Nobel Prize for Chemistry. His work was highly relevant not only for basic biomedical science but also for chemistry and physics. Zewail's research drew on participation of groups from fields as diverse as biological, electrochemical, organic, inorganic, and physical chemistry to conduct multidisciplinary research on fundamental processes in complex molecular systems. Although there were no other Nobel Prizes at Caltech in neuroscience, it did become one of America's leading centers in neurobiology in the last 25 years of the century.

The cases of the Rockefeller and Caltech suggest that—controlling for size—small organizations highly committed to excellence have a greater likelihood of having scientists receiving Nobel Prizes than large research organizations differentiated into many scientific disciplines. During the 50-year period beginning in the early 1960s, moreover, Rockefeller and Caltech have had a higher percentage of faculty who are members of the U.S. National Academy of Sciences than any other university.

Johns Hopkins Medical School. Another small research organization having a number of scientists who received Nobel Prizes in the basic biomedical sciences was Johns Hopkins Medical School. At its founding, Hopkins represented a fundamental departure from the tradition of medical schools. With a large endowment, Hopkins recruited the highest quality faculty available and had the best equipped laboratories on either side of the Atlantic. Its medical faculty was the leading one in America by 1900. Just as Simon Flexner and George Hale were great leaders who were instrumental in establishing a culture of excellence at the Rockefeller and Caltech, William H. Welch played a similar role at Hopkins. Some have argued that Welch had more influence in developing the biomedical sciences in the United States than anyone else in American history. In addition to choosing Simon Flexner as the first director of the Rockefeller, Welch served more than three decades as president of the board of the Rockefeller Institute; he also served as president of the American Association for the Advancement of Science, the National Academy of Sciences, the American Medical Association, the Association of American Physicians, and as chairman of the Executive Committee of the Carnegie Institute for some years. Because of his connections with leading centers of American science, he was able to identify and recruit some of the best scientists in America for Johns Hopkins (Fleming, 1954).

Throughout its history, the structure and culture of the Hopkins Medical School, with its great emphasis on research, provided it with a distinctive advantage in having a number of scientists who received Nobel Prizes. At Hopkins, the goal of the medical school was to exalt the scientist over the practitioner, to have the ideal of scientific research the goal of each physician and surgeon. By integrating the research laboratory with teaching and clinical practice, Hopkins brought about a revolution in medical schools. With research rather than teaching a dominant aspect of Hopkins's culture, scientists had exceptionally light teaching responsibilities. Its staff was generally expected to engage in high-risk research, and one of its major goals was to be the best biomedical research center in the world. To attain this goal, most departments in their early years developed scholarly journals, which played an important role in establishing new subdisciplines in the United States.

Like the Rockefeller and Caltech, its early culture of excellence in research, cooperation, and collegiality has remained over time. During the last third of the twentieth century, Hopkins's performance in receiving Nobel Prizes was significantly enhanced because it was among the top three research organizations in receiving funds from NIH.

Hopkins has tended to recruit scientists who internalized a great deal of scientific diversity, and its administrators have provided scientists with a rich nurturing environment. In some respects, most of the Nobel Prizes at Hopkins Medical School were in settings somewhat analogous to those at the Rockefeller and Caltech: the Hopkins scientists who received such recognition were not highly integrated in departments and not constrained by organizational inertia. Although the Hopkins Medical School has always been larger than the Rockefeller, both organizations have historically had a high degree of paternalism.

There has long been a tradition at Hopkins of deans going to basic scientists and asking what kind of resources they need for research. This, of course, is very different from the culture of most large public universities where resources have been allocated in a much more bureaucratic style. Dan Nathans (*M 78*) noted that the deans always provided him with whatever he needed: "I never had to go to the head of my department to ask for anything because he came to me before I needed to make a formal request. This type of behavior has been ingrained in the Hopkins culture" (interview of Dan Nathans by Rogers Hollingsworth, 21 July 1997).

The spirit of cooperation was pervasive across the university. Especially in the Medical School, people were very communicative, not only with colleagues in the basic sciences but also with clinicians. For many years, there tended to be a more collegial, intimate, cooperative group of faculty than in any other U.S. medical school. The emphasis among the faculty has always been on excellence in research. There was not cutthroat competition among senior scientists, as manifest in some larger U.S. medical schools and research universities. Nor was there heavy emphasis on producing many graduate students and scientific papers. Historically, the culture of the Hopkins Medical School was quite different because in most medical schools, the clinical departments dominated basic sciences.

University of Chicago. The three previous cases were research organizations founded about the time of the awarding of the first Nobel Prizes. Each had a culture highly committed to excellence and has remained a relatively small organization—not differentiated into a large number of departments. At the end of the nineteenth century, another small university (Chicago)—highly committed to excellence—was founded, one with considerable financial resources. Why has it had hardly any Nobel Prizes in the biomedical sciences? After all, it has had numerous Nobel Prizes in economics, chemistry, and physics. The answer lies in the structure of the biological sciences. If there is not a high degree of communication and integration across the various parts of a research organization, there are unlikely to be radical breakthroughs resulting in Nobel Prizes.

The University of Chicago from its beginning had a division of the biological sciences, and for decades the dean of the biological sciences has been a medical clinician. This has resulted in the basic biological sciences having lower status and influence than at the three organizations discussed above. And this has been a major reason why the University of Chicago has |lagged in receiving Nobel Prizes in physiology or medicine. On the other hand, the University of Chicago has been one of the leading medical schools producing clinicians—demonstrating that the organizational environment required for excellence in basic biomedical science is quite different from that for training excellent clinicians. The Mayo Clinic in Rochester, Minnesota, is another small, excellent biomedical organization but its research culture has focused primarily on clinical matters. However, two of its scientists (Kendall [M 50] and Hench [M 50]) shared a Nobel Prize.

Large Research Organizations and the Challenges of Change. New knowledge with the potential to be recognized with a Nobel Prize requires new specialties, new instrumentation, and other technologies that generally necessitate the hiring of personnel. But adding personnel in new specialties, increasing diversity with the required spread of talents, and providing depth in each area has led to growth in the size of research organizations. As research organizations have increased in diversity and depth, there has been a tendency for them to experience more differentiation and less integration and communication among scientists. A critical problem has been how organizations can incorporate the expansion of new knowledge without becoming too fragmented. When research organizations responded to growth by differentiating into new departments and imposing hierarchical controls, there has been a decline in communication and diminished possibility of Nobel Prize research.

Many large American research universities are organizations that have responded to changes in biological and medical knowledge by differentiating into new departments and growing in size. Many medical schools have gone through the same process. At times, several of these places appeared to be poised to be the contexts of outstanding science. They had large amounts of research funding, produced many scientific papers, and had a number of scientists in the U.S. National Academy of Sciences. But they did not have the structural, cultural, and leadership characteristics necessary for Nobel Prizes in the biomedical sciences.

All these processes have moved research universities and medical schools toward greater bureaucratization, including standardization of rules and creation of budgetary controls. Paradoxically, as research organizations have received additional sources of revenue, there have usually been considerable pressures on departments and other subunits to find more research dollars. These processes have shifted scientific research toward greater specialization and narrow projects that result in more scientific papers but not to focus on more fundamental issues. Instead, scientists spend increasing proportions of their time writing research proposals and doing administrative tasks (Ginsberg, 2011).

Most papers resulting in Nobel Prizes in the biological sciences have generally been addressed to scientists in diverse fields, not to scientists in highly specialized fields. The leading large research organizations have numerous scientists who write papers for scholars who are highly specialized, but this style of science is usually unlikely to be recognized with Nobel Prizes.

Over time, as research organizations have differentiated into more departments and other subunits, recruitment and the search for additional funding have been delegated to lower levels, quite unlike the Rockefeller. In a large multiunit university, it is difficult for provosts or even deans to have firsthand knowledge of the fields in which scientists are being recruited. Delegating the primary responsibility for recruitment to departments and other subunits heavily emphasizes disciplinary considerations in the recruitment process—unlike the Rockefeller and Caltech. Academic departments are inherently socially conservative and often select people who reproduce their thinking. Thus, differentiation has hampered the opportunities for crossing academic disciplines and generating scientific integration, so important for Nobel Prizes in biomedical science. At such large organizations, there have been occasional Nobel Prizes, but proportionate to their size, only a few. Such prizes are anomalies or singletons. This pattern has been much the same at such outstanding universities as Michigan, Minnesota, Duke, and many others.

This process has occurred not only in American universities and medical schools but also in other types of research organizations. For example, in the 1950s and 1960s NIH had several bodies of research resulting in Nobel Prizes when the various institutes were still relatively small. But massive growth in federal funding led to expansion in the size and number of labs and in their level of specialization, as well as to increasing bureaucratization of the institutes. NIH lost its magnetic attraction for scientists as other well-funded research centers developed, resulting in a dwindling in the number of Nobel Prizes at the institutes.

Strategies for Making Major Discoveries in Large Research Organizations.

Growth in size leads to diminishing communication among scientists within their organization and their capacity to do prizewinning work. The challenge for large research organizations is to respond to changes in knowledge without losing communication and integration across fields. There are various strategies that large research organizations can pursue in their quest to make major discoveries.

Keeping departments flexible.

The Harvard College of Arts and Sciences has been very successful in maintaining departments with capacity to adapt quickly to new knowledge. This strategy was facilitated by the unique role of the president of Harvard. Since the 1940s an important role of the president has been to convene an ad hoc committee of distinguished scholars—from within and outside the United States—in an effort to have a rigorous assessment for every proposed tenured appointment in the College of Arts and Sciences. The assumption is that a tenured appointment is a university's most precious asset.

These ad hoc committees, institutionalized by President Conant, frequently contested the judgment of academic departments, vetoing a tenured appointment previously approved by a department and a dean. This process, by blocking tendencies among departments to reproduce themselves, has increased scientific diversity within the college and has facilitated Harvard's flexibility in adapting to the larger world of science, giving it a distinct advantage over other universities. The key to Harvard scientists' ability to reorient themselves into new programs and departments has been the fact that their recruitment procedures have minimized the tendency of departments to reproduce their research agenda. It has been not plentiful financial resources, but the strategy for making tenured appointments that permitted Harvard for a number of years to be consistently at the frontiers of biomedical science and to have a number of scientists recognized with Nobel Prizes in the biological sciences.

Transforming mediocrity into excellence.
The biology program at MIT was so mediocre prior to the 1960s that physicists, chemists, and engineers exerted strong pressure on the administration to close the department because it could hardly attract good graduate students and postdocs. MIT's administration responded with a high-risk strategy, recruiting the distinguished biologist Salvador Luria (*M 69*) from the University of Illinois. He arrived with the plan of developing an integrated teaching program for undergraduates. This proved so successful that in a short time numerous undergraduates decided to study biology, leading to the appointment of more faculty. A decision was made that there would be only one department in the biological sciences, and it would appoint only those who could effectively communicate with others about their research. Although several research institutes were subsequently attached to the department, for many years it also attempted to limit the size of the faculty in the biomedical sciences. Within a few years, MIT became a center where several Nobel Prizes were awarded in the basic biological sciences. Others (Khorana [*M 68*] and Tonegawa [*M 87*] who did their Nobel work elsewhere) moved there. Clearly, Luria's strategy paid off handsomely. Like the Rockefeller and Caltech, MIT's strategy was facilitated by not having a medical school.

Creating a small, interdisciplinary institute within a large research organization.
The University of Wisconsin (Madison) followed this strategy between 1960 and 1990, with the creation of the Enzyme Institute and the McArdle Cancer Institute. Both were small insti-

tutes, which allowed for highly focused research and permitted intense and frequent interactions among faculty from diverse backgrounds who had *full-time* appointments in the institutes. Significantly, Wisconsin had Nobel laureates whose research emerged from these two institutes, plus other scientists who received prestigious awards.

Most large research universities have numerous research institutes. What differentiated Wisconsin's two research institutes from most of those in other American universities is that most university scientists do not have full-time appointments in an institute, but rather in disciplinary-based departments. Because university awards (promotion, salaries, etc.) are decided at the departmental level, scientists' primary loyalties are to departments, not to a research institute. The interdisciplinary institute is most effective in promoting a highly integrated scientific environment when scientists have their primary loyalties to it. Although it is very difficult to develop high-quality institutes within universities, several independent, autonomous institutes have had a number of Nobel Prizes in physiology or medicine (e.g., Salk Institute, Fred Hutchinson Cancer Center, Cold Spring Harbor).

Creating a new organization.
The Medical School of the University of Washington (Seattle) is an interesting example of the creation of a new organization that moved to the cutting edge of research. Its new medical school, created after World War II, was not hampered by the organizational inertia that has limited excellence in many medical schools. When the school was created, most medical schools were dominated by clinicians who had little interest in basic research—a reason they have received few Nobel Prizes in medicine. Largely because the University of Washington Medical School had no hospital during the early years of its existence, its first clinicians were very research oriented. Moreover, the school's first dean (Edward Turner) established a culture of excellence in research and training. Most of his departmental chairs, whether in basic or in clinical medicine, were people of extraordinarily high quality, who worked cooperatively across basic and clinical sciences. A culture of cooperation across departments and a commitment

to excellence in research has persisted into the early twenty-first century. The school grew to prominence at the same time that NIH funding increased, and a close relationship developed between the school and the NIH, thus providing funding for high-quality research. There are a number of indicators that the University of Washington has become a center of excellence for the biomedical sciences. After 1970, four of its faculty received Nobel Prizes in biomedical science, and for more than 25 years it was among the top five research organizations in funding from the NIH. Whereas in 1950 the University of Washington had only one member of the U.S. National Academy of Sciences, by 2000 it had seventy-one.

The Laboratory. Most laboratories where Nobel Prizes have occurred have not focused on narrow or highly specialized problems, and researchers have published in journals directed to scientists in many different fields (e.g., *Science, Nature, Cell Biology, Proceedings of the National Academy of Sciences*). The lab heads reflect high levels of scientific diversity and are generally well connected in multiple fields of science. Usually there is relatively easy access to instrumentation and funding for high-risk research. The heads of these labs have had high cognitive complexity, capacity to be very flexible in their thinking, the ability to be very entrepreneurial in their approach to problems, and willingness to take high risks in research. Of course, laboratories may have all these characteristics and yet have no major discoveries. On the other hand, most laboratories, especially those embedded in large research organizations, have been highly specialized, headed by scientists with relatively low levels of cognitive complexity, reluctant to cross scientific disciplines, and not inclined to take big scientific risks.

Those who have high cognitive complexity internalize the norms, habits, and conventions of more than one culture. Some scientists have high cognitive complexity because of strong identities based on ethnicity, nationality, religion, or class. A large percentage of scientists receiving the Nobel Prize in the biomedical sciences internalized multiple cultures and were both insiders and outsiders.

Their capacity to live in more than one world simultaneously was the key to their high cognitive complexity. When they were university students, it was almost second nature for them to cross from one field into another. And it is no accident that in this age of specialization, the discoveries by these Nobel laureates reflected a great deal of scientific diversity. Julius Axelrod (*M 70*), Max Delbrück (*M 69*), Gerald Edelman (*M 72*), Gertrude Elion (*M 88*), Joseph Goldstein (*M 85*), Eric Kandel (*M 2000*), Arthur Kornberg (*M 59*), Joshua Lederberg (*M 58*), Rita Levi-Montalcini (*M 86*), Salvador Luria (*M 69*), Linus Pauling (*C 54*), and Rosalyn Yalow (*M 77*) are examples of such scientists.

Although most Nobel Prizes in medicine occurred in laboratory environments with the aforementioned characteristics, most labs with these features did not make major discoveries. In other words, these attributes facilitated Nobel Prize recognition, but were not sufficient. For example, the following laboratories of scientists at the Rockefeller had the characteristics discussed in the preceding two paragraphs but were never recognized with a Nobel Prize: Oswald Avery (previously mentioned), Max Bergman (a chemist and biochemist whose major work was with peptide syntheses), René Dubos (a microbiologist who made major contributions on soil micro-organisms and antibacterial substances), Phoebus Levene (a biochemist who made fundamental contributions to the study of nucleic acids), and Leonor Michaelis (a chemist who made substantial advances in enzymology). Some have suggested that James Darnell deserved two Nobel Prizes—one for his work on messenger RNA and the other for his discovery of how signals outside cells turn on genes inside cells. Both bodies of work led directly to research by other scientists who received Nobel Prizes (Kandel, 2002).

Why did so many laboratories not receive Nobel Prizes if their profiles were similar to those receiving Nobel Prizes? Several considerations deserve attention: major breakthroughs in basic science are not the straightforward outcome of experiments. Laboratory work in the biological sciences is especially unpredictable, ambiguous, and "messy." Pauling frequently argued that every discovery contains an irrational element and that the discovery process involved a great deal of intuition. Niels Jerne (M 84) reported that his most important discovery did not grow logically or rationally, but he simply got a sudden feeling that his theory must be true. Many discoveries recognized with a Nobel Prize involve a great deal of chance and contingency. True, there have been some important experiments that were beautifully designed, with scientists planning in great detail what was to be done. But with most complex research projects, these have been more the exception than the rule.

There is also luck. A particular field of science may be in a crisis but a new set of ideas, instrument, or technique may arise. An individual who is in the right place at the right time, possessing the right skills and knowledge in multiple fields, with high cognitive complexity and propensity to integrate diverse fields of knowledge, has an opportunity to make a major breakthrough—opening up a new way of seeing a major problem—resulting in a Nobel Prize. This happened with Francis Crick (M 62) and James Watson (M 62) for their work on the structure of DNA, Marshall Nirenberg (M 68) for his work on the genetic code, and Gerald Edelman (M 72) for his work concerning the chemical structure of antibodies. Even with the "right" institutional, organizational, and laboratory characteristics as identified above, the element of luck may play an important role for scientists in their research leading to Nobel Prizes.

To understand why there have been so many U.S. Nobel laureates since 1945, it is important to recognize that for 250 years the most highly creative systems of science have been embedded only in societies that were political, economic, and military hegemons. In 2012, many observers believed that the United States was in relative economic, political, and military decline, and if this was so, should one expect that the U.S. hegemonic system of science would also begin to decline? Historically, it has been possible only retrospectively to understand when scientific hegemons were in decline. If the past is any guide to the future, one would expect the U.S. proportion of Nobel Prizes to diminish, although during the early twenty-first century, the United States continued to receive a high proportion of Nobel Prizes in basic biomedical science.

Acknowledgment.   David M. Gear provided valuable assistance in the preparation of this essay.

[*See also* **Biochemistry; Biological Sciences; Biotechnology; Chemistry; Flexner Report; Gender and Science; Genetics and Genetic Engineering; Higher Education and Science; Medical Education; Medicine; Medicine and Technology; Molecular Biology; National Academy of Sciences; National Institutes of Health; National Science Foundation; Physics; Race and Medicine; Research and Development; Rockefeller Institute, The;** *and* **Science.**]

BIBLIOGRAPHY

Bishop, J. Michael. *How to Win the Nobel Prize: An Unexpected Life in Science.* Cambridge, Mass.: Harvard University Press, 2003.

Björk, Ragnar. "Inside the Nobel Committee on Medicine: Prize Competition Procedures 1901–1950 and the Fate of Carl Neuberg." *Minerva* 39 (2001): 393–408.

Conant, James B. *My Several Lives: Memoirs of a Social Inventor.* New York: Harper & Row, 1970.

Crawford, Elisabeth. *Nationalism and Internationalism in Science, 1880–1939: Four Studies of the Nobel Population.* Cambridge, U.K.: Cambridge University Press, 1992.

Djerassi, Carl. *Cantor's Dilemma.* New York: Doubleday, 1989.

Finch, Clement A. *Fulfilling the Dream: A History of the University of Washington School of Medicine, 1946–1988.* Seattle, Wash.: Medical Alumni Association, University of Washington School of Medicine, 1990.

Fischer, Ernst Peter, and Carol Lipson. *Thinking about Science: Max Delbrück and the Origins of Molecular Biology.* New York: W. W. Norton, 1988.

Fleming, Donald. *William H. Welch and the Rise of Modern Medicine.* Boston: Little, Brown, 1954.

Friedberg, Errol C. *From Rags to Riches: The Phenomenal Rise of the University of Texas Southwestern Medical Center at Dallas.* Durham, N.C.: Carolina Academic Press, 2007.

Friedman, Robert Marc. *The Politics of Excellence: Behind the Nobel Prize in Science.* New York: Henry Holt & Company, 2001.

Geiger, Roger L. *To Advance Knowledge: The Growth of American Research Universities, 1900–1940.* New York: Oxford University Press, 1986.

Ginsberg, Benjamin. *The Fall of the Faculty and the Rise of the All-Administrative University and Why It Matters.* New York: Oxford University Press, 2011.

Goldstein, Joseph. *Scientific Duopolies.* Retrieved from http://www.laskerfoundation.org/awards/whatmerits2002.htm.

Goodstein, Judith R. *Millikan's School: A History of the California Institute of Technology.* New York: W. W. Norton, 1991.

Hager, Thomas. *Force of Nature: The Life of Linus Pauling.* New York: Simon & Schuster, 1995.

Hargittai, István. *The Road to Stockholm: Nobel Prizes, Science, and Scientists.* Oxford and New York: Oxford University Press, 2002.

Hollingsworth, J. Rogers. "Institutionalizing Excellence in Biomedical Research: The Case of Rockefeller University." In *Creating a Tradition of Biomedical Research: Contributions to the History of The Rockefeller University*, edited by Darwin H. Stapleton, pp. 17–63. New York: Rockefeller University Press, 2004.

Hollingsworth, J. Rogers, and Ellen Jane Hollingsworth. "Major Discoveries and Biomedical Research Organizations: Perspectives on Interdisciplinarity, Nurturing Leadership, and Integrated Structure and Cultures." In *Practising Interdisciplinarity*, edited by Peter Weingart and Nico Stehr, pp. 215–244. Toronto: University of Toronto Press, 2000.

Hollingsworth, J. Rogers, and Ellen Jane Hollingsworth. *Major Discoveries, Creativity, and the Dynamics of Science.* Vienna: edition echoraum, 2011.

Hunter, Graeme K. *Light Is a Messenger: The Life and Science of William Lawrence Bragg.* Oxford: Oxford University Press, 2004.

Jacob, François. *The Statue Within: An Autobiography.* Translated by Franklin Philip. Cold Spring Harbor, N.Y.: Cold Spring Harbor Laboratory Press, 1995.

Kandel, Eric. *Albert Lasker Award for Special Achievement in Medical Science Award Presentation by Eric Kandel.* Retrieved from http://www.laskerfoundation.org/awards/2002_s_presentation.htm.

Kohler, Robert E. *Lords of the Fly.* Chicago: University of Chicago Press, 1994.

Luria, Salvador E. *A Slot Machine, a Broken Test Tube: An Autobiography.* New York: Harper & Row, 1984.

Norrby, Erling. *Nobel Prizes and Life Sciences.* Singapore: World Scientific, 2010.

Opfell, Olga S. *The Lady Laureates: Women Who Have Won the Nobel Prize.* Metuchen, N.J.: Scarecrow Press, 1986.

Pringle, Peter. *Experiment Eleven: Dark Secrets behind the Discovery of a Wonder Drug.* New York: Walker & Company, 2012.

Rossiter, Margaret W. *Women Scientists in America: Forging a New World since 1972.* Baltimore: Johns Hopkins University Press, 2012.

Servos, John. *Physical Chemistry from Ostwald to Pauling.* Princeton, N.J.: Princeton University Press, 1990.

Zuckerman, Harriet. *Scientific Elite: Nobel Laureates in the United States.* New York: Free Press, 1977.

J. Rogers Hollingsworth and
Ellen Jane Hollingsworth

NOYCE, ROBERT

See Solid-State Electronics.

NOYES, ARTHUR AMOS

(1866–1936), physical chemist, educational reformer, textbook writer, academic administrator, institution builder. Noyes's research helped raise American chemistry to international stature during the period from 1890 to 1930 while he reformed scientific education at the Massachusetts Institute of Technology (MIT) and California Institute of Technology (Caltech).

Born in Newburyport, Massachusetts, Noyes obtained his B.S. in chemistry in 1886 and M.S. in organic chemistry in 1887 from MIT. In 1888 he became the first PhD student at Leipzig University, Germany, of Wilhelm Ostwald, founder of the new discipline of physical chemistry. Returning to MIT, Noyes rose from instructor in 1890 to professor in 1899 while promoting scholarly research, modernizing chemistry instruction, and broadening engineering education. In 1893 Noyes established the Research Laboratory of Physical Chemistry (RLPC), the first of its kind in the United States, partly financing it himself.

It focused on the behavior of electrolytes in solution, which Noyes had begun investigating at Leipzig, and ventured into frontier areas such as chemical bonding. Many RLPC graduates numbered among the elite of American physical chemistry.

Noyes wrote numerous textbooks while at MIT; Linus Pauling's obituary of him noted that two of them apparently "revolutioniz[ed] the teaching of both analytical chemistry and physical chemistry in America" and further asserted that "Noyes was a very good chemist…[b]ut he was a *great* teacher of chemistry" (Pauling, 1958). Noyes aimed at broadening students' education in all dimensions. When speaking with students about their work and futures, he said, "I often felt keenly how much more they need advice about *life* than about chemistry" (Noyes, 1908). From 1907 to 1909 Noyes was acting president of MIT. Because MIT increasingly favored applied over basic science and resisted his reform initiatives, Noyes became susceptible to the blandishments of astronomer George Ellery Hale, his former student.

After establishing Mount Wilson Observatory in 1904, Hale set about transforming Throop College of Technology in nearby Pasadena, California, into a worthy scientific partner. Luring Noyes to Pasadena was central to Hale's project. In 1919 Noyes became head of chemistry and a senior administrator at Throop, renamed the California Institute of Technology in 1920. Noyes and Hale were of one mind regarding the primacy of basic science at Caltech and recruited physicist Robert Millikan as president to advance that vision. They also instituted a small, elite undergraduate program that stressed broad education. By the time Noyes arrived at Caltech, his research career was ending, but while there he reached his zenith as an educational and institutional reformer.

[*See also* **Chemistry; Hale, George Ellery; Higher Education and Science; Millikan, Robert A.; Pauling, Linus;** *and* **Science.**]

BIBLIOGRAPHY

Noyes, Arthur A. "A Talk on Teaching." *Science*, New Series 28 (1908): 657–665.

Pauling, Linus. "Arthur Amos Noyes, September 13, 1866–June 3, 1936." *Biographical Memoirs of the National Academy of Sciences* 31 (1958): 322–346.

Servos, John W. *Physical Chemistry from Ostwald to Pauling: The Making of a Science in America.* Princeton, N.J.: Princeton University Press, 1990. This indispensable work describes Noyes's careers at MIT and Caltech and places them in the wider scientific, economic, institutional, and social contexts.

Stephen J. Weininger

NUCLEAR POWER

In the aftermath of World War II and the beginning of the widely hailed "atomic age," a plethora of books and articles suggested that the dangers of atomic weapons would be offset, at least partially, by the potential peaceful benefits of nuclear technology. Most of the projected applications, such as atomic automobiles and small reactors to heat and cool individual homes, were hopelessly fanciful. Proposals for building reactors to generate electricity in central power stations were more realistic, but progress was slow, especially with the Harry S. Truman administration's focus on the military uses of atomic energy.

In 1954, Congress passed a law intended to speed nuclear-power development. The 1954 Atomic Energy Act made possible for the first time the wide commercial use of atomic energy by ending the government's monopoly of the technology. It assigned the Atomic Energy Commission (AEC) responsibility for both promoting nuclear power and regulating its safety. To the frustration of the AEC and the congressional Joint Committee on Atomic Energy, many utilities refrained from making a major commitment to nuclear power because of the abundance of conventional fuels and because of economic uncertainties and unresolved safety questions about the technology.

Beginning in the mid-1960s, however, nuclear-power development experienced a sudden and unanticipated boom. This came about for several reasons, including indications that large nuclear plants could compete economically with coal, the rise of interconnected electrical grids that encouraged the construction of large plants, and intensifying concern about air pollution from fossil-fuel units. The nuclear boom produced a rapid growth not only in the number of nuclear plants but also in the size of individual plants, which in less than a decade grew from small demonstration facilities to behemoths.

The expansion of the nuclear industry took place at virtually the same time as the development of environmentalism as a potent political force. By the early 1970s, nuclear power had become a leading target of environmental activism and the subject of a highly visible and increasingly strident debate. Critics claimed that the technology was neither safe nor necessary; supporters argued that it was both safe and essential for the nation's energy future. At the center of the controversy were the unresolved issues of the likelihood and consequences of a major reactor accident and the effects of exposure to low levels of radiation. As the debate continued, public uneasiness about the risks of nuclear power increased substantially, and by the end of the 1970s orders for new plants has slowed dramatically. The slump in the industry resulted more from inflation and reduced demand for electricity than antinuclear activism, but the complaints of nuclear opponents strongly influenced public attitudes.

The debate over nuclear power intensified after the most serious accident in a U.S. nuclear power plant occurred at the Three Mile Island station near Harrisburg, Pennsylvania, in March 1979. The accident's severity was caused by mechanical failures and human error, and although only small amounts of radiation were released, the political fallout was heavy. The accident undermined the credibility of the Nuclear Regulatory Commission (NRC) and the nuclear industry while enhancing that of antinuclear critics.

After the shock of Three Mile Island, the NRC and the nuclear industry focused on a series of issues that had commanded only limited interest before the accident. These were intended to reduce the likelihood of another major accident and, if one did occur, to enhance the ability of the NRC, the utility, and the public to cope with it. At the direction of the NRC, power companies

improved plants that were operating or under construction. After a moratorium of more than one year, the NRC resumed issuing operating licenses for completed nuclear units in August 1980. By 1989, it had granted full-power licenses to more than 40 reactors, most of which had been under construction since the mid-1970s. No new nuclear-power reactors were ordered after 1978, and many earlier orders were canceled.

In 2000, 103 nuclear-power plants were operating in the United States, providing about 20 percent of the nation's generating capacity. By that time, the debate over nuclear power had faded as a national issue, although it continued to trigger heated arguments in many local areas where plants were located.

During the early twenty-first century, some commentators started discussing the possibility of a "renaissance" in the nuclear-power industry, driven by concerns about the use of fossil fuels, including new worries about the role of greenhouse gas emissions in global warming. But the talk of a renaissance in nuclear power was dealt a severe blow in 2011 by a serious nuclear accident in Japan at the Fukushima I Nuclear Power Plant.

[*See also* **Atomic Energy Commission; Electricity and Electrification; Environmentalism; Global Warming; Household Technology; Hydroelectric Power; Military, Science and Technology and the; Nuclear Regulatory Commission; Nuclear Weapons; Science; Technology;** *and* **Three Mile Island Accident.**]

BIBLIOGRAPHY

Balogh, Brian. *Chain Reaction: Expert Debate and Public Participation in American Commercial Nuclear Power, 1945–1975.* New York: Cambridge University Press, 1991.

Mazuzan, George T., and J. Samuel Walker. *Controlling the Atom: The Beginnings of Nuclear Regulation, 1946–1962.* Berkeley: University of California Press, 1985.

Morone, Joseph G., and Edward J. Woodhouse. *The Demise of Nuclear Energy? Lessons for Democratic Control of Technology.* New Haven, Conn.: Yale University Press, 1989.

Rees, Joseph V. *Hostages of Each Other: The Transformation of Nuclear Safety since Three Mile Island.* Chicago: University of Chicago Press, 1994.

Walker, J. Samuel. *Containing the Atom: Nuclear Regulation in a Changing Environment, 1963–1971.* Berkeley: University of California Press, 1992.

Walker, J. Samuel. *The Road to Yucca Mountain: The Development of Radioactive Waste Policy in the United States.* Berkeley: University of California Press, 2009.

Walker, J. Samuel. *Three Mile Island: A Nuclear Crisis in Historical Perspective.* Berkeley: University of California Press, 2004.

J. Samuel Walker;
updated by Hugh Richard Slotten

NUCLEAR REGULATORY COMMISSION

The Nuclear Regulatory Commission (NRC) was created by the Energy Reorganization Act of 1974 to assume the regulatory duties of the Atomic Energy Commission (AEC), which the law abolished. The AEC had become the target of sharp criticism in the public debate over the safety of commercial nuclear power, partly because it had a statutory mandate both to regulate and to promote the nuclear industry. The NRC's responsibilities were limited to regulating the safety of nuclear power and other civilian applications of nuclear energy.

The NRC, headed by five commissioners appointed by the president of United States, began operations in January 1975. Most of its staff members were holdovers from the AEC, but the new agency hoped to dispel the widespread public suspicion of the AEC by demonstrating its toughness as a regulator. This proved difficult, if not impossible. As the public debate over the safety of nuclear power raged on, former critics of the AEC were not inclined to regard the NRC more charitably. The NRC's efforts to overcome these suspicions were hampered by a serious fire at an Alabama nuclear power plant in 1975, highly publicized allegations that the NRC's radiation-protection regulations and reactor-safety requirements were too lax, and growing concern about nuclear weapons proliferation.

In March 1979, the worst accident in the history of commercial nuclear power in the United States occurred at Unit 2 of the Three Mile Island plant near Harrisburg, Pennsylvania. A series of mechanical failures and human errors uncovered the core of the reactor and melted about half of it. The plant suffered irreparable damage, and the credibility of the nuclear industry and the NRC fared almost as badly. Although very little radiation escaped into the environment, the accident intensified doubts about the safety of nuclear power and seriously undermined public support for the technology.

In the aftermath of Three Mile Island, the NRC devoted increased attention to a number of issues highlighted by the accident. These included ways in which a series of minor failures could lead to a major accident, the need for improved operator training, better means to assess the probability of reactor accidents, and upgraded emergency preparedness and planning. In the absence of orders for new plants, the agency allocated more of its resources to regulating the safety of existing plants, setting standards for the decommissioning of closed plants, and evaluating the complex and politically sensitive issue of the disposal of radioactive waste materials.

[*See also* Atomic Energy Commission; Environmentalism; Nuclear Power; Nuclear Weapons; Technology; *and* Three Mile Island Accident.]

BIBLIOGRAPHY

Okrent, David. *Nuclear Reactor Safety: On the History of the Regulatory Process.* Madison: University of Wisconsin Press, 1981.

Walker, J. Samuel. *A Short History of Nuclear Regulation, 1946–1990.* Washington, D.C.: U.S. Nuclear Regulatory Commission, 1993.

J. Samuel Walker

NUCLEAR WEAPONS

The history of nuclear weapons began well before the United States entered World War II. Spurred by the German discovery of nuclear fission announced early in 1939, scientists at several universities had confirmed the feasibility of an unimaginably powerful chain-reacting bomb and suggested how to build one. In August 1939, the émigré physicist Albert Einstein wrote a letter to President Franklin Delano Roosevelt (drafted by another émigré physicist, Leo Szilard) reporting these developments; in response, Roosevelt authorized a modest research program. In the summer of 1941, the federal Office of Scientific Research and Development transferred this small, scattered research program to the Army Corps of Engineers. Taking charge of what became known as the Manhattan Project, General Leslie R. Groves organized a crash program of expanded research, industrial production of fissionable materials, and bomb development.

Research was consolidated at the University of Chicago's new Metallurgical Laboratory, where Enrico Fermi and his team achieved the first controlled nuclear reaction in December 1942. Chicago also developed the health and safety measures adopted throughout the project. Construction of production facilities for enriched uranium at Oak Ridge, Tennessee, and for plutonium at Hanford, Washington, proceeded in parallel. Groves picked J. Robert Oppenheimer to direct bomb development in a new laboratory at Los Alamos, New Mexico, managed by the University of California. Buildings were still going up when scientists began work in April 1943.

By 1945, Oppenheimer's team had designed and built two fission bombs. One used enriched uranium in a gun-type assembly, a design deemed so reliable as to need no proof-testing before deployment. The other depended on the newly discovered fissionable element plutonium assembled by implosion, a much less certain technique that did demand testing. A secret test, code named Trinity, took place at Alamogordo, New Mexico, on 16 July 1945, producing energy equivalent to 21 thousand tons (21 kilotons) of high explosives.

On 6–9 August 1945, the United States launched its nuclear attack on Japan, dropping the uranium bomb on Hiroshima and the plutonium bomb on Nagasaki. At Bikini Atoll in July 1946, two more plutonium bombs furnished the firepower for a test series called Operation Crossroads. Part public spectacle intended to demonstrate America's nuclear might, part attempt to assess the effect of nuclear weapons on ships, Operation Crossroads became the Manhattan Project's last hurrah.

After heated congressional debate, the Atomic Energy Act of 1946 settled responsibility for developing future nuclear weapons on a civilian agency, the Atomic Energy Commission (AEC). Civilian control of nuclear weapons remained intact when the AEC gave way in 1974 to the Energy Research and Development Administration, itself succeeded in 1977 by the Department of Energy. The Manhattan Project officially transferred its facilities to the AEC on 1 January 1947. Its remaining, specifically military components merged under the new Department of Defense as the Armed Forces Special Weapons Project (after two subsequent name changes, it eventually became the Defense Special Weapons Agency).

Of the major transferred facilities, only Los Alamos remained concerned primarily with nuclear-weapons research and development. Its former engineering division, however, had grown rapidly after moving to Albuquerque, New Mexico, in 1945. In 1949, it became the independent Sandia Laboratories, with its management transferred from the University of California to Bell Laboratories. Its primary function was providing the engineering support to turn Los Alamos designs into working weapons.

With the Cold War now well under way, nuclear-weapons development became a high national priority. The AEC inaugurated its nuclear-weapons testing program in the spring of 1948 with Operation Sandstone. Supported by a joint army-navy task force, Los Alamos scientists tested three new fission-bomb designs at Enewetak Atoll. Part of the United Nations (UN) Trust Territory of the Marshall Islands administered by the United States, Enewetak officially became the Pacific Proving Ground, which expanded in 1951 to include Bikini. When the outbreak of the Korean War threatened to disrupt schedules for Operation Greenhouse, the next Pacific test series, the AEC selected a continental test site in Nevada, first used for Operation Ranger in January 1951.

During the 1950s, annual testing alternated between Nevada, where operations were cheaper but restrictions greater, and the Marshall Islands, which served as the site for testing very-large-yield thermonuclear weapons. A Soviet atomic-bomb test in August 1949, decidedly sooner than many expected, had severely jolted American complacency. To meet the perceived challenge, Edward Teller (among others) vigorously advocated accelerated development of the hydrogen bomb, the so-called Super, based on thermonuclear fusion, the main subject of Teller's research at wartime Los Alamos. Although no one yet knew how to design such a weapon, President Harry S. Truman in January 1950 authorized a crash program.

The conceptual breakthrough came a year later, in February and March 1951, from a suggestion by the Los Alamos mathematician Stanislaw Ulam, which Teller improved and extended. A fission first stage (primary) would provide the energy to ignite the thermonuclear fuel (deuterium and tritium, the heavy isotopes of hydrogen) in a second stage (secondary). In essence, the Ulam-Teller idea was to couple the primary's energy to the secondary via X-rays. Hydrogen bombs (H-bombs) promised yields measured in megatons rather than the kilotons of fission bombs.

Although not based on the Ulam-Teller principle, the Greenhouse George test in May 1951 showed that a fission detonation could indeed ignite small amounts of thermonuclear fuel. Teller still deemed H-bomb progress too slow, however, and with air force support and backing from the cyclotron inventor and Nobelist Ernest O. Lawrence, he successfully lobbied the AEC for a second nuclear-weapons laboratory. It opened in September 1952 as the Livermore branch of Lawrence's Berkeley Radiation Laboratory. Two decades later it became the independent Lawrence Livermore Laboratory, still under University of California management.

The new Livermore laboratory contributed little to early thermonuclear development, which remained largely a Los Alamos enterprise. The "Mike" test in Operation Ivy at Enewetak on 1 November 1952 demonstrated a full-scale thermonuclear detonation. Sixteen months later at Bikini, on 1 March 1954, the Bravo test of Operation Castle proved the design of an aircraft-deliverable H-bomb. Twice as powerful as predicted, Bravo caused heavy fallout that injured Marshall Islanders and Japanese fishermen a hundred miles and more from ground zero. Public outcry led to the test moratorium of 1958–1961 and then to the Partial Nuclear Test Ban Treaty of 1963 that ended above-ground testing. Testing moved underground.

The peak of innovation in nuclear-weapons design, with Livermore now playing a major role, came in the period 1955–1965. Despite the three-year moratorium, at least two and as many as five new types of warheads entered the stockpile each year. Gravity bombs continued to improve; the introduction in 1955 of the long-range jet-powered B-52 gave the air force a bomber that could plausibly deliver them on strategic targets. Intercontinental ballistic missiles (ICBMs) benefited even more from the trend toward efficient, lighter warheads. The first air force squadron of Atlas ICBMs became operational in 1958, followed in 1960 by the navy's nuclear-powered, missile-equipped Polaris submarine. Nuclear warheads for a variety of tactical missiles, artillery shells, torpedoes, and other munitions also proliferated.

By the mid-1960s, with nuclear-weapons development no longer posing major scientific challenges, the focus of innovation shifted from warheads to delivery systems. In 1967, the air force completed replacing its first-generation ICBMs, which used cryogenic propellants, with technically safer and more reliable missiles using solid (Minuteman) or hypergolic (Titan II) propellants. Protected in underground silos, the new missiles were ready for immediate launch. When the last Polaris submarine went to sea, also in 1967, the strategic triad of manned bombers, land-based missiles, and missile-armed submarines was in place.

The next missile generation, fitted with multiple independently targetable reentry vehicles, followed quickly. The air force deployed the first Minuteman IIIs in 1970 and the navy its first Poseidon fleet ballistic missile systems in 1971. With land-based and sea-launched missiles from multiple independently targetable reentry vehicles, the United States acquired a reliable and essentially invulnerable means of responding to, and so deterring, nuclear attack.

Delivery systems and guidance, like warheads, continued to improve, but not radically. Although the air force's Peacekeeper missile (first deployed in 1986) and the navy's Trident system (1979) marked advances in accuracy over their predecessors, their basic character remained unchanged. Efforts to develop an antiballistic missile system in the late 1960s and early 1970s produced only a modest deployment and were limited by the Antiballistic Missile Treaty of 1972. The much more ambitious Strategic Defense Initiative (Star Wars), pursued in the 1980s, cost more and produced less.

The end of the Cold War brought reductions in nuclear stockpiles and, in 1992, a halt to U.S. nuclear-weapons testing. The United States retained its nuclear arsenal at reduced levels, however, and the Department of Energy instituted a laboratory science–based "stockpile stewardship" program to insure that aging weapons would remain both safe in storage and reliable if ever required. Although the Cold War nuclear-arms race faded, nuclear weapons remained a major concern. In the 1990s, fearful that nuclear know-how might fall into dangerous hands, the Clinton administration sought to safeguard nuclear installations in the former Soviet Union. Pakistan's test of a nuclear weapon in 1998 (thereby matching India, which had exploded a nuclear device as early as 1974) stirred fears of a regional nuclear arms race.

After the 11 September 2001 terrorist attacks, the U.S. government focused on a possible nuclear attack by a rogue state or even a small terrorist band. Under President George W. Bush, the nuclear danger was subsumed into a larger preoccupation with weapons of mass destruction, including chemical and biological weapons. Allegations (later proven unfounded) that Iraqi dictator Saddam Hussein possessed weapons of mass destruction provided a rationale for the Iraq War of 2003. The Bush administration also proceeded with deployment of a missile-defense system, a limited version of President Ronald Reagan's grandiose Strategic Defense Initiative.

Fears of nuclear proliferation deepened in 2004, when Pakistan's chief nuclear scientist, Abdul Kahn, confessed that he had sold nuclear-weapons components to Libya, North Korea, and Iran. Libyan strongman Muammar al-Qaddafi agreed to abandon his nuclear weapons program in 2004, in exchange for a lifting of U.S. sanctions. North Korea continued its program, however, expelling inspectors from the UN's International Atomic Energy Agency in 2009 and conducting an underground nuclear-weapons test, as part of complex diplomatic maneuverings with the United States, South Korea, Japan, and China. Iran, strictly limiting agency inspections, admitted to enriching uranium at secret sites, but insisted it was for peaceful purposes, not weapons. Unconvinced, the UN and the United States imposed sanctions in 2006–2007, while Israel (itself a nuclear power) pondered its options. Although the nuclear threat mutated into new forms, it showed no signs of disappearing as the United States moved deeper into the twenty-first century.

[*See also* **Atomic Energy Commission; Diplomacy (post-1945), Science and Technology and; Manhattan Project; Military, Science and Technology and the; Missiles and Rockets; Nuclear Power; Nuclear Regulatory Commission;** *and* **Strategic Defense Initiative.**]

BIBLIOGRAPHY

Glasstone Samuel, and Philip J. Dolan, eds. *The Effects of Nuclear Weapons.* 3d ed. Washington, D.C.: U.S. Department of Defense, 1977.

Hacker, Barton C. *The Dragon's Tail: Radiation Safety in the Manhattan Project, 1942–1946.* Berkeley: University of California Press, 1988.

Hacker, Barton C. *Elements of Controversy: The Atomic Energy Commission and Radiation Safety in Nuclear Weapons Testing, 1947–1974.* Berkeley: University of California Press, 1994.

Hansen, Chuck. *U.S. Nuclear Weapons: The Secret History.* Arlington, Tex.: Orion Books, 1988.

Hewlett, Richard, et al. *A History of the United States Atomic Energy Commission.* 3 vols. Washington, D.C.: The Commission, 1962–1989.

Polmar, Norman, and Timothy M. Laur, eds. *Strategic Air Command: People, Aircraft, Missiles.* 2d ed. Baltimore: Nautical and Aviation Publishing Company of America, 1990.

Rhodes, Richard. *The Making of the Atomic Bomb.* New York: Simon & Schuster, 1986.

Rhodes, Richard. *Twilight of the Bombs: Recent Challenges, New Dangers, and Prospects for a World without Nuclear Weapons.* New York: Alfred A. Knopf, 2011.

York, Herbert F. *The Advisers: Oppenheimer, Teller, and the Superbomb.* San Francisco: W. H. Freeman, 1976.

Barton C. Hacker;
updated by Paul S. Boyer

NURSING

Broadly defined, the history of nursing encompasses all deliberate activities that support the care of the sick and the wounded and that create the kinds of healthy environments in which healing and health occur. Examples stretch from the long-expected work of families, through the activities of male religious brotherhoods caring for sick and wounded European Crusaders, to those working in "plague houses" that sequestered the victims of epidemics that sped across the globe, to the earliest hospitals that cared for those without families and friends (Kalisch and Kalisch, 1978, pp. 13–17). More traditionally, the history of nursing begins in the mid-nineteenth century as an attempt to find respected and respectable work for white middle-class women. It continues through the twentieth century as these women sought to codify and control the standards of their particular work and to define their place and their role within hospitals and the new project then known as scientific medicine and public health. This history is also one of confronting the challenges brought by men and women of color who also claimed the title of nurse and of challenging practice boundaries that would separate their work from that of physicians. In the end, the history of nursing is part of the story of the hospitals and health-care systems in which nurses worked. But it is also a story about how these women and men used this kind of work to create meaningful opportunities within their more personal communities of friends and families. It is a story about women and men who did the work of transforming hospitals and health-care systems into their modern form even as they used their particular form of work—nursing—to create

new choices and opportunities for themselves (D'Antonio, 2010). This trade of work for a wider range of options about how one lived one's life worked. By the early twenty-first century, nurses had emerged as the largest, most diverse, and most trusted of all health professionals (Gallup, 2010).

The Invention of Modern Nursing. Historians traditionally date the roots of modern trained nursing to the work of Florence Nightingale, the well-born, well-educated daughter of upper-middle-class British parents whose work in the Crimea nursing British soldiers in 1854 and 1855 captured the Western world's attention. Scholars debate the extent to which the work of Nightingale and her small, carefully chosen group of women nurses actually changed the appalling morbidity and mortality rates among British soldiers; and Nightingale herself later learned that the rates at her own base hospital at Scutari, Turkey, remained among the highest of all those in the Crimean peninsula. Nonetheless, the image of the "Lady with the Lamp," immortalized in Henry Wadsworth Longfellow's 1857 poem "Santa Filomena," captured the imagination of the Anglo-American world. A grateful British public raised money for a training school for nurses, eventually opened at St. Thomas's Hospital in London in 1860 (Bostridge, 2008). In the United States, health officials for what would become the Union Army in the upcoming Civil War looked to her 1859 *Notes on Hospitals* for ideas about creating effective, clean, and well-ventilated hospital structures and ward environments. And many northern American women, wanting to do their own part nursing soldiers in this war, flocked to the battlefields with Nightingale's widely serialized 1860 *Notes on Nursing* as their textbook and their inspiration.

The results were decidedly mixed. Dorothea Dix, a well-known reformer who had worked tirelessly to reform the care of the mentally ill in the United States, took formal charge of the work of women who nursed and later described it as an exasperating experience. Too many women had too many ideas about how to properly care for the sick and wounded (Brown, 1998). Nor was this experience unique to the United States. Lady Jenny Churchill, the American-born mother of the later British Prime Minister, Winston Churchill, tried to replicate Nightingale's success in the Crimea by sending women nurses on a hospital ship to the 1899 Boer War. These women were dismissed in the press and by the military as "frivolous," and nursing in the British military remained the purview of men (Kahn, 2001).

In some respects, these later failed experiences attest to Nightingale's own personal charisma. Other arguments point to Britain's need to create a heroine to combat the dismal strategic failures of and tragic loss of lives in the military in the Crimean peninsula (Helmstadter, 2010). And certainly, a few of the largest, most prestigious, and urban hospitals in the United States, Great Britain, and the British colonies of Australia and Canada followed the example of St. Thomas's and opened training schools for nurses in the 1870s and 1880s. These well-publicized and self-consciously titled "Nightingale-styled" schools succeeded in offering a secular alternative to the long traditions of the excellent nursing care given by Catholic religious sisterhoods in scattered parts of the United States and Protestant deaconesses on the European continent. But the real rise of nursing as a respected and respectable option for women depended on the later nineteenth century's new definition of scientific medicine and the need to extend its precepts to the poor and the dispossessed.

Science and Nursing. Definitions of science changed in the latter half of the nineteenth century as the laboratory and its experimental manipulations of biological, chemical, and physiological materials assumed increasing importance. Although demonstrable and effective clinical interventions needed to wait until the early decades of the twentieth century, the late-nineteenth-century laboratory's need for precise measurements, careful correlations, and replicable results infused the practices of more well-educated physicians. The personalized and sometimes idiosyncratic observations of families, still the most common and, in the value that subjective knowledge held, the most powerful source of nursing care, emerged as increasingly problematic. At the same time, new knowledge about the aseptic implications of the bacteriology for surgery and surgical wound healing made these families' homes an increasingly problematic site for these kinds of medical interventions. Throughout the closing decades of the nineteenth century, physicians and the women who would be nurses negotiated a trading of work for knowledge. Physicians would teach these women about this new science and scientific procedures in return for support of their practices and their interventions; and these women, in turn, would support these practices and precisely execute these directions in exchange for the kind of medical knowledge that would allow them to differentiate their own nursing practices from that of mothers and other lay women. In addition, this trade of work for knowledge would take place in hospitals—a new and increasingly effective public space dedicated to science and scientific healing far away from the intimate and private home. This was a trade that ultimately succeeded. By 1890, there were fewer than 500 trained nurses in the United States alone. By 1900 there were 3,500, and by 1910 there were more than 8,000 (D'Antonio, 2010, pp. 18–26).

This trade of work for knowledge took a consistent form. Students—generally called pupil nurses—worked for first two and then later three years in hospitals learning about such subjects as anatomy, physiology, biochemistry, pharmacology, operating room procedures, and nutrition while also providing increasingly complicated nursing measures. Well into the 1950s, in fact, hospital nursing care meant student nursing care in the United States and most Western countries. After graduation and the conferral of a formal nursing diploma, the new graduates left the hospital for private duty in individual patient homes or public-health nursing practice in communities. Upcoming and incoming students took their places.

Science and Society. Through the first half of the twentieth century, hospitals and their associated training schools reflected the increasingly secular and segregated societies in which they existed. The overwhelming numbers of hospital-based training schools enrolled only white women. In response, the place of religious sisterhoods in nursing became increasingly invisible, although Catholic nursing sisters would go on to establish the largest not-for-profit system of hospital care in the United States (Wall, 2005). The very small numbers of men who would nurse trained almost exclusively in schools associated with psychiatric asylums because the care of those with serious mental illnesses presumed a special need for the physical strength to deal with violent attacks. And the separate black hospitals—most often based in large northern urban areas—established their own training schools for black women to both learn nursing and care for black hospitalized patients (Hine, 1989). But as historians have pointed out, support for black women, other women of color, and underrepresented minorities' access to nursing education and practice has often been for reasons other than only health-care reform. South Africa's apartheid government, for example, championed nursing education as a way to produce a stable middle class (Mark, 1994). And the Philippine government deliberately positioned its system of nursing education at the center of an export economy determined to create remittances sent home by its nurses abroad working to meet the increasing demand for nurses and nursing care from the United States and the Continent (Choy, 2003).

As historians have long pointed out, women came to training schools from very different backgrounds and left with widely divergent experiences. The worst—and often the smallest and more remote—training schools provided negligible time in lecture halls and limited clinical experiences. The best—and often the largest—training schools accepted relatively well-educated women and provided them with a range of lectures and ward practice in nutrition and medical, surgical, obstetrical, and infectious nursing. But for much of the first half of the twentieth century, nursing leaders and educators had little direct control over their students' curriculum; training schools were controlled by hospitals and their administrators. In response, and inside their schools, educators focused on the day-to-day experiences that would turn a young and inexperienced girl into a formally trained nurse. At its worst, the transformation meant absurdly strict discipline, blind loyalty, and rote obedience (Reverby, 1987). But at its best, the transformation provided the knowledge and support nurses needed to confront and manage their patients' pain, suffering, and deteriorating clinical presentation.

The quite variable nature of nursing education quickly led nursing leadership in the United States, Great Britain, Canada, and Germany to create professional associations, to push for the same legal protection for the practice of nursing that physicians had negotiated for their practice of medicine, and to create mandatory licensing standards that would add the force of law to their campaigns for higher, voluntary standards of education for practice. These self-consciously professionalizing initiatives quickly became flash points of conflicts among nurses, hospital administrators, and other constituent groups keenly interested in standards for the care of the sick. On a very local level, nurses whose educational experiences did not match those put forward as necessary—with strong support from the hospitals in which they trained—mounted successful campaigns that acknowledged their particular contributions to the care of patients with whom they worked. On a transnational level, the creation and the work of the International Council of Nurses in the decade before World War I began with great optimism about the possibilities of professionalizing nurses of all nations but ultimately floundered on the demanding adaptations needed to accommodate the different social and political contexts of its nation-state members (Soine, 2010). The actual work of nursing—the skilled body work and the intimate emotional demands—remained largely invisible to a wider audience. In individual states in the United States, licensure requirements remained voluntary well into the 1930s and only some hospitals and public-health agencies required such credentials for employment.

Nursing and the Public's Health. By contrast, the work of those nurses protecting the public's health remained very visible. The roots of public-health nursing lay in a philanthropic impulse to care for the sick poor in their homes. In midcentury England, William Rathbone, devoted to public and private welfare work, turned to

Florence Nightingale to help create a home for nurses who would care for Liverpool's sick poor. Almost simultaneously, a small group of wealthy women in Charleston, South Carolina, formed the Ladies Benevolent Association and hired a lone nurse to care for that city's black and white sick poor in their own homes (Wilkerson, 2001). Over the next decades such individual charitable impulses grew into an international public-health movement that depended on the work of nurses for its acknowledged success.

The rise of public-health nursing drew from a very particular confluence of new scientific knowledge, appalling social conditions, and a newfound optimism about the malleability of the built environment. During the late nineteenth and early twentieth centuries, the careful determination of infectious disease vectors allowed for the possibility of the control of such deadly scourges as tuberculosis, typhoid, and pneumonia through isolation, personal hygiene, and health education. At the same time, the urban tenements and slums where hundreds of thousands of poor, immigrant, and working-class families lived became seen as places where homes could be cleaned, windows opened, and streets swept, and the sick family members were isolated from the healthy ones. Historians agree that a simultaneous fear that infectious bacteria could too easily move from the slums into middle-class neighborhoods and a wish to help the poor, dispossessed, and newly arrived immigrant groups fueled the rise of the public-health movement both in the United States and across the globe. And nurses, with their traditions of easy and trusted access to these families during times of sickness through charitable organizations, were well positioned to return to teach what other historians have called the gospel of health (Tomes, 1990).

By the 1920s, public-health nurses had joined the battle to control infectious diseases not only through case finding and care but also through general public-health campaigns focusing on the elimination of health risks. They were instrumental in the campaign to reduce maternal mortality and morbidity by providing greater access to prenatal care. They worked to substantially decrease rates of infant and childhood mortality through clean-milk campaigns, well-baby examinations, and nutrition education. And they worked with both children in schools and adults in factories and other work sites to provide healthy environments, infectious disease screening, and the medical follow-up necessary to ensure adequate treatment (Wilkerson, 1990). At the same time, public-health nurses strongly supported the aspirations of scientific medicine. In the United States, for example, public-health nurses effectively eliminated a long tradition of lay midwifery practice in regions where mothers had sufficient access to physicians and hospitals by joining with physicians to encourage mothers to have a medically attended childbirth in hospitals.

Nursing and the Nation's Health.   Nursing, like many other health-care practice disciplines, lost some hard-won gains in both illness and health care during the global Depression of the 1930s, as neither patients nor states, private philanthropies, insurance companies, or hospitals could afford the costs of all its services. But, with the advent of World War II came a sharply increased demand for nurses for both civilian and military service. Paradoxically, this demand proved to be a boon: in the United States, the demand for nurses led directly to federal funding for nursing education, loosening the financial grip of hospitals on their training schools, and to the official desegregation of, first, the Army Nurse Corps and soon thereafter the American Nurses Association (Kalisch and Kalisch, 1978, pp. 560–570).

Yet the health-care world to which these nurses returned at war's end was rapidly changing, particularly in the victorious and powerful United States. Now, the spread of health insurance made hospital care more affordable for middle-class patients; federal and state monies enshrined hospitals as the centerpiece of its health-care system; and innovative medical technologies, including penicillin, created expectations of aggressive treatment and recovery among those who sought its services. As historians have argued, the continued shortage of nurses coupled with increasing demands for their services created clinical spaces where physicians and nurses yet again rethought the nature of the trade of scientific knowledge for increasingly respected and responsible nursing practice. In newly created critical-care units, coronary-care units, and primary-care sites, supportive physicians and talented nurses renegotiated practice boundaries that had once been the sole domain of medicine (Fairman and Lynaugh, 2000; Keeling, 2007; Fairman, 2008).

The new practice demands of the postwar era resurrected older questions about the education needed for such practices. The grip of hospital-based diploma programs had begun to loosen with a small number of baccalaureate programs established in the 1920s as a basis for preparation for public-health nursing. But this accelerated in the 1950s and 1960s with the establishment of nursing education as a cornerstone of the community college movement in the United States and passage of the federal Nurse Training Act that poured over $4 billion into basic and advanced nursing education over a 10-year period. Midcentury nursing leaders had great hopes that these initiatives would establish a hierarchical system of practice with baccalaureate-prepared "professional" nurses supervising the practice of associate-degreed "technical" nurses. But as now mandatory state licensure laws ultimately determined who had the right to practice the full scope of nursing's responsibilities, the imagined differentiation dissolved in the press of day-to-day practice. Today, the United States shares with other nations across the globe multiple pathways to professional nursing practice. But it has the most secure foothold in university and collegiate settings, allowing it to develop a robust program of education for advanced practice and research into illness, health, and wellness care.

More fundamentally, the postwar changes in nursing's funding opportunities, curricular opportunities, and practice patterns affected not only the numbers but also the social, racial, and gendered backgrounds of nurses. Even as the absolute numbers of white women nurses grew, nursing became less and less exclusively white women's work as the numbers of men and women of color grew dramatically. Moreover, nurses of color were more likely to take advantage of the multiple pathways to professional nursing practice: they may have entered as diploma or community-college

graduates because these venues demanded less financial and material resources; but they were also more likely to eventually earn a baccalaureate and the opportunity to expand their practice (D'Antonio, 2010, pp. 170–179). Their particular experiences illustrate the place of nurses and nursing at the fulcrum of both public as well as private concerns and professional as well as personal achievements in hospitals and health-care systems in the United States and across the globe.

[*See also* **Anatomy and Human Dissection; Biochemistry; Biological Sciences; Disease; Food and Diet; Foundations and Health; Gender and Science; Germ Theory of Disease; Health and Fitness; Health Insurance; Health Maintenance Organizations; Hospitals; Hygiene, Personal; Influenza; Medical Education; Medical Specialization; Medicine; Medicine and Technology; Mental Health Institutions; Mental Illness; Midwifery; Penicillin; Pharmacology and Drug Therapy; Physiology; Psychiatry; Public Health; Race and Medicine; Religion and Science; Surgery; Tuberculosis; Typhoid Fever; Typhus; War and Medicine;** *and* Yellow Fever.]

BIBLIOGRAPHY

Bostridge, Mark. *Florence Nightingale: The Making of an Icon.* New York: Farrar, Straus and Giroux, 2008.

Brown, Thomas. *Dorothea Dix: New England Reformer.* Cambridge, Mass.: Harvard University Press, 1998.

Choy, Catherine Cenzia. *Empire of Care: Nursing and Migration in Filipino American History.* Durham, N.C.: Duke University Press, 2003.

D'Antonio, Patricia. *American Nursing: A History of Knowledge, Authority, and the Meaning of Work.* Baltimore: Johns Hopkins University Press, 2010.

Fairman, Julie. *Making Room in the Clinic: Nurse Practitioners and the Evolution of Modern Health Care.* New Brunswick, N.J.: Rutgers University Press, 2008.

Fairman, Julie, and Joan Lynaugh. *Critical Care Nursing: A History.* Philadelphia: University of Pennsylvania Press, 2000.

Gallup. "In U.S., Nurses at Top of Ethics List, Lobbyists at Bottom." 10 December 2010. http://www.gallup.com/video/145199/nurses-top-ethic-list-lobbyists-bottom.aspx (accessed 11 April 2012). Nurses have topped Gallup's Honesty and Ethics ranking every year but one since they were added to the Gallup list of most honest professions in 1999. The only exception is 2001 when firefighters earned a record high of 90% in the aftermath of the September 11 terrorist attacks. http://www.gallup.com/poll/112264/nurses-shine-while-bankers-slump-ethics-ratings.aspx (accessed 11 April 2012).

Helmstadter, Carol. "Navigating the Political Straits in the Crimean War." In Notes on Nightingale: The Influence and Legacy of a Nursing Icon, edited by Sioban Nelson and Anne Marie Rafferty, pp. 28–54.. Ithaca, N.Y.: Cornell University Press, 2010.

Hine, Darlene Clark. Black Women in White: Racial Conflict and Cooperation in the Nursing Profession. Bloomington: Indiana University Press, 1989.

Kahn, Richard J. "Women and Men at Sea: Gender Debate aboard the Hospital Ship Maine during the Boer War, 1899–1900." Journal of the History of Medicine and Allied Sciences 56 (April 2001): 111–139.

Kalisch, Philip A., and Beatrice Kalisch. The Advance of America Nursing. Boston: Little, Brown and Co., 1978.

Keeling, Arlene. Nursing and the Privilege of Prescription, 1893–2000. Columbus: Ohio State University Press, 2007.

Mark, Shula. Divided Sisterhood: Race, Class, and Gender in the South African Nursing Profession. London: Palgrave Macmillan, 1994.

Melosh, Barbara. The Physician's Hand: Nurses and Nursing in the Twentieth Century. Philadelphia: Temple University Press, 1982.

Reverby, Susan. Ordered to Care: The Dilemma of American Nursing, 1850–1945. New York and London: Cambridge University Press, 1987.

Soine, Aeleah. "The Relation of the Nurse to the Working World: Professionalization, Citizenship, and Class in Germany, Great Britain, and the United States before World War I." Nursing History Review 18 (2010): 51–80.

Tomes, Nancy. Gospel of Germs: Men, Women and the Microbe in American Life. Cambridge, Mass.: Harvard University Press, 1998.

Wall, Barbra Mann. Unlikely Entrepreneurs: Catholic Sisters and the Hospital Marketplace. Columbus: Ohio State University Press, 2005.

Wilkerson, Karen Buhler. False Dawn: The Rise and Decline of Public Health Nursing in America, 1900–1930. New York: Garland Publishing, 1990.

Wilkerson, Karen Buhler. No Place Like Home: A History of Nursing and Home Care in the United States. Baltimore: Johns Hopkins University Press, 2001.

Patricia D'Antonio

NYLON

Nylon, when it was publicly announced in 1938, was heralded as a chemical breakthrough that would soon replace silk in women's stockings. A high-technology polymer product that had outstanding physical properties, nylon demonstrated that synthetic materials were not just inferior substitutes for natural ones. Over the following decades, nylon lived up to its early promise, making it the most important innovation in the history of the DuPont Company. Nylon emerged from the research of Wallace H. Carothers, a chemist in DuPont's fundamental research program initiated in 1927 to do basic research in certain fields of chemistry. After arriving at DuPont from Harvard in 1928, Carothers began to study the structure of large molecules. At the time was there a scientific controversy over whether these molecules were just larger versions of ordinary compounds.

Carothers's experiments proved that this was indeed the case with the development of methods for constructing long-chain molecules or polymers. In 1930, Carothers's associate, Julian Hill, made a polymer chain that was so long that the resulting material could be drawn into very strong fibers. Over the next four years, Carothers's team made fibers from various polymers, hoping to find one that had all the properties necessary for a commercial fiber. In May 1934, Donald Coffman made a polyamide material, later named nylon, which yielded fibers that were strong and elastic and melted at a very high temperature. DuPont research director Elmer K. Bolton immediately concluded that nylon had commercial potential despite the many technological obstacles that researchers would need to overcome. First, nylon was made from two basic chemicals, both exotic compounds that were only produced on a laboratory scale. Reacting these two chemicals to produce a standardized polymer suitable for synthetic fibers was another major challenge. Then, the polymer would have to been turned into fibers that could be woven or knitted into fabrics that would be attractive to consumers.

To commercialize nylon, DuPont launched a major development project directed by Crawford Greenewalt, who would later play a key role in the Manhattan Project and serve as DuPont president from 1948 to 1962. While Greenewalt was learning how to make nylon, Bolton decided that silk stockings would be the first large target market. In the modern era of knee-length dresses, stockings had become a fashion necessity. In the 1930s virtually all of the silk used in stockings came from an increasingly belligerent Japan, creating a favorable climate for a domestic substitute. Nylon stockings first went on sale to the public in 1940; they proved popular mainly because they lasted longer than fragile silk ones. Consumers, however, did not get to enjoy their nylons for long. After Pearl Harbor, DuPont's limited output of nylon was commandeered for military uses, such as parachutes and tire cord. After the war, when DuPont reintroduced nylons, consumers greeted them with such enthusiasm that police were sometimes needed to maintain order. In the postwar era DuPont developed many new plastic and textile products from versatile nylon. Probably the most important new application was a bulked continuous filament commercialized in 1964 that was used in the ubiquitous nylon carpeting of the late twentieth and early twenty-first centuries.

[*See also* **Carothers, Wallace Hume; Chemistry; Military, Science and Technology and the; Plastics; Research and Development;** *and* **Technology.**]

BIBLIOGRAPHY

Hadley, Susannah. *Nylon: The Story of a Fashion Revolution*. Baltimore: Johns Hopkins University Press, 1999.
Hounshell, David A., and John Kenly Smith Jr. *Science and Corporate Strategy: DuPont R&D, 1902–1980*. New York: Cambridge University Press, 1988.

John Kenly Smith Jr.

O

OBESITY

In June 2013 the American Medical Association made front-page headlines across the United States when the organization recognized obesity as a disease. This formal recognition, claimed board member Patrice Harris, would transform the ways in which American physicians dealt with the complex issue that affects nearly one in three Americans. Such recognition would also assist the medical profession's efforts to reduce the extent of type 2 diabetes and heart disease, two major diseases associated with obesity affecting numerous Americans since the mid-twentieth century. The American Medical Association's stand was controversial even among its own members. Although some welcomed the development, others criticized the identification of obesity as a disease because, among other things, the metric for defining obesity, the body mass index, was both simplistic and flawed.

No one disputed that obesity, defined by the Centers for Disease Control and Prevention (CDC) in Atlanta as having a body mass index greater than 30, had become a highly visible problem in American society. Since 2001, the U.S. Public Health Service has considered obesity epidemic not only in the United States, but also globally. "There's a pandemic of obesity we are experiencing in this country," asserted Dr. Julie Gerberding, director of the CDC. "If you looked at any epidemic—whether it's influenza or plague from the Middle Ages—they are not as serious as the epidemic of obesity in terms of the health impact on our country and our society" (Gibbs, 2005). The obesity pandemic has spawned a flourishing scholarly literature; anthropologists, sociologists, political scientists, and, more recently, historians of science and medicine have focused on obesity and its histories.

Measuring Obesity. The body mass index, used by the CDC and such international health bodies as the World Health Organization, relies on a formula originally developed by the Belgian mathematician and astronomer Adolphe Quetelet

(1796–1874). Seeking to define the characteristics of normal human beings (and not obesity), Quetelet studied changes in weight and height in newborns, children, and adults, which led him to conclude that in normal humans "weight increases as the square of the height." His 1835 volume, *A Treatise of Man*, described as "one of the greatest books of the nineteenth century" by his biographer, George Sarton, was translated into several languages and influenced such health-care leaders as the British nurse Florence Nightingale (1820–1910), who relied on Quetelet's statistical methods to advocate radical reforms in nursing care.

In 1972, Ancel Keys (1904–2004) an influential physiologist and epidemiologist at the University of Minnesota, adopted Quetelet's formula (weight divided by height squared) as the most useful available metric to characterize changes in the weights of individuals and to compare the obesity of men and women who differed in height but had the same weight. As the lead investigator of the Seven Countries Study, launched in 1956 to analyze the relationship among diet, lifestyle, coronary artery disease, and stroke, Keys needed a reliable standard to compare more than 12 thousand men from seven countries in North America, Europe, and Japan inducted into the study. Although not without limitations, the formula devised by Quetelet, subsequently renamed the body mass index (BMI) by Keys, became the metric. In 1979 at the first international conference on obesity, George Bray, an investigator at the National Institutes of Health, similarly advocated the classification of body weights based on BMI numbers. By the 1990s, the BMI had become the standard method for measuring and defining obesity. In 2006 a CDC School Health Policies and Programs study reported that 21 American states required school districts to measure and assess the height and weight or body mass of students, and 15 of those states required parental notification (including the so-called BMI report cards in Arkansas schools).

Treating Obesity. The meaning and burdens of obesity have changed over time. In the early

nineteenth century the health reformer Sylvester Graham (1794–1851) identified gluttony as the greatest source of disease. An individual whom Ralph Waldo Emerson described as "a prophet of bran bread and pumpkins," Graham urged his followers to abstain from alcohol, spices, coffee, and tea, and instead live on whole wheat bread, vegetables, and water. In the late nineteenth century, the physician and health reformer John Harvey Kellogg (1842–1943) similarly urged a vegetarian diet, abstinence from alcohol and tobacco, and daily exercise. The author of best selling health, sex, and dietary manuals, Kellogg conceded that many individuals inherited a predisposition to obesity, even as he condemned excessive eating and insufficient exercise. "Gluttony and laziness have long been recognized as the two great causes of obesity, so that it has become customary to regard an excessively fat man as one who has been given to the gratification of appetite and is of an indolent disposition" (Kellogg, 1881, p. 847).

Since the late nineteenth century, tolerance for fat bodies has dramatically declined in the United States (and elsewhere). As the historian Hillel Schwartz pointed out, the Connecticut Fat Man's Club, formed in 1866, closed its doors in 1903, citing the lack of members and the fact that "a great weight is no longer associated with success." One unhappy fat man was Secretary of War William Howard Taft, who in 1905 engaged an English physician and dietary expert to treat his obesity. Concerned about his health and his political future, Taft, weighing 354 pounds, became the nation's largest president in 1909. Taft was the butt of numerous jokes and questions about his self-control, and his subsequent weight loss (70 pounds in 1913) under the treatment of the physician George D. Blumer, dean of the Yale School of Medicine, made front-page headlines across the country (Levine, 2013).

Over the course of the twentieth century, physicians and others have developed treatments—dietary, hormonal, psychological, pharmaceutical, and surgical—for obese men, women, and children. Schwartz (1986) has elegantly analyzed the myriad ways in which Americans before the end of the 1980s had embraced medical approaches to reduce weight, including the use of thyroid extract (to increase metabolic rate), dinitrophenol (popular in the 1930s until users developed skin rashes, blindness, and neurological complications), and amphetamines (by reducing food intake but also creating addiction).

In the 1990s, physicians and patients expressed excitement at the prospect of a combination of two drugs, fenfluramine (which acted on the serotonin system in the body to reduce appetite) and the diet drug phentermine (a stimulant that counteracted the drowsiness produced by the other drug). Amid the excitement over this effective drug combination came reports in 1997 that the drugs damaged the heart valves of users; the Food and Drug Administration established that nearly 30 percent of some 7 million users might develop severe valvular disease. The same year the Wyeth pharmaceutical company pulled the drugs from the marketplace. The lawsuits against the pharmaceutical company, which ended in settlements exceeding $16 billion, prompted intense media and congressional interest in pharmaceutical marketing practices, which included paying academic physicians to ghostwrite articles and fostering changes in conflict-of-interest policies at universities and the federal government (Elliott, 2004).

In the same decade, surgical interventions for treating severe obesity increased dramatically. Whereas surgeons performed approximately 16,000 bariatric procedures (including gastric bypass and surgical stapling) on Americans in the early 1990s, by 2003 the number exceeded 103,000. Between 2006 and 2010, nearly 280,000 patients underwent these procedures in American hospitals. The implications of the tremendous popularity of these surgical operations, the costs to the health-care system, and the lifelong effects on the postsurgical lives of these patients remain to be seen, but they have already profoundly affected the existence of this complex disease, disorder, or condition (depending on one's definition) for many Americans.

[*See also* **Centers for Disease Control and Prevention; Diabetes; Disease; Food and Diet; Health and Fitness; Medicine; Public Health;** *and* **Surgery.**]

BIBLIOGRAPHY

Elliott, Carl. "Pharma Goes to the Laundry: Public Relations and the Business of Medical Education." *Hastings Center Report* 34 (2004): 18–23.
Fletcher, Isabel. "Defining an Epidemic: The Body Mass Index in British and US Obesity Research 1960–2000." *Sociology of Health & Illness* 20 (2013): 1–16.
Gibbs, W. Wayt. "Obesity: An Overblown Epidemic?" *Scientific American* 292 (2005): 70–77.
Jafari, Mehraneh D., Fariba Jafari, Monica T. Young, Brian R. Smith, Michael J. Phalen, and Ninh T. Nguyen. "Volume and Outcome Relationship in Bariatric Surgery in the Laparoscopic Era." *Surgical Endoscopy* 27 (2013): 4539–4546.
Kellogg, John H. *The Home Hand-book of Domestic Hygiene and Rational Medicine*, 2 vols. Oakland, CA: Good Health Publishing, 1881.
Levine, Deborah I. "Corpulence and Correspondence: President William H. Taft and the Medical Management of Obesity." *Annals of Internal Medicine* 159 (2013): 565–570.
Mundy, Alicia. *Dispensing with the Truth: The Victims, the Drug Companies, and the Dramatic Story behind the Battle over Fen-Phen.* New York: Macmillan, 2010.
Schwartz, Hillel. *Never Satisfied: A Cultural History of Diets, Fantasies, and Fat.* New York: Free Press, 1986.
Stearns, Peter N. *Fat History: Bodies and Beauty in the Modern West.* New York: New York University Press, 1997.

Susan E. Lederer

OCCUPATIONAL DISEASES

Throughout the nation's history, most American adults (and many children) have spent the largest share of their time working. Accordingly, even in occupations that do not seem especially dangerous, extended exposure to the environmental conditions and other parameters of the workplace commonly produce virtually unavoidable adverse effects. Particularly since the advent of industrialism, technological innovation has continually brought American workers into contact with unprecedented challenges to their well-being. Yet perhaps as remarkable as the constant invention of human-made occupational risks has been the persistence of ancient naturally occurring hazards, including some long recognized as deleterious.

The Etiological Spectrum. From the pre-industrial era to the present, American workers have encountered a wide range of disease hazards on the job. Surveying the biological agents, toxic chemicals, physical forces, psychosocial stressors, and temporal factors that can cause acute or chronic illness provides some sense of the enormity and intractability of this public-health problem.

Biological agents have always menaced working men, women, and children in the United States. Laborers in agriculture, construction, and transportation faced mosquitoes, ticks, lice, and other vectors of infectious disease. Cutting canals through malarial swamps, for example, offered one of countless chances to incur an infection while at work. Health-care employees confronted blood-borne pathogens long before the emergence of human immune-deficiency virus. Epidemic outbreaks of cholera, yellow fever, influenza, and bubonic plague attacked not only providers of medical services but also police, sanitation workers, and other public employees on the front lines.

Toxic chemicals loomed as a significant category of hazards long before the Industrial Revolution. Lead, mercury, and other heavy metals poisoned artisans in diverse crafts, from printing to pottery. Silica and other dusts penetrated the respiratory systems of miners before the arrival of power drills. Environmental tobacco smoke has afflicted the staff serving in commercial eating and drinking establishments since the seventeenth century. Of course, the novel hazards unleashed by industrializing capitalism exacerbated preexisting problems and generated many new ones. Industrialization unleashed a torrent of synthetic compounds that enveloped members of the workforce using acids, dyes, solvents, pesticides, and a host of other materials. Vinyl chloride, an ingredient in the widely produced plastic polyvinyl chloride, induced cancer in those who manufactured it. Household workers routinely handled ammonia and other toxic cleaning agents. Carcinogenic formaldehyde attacked woodworkers and clerical employees in carpeted office buildings.

Perhaps even more insidious than the largely invisible chemical hazards were the physical forces operating in diverse situations. Ultraviolet radiation caused countless workers exposed in the course of maritime, construction, and recreation services work to develop skin cancer. Extremes of heat and cold also took their toll on employees whose duties kept them outdoors. In enclosed environments, high levels of noise deafened weavers in textile mills, boilermakers in locomotive works, stamping-press operators in auto plants, and anyone placed in close proximity to loud machinery for extended periods. Subtle biomechanical imbalances associated with repetitive strains brought back problems to caregivers wrestling with disabled patients, carpal tunnel syndrome to sewing-machine operators, and other ergonomic disorders of the musculoskeletal system to anyone bearing excessive or awkward loads.

Psychosocial stressors eroded employee well-being when jobs presented either overloads or, paradoxically, underloads. The social isolation experienced by many domestic workers fostered depression; the ill-defined extent of their duties also promoted among household servants a sense of being overwhelmed by endless obligations. Bad bosses' tyrannous behavior caused stress that for female workers included fears of sexual harassment and assault. Especially for caring individuals in human services, the disparity between the demands of their jobs and the resources—personal and organizational—to meet those demands have always taken an emotional toll, sometimes manifested in the exhaustion recently labeled "burnout."

The temporal factors of employment have, in and of themselves, caused occupational disease. The common combination of long hours and nonstandard scheduling has afflicted a sizable share of the workforce with shift-work sleep disorder and other sequelae of sleep deprivation. In the transportation sector, railroad crews in the nineteenth century shared essentially the same physiologically unnatural patterns of deranged working time with airline crews in the twenty-first century.

Remedial Action. Recognition of occupational disease is obviously a prerequisite for effective prevention. But widening such recognition has always been fraught with difficulties in America. A shortage of biomedical expertise in the relevant scientific fields has perennially hampered remedial efforts. Alice Hamilton, whose authoritative *Industrial Toxicology* was published in 1934, and Wilhelm Hueper, whose comprehensive *Occupational Tumors and Allied Diseases* appeared eight years later, were exceptional for their pioneering insights. The denials and obfuscation of employers posed the most fundamental, abiding obstacle to expanded awareness of occupational illnesses. In a society and a polity in which the business community has invariably held considerable influence, the advocates of fuller recognition of the health costs of producing goods and services have waged an uphill struggle for private and public reforms.

Public interventions to curtail occupational disease had only minimal success prior to 1970. A century's accumulation of piecemeal, state-level laws regulating conditions in mines, factories, and other facilities concentrated on the prevention of traumatic injury, not illness. Workers' compensation legislation took a similarly narrow focus, with corporate interests fighting proposals to bring work-related diseases within the scope of protection. A 1980 report to Congress by the Department of Labor estimated that only one in twenty workers severely disabled by occupational disease won workers' compensation benefits. Hence, the assertion of federal responsibility embodied in the Occupational Safety and Health Act of 1970 represented a historic breakthrough. Under this statute, federal regulators managed set national standards to control (if not eradicate) a number of major threats, including lead, asbestos, coke oven emissions, and blood-borne pathogens.

The passage of the landmark law in 1970 precipitated a substantial amount of private preventive activity. A more sizable cohort of academic specialists in epidemiology, toxicology, physiology, ergonomics, and clinical medicine arose to tackle both long-neglected and emerging hazards. Numerous community-based committees on occupational safety and health (the so-called COSH groups) brought together conscientious professionals and worker activists. Many unions awakened to a deeper sense of commitment to safeguarding their members, retaining experts, and educating the rank and file. In a radical program to make blue-collar laborers into epidemiological investigators, the United Auto Workers trained its members to gather data to detect cancer patterns among their coworkers. Such ventures into self-help became all the more essential as unsympathetic presidential administrations in the late twentieth and early twenty-first centuries retreated from their mandate to provide American workers with a place of employment free from major threats of illness.

[*See also* **Agricultural Technology; Airplanes and Air Transport; Cancer; Centers for Disease Control and Prevention; Chemistry; Cholera; Deafness; Disease; Entomology; Environmental Protection Agency; Health Insurance; HIV/AIDS; Hospitals; Influenza; Machinery and Manufacturing; Malaria; Medicine; Pesticides; Physiology; Public Health; Railroads; Technology;** *and* **Yellow Fever.**]

BIBLIOGRAPHY

Cherniack, Martin. *The Hawk's Nest Incident: America's Worst Industrial Disaster*. New Haven, Conn.: Yale University Press, 1986.

Dembe, Allard E. *Occupation and Disease: How Social Factors Affect the Conception of Work-Related Disorders*. New Haven, Conn.: Yale University Press, 1996.

Derickson, Alan. "'Asleep and Awake at the Same Time': Sleep Denial among Pullman Porters." *Labor: Studies in Working-Class History of the Americas* 5 (2008): 13–41.

Derickson, Alan. *Black Lung: Anatomy of a Public Health Disaster*. Ithaca, N.Y.: Cornell University Press, 1998.

Markowitz, Gerald, and David Rosner. *Deceit and Denial: The Deadly Politics of Industrial Pollution*. Berkeley: University of California Press, 2002.

Murphy, Michelle. *Sick Building Syndrome and the Problem of Uncertainty: Environmental Politics, Technoscience, and Women Workers*. Durham, N.C.: Duke University Press, 2006.

Rosner, David, and Gerald Markowitz. *Deadly Dust: Silicosis and the Ongoing Struggle to Protect Workers' Health*. Ann Arbor: University of Michigan Press, 2006.

Alan Derickson

OCEANOGRAPHY

Although oceanography—the study of the ocean and its physical, chemical, and biological components and processes—is one of the newest professional disciplines in the natural sciences, its roots extend back thousands of years. The oceans have been used for millennia for transportation and sustenance. Sailors, fishermen, and explorers all observed and used information about storms, tides, currents, and winds. However, oceanography as a structured discipline began less than two hundred years ago. During the antebellum period, American scientists made substantial contributions to the field. Still, intense and systematic scientific study of the oceans is a twentieth-century phenomenon, largely driven by private foundations (which sought new avenues to scientific knowledge) and the federal government (with support dramatically increasing during and after World War II to assist with numerous issues in areas as diverse as amphibious landings and submarine warfare). By the early twenty-first century oceanographers became vigorous participants in national policy issues and scientific endeavors.

The Age of Exploration. Oceanic exploration accelerated rapidly during the sixteenth to early nineteenth centuries. By the late seventeenth century many voyages included efforts to examine the seas through which ships sailed. During the 1600s scattered observations at sea even included a few by American colonists. In one of the earliest examples of attempts at deep-sea research, the Royal Society in London asked John Winthrop, the governor of Connecticut, to undertake experiments with sounding leads and sample bottles. The society made the request as part of its work in determining which apparatus and methods of research might prove useful for accumulating the information necessary to improve safety during passages across the ocean. Both of Winthrop's experiments failed because of wind and leakage of the collection materials.

With a few notable exceptions, American colonists did not venture deeply into the field of marine natural science. Even so, information about the waters off the American coast did accumulate. As American ships became increasingly prominent and experienced in North Atlantic voyages, informal knowledge of that area increased commensurately. In particular, ship captains acquired increasing understanding of the currents that dominate the seas off the North American coast. These currents had dramatic impacts on sailing colonial voyages, a fact that did not go unnoticed. While serving as postmaster general of the colonies, Benjamin Franklin heard complaints about the delays experienced in mail deliveries from England. With the help of the American whaling captain Timothy Folger, Franklin drew a chart of the surface currents of the North Atlantic. British colonial officials also took notice. The London publication in 1787 of the British politician Thomas Pownall included not only notes about his observations and discussions with sea captains during his term as secretary to the Massachusetts governor from 1753 to 1760, but also a chart of northern Atlantic currents. Although now known to be oversimplified renderings of the Gulf Stream and North Atlantic currents, these charts helped stimulate interest in the physical characteristics of the Atlantic. These were not the only efforts at understanding the oceans. Individuals, including Franklin, recorded temperature observations at sea and conducted other experiments.

The Age of Commercial Ventures. In the nineteenth century, Western nations, led by Great Britain, increasingly looked to commerce and capitalism in determining national policy. Because oceans played a major role in commerce, both scientists and national leaders considered how ocean research could help advance the nation's business. By midcentury, the United States had become an active leader in this effort. Within decades of independence, Congress laid the foundations for ocean research in support of commerce with the establishment of two agencies—the U.S. Coast Survey in 1807 and the Depot of Charts and Instruments in the U.S. Navy in 1830—and the authorization of an exploratory expedition in the mid-1830s. Although these three actions did not initially result in significant published research or commercial opportunities, they provided a waiting framework for future leaders.

The 1838–1842 U.S. Exploratory Expedition, commonly known as the Wilkes Expedition, became the first U.S. effort at worldwide collection of data from both land and sea. As with many governmental endeavors in the antebellum period, three purposes underlay this expedition: enhancing scientific knowledge, showing the flag, and increasing commercial prospects. However, when the expedition returned almost four years later, it generated little interest in the governmental or business community. Some of the specimens and data were lost, and the expedition's 20-volume report, which included sections on hydrography and marine animals, was limited to one hundred copies.

Shortly thereafter, however, new American governmental activities threatened British dominance in physical oceans science. The peak of nineteenth-century American involvement in ocean research occurred during the tenures of Alexander Dallas Bache and his great rival, Matthew Fontaine Maury, at two agencies, one funded directly through Congress and the other reliant upon limited naval funding. Through these agencies, Bache and Maury dominated American ocean research in the late antebellum period.

The first agency, the U.S. Coast and Geodetic Survey, which was authorized during the Jefferson administration, initially limited its activities to a slow survey of American harbors and coasts. Under its second superintendent, Bache, appointed in 1843, the Survey expanded its core missions of coastal surveys, hydrography, topography, and geodesy. Greatly increased funding also enabled it to undertake new activities in the late antebellum period that included study of the Gulf Stream, meteorological observations in coastal areas, geomagnetic studies, new mathematical techniques for triangulation and calculation of tides, and examination of bottom sediments.

In contrast, throughout his almost 20-year career as the navy's chief oceans scientist, Lieutenant Matthew Fontaine Maury obtained only limited financial support from the navy, supplemented on occasion by direct congressional approval of specific activities and expeditions. Despite this limited backing, Maury displayed both innovation and persistence in developing new research and analytic techniques while back-strapping scientific research onto navy expeditions. His popularization of oceans science has earned him the title "Father of Oceanography." As the newly installed officer in charge of the Depot of Charts and Instruments—later designated the Naval Observatory and Hydrographic Office—Maury recognized the opportunities available in dusty drawers of archived wind and current observations. He not only organized and correlated these observations into useful data, but also dramatically increased the amount of available information by developing standardized observation logs that were made available to all ship captains. The resulting charts, initially published in 1847, provided a comprehensive compilation of wind and current averages and variations for the North and mid-Atlantic Ocean. These charts helped ships departing the American east coast dramatically reduce their sailing time to China. Later charts also included whale location information.

Maury also dispatched the first open-ocean sounding expeditions in the early 1850s. His mathematical analysis of a number of especially deep soundings eliminated several readings of exaggerated depths. Under his command, deep-sounding sediment collection also provided the first deep-ocean samples for microscopic examination. As the editor of the London *Nautical Magazine* remarked, British and European scientists recognized that the Americans had taken the lead in this type of marine research.

Maury's most ambitious collection scheme involved the encouragement of an International Maritime Meteorological Conference that met in 1853 at Brussels. At the conference, Maury advocated the extension of his abstract log form system to ships of all nations. Eventually, 19 nations joined this effort.

Maury's collection of information and notes concerning the oceans led to his publication, *Physical Geography of the Sea*, the first American book devoted to ocean processes. Although his hypotheses, assumptions, and reliance on natural philosophy were often criticized, the book's popularity led to greatly increased familiarity of the public with the oceans. Although many hypotheses in the book were both contradictory and wrong, they had the benefit of spurring further research by individuals, including his rival Bache, attempting to prove him wrong. Maury also recognized the tentativeness of his conclusions in the book, noting that his opinions were not full theories, but rather hypotheses, which he hoped would lead to further research.

The late antebellum period proved to be the high watermark for American prominence in nineteenth-century oceans science, as steam power reduced the significance of winds and currents to commerce. Following the Civil War, although the Coast Survey continued its research, federal funding was limited. Several scientists in the later decades continued modest research, particularly in marine biology, an area of special interest to the fisheries industry. In 1871 Congress established the U.S. Fish Commission, with its promoter, Spencer Fullerton Baird (future secretary of the Smithsonian Institution) being named the first commissioner. Through Baird's persistence, Congress funded the first ship built specifically for oceanographic research, the 234-foot, 1,074-ton steamer *Albatross*, which entered service for the Commission in 1882.

As an advocate of basic fisheries research and a structured national fisheries policy, Baird selected Woods Hole, Massachusetts, as the Commission's first summer marine biological research facility. Baird and subsequent directors of the facility encouraged an integrated approach to research of marine fauna. Formally chartered in 1888, the Marine Biological Laboratory settled into a dual role of research laboratory and natural history school. Throughout its history the Marine Biological Laboratory emphasized innovation, the combination of education with investigation, and independence. Four years later a marine biological laboratory—later to become the Scripps Insti-

tution of Oceanography—began operation on the west coast in 1892, although initially it concentrated on education more than research.

With limited federal funding available through much of the late nineteenth century, research relied upon private individuals and philanthropist-funded foundations. For example, during the last decades of the nineteenth century and into the early twentieth century, ichthyologist and mining entrepreneur Alexander Agassiz—the son of renowned zoologist and natural scientist Louis Agassiz—conducted research expeditions to consider issues such as azoic zones, similarities of Caribbean and Pacific sea life, distribution of corals, and methodologies of dredging. Uniquely, Agassiz also acted as a philanthropist for the voyages, funding not only ship renovations, but also most running expenses. On several occasions Agassiz utilized government vessels. His first such cruise on the Coast and Geodetic Survey ship *Blake* conducted dredging studies in 1877–1880. Agassiz subsequently made three voyages on the *Albatross*. The initial 1891 voyage took the ship through the Gulf of Mexico and into the Pacific while conducting midlevel trawls and then concluded with dredging at the Galapagos. Agassiz led two more cruises on the *Albatross*, one in 1899–1900 and the final one in 1904–1905, both examining sea life in the South Pacific. Other privately funded research included the Carnegie Institution of Washington's investigation of oceanic magnetic variations by the nonmagnetic ship *Carnegie*.

Oceanographic research and funding followed a similar course during the first 40 years of the twentieth century. Federally sponsored marine research, particularly when relevant for submarine warfare, expanded during World War I, but quickly waned following the armistice. In contrast, foundations and private individuals sponsored even more research as American marine scientists sought ways to improve scientific knowledge of oceanic processes. Two events with dramatic significance for the future of oceanography in America occurred in the decade following 1924. First, Scripps Institution broadened its mission from biological research to oceanography in 1925. Second, and equally important, discussions with the Rockefeller Foundation led to the appointment of a

National Academy of Science Committee on Oceanography that quickly recommended establishment of an independent research laboratory on the east coast. This recommendation, along with a $3 million grant from the Rockefeller Foundation, ultimately created the Woods Hole Oceanographic Institution and resulted in the commissioning of the *Atlantis*, a 142-foot research ketch. The institution joined other research facilities at Woods Hole, including the Marine Biological Laboratory and the National Marine Fisheries Service. Under the leadership of Henry Bryant Bigelow of Harvard University and Frank R. Lillie (director of the Marine Biological Laboratory), Woods Hole centered its work on seagoing research—primarily physical oceanography—aboard its newly constructed sailing ship. Unfortunately, the economic recession of the 1930s resulted in reduced funding, dramatically slowing oceanographic research at virtually all marine laboratories.

Expanding Horizons: World War II, the Cold War, and Maturity.

Oceanographic research both dramatically expanded and changed direction as preparations began for World War II. As the importance of oceanographic research to U.S. Navy fleet operations became of paramount concern, oceanographic research shifted from the biological to a much greater emphasis on the physical and chemical branches of oceanography. During World War II, the U.S. government and oceanographers forged new partnerships. These new relationships provided support for research in a multitude of areas, including submarine warfare, ship maintenance, mine warfare, fleet operations, and island and beach landings. As one of the primary research facilities on the east coast, Woods Hole provided extensive support to naval research, including geophysicist W. Maurice Ewing's pathbreaking work in underwater sound transmission and other important studies of the effectiveness of underwater explosives and prevention of marine fouling, a project later awarded the U.S. Navy's highest civilian award. Physical oceanographers, many trained at Scripps, accurately predicted surf, swell, and tide conditions for amphibious landings, including those at Normandy in 1944.

Defense-oriented research at Woods Hole and other institutions further expanded during the Cold War, resulting in greater knowledge about many physical and chemical marine processes, as well as the development of manned submersibles and numerous other research tools. During the early 1950s support for Woods Hole's research again expanded as the National Science Foundation (NSF) and other agencies began funding ocean research at Woods Hole and numerous other marine institutions, particularly in marine biology fields. In the early twenty-first century, Woods Hole provided leadership in numerous ocean science and engineering fields such as microbial research, innovative tools and techniques, deep-ocean thermal vent research, and the impacts of hydrocarbons, as well as oceanographic education.

Postwar oceanography research continued its heavy reliance on U.S. Navy funding, resulting in increasing questions about the independence of the oceanography research community. Many active oceanographers wore the dual hats of independent oceanographers and naval contractors. During the war, oceanographer Roger Revelle, at the time on active duty while on leave from Scripps, advised the navy on ocean processes that could influence naval operations. Shortly following the war's conclusion, then-commander Revelle organized the Geophysics Branch of the Office of Naval Research (ONR), the navy's conduit for scientific research funding. Not long afterward, the ONR made a firm commitment to lay groundwork for future understanding of the oceans by providing financial support to existing oceanographic laboratories, helping to establish new laboratories, and encouraging the entrance of new scientists to the field of oceanography.

By 1950, the six established oceanographic laboratories—including Woods Hole and Scripps—experienced new growth. In addition, four new university departments or institutes—including the Chesapeake Bay Institute of Johns Hopkins University—had commenced operations through U.S. Navy support. Most of the funding for this growth came through block grants, allowing wide latitude in how the institution utilized the funding, generally supporting not only laboratories and departments but also ships, operating expenses, overhead, travel, and, in many cases, salaries. ONR justified the contracts based upon the value of basic oceanographic knowledge to naval operations, including submarine, mine, and amphibious warfare, even if there was no direct operational relevance. Oceanographic support covered a wide range of research as diverse as Arctic studies, deep-sea submersibles, fixed buoy systems, and world-wide surveys; these funds also helped efforts to improve oceanographic institutions.

Historians have debated about the significance and effects of this generosity, some arguing that the Cold War navy controlled oceanographic research, even if indirectly. However, there is no doubt that this source of revenue greatly accelerated oceanographic research and education in the United States during the two decades following World War II (see Hamblin, 2005).

Other agencies, including the Atomic Energy Commission, the Bureau of Commercial Fisheries, and the NSF, began augmenting the navy's efforts in the early 1950s. Gradually, targeted research funding expanded from physical studies such as underwater acoustics, underwater sediment charts, and wave studies to broader biological and chemical areas.

The International Geophysical Year of 1957–1958 was a pivotal period for oceanography as international attention focused on the geophysical sciences. That year, tens of thousands of scientists from over 60 countries undertook the largest international scientific research program of the twentieth century. Planning for the event and subsequent research efforts highlighted the paucity of information then available about the ocean depths. Following the International Geophysical Year, marine research received a boost as the NSF first increased its funding and then in 1962 promulgated a 10-year program for oceanography support. As the NSF and other agencies increased their funding, research became more closely tied to large-scale projects, such as deep-sea drilling, Sealab, deep-sea submersibles, the ocean's role in global warming, and international coordinated research. One of the first large-scale interdisciplinary activities—drilling into the Earth's crust at

sea—proved a partial success. This achievement established the NSF as a federal patron of comprehensive oceanic research and generated considerable excitement among scientists and petroleum companies. Its subsequent outgrowth, Project Mohole, which eventually shut down because of escalating costs as well as scientific and political squabbles, introduced the NSF to the difficulties of planning and funding big science. However, the follow-up Deep Sea Drilling Project again demonstrated the worth of substantial national funding for geophysical research related to the ocean because it supplied crucial evidence verifying the theory of seabed spreading and continental drift.

With increasing funding came closer cooperation of the involved agencies. In 1954 the navy and four other federal agencies began to coordinate their activities and planning. The Informal Coordinating Committee on Oceanography was created in 1954. The Interagency Committee on Oceanography superseded it in 1959. Later, in 1966, Congress authorized the National Council for Marine Resources and Engineering Development. These increasingly sophisticated organizations ultimately resulted in the establishment of the National Oceanic and Atmospheric Administration in October 1970. For the first time, almost all civilian federal oceans activity centers resided under one roof. Hence, the National Oceanic and Atmospheric Administration subsumed research domains previously administered by the Coast and Geodetic Survey, the Environmental Science Services Administration, the Bureau of Commercial Fisheries, and the Marine Mineral Technology Center.

Federal agencies soon recognized that the ability to dramatically increase research depended upon too small a pool of suitably trained scientists. Oceanographic institutions were not educating ample researchers for the expanding discipline. Once again, the navy provided the first impetus to advance the field. In 1958 the Geophysics Branch of the ONR had proposed a major 10-year commitment to oceanographic research and education that it called Project TENOC. Through this program the navy not only provided support to existing institutions, but also helped establish a number of fledgling oceanographic programs in the United States, such as at Oregon State University, substantially increasing both research and the supply of oceanographic scientists.

Other agencies, including the NSF, quickly joined in this effort. Although established in 1950, the NSF, which came about as a result of presidential science advisor Vannevar Bush's seminal 1945 report, *Science—The Endless Frontier*, did not begin operations until 1951. Although many members of its staff were alumni of the ONR, its limited funding meant very limited initial support for oceanography.

This changed in the wake of *Sputnik*'s launch by the Soviet Union in 1957. The combined launch of *Sputnik* and the failure of the United States' own rocket helped place renewed U.S. governmental emphasis on support for science. During the long-anticipated International Geophysical Year of 1958, NSF funding increased to $43 million, of which $2 million was used to support oceanography (Van Keuren, 2000, p. 93). This was but the beginning of an expansion in funding oceanographic research. Immediately following the International Geophysical Year, the National Academy of Science's Committee on Oceanography issued a report on the current state and needs of oceanography. A few days later Roger Revelle, director of the Scripps Institution of Oceanography, warned House Appropriation Committee member Albert Thomas that "Man's knowledge of the oceans" was "meager indeed when compared with their importance to him…[N]eglect… might well result in our being placed in a precarious position" (Van Keuren, 2000, pp. 90–91). As a result of this meeting and other congressional contacts, within two years the NSF had the funding to develop its own 10-year plan for oceanographic research.

A more formalized program quickly followed. At a 1963 meeting of the American Fisheries Society, the University of Minnesota geophysicist and oceanographer Athelstan Spilhaus—noted for his development of the bathythermograph, an instrument used to measure ocean depths and temperatures—called for the formal establishment of sea grant colleges in universities. He argued that just as land grant colleges supported agriculture and forestry products, sea grant colleges should support marine research and sustainable development of coastal resources. Two years later Congress passed the National Sea Grant College and Program Act of 1966. The program awarded the first grants in 1968 and two years later became part of the National Oceanic and Atmospheric Administration. In 1971 four universities achieved Sea Grant College status: Oregon State University, University of Rhode Island, Texas A&M University, and the University of Washington. In 2012, more than 30 institutions and over three thousand scientists participated in the Sea Grant program, examining a diverse host of marine and environmental topics.

Following the end of the Cold War, oceanography continued to provide important data and information for U.S. national security. Oceanographers became vital participants in evaluating the effects of oceans on the climate, as well as the effects of climate change on the oceans and their inhabitants. Modeling and forecasting of hurricanes, as well as El Niño and La Niña events, depended upon a host of oceanographic research and data points. In the early twenty-first century, marine scientists used a vast array of instruments and resources to collect data about the oceans. These included a wide variety of ships and boats, deep submersibles, remotely operated vehicles, autonomous underwater vehicles, free-floating drift buoys, underwater laboratories, and even satellites and high-level photography.

During the course of the nineteenth and twentieth centuries oceanography repeatedly demonstrated its importance to America's commercial health and national security. Oceanographic institutions, scientists, and businesses became vital components in the nation's technical and educational infrastructure. During the early twenty-first century, oceanography increasingly assumed an even wider and more intense role in national environmental, commercial, and security policies.

[*See also* **Biological Sciences; Chemistry; Geography; Geological Surveys; Geophysics; Higher**

Education and Science; Meteorology and Climatology; Military, Science and Technology and the; National Science Foundation; Physics; *and* Scripps Institution of Oceanography.]

BIBLIOGRAPHY

Bruce, Robert V. *The Launching of Modern American Science, 1846–1876*. New York: Alfred A. Knopf, 1987. Excellent survey of the works of Bache, Maury, and Louis Agassiz in the antebellum period.

Deacon, George E. R. "The Woods Hole Oceanographic Institution: An Expanding Influence." In *Oceanography: The Past*, edited by M. Sears and D. Merriman, pp. 25–31. New York: Springer-Verlag, 1980.

Deacon, Margaret. *Scientists and the Sea, 1650–1900: A Study of Marine Science*. London: Academic Press, 1971. Pathbreaking account of early marine science, with numerous details of early American involvement.

Deacon, Margaret. "Some Aspects of Anglo-American Cooperation in Marine Science, 1660–1914." In *Oceanography: The Past*, edited by M. Sears and D. Merriman, pp. 101–113. New York: Springer-Verlag, 1980.

Doel, Ronald E. "Constituting the Postwar Earth Sciences: The Military's Influence on the Environmental Sciences in the USA after 1945." *Social Studies of Science* 33, no. 5 (2003): 635–666. Describes how the U.S. Navy provided critical support to oceanography in furtherance of its security missions.

Dupree, A. Hunter. *Science in the Federal Government: A History of Policies and Activities*. Baltimore: Johns Hopkins University Press, 1986.

Hamblin, Jacob Darwin. *Oceanographers and the Cold War: Disciples of Marine Science*. Seattle: University of Washington Press, 2005. Demonstrates the close connections between oceanographers and the U.S. Navy post–World War II.

Idyll, C. P., ed. *Exploring the Ocean World: A History of Oceanography*. New York: Thomas Y. Crowell Co., 1970.

Lill, Gordon G. "The Earth Sciences Program of the Office of Naval Research." *The Scientific Monthly* 68, no. 4 (1949): 284–287. An insider's account of the early work at the ONR.

Mills, Eric L. *Biological Oceanography: An Early History, 1870–1960*. Ithaca, N.Y.: Cornell University Press, 1989. The definitive work on biological oceanography.

Mills, Eric L. *The Fluid Envelope of Our Planet: How the Study of Ocean Currents Became a Science*. Toronto and London: University of Toronto Press, 2009. Provides important insights into national styles of research and the rise of mathematical oceanography.

Rainger, Ronald. "Science at the Crossroads: The Navy, Bikini Atoll and American Oceanography in the 1940s." *Historical Studies in the Physical and Biological Sciences*. 30, no. 2 (2000): 349–371.

Revelle, Roger. "The Oceanographic and How It Grew." In *Oceanography: The Past*, edited by M. Sears and D. Merriman, pp. 10–24. New York: Springer-Verlag, 1980.

Rozwadowski, Helen M. *Fathoming the Ocean: The Discovery and Exploration of the Deep Sea*. Cambridge, Mass.: Harvard University Press, 2005. Contains an excellent account of the importance of Maury's work.

Sapolsky, Harvey M. *Science and the Navy: The History of the Office of Naval Research*. Princeton, N.J.: Princeton University Press, 1990.

Schlee, Susan. *The Edge of an Unfamiliar World: A History of Oceanography*. New York: E. P. Dutton & Co., 1973.

Slotten, Hugh Richard. *Patronage, Practice, and the Culture of American Science: Alexander Dallas Bache and the U.S. Coast Survey*. Cambridge, U.K.: Cambridge University Press, 1994.

Spencer, Larry T. "Four Men and an Albatross: The Growth of American Oceanography, 1882–1921." In *Oceanographic History: The Pacific and Beyond*, edited by Keith R. Benson and Philip F. Rehbock, pp. 288–297. Seattle: University of Washington Press, 1993.

Van Keuren, David K. "Building a New Foundation for the Ocean Sciences: The National Science Foundation and Oceanography, 1951–1965." *Earth Sciences History*. 19, no. 1 (2000): 90–109.

Weir, Gary E. *An Ocean in Common: American Naval Officers, Scientists, and the Ocean Environment*. College Station: Texas A&M University Press, 2001. Argues that the convergence of naval and scientific interests since World War I laid the foundation for the establishment of oceanography as a distinct discipline and its subsequent exponential growth.

Williams, Frances Leigh. *Matthew Fontaine Maury, Scientist of the Sea*. New Brunswick, N.J.: Rutgers University Press, 1963. To date, the best biography of Maury, but lacks deep consideration of his science.

Craig Biegel

ODUM, EUGENE AND HOWARD

(1913–2002) and (1924–2002), respectively, ecologists. Brothers Eugene Pleasants and Howard Thomas Odum played pivotal roles in establishing ecosystem ecology during the second half of the twentieth century. They were sons of the prominent sociologist Howard Washington Odum. Following their father's progressive political views, both sons embraced the idea that scientists have a social responsibility to solve practical problems. This perspective permeated Eugene Odum's *Fundamentals of Ecology*, which went through five editions. Howard Thomas Odum pioneered the emerging specialties of ecological economics and ecological engineering.

Eugene Odum began his research in physiological ecology; organismal analogies later became a prominent part of his thinking about ecosystems. He emphasized the importance of ecological succession as a developmental process through which a biotic community matures toward a predictable climax. He also believed that ecosystems maintain stability through a form of homeostasis analogous to the self-regulation in organisms. These organismal analogies were part of the broad mainstream of biological thought during the 1950s when Eugene Odum first popularized them, but were later criticized by evolutionary ecologists who championed more individualistic and competitive views of nature.

Eugene Odum spent his professional career at the University of Georgia. Its location near the Savannah River nuclear power facility provided a unique opportunity for research. Beginning in the early 1950s Eugene was awarded contracts by the Atomic Energy Commission (AEC) for ecological research in the areas surrounding the nuclear plant. Together with his brother, he also conducted an AEC-sponsored study of energy flow on a coral reef near the testing site for nuclear weapons at Eniwetok Atoll. This study won the Mercer Award from the Ecological Society of America. Eugene Odum's connections with the AEC provided a springboard for founding the Institute of Ecology at the University of Georgia, which became a major center of ecological research. His prominence among ecologists was recognized in 1964 when he was elected president of the Ecological Society of America. Eugene's presidential address, "The Strategy of Ecosystem Development," became a Science Citation Classic, but also a flashpoint for criticism from ecologists who opposed his views about development, stability, and self-regulation in ecosystems.

Howard Thomas Odum studied under G. Evelyn Hutchinson at Yale University shortly after World War II. His dissertation dealt with the biogeochemical cycling of strontium, a topic that gained prominence during the Cold War. Shortly after completing his PhD, Howard Thomas conducted a large-scale study of energy flow through an aquatic ecosystem at Silver Springs, Florida. Both the study and the diagrams that he used to illustrate energy flow are still widely used in textbook accounts of ecosystem energetics. Howard Thomas continued large-scale experimental studies in tropical rainforests, estuaries, and other ecosystems, but he also gained prominence in the field of ecological modeling. Inspired by the analog computers that he used to simulate energy flow in ecosystems, Odum created pictorial models reminiscent of electronic circuits. He used these models to explore the economic, social, and environmental consequences of ecological energetics.

Eugene and Howard Thomas Odum were jointly awarded two international prizes for their contributions to ecology: the Institute de la Vie Prize (1975) and the Crafoord Prize (1987).

[*See also* **Atomic Energy Commission; Biological Sciences; Ecology; Engineering; Evolution, Theory of; Hutchinson, G. Evelyn; Nuclear Power;** *and* **Physiology.**]

BIBLIOGRAPHY

Craige, Betty J. *Eugene Odum: Ecosystem Ecologist and Environmentalist.* Athens, Ga.: University of Georgia Press, 2001.

Hagen, Joel B. *An Entangled Bank: The Origins of Ecosystem Ecology.* New Brunswick, N.J.: Rutgers University Press, 1992.

Hall, Charles A. S., ed. *Maximum Power: The Ideas and Applications of H. T. Odum.* Niwot: University Press of Colorado, 1995.

Taylor, Peter J. "Technocratic Optimism, H. T. Odum, and the Partial Transformation of Ecological Metaphor after World War II." *Journal of the History of Biology* 21 (1988): 213–244.

Joel B. Hagen

OFFICE OF SCIENCE AND TECHNOLOGY POLICY

The Office of Science and Technology Policy (OSTP) in the Executive Office of the President was established in 1976 as a result of the National Science and Technology Policy, Organization, and Priorities Act that President Gerald Ford signed into law that year. Since that time, it has functioned as the institutional focal point through which presidents have coordinated and implemented national science and technology policies or policies in areas with strong technical components such as the economy, education, energy, environment, health, national security, and space.

The Office of Science and Technology Policy had its predecessor in the nonstatutory office of the Special Assistant to the President for Science and Technology in the White House, which was established in 1957 when President Dwight D. Eisenhower appointed James R. Killian Jr. as the first such assistant or science adviser in the wake of the Soviet launching of the satellite *Sputnik.* Because the science adviser also chaired the President's Science Advisory Committee (PSAC), a group of science advisers mainly from outside of the federal government, as well as the Federal Council for Science and Technology (FCST), which consisted of technical representatives from federal agencies, his office provided staff support for these organizations as well and quickly grew to be one of the largest offices in the White House. Concerns about its size and congressional demands for accountability in executive science policy led President John F. Kennedy to establish, with the consent of Congress, the statutory Office of Science and Technology (OST) in the Executive Office of the President in 1962. The president's science adviser always held the position of director of the OST but now could be called on to testify in Congress in his latter capacity. The office and much of the rest of the presidential science advisory system were, however, abolished in 1973 by President Richard M. Nixon, who was antagonized by the opposition of many scientists, including some associated with PSAC, to his Vietnam War and technology policies and was convinced that the science advising system served more the interests of the scientific community than his.

Prodded in part by a report of the National Academy of Sciences in July 1974 that advocated the reestablishment of a science advising system in the White House, Gerald Ford, who took over the presidency from Richard Nixon following the Watergate scandal in August 1974, set in motion a process that led to the passage of the 1976 act that established the OSTP. Created thus by a specific congressional act, the OSTP enjoyed a more secure position in the federal bureaucracy than the earlier OST. The act also formalized the Federal Council for Science and Technology in the form of a Federal Coordinating Council for Science, Engineering, and Technology, which was upgraded under President Bill Clinton to the National Science and Technology Council, with the president as chairman. PSAC, however, was not revived until President George H. W. Bush established the President's Council of Advisers on Science and Technology (PCAST) in 1990.

As in the OST/PSAC days, the president's science adviser always headed the OSTP and chaired or co-chaired the PCAST after it was established. Starting with H. Guyford Stever under Ford, OSTP directors have included Frank Press under Jimmy Carter, George Keyworth and William Graham under Ronald Reagan, D. Allen Bromley under George H. W. Bush, John Gibbons and Neal Lane under Bill Clinton, John Marburger under George W. Bush, and John Holdren under Barack Obama.

[*See also* **Environmentalism; Killian, James Rhyne, Jr.; National Academy of Sciences;**

President's Science Advisory Committee; Science; Space Program; Space Science; *and* Technology.]

BIBLIOGRAPHY

Bromley, D. Allan. *The President's Scientists: Reminiscences of a White House Science Adviser.* New Haven, Conn.: Yale University Press, 1994.

Herken, Gregg. *Cardinal Choices: Presidential Science Advising from the Bomb to SDI.* New York: Oxford University Press, 1992.

Smith, Bruce L. R. *The Advisers: Scientists in the Policy Process.* Washington, D.C.: The Brookings Institution, 1992.

Wang, Zuoyue. *In Sputnik's Shadow: The President's Science Advisory Committee and Cold War America.* New Brunswick, N.J.: Rutgers University Press, 2008.

Zuoyue Wang

OFFICE OF SCIENTIFIC RESEARCH AND DEVELOPMENT

Established in June 1941, the Office of Scientific Research and Development, always referred to by its initials, OSRD, quickly became the most famous and effective organization at harnessing academic American science for World War II. Identified with its director, Vannevar Bush, a prominent administrator from the Massachusetts Institute of Technology (MIT) as well as a pioneering analog computer designer, the OSRD embodied the assumptions of the interwar political economy of science and technology. Far from seeing the OSRD as a test bed for a future in which the military would become the dominant patron of the physical sciences and engineering disciplines, Bush and his colleagues, especially James Bryant Conant, then Harvard University president, created an institution that would preserve and protect the boundaries separating science from politics. OSRD's mode of operation was part of this larger goal. First, OSRD decided whenever possible to use existing university and industrial facilities rather than establish new government

laboratories as the main sites for research. Second, OSRD used the contract rather than the grant for funding investigation. By the war's end, Bush understood that the very world he had created the OSRD for no longer existed, in large measure because of the OSRD's success in forging connections among academic researchers, industrialists, and the armed services.

OSRD incorporated Bush's first attempt at organizing science, the National Defense Research Committee (NDRC), established in June 1940 and the nascent Committee for Medical Research, a new organization under the direction of Alfred N. Richards of the University of Pennsylvania that attempted to manage medical research. Although the NDRC had proved successful at bringing American academic researchers to bear upon problems of military interest, it possessed one original defect—an inability to provide a mechanism for the actual development of devices invented by researchers. It is one thing to make a weapon that works on a laboratory bench; it is an entirely different affair to design a device that workers without advanced degrees might manufacture in quantity. OSRD acquired the legal authority as part of the Office of Emergency Management, under the president, to authorize and fund development work in both universities and corporations.

Rather than create new institutions, the OSRD sought to use existing university facilities whenever possible, although this sometimes involved the creation of new laboratories on university campuses. Among the most famous were the MIT Radiation Laboratory, the preeminent Allied radar research facility, and the Harvard Radio Research Laboratory, the site of Allied work on radar countermeasures. The MIT laboratory quickly became a hotbed of research in which physicists from around the country toiled to take radar from the laboratory to the battleship, the bomber, and the night fighter. Radiation Laboratory researchers worked with industrial scientists and designers to develop weapons that American firms might mass produce. At the Harvard laboratory, researchers devised measures to block Axis radar, including chaff, strips of aluminum foil, each of which reflected Axis radar and confused German radar operators.

Another central OSRD innovation was the research contract. Rather than contract for the development of a particular device or technology, OSRD contracts called for investigators to make good efforts toward understanding a particular problem; in turn, these contracts were easily amended to take into account unexpected research developments. Equally important, should research under such contracts meet a dead end, it was quickly canceled and resources were redeployed along more promising lines of investigation. Contracts also allowed universities to charge for overhead as wartime research overran their campuses, with an important caveat—no institution was to make a profit from the wartime effort.

Among OSRD's many successes were the DUKW, an amphibious landing craft that functioned as a boat in the water and as a truck on land; radar; the proximity fuse, a technology that allowed artillery shells to detonate at a prespecified distance from their target; and the mass production of penicillin. The latter was among the OSRD's greatest accomplishments, dramatically reducing the amount of time lost treating one of war's most prevalent afflictions, venereal disease.

By war's end, OSRD had spent over $536 million and employed researchers across the United States. Despite Bush's efforts to centralize research and development, OSRD was not its largest patron. The funds of the armed services dwarfed those of the OSRD. For example, whereas the NDRC originally incorporated the efforts of the preexisting Uranium Committee under National Bureau of Standards director Lyman Briggs, Bush transferred the Manhattan Project to General Leslie R. Groves of the Army Corps of Engineers shortly after Enrico Fermi demonstrated the chain reaction in uranium in December 1942. The Manhattan Project alone cost approximately $2 billion, a figure towering over OSRD's large, but comparatively small overall budget. Despite its relatively modest budget and Bush's overwhelming desire to end the OSRD, researchers and government officials would often call for a new OSRD at various crisis points in the early Cold War.

[*See also* **Bush, Vannevar; Conant, James B.; Engineering; Manhattan Project; Military,** **Science and Technology and the; Penicillin; Physics; Research and Development (R&D); Science; Sexually Transmitted Diseases; Technology;** *and* **War and Medicine.**]

BIBLIOGRAPHY

Baxter, James Phinney. *Scientists against Time.* Boston: Little, Brown, 1946. The original history of the wartime agency; still used by many as a first source.

Kevles, Daniel J. *The Physicists: The History of a Scientific Community in Modern America. With a New Preface by the Author.* Cambridge, Mass.: Harvard University Press, 1995.

Owens, Larry. "The Counterproductive Management of Science in the Second World War: Vannevar Bush and the Office of Scientific Research and Development." *Business History Review* 68 (1994): 515–576. Using heretofore unexploited archival materials, this remains the most sophisticated and nuanced account of the OSRD.

Swann, John Patrick. "The Search for Synthetic Penicillin during World War II." *The British Journal for the History of Science* 16, no. 2 (1983): 154–190.

Michael Aaron Dennis

OFFICE OF TECHNOLOGY ASSESSMENT, CONGRESSIONAL

Congress created the Office of Technology Assessment (OTA) in 1972. The principal advocate, Connecticut Congressman Emilio Q. Daddario, became the first director. The founding legislation charged the OTA with helping legislators understand the potential impact and public-policy implications of emerging technologies. The immediate impetus behind the OTA's founding was Congress's desire for technological and scientific advice independent of the Executive Branch, following a series of contentious debates over technology-related environmental issues and strategic matters such as ballistic-missile defense and funding for the supersonic transport (SST). With an annual budget eventually reaching $22 million and some two hundred employees at its peak, including specialists in various scientific and technological fields, the OTA issued reports on a wide range of technology-related issues. The OTA remained under congressional control, with its research agenda dictated by requests from congressional committees and its operations overseen by a 12-member congressional board, half from the Senate and half from the House of Representatives and equally divided between Republicans and Democrats. This board approved each report before publication. The process of preparing reports, typically completed in one to two years, included intense study of the issue by staff members plus expert panels recruited for their knowledge of specific topics. As its workload increased, the OTA divided into two main divisions, one focused on industry, commerce, and international security and the other on health, education, and environmental issues, each with various subsections.

From the first, the OTA precariously navigated Washington's political cross-currents. In the early years, Republicans on the oversight committee accused the Democrats, notably Senator Edward M. Kennedy, of seeking to control the OTA for partisan purposes. Greater stability came under director John H. Gibbons, a physicist who served from 1979 to 1993. Nevertheless, reports on such politically charged issues as the effects of nuclear war (1979) and two on missile defense (1985, 1988), as proposed in President Ronald Reagan's 1983 Strategic Defense Initiative, proved controversial. In the 1994 midterm election, the Republicans' "Contract with America" campaign manifesto pledged to close down the OTA. True to its word, the new Republican majority terminated the OTA in 1995.

In its 23-year history, the OTA produced nearly 750 reports, background papers, technical memoranda, and related documents addressing contemporary technological issues, including genetic engineering, climate change, the space program, new information technologies, and much more. Praised for their objectivity and analytic depth, these reports were published by the U.S. Government Printing Office and frequently reissued by commercial publishers. Some, especially *The Effects of Nuclear War,* reached a wide audience. Foreign delegations studied the OTA as a model for addressing emerging technologies and their effects. OTA staff frequently testified before congressional committees. But the OTA never escaped Washington's political pressures. By congressional direction, it could not make policy recommendations, only present options. An inherent contradiction existed between its mandate to take a long-term view and politicians' preoccupation with immediate—and often intensely partisan—matters. Although the vision of a nonpartisan agency offering objective analyses that could then shape the legislative process was never fully realized, the OTA did contribute significantly to public understanding of complex issues.

[*See also* **Genetics and Genetic Engineering; Global Warming; Internet and World Wide Web; Meteorology and Climatology; Military, Science and Technology and the; National Academy of Sciences; Nuclear Weapons; Office of Science and Technology Policy; President's Science Advisory Committee; Research and Development (R&D); Satellites, Communications; Space Program; Strategic Defense Initiative;** *and* **Technology.**]

BIBLIOGRAPHY

Bimber, Bruce. *The Politics of Expertise in Congress: The Rise and Fall of the Office of Technology Assessment.* Albany: State University of New York Press, 1996.
Office of Technology Assessment. http://www.princeton.edu/~ota/ns20/proces_f.html (accessed 20 March 2012).

Paul S. Boyer

OFFICE TECHNOLOGY

U.S. inventors built mechanical prototypes of typewriters and computing machines as early as the mid-nineteenth century, but little demand for them arose until the economy became more sophisticated after the Civil War. Christopher

Latham Sholes and James Demsmore convinced E. Remington and Sons, a Hartford, Connecticut, arms manufacturer, to advertise the first mass-produced typewriting machine in the 1870s. In the 1890s both Underwood and Royal marketed more efficient versions of the typewriter, which by 1900 was ubiquitous in North American offices. After William Patterson devised cash registers (adding machines with drawers) for use in his Dayton, Ohio, coal business in 1882, he founded the National Cash Register Company. Joseph Burroughs, Frank Baldwin, and Jay Monroe were among the entrepreneurs and inventors who established adding-machine companies at the turn of the twentieth century. The Felt and Tarrant Company of Chicago produced a popular lightweight "comptometer," which could execute all the basic arithmetic functions.

Herman Hollerith adapted Jacquard loom technology in the 1880s to develop sorting machines using punched cards, allowing for more efficient production and analysis of cost-accounting records, census data, and actuarial tables. First used in the federal census of 1890, the Hollerith machines were soon installed at large offices such as the Baltimore Department of Health, the New York Central Railroad, and the Marshall Field department store in Chicago. Hollerith's Computing Tabulating and Recording Company merged with the smaller International Business Machine (IBM) Corporation in 1924 and took its name. By leasing machines and selling keypunch cards to large business establishments, IBM became one of America's most powerful and profitable corporations, eventually dominating the office-machine industry.

Other office machines complemented this basic computing, typewriting, and tabulating technology. Mimeograph machines used typewritten stencils to reproduce office documents. "Addressograph" machines (featuring detachable metal name-and-address plates on a mimeographing device) and bookkeeping and billing machines (combinations of adding and typewriting machines) made billing, tax collecting, and advertising more efficient. With the dictaphone, a combination of the sewing machine, the phonograph, and the telephone that reproduced the human voice on a wax cylinder, business correspondence could be dictated for later transcription by someone using a typewriter. Along with the telephone and switchboard, these machines completed the modern office and allowed scientific management experts to rationalize most office functions, making the organization of office workers and their use of machines akin to light factory work.

U.S. employers created 3 million new clerical jobs between 1900 and 1920. Functions that could be mechanized and routinized were often "feminized" as well, and by 1930, 82 percent of all bookkeepers, cashiers, stenographers, and typists were female. These mostly young women were paid far less than men and subjected to discrimination based on marital status (the so-called marriage bar). Business colleges and high school business-education courses prepared tens of thousands of them for office machine jobs, and young women flocked to major cities to take up clerical work. These urban pioneers helped create new standards of female dress, sexual behavior, and independence from family supervision, and they soon appeared as standard characters in movies and novels. During the Great Depression of the 1930s, some of them overcame the resistance of employers and male-dominated unions and organized office-worker unions, protesting low wages, uncompensated overtime, and the increased pace of mechanized work. By 1950 more than 4.5 million women were employed in office work, far outnumbering those in factories.

Beginning in the 1920s, electrification amplified the efficiency of some office machines, and after World War II, early prototypes of the digital computer, financed largely by the federal government, allowed for still more elaborate compilations of data. The widespread introduction of personal-computer stations after 1980 integrated multiple office-work functions into the same machine. Some workers used the new technology for creative and varied work, but many found their computerized jobs more routinized than ever. By the end of the century, some clerical functions were being assigned to home offices or back-office electronic sweatshops in inexpensive labor markets, some of them outside the United States. Clerical workers (mostly female) and better-paid middle managers (mostly male) were particularly hard hit in the 1990s by the disappearance or downgrading of their jobs.

Office technology facilitated the growth of the modern corporation and the sophisticated nation-state after 1900. North America's development and dominance of that technology made the United States a major exporter of office machinery and of-fice-management methods. By the end of the twentieth century, thanks to ever more sophisticated office technology, white-collar workers dominated the U.S. job market, and the continued refinement of microchip and telecommunications technology had made office functions fundamental to an increasingly integrated global economy.

[See also Automation and Computerization; Computer Science; Computers, Mainframe, Mini, and Micro; Electricity and Electrification; Gender and Technology; Printing and Publishing; Technology; and Telephone.]

BIBLIOGRAPHY

Austrian, Geoffrey D. *Herman Hollerith*. New York: Columbia University Press, 1982.

Cortada, James W. *Before the Computer: IBM, NCR, Burroughs, and Remington Rand and the Industry They Created, 1865–1956*. Princeton, N.J.: Princeton University Press, 1993.

Fine, Lisa M. *The Souls of the Skyscraper: Female Clerical Workers in Chicago, 1870–1930*. Philadelphia: Temple University Press, 1990.

Garson, Barbara A. *The Electronic Sweatshop*. New York: Simon and Schuster, 1988.

Hartmann, Heidi I., Robert E. Kraut, and Louise A. Tilly, eds. *Computer Chips and Paper Clips*. Washington, D.C.: National Academy Press, 1986.

Strom, Sharon Hartman. *Beyond the Typewriter*. Urbana: University of Illinois Press, 1992.

Zuboff, Shoshana. *In the Age of the Smart Machine*. New York: Basic Books, 1988.

Sharon Hartman Strom

OPHTHALMOLOGY

Ophthalmology became an important specialty in America only after 1860, but the conditions that made its existence possible can be traced to the early years of the nineteenth century. At that time clinical ophthalmology mainly involved surgery practiced by general surgeons. Patients' eyes were examined externally, using no instrument other than a magnifying glass. Even after the ophthalmoscope was invented in the middle of the nineteenth century, many years passed before it was widely used and before correlations could be made with disease in a living patient.

Organized ophthalmic institutions actually preceded the appearance of trained ophthalmologists. The first eye hospital anywhere opened in Vienna in 1786, but it was a small, private institution controlled by the chairman of ophthalmology at the university clinic, Georg Beer. The first public hospital devoted exclusively to treatment of diseases of the eye and ear was established in 1805, the London Infirmary for Curing Diseases of the Eye and Ear, now known as Moorfields Eye Hospital.

The first institution in the United States for eye care alone was the New London Eye Infirmary, established by Elisha North in 1817 in Connecticut. It existed for about 17 years but had little lasting influence. Continuous specialty care in ophthalmology in America began in 1820 when Edward Delafield and John Kearney Rodgers, recent graduates of the College of Physicians and Surgeons (now the medical school of Columbia University), established the New York Eye Infirmary. It was modeled on the London Eye Infirmary. Apparently Delafield and Rodgers were unaware of North and his infirmary in Connecticut. The Baltimore Dispensary for the Cure of Diseases of the Eye was established in 1823, primarily by George Frick. He emulated the methods of Beer, whose teaching dominated the practice of ophthalmology in Europe. Frick may have been the first American to restrict his practice to diseases of the eye. In Boston two young men, Edward Reynolds and John Jeffries, established the Massachusetts Charitable Eye and Ear Infirmary in 1824, again following the pattern of the London Eye Infirmary. Physicians at these infirmaries treated such conditions as eye wounds, cancers, abscesses, and even cataracts.

After a medical field has been established, the dissemination of ideas follows, usually through demonstrations and later through publications and lectures. The first American textbook on ophthalmology was Frick's *Treatise on the Diseases of the Eye* of 1823, which used the format established by Beer in Vienna. About eight years later came John Jeffries's series of lectures based on ideas derived from English teachings (Jeffries, 1998). These were major steps that improved on the previous standard of providing information about the pathology and treatment of diseases and abnormalities of vision only through general lectures on surgery. Prior to 1820 what was taught was based largely on personal experience.

The first ophthalmic journal in the United States, the *American Journal of Ophthalmology*, created by Julius Homberger in 1862, survived only briefly. The *Archives of Ophthalmology*, still an important journal in the early twenty-first century, started publishing in 1869. The first editor, Herman Knapp, had left Heidelberg, Germany, and an esteemed professorship for the uncertainty of private practice in New York City. Knapp was the first ophthalmologist with an international reputation who immigrated to the United States. The new version of the *American Journal of Ophthalmology* began publication in 1884.

Trends Favoring Specialization.

By the 1860s, conditions favored specialization in ophthalmology. There were special eye institutions, a group of men trained in medicine who were interested in diseases of the eye, and large urban populations with a high incidence of disease who were socially and culturally prepared to consult specialists. But to flourish, a specialty requires bonds between colleagues within an association based on shared interests and problems. The creation of the American Ophthalmological Society in 1864 was thus a pivotal point that solidified ophthalmology's position as a formal specialty in America, although this society has remained a small group. The expanding needs for education, public policy, and socialization were met by the founding of the American Academy of Ophthalmology and Otology in 1896. (Ophthalmology and otology separated amicably in 1979.) The American Academy of Ophthalmology has become the largest association of eye care providers in the world and sponsors the largest annual ophthalmological conference in the world. In 2012, it had about 20 thousand U.S. ophthalmologists and 7 thousand international members (American Academy of Ophthalmology, 2012). From 1878 to 1971 the section on ophthalmology of the American Medical Association served similar functions as the American Academy of Ophthalmology, but the American Medical Association has discontinued providing medical educational meetings to concentrate on public policy and its family of medical journals, including the *Archives of Ophthalmology*.

Standards.

Until the eighteenth century eye diseases received little attention from the medical profession and there was little they could do. Quacks and charlatans were able to fill this void. Cataract surgery was the province of itinerant practitioners in the United States until the latter part of the nineteenth century. Peripatetic eye care practitioners were held in low esteem, which contributed to slow growth of the specialization. Most physicians were antagonistic to specialization. In part, their rationale was that medical science was unique and indivisible and that the clinical practice of medicine should be no different. Economic competition was another major factor. General practitioners felt that specialization implied that they were not competent to treat certain diseases and limited their opportunities to treat. Scientific advances, improved skills, and a shift in public attitude eventually drove acceptance of specialization.

Ophthalmology did not develop as rapidly in the United States as it did in Europe (Hubbell, 1908, p. 128). Early medical institutions in America, with few exceptions, were the products of private enterprise, unlike the European governmental schools and hospitals. In the American spirit of free enterprise, little governmental regulation and low standards for medical school graduates resulted in too many doctors and weak professionalism until the 1860s. The first university professorships in ophthalmology were established at Cincinnati (Elkanah Williams, 1860), the College of Physicians and Surgeons in New York (Cornelius Agnew, 1869), Harvard (Henry Williams, 1871), and Michigan (George Frothingham,

1872). Training programs were not well defined for decades and preceptorships under individual physicians were the alternative method of learning for many years.

The need for rational standards in medical practice resulted in the establishment of the American Board of Ophthalmology in 1916, the first U.S. specialty board. In 2012, more than 27 thousand people had met its rigorous standards for certification (American Academy of Ophthalmology, 2012). Board-certified ophthalmologists have been eligible for full membership in the American Academy of Ophthalmology. In the early twenty-first century, the vast majority of American ophthalmologists were members.

Another eye care group, optometry, arose from lens makers who, with advances in the studies of optics, began to apply scientific understanding to problems of vision. By the end of the nineteenth century anyone could call himself an optometrist, since there were no regulations or licensure requirements (Albert and Edwards, 1996, pp. 303–310). The American Optometric Association had high educational standards and professional goals to promote the visual health of the general population. The field of optometry has evolved not only to prescribe lenses to improve vision but also to treat some eye diseases, although the scope of optometry (which is not a medical field and provides less educational experience in training) remains a point of dispute between the two professions.

Europeans dominated ophthalmic research during the nineteenth and early twentieth centuries, but momentum shifted to the United States following World War II. The federal government became an important source of support for ophthalmic research. By the early twenty-first century, the National Institute of Health's National Eye Institute was regularly providing major grant support for research to hundreds of medical centers and hospitals. American ophthalmologists have made many contributions to the field. Although the ophthalmoscope was a European invention, Americans made many of the important refinements to the instrument. Elkanah Williams of Cincinnati was a pioneer in the use of the ophthalmoscope. Henry Williams, in Boston, was the first to use sutures in cataract surgery. Other examples of American research leadership in ocular science in the early twenty-first century included ultrasonic energy for cataract surgery, the excimer laser to alter the shape of a human cornea and correct refractive errors, the artificial cornea, fluorescein angiography, modern indirect ophthalmoscopy, and new forms of vitreoretinal surgery.

[*See also* **Medical Specialization; Medicine; Optometry;** *and* **Surgery.**]

BIBLIOGRAPHY

Albert, Daniel M., and Diane D. Edwards, eds. *The History of Ophthalmology*. Cambridge, Mass.: Blackwell Science, 1996.

Albert, Daniel M., and Marvin L. Sears. "Dr Elisha North and the First Eye Infirmary in the United States." *American Journal of Ophthalmology* 71, no. 2 (1971): 578–587. Discusses the New London (Connecticut) Eye Infirmary, established by Elisha North in 1817.

American Academy of Ophthamology. http://www.aao.org/.

Collins, E. Treacher. *The History & Traditions of the Moorfields Eye Hospital*. London: H. K. Lewis, 1929. Discusses the London Institution, which was the first public hospital devoted exclusively to treatment of diseases of the eye and ear.

Hubbell, Alvin A. *The Development of Ophthalmology in America 1800 to 1870*. Chicago: W. T. Keener & Co., 1908.

Jeffries, John. *Lectures on the Diseases of the Eye, First Delivered 1831*. Edited by Daniel M. Albert. Oostenede, Belgium: J. P. Wayenborgh, 1998.

Newell, Frank W. *The American Ophthalmological Society 1864–1989*. Rochester, Minn.: Johnson Printing Co., 1989. Includes discussion of the creation of the society in 1864.

Rosen, George. "Changing Attitudes of the Medical Profession to Specialization." *Bulletin of the History of Medicine* 12 (1942): 343–354.

Rosen, George. "New York City in the History of American Ophthalmology." *New York State Journal of Medicine* 43 (1943): 754–758. Discussion of ophthalmology in New York City, including details about establishment of the New York Eye Infirmary in 1820 by Edward Delafield and John Kearney Rodgers.

Rosen, George. *The Specialization of Medicine with Particular Reference to Ophthalmology*. New York: Froben Press, 1944.

James Ravin and Michael F. Marmor

OPPENHEIMER, J. ROBERT

(1904–1967), physicist. Born in New York City, J. Robert Oppenheimer attended Harvard University, graduating summa cum laude in 1925. In 1927 he received a PhD in theoretical physics from Germany's Göttingen University, where he studied with Max Born. His dissertation used quantum mechanics, an emerging field at that time. In 1929, after postdoctoral study and lecturing at Europe's leading centers of physics, he accepted an unusual joint appointment at the University of California, Berkeley, and the California Institute of Technology (Caltech). While teaching half-time at Caltech (and seriously studying the arts, languages, and literature), he nevertheless transformed Berkeley into the top U.S. center for quantum physics. He also became involved with several left-wing groups. He was friendly with members of the Communist Party in Northern California, married the widow of a party official, and supported causes championed by the party.

In 1942, despite opposition by security officers, General Leslie Groves, military head of the Manhattan Project, appointed Oppenheimer director of the Los Alamos laboratory responsible for designing and constructing atomic bombs. He proved an effective leader and on 16 July 1945 the first atomic device was tested at Alamogordo, New Mexico. On 6–9 August, atomic bombs obliterated the Japanese cities of Hiroshima and Nagasaki. Transformed into a national hero, "the father of the atomic bomb," Oppenheimer used his newfound fame to promote the Acheson–Lilienthal plan for the international control of atomic energy. He resigned as director of the project in 1945 and returned to teaching.

From 1947 to 1953, while directing the Institute for Advanced Study in Princeton, New Jersey, he served on numerous government advisory committees and chaired the General Advisory Committee of the Atomic Energy Commission (AEC). During this period, as the Cold War intensified, the American government became increasingly concerned about security and the loyalty of its advisors. Oppenheimer's former Communist associations and his opposition to the hydrogen-bomb project led in 1953 to the suspension of his security clearance—an action coordinated by Lewis L. Strauss, appointed by President Dwight D. Eisenhower as AEC chairman. In 1954 a biased and inquisitorial AEC hearing board, while affirming Oppenheimer's loyalty, nevertheless declared him a security risk. Although many members of the physics community supported Oppenheimer before the hearing, Edward Teller was an important exception. Oppenheimer and Teller had a long-running dispute over the hydrogen bomb. The decision of the AEC hearing ended Oppenheimer's career as a government adviser but made him a martyr in the eyes of many. Oppenheimer stayed in his position at the Institute for Advanced Study. Under his guidance, the Institute became a prominent academic center. In 1963, in a gesture of reconciliation with the government, President Lyndon B. Johnson awarded Oppenheimer the prestigious Enrico Fermi Prize.

[*See also* **Atomic Energy Commission; Fermi, Enrico; Manhattan Project; Military, Science and Technology and the; Nuclear Weapons; Physics; Quantum Theory; Science;** *and* **Teller, Edward.**]

BIBLIOGRAPHY

Bird, Kai, and Martin J. Sherwin. *American Prometheus: The Triumph and Tragedy of J. Robert Oppenheimer*. New York: Vintage Books, 2005.

Cassidy, David C. *J. Robert Oppenheimer and the American Century*. New York: Pi Press, 2004.

Herken, Gregg. *Brotherhood of the Bomb: The Tangled Lives and Loyalties of Robert Oppenheimer, Ernest Lawrence, and Edward Teller*. New York: Henry Holt and Co., 2002.

McMillan, Priscilla J. *The Ruin of J. Robert Oppenheimer and the Birth of the Modern Arms Race*. New York: Viking Press, 2005.

Sopka, Katherine R. "Oppenheimer, J. Robert (1904–1967)." In *The History of Science in the United States: An Encyclopedia,* edited by Marc Rothenberg, pp. 414–415. New York and London: Garland Publishing, 2001.

Martin J. Sherwin;
updated by Elspeth Knewstubb

OPTOMETRY

The word "optometry," from the Greek *optos* and *metron* meaning "visible" and "measure," was apparently first used in the 1890s to describe a profession that today encompasses doctors trained and licensed to diagnose and treat diseases and disorders of the visual system. Colonial merchants selling European-made spectacles and lenses launched what would become professional optometry in the United States. Two developments by Americans, bifocal lenses and better spectacle frames, helped move optometry from a vendor trade toward a recognized profession by making the process of fitting and selecting eyeglasses more complicated. In 1760, Benjamin Franklin instructed a London firm to make him spectacles with two types of lenses fitted together, thus inventing bifocals. Late in the eighteenth century, American inventors, like those overseas, began patenting lighter-weight rims and springs and pads for comfort, as well as improved construction techniques.

Nineteenth-century American optometry made further advances with the growth of optical companies, the development of new diagnostic equipment, and cooperative efforts by prescriber-purveyors of spectacles to gain professional status as optometrists. Many of the diagnostic advances, such as Bausch and Lomb's 1902 retinoscope and the improved ophthalmoscopes made in 1905 by the New Jersey–based DeZeng Standard Company, extended technologies developed earlier in Europe. More grounded in American soil were the optical companies, which also influenced an emergent occupation of opticians. Denied traditional supplies from Europe during the Revolutionary War, American manufacturers and merchants built a domestic industry. John McAllister, a Philadelphia cane and whip manufacturer who began selling spectacles in 1783, became the first U.S. optician and his firm the first American optical company. Several frame-making factories followed, often begun by jewelers or by European-trained immigrants. When the Civil War again disrupted glass imports from Europe, the American Optical Company and other firms began production of their own lenses. In consultation with those who sold spectacles, American Optical and Bausch and Lomb, among others, developed improved sets of trial lenses to determine patient prescriptions. By 1904 the United States was exporting lenses to Europe.

With improved tools and clinical expertise, practitioners who once labeled themselves refracting or applied opticians now identified themselves as more highly trained optometrists; took steps to establish optometry's professional identity and prestige; and launched specialized periodicals such as *Johnson's Eye Echo* (1886), *The Optician* (1891), *Optical Journal* (1895), and *Optical Review* (1907).

With professionalization came controversies over licensing laws and government regulations. Until the late nineteenth century, the field had no official standards of practice, education, or competency. In 1896, seeking stricter controls over who could prescribe eyeglasses, Charles F. Prentice and Andrew Jay Cross formed the Optical Society of New York. As other state societies arose, practitioners lobbied legislatures for regulatory statutes. Minnesota imposed the first regulations, in 1901, and by 1925 all of the states and the District of Columbia had passed such legislation.

Inspired by the early lobbying efforts, periodical editors, officials of state organizations, and practitioners founded the American Association of Opticians in New York City in 1898. Initially, anyone interested in optics could join, but the retail merchants soon dropped out and over the next decade stricter education and professional standards resulted in a more exclusive membership. In 1910 the organization was renamed the American Optical Association and in 1919 the American Optometric Association. In 1929 it launched its own *AOA Organizer*, renamed the

Journal of the American Optometric Association in 1930.

In 1915 the National Board of State Examiners in Optometry (established by the national association in 1919) set two 26-week school terms as a minimum education standard for certification. This reflected a continuing emphasis on education as one guarantee of quality care. Around 1900, America had an estimated 60 optometry schools of varying quality; by 2000, fewer than 20 were accredited by the Council on Optometric Education. Four-year programs included anatomy, pharmacology, pathology, vision screening, optics, and applied lens technology. Graduates needed to pass a state board examination to practice, and nearly all states required continuing-education courses for license renewal.

The scope of optometric practice expanded in the 1970s as some states authorized optometrists to treat certain eye diseases with pharmaceuticals. By 1989 all states had authorized specifically trained optometrists to use drugs for diagnostic purposes. By 2000, changing Medicare regulations, the growth of managed-care systems, and cooperative networks with ophthalmologists and other specialists were altering optometric practices. But America's 30 thousand optometrists, 25 percent of whom were women, still performed over 60 percent of the nation's primary eye examinations.

[*See also* **Anatomy and Human Dissection; Franklin, Benjamin; Health Maintenance Organizations; Journals in Science, Medicine, and Engineering; Medicare and Medicaid; Medicine; Ophthalmology;** *and* **Pharmacology and Drug Therapy.**]

BIBLIOGRAPHY

Gregg, James R. *American Optometric Association: A History*. St. Louis: American Optometric Association, 1972.

Gregg, James R. *The Story of Optometry*. New York: Ronald Press, 1965.

Koetting, Robert. *The American Optometric Association's First Century*. St. Louis: American Optometric Association, 1997.

Diane D. Edwards

ORGAN TRANSPLANTATION

Organ transplantation is one of the most significant surgical interventions of the twentieth century. Since the 1950s, when the first successful kidney transplants were performed, thousands of Americans have lived with "replacement" organs or "spare parts" taken from the bodies of people both living and dead. The success of transplanting kidneys, lungs, hearts, corneas, and, more recently, faces has seemingly created a critical shortage of these organs. In the United States, potential recipients of organs are placed on lists managed by the United Network of Organ Sharing, an organization created by the National Organ Transplant Act enacted by Congress in 1984. Many individuals waiting on such lists die before an acceptable organ becomes available. The United Network of Organ Sharing relies on voluntarily donated organs; the National Organ Transplant Act explicitly outlaws the buying and selling of human tissues and organs. The intensifying need for organs for transplantation has fostered new and still controversial systems for increasing the supply of transplantable organs, including financial incentives for organ donation and presumed consent (which assumes that a dead person would want organs to be harvested unless explicitly indicated).

Before the 1950s. The idea of replacing injured or diseased tissue with healthy tissue has an ancient history and an ongoing appeal. In the United States the first tissue transplants began in the 1850s, when the New York surgeon Frank Hamilton transplanted skin from one person to treat the ulcerated body of another patient. By the early twentieth century, following European medical developments, American surgeons were attempting to transfer skin, bone, and even such organs as the thyroid gland from one patient to another (and in some cases from one nonhuman animal to a patient).

Surgical developments in the attachment of blood vessels and arteries, especially the work of the French surgeon Alexis Carrel (1873–1944), fostered the potential for organ and limb transplantations. In France, where Carrel received his medical training, he developed a technique for joining together the ends of blood vessels, a delicate surgical feat that enabled both direct blood transfusion and the transplantation of whole organs. At the Rockefeller Institute for Medical Research (opened in New York in 1904), where he headed the Department of Experimental Surgery, Carrel cultivated his image as a surgical miracle worker, even claiming that he had performed the medieval miracle of "the black leg." But whereas Saints Cosmas and Damian had miraculously substituted the diseased leg of a European churchman with the healthy leg from a Moor, Carrel, who received the Nobel Prize in 1912 for his work, confined his miracles to animals, claiming to have successfully grafted the leg from a black dog onto the body of a white dog.

The idea of surgically replacing diseased organs with healthy organs became very popular in the 1920s. Before the successful isolation of testosterone and estrogen, surgeons and patients looked to surgery to rejuvenate aging bodies with transplants of gonadal tissue (testes and ovaries). Here again, supply was problematic. In the absence of sufficient testicular sources, surgeons in the United States and Europe used glands taken from monkeys, apes, goats, and sheep in the effort to restore function. Despite the popularity of the idea of spare-part surgery, medical understanding of the complex immunology of joining together bodies of different individuals and different species took several decades.

Success with Kidneys. In the early 1950s, on the heels of pioneering work by such scientists as Sir Peter Medawar (1915–1987; Nobel Prize, 1960), who investigated how cells acquired the ability to differentiate self from non-self, surgeons in the United States and France performed the first successful kidney transplants. In 1954, the surgeons Francis Moore (1913–2001), John Merrill (1917–1984), and Joseph Murray (1919–2012) at the Peter Bent Brigham Hospital in Boston, Massachusetts, removed a healthy kidney from Ronald Herrick and transplanted it into the body of his identical twin, Richard. Richard lived for eight years with the kidney; his brother lived with just one until 2010. The fact that the donor

and recipient were genetically identical meant that they did not face the biological rejection of foreign tissue.

The successful transplantation of the kidney inspired hope for transplantation of other organs. Whereas the kidney was a paired organ, heart transplantation demanded the death of the donor. In 1967 an obscure South African surgeon, Christiaan Barnard (1922–2001), captured the world's attention when he transplanted the heart of a young woman into the chest of Louis Washkansky. Washkansky lived for 18 days with the transplanted heart. Such American surgeons as the Stanford physician Norman Shumway, who believed that an American would perform the first heart transplant, were stunned by the so-called "Capetown miracle." However, Americans quickly led the world in performing heart transplants. By 1972, American surgeons had performed 132 of the world total of 202 heart transplants and accounted for 22 of the 26 survivors of the operation. Unfortunately, most recipients did not survive the surgery. In the face of extremely high mortality rates, surgeons around the world called for a moratorium on heart transplants until the problems of tissue rejection and immune response could be resolved.

The transplantation of organs was greatly facilitated by developments in immunology. Relying on the discovery of the human leukocyte antigens by the French biologist Jean Dausset (1916–2009), immunologists were able to type tissues in an effort to have better matched transplants (reducing the potential for rejection). The discovery of chemical and physical means (e.g., radiation) to depress immune response also facilitated the spread of organ transplantation. In 1980, the introduction of cyclosporine to suppress immune response by the University of Pittsburgh surgeon Thomas Starzl launched a new era in organ transplantation. The Food and Drug Administration approved the drug in 1983. The availability of this agent greatly increased the transplantation of bone marrow, kidneys, and hearts.

New hopes for kidney transplants prompted old concerns about the sources of organs. The prospect of a commercial kidney-supply business was one factor in Congress's decision to outlaw the buying and selling of human organs. Even before the legislation, such novels as *Coma* (1977) fanned fears of a "black market" in organs. Despite the legislation, the buying and selling of organs seems to have occurred in the United States. Although documenting such sales is difficult, it is certain that some Americans have participated in so-called "transplant tourism," in which they travel to countries where organ traffic is permitted for the surgery and then return to the United States for their medical care.

Organ transplantation raises other profound ethical concerns. Since the first human heart transplant in 1967, the status of the donor's heart at the time of heart removal has been at issue. If surgeons wait until the heart stops beating, the chances for successful transplantation diminish. But if the donor's heart is still beating, is the donor still alive? What does alive mean in this context? One effort to redress this issue was the introduction of a new definition for death. In 1968 Harvard Medical School convened the Harvard Ad-Hoc Committee on Brain Death to produce new criteria for determining death. The committee published an influential report that defined a new kind of death, brain death, determined by diagnostic tests that established whether a person had a "permanently nonfunctioning brain" (including the absence of electrical activity in the brain). Brain death has been and continues to be controversial.

[*See also* **Animal and Human Experimentation; Death and Dying; Ethics and Medicine; Medical Specialization; Medicine;** *and* **Surgery.**]

BIBLIOGRAPHY

Fox, Renée C., and Judith P. Swazey. *Spare Parts: Organ Replacement in American Society*. New York: Transaction Publishers, 2013.
Lederer, Susan E. *Flesh and Blood: Organ Transplantation and Blood Transfusion in Twentieth-Century America*. New York: Oxford University Press, 2008.
Lock, Margaret. *Twice Dead: Organ Transplants and the Reinvention of Death*. Berkeley: University of California Press, 2001.
Schlich, Thomas. *The Origins of Organ Transplantation: Surgery and Laboratory Science, 1880–1930*. Rochester, N.Y.: University Rochester Press, 2010.
Tilney, Nicholas L. *Transplant: From Myth to Reality*. New Haven, Conn.: Yale University Press, 2003.
                                    Susan E. Lederer

OSLER, WILLIAM

(1849–1919), physician and medical educator. Arguably the greatest physician of his time, Osler played a crucial role in defining the modern profession of medicine. He was born at Bond Head, Canada, the son of the Reverend Featherstone Lake Osler and Ellen Free Picton Osler. He entered medical study at the University of Toronto, but transferred to the University College of Medicine at McGill because it allowed students better access to clinical experience. He graduated M.D., C.M., from McGill in 1872. Supported financially by his brother, he traveled to London, Berlin, and Vienna for advanced training in medicine, pathology, and laboratory science.

Osler returned to McGill as professor of the institutes of medicine in 1874. As well as giving traditional lectures, he developed the new teaching technique of bedside instruction at the Montreal General Hospital. He also introduced a course on clinical microscopy and established a pathology laboratory. To supplement his income as a professor of medicine, he operated a private practice and taught veterinary pathology at the Montreal Veterinary College. In 1884 he moved to the University of Pennsylvania to take up the position of chair of clinical medicine. Five years later, Johns Hopkins University appointed him professor of medicine and physician in chief at the university hospital.

Drawing on European models, Osler introduced to the Johns Hopkins Medical School, which opened in 1893, a system of clinical clerkships similar to the practice in England that allowed senior students to practice as junior doctors in a supervised context. He also put a premium on bedside instruction. Osler taught students beginning with their third year of study. A charismatic teacher, he became a role model for a generation of U.S. medical students. His influence was further extended through his best-selling textbook, *The Principles and Practice of Medicine* (1892), and through numerous essays on the medical life. He received honorary degrees from McGill, Michigan, Jefferson, Aberdeen, Edinburgh, Trinity College, and Toronto universities. In 1905, wishing for a change of pace, he became Regius Professor at Oxford. In 1911 he was made a baronet. In England, Osler and his wife made their home a haven for a generation of Rhodes scholars and other visiting Americans. He died at Oxford in 1919.

A clergyman's son, Osler became a high priest of modern medicine and contributed greatly to America's rise to international medical prominence. His patient-centered teaching and his genteel, bibliophilic scholarship inspired later medical humanists. His legacy is perpetuated through various clubs, lectureships, and the American Osler Society. A large collection of Osler papers and books bequeathed by him is held at the Osler Library at McGill University.

[*See also* **Hospitals; Medical Education; Medicine; Science; Societies and Associations, Science;** *and* **Welch, William H.**]

BIBLIOGRAPHY

Bliss, Michael. *William Osler: A Life in Medicine.* Oxford and New York: Oxford University Press, 1999.
Cushing, Harvey. *The Life of Sir William Osler.* 2 vols. Oxford: Clarendon Press, 1925.
Murray, Jock. "Osler, William." In *Dictionary of Medical Biography,* edited by W. F. Bynum and Helen Bynum, Vol. 4, pp. 947–951. Westport, Conn., and London: Greenwood Press, 2007.

Michael Bliss; updated by
Elspeth Knewstubb and
Hugh Richard Slotten

OWEN, DAVID DALE

(1807–1860), geologist and surveyor. Born in New Lanark, Scotland, to a family of social reformers (father Robert), politicians (brother Robert Dale Owen), and scientists (brother Richard and sister Jane Dale Owen Fauntleroy), David Dale Owen immigrated to the United States in 1827, intending to work as a chemist in the science-oriented Utopian community of New Harmony, Indiana, established by his father and led, at the time, by geologist William Maclure. He married Caroline Neef, daughter of a New Harmony school teacher in 1837, with whom he had four children.

Although New Harmony would remain his home for the rest of his life, it did not offer the career he had anticipated. Between 1830 and 1837 he worked in New York (as a printer) and studied in London (chemistry) and Cincinnati (medicine).

In 1837, he was appointed head of the first geological survey of Indiana, launching his career as a federal and state geologist. For the General Land office, he conducted surveys of minerals located in portions of Wisconsin, Illinois, and Iowa from 1839 to 1840 and of the Chippewa land district in Iowa, Wisconsin, and Minnesota from 1847 to 1852. He subsequently held overlapping appointments as state geologist for Kentucky (1854 to 1860), Arkansas (1857 to 1860), and Indiana (1859 to 1860).

Owen was a meticulous and careful stratigrapher and his reports are noteworthy for their detail and high-quality illustrations. Collectively, they provided the first overall picture of the geology of the upper Midwest. At the same time, he was very much a practical, economic geologist who intended his findings to aid in the development of the region's mineral resources.

One key to his success was his ability to gather, train, and organize a talented group of assistants. He made New Harmony a base and training ground for a generation of field geologists, effectively creating a geological research school there. He built a geological laboratory and museum where he and his assistants analyzed and organized the specimens collected during their field work. Many of these assistants and students including E. T. Cox, F. B. Meek, J. G. Norwood, C. C. Parry, and B. F. Shumard would go on to successful careers in geology or other scientific disciplines.

[*See also* **Chemistry; Geological Surveys; Geology;** *and* **Medicine.**]

BIBLIOGRAPHY

Hendrickson, Walter B. *David Dale Owen, Pioneer Geologist of the Middle West.* Indianapolis: Indiana Historical Bureau, 1943. This is the seminal biography upon which all work on Owen depends. Available free online through Hathitrust at http://hdl.handle.net/2027/uc1.31822007454515 (accessed 11 April 2012).

Kimberling, Clark. "David Dale Owen and Joseph Granville Norwood: Pioneer Geologists in Indiana and Illinois." *Indiana Magazine of History* 92 (1996): 2–25. A detailed discussion of the lives of the two men, their disputes, and their collections, it situates them clearly in their cultural and scientific contexts.

Daniel Goldstein

P

PACKARD, DAVID

See Computers, Mainframe, Mini, and Micro.

PAGE, LARRY

See Software.

PALEONTOLOGY

In the late eighteenth century, when early modern science was largely confined to Europe, American fossils played a crucial role in the development of paleontology in France and Great Britain. British anatomist William Hunter, for example, described fossils collected at Salt Lick, Kentucky, as gigantic, elephant-like carnivores and suggested that they were probably extinct. Likewise, Georges Cuvier, a French comparative anatomist and the founder of modern vertebrate paleontology, used American fossil mastodons to argue convincingly for the fact of extinction in 1796. Charles Willson Peale's "mammoth" fossil, exhibited with great fanfare at Philadelphia's American Philosophical Society late in 1801, was the world's second mounted fossil vertebrate skeleton. A second skeleton toured England with Peale's son Rembrandt, to mixed reviews.

By the 1830s, Americans had adopted Cuvier's pioneering methods, and they soon began making important contributions to paleontology. Philadelphia physician Richard Harlan and his *Basilosaurus*, for example, featured prominently in European debates about the antiquity of fossil mammals. Harlan, collaborating with London's Richard Owen, determined that *Basilosaurus* was a fossil whale and not a reptile as Harlan had originally believed. The important point, however, is that Europeans had greater respect both for American fossil descriptions and for their interpretations after 1830.

James Hall, working for the state geological survey of New York, made many important contributions in stratigraphy and invertebrate paleontology beginning in the 1840s. He worked later for other state surveys and amassed enormous fossil collections. Hall's publications, especially his encyclopedic, multivolume *Palaeontology of New York*, were largely responsible for establishing the stratigraphy of the eastern United States.

An Embarrassment of Fossil Riches. Various federal surveys organized before and after the Civil War produced an abundance of fossils from the trans-Mississippi West. Fielding B. Meek, a stratigraphical paleontologist trained, in part, by Hall, took charge of these collections at the Smithsonian Institution's U.S. National Museum. Meek collaborated with explorer Ferdinand Vandiveer Hayden in research and in the field. Federal paleontology was later organized around the U.S. Geological Survey, established in 1879 to do field-oriented research, and the Smithsonian Institution, where specimens were curated. In 1907, invertebrate paleontologist Charles Doolittle Walcott resigned as director of the geological survey to become secretary of the Smithsonian, where he continued to pursue his paleontological research program. The significance of Walcott's discovery, in 1909, of spectacularly preserved, soft-bodied invertebrate fossils from the Cambrian Period was not fully appreciated until a reassessment of the bizarre Canadian fossils was made in the 1960s.

Joseph Leidy, considered the father of American vertebrate paleontology, described the first American dinosaurs, in 1856, based on fragmentary fossil teeth collected by Hayden in present-day Montana. In 1858, he described a relatively complete Cretaceous dinosaur, *Hadrosaurus foulkii*, from a fossil found in Haddonfield, New Jersey. *Hadrosaurus*, which featured greatly reduced forelimbs and a kangaroo-like posture, created a sensation at Philadelphia's Academy of Natural Sciences when it was exhibited to the public in 1868—it was the world's first mounted dinosaur. In 1869, Leidy published a monograph on the extinct fauna of Dakota and Nebraska, which added more than 70 genera and numerous species—including representatives of many of the principal mammalian orders—to the fossil fauna of America. Hayden collected most of these specimens also.

Othniel Charles Marsh and Edward Drinker Cope took the mantle from Leidy in the 1860s. Marsh became America's first professor of paleontology at Yale in 1866 and launched the first of his four western paleontological expeditions in 1870. In 1882, Marsh was appointed vertebrate paleontologist of the U.S. Geological Survey, which relieved him of some of the financial burden of his research program. Marsh's paper restorations of extinct animals, often reproduced in textbooks and newspapers, served as important visual aids in an era when mounted fossils in museums were still a rarity. One of Marsh's most important contributions was his 1880 monograph *Odontornithes*. Charles Darwin hailed this book on toothed birds as the best empirical support for evolution in decades. Certain members of Congress, however, were less impressed. In 1892, "Birds with teeth!" became a rallying cry for opponents of wasteful government spending on science.

Philadelphia's Edward Drinker Cope was Marsh's contemporary and arch-rival. Brilliant, productive, and combative, Cope's most renowned work is *Vertebrata of the Tertiary Formations of the West* (1883). With more than a thousand pages and 80 plates, this book today is known as "Cope's Bible." Cope, along with invertebrate paleontologist Alpheus Hyatt, was one of America's leading neo-Lamarckian evolutionary theorists. Cope and Marsh competed for access to fossils and for priority of description, often resorting to underhanded tactics to gain an advantage. Their ungentlemanly competition eventually drove Leidy out of paleontology.

In 1877, enormous, well-preserved Jurassic dinosaurs were discovered in prolific numbers in several localities in Colorado and Wyoming. Cope and Marsh raced to describe these new forms first, including *Apatosaurus*, *Camarasaurus*, *Stegosaurus*, and many other iconic dinosaurs. Their hastily penned and often poorly illustrated descriptions left a legacy of synonymous forms for the next generation of American paleontologists. Both of their reputations were tarnished when their rivalry became public scandal in 1890.

Shifting into Museums. The institutional setting for American vertebrate paleontology shifted into large, urban museums in the 1890s. Henry Fairfield Osborn of New York's American Museum of Natural History was one of the pioneers. A competition ensued to build museum collections, which led to a number of important developments. Improved field techniques yielded exhibit-quality fossils for museum paleontologists. Osborn and his staff developed new techniques for displaying mounted fossils in life-like poses and for reconstructing prehistoric life in colorful murals. Osborn's colleague Adam Hermann and Elmer Riggs, at Chicago's Field Columbian Museum, invented efficient, labor-saving techniques for cleaning fossils, many still in use in the early twenty-first century. Spectacular fossil exhibits, especially gigantic mounted sauropod dinosaurs and Osborn's *Tyrannosaurus rex*, brought record crowds into museums. Newspapers, movies, and books helped make dinosaurs and other extinct animals into popular media stars. Meanwhile, casts of the Carnegie Museum's *Diplodocus* mounted in European and Latin American museums aided the international spread of *dinomania*.

In the 1920s, American museums organized a number of ambitious and hugely expensive expeditions to scour the globe for fossils. These well-publicized expeditions were a boon for paleontology. Walter Granger, for example, found dinosaur eggs and several new kinds of Cretaceous dinosaurs during a high-profile American Museum expedition to the Gobi Desert of China and Mongolia. The Field Museum sent a similarly ambitious, although far less extravagant, expedition for fossil mammals to South America.

Moving toward Biology. George Gaylord Simpson, perhaps the most influential vertebrate paleontologist of the twentieth century, was one of the architects of the Modern Evolutionary Synthesis of the 1940s and 1950s. By introducing rigorous quantitative methods into paleontology and stressing the importance of causal explanations, Simpson brought his field into closer contact with biology. Simpson's *Tempo and Mode in Evolution* (1944) is a classic in the field.

Invertebrate paleontologist Norman Newell worked to promote the biological aspects of paleontology in the 1950s and 1960s and, because he trained many of the next generation of paleobiologists, his impact was profound. Newell applied statistical methods to study broad patterns in the fossil record as well as the significance and possible causes of mass extinctions. For his work on the latter, he seriously addressed the hitherto taboo topic of catastrophism in the fossil record. He was also a pioneer in the subfield of paleoecology. Newell's appreciation of the quality of the fossil record stands in stark contrast to Darwin's preoccupation with its deficiencies.

A dinosaur renaissance began in the postwar period. In 1947, Edwin H. Colbert opened a quarry near Ghost Ranch, New Mexico, that produced a spectacular series of near-perfect skeletons of the primitive Triassic dinosaur, *Coelophysis*. Likewise, a global expansion of collecting produced thousands of new specimens. New techniques, like histology, were applied to dinosaurs, raising new questions regarding physiology, behavior, and evolution. John Ostrom and Robert Bakker worked on the problem of dinosaur metabolism, for example, in the 1960s and 1970s. They argued that dinosaurs were warm-blooded. John Horner used fossils and a profusion of trace evidence to draw novel conclusions about dinosaur nesting behavior and ontogeny among *Maisaura* in the 1980s.

The period from 1970 through 1985 has recently been styled a paleobiological revolution. Stephen Jay Gould and Niles Eldredge's landmark paper, "Punctuated equilibria: An alternative to phyletic gradualism" (1972), set much of the agenda for this movement. Important papers by David Raup, J. John Sepkoski Jr., Steven Stanley, and others on species diversity, taxonomic survivorship, and rates of evolution and extinction drew heavily on quantitative techniques adapted from population biology. In 1975, a new journal, *Paleobiology*, provided a ready outlet for nontraditional, quantitative paleontology. Controversial topics like macroevolution and extinction have become mainstays of present-day paleobiology.

Paleontology is firmly embedded in American popular culture. Roadside dinosaurs populate the

U.S. West. Dinosaur books are often best-sellers; movies like *Jurassic Park* and *Ice Age* are blockbusters. Natural history museums are judged by their dinosaurs—those with the biggest and best attract appreciative crowds. Modern paleontology research, which continues to draw ideas and methods from biology, like divergence dating and DNA/protein analysis, thrives at American universities and museums.

[*See also* **Academy of Natural Sciences of Philadelphia; American Museum of Natural History; American Philosophical Society; Biological Sciences; Cope, Edward Drinker; Dinosaurs; DNA Sequencing; Evolution, Theory of; Geological Surveys; Geology; Gould, Stephen Jay; Leidy, Joseph; Marsh, Othniel Charles; Museums of Science and Natural History; Peale, Charles Willson; Simpson, George Gaylord;** *and* **Smithsonian Institution.**]

BIBLIOGRAPHY

Brinkman, Paul D. *The Second Jurassic Dinosaur Rush: Museums & Paleontology in America at the Turn of the Twentieth Century*. Chicago and London: University of Chicago Press, 2010. Draws heavily on archival sources; tells the lesser-known story of American paleontology in the post Cope–Marsh era.

Buffetaut, Eric. *A Short History of Vertebrate Palaeontology*. London and Wolfeboro, N.H.: Croon Helm, 1987. A concise and excellent volume on the history of vertebrate paleontology.

Gerstner, Patsy A. "Vertebrate Paleontology, an Early Nineteenth Century Transatlantic Science." *Journal of the History of Biology* 3 (1970): 137–148.

Lanham, Url. *The Bone Hunters*. New York: Columbia University Press, 1973. A colorful account of American bone diggers.

Rainger, Ronald. *An Agenda for Antiquity: Henry Fairfield Osborn and Vertebrate Paleontology at the American Museum of Natural History, 1890–1935*. Tuscaloosa: University of Alabama Press, 1991. An excellent source on Osborn's vertebrate paleontology program at the American Museum in New York.

Sepkoski, David, and Michael Ruse, eds. *The Paleobiological Revolution: Essays on the Growth of Modern Paleontology*. Chicago and London: University of Chicago Press, 2009. An invaluable edited collection of essays, many written by the revolutionary scientists themselves.

Paul D. Brinkman

PANAMA CANAL

A 51-mile ship canal through the Isthmus of Panama that connects the Caribbean Sea with the Pacific Ocean. The Spanish recognized the importance of such a canal as early as the sixteenth century. From 1879 to 1881, the French engineer Ferdinand de Lesseps attempted to build a canal at Panama, but the project failed because of disease, poor planning, and lack of funding. Late-nineteenth-century commercial and military interests prompted the U.S. government to undertake the project. After actively promoting Panama's independence, the Theodore Roosevelt administration completed the Hay–Bunau–Varilla Treaty in 1903, negotiated by Secretary of State John Hay, by which Panama granted the United States the right to construct, maintain, operate, and defend the canal.

Between 1907 and 1914, after a major public-health program to eradicate the mosquitos that transmitted yellow fever, the U.S. army colonel George W. Goethals (1858–1928) directed nearly 35 thousand workers, who completed the greatest construction project the world had seen to that time. Seven sets of locks raise and lower approximately 50 ships every 24 hours en route between the Caribbean Sea and Pacific Ocean. Passage through the canal takes approximately eight hours. For ships traveling between the east and west coasts of the United States, the canal route is some 8,000 nautical miles shorter than the route around the tip of South America. On voyages between the east coast of North America and the west coast of South America and Asia, the savings is some 3,500 miles.

Almost immediately after the signing of the Hay–Bunau–Varilla Treaty, the Panamanian government protested its provisions that granted the

United States titular sovereignty and economic control over the 10-mile-wide Canal Zone. As a result of the Hull–Alfaro Treaty (1936) and the Eisenhower–Remón Treaty (1955), the Republic of Panama's share of administrative responsibilities in the Canal Zone was increased, and Panamanians gained greater economic opportunities in the Canal Zone.

A rising wave of Panamanian nationalism after World War II demanded more. After violent demonstrations in Panama in 1958 and 1964, new treaty negotiations began. Finally, the 1977 New Panama Canal treaties provided for a joint U.S.–Panamanian Commission that administered the canal's operations until the year 2000, when the canal was turned over to the Panamanian government. The treaties included safeguards for U.S. security interests. Although Panamanians readily approved the treaties in a plebiscite, the U.S. Senate ratified them only after a bitter debate over the "abandonment" of a prized U.S. possession.

[See also **Canals and Waterways; Disease; Maritime Transport; Military, Science and Technology and the; Public Health;** and **Yellow Fever.**]

BIBLIOGRAPHY

Leonard, Thomas M. *Panama, the Canal and the United States: A Guide to Issues and References.* Claremont, Calif.: Regina Books, 1993.

Major, John L. *Prize Possession: The United States and the Panama Canal, 1903–1977.* Cambridge, U.K.: Cambridge University Press, 1993.

Missal, Alexander. *Seaway to the Future: American Social Visions and the Construction of the Panama Canal.* Madison: University of Wisconsin Press, 2008.

Parker, Matthew. *Panama Fever: The Epic Story of One of the Greatest Human Achievements of All Time—The Building of the Panama Canal.* New York: Doubleday, 2007.

Thomas M. Leonard

PARAPSYCHOLOGY

The term "parapsychology" was adopted by Joseph Banks Rhine in his first monograph, *Extra-Sensory Perception* (1934), to denominate a new field of academic scientific research dealing with purported human abilities that, *prima facie*, appeared to have no obvious explanatory mechanism in sensory or physical transmission, often termed "ESP."

Three such abilities concerned information transmission and reception (*telepathy*—mind reading; *clairvoyance*—gaining information of unobserved physical situations; and *precognition*—gaining information about future events) and one dealt with mental impact on physical situations (*psychokinesis*). The experimental investigations of these four purported abilities by Rhine and his students at Duke University were the basis of the field's most sustained attempt to achieve recognition as a valid scientific field, an attempt that was, at best, only partially successful.

The investigations at Duke worked in a tradition that studied incredible abilities and strange phenomena and that harked back to the spiritualist movement of the nineteenth century. In 1882, the Society for Psychical Research was founded in London by several prominent intellectuals, including scientists, to investigate scientifically the range of phenomena associated with spiritualism as well as purported abilities like the ones mentioned above. Two years later, the American Society for Psychical Research was founded, with its principal advocate the distinguished psychologist William James.

There was something of a recession of interest and marginalization of psychical research during the first few decades of the twentieth century. In the United States, members of the rapidly developing field of experimental psychology were almost uniformly skeptical and hostile to psychical research, although James remained strongly committed to it until his death in 1910. The American Society for Psychical Research, which disbanded before the end of the decade in which it was founded, was refounded in 1907 but with a more spiritualist orientation than that of the original society. Nevertheless, in the next decade, two American universities, Stanford and Harvard, established psychical research fellowships. The second holder of the Harvard fellowship, Gardner Murphy, became both a distinguished psychologist and a lifelong advocate for psychical research/ parapsychology.

Moreover, in 1920, the English psychologist William McDougall accepted the chair of psychology at Harvard. He had been active in psychical research in England and continued his activity in the United States. In 1927, he left Harvard to become chairman of the psychology department at the newly founded Duke University. Soon after McDougall's arrival at Duke came J. B. and Louisa E. Rhine. They were trained scientists (in plant physiology) but, while doing graduate work at the University of Chicago, had become interested in psychical research. They hoped to pursue this field at Duke under McDougall's patronage. In this, they were successful; by 1930, J. B. Rhine had received an academic appointment and began the experimental research that would be synthesized four years later in *Extra-Sensory Perception*.

Testing for telepathic and clairvoyant abilities came to be based on the use of a 25-card deck composed of equal numbers of five geometric symbols. Test results were evaluated statistically (with average scores above or below the chance average of five of twenty-five correct guesses being quantitatively evaluated). Rhine's subjects largely came from his students, undergraduate and graduate, a number of whom scored at unprecedentedly high extra-chance levels under systematically varied physical conditions (e.g., the distance between sender and receiver in telepathy experiments) and psychological conditions (e.g., formal versus informal settings of experiments).

Rhine's results received considerable publicity as well as criticism from skeptical psychologists. Nevertheless, during the 1930s, Rhine attempted to develop the new field as an academic discipline, establishing the *Journal of Parapsychology* as a research-oriented publication (1937). Moreover, in the early 1940s, there appeared to be major confirmation of Rhine's approach and claims in England (subsequently called into question). In 1940, Rhine and his research associates summarized their research (including that on precognition and psychokenisis) in *Extra-Sensory Perception after Sixty Years: A Critical Appraisal of the Research in Extra-Sensory Perception*. In 1947, an independent "Parapsychology Laboratory" was established at Duke, with Rhine as the director.

Starting in the 1940s, Louisa Rhine began research that complemented J. B. Rhine's experimental focus by collecting cases of "spontaneous" ESP. Also, after World War II, the Parapsychology Laboratory became engaged from time to time in investigating reports of paranormal occurrences such as poltergeists, although J. B. Rhine was ambivalent about investigations of sensational claims that lay beyond laboratory testing.

But parapsychology ultimately failed to capitalize on its promising initiation in the 1930s. Some new institutional developments did take place, such as the inception of the international Parapsychological Association in 1957 (affiliated with the American Association for the Advancement of Science since 1969) and the formation of the Foundation for Research on the Nature of Man in Durham, North Carolina, in 1965, after Rhine had retired from Duke. But with the exception of some academic activity in New York City, the legacy of Gardner Murphy, there was virtually no academic development in the United States after 1950 (one exception was the Princeton Engineering Anomalies Research program at Princeton University, established in 1979 by Robert G. Jahn, the dean of the School of Engineering and Applied Design, and terminated in 2007).

Starting in the early 1970s, significant government-funded research (from the Central Intelligence Agency and the Department of Defense) focused on "remote viewing," a subspecies of clairvoyance whereby "psychics" (people with clairvoyant abilities) could be trained to "view" secret sites in adversarial countries, particularly, at this time, the Soviet Union. A major impetus was the fear that the Soviet Union had already embarked on this kind of research. It went under various code names, the collective name being *Project Star Gate*. An early locus of the research was at the Stanford Research Institute (Menlo Park, Calif.), directed by Harold E. Puthoff and Russell Targ. Although reviewed unfavorably by the National Research Council of the National Academy of Sciences, military- and intelligence-supported research continued until 1995.

To skeptics of the field, the reasons for the failure of these experiments are all too obvious. But from a historical perspective, the failure is more problematic and demanding of explanation. One—to give credit to the skeptics—lies in the methodological difficulties that even researchers convinced of the veracity of the phenomena and abilities encountered. Added to this was widespread a priori skepticism and hostility in the American scientific community, no doubt abetted by the sensationalist associations of psychical research and parapsychology in spiritualism and associated phenomena such as haunting and poltergeists that have persisted from the nineteenth century to the early twenty-first century.

Nevertheless, the field of parapsychology as a serious research endeavor in the United States has always had a few supporters and patrons among scientists with established reputations. These have included William James, Gardner Murphy, and, most recently, Daryl Bem, social psychologist at Cornell University. In addition, the field has attracted material support from wealthy patrons, such as Chester Carlson, the inventor of the Xerox photocopying process. Such support and patronage has contributed to the perseverance of the field in the face of the generally severe hostility and skepticism of the scientific establishment.

In 2011, David Kaiser, a historian of modern physics, argued that a group of young, unconventional (and largely unemployed) physicists, gathering together in San Francisco in the 1970s under the name "Fundamental Fysiks Group," deployed their interest in such topics as philosophy, Eastern mysticism, and parapsychology to bring to the fore Bell's theorem (quantum entanglement); this subsequently has become an important area of contemporary thought and research in physics and information theory.

[See also Physics; Pseudoscience and Quackery; Psychology; Religion and Science; Social Sciences: Before 1945; and Social Sciences: Post–World War II.]

BIBLIOGRAPHY

Beloff, John. Parapsychology: A Concise History. London: Athlone, 1993.

Horn, Stacy. Unbelievable: Investigations into Ghosts, Poltergeists, Telepathy, and Other Unseen Phenomena from the Duke Parapsychology Laboratory. New York: Ecco, 2009.

Kaiser, David. How the Hippies Saved Physics: Science, Counterculture, and the Quantum Revival. New York: W. W. Norton, 2011.

Mauskopf, Seymour H., and Michael R. McVaugh. The Elusive Science: Origins of Experimental Psychical Research. Baltimore: Johns Hopkins University Press, 1980.

Moore, R. Lawrence. In Search of White Crows: Spiritualism, Parapsychology, and American Culture. New York: Oxford University Press, 1977.

Putoff, H. E. "CIA-Initiated Remote Viewing Program at Stanford Research Institute." Journal of Scientific Exploration 10, no. 1 (1996): 63–76.

Schnabel, Jim. Remote Viewers: The Secret History of America's Psychic Spies. New York: Dell, 1997.

Smith, Paul H. Reading the Enemy's Mind: Inside Star Gate: America's Psychic Espionage Program. New York: Macmillan, 2005.

Targ, Russell. "Remote Viewing at Stanford Research Institute in the 1970s: A Memoir." Journal of Scientific Exploration 10, no. 1 (1996): 77–88.

Seymour Mauskopf

PARK, ROBERT

(1864–1944), sociologist. Born in Pennsylvania and reared in Red Wing, Minnesota, where his father ran a wholesale grocery firm, Park studied at the University of Minnesota, switching to the University of Michigan after his first year. His teachers included John Dewey and Calvin Thomas. Park graduated with a bachelor's degree in philology in 1887 and moved to Minneapolis to work as a reporter. He also worked in Detroit, Denver, and New York.

Park believed that better news reporting might prove capable of reforming society and reducing depression and violence. His interest in the potential of news reporting led to his decision to study philosophy at Harvard University. After a year at Harvard, he went abroad and studied at Strasbourg and Heidelberg in Europe. At Harvard, Park was taught by William James and the idealist philosopher Josiah Royce. In Germany, he attended lectures by the social theorist Georg Simmel and wrote a dissertation under the neo-Kantian philosopher Wilhelm Windelband on the problem of the crowd and the public. Back in America, he put scholarship aside to work with the Congo Reform Association. Through this job he became aware of inequality in Africa. He believed inequality to be inherent in colonial relationships and planned a trip to Africa to study colonialism. In preparation for this journey, he sought the advice of Booker T. Washington at the Tuskegee Institute. This resulted in his employment as an assistant to Washington. He never made his planned trip to the Congo.

In 1913, he took his first academic post, in the sociology department at the University of Chicago. Joining an already distinguished group of sociologists, he emerged as leader of the Chicago school of urban sociology. In an important 1915 essay, "The City," and in his textbook *Introduction to the Science of Sociology* (1921), coauthored with Ernest W. Burgess, Park conceptualized the American urban experience within a holistic ecological framework that combined economic, demographic, and cultural factors. The tension between the civilizing process of urbanization and the persistence of discrete cultural enclaves remained a consistent theme through his work, which drew upon what he and his students observed in the dynamic "laboratory" of early-twentieth-century industrial Chicago. Park's integrative vision continued long after his death to appeal to students of ethnicity, race, and the social geography of the city.

[*See also* **Demography** *and* **Social Sciences.**]

BIBLIOGRAPHY

Austin, Duke W. "Park, Robert E. (1864–1944)." In *Encyclopedia of Race, Ethnicity, and Society*, edited by Richard T. Shaefer, Vol. 2, pp. 1027–1028. Los Angeles: Sage Publications, 2008.

Matthews, Fred H. *Quest for an American Sociology: Robert E. Park and the Chicago School*. Montreal: McGill–Queens University Press, 1977.

Shils, Edward. "Robert E. Park, 1864–1944." *American Scholar* 60 (Winter 1991): 120–127.

J. Nicholas Entrikin; updated by Elspeth Knewstubb

PARSONS, TALCOTT

(1902–1979), sociologist. Born in Colorado Springs, Colorado, Talcott Parsons was the son of a Congregational minister, Edward Smith Parsons, and a suffragette, Mary Augusta Ingersoll Parsons. Talcott Parsons studied at Amherst College (1920–1924). He majored in biology, but became interested in economics and sociology. After graduating from Amherst, he attended the London School of Economics and the University of Heidelberg (1924–1926). Although his education included little formal training in sociology, it introduced him to the institutional economics of Thorstein Veblen, the functionalism of the anthropologist Alfred Radcliffe-Brown, and the sociology of Max Weber. Parsons translated Weber's famous *The Protestant Ethic and the Spirit of Capitalism* from German, which led to the wider dissemination of Weber's theories in America. In 1926, Parsons returned to the United States and took a position teaching economics at Amherst. In 1927 he joined Harvard University's sociology department.

Parsons's sociological theory developed in several phases. During his first two decades at Harvard, and particularly in *The Structure of Social Action* (1937), he elaborated a voluntaristic "action" theory that he traced to Weber, Alfred Marshall, Emile Durkheim, and Vifredo Pareto. In this, he moved American sociology away from its then more common forms of empirical research and ethnography and toward the use of a more abstract form of analysis. Parsons sought to construct a "grand theory" for social science. He drew on a functionalist tradition, proposing that society was a system made up of structures and substructures, each serving their own function in support of the overall system. In the two decades after Harvard's establishment of a new department of social relations in 1946, and notably in *The Social System* (1951), Parsons treated social structures in terms of the functions they served. He called his work "structural-functionalism" and "systems theory." Beginning in the late 1950s, returning to interests evident in his earlier work on the professions, he refined his systems theory to deal with the interaction of social subsystems and to develop a cybernetic model of the ways in which culture controls social change.

From 1945 to the early 1960s, Parsons was the major figure in American sociology, serving as president of the American Sociological Association in 1949. During the 1960s, criticism of his system mounted on the left, from the sociologists C. Wright Mills and Alvin Gouldner, and from feminists, as in Betty Friedan's *The Feminine Mystique* (1963). A revival of interest in the 1980s, however, reestablished his preeminence among American sociologists.

[*See also* Social Sciences.]

BIBLIOGRAPHY

Buxton, William. *Talcott Parsons and the Capitalist Nation-State: Political Sociology as a Strategic Vocation.* Toronto and Buffalo, N.Y.: University of Toronto Press, 1985.
Gerhardt, Uta. *Talcott Parsons: An Intellectual Biography.* Cambridge, U.K., and New York: Cambridge University Press, 2002.
Salerno, Roger A. "Talcott Parsons: The Systems Society." In *Beyond the Enlightenment: Lives and Thoughts of Social Theorists*, pp. 175–180. Westport, Conn.: Greenwood Press, 2004.

Robert C. Bannister;
updated by Elspeth Knewstubb

PAULING, LINUS

(1901–1994), chemist, peace activist, and Nobel laureate. Born to an Oregon family of modest means, Pauling's early readings included the phar-

macopoeia and dispensatory of his pharmacist father, who died when Pauling was a young boy. Pauling attended Oregon Agricultural College in Corvallis. Pauling's knowledge of chemical engineering so impressed his teachers that they asked him to teach freshman and sophomore chemistry courses when he was still a student. After completing his undergraduate study, Pauling found a scientific home at the California Institute of Technology (Caltech), where he earned his doctorate in 1925 and taught for nearly 40 years.

While traveling in Europe on a Guggenheim Foundation Fellowship, Pauling learned quantum mechanics as it was being discovered, studying with Arnold Sommerfeld in Munich, Niels Bohr in Copenhagen, and Erwin Schrödinger in Zurich. Upon returning to Caltech in 1927, Pauling became an assistant professor of chemistry and then a full professor in 1931. In the same year the American Chemistry Society awarded him the inaugural Langmuir Prize for the most promising young chemist in the nation. At Caltech he helped revolutionize chemistry by aligning it with the new physics, popularizing his ideas through an intuitive mix of bold theory and empirical research, memorable lectures, persuasive papers, and best-selling textbooks. In 1937, he became director of the Gates Laboratory and chairman of the division of chemistry and chemical engineering at Caltech. His *Nature of the Chemical Bond* (1939) proved particularly influential.

Starting in the late 1920s, Pauling participated in biology seminars offered at Caltech. His work with biologists shaped his thinking about chemistry and he began to work in biochemistry. Convinced that the structure of molecules explained their activity, Pauling made his point brilliantly in a series of groundbreaking discoveries about biomolecules, explaining the workings of hemoglobin and antibodies, the cause of sickle-cell anemia, and the secondary structure of proteins. He won the Nobel Prize in Chemistry in 1954.

After World War II, at the urging of his wife, he focused his attention on political causes, especially efforts to end nuclear-bomb testing. He persevered despite government harassment, becoming a world leader in the peace movement. His activism did have an impact on his career as a professional scientist, however. In 1958 Caltech asked him to resign as the chairman of the chemistry and engineering division on the grounds that he could not commit all his time to that position. In 1963, Pauling resigned from Caltech after the president of the university, Lee DuBridge, acknowledged the conflict involving Pauling's anti-nuclear campaign. His activism, however, brought him the 1962 Nobel Peace Prize, making him the only person to win two unshared Nobels. Pauling spent his last years at a California research institute he cofounded in 1973, studying the health effects of vitamin C and other nutrients.

[*See also* Biochemistry; Biological Sciences; Chemistry; Engineering; Health and Fitness; Medicine; Nobel Prize in Biomedical Research; Nuclear Weapons; Physics; Quantum Theory; *and* Sickle-Cell Disease.]

BIBLIOGRAPHY

Hager, Thomas. *Force of Nature: The Life of Linus Pauling*. New York: Simon and Schuster, 1995. Most comprehensive biography of Pauling.

Marinacci, Barbara, ed. *Linus Pauling in His Own Words*. New York: Simon and Schuster, 1995. Edited selections from his writings, speeches, and papers divided into sections on autobiography, "The Structure of Matter," "The Nuclear Age," and "Nutritional Medicine."

Mead, Clifford, and Thomas Hager, eds. *Linus Pauling, Scientist and Peacemaker: A Centenary Volume*. Corvallis: Oregon State University Press, 2001. Furnishes a good introduction to Pauling's life and thought.

Nye, Mary Jo. "Pauling, Linus Carl." In *Complete Dictionary of Scientific Biography*. Vol. 24, pp. 36–44. Detroit: Charles Scribner's Sons, 2008.

The Research Notebooks of Linus Pauling. 46 vols. Digitized and released online by Oregon State University Special Collections. http://osulibrary.orst.edu/specialcollections/rnb/index.html (accessed 15 January 2013).

Thomas Hager;
updated by Elspeth Knewstubb and
Hugh Richard Slotten

PEALE, CHARLES WILLSON

(1741–1827), museologist, artist, artisan, and inventor. Charles Willson Peale was born on the eastern shore of Maryland. His father, convicted of embezzlement in London and transported to the colonies, where he taught school, died young, throwing his widow and five children into poverty. Peale was apprenticed to a saddler and taught himself additional artisanal trades and portrait painting, displaying sufficient skill in the latter to convince Maryland's generous and public-spirited planters to send him to London to study with the American ex-patriot Benjamin West. He returned to become one of the most successful artists of the early republic, painting over one thousand portraits, including seven live sittings of George Washington. In his mid-forties this self-made man remade himself again, beginning an enormous lifelong undertaking: the creation of a natural history museum in Philadelphia. His museum was to be a new institution, designed by Peale for a republic. Specimens were carefully preserved as lifelike (Peale taught himself taxidermy) and labeled with their scientific names in the Linnaean classification. It was as unlike the proprietary museums with their jumble of specimens as the scientific institutions in Europe with their specimens pinned flat to white cloths and placed in drawers. Anyone with the 25-cent admission could enter, unlike European institutions requiring special application. Peale's museum was designed to engage large numbers of Americans in an educational experience, to play an important role in producing knowledgeable and virtuous citizens for a republic. In the first two decades of the nineteenth century—its years of greatest success—more than 40,000 people may have visited the museum yearly, in a city whose population was little more than 100,000. Peale's museum received national and international acclaim when in 1801 he exhumed and mounted two mastodon skeletons, only the second reconstruction of an extinct animal in the world. In addition to the museum, Peale often returned to his artisan roots and his fascination with mechanical pursuits: he held patents for fireplaces and stoves and the first patent for a bridge design in America; he was the coinventor of the polygraph, a copying device used by Jefferson and Benjamin Latrobe; and in his eighties he became a pioneer in American dentistry, becoming the first in this country to make false teeth out of porcelain.

[*See also* **Dentistry; Dinosaurs; Jefferson, Thomas; Latrobe, Benjamin;** *and* **Museums of Science and Natural History.**]

BIBLIOGRAPHY

Hart, Sidney. "The Enlightened City: Charles Willson Peale's Philadelphia Museum in Its Urban Setting." In *Shaping a National Culture. The Philadelphia Experience, 1750–1800*, edited by Catherine E. Hutchins, pp. 213-241. Winterthur, Del.: Henry Francis DuPont Winterthur Museum, 1994.

Hart, Sidney, and David C. Ward. "The Waning of an Enlightenment Ideal: Charles Willson Peale's Philadelphia Museum, 1790–1820." *The Journal of the Early Republic* 8, no. 4 (Winter 1988): 389–418.

Miller, Lillian B., Sidney Hart, David C. Ward, and Toby A. Appel, eds. *The Selected Papers of Charles Willson Peale and His Family*. 5 vols. New Haven, Conn., and London: Yale University Press, 1983–2000.

Sellers, Charles Coleman. *Charles Willson Peale*. New York: Charles Scribner's Sons, 1969.

Sidney Hart

PEARL, RAYMOND

(1879–1940), biologist and statistician, influential also in agriculture. Pearl was born in Farmington, New Hampshire, the only child of Frank Pearl, a grocery store clerk and shoe factory foreman, and Ida May (McDuffee). He attended grammar school and high school in New Hampshire and graduated from Dartmouth College in 1899 with the degree of A.B. That fall, Pearl followed his mentor, Herbert Spencer Jennings, to the University of Michigan, where he entered graduate school. As a graduate student, he was an assistant in zoology and participated in the Biological Survey of the Great Lakes, sponsored by the U.S. Fish Commission. In 1902 he was awarded the doctorate for his work on the reactions and behavior of Planarians. He married Maud Mary DeWitt in 1903, with whom he had two daughters.

Pearl spent the next four years as an instructor in zoology at the University of Michigan. In 1905 he spent a year working with the famed statistician Karl Pearson at University College, London, and visiting the University of Leipzig and the Naples Zoological Station. His year abroad yielded numerous publications and an appointment as associate editor of *Biometrika* (1906–1910). In 1906, he taught zoology at the University of Pennsylvania and a year later headed the department of biology at the Main Agricultural Experiment Station, University of Maine, Orono. During his 11-year tenure there, Pearl worked primarily on genetics and variation in domestic animals.

From 1917 to 1919 Pearl became chief of the statistical division of the newly organized U.S. Food Administration, under Herbert Hoover. In 1918 Pearl became the first Professor of Biometry and Vital Statistics, School of Hygiene and Public Health, Johns Hopkins University. From 1919 to 1930 he was a statistician at Johns Hopkins Hospital. From 1925 to 1930 he directed the Institute for Biological Research in that school. At Hopkins, Pearl published articles and books on human population, longevity, fertility, and disease. In 1928 he became the first president of the International Union for the Scientific Investigation of Population Problems.

Pearl founded two scientific journals: *Quarterly Review of Biology* (1926) and *Human Biology* (1929). He published 17 books and over seven hundred articles. His work on predicting population growth, studies on tuberculosis, and public criticism of eugenics sparked heated debate. Pearl was a member of numerous professional organizations including the National Academy of Sciences, American Philosophical Society, and American Academy of Arts and Sciences.

[*See also* **Agricultural Education and Extension; Agricultural Experiment Stations; Agricultural**

Technology; American Philosophical Society; Biological Sciences; Eugenics; Fish and Wildlife Service, U.S.; Fisheries and Fishing; Genetics and Genetic Engineering; Journals in Science, Medicine, and Engineering; Mathematics and Statistics; National Academy of Sciences; Public Health; Tuberculosis; *and* Zoology.]

BIBLIOGRAPHY

Glass, Bentley. *A Guide to the Genetics Collections of the American Philosophical Society*, pp. 58–66. Philadelphia: American Philosophical Society Library, 1988. Provides a detailed overview of the Pearl papers held at the American Philosophical Society.

Jennings, Herbert S. "Raymond Pearl (1979–1940)." *Biographical Memoirs of the National Academy of Sciences* 22 (1943): 295–347. Biographical memoir written by Pearl's longtime mentor containing an extensive bibliography of Pearl's many publications.

Mateo Muñoz

PEDIATRICS

Pediatrics has often been described as a holistic specialty, defined by an age group rather than an organ system. How it arose in the United States has much to do with the social context of late-nineteenth-century child mortality.

Historians estimate that between 15 and 20 percent of infants born in the United States in the second half of the nineteenth century never lived to see their first birthday. This astonishing loss was most evident in the immigrant wards of eastern cities, where entire families could be crowded into poorly ventilated tenements lacking a safe water supply. Even as sanitarians began to improve these conditions, infants rarely had access to pure milk. Women from the laboring classes typically weaned early and fed their infants whole or condensed milk transported in unrefrigerated bulk containers, often adulterated with sugar or molasses to disguise spoilage. Diarrhea epidem-

ics consequently swept the foreign wards every summer, killing many infants from dehydration and leaving survivors malnourished and vulnerable to subsequent illness. Those who lived past infancy had to face the traditional infections of childhood such as measles, whooping cough, and scarlet fever. Although the slow suffocation characterizing death from diphtheria was particularly agonizing to watch, all of these infections carried substantial mortality.

In this context, the socialist physician Abraham Jacobi laid the foundations for a new specialty directed at the medical problems of infancy and childhood. An associate of Karl Marx who had fled Germany following the aborted revolution of 1848, Jacobi founded the German Dispensary of New York to treat the poor free of charge. The clinic provided an unmatched opportunity to study and treat the diseases of childhood. Jacobi used his experience to become Professor of Pediatrics at New York Medical College in 1860—the first such position dedicated to pediatrics in the world at the time. His great insight was that children needed their own specialists not so much because they had distinct diseases, but because illness itself presented distinctly at different ages. Jacobi and his colleagues thus called the public's attention to the fact that the number one killer of infants was diarrhea, a condition often trivial in adults but deadly in babies. He argued that physiological knowledge of infants and children should guide therapy.

The management of infant feeding became the hallmark of the first generation of pediatric specialists. Jacobi's colleague Thomas Rotch at Harvard developed what became known as the "percentage system" by which practitioners employed slide rules and elaborate calculations to prescribe milk "formula" according to the proportions of its constituents. The method drew upon the nutritional theories of Justus von Liebig and certainly conferred an aura of scientific authority to these early practitioners who otherwise had little to offer sick infants. Supervising infant feeding in middle-class families also provided income to allow for time attending the children of the poor in hospitals and dispensaries.

The children's hospital provided another foundation for the new specialty. L. Emmett Holt, who became the leading figure of early-twentieth-century American pediatrics, developed his expertise through many years attending children at the New York Babies' Hospital. Like his colleagues, he had little to offer in the way of therapy. Parents only entrusted their infant to the hospital after all else had failed, and many babies arrived so moribund that they would never return home. A few children were actually saved by a biomedical intervention such as the newly discovered antitoxin to diphtheria; others somehow regained their health through a combination of nutritional care, skilled nursing, and a homelike hospital setting replete with outdoor fresh-air patios. All provided an unparalleled opportunity to study the clinical pathology of the diseases of childhood, enabling Holt to produce the new specialty's paradigmatic textbook, *The Diseases of Infancy and Childhood*, in 1897.

Two Visions of a New Profession. In 1887, 43 physicians came together to form the American Pediatric Society (APS). Jacobi, the country's best known pediatric specialist, became its first president and lived a quarter century longer to become its chief elder statesman. It was Holt, however, who did more than any other individual to shape the new profession's agenda. He envisioned pediatrics as a relatively elite specialty of hospital-based consultants. Their chief role would be to manage severe childhood illness referred by general practitioners and to produce scientific knowledge to improve practice. Holt imagined pediatrics, in other words, as evolving along the lines of the path it would take in countries such as Britain, where it has remained a profession of hospital consultants.

In fact, American pediatrics developed in a very different direction. The early-twentieth-century Progressive Era unleashed a powerful infant welfare movement that would profoundly undermine Holt's expectations. At its heart was a network of female reformers who argued that the health problems of children would never be addressed until *women* became involved. Graduates of women's medical colleges, often very interested in the diseases of children but excluded from the American Pediatric Society, invented their own

counterpart to pediatrics in the form of infant public health. Their exemplar was S. Josephine Baker, who in 1908 became the first director of the newly created child hygiene division of New York City's health department. Baker won national recognition by promoting a new approach to reducing infant mortality based on maternal education. The city had previously relied upon largely ineffectual "milk stations" to provide pure milk that often spoiled in unrefrigerated tenements. Baker sent visiting home nurses into the homes of the poor, providing instruction on hygiene and breast-feeding and referring infants for consultations at city-run infant welfare stations. There the baby would be examined by a physician (often a woman) who provided advice—the beginnings of what would later be called "well-child care." Maternal education soon replaced clean milk as the great slogan of child welfare crusaders around the country.

The aspirations of the infant welfare movement eventually led to a showdown with organized medicine. In the wake of the Nineteenth Amendment granting women the right to vote, Congress in 1921 passed the Sheppard–Towner Act, which provided matching funds to extend child health supervision to rural areas in the south and west, as well as extending its scope to include preschool children. The American Medical Association (AMA) reacted furiously, denouncing the law at its 1922 meeting as tantamount to socialism. Its pediatric section dissented, however, and passed its own counterresolution supporting Sheppard–Towner. A new generation of pediatricians was coming to realize that the infant welfare movement had generated enormous demand for well-child supervision.

Represented by neither the American Pediatric Society nor the AMA, these office-based pediatricians eventually formed an organization of their own, the American Academy of Pediatrics (AAP), in 1931. Well-child care was a major part of the daily work for these physicians. It now took place, however, largely within private offices; the Sheppard–Towner Act was allowed to expire in 1929 and state-run child health supervision became marginalized. The American Academy of Pediatrics quickly set up a certifying body, the American

Board of Pediatrics, in 1933. Residency programs and training requirements followed in the next decade. By the mid-1930s, American pediatrics had thus expanded far beyond the American Pediatric Society vision of a small body of hospital-based specialists to a much larger body of generalists providing primary care.

Science and Subspecialization.

The antibiotic revolution of the 1940s exemplified the most important trend in pediatric practice of the mid-twentieth century, a therapeutic revolution made possible by science. To be sure, penicillin was hardly the first breakthrough therapy for child illness. Antisera and sulfa drugs had already lowered the mortality from infectious diseases such as meningococcal meningitis and pneumococcal pneumonia. The discovery of insulin in 1922 had deeply impressed the public with images of comatose and emaciated children being virtually resurrected. Penicillin demonstrated the power of scientific medicine on a far wider scale and embodied a new confidence in the pediatrician's ability to treat illness.

But for many chronic and congenital conditions, these new therapies transformed rather than cured illnesses. Insulin allowed children with diabetes to survive, but was followed by a range of unanticipated complications. Antibiotics and enzyme replacement therapy allowed children with cystic fibrosis to live beyond early childhood, creating a need for a new level of health supervision.

These science-driven innovations and the emergence of new chronic diseases were accompanied by the rise of pediatric subspecialization. The first academic department of pediatrics at an American medical school, led by John Howland at Johns Hopkins, had encouraged laboratory research in biochemistry but made almost no provision for clinical research. This situation changed under the department's second chairman, Edwards Park, starting in the late 1920s. Physicians were appointed to newly created subspecialty clinics, providing in-depth experience with diseases that otherwise would be rarely encountered. One of Park's most successful appointments was Helen Taussig, who had been denied a position at Harvard but went on to propose a dramatic cardiac procedure with surgeon Alfred Blalock that won international acclaim in 1944 as the "blue baby operation." Another example was Lawrence Wilkins, who played a pivotal role in the founding of pediatric endocrinology and author of its classic textbook. Many of the first pediatric subspecialists learned their profession on the job, becoming experts through the care of the children seen in their clinics.

By the 1950s, subspecialists dominated the teaching of pediatrics in medical schools. Training had become standardized through fellowships after residency that included formal research experience. Research, boosted by the postwar expansion of the National Institutes of Health as well as private foundations such as the March of Dimes, was an integral part of these academic careers. At the same time, the "generalist" ethos of earlier pediatrics remained strong. Many subspecialties developed comprehensive care clinics providing not only medical interventions but also psychological support and education for children and families. Cystic fibrosis became a paradigmatic example. Profound advances in understanding this disease as a disorder in exocrine gland function led not to a single "cure," but to a set of interventions addressing nutrition, pulmonary function, superinfections, and a range of complications. The integration of these therapies in a team approach in the 1950s and 1960s transformed the disease from one that had been almost universally fatal by early childhood to a chronic illness with the potential of living into adulthood. Analogous programs arose for other pediatric conditions ranging from sickle-cell disease and childhood cancer to cerebral palsy and diabetes. It was common for practitioners in such clinics to develop the kinds of close relationships with families traditionally associated with primary care.

In addition, a new generation of vaccines profoundly transformed general pediatrics. As late as 1950, pediatricians had few effective vaccines beyond smallpox and the diphtheria–tetanus–pertussis (DTP) combination. The development of viral tissue culture techniques by John Enders in the late 1940s set off a succession of new vaccine discoveries over the next 20 years. Jonas

Salk's inactivated polio vaccine, demonstrated in 1955 to be "safe, potent, and effective" in the largest clinical trial that had ever taken place, excited the American public more than had any medical innovation besides penicillin. Polio rates dropped sharply and finally vanished following the introduction of Albert Sabin's attenuated vaccine in 1963. Live vaccines for measles, mumps, and rubella followed in the 1960s; measles in particular had once killed more children than polio and continued to have enormous mortality in the developing world. Pediatricians played a critical role in promoting these new vaccines both in their offices and by advocating for government support. Vaccines brought parents to the physician more often and in great part determined the well-child visit schedule.

The New Pediatrics.   In the 1960s, academic generalists coined the phrase "new morbidity" to express how pediatricians now faced a very different set of problems than those confronting their predecessors a generation earlier. They argued that general pediatrics would lose its relevance unless practitioners embraced the psychosocial dimensions of childhood. Pediatricians in the final decades of the twentieth century did in fact find themselves dealing more with nonmedical issues such as behavioral and developmental problems, academic failure, and the emotional consequences of rising divorce rates and split families. Adolescence was becoming increasingly recognized as a distinctive developmental phase in its own right in which pediatricians (and eventually adolescent specialists) could play an important role. The recognition of child abuse in the early 1960s spurred the development of child protection teams.

The new morbidity generated calls for a new pediatrics. Advocacy again assumed a central role for the American Academy of Pediatrics, recalling the spirit so dominant in the Progressive Era. Fittingly, women began to reclaim their legacy as the inventors of well-child care, entering the profession in ever greater numbers. By the early twentieth-first century they accounted for the majority of new general pediatricians.

A claim could also be made, however, that another "new pediatrics" emerged in the guise of high-technology pediatric care. Bone-marrow transplantation, intensive-care units, surgery for congenital heart disease, and spectacular organ transplantations have become symbols of how far the modern children's hospital has progressed from the modest institutions of Holt's day. The rise of neonatology is particularly striking. Premature infant care was conspicuous mainly by its absence in the early twentieth century; the eugenic spirit so prevalent at that time raised doubts over the wisdom of rearing even mildly premature infants (known popularly as "weaklings"). Smaller premature babies with immature lungs died within hours. The development of neonatal intensive-care units in the 1970s equipped with mechanical ventilators, monitors, and specialized nursing staff led to one of the most remarkable advances of twentieth-century child health: the survival of premature infants down to 24 weeks' gestation and even earlier. The new technology also became the battleground for the most public bioethical debates of the late twentieth century, raising difficult questions regarding how early in pregnancy it should be applied and who should decide when it should be withdrawn.

Between the extremes of psychosocial and high-technology pediatrics was a less celebrated but arguably still momentous set of preventive interventions made possible by scientific research. New vaccine technology led to effective immunizations against diseases such as meningitis and hepatitis. Newborn screening identified an ever-growing list of childhood diseases ranging from phenylketonuria to sickle-cell disease and cystic fibrosis. Pediatric investigators showed that antiretroviral drugs could prevent the perinatal transmission of HIV. Artificial surfactant reduced the need for mechanical ventilation for premature infants, leading to better outcomes and more cost-effective care.

As the twenty-first century opened, many American pediatricians looked to advances such as the sequencing of the human genome as potentially generating a new wave of preventive innovations. Their enthusiasm was tempered by the rising prevalence of conditions with presumed multifactorial causation such as childhood obesity, mental-health problems, and autism. Pediatricians continued to debate the scope of their practice and the questions of how far to focus on biomedical research versus community advocacy. The specialty nonetheless has remained striking for the ways it has drawn from both paradigms, maintaining its identity as a "holistic specialty."

[*See also* **American Medical Association; Autism;** *Baby and Child Care;* **Biochemistry; Blalock, Alfred; Cancer; Diabetes; Diphtheria; Disabilities, Intellectual and Developmental; Disease; DNA Sequencing; Ethics and Medicine; Germ Theory of Disease; HIV/AIDS; Hospitals; Human Genome Project; Hygiene, Personal; Medical Education; Medical Specialization; Medicine; Medicine and Technology; Mental Health Institutions; Mental Illness; National Institutes of Health; Nursing; Penicillin; Poliomyelitis; Psychiatry; Psychology; Public Health; Salk, Jonas; Sickle-Cell Disease; Smallpox;** *and* **Societies and Associations, Science.**]

BIBLIOGRAPHY

Apple, Rima D. *Perfect Motherhood: Science and Childrearing in America.* New Brunswick, N.J.: Rutgers University Press, 2006. History of how the ideal of "scientific motherhood" evolved among child health experts and mothers in the twentieth century.

Baker, Jeffrey P. *The Machine in the Nursery: Incubator Technology and the Origins of Newborn Intensive Care.* Baltimore: Johns Hopkins University Press, 1996. A study of early premature infant care analyzing how technology has shaped child health; it provides much background on the early history of pediatrics and obstetrics.

Colgrove, James K. *State of Immunity: The Politics of Vaccination in Twentieth-Century America.* Berkeley: University of California Press, 2006. A definitive history of American vaccine policy and its interaction with pediatrics.

Cone, Thomas E. *History of American Pediatrics.* Boston: Little, Brown, 1979. Although a more traditional history focusing on personalities and medical advances, Cone's work remains valuable for clinician-historians for its breadth and extensive bibliography.

English, Peter C. *Rheumatic Fever in America and Britain: A Biological, Epidemiological, and Medical History.* New Brunswick, N.J.: Rutgers University Press, 1999. A sophisticated study of the decline of a major pediatric illness, incorporating perspectives from medical science as well as social history.

Feudtner, Chris. *Bittersweet: Diabetes, Insulin, and the Transformation of Illness.* Chapel Hill: University of North Carolina Press, 2003. A ground-breaking analysis showing how the discovery of insulin transformed childhood diabetes into a chronic illness, with implications for other pediatric diseases.

Golden, Janet, Richard A. Meckel, and Heather Munro Prescott. *Children and Youth in Sickness and in Health: A Historical Handbook and Guide.* Westport, Conn.: Greenwood Press, 2004. Contains outstanding essays addressing broad historical topics in child health, as well as a useful collection of primary sources.

Grant, Julia. *Raising Baby by the Book: The Education of American Mothers.* New Haven, Conn.: Yale University Press, 1998. An introduction to the history of child advice books in the twentieth century, Grant's book stands out for her spotlight on mothers' responses to the professional literature.

Halpern, Sydney A. *American Pediatrics: The Social Dynamics of Professionalism, 1880–1980.* Berkeley: University of California Press, 1988. Innovative sociological analysis of the rise of pediatrics as a profession.

Meckel, Richard A. *Save the Babies: American Public Health Reform and the Prevention of Infant Mortality, 1850–1929.* Ann Arbor: University of Michigan Press, 1998. An indispensable resource for understanding the rise of pediatrics in the context of the infant mortality crusades of the turn of the past century.

Pernick, Martin. *The Black Stork: Eugenics and the Death of "Defective" Babies in American Medicine and Motion Pictures since 1915.* Oxford: Oxford University Press, 1996. Fascinating examination of how eugenics shaped American attitudes toward disabled children.

Prescott, Heather Munro. *A Doctor of Their Own: The History of Adolescent Medicine.* Cambridge, Mass.: Harvard University Press, 1998. A history of adolescent medicine emphasizing the agency of patients as well as professionals.

Stern, Alexandra M., and Howard Markel, eds. *Formative Years: Children's Health in the United States,*

1880–2000. Ann Arbor: University of Michigan Press, 2002. Excellent collection of essays illuminates, both important themes in pediatric history, ranging from Abraham Jacobi's socialist background to the discovery of child abuse.

Jeffrey P. Baker

PENICILLIN

Penicillin was first used to treat patients during World War II. It destroys several families of bacteria and for most patients was found to be almost nontoxic. Produced from a fungus, it was the first safe "antibiotic." Drugs of any kind, including the synthetic sulfanilamide and the natural but toxic tyrothricin, which could kill bacteria, had predated its introduction by only a few years. Among all the antibiotics (antibacterials produced from chemicals produced by living organisms) developed over the subsequent 20 years, the impact of penicillin itself was so great as to symbolize the entire history of antibacterial drugs.

The history of penicillin in America has three phases. The first was the extraordinarily quick development of a radically new type of medicine and its manufacture during World War II; the second was the introduction of penicillin, its competitors, and derivatives, particularly over the subsequent 20 years; and the third was the era of widespread concern about antibiotic resistance that achieved widespread recognition from the mid-1990s. The three eras were linked by the exuberance with which the drug, for most patients with neither precedent nor limits, was received into clinical practice. It was subsequently overused and abused as it served the social and cultural, as well as the medical, needs of both clinicians and patients.

Wartime Development. In 1929, the London-based bacteriologist Alexander Fleming reported the antibacterial effects of the liquid produced by a culture of the penicillium mold. Over the next few years flickers of interest in his results were shown by both academic and industrial scientists both in Britain and in the United States. Neither Fleming nor others, however, succeeded in extracting whatever was responsible for the destruction of bacteria. Only in March 1940 did a scientist in wartime Oxford University, Ernst Chain, successfully extract the active principal from the small quantities of liquid produced by the mold. By early the next year the Oxford team were testing small quantities of the albeit impure product on a few sick human patients. The difficulties of manufacture, even without the additional problems of wartime, meant that supplies were very limited. The Rockefeller Foundation therefore arranged that the head of the Oxford group, Howard Florey, and his colleague the chemist Norman Heatley make the difficult and perilous airtrip to the United States in June 1941 to share their experience and knowledge and obtain supplies.

The biggest problem in the growth of these fungi was that they needed air to breathe and were thus typically grown slowly on the surface of space-consuming dishes rather than in tanks like beer-making yeast. The centers of expertise in conquering this problem through aeration of slurries in tanks were in German-occupied Europe, particularly Delft and Prague. However, since the early 1920s, scientists in the United States had been working on the production of organic acids by such molds, keeping in close touch with European colleagues and exploiting the cheap agricultural by-products of the American Midwest. The two centers were the so-called Color Laboratory of the U.S. Department of Agriculture, where a method of producing citric acid from penicillium mold was developed by the chemist James Currie, and the small Brooklyn-based Pfizer Corporation, where Currie had moved. Other small groups in the United States kept an interest, such as the Merck Corporation and the University of Wisconsin's biochemistry group.

Arriving in the United States, Florey and Heatley were directed to the Peoria laboratory, where they almost immediately found a method for growing the mold in a deep tank. Not long after, a new strain of penicillium that was particularly productive was found on a melon bought in a Peoria market. Pfizer would develop semitechnical-scale deep fermentation within two years and then immediately moved to invest in a large fermentation plant. The efforts of corporate, government, and academic laboratories were also coordinated from the top. War already seemed to be impending by the middle of 1941 when the British scientists had arrived, and a Committee for Medical Research (CMR) was established within the federal government's newly convened Office of Scientific Research and Development. CMR convened a meeting of industrialists as early as September to win support for collaboration on penicillin production. From 1943 the War Production Board coordinated manufacture. By 1944 the United States could supply all its own troops on the beaches and shortly afterward made supplies available to civilians in U.S. hospitals.

Postwar Enthusiasm. The opportunity to produce penicillin and soon other antibiotics for a huge American and global market transformed such hitherto small corporations as Pfizer and Merck. Despite expectations, production from natural mold continued to be cheaper than any solely synthetic route. Corporate expertise and products were sold to countries across the postwar world. The perceived powers of the medical profession were also transformed. Infections that had been hitherto difficult to manage, such as syphilis and pneumonia, were now generally easily treatable, and the more minor but painful ailments of infant earaches and infected fingers could be immediately cured. Complex surgery and transplants involving the reduction of patient immunity could both be conducted without apparent fear of infection. The result was the often haphazard use of the drug, with many sociological studies showing that physicians prescribed the use of penicillin and other antibiotics to treat virus-induced infections, with no medical benefit, and that hospitals used antibiotics excessively and carelessly.

Penicillin-resistant Germs. From the mid-1950s this newfound enthusiasm was challenged by the spread in hospitals of penicillin-destroying staphylococci known as staph 80/81.

Weaning babies, recovering hospital patients, and elderly people already suffering from influenza were too often fatally affected. However, chemically produced variants of penicillin resistant to the bacterially produced enzyme were developed. In the United Kingdom, it was first known as "methicillin" (sold in the United States under a number of trade names such as Staphcillin). Introduced in 1960, the new drug seemed the perfect solution until physicians encountered methicillin-resistant *Staphylococcus aureus* (MRSA). The penicillin did not produce these bacteria; rather, they occurred through natural mutations and prospered when penicillin destroyed other competing bacteria. Where penicillin was most used and least controlled, often in hospitals and in poor countries to which well-meaning physicians brought huge quantities, antibiotic-resistant bacteria began to multiply. By the 1990s this had become a worldwide problem. The world entered a new era characterized by widespread anxiety that ultimately antibiotics would cease to be effective in the majority of cases of bacterial infection. Public-health authorities encouraged the public not to think of these medicines as cure-alls.

Germs, Guilt, and Wonder Drugs. These three eras were associated not only with changing attitudes to drugs but also with two revolutions in attitudes to germs. Previously, infection was controlled primarily by prevention, discipline, and good behavior, managed by guilt. The introduction of penicillin led to great optimism that medical science had conquered infections. Whereas once parents had worried about diphtheria and tuberculosis, syphilis and pneumonia were now staples of literature, and anxieties about germs vanished. From the emergence of AIDS in the 1980s and the subsequent growth of antibiotic-resistant bacteria, attitudes changed once again. Yet even at the beginning of the twenty-first century such derivatives of penicillin as amoxicillin and flucoxicillin are still major drugs, particularly for use in the community.

[*See also* **Agricultural Technology; Agriculture, U.S. Department of; Biochemistry; Disease; Germ Theory of Disease; Hospitals;**

Influenza; Military, Science and Technology and the; Office of Scientific Research and Development; Pediatrics; Pharmacology and Drug Therapy; Public Health; Surgery; *and* War and Medicine.]

BIBLIOGRAPHY

Brockman, Maxwell C., et al. *The History of Penicillin Production.* New York: American Institute of Chemical Engineers, 1970. This is the authoritative account of early production, several of whose authors were themselves involved.

Bud, Robert. *Penicillin: Triumph and Tragedy.* Oxford: Oxford University Press, 2007. The present author's interpretation. Links the excitement of the early years to later anxieties over antibiotic resistance.

Hobby, Gladys L. *Penicillin: Meeting the Challenge.* New Haven, Conn.: Yale University Press, 1985. An authoritative historical account of penicillin's early development in America by a woman who was herself a distinguished participant.

Robert Bud

PESTICIDES

The history of pesticides is closely linked to the history of pests in agriculture and public health. The agricultural revolution at the end of the eighteenth century was facilitated by increased mechanization and fertilization, which enabled farmers to plant extensive crops consisting of monocultures. Successful harvests could be spectacularly profitable. Nevertheless, monoculture left crops profoundly vulnerable to insect invasions, which could quickly bankrupt farmers. Farmers sought effective means to control insect infestations, and economic entomologists answered their hopes. Particularly promising was an insecticide extracted from the pyrethrum flower, a chrysanthemum. Drying and crushing the stamens of the flowers produced a powerful insecticide. Pyrethrum, as the insecticide became known, was prohibitively expensive because farmers in the Caucasus guarded their monopoly on the plant.

Economic entomologists sought a synthetic insecticide as effective as pyrethrum. In 1867, entomologists answered farmers' prayers with Paris Green, a copper acetoarsenite. Some journalists warned against adding arsenic to agriculture; but farmers soon adopted Paris Green to fight a range of insect pests. In the five years after its introduction, Paris Green became the preferred pesticide. Inexpensive and effective against a variety of insects, Paris Green was popular with farmers (Whorton, 1974, p. 21). The wonder insecticide failed to control gypsy moth caterpillars, however, when the invasive species threatened to destroy orchards and forests in New England. Between its introduction in 1892 and the turn of the century, lead arsenate became the preferred insecticide. In the decade between 1919 and 1929, use of arsenates quadrupled from 14.5 million pounds to 58 million pounds. The arsenates appealed to farmers as broad-spectrum insecticides, which is to say they were very effective against a wide range of insects. However, consumer advocates argued that the toxic residues of lead and arsenic contaminated fruits and vegetables, which led to chronic poisonings (Whorton, 1974, pp. 81–82).

Dichlorodiphenyltrichloroethane (DDT) was initially synthesized by an Austrian chemistry student named Othmar Zeidler in 1873. Not until 1939 did Paul Müller, a staff scientist at the Geigy firm in Basel, Switzerland, discover that DDT was extraordinarily effective in killing insects on contact, with long-lasting effects after application. Geigy, with its base in neutral Switzerland, patented DDT in the Third Reich in 1943, whereas its American subsidiary sent samples to officials at the Bureau of Entomology in the United States late in 1942. Early tests on target organisms such as flies, lice, and mosquitoes thrilled economic entomologists, although toxicity testing on mammals, including humans, yielded mixed results. American forces used DDT to avert a typhus epidemic (carried by lice) in Naples, Italy. DDT played a significant role in reducing cases of malaria and other insect-borne diseases in the South Pacific during World War II. By the close of the war in 1945, several U.S. chemical companies were producing 3 million pounds of DDT *per month* (Russell, 2001, p. 161).

Like DDT and other chlorinated hydrocarbons, the organic phosphate (later organophosphate) pesticides were first developed by German chemists during World War II as potential nerve gases to be used in combat. Among the compounds investigated for this purpose was diisopropyl fluorophosphate (DFP). The Germans eventually discarded DFP as a nerve gas, but their experiments indicated that it inhibited cholinesterase, an enzyme that facilitates nerve function. The first organophosphate insecticide hexaethyl tetraphosphate (HETP) emerged from Gerhard Schrader's laboratory at Farbenfabriken, Germany, in the early 1940s. The Toxicity Laboratory at the University of Chicago carried out the toxicological analysis of the new chemicals. Kenneth DuBois and his associates recognized cholinergic symptoms produced by the new chemicals. The Tox Lab also studied parathion, one of the most toxic pesticides to insects and other life forms.

After World War II, farmers and public officials deployed the new chlorinated hydrocarbons like DDT and organophosphates in the ongoing fight against insect pests. DDT replaced many of the older arsenate pesticides. In 1959, DDT use in U.S. agriculture reached a peak of approximately 79 million pounds (U.S. production peaked at 179 million pounds in 1963) (World Health Organization, 1979, p. 8). In cases where the new insecticide proved to be ineffectual (for example, aphids), farmers turned to organophosphates. Through the 1950s, some scientists, consumers, and legislators expressed concern about the toxicity of the new insecticides. But it was not until 1962, when Rachel Carson published *Silent Spring*, that the American public discovered the potential dangers of synthetic insecticides. Drawing on scientific and medical sources, Carson criticized indiscriminate use of insecticides and revealed widespread contamination of ecosystems, wildlife, and even humans. DDT and other chlorinated hydrocarbons accumulated in the environment and concentrated in the food chain to the detriment of top-line predators such as bald eagles, ospreys, and peregrines. Meanwhile, organophosphates were so acutely toxic as to cause convulsions, paralysis, and even death in farm workers and animals. Carson called for restraint in the use

of both chlorinated hydrocarbons and organophosphates. *Silent Spring* inspired further investigations and hearings at the federal level. Significant changes in the regulatory landscape, however, followed prolonged litigation as environmental groups challenged state and federal spraying campaigns. The U.S. Environmental Protection Agency's ban on DDT in 1972 signaled a milestone in the environmental movement.

The story of pesticides took an ironic turn during the 1970s as farmers substituted highly toxic organophosphates for the banned chlorinated hydrocarbons like DDT. In banning DDT, regulators responded to litigation and followed only part of Carson's recommendation, which was to reduce the use of both chlorinated hydrocarbons and organophosphates. As a result, use of organophosphates in the United States grew to more than 100 million pounds per year (Gianessi and Reigner, 2006) and billions of pounds worldwide, with continuing consequences for wildlife and farm workers (Anonymous, 1996).

[*See also* **Agricultural Technology; Animal and Human Experimentation; Carson, Rachel; Chemistry; Entomology; Environmentalism; Environmental Protection Agency; Fish and Wildlife Service, U.S.; Fisheries and Fishing; Malaria; Public Health; Typhus;** *and* **War and Medicine.**]

BIBLIOGRAPHY

Anonymous. "Organophosphate Insecticides." *Pesticides News* 34 (December 1996): 20–21.

Carson, Rachel. *Silent Spring*. Boston: Houghton Mifflin, 1962.

Davis, Frederick Rowe. "Pesticides and Toxicology: Episodes in the Evolution of Environmental Risk Assessment." PhD diss. Yale University, 2001.

Dunlap, Thomas. *DDT: Scientists, Citizens, and Public Policy*. Princeton, N.J.: Princeton University Press, 1981.

Gianessi, Leonard P., and James Earl Anderson. *Pesticide Use Trends in U.S. Agriculture: 1979–1992*. Washington, D.C.: National Center for Food and Agricultural Policy, 1993.

Gianessi, Leonard, and Nathan Reigner. *Pesticide Use in U.S. Crop Production: 2002*. Washington, D.C.: CropLife America, 2006.

Russell, Edmund. *War and Nature: Fighting Humans and Insects with Chemicals from World War I to Silent Spring*. Cambridge, U.K.: Cambridge University Press, 2001.

Whorton, James. *Before* Silent Spring: *Pesticides and Public Health in America in pre-DDT America*. Princeton, N.J.: Princeton University Press, 1974.

World Health Organization. *Environmental Health Criteria 9: DDT and Its Derivatives*. Geneva: World Health Organization, 1979.

Frederick R. Davis

PETROLEUM AND PETROCHEMICALS

The history of the U.S. petroleum industry is typically divided into two periods: the age of illumination and the age of energy, with the transition occurring in the early twentieth century. In the first period, refiners mainly produced kerosene for use as lamp oil and viewed gasoline as a by-product with limited use. The dissemination of electric lighting and the introduction of the automobile, which reduced the demand for kerosene and provided a market for gasoline, dramatically changed both the focus and the scale of the industry. A shift from coal-burning to oil-burning ships and locomotives further facilitated its growth, as did the sale of natural gas for use in home heating. In addition, in the years after World War II, petroleum—long used to produce by-products such as solvents and lubricants—also came to be used to produce the petrochemicals from which products such as plastics, synthetic fibers, and pesticides are made.

Since the advent of the petroleum industry, companies have sought to innovate in four general areas: exploration (locating new deposits of petroleum), production (extracting oil and gas by drilling wells), transportation (getting oil and gas to refineries and markets), and refining (transforming oil into marketable products). In the first half of the nineteenth century, little incentive to search for petroleum existed. The location of many petroleum seeps was known but the market for this material was limited. At the time, illumination was provided by material such as whale oil, beeswax, vegetable oils, and tallow. Wood and coal served as the main fuel for steam engines and heating homes. Only when scientists demonstrated that kerosene could serve as a replacement for whale oil did entrepreneurs turn their attention to petroleum. Other distillates of petroleum, such as gasoline (too volatile for use as lamp oil) and diesel oil (not volatile enough), had less of a market.

At first, in the 1850s, companies that manufactured kerosene obtained their petroleum from hand-dug wells near known petroleum seeps. In the United States, that changed in 1859, when a group of investors sent Edwin Drake to drill for oil in central Pennsylvania. Drake used the method employed by local brine drillers, which was to attach a heavy, chisel-like tool to a rope and continually raise and drop it, pulverizing rock and gradually deepening the well. In Drake's case, a steady flow of petroleum began seeping out of the well after 69 feet of drilling, motivating others to drill for the increasingly valuable fluid as well.

Over the next half century, as the depth of wells increased, challenges associated with removing the pulverized rock and preventing oil from blowing out of higher pressure formations, along with a desire to drill faster, stimulated a number of innovations. A key development involved the shift to rotary drilling, which involved attaching a rock-grinding tool to a rotating pipe. To drill deeper, crews simply added another segment of pipe. They removed pulverized rock by pumping a heavy fluid (drilling mud) down the pipe and allowing it to flow back to the surface via the outside of the pipe. The drilling mud also stopped petroleum under pressure from escaping in an uncontrolled manner. Drillers eventually discovered that they could cause a rotary-drilled well to curve in a desired direction, allowing them to reach under neighboring tracks of land, sometimes illegally so.

Before the 1930s, oil fields in the United States operated under the rule of capture, which meant that any landowner who extracted oil owned it. As a result, oil fields tended to be chaotic places as lease-holders raced to drill more wells and extract more oil than their neighbors, flaring gas and running brine (lifted with the oil) into streams. In the end, however, much petroleum remained underground, drained of viscosity-reducing gases and unable to flow through the porous rock that held it. In the 1930s, regulations that required oil deposits to be managed as an entity brought order to most fields and facilitated innovations that depended on some level of cooperation, including the reinjection of excess gas and waste brine to maintain pressure and viscosity. Although rotary drilling of wells into oil-bearing rock formations remains the dominant system for extracting oil, numerous innovations have since increased the efficiency and precision of the process. For all practical purposes, crews can now steer a several-mile-long drilling string and position a well, vertically and horizontally, precisely where they want it. Special methods for extracting oil from oil sands, which involves oil too thick to flow into wells, have also been developed.

Computer modeling has also contributed to the exploration and extraction process. In the first half of the twentieth century, petroleum geologists developed a variety of methods and tools for locating layers of petroleum-bearing porous rock, but trial and error—drilling exploratory wells and hoping that one discovered oil—played a far greater role than scientific instruments and models. Today, computers are used to process massive amounts of data produced through the generation, propagation, and detection of seismic waves, resulting in three-dimensional models of underground formations that eliminate a significant portion of the guesswork.

In refineries, the distillation process remains central. The incoming oil is vaporized and the different fractions (kerosene, gasoline, diesel fuel, etc.) condense out at different temperatures. Initially, refiners could not convert any of their gasoline or diesel oil into kerosene, which meant that that they had to find markets for those fractions or dispose of them as waste. Refiners also faced the challenge of removing impurities, especially sulfur compounds, which they did by mixing the kerosene with sulfuric acid. When they separated the two liquids, the impurities stayed with the sulfuric acid, forming a sludge that had to be dumped.

Over time, refiners have developed methods for converting one fraction of oil into another, allowing them to secure a greater quantity of marketable products from each barrel of oil. The first step in this direction involved using heat to "crack" longer molecules (heavier oils) into shorter ones (gasoline). Later, companies began using catalysts to facilitate chemical transformations, with the first commercial-scale process being a form of catalytic cracking adopted in 1937. Refiners have since developed a variety of other catalytic processes, including methods for removing sulfur without the need for sulfuric acid. In the 1970s, policies prohibiting refineries from adding octane-boosting tetraethyl lead to gasoline also encouraged the dissemination of catalytic processes capable of converting low-octane molecules into higher-octane ones. Catalytic processes also facilitate the production of petrochemicals such as ethylene and propylene.

[*See also* **Automation and Computerization; Chemistry; Computers, Mainframe, Mini, and Micro; Electricity and Electrification; Heating Technology; Household Technology; Illumination; Maritime Transport; Mining Technology; Motor Vehicles; Pesticides; Plastics; Railroads;** *and* **Shipbuilding.**]

BIBLIOGRAPHY

Anderson, Robert O. *Fundamentals of the Petroleum Industry*. Norman: University of Oklahoma Press, 1984.

Priest, Tyler. *The Offshore Imperative: Shell Oil's Search for Petroleum in Postwar America*. College Station: Texas A&M University Press, 2007.

Spitz, Peter H. *Petrochemicals: The Rise of an Industry*. New York: John Wiley & Sons, 1988.

Williamson, Harold F., and Arnold R. Daum. *The American Petroleum Industry: The Age of Illumination, 1859–1999*. Evanston, Ill.: Northwestern University Press, 1959.

Williamson, Harold F., et al. *The American Petroleum Industry: The Age of Energy, 1899–1959*. Evanston, Ill.: Northwestern University Press, 1963.

Hugh S. Gorman

PHARMACOLOGY AND DRUG THERAPY

In the early twenty-first century, the American pharmaceutical market was the largest in the world, with a total of 3.9 billion prescriptions filled in 2009—enough for 12 prescriptions a year for every man, woman, and child in the country. Pharmaceuticals elicit powerful historical narratives in American society: they are recruited simultaneously into triumphant accounts of the expanding power of modern medicine and critical accounts of the corrosive effects of market and consumer logics in the realm of health care. The moral appeal of such grand narratives unfortunately leads many to overlook the more complex social and cultural histories that pharmaceuticals can reveal. Pharmaceuticals are material objects that relate ailing bodies to bodies of knowledge, patients to practitioners, and biosciences to bioindustries; as historical artifacts they can help recapture some of the substance of everyday life in American history.

America's position in global economies of knowledge and goods has been pharmaceutically mediated since the original voyages of discovery. The spices sought by Columbus and others developing the West Indies trade were understood to be powerful therapeutic objects, and many of the new objects brought back—including antisyphilitic guaiac bark, antipyretic Peruvian bark, and stimulant coca leaves—would pose significant challenges to previously stable Galenic *materia medica* and enable new systems of thinking about therapeutics, from the sixteenth-century iatrochemistry of Paracelsus to the seventeenth-century *Pharmacopia Londoniensis* of Nicolas Culpeper.

That Culpeper's first pharmacopoeia, *The English Physician*, was one of the first medical texts printed in the United States (in 1708) is an illustration of the largely European-oriented gaze of American medical therapeutics in the North American colonies. Reflecting a therapeutic preoccupation with a body not only composed of humors and complexions but also complicated by obstructions and flows and astrological associa-

tions with organs, afflictions, and remedies, Culpeper's eclectic approach to therapeutic rationality was a good match for the pragmatic eclecticism of colonial therapeutics. Although much of the practical *materia medica* was homegrown, when early Americans bought pharmaceuticals in the seventeenth and eighteenth centuries they overwhelmingly purchased British drugs like Epsom salt, Glauber's salt, or British "patent medicines"—secretive cures whose extravagant promises of cures were matched only by their lack of disclosure as to their ingredients.

The first manufacturing laboratory of pharmaceuticals in the United States opened in Carlisle, Pennsylvania, in 1778 to supply medicines to Washington's army. Other firms soon emerged in New York and Philadelphia vending standard items from the *materia medica* such as opium, jalap, and calomel. However, in 1796 the secretive "Lee's Bilious Pills" received the first U.S. patent for a pharmaceutical product, an early entry in what would become a burgeoning U.S. trade in patent medicines. Made in Connecticut, packages of Bilious Pills emblazoned with an American eagle could nonetheless be found in St. Louis soon after the Louisiana Purchase. The expanding popularity of American patent medicines in the first half of the nineteenth century is now partly understood as an attractive consumer alternative to the harsh mineral and instrumental cures of allopathic heroic medicine: calomel and the lancet. This marketplace of therapeutics expanded greatly in antebellum America to include a dizzying array of therapeutic systems, from Thomsonian herbalism to the appealingly dilute offerings of the homeopathic pharmacy. Although the first synoptic *United States Pharmacopoeia* was first published in 1820, any notion of drug therapy in antebellum America this time must be understood to be pluralistic and highly regionalized. By the outbreak of the Civil War, an entirely different set of medicines could be found in the pharmacopoeia of the Union Army compared with that of the Confederate.

The massive casualties of the Civil War demanded mobilization of *materia medica* on an unprecedented scale. As small manufacturers such as the Brooklyn-based E. R. Squibb experimented with new mechanized modes of pill production (rather than hand-rolling), they were rewarded with large-scale contracts to produce quinine and opium for the Union Army. These contracts and the postwar emergence of a unified American mass consumer market in turn helped to develop the firm structure of the American pharmaceutical industry—at least in part. Largely based in the Northeast and the northern Midwest, firms like Squibb, Lilly, Mulford, Upjohn, Sharp & Dohme, and Smith, Kline & French, distinguished themselves as ethical manufacturers who—in contradistinction to patent medicine manufacturers—produced standardized formulations of well-known therapeutic objects. In the 1890s, for example, American firms such as Mulford and Parke–Davis capitalized on techniques of producing diphtheria antitoxin developed by French and German pharmacologists such as Emile Roux and Emil von Behring. By the onset of World War I, however, almost all American patents for innovative drugs were owned by German firms, largely from the dyestuff conglomerates that had developed innovative synthetic chemotherapeutic forms such as barbiturates, acetylsalicylic acid, and Salvarsan: Paul Ehrlich's antisyphilitic "magic bullet."

The early forms of innovation that came out of the laboratories of Squibb and other American firms in the latter part of the nineteenth century tended to relate to standardization and quality control of products rather than the development of new therapeutic agents. However, at a slow pace from the turn of the century to World War I, and at a much faster pace in the interwar years, American pharmaceutical firms began to create their own autonomous research laboratories. These included the Merck Research Laboratory (1933), Lilly Research Laboratories (1934), the Squibb Institute for Medical Research (1938), the Abbott Research Laboratories (1938), and many more thereafter. During this time a previously standoffish relationship between academic pharmacologists and industrial laboratories gave way to a far more interpenetrated vision. New collaborations among the pharmaceutical industry, academic pharmacologists, and academic clinicians would become crucial to the development

of many successful new agents, from insulin to amphetamines to anticoagulants. The basic collaborative research structure established in the interwar years would undergird the massive expansion in the scale and pace of innovative pharmaceutical products in the post–World War II era, from antibiotics to antipsychotics to antihypertensives to antidepressants.

The commercial implications of such relationships, however, were troubling to many writers inside and outside of academic medicine. Martin Arrowsmith, the protagonist and avatar of rational therapeutics in Sinclair Lewis's medical bildungsroman, *Arrowsmith* (1925), was dismayed to see his research mentor Max Gottleib begin working in an industrial laboratory as a "pill-pusher." Likewise, a moral tone of anticommercialism permeated the early pronouncements of the Council on Pharmacy and Chemistry of the American Medical Association, which issued professional guidelines for rational drug use in the first half of the twentieth century based on its own review of the laboratory and clinical data on new drugs. Anticommercialism and suspicion of the marketplace would likewise be key to the passage of the Pure Food and Drug Act of 1906, which created the embryonic Food and Drug Administration (FDA) and charged it with control over the proper "labeling" of pharmaceutical products to ensure consumer safety.

A parallel history of pharmaceuticals in the twentieth and twenty-first centuries can be told in terms of regulatory responses to perceived crises. The Harrison Act (1914), restricting accessibility of narcotic agents to prescription-only status, was passed in response to a perceived "social panic" regarding the menace such "toxicomanic" drugs posed to individuals and society. The Food Drugs and Cosmetics Act (FDCA, 1938), which extended the concept of "prescription-only" drugs beyond narcotics and transformed the FDA into the gatekeeper of the pharmaceutical market, was passed in response to public outcry over the deaths of over one hundred children after consuming tainted sulfanilamide in 1937. Likewise, it was the publicity of the thalidomide tragedy, with graphic images of deformed children whose mothers had consumed the supposedly innocuous sleeping pill while pregnant, that emboldened Congress to pass the Kefauver–Harris amendments (1962) to the FDCA, giving rise ultimately to the three-phase system of clinical trials now required to demonstrate the efficacy of new drug products prior to approval. More recently, the Vioxx scandal of the early 2000s precipitated the sweeping FDA Amendments Act (FDAAA, 2007), which has increased the role of the agency in maintaining "pharmacovigilance" programs to monitor the usage of drug products with yet finer surveillance tools.

Since the early 1960s, critics of the pharmaceutical industry have been joined by a number of voices outside of professional, regulatory, and policy spheres. Health feminists mobilized powerful "lay epidemiology" campaigns to criticize the pharmaceutical industry regarding the hidden safety risks of medications for women, such as the association of oral contraceptives and hormonal replacement therapies with deep-vein thromboses and various forms of cancer. Consumerist groups from the Consumer's Union to Ralph Nader's Public Citizen began to call for closer examinations of the "irrational" influence of pharmaceutical marketing on physicians and consumers. These critiques would later be extended by communities of HIV/AIDS activists, and, separately, by those of racial and ethnic groups all claiming to have been excluded from the process of research and regulatory protocols. Over the 1970s and 1980s, activist critiques of the pharmaceutical industry and the FDA often moved in contradictory ways: some groups focused on the problems of relative neglect and lack of access to medications, whereas others focused on problems of overmedication and medicalization of daily life.

Although pharmaceuticals can be understood to have moved in global markets for five hundred years, if not longer, the structure of the research-based pharmaceutical industry shifted dramatically in the second half of the twentieth century toward a more explicitly globalizing model, in which research, production, and distribution of drugs within a single company could take place in a series of 10 to 20 countries scattered across several continents. It has been a bitter irony that despite this increased globalization, the business of pharmaceutical production and research did not result in global equity in pharmaceutical access. Problems of access to drugs in the poorer countries of the global South—already tenuous for most of the late twentieth century despite efforts by the World Health Organization to build a list of affordable, accessible "essential drugs"—became more difficult still in the face of the international harmonization program of the World Trade Organization, which many perceive as an "Americanization" of global intellectual property regimes.

As the innovative edge of the American *materia medica* has changed from botanical to mineral to chemical to biological, pharmaceuticals continue to mediate relationships among suffering bodies, bodies of knowledge, healers and practitioners, industries, and scientific fields.

[*See also* **Advertising, Medical; American Medical Association; Biological Sciences; Botany; Cancer; Centers for Disease Control and Prevention; Chemistry; Diabetes; Diphtheria; Ethics and Medicine; Food Processing; Gender and Science; Health Insurance; HIV/AIDS; Hospitals; Influenza; Journals in Science, Medicine, and Engineering; Machinery and Manufacturing; Malaria; Medicine; Mental Illness; Military, Science and Technology and the; Penicillin; Psychiatry; Psychopharmaceutical Drugs; Public Health; Pure Food and Drug Act; Race and Medicine; Research and Development (R&D); Sexually Transmitted Diseases; Typhoid Fever; Typhus; War and Medicine; World Health Organization;** *and* **Yellow Fever.**]

BIBLIOGRAPHY

Carpenter, Daniel P. *Reputation and Power: Organizational Image and Pharmaceutical Regulation at the FDA.* Princeton, N.J.: Princeton University Press, 2010.

Flannery, Michael. *Civil War Pharmacy: A History of Drugs, Drug Supply and Provision, and Therapeutics for the Union and Confederacy.* New York: Pharmaceutical Products Press, 2004.

Greene, Jeremy A., and Elizabeth Siegel Watkins. *Prescribed: Writing, Filling, Using, and Abusing the Prescription in Modern America*. Baltimore: Johns Hopkins University Press, 2012.

Liebenau, Jonathan. *Medical Science and Medical Industry: The Formation of the American Pharmaceutical Industry*. Basingstoke, U.K., and Baltimore: Macmillan and Johns Hopkins University Press, 1987.

Mahoney, Thomas. *The Merchants of Life: An Account of the American Pharmaceutical Industry*. New York: Harper, 1959.

Marks, Harry M. *Progress of Experiment: Science and Therapeutic Reform in the United States, 1900–1990*. Cambridge, U.K.: Cambridge University Press, 1997.

Schiebinger, Londa, and Claudia Swan, eds. *Colonial Botany: Science, Commerce, and Politics in the Early Modern World*. Philadelphia: University of Pennsylvania Press, 2004.

Swann, John. *Academic Scientists and the Pharmaceutical Industry*. Baltimore: Johns Hopkins University Press, 1988.

Watkins, Elizabeth Siegel, and Andrea Tone, eds. *Medicating Modern America: Prescription Drugs in History*. New York: New York University Press, 2007.

Young, James Harvey. *The Toadstool Millionaires: A Social History of Patent Medicines in the US before Federal Regulation*. Princeton, N.J.: Princeton University Press, 1961.

Jeremy A. Greene

PHOTOCOPYING

When the small Haloid Xerox Corporation introduced its Model 914 Copier in 1960, the size of the market for photocopying was uncertain. Before deciding to manufacture such a complex machine on its own, the company had approached the business machine giant IBM about a possible joint venture, but IBM, which was focusing on computers, declined to participate. The consulting firm, Arthur D. Little, had advised IBM that there would be a limited market for such an expensive and complex machine. Within a year, however, the overwhelming success of the 914 demonstrated the widespread demand for cheap and fast copies

of documents. Photocopying machines soon became a necessary item in nearly every office. By 1966, the now-renamed Xerox Corporation estimated that 14 billion copies were being made every year. In the 1960s photocopying launched an information revolution—it was now cheap and easy to have personal copies of documents—three decades before the Internet.

The development of a commercially successful copier had taken over two decades since independent inventor Chester Carlson began experimenting in the late 1930s. Born in 1906, Carlson grew up in poverty but was precocious enough to earn a degree in physics from Caltech. While employed in the patent division of a small New York City electronics firm, Carlson became intrigued with the phenomenon of photoconductivity, that the electric charge on the surface of a material can be changed upon exposure to light. Initially working in his apartment with sulfur, he frequently annoyed his neighbors with unpleasant odors. In 1939 he filed his patent on what he called "electrophotography." To make a copy, the original would be placed on a plate (or later drum) of photoconductive material and exposed to a bright light. The print on the original would block the light from hitting the drum, creating a print pattern that maintained an electric charge while the rest of the plate became uncharged by the light. Next, an oppositely charged dry powdered ink (toner) was dusted across the plate, sticking to the charged areas. After the excess toner was swept away, the attached toner had to be carefully melted to create the permanent copy.

Although the process was straightforward, building a machine to perform it was not. In 1944 Carlson received funding from the Battelle Memorial Institute, a private contract research and development organization in Columbus, Ohio. A year later, the Haloid Company, maker of photographic paper and related supplies, began to fund research at Battelle. Soon, Haloid then embarked on a 15-year effort to produce the 914 copier. Carlson worked at Haloid until 1955, when a new agreement was worked out that gave him a royalty based on the number of copies made. After the success of the 914, Carlson accumulated a considerable fortune, much of which he gave away. Xerox was able to dominate the photocopying business into the 1970s in part because Carlson, who died in 1968, had used his expertise in patents to thoroughly protect his invention.

[*See also* Photography; Printing and Publishing; *and* Research and Development (R&D).]

BIBLIOGRAPHY

Owen, David. *Copies in Seconds: How a Lone Inventor and an Unknown Company Created the Biggest Communication Breakthrough since Gutenberg—Chester Carlson and the Birth of the Xerox Machine.* New York: Simon and Schuster, 2004.

John Kenly Smith Jr.

PHOTOGRAPHY

Western European scientists and artists had developed chemical image-making by 1840 and soon introduced photography as a budding tool in science, especially in astronomy and microscopy. By 1900 America had seized leadership in the industry with dry gelatin emulsion, roll film photography and maintained world dominance for nearly a century. Digital photography then quickly replaced chemical image-making and facilitated instantaneous transmission of images in space and throughout the world.

Early Photography, 1839–1880. French artist Louis Jacques Mande Daguerre, with the help of leading members of the French scientific community, publicly disclosed the details of the daguerreotype process on 19 August 1839 in Paris. His manual explicating the process quickly circulated throughout Europe and to Britain and the United States.

Telegraph pioneer Samuel F. B. Morse and his chemistry-professor friend John William Draper introduced the daguerreotype process in New York City in September 1839. Among the earliest of photographic processes then emerging, the daguerreotype dominated photographic practice in America from 1839 to the mid-1850s. The direct positive technique employed a camera obscura, the lens of which projected into the darkened chamber an image from nature onto a thin, silvered copper plate that had been exposed to iodine vapors, creating a photosensitive silver iodide layer, thereupon recording a latent black-and-white image. The daguerreotypist then developed the latent image with mercury vapor and subsequently "fixed" the developed image with a wash then known as hyposulfite of soda (sodium thiosulfate).

The complicated process mandated production of the photosensitive material at the site of picture taking. Requiring long exposure times and being relatively expensive, daguerreotypy attracted only a few amateurs. Instead, professional photographers operating from well-lit urban studios dominated the practice, producing large portraits of individuals or families (Newhall, 1968; Jenkins, 1975).

Introduced in the early 1850s, the wet collodion negative/positive process attracted professional photographers. They coated thin glass plates with a freshly prepared photosensitive silver halogen material held in a wet collodion solution, placed the plate in the camera, and made the exposure. Developing and fixing the negative image, photographers then, at any time thereafter, produced less expensive positive paper prints. The new process boasted of an increase in photosensitivity. Wet collodion photography dominated American photography until the early 1880s.

Making the photosensitive materials and developing the negatives at the site of exposure, studio photographers continued to dominate the practice. Although factories produced albumenized print paper, photographers still photosensitized the paper in their studios. Highly skilled optical specialists produced the cameras and lenses for many of the professional photographers, whereas small studios and a small number of amateurs employed factory-produced cameras and lenses. Specialized New York City wholesalers dominated the industry, distributing the necessary photographic chemicals, cameras, lenses, and miscellaneous supplies (Jenkins, 1975).

Some scientists and medical researchers enthusiastically embraced photography to replace hand-drawn illustrations and atlases. They perceived it as producing objective representation. While French medical researcher Alfred François Donné and his student Léon Foucault pioneered in the early 1840s in making daguerreotypes of microscope images, John William Draper also produced early photomicrographs. He, among other Americans, also took daguerreotypes of the moon. His son, Henry Draper, produced in the 1860s a popular stereopticon image of the full moon and used photography in his spectral studies.

The Boston photographer John Adams Whipple, the Harvard College astronomy professor William Cranach Bond, and his son, the Harvard Observatory director George Phillip Bond, collaborated in astronomical daguerreotypy. Using Harvard's 15-inch refracting telescope, then the nation's largest, they daguerreotyped in the early 1850s the star Alpha Lyrae (Vega), the moon, and a partial solar eclipse (Newhall, 1968, pp. 92–94).

Gelatin Emulsion Photography, 1880–1990.

Use of gelatin dry plates came to the United States from England about 1880. They consisted of glass plates coated with a photosensitive gelatin silver halide emulsion. The sensitivity of these plates endured for months. Accordingly, photographers no longer had to make the photosensitive materials at the site of the picture taking. By the mid-1880s several gelatin dry plate factories arose at locations across America.

George Eastman, a pioneer dry plate producer in the United States, introduced in the mid-1880s gelatin roll film on paper in place of the heavy glass plates. By the late 1880s he began to market factory-produced photosensitized print paper for professionals and the Kodak camera system for amateurs. At first, new well-to-do amateurs purchased Kodak cameras already loaded with photosensitized roll film and took up to one hundred pictures. They mailed the camera to the factory, where workers developed the film and made prints. They reloaded the camera with fresh film and returned the camera and prints to the owner.

The company advertised, "You press the button and we do the rest."

By the late 1890s the Eastman Kodak Company's numerous improvements in the film, camera, and distribution as well as a substantial lowering of cost prompted a vast expansion in the practice of photography, creating mass amateur photography. Improving the photosensitive emulsion while keeping it a trade secret, Eastman's company commanded worldwide production and distribution in nearly all areas of professional and amateur photography. It also possessed nearly exclusive film production for the then-emerging motion picture industry. The establishment of the Eastman Kodak Research Laboratory in 1912, led by the former English photochemist Dr. C. E. Kenneth Mees, placed the company at the forefront of scientific and technical developments in photography (Jenkins, 1975).

Experimenters in Europe and the United States from the latter part of the nineteenth century had sought to produce practical systems of color photography. Notable efforts included the introduction in 1907 in France of autochromes, impressively beautiful but highly costly screen-process color photographs. A decade later in Massachusetts the Technicolor Corporation began innovations in color motion pictures. The Eastman Kodak Research Laboratory sought to produce for amateurs both color movies and a practical negative/positive color system. In 1935 the company marketed Kodachrome color film and prints. By the 1960s improved quality and lower costs attracted a majority of American amateurs to color film (Hirsch, 2011; Mees, 1961).

Although German producers traditionally dominated the world market for high-quality cameras and fine optics, after World War II Japanese high-end camera producers gained the edge in the American market. Somewhat later, Japan's Fuji Photo Film Company gradually replaced Germany's AGFA as Eastman Kodak's principal competitor in the world film market.

In 1948 Polaroid Corporation's Edwin H. Land introduced instant photography, a system that exposed, developed, and fixed a direct-positive paper print in a special camera. Polaroid prints attracted impatient consumers, especially at holiday times. Land, the technical leader, ultimately produced instant color prints and an amateur instant motion picture system. Unbeknown to most people, Eastman Kodak produced the highly profitable Polaroid film until the mid-1970s, when it introduced a system that infringed upon Polaroid-owned patents. After the death of Land and the subsequent failure of Polaroid's digital efforts, the firm filed for bankruptcy in 2001 (Wensberg, 1987).

With the advent of gelatin emulsion photography, its use permeated science, technology, and medicine. For example, astronomers adopted gelatin dry plates because of their ease of use and increased photosensitivity. Images of distant celestial objects obtained in ever larger telescopes contributed to a revolution in astronomy and cosmology. American astronomer Edwin Hubble, for example, identified galaxies beyond the Milky Way and also suggested that the greater a star's spectral redshift, the greater its distance from the Earth. Such work prompted views of an expanding universe and, ultimately, evidence supporting the Big Bang Theory.

Industrial engineering pioneers Frank and Lillian Gilbreth employed motion pictures to microanalyze workflow in time and motion studies. Also, medical X-ray photography emerged shortly after the German physicist Wilhelm Conrad Röntgen's discovery of X-rays in 1895. Its use in America grew in medical research and as a diagnostic tool in hospitals and in the offices of physicians and dentists. At first, professionals used glass dry plates but eventually moved to flat film for recording X-rays.

Digital Photography, 1990–2012. The development of television beginning in the 1930s and video recording in the 1950s and 1960s inaugurated a gestation period of innovations in electronic imaging that ultimately unleashed the digital revolution in popular photography at the beginning of the twenty-first century. Whereas in the 1960s the U.S. military employed early electronic sensing for Cold War spy satellites, in 1969 Bell Laboratory physicists Willard Boyle and George E. Smith assembled the charge-coupled device (CCD), an electrical sensor central to modern digital imaging. In 1975 Steven Sasson, an electrical engineer at Eastman Kodak, used a CCD in the first digital still camera.

In 1976 the United States launched a spy satellite equipped with a camera employing the CCD. Over the next quarter century, the U.S. military and the National Aeronautics and Space Administration's need for real-time electronic imaging data from satellites fostered digital photography. They also joined commercial enterprises in developing related enhancements in computer processing and the Internet.

The Hubble space telescope gave the public dramatic evidence of the value of digital photography. The National Aeronautics and Space Administration launched the Hubble telescope into orbit in 1990. Digital photography efficiently recorded telescope images and facilitated electronic transmission of the data to Earth. Rapid advances were incorporated as four of the five service missions between 1993 and 2009 either updated or replaced the initial two digital cameras.

By the beginning of the twenty-first century, American consumers had access to expensive digital cameras and cell phones with cameras. Soon digital quality improved and prices fell. Digital rapidly replaced film photography. With profits wedded to film, the once-dominant Eastman Kodak Company filed for bankruptcy on 19 January 2012.

[*See also* **Film Technology; Research and Development (R&D); Science; Technology;** *and* **Television.**]

BIBLIOGRAPHY

Evans, Mona. "Photography and the Birth of Modern Astrophysics." Bella Online, the Voice of Women. http://www.bellaonline.com/articles/art19545.asp

"George Eastman House, International Museum of Photography and Film." http://www.eastmanhouse.org/. Oldest photographic museum and collections in America. Select from detailed site map. Outstanding collections of artifacts, images, and books.

Hirsch, Robert. *Exploring Color Photography: From Film to Pixels.* 5th ed. Oxford, U.K., and Burlington, MA: Elsevier/Focal Press, 2011. New edition with emphasis on digital color photography by director of Light Research and faculty member at SUNY Buffalo. Chapter 2 is an excellent brief overview of the history of color photography

"History of Photography in Astronomy." McCormick Museum, Department of Astronomy, University of Virginia. http://www.astro.virginia.edu/~rjp0i/museum/photography.html.

Jenkins, Reese V. *Images and Enterprise, Technology and the American Photographic Industry, 1839 to 1925.* Baltimore: Johns Hopkins University Press, 1975. Older institutional study of the first 90 years of the photographic industry in the United States. Emphasis on the role of radical technological change on the structure of the industry. Considerable use of the George Eastman correspondence.

Mees, C. E. Kenneth. *From Dry Plates to Ektachrome Film: A Story of Photographic Research.* New York: Ziff-Davis, 1961. Insider's view of science/technological change in photography at Kodak, especially developments in color photography by the Eastman Kodak Research Laboratory's first director.

Newhall, Beaumont. *The Daguerreotype in America.* New York: New York Graphic Society, 1968. Excellent, detailed older technical/artistic study of the birth of photography in the United States by America's pioneer art photography historian.

"Photography." National Museum of American History, Smithsonian Institution. http://americanhistory.si.edu/collections/search/main?edan_q=Early+photography&op=Search

Rosenblum, Naomi. *A World History of Photography.* New York: Abbeville Press, 2008. A most comprehensive scholarly study of the history of art photography that includes brief chapters on the technology of photography.

Wensberg, Peter C. *Land's Polaroid, A Company and the Man Who Invented It.* Boston: Houghton Mifflin, 1987. A balanced biography of Edwin Land and his company written by a member of Polaroid's advertising department after Land's retirement in 1982.

Reese V. Jenkins

PHRENOLOGY

Phrenology was a theory of human psychology and brain structure prevalent in the United States in the antebellum era. It was based on the extensive writings on cranial research by the Austrian physician Franz Joseph Gall, who maintained that all mental activity was a product of the operation of the brain and that all traits of human intellect and personality were controlled by 37 specific regions of the brain known as "organs." He further maintained that the relative influence of these organs on the development of individual character could be determined by examining the shape and contours of the skull. In the early nineteenth century Johann Gaspar Spurzheim and George Combe modified the deterministic character of Gall's original theory, and it was through their writings and lecturing that phrenology gained a sizeable following in the United States during the 1830s.

Phrenology was popular among scientists and physicians because it was at that time the only comprehensive theory of mental functioning based on what appeared to be solid empirical investigation. Its concept of localized brain functions was an advance over the imprecise and moralistic faculty psychology of Scottish realism, the dominant intellectual trend of that era. It appeared to offer new and fruitful avenues of research in anatomy and physiology and practical applications in such fields as education, criminology, and psychological medicine. Furthermore, by emphasizing the malleability of human nature, phrenology also appealed to the optimistic attitude in antebellum America toward reforming and perfecting the moral character of both individuals and society.

Phrenology was always surrounded by controversy, however. Popularizers of the theory, like Orson Fowler and Samuel Wells, commercialized it and turned it into a crude self-improvement program for mass consumption. A large segment of learned opinion opposed it because its materialistic assumptions undermined Christian theology and ethics. Finally, other medical researchers demonstrated that the origin of various kinds of mental functions did not correspond to the locations of Gall's organs. In the latter half of the nineteenth century phrenology lost its respectability as a scientific theory and came to be regarded as a pseudoscience and popular delusion.

[*See also* **Anatomy and Human Dissection; Physiology; Psychology; Religion and Science;** *and* **Science.**]

BIBLIOGRAPHY

Combe, George. *The Constitution of Man Considered in Relation to External Objects.* Boston: Carter and Hendee, 1829. The first American edition of the most popular and influential book on phrenology in the United States.

Davies, John D. *Phrenology, Fad and Science: A 19th-Century American Crusade.* New Haven, Conn.: Yale University Press, 1955. The only comprehensive study of the history and influence of phrenology in America.

"Phrenology." *The North American Review* 37, no. 80 (July 1833): 59–83. The first expression of American learned opinion against phrenology.

Spurzheim, Johann Gaspar. *Observations on the Deranged Manifestations of the Mind; or Insanity.* 3d American ed., with notes, improvements and plates; with an appendix by Amariah Brigham. Boston: Marsh, Capen & Lyon, 1836. A treatise on the application of phrenological principles to the diagnosis and treatment of insanity.

Loren A. Broc

PHYSICS

The study of physics had modest origins in early America, sheltered within a few of the earliest colleges and learned societies. Increased professionalization followed in the nineteenth century, bolstered by the emergence of professional societies and modern universities prioritizing original research. The fledgling U.S. physics community began to earn some international recognition in the early twentieth century, as it benefited from increased contact with European physicists and centers of research. Prior to World War II, university and corporate patrons dominated funding for American physics. During and following the wars, however, the federal government (especially the military) swamped all other sources of support. American physics exploded in the postwar era, in terms of funds, numbers of practitioners and publications, and the scale and quality of research. Physicists assumed a new cultural and political prominence even as they faced increased scrutiny during the Cold War. The market for physicists tumbled in the 1970s amid worsening economic conditions and a dip in defense spending for basic research. A brief resurgence in the 1980s did not permanently restore the postwar pattern, and a more complex institutional and funding environment for physics has prevailed into the early twenty-first century.

Colonial Period. Physics—the study of matter, forces, and their spatial and temporal relationships—was not recognized as a distinct branch of the natural sciences until the early nineteenth century. Physics in its modern sense evolved from natural philosophy, whose ancient pedigree dated back at least to the writings of Aristotle and whose object of study was the whole furniture and causal structure of the natural world. In early America the study of natural philosophy was taken up where formal learning and culture were traditionally nurtured: among the clergy, by members of the propertied elite, and in the first colleges.

Protestant ministers in the American colonies had the best access to literacy and education (and to European scholarly texts), and they produced some of America's earliest original scientific writing. New England clergyman Cotton Mather, for example, was not only centrally involved in the Salem witch trials in the 1690s, but also read natural philosophy avidly and even wrote a tract attempting to explain the aurora borealis in 1719. In pious Puritan New England throughout the seventeenth and eighteenth centuries, work and study in natural philosophy was integrated within the wider intellectual project of natural theology. The intricacy of nature's workings, it was believed, revealed divine intention and design; to know nature was to limn the power and providence of God. The English naturalist John Ray's *The Wisdom of God Manifested in the Works of Creation* (1691) was read widely in America and served as a model for the integration of natural and revealed knowledge.

After the founding of the Royal Society of London in 1660, some members of the American gentry could keep abreast of the latest scientific developments in Europe through correspondence with the society's members. John Winthrop Jr.—governor of the Connecticut Colony, designer of iron works, and owner of a three-foot telescope (in 1664 Winthrop famously claimed to have observed a fifth moon of Jupiter)—was the first American elected Fellow of the Royal Society, during his visit there in 1661–1663.

The curricula offered at the oldest colleges—Harvard (founded 1636), William and Mary (1693), and Yale (1701)—typically included instruction in Aristotelian natural philosophy, following European conventions. The colleges also provided an institutional base for a few of the earliest vocational scientists in America. Thomas Brattle, the son of a prominent merchant family and graduate of Harvard College, whose astronomical observations of Halley's Comet were cited in Newton's *Principia*, taught astronomy informally at Harvard and used his inheritance to endow a mathematics professorship just before his death in 1713. Isaac Greenwood, author of the first mathematical text published on American soil, took up the inaugural Hollis Chair of Mathematics and Natural Philosophy at Harvard in 1727.

American science was often regarded as provincial, uneven in quality, and lagging behind the currents of European thought. Cadwallader Colden, the lieutenant governor of New York and an aspiring scientist, endured harsh European criticism when his 1745 treatise, *An Explication of the First Causes of Action in Matter; and the Cause of Gravitation*, appeared to be innocent of the basic features of Newtonian mechanics. Still, the Scientific Revolution and strains of Enlightenment secularism sweeping Europe in the 1700s would eventually make their impact in America. The polymath Benjamin Franklin soon emerged as America's most renowned man of science, and his practical electrical and optical research was revered throughout England and the Continent. In Philadelphia in 1743 Franklin helped to establish one of the earliest American forums for the presentation of scientific work, the American Philo-sophical Society, where gentlemanly enthusiasts could gather to share their studies. But aspiring natural scientists would have to await the following century, and the founding of the Republic, for more formal institutional support for scientific research and publication.

Nineteenth Century.   The fledgling ranks of American physicists struggled to gain a stronger professional footing during the nineteenth century. Theology, classics, and moral philosophy continued to overwhelm scientific instruction in American universities, and physics research received little material support outside the academy. Modest federal provisions for science in the early nineteenth century—chiefly efforts in standardization, patent regulation, exploration, and surveying, all designed to enhance the government's administrative control over the territory and commerce of the new nation—slowly began to encourage the professionalization of science. Scientists of the day were by no means specialists, however, often mixing expertise in separate areas. The U.S. Coast Survey, for example, revived in the 1830s under the leadership of Swiss émigré Ferdinand Hassler (a former instructor at the new U.S. Military Academy at West Point, the first engineering school in the country) and Alexander Dallas Bache (an Academy graduate and instructor), drew on a wide range of physical knowledge and techniques from astronomy, geodesy, and geomagnetism.

Physicists were central to the earliest efforts to build national scientific institutions for the promotion of advanced research. Joseph Henry—one of the few American physicists to gain respect within European scientific circles for his celebrated experiments in magnetism and induction at the Albany Academy and Princeton University in the 1820s and 1830s—helped found the American Association for the Advancement of Science in 1840 and campaigned tirelessly for basic science in the United States. In 1846, after years of intense debate in Congress over how best to use the gift of wealthy English donor James Smithson, the Smithsonian Institution was established in Washington, D.C., with Henry as its first secretary.

The presence of distinct pedagogical cultures in the years after the Civil War made it less than clear where and how U.S. physicists should receive their training. On one hand, the private colleges spurned laboratory research, remaining devoted to a liberal arts curriculum for the cultivation of civic and religious virtue. On the other, the United States in the late 1800s was becoming more and more a nation of energetic planners and builders. As the country expanded its industrial capacity, mapped its interior, built its railroads, and aggressively conquered the Western frontier, the "practical arts" (including agricultural science and the various branches of engineering) dominated over the pursuit of abstract knowledge. A new kind of educational institution—the technical college—fueled the engine of American progress. Private schools like the Rensselaer Polytechnic Institute (founded 1824) and the Massachusetts Institute of Technology (1861) were training scores of new engineers, many of whom put their training to work in the expanding railroad, oil, and electrochemical industries. Public colleges established by the Morrill Land Grant Acts of 1862 and 1890 contributed to the flood of academically trained technicians. But any students aspiring to professional physics research would have found few American educational venues welcoming of their interests and hardly any well-stocked laboratories in which to conduct their work.

Even by the 1870s the number of professional research physicists in America probably totaled no more than 75. Yale University awarded the first American doctoral degree in physics in 1861—although only a quarter of American physicists in the late nineteenth century actually held PhD's in physics, and fewer still had acquired their doctorates in the United States. Yet there were signs of growth, and spurts of brilliance, as well. In 1876 Johns Hopkins University was founded with Henry Augustus Rowland, the talented spectroscopist and designer of diffraction gratings, installed as the first chair of physics. At the Case School of Applied Science in Cleveland during the 1880s, Albert Michelson and collaborator Edward Morley performed exhaustingly precise measurements of the speed of light using an interferometer of their own design—work that in 1907 would earn Michelson the first Nobel Prize in Physics for an American. And Yale University in New Haven sheltered the stunning homegrown talent of mathematical physicist Josiah Willard Gibbs. His rigorous theoretical work in thermodynamics, constructed with elaborate mathematical rigor, culminated in his 1902 masterpiece *Elementary Principles of Statistical Mechanics*.

Early Twentieth Century. During the closing years of the nineteenth century, physicists in the United States began to establish more firm institutional frameworks for their discipline. Physics professors at Cornell University founded the *Physical Review* in 1893, the first professional journal in the United States to cater exclusively to basic research in physics. A few years later, in 1899, three dozen physicists met at Columbia University to establish the American Physical Society. Reflecting the growing number of researchers in physics-related areas, other groups organized their own professional societies, such as the Optical Society of America (founded in 1916); the Acoustical Society of America (1929); the Society of Rheology (1929), focused on the structure and properties of materials; and the American Association of Physics Teachers (1930). These groups banded together under a new organization, the American Institute of Physics, in 1931. Hard hit by the Depression, the Institute aimed to achieve economics of scale, centralizing the journal-publication efforts of its member societies and lobbying various industries and philanthropies for increased financial support for research.

As the research-university model became more central throughout American higher education—with more and more American universities granting PhD's based on dissertations composed of original research—physicists placed greater emphasis on training new recruits. The annual number of physics PhD's granted in the United States grew steadily, from 20 in 1900 to 106 in 1930. The nature of the training began to shift as well. Soon after World War I, young physicists began to compete for new postdoctoral fellowships, to hone their professional preparation beyond the PhD degree. The new fellowships were funded by the Rockefeller Foundation and administered by the National Research Council, an arm of the National Academy of Sciences, and were established at the urging of prominent physical scientists George Ellery Hale, Robert Millikan, and Arthur Noyes. Hale, Millikan, and Noyes had been disappointed by the limited contributions that scientists in the United States had made to the war effort and sought some means of bolstering the scientific strength of the nation.

Many of the first recipients of the postdoctoral fellowships used the funds to complete their studies in Europe. Only there, I. I. Rabi famously remarked, could young American physicists learn the music, and not just the libretto, of world-class research in physics. While studying in Germany, Rabi also encountered typical European views of American physics. As late as 1927, during Rabi's visit, university librarians at Hamburg saw no need to receive the *Physical Review* upon publication, opting instead to order a full year's worth of the journal at a time.

Back in the United States, the new cadres of physicists took up positions in a variety of institutional settings: in universities but also in fast-growing corporate laboratories, including the fabled Bell Laboratory, founded in New York City in 1925 and affiliated with the American Telephone and Telegraph Company (AT&T). Physicists in several universities struck up active collaborations with neighboring industries as well, especially at the Massachusetts Institute of Technology and Stanford University. In fact, nearly all funding for academic research in physics between the world wars came from (modest) university budgets, private philanthropies like the Rockefeller Foundation, or corporate partners. The federal government played virtually no role in funding physics research before World War II, in large part because many conservative administrators at leading universities resisted anything that smacked of centralized, statist intervention in local educational affairs.

Most of the research pursued by physicists during the opening decades of the twentieth century focused on experimental physics rather than theoretical topics and often stayed close to areas like thermodynamics, optics, and acoustics—topics of longstanding expertise for American researchers, hearkening back to the efforts of Gibbs, Rowland, and Michelson. Physicists in the United States were relatively slow to turn attention to the new topic of quantum theory, physicists' account of matter and forces at the atomic scale that was honed in Europe during the first quarter of the twentieth century. Yet quantum theory began to make inroads among American physicists after young leaders of the field, such as John Slater, I. I. Rabi, and J. Robert Oppenheimer, returned from their European postdoctoral stints and began to teach the new material to advanced students.

Their efforts were aided by a series of visits by European experts in quantum theory, including Max Born's visit to the Massachusetts Institute of Technology in 1926 and Werner Heisenberg's visit to the University of Chicago in 1929. Such international contact became more systematic with the founding in 1928 of the annual Summer Symposium in Theoretical Physics at the University of Michigan, organized by department chair Harrison Randall along with émigré physicists Samuel Goudsmit and George Uhlenbeck. Collaboration became even more pronounced during the mid-1930s. About one hundred physicists and mathematicians fled fascism in Europe and settled in the United States. The émigrés included renowned physicists like Albert Einstein as well as scores of younger researchers, such as Enrico Fermi, Hans Bethe, Victor Weisskopf, Felix Bloch, Edward Teller, Eugene Wigner, and John von Neumann. The influx of talent bolstered what had already grown into a well-established discipline in the United States, and several émigrés assumed leading roles during and after World War II.

World War II.   By any measure, World War II was a watershed moment for physics in America. In fact, physicists began to mobilize even before the attack on Pearl Harbor. Several leading scientists and engineers, including Vannevar Bush, James Conant, and Karl Compton, convinced President Franklin Roosevelt that scientists should be better utilized in the coming conflict than the lackluster efforts during World War I. Following Bush's advice, Roosevelt established the

National Defense Research Committee (NDRC) in June 1940. One year later—still six months before the United States entered the war—Roosevelt created the Office of Scientific Research and Development (OSRD) to further coordinate research projects and to help see them through the development stage into working devices for combat use.

The OSRD was based on a contract model. The federal government (in particular its military branches) entered into contracts with researchers at universities, in corporate laboratories, and increasingly at purpose-built government facilities. The use of contracts, rather than block grants or other forms of patronage, helped to appease conservative administrators such as Bush who feared any semblance of New Deal–style centralized bureaucracies.

The largest project administered under the NDRC was the Radiation Laboratory (or "Rad Lab") housed at the Massachusetts Institute of Technology. The Rad Lab became the headquarters of the Allied effort to design and improve radar systems. The lab was founded hastily in the autumn of 1940 after a top-secret mission of British scientists and engineers visited with physicist and MIT president Karl Compton (among others) to reveal a new piece of equipment the British team had invented: a cavity magnetron that could generate short-wavelength electromagnetic radiation, in the microwave region of the spectrum. Such waves were short enough that they could provide much-improved resolution to existing radar systems—short enough to spot the tiny periscope from an otherwise-submerged German U-boat, for example. In short order, the Rad Lab grew from an initial staff of two dozen physicists, three security guards, two stockroom clerks, and a secretary to a sprawling staff of four thousand and a *monthly* operating budget of $1 million (more than $12 million per month in 2014 dollars). Led by physicist Lee DuBridge, the Rad Lab brought together young physicists with electrical engineers, metallurgists, chemists, and earth scientists. By the end of the war, the Rad Lab staff had developed more than one hundred different types of radar systems and had also trained more than 8,500 servicemen in how to use and maintain the units.

The OSRD assumed responsibility for a comparable project: the Manhattan Engineering District, or "Manhattan Project," to design and build nuclear weapons. As with radar, some physicists had begun to work on the topic before the United States entered World War II, but the project only received high priority and massive support following the attack on Pearl Harbor. One year later, in December 1942, a team led by Enrico Fermi at the University of Chicago created the first self-sustaining chain reaction—a crucial step in demonstrating that the still-new phenomenon of nuclear fission, in which heavy atomic nuclei such as uranium split into smaller pieces, could lead to an explosive release of energy. Within months, the OSRD had set up major industrial-scale facilities across the country to further the effort. The largest became the laboratories in Oak Ridge, Tennessee, which focused on separating the highly fissionable type of uranium from the common, more stable, variety; in Hanford, Washington, which focused on fabricating a new element, plutonium, even heavier than uranium and more likely to fission; and in Los Alamos, New Mexico, which took on the tasks of designing working bombs from the nuclear materials. Los Alamos alone grew to rival the Rad Lab in size, and like the Rad Lab, Los Alamos was headed by a physicist: J. Robert Oppenheimer. All told, the Manhattan Project included more than 30 sites across the United States and Canada and employed about 125,000 people, most of whom had little idea of the real nature or extent of the top-secret project. It culminated in the use of atomic bombs on the Japanese cities of Hiroshima and Nagasaki in August 1945.

Beyond the Rad Lab and Manhattan Project, physicists contributed to dozens of wartime projects alongside other scientists and engineers, most of them under NDRC and OSRD supervision. The scale of the largest undertakings, like radar and the atomic bombs, dwarfed any previous scientific projects conducted in the United States (or elsewhere). Whether measured by budgets, personnel, or the size of equipment—including the factory-size particle accelerators and nuclear reactors that became central to the Manhattan Project—the projects that physicists and their colleagues embarked on simply had no precedent. The source of support was also new: federal funding, largely military in origin, eclipsed the prewar patterns of patronage from private philanthropies or corporations. The modular, interdisciplinary nature of the research projects likewise broke with the interwar trend. In each of the major wartime projects, physicists worked alongside engineers of various stripes, physical chemists, metallurgists, and more. These massive endeavors demanded pragmatic focus on applications rather than basic research per se and were managed on tight timelines to ensure usefulness during the war effort.

The Cold War. Physics in the United States looked quite different after World War II than before it. Riding on the heels of the wartime projects, physics became the fastest-growing academic field in the country. Undergraduate and graduate-level enrollments in all fields, from history and literature to economics and sociology, grew exponentially after the war, aided by programs like the GI Bill; but graduate-level enrollments in physics doubled nearly twice as quickly as the rate for all other fields combined. The annual number of physics PhD's granted by U.S. institutions doubled every 1.7 years between 1945 and 1951 and took off exponentially again after the surprise launch of the Soviet *Sputnik* satellite in 1957. Whereas American universities had produced around 150 new physics PhD's per year in the late 1930s, that number zoomed to 500 per year in the early 1950s and 1,500 per year by the late 1960s. The number of university physics departments that granted PhD degrees likewise tripled between 1950 and 1970.

Remarkably, demand for young physicists expanded even more quickly than supply during the 1950s and 1960s. Within a few years after the war, physicists in the United States could select among well-paying positions in universities, corporate laboratories, or the brand-new network of national laboratories organized by the Atomic Energy Commission (the Commission had been founded in 1946 as the successor to the Manhattan Engineering District, inheriting the nuclear-weapons complex and much of the wartime research infra-

structure). Emblematic of the new possibilities, physicists John Bardeen, Walter Brattain, and William Shockley invented the point-contact transistor at Bell Labs in 1947—a development that earned them a Nobel Prize and jumpstarted the postwar boom in electronics and communication technologies. In 1953, for the first time, more PhD-level physicists took jobs in industry rather than academia.

Funding for research in physics continued on the wartime model, rather than reverting to the prewar pattern. Even adjusting for inflation, annual expenditures on basic physics research in the United States in 1953 were 25 times greater than what they had been in 1938, and they continued to rise exponentially into the mid-1960s. Those funds came overwhelmingly from the federal government, mostly from defense-related agencies like the Office of Naval Research and the Atomic Energy Commission. In 1949, 96 percent of funds for basic research in physics came from federal defense agencies. That proportion rose to 98 percent in 1954, despite the founding, in 1950, of the civilian National Science Foundation. By the early 1960s, not long into the "space race," additional resources for physics research came from new federal agencies like the National Aeronautics and Space Administration (NASA) and the Advanced Research Projects Agency (ARPA).

The research conducted by physicists in the United States commanded newfound respect among the world's physicists. Unlike Rabi's experiences in Europe before the war, European physicists now often looked to the United States for intellectual leadership—a testament, in part, to the lavish resources available for research in the United States after the war, which were all out of proportion to the privations of war-ravaged Europe. Between 1945 and 1975, for example, physicists in the United States earned 28 Nobel Prizes in Physics, more than four times the total that had been awarded to American physicists between 1900 and 1940. The *Physical Review*, once a backwater journal compared with the physics journals in Europe, became the dominant publication in the field. In 1953, articles in the *Physical Review* were cited eight times more often in the world's physics literature than articles in its nearest competitor.

On campus and off, physicists' research efforts turned more squarely to quantum theory than before the war. Two lines of research became prominent: applying quantum theory to very-high-energy phenomena in nuclear physics and elementary-particle physics and applying quantum theory to systems with many interacting particles. By the mid-1960s, those two areas—nuclear physics and solid-state physics—accounted for three quarters of all physics PhD's completed in the United States.

The research in high-energy physics benefited from theoretical breakthroughs by several young American physicists, veterans of the wartime projects, such as Julian Schwinger and Richard Feynman. (Schwinger, in particular, later credited his crash-course lessons at the Rad Lab in how to calculate pragmatically with influencing his postwar approach to quantum theory.) Alongside theoretical advances, research in nuclear and particle physics also benefited from the raft of new particle accelerators across the country financed by the Atomic Energy Commission. One prominent physicist quipped in the early 1950s that hardly a month went by without the announcement that another brand-new particle had been discovered in the huge machines. Driven by the advances in both theory and experiment, many physicists in the United States pursued a deeper understanding of the fundamental nuclear forces.

Work in solid-state physics likewise galloped ahead after the war. One crowning achievement was the first successful theoretical explanation of superconductivity, a striking phenomenon in which electrical resistance vanishes in certain materials under specific conditions. The phenomenon had been discovered in a laboratory in Leiden decades earlier, but received its first compelling theoretical explanation, rooted in quantum theory, in 1957 by American theorists John Bardeen, Leon Cooper, and Robert Schrieffer. The feat earned Bardeen a rare second Nobel Prize in Physics.

Research on fundamental nuclear forces or exotic phenomena like superconductivity had little immediate application to weapons projects.

Basic research was funded by defense-related agencies of the federal government largely to keep cadres of young physicists well trained and close at hand, in case the Cold War with the Soviet Union ever boiled over into open combat. In 1953, for example, three quarters of all physics PhD's trained in the United States who had earned part of their support from the Atomic Energy Commission took jobs with the Commission upon graduation. Military planners and science-policy experts at the time often used military metaphors to describe the fast-growing ranks of young physicists, trained on the government's dime—terms like "manpower" and "a standing army" of physicists became common, as did talk of "stockpiling" and "rationing" the nation's labor pool of physicists.

Physicists in the United States after the war enjoyed more than just new job opportunities and new research frontiers; they moved to the spotlight as well. *Harper's* magazine noted in the late 1940s, "Physical scientists are in vogue these days. No dinner party is a success without at least one physicist." Lionized in local civic clubs, physicists were frequently called upon to advise the government, often on topics removed from their domain of expertise. Within weeks of the launch of *Sputnik*, President Dwight Eisenhower created a new President's Science Advisory Committee staffed with notable physicists including I. I. Rabi, Hans Bethe, Robert Bacher, Edward Purcell, Herbert York, and Jerrold Zacharias.

The new publicity had a darker side as well. Physicists found themselves subject to unprecedented political scrutiny, especially during the heyday of postwar domestic anti-Communism. Politicians and journalists expressed widespread fears that physicists harbored an "atomic secret," some special knowledge about how to make nuclear weapons that could be written on a scrap of paper and smuggled to foreign powers. Amid the frenzy, the Atomic Energy Commission revoked the security clearance of J. Robert Oppenheimer in 1954. By that time, several powerful leaders in the military and the Atomic Energy Commission feared that Oppenheimer, the wartime director of Los Alamos, had too many left-leaning friends to be trusted. Oppenheimer's high-profile hearing—which was originally conducted in secret, but whose transcript was later released to the public in a further embarrassment to the physicist—was only the most famous example of the new political tests that physicists faced. Between 1945 and 1955, more physicists were called to testify before the House Un-American Activities Committee (HUAC) than members of any other academic discipline. Security clearances were routinely suspended or revoked for young physicists working at national laboratories and passports and visas were denied for foreign travel.

Beyond HUAC, and lasting longer than the political grandstanding of Senator Joseph McCarthy, physicists engaged with many political issues during the postwar decades, both within and beyond the spotlight. Most activity centered on nuclear-weapons policy and debates over the feasibility of ballistic missile defense.

The boom years for physics lasted about a quarter century after the end of World War II and were followed by a major, rapid contraction. A combination of factors coalesced between the late 1960s and early 1970s to change the fortunes for physics. Internal audits in the Department of Defense, culminating in the "Project Hindsight" report of 1969, concluded that the Pentagon was not getting an adequate return on its investment by funding open-ended, basic research on university campuses rather than mission-oriented projects. Around the same time, the escalation of fighting in the Vietnam War triggered a wave of protests across American campuses, spotlighting the prevalence of military-funded research by academic scientists and engineers. Physics laboratories in particular were often targeted by protesters. On top of the political turmoil came an economic downturn, which brought massive cuts in federal spending on education and defense. As the end result, funding for physics research, enrollments in classrooms, and job opportunities for young physicists fell faster than for any other academic discipline in the country.

Resources for the discipline began to pick up again during the early 1980s, buoyed by Reagan-era investment in new defense projects like the Strategic Defense Initiative, nicknamed "Star Wars" by its critics. The new projects also brought physicists into renewed political debate. The American Physical Society released a major report in 1987 arguing that the exotic antimissile technologies proposed by the Strategic Defense Initiative were far less feasible than military officials had promised. Other notable physicists, such as Edward Teller, continued to advise highly placed politicians that such systems were well within reach. Similar debates pitted physicists against each other on issues such as the safety of nuclear power and even the moral and intellectual appropriateness of physicists' postwar dependence on the federal government. Activist groups such as the Union of Concerned Scientists and Science for the People—formed by physicists during the Vietnam War amid protesters' claims that American science had been coopted by the military—strove to turn physics to more "socially responsible" ends in the late twentieth century.

After the Cold War. The Reagan-era boom in physics funding and enrollments came to a sudden halt with the unexpected end of the Cold War. Just as in the early 1970s, the rapid reversal of fortunes for the discipline sent a glut of young PhD's scrambling to find jobs outside the field. In fact, the dramatic mismatch between supply and demand of young scientists in the early 1990s became the subject of heated Congressional hearings and resulted in the closure of the department within the National Science Foundation that had produced the faulty predictions of how many young researchers in physics and allied areas the nation would need or the job market could absorb.

Among high-energy physicists, the most visible sign that times had changed came when Congress canceled funding for the Superconducting Supercollider in October 1993. The massive particle accelerator, which had been approved during the mid-1980s and was already under construction near Dallas, Texas, had suffered from cost overruns and accusations of mismanagement—challenges that had often been overlooked during the Cold War, but which left the project vulnerable amid the new political realities. Even more striking, the debates in Congress over whether to continue funding the project pitted physicists from one specialty, high-energy physics, against vocal leaders of other specialties, including condensed-matter physics. Amid tight constrictions on overall federal spending for science, internal divisions and rivalries among the nation's physicists came into view.

Funding for basic research in physics continued to slide for the remainder of the 1990s, although the trend reversed modestly early in the twenty-first century. The Laser Interferometer Gravitational-Wave Observatory (LIGO), a large-scale project with two major facilities and collaborators at more than 50 institutions, was built in 1999, becoming the most expensive project ever supported by the National Science Foundation. Although substantial, LIGO's cost, at roughly $490 million in 2014 dollars, was a mere fraction of the $8 to $15 billion that the Superconducting Supercollider would have required. (The supercollider, like most experimental research in high-energy physics, had been supported by the Department of Energy, successor to the Atomic Energy Commission, rather than the National Science Foundation.)

Cutting-edge basic research in high-energy physics, astrophysics, and cosmology has been buoyed in the 1990s and 2000s by projects like LIGO, as well as NASA-supported satellite missions like the Cosmic Microwave Background Explorer (COBE) and the Wilkinson Microwave Anisotropy Probe (WMAP). At the same time, transdisciplinary research in areas like biophysics, medical physics, geophysics, and nanotechnology has grown especially rapidly since the end of the Cold War.

Just as physics participated in the transformation of America from a colonial hinterland in the seventeenth century to a global superpower in the twentieth, it too was transformed by the forces of modernization and war. Although the discipline has changed dramatically in terms of patronage, political engagement, and intellectual trajectory, physics remains a vibrant and many-faceted enterprise in the new millennium.

[*See also* **American Association for the Advancement of Science; American Institute of Physics; American Philosophical Society; Astronomy and Astrophysics; Atomic Energy Commission; Bache, Alexander Dallas; Bardeen, John; Bell Laboratories; Bethe, Hans; Bush, Vannevar; Chemistry; Colden, Cadwallader and Jane; Compton, Karl Taylor; Conant, James B.; Defense Advanced Research Projects Agency; Einstein, Albert; Fermi, Enrico; Feynman, Richard; Franklin, Benjamin; Geophysics; Gibbs, Josiah Willard; Hale, George Ellery; Henry, Joseph; Higher Education and Science; Instruments of Science; Manhattan Project; Mathematics and Statistics; Meteorology and Climatology; Michelson, Albert Abraham; Military, Science and Technology and the; Millikan, Robert A.; Morrill Land Grant Act; Nanotechnology; National Academy of Sciences; National Aeronautics and Space Administration; National Laboratories; National Science Foundation; Nobel Prize in Biomedical Research; Noyes, Arthur Amos; Nuclear Power; Nuclear Weapons; Office of Scientific Research and Development; Oppenheimer, J. Robert; President's Science Advisory Committee; Quantum Theory; Rabi, Isidor I.; Railroads; Religion and Science; Rockefeller Institute, The; Rowland, Henry A.; Shockley, William; Smithsonian Institution; Space Program; Space Science; Strategic Defense Initiative; Teller, Edward; Von Neumann, John;** *and* **Wigner, Eugene.**]

BIBLIOGRAPHY

Bird, Kai, and Martin J. Sherwin. *American Prometheus: The Triumph and Tragedy of J. Robert Oppenheimer.* New York: Alfred A. Knopf, 2005. A definitive biography of J. Robert Oppenheimer, from his childhood and early career as a physicist to his leadership of the Manhattan Project and subsequent fall from grace during the height of the Cold War.

Bruce, Robert V. *The Launching of Modern American Science, 1846–1876.* New York: Alfred A. Knopf, 1987. A history of the development of institutional support for U.S. science—from private organizations and philanthropies to federal projects and the military—in the decades leading up to the Civil War.

Burns, William E. *Science and Technology in Colonial America.* Westport, Conn.: Greenwood Press,

2005. A wide-ranging survey of the forms of natural knowledge and technical skill in colonial America. Whereas science and technology in the earliest decades were focused on subsistence and survival, the establishment of the first colleges and learned societies provided more formal platforms for the growth of natural philosophy in America.

Dupree, A. Hunter. *Science in the Federal Government: A History of Policies to 1940.* Cambridge, Mass.: Belknap Press of Harvard University Press, 1957. A history of the halting growth of federal support of U.S. science, from the ratification of the Constitution until World War II. Dupree emphasizes the central place of science in the development of the nation, but argues that science failed to achieve a central place in the federal government as well as a set of comprehensive federal policies for its promotion.

Forman, Paul. "Behind Quantum Electronics: National Security as Basis for Physical Research in the United States, 1950–1960." *Historical Studies in the Physical Sciences* 18 (1987): 149–229. An exhaustive survey of the postwar influx of military financial support for research in the field of quantum electronics. Forman argues that the Cold War altered the style and character of U.S. physics, making it more oriented toward the solution of practical military problems, and argues controversially that postwar funding patterns compromised the genuine intellectual freedom of American physics.

Galison, Peter. *Image and Logic: A Material Culture of Microphysics.* Chicago: University of Chicago Press, 1997. A vast and wide-ranging history of modern particle and nuclear physics in the United States. Galison emphasizes the materiality of physicists' practices and the interaction between the distinct subcultures of instrumentalists, experimentalists, and theorists.

Galison, Peter, and Bruce Hevly, eds. *Big Science: The Growth of Large-Scale Research.* Stanford, Calif.: Stanford University Press, 1992. A collection of essays sketching the classic characteristics of postwar "big science," featuring big particle physics machines at the Lawrence Berkeley Laboratory and the Stanford Linear Accelerator Center; funding for science provided by sponsors like NASA and Du Pont; and military science from World War II to the Cold War.

Hewlett, Richard G., and Oscar E. Anderson. *The New World, 1939–1946: A History of the United States Atomic Energy Commission.* University Park: Pennsylvania State University Press, 1962. The first volume of an extensive two-volume study of the formation of the Atomic Energy Commission. This volume tracks the political and military decision making from the discovery and announcement of nuclear fission to the passage of the first Atomic Energy Act in 1946.

Kaiser, David. "The Atomic Secret in Red Hands? American Suspicions of Theoretical Physicists during the Early Cold War." *Representations* 90 (2005): 28–60. An account of how anti-Communist suspicion in the postwar years was heaped disproportionately on a particular segment of the scientific community: theoretical physicists. Kaiser shows how, from media accounts to the House Un-American Activities Committee, the belief that theoretical physicists were both uniquely responsible for the creation of atomic weapons and also inordinately susceptible to leftist ideologies dominated the national discussion.

Kaiser, David. "Cold War Requisitions, Scientific Manpower, and the Production of American Physicists after World War II." *Historical Studies in the Physical and Biological Sciences* 33 (2002): 131–159. Although many studies have been concerned with measuring the "bigness" of postwar science funding and the size of postwar scientific equipment, Kaiser argues that a third kind of "bigness" was just as important: enrollment of graduate students in physics. In two successive waves of expansion—one following the Korean War in 1950 and the second following the *Sputnik* launch in 1957—the production of PhD scientists outpaced the production of experts in all other fields, and physics outpaced every other scientific discipline.

Kaiser, David. "The Postwar Suburbanization of American Physics." *American Quarterly* 56 (2004): 851–888. Argues that the cultural history of American physics offers a window onto postwar academics' changing views about the proper role of the American intellectual and more specifically that physicists assimilated the symbolism and language of suburbanization and mass consumption.

Kevles, Daniel J. *The Physicists: The History of a Scientific Community in Modern America.* 3d ed. Cambridge, Mass.: Harvard University Press, 1995 [1978]. The classic account of the professionalization of American physics and the political fortunes of the discipline from the nineteenth century onward. Kevles highlights the enduring tension between physics as an elite, technocratic discipline and its proper role within American democracy.

Leslie, Stuart W. *The Cold War and American Science: The Military–Industrial–Academic Complex at MIT and Stanford.* New York: Columbia University Press, 1993. Studies the predominance of military funding and projects in major research, teaching laboratories, and classrooms at MIT and Stanford. It focuses on the Cold War years leading up to the student-led antimilitary protests in each of these campuses.

Moore, Kelly. *Disrupting Science: Social Movements, American Scientists, and the Politics of the Military, 1945–1975.* Princeton, N.J.: Princeton University Press, 2008. A study of scientists' affiliations with various peace and social change movements, from Quaker pacifism to anti-Vietnam War activism and the radical New Left group Science for the People. Moore argues that through their association with such activism, scientists played a key role in eroding their own scientific authority.

Moyer, Albert. "History of Physics." *Osiris* 1 (1985): 163–182. Special issue on "Historical Writing in American Science," edited by Sally Gregory Kohlstedt and Margaret W. Rossiter. A historiographical essay that argues historians have paid too much attention to a certain kind of physicist—the "physicist-politician" dominant in, for example, Kevles's *The Physicists*—and have tended to ask only two (among many possible) questions. One: how did the U.S. physics community reach maturity just prior to the Manhattan Project to make that undertaking so successful?; and two: what effect did the Manhattan Project have on the character of U.S. physics?

Owens, Larry. "MIT and the Federal 'Angel': Academic R&D and Federal–Private Cooperation before World War II." *Isis* 81 (1990): 188–213. A history of the failed partnership between MIT and the federal government during the 1930s, when the Tennessee Valley Authority attempted to contract MIT to produce a new power transmission system in return for funding for its research programs in physics and electrical engineering. Although the effort failed, it prefigured (especially in its use of the contract system) the much tighter science–government relationship of years to come.

Reingold, Nathan. "Vannevar Bush's New Deal for Research: Or the Triumph of the Old Order." *Historical Studies in the Physical Sciences* 17 (1987): 299–344. An account of the development of Vannevar Bush's highly idiosyncratic thinking about the relationship between science and government during the 1940s. Reingold argues that although Bush was thoroughly conservative, his vision of postwar federal patronage for research was in many ways reminiscent of New Deal policies and programs.

Schweber, Silvan S. "The Empiricist Temper Regnant: Theoretical Physics in the United States, 1920–1950." *Historical Studies in the Physical Sciences* 17 (1986): 55–98. Schweber argues that theoretical physics in the United States took on a particularly instrumentalist and pragmatist style as it reached maturity in the first half of the twentieth century. This style emerged naturally from the innate characteristics of American culture and philosophical outlook (as represented especially by the pragmatist philosophy of William James and Charles Sanders Peirce) and was reinforced institutionally in the education of American researchers and the close collaboration of experimentalists and theorists.

Schweber, Silvan S. "The Mutual Embrace of Science and the Military: ONR and the Growth of Physics in the United States after World War II." In *Science, Technology, and the Military*, edited by Everett Mendelsohn, Merritt Roe Smith, and Peter Weingart, pp. 1–45. Boston: Kluwer Academic, 1988. An article describing the close partnership between U.S. physics and military research and development agencies in the postwar era, with a special focus on the Office of Naval Research (ONR), known for funding wide-ranging basic science alongside research of more direct military relevance. The establishment of ONR on the model of the wartime Office of Scientific Research and Development meant that support for American physics in the postwar era would remain predominantly military, rather than civilian, in origin.

Schweber, Silvan S. *QED and the Men Who Made It: Dyson, Feynman, Schwinger, and Tomonaga.* Princeton, N.J.: Princeton University Press, 1994. A technically detailed history of physicists' efforts after World War II to overcome difficulties in the theory of quantum electrodynamics—namely, the troubling appearance of infinities in routine calculations related to the interaction between light and charged particles like electrons—by forging new theoretical techniques and concepts.

Wang, Jessica. *American Science in an Age of Anxiety: Scientists, Anticommunism, and the Cold War.* Durham: University of North Carolina Press, 1999. A history of the encounter between scientists and domestic anti-Communism during the late 1940s. Wang claims that national science advocacy organizations largely failed to make a rigorous public defense of scientists' civil liberties when they came under siege by anti-Communist witch-hunters, even before Senator McCarthy had risen to prominence.

Weart, Spencer. "The Physics Business in America, 1919–1940: A Statistical Reconnaissance." In *The Sciences in American Context: New Perspectives*, edited by Nathan Reingold, pp. 295–358. Washington, D.C.: Smithsonian Institution, 1979. A discussion of growth trends in the community of U.S. physicists during the 1920s and 1930s, supplemented with statistics on numbers of PhD physicists graduated, national research and development expenditures, physicists' salaries, employment patterns, and so forth. Weart documents the nearly unbroken growth of American physics in these decades.

Weart, Spencer. "The Solid Community." In *Out of the Crystal Maze: Chapters from the History of Solid-State Physics*, edited by Lillian Hoddeson, Ernest Braun, Jurgen Teichmann, and Spencer Weart, pp. 617–669. New York: Oxford University Press, 1992. A study of the intellectual, social, and institutional formation of the field of solid-state physics in Europe and the United States between the 1920s and 1970s. Weart uses the writings and recollections of prominent physicists, along with statistical analyses of publications, to show how solid-state physics cohered as a distinct field of expertise, especially in the years following World War II.

Benjamin Wilson and David Kaiser

PHYSIOLOGY

Physiology is the experimental study of the function of biological processes within living organisms. Until the 1870s, physiology in the United States was primarily a popular discourse related to personal hygiene and health reform. The first American Physiological Society was founded in 1837 by the health reformers William Alcott and Sylvester Graham as a diet reform and self-help organization for men and women in New England. In the first part of the nineteenth century, ladies' physiological institutes were created to teach women how to maintain their health.

Before 1870. American medical schools offered limited instruction to aspiring physicians. No U.S. institution offered comprehensive instruction in physiological experimentation akin to that offered in the universities of France and Germany. Some American physicians conducted research if they possessed both an interest in the subject and a private income to fund their work. The Philadelphia physician John Richardson Young worked on the chemistry of food and digestion, and the doctor and educator Robley Dunglison wrote a textbook of physiology. The only American to achieve international fame for physiological research was William Beaumont (1785–1853), an army surgeon who proved that digestion was a chemical process. In 1822, Beaumont was stationed on Mackinac Island in Michigan when he was called upon to treat Alexis St. Martin, a Canadian voyageur who had been shot in the stomach. St. Martin's wound healed imperfectly, leaving a gastric fistula. Beginning in 1824, Beaumont performed hundreds of digestion experiments on St. Martin. An apprentice-trained physician with no previous experience in research, Beaumont took advantage of this "experiment in nature" by tying string around various foodstuffs and dangling them into St. Martin's stomach to measure how long it took for the food to digest. St. Martin was not always a willing participant in the experiments because they caused him pain; he would periodically escape to Canada, finally leaving the army surgeon for good in 1834.

During the 1820s and early 1830s Beaumont took measures to keep St. Martin available for experiments, including having him sign a contract that promised money, food, and shelter in exchange for submitting to his investigations and performing household chores. Beaumont also enlisted the Canadian as an orderly in the U.S. Army to further compel him to remain in his care. Beaumont had few contacts with physicians outside of the army until 1832, when he traveled to the East Coast to meet Dunglison and other scientists. In 1833 he published *Experiments and Observations on the Gastric Juice, and the Physiology of Digestion*. The book became well known in the United States and abroad. In French and German physiological circles it took on importance because it proved that digestion was not caused by vital forces, but by chemical ones, strengthening the hand of advocates of an empirical study of life as opposed to speculative or philosophical investigations. Beaumont's work inspired the French physiologist Claude Bernard (1813–1878) to conduct his own experiments inducing gastric fistulae in animals. Although Beaumont was celebrated by the American medical establishment, his research did not spur further experimental work in the United States. A more significant response came from health reformers, who quickly adopted Beaumont's tables on the speed of digestion of different foods to validate their own dietetic theories. Beaumont's work was also integrated into hygiene and physiology textbooks for primary and secondary students from the 1830s to 1900, so that most students were familiar with it (Numbers and Orr, 1981).

Professionalization of American Physiology. After the Civil War, scientists and physicians in the United States began to employ the term "physiology" to refer to experimental studies of the functions of living organisms. Histories of physiology in the United States have tended to focus on the social and institutional contexts of the discipline, rather than the intellectual development of the science (Fye, 1987; Geison, 1987). The physiologists who built the discipline in the United States had received their training in Europe in the 1850s and 1860s, studying in the research laboratories of such prominent scientists as Bernard in Paris and Carl Ludwig in Leipzig. There these scientists learned advanced microscopy, physiological chemistry, the use of instruments like the kymograph and galvanometer, and advanced surgical and experimental techniques, as well as an ethos of experimental rigor, all of which they

brought back to the United States. No research infrastructure analogous to the physiology departments in Europe existed at American universities in the mid- to late nineteenth century. Therefore, the first American physiologists were primarily clinicians who carried out some physiological research in their spare time, while advocating for changes in American medical education that would grant a more prominent place for their discipline. For example, Silas Weir Mitchell carried out work on the physiology of poison while keeping up a medical practice, although his two bids to obtain a research position at Philadelphia-area medical schools were unsuccessful. Experimental physiology along European lines was initially thought to have little relevance for American medical education (Fye, 1987). One important exception to this perspective was John Call Dalton, the chair of physiology and microscopic anatomy at the College of Physicians and Surgeons in New York City. Dalton taught physiology to medical students along the same lines as his mentor Bernard, using vivisection to demonstrate various physiological functions. However, his original research on gastric digestion and the brain were carried out in his own house and paid for with his own funds. Dalton was additionally an advocate for animal research, speaking publicly against anti-vivisection groups who called for legal restrictions on the use of animals in scientific research and medical teaching.

Between 1870 and World War I, increasing numbers of elite American medical students traveled to German universities to receive advanced training in physiology. Dalton and Mitchell were joined in their advocacy of physiology by other researchers who positioned the science as an important component of medical education reform, then taking place at some U.S. universities. These reformers argued that doctors would learn a scientific mind-set through studying physiology, biochemistry, anatomy, and pharmacology. This new ethos would bring improvements in medical practice and a rise in the status of physicians. The reform movement led to the establishment of laboratories at some medical schools for hands-on training in experimental medicine, staffed by professional physiologists. The first was founded in

1871 by Henry P. Bowditch (1840–1911), who was invited by Harvard University's president, Charles Eliot, to become the chair of physiology at the medical school. Bowditch used university funds and some of his family's money to outfit a space in the attic of a medical school building with instruments and animal quarters. Advanced medical students were allowed to conduct research under Bowditch's supervision. Bowditch himself conducted research on cardiac physiology; he also trained a number of influential American scientists, including G. Stanley Hall and Charles Minot. In Connecticut, Russell Chittenden (1856–1943) became a professor of physiology at Yale's Sheffield Scientific School in 1882 after studying physiological chemistry with Willy Kühne in Heidelberg. At the Sheffield School he taught basic courses in chemistry alongside physiology and nutrition. Chittenden's own research was centered on the action of enzymes on proteins and on human dietary requirements.

Physiology developed at elite American medical schools along a pattern similar to that of Harvard and Yale, with some exceptions. At the Johns Hopkins University, built in part on the model of the German university, the department of physiology preceded the establishment of the medical school. H. Newell Martin's physiological laboratory at Hopkins was created as part of the biology department in 1876. Physiology was also considered part of biology at the University of Chicago, largely because of the work of Jacques Loeb (1859–1924). The general or biological physiology that took root at these schools was conceived of as a fundamental natural science dedicated to unraveling the phenomena of life common to all living things, using the tools of biochemistry and biophysics. This was not the dominant model, however. General physiology remained a minor part of biology, and medically oriented physiologists dominated the discipline. At women's colleges physiology was frequently taught by female physiologists who conceived of the discipline as a branch of hygiene as well as a biomedical science.

Physiology's arrival as an independent discipline in the United States can be pegged to the founding in 1887 of the second American Physiological Society (APS) by Bowditch, Mitchell, Martin, Chittenden, and John Green Curtis. The first APS was a social reform movement that dissolved in 1839; the new APS was one of the first disciplinary societies in the United States, founded with the intent of promoting physiology as an experimental science and to provide a forum for physiologists to present their research. Although only a handful of the original 28 members were professional physiologists—the rest were largely practicing physicians—membership was restricted to scientists who had published original research, which kept the society small and exclusive. It also kept women from joining the group because few were able to obtain research posts at universities in the late nineteenth century. The first female member joined in 1902. The group's ranks soon swelled with eligible scientists who had entered the discipline. There were 128 members by 1906 and 230 members by 1913.

Physiology in the Twentieth Century. American physiology had attained international prominence by the close of World War I. The well-equipped laboratories established at elite universities became attractive places to study for American students, obviating the need to go abroad for advanced training. In addition, the war's disruption of European and British physiologists' work allowed Americans to keep pace with, and even surpass, the productivity of their European colleagues, despite the fact that physiology remained a niche discipline dominated by research groups at the major universities through the 1930s (Geison, 1987). Histories of physiology in the twentieth century tend to focus on the contributions of individual physiologists within their respective subdisciplines. The most prominent physiologist of the early twentieth century was Walter Bradford Cannon (1871–1945). While a medical student at Harvard, Cannon was one of the first to use X-rays to observe the function of the digestive tract. After he succeeded his mentor Bowditch as professor of physiology at Harvard in 1906, Cannon studied how emotions such as fear or excitement might cause changes in the nervous system or digestive tract. In addition, he built on Bernard's concept of the *milieu intérieur* to develop the notion of homeostasis. He coined the term in

1926 to describe the ways in which the body regulates its own internal properties, such as blood glucose levels and temperature, to maintain an equilibrium. Cannon was also quite active in arguing for the medical utility of animal experimentation on behalf of the American Medical Association's Committee on Defense of Medical Research in the 1910s and 1920s.

Physiology in the twentieth century has been marked by the mushrooming of specialized fields within the discipline. The burgeoning interest in disciplines such as biochemistry, cell biology, and endocrinology led to scientists taking on the disciplinary identity of their specialized field of research rather than of physiology. The fragmentation of the discipline can be seen through the formation of specialist societies, which began to happen as early as 1906, when a number of APS members founded the American Society of Biological Chemists. The American Society for Pharmacology and Experimental Therapeutics, a further spin-off, was founded in 1908, with separate organizations for nutritionists, biophysicists, general physiologists, and neurophysiologists to come in the following decades. Many of the members of the new societies remained members of APS, and the specialty groups would hold joint annual meetings under the APS umbrella. The relationship among APS and its splinter organizations became more fraught after World War II, as the number of self-identified physiologists declined. Beginning in the 1940s, physiologists themselves began to think of their discipline not as a science but as a point of view: essentially, a cluster of disciplines centered around understanding the relationship of biological processes to the functioning of whole organisms (Long Range Planning Committee, 1990). Although this perspective differs from the medically oriented animal physiology of the founders of American physiology, it reflects the growth and development of the discipline. In the early twenty-first century, physiology has become more diffuse as a discipline. This is reflected in the fact that many physiology departments at American medical schools have been reorganized, merged with other departments, and renamed to reflect their faculty's more specialized research, such as cell biology or neuroscience.

[*See also* **Anatomy and Human Dissection; Animal and Human Experimentation; Biochemistry; Biological Sciences; Chemistry; Medical Education; Medicine;** *and* **Public Health.**]

BIBLIOGRAPHY

American Physiological Society (1887–). *History of the American Physiological Society: The First Century, 1887–1987.* Bethesda, Md., and Baltimore: The Society; distributed for the American Physiological Society by the Williams & Wilkins Co, 1987. A collection of detailed essays on the founding, membership, and activities of the APS.

Appel, Toby A. "Physiology in American Women's Colleges: The Rise and Decline of a Female Subculture." *Isis* 85, no. 1 (1994): 26–56.

Benison, Saul, A. Clifford Barger, and Elin L. Wolfe. *Walter B. Cannon: The Life and Times of a Young Scientist.* Cambridge, Mass.: Belknap Press, 1987. A biography of the physiologist focusing on his research and administrative work.

Fye, Bruce. *The Development of American Physiology: Scientific Medicine in the Nineteenth Century.* The Henry E. Sigerist Series in the History of Medicine. Baltimore: Johns Hopkins University Press, 1987. Tracks the growth of a "research ethic" among four of the founders of the APS.

Geison, Gerald L., ed. *Physiology in the American Context, 1850–1940.* Bethesda, Md.: American Physiological Society; distributed by Williams & Wilkins, 1987. Intended by its editor as a "base camp" from which further explorations of the history of physiology could be launched. The book is primarily focused on the institutional and social context of physiology.

Kohler, Robert E. *From Medical Chemistry to Biochemistry: The Making of a Biomedical Discipline.* Cambridge, U.K.: Cambridge University Press, 1982. Outlines the development of biochemistry in American universities; notes that discipline's relationship to physiology.

Long Range Planning Committee of the American Physiological Society. "What's Past Is Prologue: A 'White Paper' on the Future of Physiology and the Role of the American Physiological Society in It." *The Physiologist* 33 (1990): 161–177, 180.

Numbers, Ronald L., and William J. Orr. "William Beaumont's Reception at Home and Abroad." *Isis* 72, no. 4 (1981): 590–612.

M. S. Laas

PICKERING, EDWARD CHARLES

(1846–1919), American physicist and astronomer. Pickering was the director of the Harvard College Observatory from 1877 until his death and the elder brother of fellow astronomer William Henry Pickering (1858–1938).

A child of the Boston elite, Pickering attended Boston Latin School and graduated from the Lawrence Scientific School at Harvard University on his 19th birthday. He remained at Lawrence for two years as a mathematics instructor, but left to teach physics at the Massachusetts Institute of Technology (MIT) in 1867. During his decade-long tenure at MIT, Pickering developed one of the first teaching laboratories in the United States and published a pioneering laboratory manual, his *Elements of Physical Manipulation*. He married Elizabeth Wadsworth Sparks in 1874.

In early 1877, Pickering was appointed director of the Harvard College Observatory. Trained as a physicist rather than as an astronomer, he was not Harvard's first choice to replace the late Joseph Winlock (1826–1875). The position lay vacant for more than a year before Harvard University president Charles William Eliot (1834–1926), himself a Lawrence graduate and former MIT professor, turned to Pickering.

As director, Pickering expanded the Harvard College Observatory dramatically and shifted its research emphasis from celestial mechanics and astrometry toward the relatively new science of astrophysics. Adept at fundraising and suspicious that contemporary astronomical theory suffered from a paucity of data, he quadrupled the observatory's endowment, launched observational projects requiring large staff and expensive instruments, and increased the observatory's publication output several times over. Geographically, he extended its reach by establishing a station outside Arequipa, Peru, thus providing access to data that could be pulled only from the skies of the southern hemisphere.

Pickering became known for running the observatory like a mass-production line and hiring women "computers" to conduct daytime observations on photographic plates. He is known especially for two large projects he administered, the Henry Draper Memorial Catalogue for Stellar Spectra and the so-called Harvard Photometry. Using primarily photographic methods, his staff developed standardized classification systems for stellar spectra and magnitudes. Pickering campaigned vigorously for both systems' adoption by the International Union for Cooperation in Solar Research and succeeded in 1913.

Pickering survived his wife and died without heirs in 1919, leaving most of his estate to the Harvard College Observatory.

[*See also* **Astronomy and Astrophysics; Higher Education and Science;** *and* **Physics.**]

BIBLIOGRAPHY

Campbell, W. W. "Edward Charles Pickering, 1846–1919." *Publications of the Astronomical Society of the Pacific* 31, no. 180 (1919): 73. Obituary of Pickering by a fellow astronomer.
Jones, Bessie Zaban, and Lyle Gifford Boyd. *The Harvard College Observatory: The First Four Directorships, 1839–1919.* Cambridge, Mass.: Belknap Press, 1971. The standard, celebratory history of the early period of the Harvard College Observatory.
Osterbrock, Donald E. "The Appointment of a Physicist as Director of the Astronomical Center of the World." *Journal for the History of Astronomy* 23, no. 3 (1992): 155–165. Discusses the controversy of Pickering's appointment as Harvard College Observatory director.
Plotkin, Howard. "Edward C. Pickering." *Journal for the History of Astronomy* 21 (1990): 47–58. A short review of Pickering's professional life.
Plotkin, Howard. "Edward C. Pickering, the Henry Draper Memorial, and the Beginnings of Astrophysics in America." *Annals of Science* 35 (1978): 365–377. Discusses Pickering's preference for data over theory, his fundraising skill, and the origins of early big science in astronomy.

Catherine Nisbett Becker

PINCUS, GREGORY GOODWIN

(1903–1967), pioneer of the oral contraceptive. Gregory Goodwin Pincus was born in New Jersey in 1903. Inspired to follow in the footsteps of family members in the agricultural sciences, Pincus headed to Cornell University in 1920. His interests turned toward general biology and, following his graduation in 1924, Pincus began graduate studies in genetics and physiology under William E. Castle and William J. Crozier at Harvard University.

Receiving his ScD in 1927, a National Research Council fellowship in Europe kindled Pincus's interest in mammalian reproductive physiology. Upon returning to Harvard as an instructor in 1930, Pincus's research focused on the influence of ovarian hormones on ovum development. His work drew disapproval when he made the controversial claim that he could cause unfertilized rabbit eggs to mature through the manipulation of sex hormones. This criticism, among other factors, precipitated the school's decision in 1937 not to grant him reappointment. Luckily, Hudson Hoagland, a former graduate school colleague, lobbied for Pincus to join him at Clark University in 1938.

In 1944, Pincus and Hoagland cofounded the Worcester Foundation for Experimental Biology, which grew into an international hub for steroid hormone research. As director of the foundation, Pincus became a skilled administrator, fostering young scientists and innovative methods. The mid-1940s also found Pincus organizing the Laurentian Hormone Conference, an influential and long-running annual forum for hormone researchers.

Pincus extended his research after World War II toward controlling fertility through hormonal intervention. This work attracted the attention of the birth control advocate Margaret Sanger, who asked Pincus to develop an oral contraceptive, and the philanthropist Katharine McCormick, who underwrote the project. By 1956, Pincus and his colleagues honed in on synthetic progesterone compounds that successfully inhibited ovulation in rabbits and rats. Pincus enlisted the physician John Rock to help conduct tests in humans. Subsequent large-scale trials yielded successful results and the Food and Drug Administration's 1960 approval of the new drug.

Pincus passed away in 1967. Beyond his crucial role in bringing about an effective hormonal con-traceptive, Pincus left a legacy as an important scientific leader and organizer for the growing area of hormone research.

[*See also* **Biological Sciences; Birth Control and Family Planning; Genetics and Genetic Engineering; Physiology; Sanger, Margaret; Sex and Sexuality;** *and* **Sex Education.**]

BIBLIOGRAPHY

Ingle, Dwight J. "Gregory Goodwin Pincus: 1903–1967." *National Academy of Sciences Biographical Memoirs* 42 (1971): 228–270.
Speroff, Leon. *A Good Man: Gregory Goodwin Pincus: The Man, His Story, the Birth Control Pill.* Portland, Ore.: Arnica Publishing, 2009.

Tulley Long

PLASTICS

Plastics are resinous substances molded, cast, or extruded into desired shapes. Until 1869, when John Wesley Hyatt invented celluloid by combining cellulose and camphor, the only plastics were such natural materials as shellac, hard rubber, and gutta percha, used for daguerreotype cases, buttons, and other small artifacts. Celluloid, a sheet material shaped with heat, replaced ivory or tortoiseshell in combs and accessories. Celluloid addressed such issues as the uncertain supply of raw materials, the need for precisely dimensioned manufacturing materials, and the demand for democratization of goods. From the first, its imitative qualities signified both technological ingenuity and second-rate cheapness.

After finding a shellac substitute for electrical insulation in 1907, Leo Baekeland realized that his durable phenolic resin had many applications—from pipe stems to skillet handles—and commercialized it as "the material of a thousand uses." While Bakelite became a household word during the 1920s and 1930s, other plastics appeared: colorful cast phenolic, pastel-colored urea formaldehyde, cellulose acetate, vinyl, and transparent acrylic—all promoted as utopian materials derived from such abundant sources as coal, water, and air. Independent custom molders, who made marketable parts and products, experimented in the 1930s with injection molding of thermoplastics, which eventually almost replaced compression molding of thermoset resins. A journal (*Modern Plastics*, 1925) and a trade association (the Society of the Plastics Industry, 1937) served the fledgling industry.

The DuPont Corporation's introduction of nylon in 1938 marked a major transition. Rather than trying to commercialize a random laboratory gunk, Wallace Carothers and Julian Hill set out to synthesize a precise substitute for silk. Nylon's success as a fiber for stockings and as a molding resin signaled the dominance of large chemical companies. The industry came to maturity during World War II, providing cockpit enclosures, mortar fuses, and even bugles. Its wartime advertising promised a plastic miracle world, but home-front substitutes reinforced an image of cheapness. Many new plastics—among them polyethylene, polypropylene, and polyester—were commercialized after the war. Mirroring an expanding economy, a host of new products—Tupperware, hula hoops, fiberglass chairs, Formica laminate, bubble packaging, dry-cleaning bags, Teflon-coated pans—moved so quickly into everyday life that moviegoers laughed nervously in 1968 when a booster in *The Graduate* told Dustin Hoffman, "Just one word. Plastics. There's a great future in plastics."

Although vinyl go-go boots and inflatable domes expressed the youth culture of the 1960s and 1970s, distrust of plastic developed into hostility. Journalists and writers expressed fears of toxicity, flammability, and overflowing landfills (themes used to great effect by the novelist Norman Mailer). Plastic, once a symbol of humanity's power to transcend natural limits, became instead a metaphor of technology out of control and a pejorative adjective meaning fake or phony. Eventually, as engineering resins and composites revolutionized sports equipment and other consumer goods in the 1980s and 1990s, plastic regained its good name. At the same time, as cultural attention shifted from intractable natural materials to more malleable plastics and finally to virtual environments electronically synthesized by computer, the concept of plasticity embodied a traditional American faith in an ability to remold the world.

[*See also* **Carothers, Wallace Hume; Chemistry; Environmentalism; Military, Science and Technology and the; Nylon; Science;** *and* **Technology.**]

BIBLIOGRAPHY

DuBois, J. Harry. *Plastics History U.S.A.* Boston: Cahners Books, 1972.
Meikle, Jeffrey L. *American Plastic: A Cultural History*. New Brunswick, N.J.: Rutgers University Press, 1995.

Jeffrey L. Meikle

PLATE TECTONICS, THEORY OF

The idea that regions of the Earth have undergone very large motions relative to each other is a scientific finding of the second half of the twentieth century. The first theory to propose this addressed only the motion of continents and so was called continental drift; it was first put forward in detailed form by the German scientist A. Wegener in 1915. After much controversy this idea was accepted in the 1960s in the somewhat different form of plate tectonics. Plate-tectonic theory says that there are large areas of the Earth, the plates, which may include oceans and continents. Within these regions, there is little relative motion, so most of the motion takes place at the boundaries between these plates, where plate material can be created or destroyed—and where these relative motions cause most of the world's mountains, volcanoes, and earthquakes. Although the rates of motion are a few inches per year or less, over geological time they can result in relative motions of thousands of miles.

American scientists played important roles in the history of this idea: first as opponents of it, then as contributors of data and concepts which led to it, and finally as investigators of the consequences of it and measurers of the plate motions.

As a novel account of large-scale change over geologic time, Wegener's theory was much discussed in the 1920s and 1930s. In the United States the result of these discussions was that several prominent American geologists dismissed it, and it was generally rejected, in preference to the theory that the present configuration of continents and oceans was as it had always been. This rejection seems to have been in part because of the preference of American geologists for theories built up only from accumulations of facts—which Wegener's theory was felt not to be. Other reasons were a belief that observations of gravity indicated a difference between continents and oceans that was incompatible with the former drifting through the latter and a commitment to a strong version of the idea that the past must resemble the present. And some of the strongest geologic evidence for Wegener's theory came from South America, not the more familiar North America.

Although the status of continental drift did not change after World War II, the areas studied by American geologists did, to encompass the whole world, especially the oceans. Substantial funding from the Office of Naval Research and (later) the National Science Foundation supported many oceangoing expeditions by a number of institutions, notably Lamont–Doherty Geological Observatory in New York and Scripps Institution of Oceanography in California, as well as by government agencies such as the U.S. Coast and Geodetic Survey. These surveys sampled rocks from the ocean floor and measured its topography and the gravity and magnetic fields over it. The topography showed long, straight features, called fracture zones, and a system of rises and rifts that seemed to reach all through the world ocean. An influential explanation for some of this was provided in 1960–1961 by the geologists H. Hess (Princeton) and R. S. Dietz (U.S. Navy and Scripps), who proposed the concept called seafloor spreading. This model was that, at the ocean rifts, molten rock was rising to create new seafloor, which then moved away from the rift;

like continental drift, this theory suggested large motions, but its focus was on the oceans, not the continents.

Independently of these investigations and theories, American and other scientists were reconstructing the behavior of the Earth's magnetic field over geologic time. These results strongly suggested relative motions of the continents; more importantly, they came to be recognized as showing that the field direction had reversed (magnetic south and north changing places) many times. Because rocks acquire magnetism when they cool, it was proposed that seafloor spreading away from rifts would act as a kind of "tape recorder," with the magnetic field over the ocean showing a pattern of stripes parallel to the rifts. Such a pattern had been observed in surveys off the west coast of the United States and Canada, but was not initially viewed as supporting the tape-recorder hypothesis. But in 1966 and 1967 it was realized that this and other observed patterns of seafloor magnetism could in fact be explained in terms of this hypothesis and closely matched the temporal pattern of field reversals measured in rocks on land. At the same time, the original idea of seafloor spreading was extended to explain the fracture zones in terms of a new kind of structure, called a transform fault, that would develop when new seafloor was created at a rift. These ideas were combined into plate tectonics, proposed in 1967 both by W. J. Morgan, at Princeton, and by D. P. McKenzie and R. L. Parker, working at Scripps; they created a quantitative description of the spreading and other motions at plate boundaries.

Although American scientists had produced most of the data that gave rise to seafloor spreading and plate tectonics, many of the concepts had come from scientists from other countries, especially Great Britain and Canada. But Americans were the first to exploit the data that they now saw in a new light. This included data from the oceans, which allowed reconstructions of continental motions and the evolution of plate boundaries. Another data type was records of earthquakes, collected on an extensive global array of seismometers that was installed by the United States in the 1960s as part of an effort to monitor underground

264 • POLIOMYELITIS

nuclear explosions and analyzed by American seismologists. These data gave a more precise picture of where earthquakes happened (mostly at plate boundaries), and seismological and plate-tectonic ideas were rapidly integrated into a global description of where, how often, and in what ways earthquakes occur.

Finally, American and other scientists, with funding from the National Aeronautics and Space Administration, pioneered the use of space measurements to find accurate distances between points on the earth. Starting in the 1970s, these measurements began to show the motion of the plates as they occur. From the 1980s on, the construction of the Global Positioning System (GPS) by the U.S. Department of Defense made such measurements much easier and less expensive. In 2012, there were thousands of GPS receivers around the world, measuring the motions of all of the plates.

[*See also* **Geography; Geological Surveys; Geology; Geophysics; National Aeronautics and Space Administration; National Science Foundation; Oceanography;** *and* **Scripps Institution of Oceanography.**]

BIBLIOGRAPHY

Le Grand, H. E. *Drifting Continents and Shifting Theories: The Modern Revolution in Geology and Scientific Change.* New York: Cambridge University Press, 1988. Describes the data and theories that led to the acceptance of plate tectonics.
Menard, H. W. *The Ocean of Truth: A Personal History of Global Tectonics.* Princeton, N.J.: Princeton University Press, 1986. Similar to LeGrand, Menard examines the theories that led to the acceptance of plate tectonics.
Oreskes, Naomi. *The Rejection of Continental Drift: Theory and Method in American Earth Science.* New York: Oxford University Press, 1999. Covers ideas of continental drift before 1960 in detail.
Oreskes, Naomi, ed., with Homer Le Grand. *Plate Tectonics: An Insider's History of the Modern Theory of the Earth.* Boulder, Colo.: Westview Press, 2001. Presents personal accounts by researchers, scientists, and experts who formu-
lated the theory of plate tectonics and made early use of it.
Warner, Deborah J. "From Tallahassee to Timbuktu: Cold War Efforts to Measure Intercontinental Distances." *Historical Studies in the Physical Sciences* 30 (2000): 393–415. Describes how geodetic measurements advanced to the level of being able to detect continental drift.

Duncan Agnew

POLIOMYELITIS

Until 1894 when Vermont reported 132 paralytic cases, poliomyelitis, then known as infantile paralysis, was seen as rare. Between 1905 and 1909, however, as the United States reported two thirds of the world's 8,000 cases, it became a peculiarly American epidemic. Although never a major factor in overall morbidity or mortality rates, by the 1930s paralytic polio had become one of America's most feared diseases because it tended to strike children and had no known prevention or cure. In 1909, pathologist Simon Flexner at New York's Rockefeller Institute of Medical Research, building on pathologist Karl Landsteiner's work, demonstrated that polio was caused by a virus, but a full understanding of how the virus entered and left the body or why only some but not all children in a family developed paralysis eluded investigators for many decades.

In 1921, polio left 39-year-old Franklin Delano Roosevelt partially paralyzed. Although Roosevelt hid the extent of his disability, he turned Warm Springs, Georgia, into a polio rehabilitation center and inspired the founding of two philanthropies: the President's Birthday Ball Commission in 1933 and the National Foundation for Infantile Paralysis in 1937. The National Foundation, directed by Roosevelt's law partner Basil O'Connor, became America's largest, most successful disease philanthropy. By 1945 its March of Dimes campaign had raised more than $20 million. Organized through local chapters directed by a national office in New York City, the National Foundation paid for medical and hospital care of polio patients, as well as orthopedic apparatus such as braces and crutches. It used a portion of its funds to pay for scientific research along with specialized training for doctors, nurses, and physical therapists.

Until the late 1940s American scientists, despite significant funding from the National Foundation, made only limited contributions to the understanding of polio's virology, epidemiology, and physiology. The National Foundation's most dramatic recipient was Australian nurse Elizabeth Kenny (known as Sister Kenny) who, with the support of physicians at the University of Minnesota, gained National Foundation funding in the early 1940s; this enabled her to offer courses on her distinctive methods to medical professionals. The Kenny method of treating polio spread rapidly around the United States and transformed polio care from a system of immobilization to one of careful, active physical therapy. Dissatisfied that she was acclaimed as a clinician but not also as a scientific innovator, Kenny disassociated herself from the National Foundation and set up her own Kenny Foundation, a small philanthropy that paid for patient care and for the training of Kenny technicians.

Vaccine Creation. O'Connor and his medical advisors hoped that a virological breakthrough would lead to a safe polio vaccine or antipolio drug, which two major Foundation-funded discoveries did. In 1948 tissue-culture experiments by John Enders, Frederick Robbins, and Thomas Weller at the Boston Children's Hospital (which won them a Nobel Prize in 1954) demonstrated that the polio virus could be grown in nonneurological tissue; and in 1952 virologists David Bodian and Dorothy Horstmann identified a previously unrecognized "viremia," which suggested that the virus traveled through the blood stream. These insights gave University of Pittsburgh virologist Jonas Salk (1914–1995) the means to develop the first safe and effective polio vaccine.

In 1954 the National Foundation organized the world's largest clinical trial, in which 1.8 million U.S. schoolchildren were injected with Salk's killed-virus vaccine or a placebo. With the approval of the U.S. Public Health Service, the Salk vaccine was then administered widely, bringing a dramatic decline in America's polio cases. In the late 1950s, virologist Albert Sabin (1906–1993) at the University of Cincinnati developed an attenuated live-virus vaccine that he tested in the Soviet Union. Between 1961 and 1998 Sabin's oral vaccine, which was riskier but more effective than Salk's vaccine, remained the officially recommended U.S. polio vaccine. Responding to a larger global effort to eliminate polio, the U.S. Public Health Service then began to reintroduce the Salk vaccine.

The vaccine victory over polio, a story well crafted by the National Foundation's publicity department, erased almost all previous versions of polio's history, especially around therapy. The National Foundation organized a special ceremony at Warm Springs to honor 17 polio heroes in a new Polio Hall of Fame in 1958, selecting mostly twentieth-century scientists whose Foundation-funded work had led to the polio vaccine, along with Roosevelt, O'Connor, and three nineteenth-century physicians. There were no modern orthopedists or physical medicine experts, much less any physical therapists or nurses. The polio vaccines, indeed, became the epitome of American control over disease, a high-tech solution to a messy, frightening plague now gone forever. As epidemic polio disappeared and the term "infantile paralysis" lost its meaning, the National Foundation renamed itself the March of Dimes and expanded its mission beyond polio, focusing on "crippling" diseases such as arthritis before finally settling on birth defects.

Polio Disability and Rights. By the late 1950s polio had become mostly a chronic disease, the source of disability for survivors who tended to see themselves as individuals who just had to "work harder," as their physicians and physical therapists had told them. A few survivors in wheelchairs and iron lungs were part of a small polio community, knitted together by newsletters such as the *Toomeyville Gazette*. In the 1960s and 1970s, however, some courageous and frustrated survivors began to articulate a new kind of disability rights. In 1962 Edward Verne Roberts (1939–1995)—who required an iron lung or a ventilator to help him breathe—successfully sued the University of California at Berkeley for admission, becoming the first seriously disabled student to attend the university. A founder of the Rolling Quads, Roberts led the emerging Independent Living Movement. Judith Heumann (1947–) fought for the right to attend public school and then for the right to teach, becoming the first person in a wheelchair to teach public school in New York City. In 1970 she established Disabled in Action, which argued that civil rights legislation should protect people with disabilities. She also organized sit-ins at U.S. Department of Health, Education, and Welfare offices (HEW), which led to HEW Secretary Joseph Califano signing the Rehabilitation Act's Section 504 regulations, the first federal civil rights law guaranteeing equal opportunity for people with disabilities. Justin Dart Jr. (1930–2002), a business entrepreneur, expanded his civil rights activism to disability rights. From 1980 to 1985 he was a member and then chair of the Texas Governor's Committee for Persons with Disabilities. President Ronald Reagan appointed him as vice chair of the National Council on Disability and then as head of the Rehabilitation Services Administration, a $3 billion federal agency. In 1988 Dart became co-chair of the Congressional Task Force on the Rights and Empowerment of Americans with Disabilities and lobbied for the Americans with Disabilities Act. President George H. W. Bush signed the Act into law in 1990 along with related legislation, the Individuals with Disabilities Education Act, which required that all disabled children be provided with appropriate public education to prepare them for further education, employment, and independent living. Working with other activists to fight congressional attempts to weaken these acts, Dart later founded the group Justice for All. He received the Presidential Medal of Freedom in 1998 (Shapiro, 1993; Barnartt and Scotch, 2001).

After decades as a symbol of America's victory over infectious disease, polio won renewed scientific and public interest in the 1980s with the identification of the post-polio syndrome. Frustrated at the growing weakness in muscles they had "normalized" through hard work—as well as joint pain, sensitivity to cold, and extreme fatigue—

polio survivors sought medical advice and were shocked to find how little physicians knew about polio or its aftereffects. Survivors created a new specialty with a new set of experts, most prominently polio survivor and rehabilitation specialist Lauro Halstead, who organized the first international post-polio syndrome conference in 1984 at Warm Springs. The lessons taught by physical therapists and other medical professionals during polio's epidemic years, post-polio syndrome activists now argued, had been counterproductive. In a devastating new study of muscle physiology it became clear that extensive physical therapy did not result in stable physical achievements. Medical research now suggested that survivors may have originally recovered muscle function when surviving nerve cells developed extra branches (axonal sprouts) that had reattached themselves to orphaned muscle fibers, but under heavy demand these branches began to age more quickly.

Post-polio syndrome survivors joined other disabled activists to fight for universal design and for the least restrictive environment for schools and workplaces. Using provocative terms like "crip" and "quad," activists attacked discrimination and paternalism through magazines like *Disability Rag* (f. 1980), renamed in 1997 the *Ragged Edge* (http://www.raggededgemagazine.com). Founded in the 1980s, the Society for Disability Studies and its journal, *Disability Studies Quarterly*, helped to make disability studies a respectable new academic field. A profusion of polio survivors' memoirs as well as post-polio syndrome newsletters and websites offered new ways of thinking about the family, education, medical care, welfare services, the "medical model" of disability, authoritarian and paternalistic physicians, and previously ignored voices and needs of people with disabilities. In a significant victory, polio survivors joined other activists to pressure National Park Service officials to agree to add a statue of Franklin Roosevelt seated in his wheelchair to the Roosevelt memorial on the Washington Mall, a statue that opened in 2001. Although Roosevelt had hidden his disability, activists argued, he could now be reclaimed as an inspiring disabled hero.

[*See also* Biological Sciences; Disease; Hospitals; Medicine; Nobel Prize in Biomedical Research; Nursing; Pediatrics; Physiology; Public Health; Public Health Service, U.S.; Rockefeller Institute, The; *and* Salk, Jonas.]

BIBLIOGRAPHY

Barnartt, Sharon N., and Richard K. Scotch. *Disability Protests: Contentious Politics, 1970–1999.* Washington, D.C.: Gallaudet University Press, 2001. A history of the recent disability rights movement in the United States.

Black, Kathryn. *In the Shadow of Polio: A Personal and Social History.* Reading, Mass.: Addison–Wesley, 1996. The author combines the history of the disease and medical institutions with personal reflections about her mother's experience with polio.

Colgrove, James. *State of Immunity: The Politics of Vaccination in Twentieth-Century America.* Berkeley: University of California Press, 2006. Analyzes the history of vaccination in the twentieth century, focusing especially on how it became accepted as a public-health technique.

Finger, Anne. *Elegy for a Disease: A Personal and Cultural History of Polio.* New York: St. Martin's Press, 2006. A memoir interweaving the social and cultural history of polio with the author's personal experiences with the disease.

Fleischer, Doris Zames, and Frieda Zames. *The Disability Rights Movement: From Charity to Confrontation.* 2d ed. Philadelphia: Temple University Press, 2011. A history of the disability rights movement in the United States based partly on interviews with activists.

Gallagher, Hugh Gregory. *FDR's Splendid Deception: The Moving Story of Roosevelt's Massive Disability—And the Intense Efforts to Conceal It from the Public.* Arlington, Va.: Vandamere Press, 1994 [1985]. A history of President Roosevelt's successful efforts to hide the severe paralysis of his legs and the wider cultural acceptance of this deception.

Gould, Tony. *A Summer Plague: Polio and Its Survivors.* New Haven, Conn.: Yale University Press, 1995. A history of the disease in the twentieth century that includes the personal histories of people who contracted polio during the 1940s and 1950s in the United States and Great Britain.

Longmore, Paul K., and Lauri Umansky, eds. *The New Disability History: American Perspectives.* New York: New York University Press, 2001. Edited collection emphasizing themes of "autonomy and agency" in the history of disability.

Oshinsky, David M. *Polio: An American Story.* New York: Oxford University Press, 2005. History of the polio epidemic of the mid-twentieth century, focusing especially on medical efforts to discover a cure and the social impact of the disease on Americans.

Paul, John R. *A History of Poliomyelitis.* New Haven, Conn.: Yale University Press, 1971. A medical history of polio that includes an analysis of the research undertaken to find a cure and the effort to prevent occurrences of the disease.

Rogers, Naomi. *Dirt and Disease: Polio before FDR.* New Brunswick, N.J.: Rutgers University Press, 1992. A history of the 1916 polio epidemic in the northeastern United States, and the public and public health responses to the outbreak.

Shapiro, Joseph. *No Pity: People with Disabilities Forging a New Civil Rights Movement.* New York: Times Books/Random House, 1993. A history of the disability rights movement and its relations to the civil rights movement.

Whatever Happened to Polio? Staff, National Museum of American History, Behring Center. http://amhistory.si.edu/polio/ (accessed 25 January 2013).

Wilson, Daniel J. *Living with Polio: The Epidemic and Its Survivors.* Chicago: University of Chicago Press, 2005. An analysis of the experiences of polio survivors since the 1940s with a nuanced attention to disability, culture, and sexuality.

Naomi Rogers

POPULAR SCIENCE MAGAZINE

See Popularization of Science.

POPULARIZATION OF SCIENCE

The popularization of science—that is, the translation of scientific knowledge so that it might be understood and used by nonspecialists—has fit comfortably within the political and social framework of the United States. Democracy, capitalism, and the nation's cultural and legal defense of free expression have resulted in few inhibitions imposed on public communication of scientific ideas and, often to the dismay of scientists, have encouraged a proliferation of interpretive voices through emergent new communications media. The development of mass-circulation newspapers and magazines, motion pictures, radio, and television not only expanded commercial markets for popular science, but also increased opportunities for creative incorporation, appropriation, and misrepresentation of science-related images and ideas. The resulting coexistence of intentional and unintentional communication of science, of educational and sensational science-related content, contributed to many scientists' discomfort with all popularization.

Each era and each communications technology has been distinguished by distinctive types of popularizers, purposes, and levels of acceptable complexity. Early in the history of the United States, descriptions of the natural world and scientific experiments were integrated within general cultural discourse. During the nineteenth century, prominent scientists delivered carefully constructed, pedagogical public lectures and some wrote for magazines like *Popular Science Monthly*. A century later, professional communicators, not scientists, primarily controlled the major popularization efforts. Sparsely narrated but visually dynamic television series like *NOVA*, created by documentary filmmakers, tapped scientists for advice but aimed to entertain as well as inform. For each genre, the level of acceptance by and cooperation from scientists and their professional associations varied in relation to perceptions of sensationalism and who controlled the final content. Throughout the twentieth century, scientists themselves have thus tended to favor popularization via print (writing books or magazine articles) and to leave the production of films, radio, and television to others.

Popularized science has also existed in a delicate relationship to scientists' professional communications, especially the periodicals and peer-review system. Popularizers, whether scientists or not, exploit the permeable intellectual boundaries between scientific culture and mass communication whenever content created in one forum is refashioned and incorporated within another. Economic forces influence significantly the flow of this knowledge. During the early twentieth century, the same firms that produced textbooks and laboratory manuals would publish popular science books and market technical materials to amateurs. Because their disciplinary-based systems validated authenticity, established credit and priority, and defined publication standards, scientists often assumed that they had the right to control the knowledge they produced, a circumstance that exacerbated conflicts with those who acknowledged no such barriers to the adaption and translation of ideas.

For popularization through print and broadcast news, economic forces have also influenced the type and amount of science discussed. The establishment of commercial and nonprofit organizations dedicated to disseminating scientific information offered employment to science writers and reinforced the professionalization of science journalism during the first decades of the twentieth century. Competition in the news business spurred markets for "timely" news, which conflicted with researchers' desire to reinforce credit by publishing first in peer-reviewed journals. During the 1940s, scientific information deemed important to national security or commercial interests began to be withheld, censored, or delayed from dissemination in ways that directly influenced popular science content. And by the end of the twentieth century, expansion of cable television and the development of the Internet contributed to fragmentation of potential audiences for popular science and facilitated a rise in politically or commercially motivated popularization.

Pre-1900 Popularization of Science in America. During the eighteenth and early nineteenth centuries, American popular science reflected national interest in economic progress, exploration, and appreciation for natural wonders. General magazines and newspapers aimed to inform readers about current ideas and events, rather than engage in intentional campaigns to diffuse scientific knowledge. Botanists and geologists wrote about the North American continent, enthusiastic amateur experimentalists and inventors described their latest work, and professional writers explained new agricultural techniques and medical treatments. Publications gave modest attention to astronomical phenomena, fossils, and newly discovered flora and fauna, but these serious articles would appear alongside dubious descriptions of "sea-serpents" or "mermaids."

Burnham (1987) argues that the practice of deliberate, intentional popularization emerged during the nineteenth century and that the term "popularize" began to be used with frequency only after the 1840s. Such diffusion was initially practiced by scientists who identified their efforts with acculturation of the masses and who saw themselves as engaged in moral missions to evangelize about science.

Natural history museums. America's first science museums drew inspiration from wealthy amateur naturalists who had assembled extensive private collections. The focus of these nascent scientific and cultural institutions soon veered away from elite agendas. Artist and inventor Charles Willson Peale, who established the first public natural history museum in the United States in 1786, envisioned his Philadelphia institution as an instrument for democratic education rather than a "cabinet of curiosities." By displaying biological, botanical, and mineral collections within the same galleries (over 90 species of animals were represented in the mammal room, and one wall of cases contained over four thousand species of insects) and by superimposing a template of moral lessons on the presentations, Peale prefigured twentieth-century approaches to popular science, from their inclusiveness to their attentiveness to social and ethical issues. When Peale exhibited a mastodon fossil uncovered in 1809, the missing bones were carved in wood and the head fabricated in *papier mâché*, much as television broadcasts would later "recreate" contemporary and prehistoric nature through drama and computer-assisted animation.

The Smithsonian Institution in Washington, D.C., founded in 1846, exemplified how the context for popular science was evolving. The Smith-

sonian's initial endeavors focused on creation of knowledge. In 1858, when the institution accepted custody of the U.S. Patent Office's "National Cabinet of Curiosities," the Smithsonian's first building (the "Castle") was transformed into a venue for diffusing science, with natural history exhibits installed on the first floor. The building became a center for cultural life in the city, including public lectures by scientists. At the American Museum of Natural History in New York (established 1869), the Columbian Museum of Chicago (established 1893, later renamed the Field Museum), and the Smithsonian's U.S. National Museum (established 1909, later renamed the National Museum of Natural History), scientists and curators encapsulated the current state of knowledge within dioramas or interpretive cases of stuffed animals and paleontological specimens.

These museums, although devoting public areas to popularization, were also places for research, as were most zoos, aquaria, and arboreta established during the nineteenth century. Chicago's Lincoln Park Zoo (established 1868) and the Missouri Botanical Garden in St. Louis (established 1859), for example, had staff scientists, governing boards dominated by scientists, and scientists at the helm. Such close connections meant that displays and labels diffused knowledge in terms acceptable to scientists.

At the same time, private entrepreneurs such as P. T. Barnum were engaging in exuberant popularization within smaller museums and traveling side shows. As with late twentieth-century television, accurate and inaccurate messages about natural history coexisted in these exhibitions. Their visualizations of "science" combined the real with the fantastic, the credible with the hoax. Because visitors to the Smithsonian, for example, may well have also sampled Barnum's entertainments, historians attempting to understand nineteenth-century popular science must take into account the dynamics of such contemporaneous experiences. Each museum visitor drew on images and ideas from multiple sources, often with different or conflicting economic and social goals.

Public lectures. During the nineteenth century, public lecture halls afforded scientists more familiar contexts in which to explain their work. Many lecture programs, like popular books and magazines of the day, at first featured European science. English physicist John Tyndall, for example, used lanternslides and live demonstrations to explain optics and magnetism to crowded halls in New York and Boston. The growth of the lyceum movement soon offered opportunities for dynamic American scientists like botanist Asa Gray and chemist Benjamin Silliman. When these scientists' lectures were reprinted later within popular magazines and newspapers, the publicity helped to reinforce new pride in the vitality of American science.

Magazines. After the Civil War, the market for specialized, authenticated popular science expanded and changed once more. In periodicals, as in mass-circulation newspapers, the practice of mixing dedicated (intentional) with incorporated (inadvertent) popular science continued, but popularization became linked more closely to profit motives and utility than to education. Science articles appeared within commercial literary magazines like *Harper's*, and the general-content weeklies like *Saturday Evening Post* carried scientists' forecasts of how research would benefit public health, agriculture, and industry. Commercial publishing firms established specialized magazines, such as *Scientific American*, *Popular Science Monthly*, and *Science*.

Scientific American, which became the most influential science magazine of the mid-twentieth century, was founded in 1845 by Yankee inventor Rufus M. Porter and initially concentrated on the patent business. In its first issues, lists of new patents ran alongside review articles on mechanics and sentimental poems blessing "the honest laborer,/The hardy son of toil." Two years later, the magazine was acquired by Munn and Company, which published it for the next one hundred years, quickly tripling circulation and expanding the content.

From its first issue in 1872, *Popular Science Monthly* promoted the cause of popularizing science and the importance of expertise. Established by science popularizer Edward Livingston Youmans and D. Appleton and Company as an outlet

for material written by English philosopher and sociologist Herbert Spencer, the magazine soon traded on its connections to the emerging American scientific community to serve as forum and cheerleader. Articles documented scientific progress and advocated educational and social reform. Youmans edited *Popular Science Monthly* for 15 years (co-editing from 1877 until 1887 with his brother William Jay Youmans, who then ran the publication until 1900). E. L. Youmans was described as having a missionary, almost evangelistic, spirit, especially on topics like evolution, and he regarded civic education on science as essential to national success. In 1900, Appleton sold the publication to psychologist James McKeen Cattell, who edited it until 1915, while also heading the third influential science publication founded during the late nineteenth century.

The inaugural issue of *Science* magazine in July 1880 signaled a new era for American scientists. A weekly journal, published by a commercial firm, backed financially by inventors Thomas A. Edison and Alexander Graham Bell and intended to document "scientific progress," *Science* was the first publication in the United States edited specifically for scientists from all disciplines. It was also a "boundary publication," in that well-educated nonscientists could also find many of the articles accessible. Even after *Science* became the official journal of the American Association for the Advancement of Science (AAAS) in 1900, the publication remained an essential link between professional scientists and their supporters within the business and political communities. In 1895, ownership was transferred to James McKeen Cattell, who controlled the publication for almost 50 years.

In 1915, *Popular Science Monthly* had been sold to popularizers trained in journalism or publishing rather than science. Waldemar Kaempffert, who had worked for *Scientific American* and just qualified as a patent attorney, edited *Popular Science Monthly* from 1915 to 1920. Meanwhile, Cattell, convinced that scientists are amateurs in every discipline but their own, created another magazine, *Scientific Monthly*, aimed not at the masses but at explaining science to scientists and other well-educated readers.

Another publication whose influence grew exponentially from the nineteenth throughout the twentieth century and provided consistently positive publicity for its nonprofit owner was *National Geographic Magazine* (1888). With accounts of expeditions, wildlife, and exotic places and illustrated with steadily improving photographic reproductions, *National Geographic* tapped American fascination with the rest of the world and played an important role in the popularization of archaeology and anthropology.

Commercial publishers capitalized on these expanding audiences for popular science by establishing book series, subscription sets, and encyclopedias. By 1900, for example, the successful Appleton "International Scientific Series" included one hundred volumes and, in response, a rival firm founded an "American Science Series" emphasizing U.S. scientists.

Goal-oriented Popularization and New Partnerships. By 1900, magazines and newspapers were paying more attention to medical research and public health, linking it to social progress, just as other parts of science were being linked to economic growth. An expanding consumer marketplace for new technologies, a cadre of prominent scientists willing to use their fame in support of all science, and concern among the political and social elite about the need for improved technical education all combined in the early twentieth century to create a climate favorable to the establishment of organizations devoted to popularization through the mass media.

Electrification of the home and widespread adoption of typewriters, treadmill sewing machines, automobiles, electric irons, Victrolas, and radios opened new markets for publication of handbooks and how-to texts as well as articles within magazines and newspapers that explained the scientific principles underpinning technological innovation. Owners of the new devices needed to know how to assemble, operate, and fix their purchases. Periodicals like *Popular Mechanics*, founded in 1902, met this demand by explaining the "mechanics" behind consumer inventions. After 1915, publications like *Popular Science Monthly* also focused more

on the science assumed to interest consumers and hobbyists.

Scientific celebrities and public relations. The names and accomplishments of such men as Edison, horticulturist Luther Burbank, and mathematician Charles Proteus Steinmetz were becoming familiar to millions of Americans. In addition to being skilled communicators, these men were unafraid of interacting with journalists. Their stories of achievement and accomplishment, of rising from humble or immigrant beginnings, fit the emerging national narrative and their fame helped to attract favorable attention to all of science. Other prominent scientists, most notably physicist Robert Andrews Millikan and astronomer George Ellery Hale, engaged in deliberate publicity seeking, with the goal of securing political support for government funding of basic research.

Although Progressive-Era political rhetoric was linking research with economic progress and social improvement, not every scientific advance brought positive media attention. The creation and use of chemical weapons during World War I had resulted in unflattering and occasionally negative comments about the discipline of chemistry within popular magazines and newspapers. In response, the American Chemical Society joined with corporations and private foundations in a public-relations campaign aimed at "popularizing" chemistry. This coalition eventually subsidized the production of books that extolled "The Progress—The Romance—The Necessity of Chemistry!" Such publications could not educate an entire nation, however. Bolder endeavors would be necessary.

Science Service. In collaboration with zoologist William E. Ritter, the wealthy newspaper publisher E. W. Scripps decided to found and endow an organization aimed at influencing the volume and quality of popular science. The two friends espoused a democratic vision of popularization. Communication should serve "the masses as well as the classes," be guided by audience preferences, and be not merely publicity for scientists. Scripps was convinced that, although the public was interested in science, most scientists had little interest in communicating about their work to the public. The publisher's generosity allowed the resulting organization, Science Service, to be self-sufficient, engage in entrepreneurial popularization, and experiment with different communications forms, from cartoons to poetry contests. Weekly "Star Maps" and "Why the Weather" columns about meteorology were syndicated at modest prices to newspapers around the country, and the circulation and reputation of the weekly *Science News-Letter* (later named *Science News*) grew rapidly. Other material, such as scripts that could be read on local radio stations, were offered for free, with the goal of incubating markets for scientific content.

Although trained in chemistry, the organization's first director, Edwin Emery Slosson, had abandoned an academic career in 1903 to become literary editor of *The Independent*. By 1921, when Science Service began operations, Slosson had a national reputation as a science popularizer (his *Easy Lessons on Einstein* was already in a fourth edition). Slosson's colorful rhetoric and dramatic flair had also brought him fame as a public speaker, balancing deep interest in scientific theory with a romantic vision of science. In January 1924, he raised over $2,500 for the organization in 16 lectures throughout the midwestern United States. Slosson (1927) argued that communicators should exhibit sympathy and sensitivity to their audiences' experiences and educational backgrounds, and he dared fellow scientists to "descend from the platform to the street."

Science Service's organizational structure represented a model seen in many subsequent popularization projects, from book series to television, where an advisory board lent authority and imprimatur to the popular content. Science Service's trustees during the 1920s and 1930s included the presidents of the National Academy of Sciences and the American Association for the Advancement of Science and the head of the Smithsonian Institution, among other prominent scientists.

Brokering Popular Science. The idea of underwriting a science news service proved a success. Science Service capitalized on the American visits of celebrities like physicists Albert Einstein and Marie Curie and on events like the 1925 John T. Scopes anti-evolution trial to offer special coverage and attract new readers.

Science Service also brokered (and thereby helped to validate) scientists' manuscripts to commercial book and magazine publishers. The publishing market for science grew steadily during the 1920s. The Scientific Book Club was established in 1921. In 1923, P. F. Collier & Son began selling a 16-volume *Popular Science Library* ("A Complete Education in a Single Set"), with a 10-year "loose-leaf revision service" guaranteeing to keep subscribers abreast of future discoveries. Such projects coexisted with expanding shelves of science fictionalizations—stories about rockets and space adventures, *Tom Swift* novels, and Hugo Gernsback's *Amazing Stories* (a science fiction magazine established in 1926). Americans were craving fantastic versions of future science and predictions of "the world to come," just as they were marveling at equally amazing contemporary achievements.

The Professionalization of Science Journalism.
By the 1930s, popular science books and magazine articles were being written more by professional writers than scientists. Tobey (1971) attributes scientists' declining participation in popularization to the lack of professional credit, and although there is evidence to support that explanation, the scientists were also by then replaceable by skilled alternatives, by professional writers who understood technical material and were attuned to what magazines, newspapers, book publishers, and, eventually, radio and television producers required. Writer Paul de Kruif, for example, who helped novelist Sinclair Lewis research his 1925 novel *Arrowsmith*, then published his own nonfiction best-seller *Microbe Hunters* the following year.

When E. E. Slosson died in October 1929, he was not replaced immediately as director of Science Service, and the ensuing fight over his successor, which dragged on for years, reflected continuing friction over the terms of popularization. To scientists, the ideal popularizer was another scientist.

To those who endorsed a vision of popularization as free expression in a free society, with the goal of informing citizens rather than promoting scientists, what mattered most were professionalism, accuracy, and the production of good-quality products attractive to mass audiences. When Slosson's longtime deputy, civil engineer and journalist Watson Davis, was finally appointed director in 1933, he epitomized the new type of popularizer—an enthusiastic supporter of science who regarded all forms and genres of communication as suitable for popular science. Davis believed in the power of the marketplace. Popularization was an art, requiring creativity, and if the science was presented well, then audiences would consume it.

Davis navigated deftly between the scientific and journalism/publishing communities, and he experimented with modes of science communication, from photography and radio to microfilm, both popular and professional. He understood scientists' discomfort with popularization, distrust of sensationalism, and disdain for thoughtless simplification. Davis embraced capitalism and cooperated with corporate, advertising, and public relations executives at companies like DuPont and General Electric to bring news of industrial and engineering advances to the public.

Professionalization. The founding of the National Association of Science Writers (NASW) in 1934, with Davis as a charter member, signaled the professionalism of science journalism. Major U.S. newspapers were assigning reporters to cover science, medicine, and technology exclusively. NASW founders included Associated Press reporter Howard W. Blakeslee, Scripps–Howard News Service editor David Dietz, Hearst science editor Gobind Behari Lal, *New York Times* reporter William L. Laurence, *New York Herald–Tribune* science editor John J. O'Neill, and Science Service medical editor Jane Stafford. NASW members eventually included most major science reporters in the country, including Waldemar Kaempffert, who had turned from magazine to newspaper journalism (serving as *New York Times* science editor from 1927 to 1928 and, after a brief hiatus to run a science museum, also from 1931 to 1956).

Broadcasting Science: Radio. One source for increased tension between scientists and journalists had less to do with print journalism than with the emergence of electronic mass media dominated by entertainment. Even the most serious and accurate radio talk could be tainted, in scientists' minds, by the brash commercials or screwball comedians that often preceded or followed on traditional radio shows of the time. Scientists' initial use of radio, in fact, differed little from nineteenth-century public lectures. The first regularly produced radio science series in the United States, a 1923 innovation of Smithsonian Institution biologist Austin Hobart Clark, began as a series of "talks" during which scientists read narrative descriptions of their work. Science Service and AAAS created similar radio talk series during the 1920s.

When more dynamic, entertaining content began to dominate the radio schedule and airtime became a more valuable commodity, the scientists' talks were canceled. To compete, science programs had to either accommodate to radio's entertainment goals or allow commercial sponsorship. Most 1930s series developed by nonprofit organizations compromised on the former strategy, although they relinquished considerable control over the content. Watson Davis worked directly with CBS to develop Science Service's *Adventures in Science*, broadcast weekly from 1938 to 1957 in airtime provided by the commercial network. Davis became a proficient interviewer and secured top scientists for his program. The Smithsonian Institution's *The World Is Yours* (1936–1942), part of an experimental Works Progress Administration radio project with the U.S. Office of Education and NBC, included segments on research with dramatized content and continuing fictional characters. From 1936 to 1940, AAAS worked with NBC on *Science in the News*, *Science Everywhere*, and *Science on the March*, series that attempted to convey the excitement and relevance of scientific research.

Other projects focused more on public education. NBC's successful *National Farm and Home Hour* integrated technical advice about pest control and soil enhancement with informational segments on home canning. Government agencies, dairy councils, pharmaceutical companies, and insurance firms all produced public-health broadcasts during the 1930s. The American Medical Association *Your Health* series (1935–1940), one of many underwritten by the association, combined dramatizations with expert discussions. Corporations even sponsored radio talks by scientists during the intermissions of symphony concerts.

Conflicting Agendas. By the late 1930s, Americans could select from multiple sources of scientific information and science fictionalizations, from museum exhibitions and books to radio dramas and Hollywood movies. Popular magazines continued to be important means for conveying science. The American Museum of Natural History, which had already tried radio outreach (and would later cooperate with television ventures), established *The Sky* in 1936 to offer regular "bulletins" from its Hayden Planetarium. In 1939, the museum sold the publication to a commercial publisher that transformed it eventually into *Sky and Telescope*.

Concurrent with these efforts at what sociologist W. F. Ogburn characterized at the time as *didactic popularization*, which sought to explain scientific discoveries and fundamental knowledge, were the scientific community's own *evangelistic popularization* efforts, directed at extolling the value of science as a way of life and knowing. There was little consensus among scientists over the most appropriate techniques to achieve either goal. Bart J. Bok, in a 1939 report to fellow astronomers, expressed representative concern that "dramatizations" of science within museum displays or radio broadcasts cheapened science and eroded its dignity. Popularization should relate to educational goals, such as through coordination with school curriculum. Sanctioned and vetted popularization was also perceived as a potential defense against "pseudoscience," superficiality, and deliberate distortion within commercial advertisement and political propaganda. For intellectuals who regarded the majority of all mass media content as vacuous and vulgar, any cooperation with mass culture producers represented an unacceptable option. Scientists must control their public communications or else risk misinterpretation and misuse of their knowledge.

To other social critics, such criticisms perpetuated a self-defeating elitism. Scripps and Ritter had openly challenged the status quo by questioning scientists' presumptions about popularization; in their view, the needs and interests of society, not science, should prevail when journalists choose topics and presentation approaches. From the late 1930s on, responding in part to audience preferences and propelled by those scientists who regarded public communication as a matter of civic responsibility, popular science began to be more attuned to ethics, politics, and social context, although such discussion was increasingly incorporated within entertainment and Hollywood-created illusion.

Visualizing Science: Motion Pictures. Motion pictures afforded popularizers new ways to visualize science in the laboratory and to show the scientists being discussed in print. Although film was used effectively for educational purposes, its primary contribution to science popularization came through blending images and information in entertainment-based documentaries and fictional movies.

Nineteenth-century scientists such as biologist Eadweard Muybridge first exploited motion picture technology to record and gather data for professional use. By the early twentieth century, Edison and others had recognized film's potential for public education. Edison's melodramatic "health propaganda" films for the Tuberculosis Association in the 1910s were shown in schools, factories, and commercial movie houses. Films began to be used regularly for health, engineering, and other practical public education, as well as classroom instruction.

Natural history motion pictures soon broke the boundaries between films shot for professional reasons and those created to entertain. Robert Flaherty's *Nanook of the North* (1922) attracted large audiences, and natural history museums helped to underwrite and promote productions like Martin and Osa Johnson's *Trailing African Wild Animals* (1923), one of the first commercially successful feature-length animal pictures. Their practice of editing expedition films and later "recreating" scenes or situations contributed to the acceptability of merging of fact and dramatization within popular science.

The same audiences who enjoyed those documentaries were also likely to be watching Hollywood visions of science that bore little resemblance to reality. Beginning with the Edison Company's *Frankenstein* in 1910, movie versions of Mary Shelley's novel perpetuated melodramatic images of a villainous scientist, with similar characterizations continuing uninterrupted into the twenty-first century. Whether using scientific expertise for self-experimentation, as in adaptations of Robert Louis Stevenson's *Dr. Jekyll and Mr. Hyde*, or being manipulated by criminals in *Superman* serials, fictional scientists in the movies could be unpleasant characters, only sporadically counterpoised by the heroic researchers portrayed in *Arrowsmith* (1931), *The Story of Louis Pasteur* (1936), or *Madame Curie* (1943) or by awed attention to Albert Einstein in *The March of Time* newsreels. In Flash Gordon serials and movies such as *The Things to Come* (1936), science was used to pave a route to the future, advancing positive, if exaggerated, images of scientists.

As with other forms of visual culture, the movies simply adapted "science" to fit plot necessities, while conveying powerful messages about scientists' motivations, the usefulness of basic research, and the adaptability of knowledge as a force for good or evil. Hansen's (2004) conclusions about comic books could be applied with equal validity to popular movies, in that the latter included potent statements about scientific evidence, values, and experimentation even when the plots centered on unrelated aspects of American life and culture.

Popular Science and Politics. Popular science communications had long been used for political goals. Eugenicists wrapped their social agendas with technical explanations of genetics and biology. Talking about evolution on the radio or through a museum exhibition could attract criticism from those who rejected non-Biblical explanations for the creation of the world. Beginning in the late 1930s, however, science popularizers confronted other difficult challenges related to the development and politics of atomic power. When wartime fears intensified in 1938 and 1939, many scientists and publishers had engaged in voluntary self-censorship, exercising discretion in both their professional and their popular discussion of atomic physics. Once war began, all items published in the United States, from textbooks to comic books, came under the control of the U.S. Office of Censorship. Government officials nevertheless strived to keep scientific and technical information flowing to military personnel, factory workers, and other citizens, even enlisting department stores in the effort; R. H. Macy's in New York carried between two thousand and three thousand technical books during 1942, five times the prewar amount (Thompson, 1942).

After the war, scientists, government officials, and the media did not necessarily agree on which, when, or if information on atomic energy should be shared with the public. Decision-making grew more ambiguous and the resulting censorship more contentious. Manhattan Project administrators had so valued the power of publicity that they had arranged for *New York Times* reporter William L. Laurence to be present at the July 1945 Trinity test at Alamogordo, New Mexico, and to accompany, and write about, the mission to bomb Nagasaki, Japan. In 1946, Laurence and other journalists were invited to observe U.S. atomic-bomb tests in the Pacific, part of a government effort to shape public opinion through popularization. Nevertheless, as the Cold War deepened, popularizers found themselves caught between pressure from government censors and their responsibility to their audiences. When General Leslie Groves refused to allow *Popular Science Monthly* to use photos of nonsecret devices within a 1946 article on atomic medicine, for example, the magazine protested by leaving the illustration locations blank.

After purchasing *Scientific American* in 1947, editors Gerard Piel and Dennis Flanagan broadened the magazine's scope to include more articles by scientists about such social and political issues as arms control and environmental policy. In 1950, concerned about ongoing plans to build a hydrogen bomb, the U.S. Atomic Energy

Commission (AEC) directed all employees and consultants, past and present, to cease public discussion of thermonuclear reactions and then extended this directive to include unclassified as well as classified information. Physicist Hans A. Bethe had just completed an article for *Scientific American* when, after the issue had gone to press, the editors received a telegram from the AEC requesting deletion of the article's technical sections, although that text contained no classified material. Eventually, the government requested that all copies of the original article be destroyed and a security officer visited the printing plant and supervised destruction of the type, printing plates, and three thousand copies of the April 1950 issue already printed. The episode signaled a change in the political context for popularization, far removed from the poetry that had marked *Scientific American's* first issues.

Televising and Dramatizing Science.

The use of radio dramatization had represented an important shift in popularization approaches, paving the way for how television would further transform popular science's prevailing tone and topics. Radio series like *The Human Adventure*, produced by the University of Chicago from 1939 to 1946, used science dramas to inform listeners accustomed to fast-paced comedies, mysteries, and quiz shows. Hundreds of radio documentaries about atomic energy exploited similar entertainment techniques, entwining recitation of facts with fictional reenactments or interspersing interviews with real scientists and dialog delivered by professional actors. In the spring of 1946, the Library of Congress sponsored a radio discussion among scientists, politicians, and ordinary citizens about the forthcoming Pacific atomic-bomb tests, whereas other broadcasts that year imagined the aftereffects of atomic warfare or facilitated debate over international control of the atom.

Television offered the prospect of popularization through visualization delivered directly to American living rooms. Cameras could provide the illusion of taking viewers into a laboratory to observe researchers at work. During television's first decades, a few scientists took advantage of this creative potential, but the scientific community and its professional organizations never fully exploited the opportunities. Groups like AAAS acknowledged their responsibility to increase public understanding of science through television, yet seemed deterred by the substantial costs and by their own lack of appreciation for the medium. Offended by television pitchmen who attempted to acquire scientific credibility by wearing white coats and by Hollywood's propensity to erect myths around science in an effort to accommodate it to a world of fantasy, the mainstream scientific community reached out tentatively, leaving television popularization to ambitious entrepreneurs, corporate underwriters, and, eventually, the commercial purveyors of illusion and entertainment.

The first two primetime science series in the United States had strong academic roots and their hosts exemplified the two predominant types, either charismatic scientists willing to be transformed into celebrities or nonscientist performers who played dignified surrogates and translators. Astronomer Roy Kenneth Marshall, who created *The Nature of Things* in 1948, was director of the Fels Planetarium in Philadelphia and later became a frequent celebrity guest on variety shows. Johns Hopkins University public-relations director Lynn Poole created three different science-related series, including the highly acclaimed *Johns Hopkins Science Review*, telecast from 1948 to 1954.

Many of television's early attempts at popularization were "science actualities" (programs revolving around live broadcasts). In March 1948, a Washington, D.C., station telecast views of Mars, Saturn, and the Moon projected through an observatory telescope, and the next year, that station connected a camera to a microscope to show blood circulation in a mouse. Throughout the 1950s, lunar eclipses, solar eclipses, and the atmospheric testing of atomic weapons allowed television viewers to "experience" science in real time. Programs broadcast from zoos and museums offered similar immediacy, and zookeepers would bring live animals, birds, and reptiles to local studios. Although minimal scientific information was transmitted in these demonstrations, natural history programs eventually became effective platforms for messages about endangered species and conservation.

Another persistent model for early television, one used by both Marshall and Poole, was to have a guest scientist perform a carefully rehearsed simulation of an experiment. *Science in Action*, created in 1950 by the California Academy of Sciences, encouraged viewers to believe that visiting scientists were in a real laboratory, not on a set, while the academy's curator of aquatic biology, Earl S. Herald, wore a white lab coat and engaged in affable banter. The most famous such television scientist was Donald Herbert, who for over 40 years reigned as "Mr. Wizard," guiding child actors through simple experiments designed to explain basic scientific principles. Other 1950s series, such as the American Museum of Natural History's *Adventure* program, produced with CBS, began as showcases for research but evolved into presentations of science within culture, with hosts and presenters mostly professional entertainers or public figures.

From the mid-1950s through the 1960s, Bell Telephone Company underwrote seven notable documentaries (including *Our Mr. Sun* (1956), *Hemo the Magnificent* (1957, directed by Frank Capra), and *The Thread of Life* (1962)), first shown on primetime television and then in thousands of classrooms, combining animation, humor, and professional actors in the service of science education, frequently layered with references to religion and philosophy. Dreams of using the television studio as a national classroom soon faded. *Sunrise Semester* and *Continental Classroom* enlightened hundreds of thousands of adults who signed up for college credit, but could not compete with the creativity of commercial programming. When University of Michigan pollsters asked viewers in 1958 which television programs provided their prime source of information about science, over half named either *Disneyland*, *Science Fiction Theater*, or the medical drama *Medic* and fewer than one-third mentioned educational series like *Science in Action*, the Bell Telephone specials, or *Watch Mr. Wizard*.

Television enthusiastically adapted techniques of dramatization and reenactment long exploited in nature films, combining simplistic, anthropomorphized narratives with bits of scientific information. Zoo director Marlin Perkins led the way with *Zoo Parade* (1950–1957) and *Wild Kingdom* (1962–1988), along with Walt Disney's "True-Life Adventures" feature films (for example, *The Living Desert*, 1953). French oceanographer Jacques-Yves Cousteau became another favorite with American audiences, thanks to his spectacular cinematography and passionate messages about ocean conservation. Beginning in 1964, documentaries produced by the National Geographic Society set high standards for production and reinforced the magazine's messages about the practical technologies flowing from the sciences. Those specials helped to propel photogenic scientists like primatologist Jane Goodall to celebrity status.

From television dramas about hospitals, operations, diseases, and charismatic physicians, viewers could assimilate information (both accurate and misleading) about the effectiveness and promise of medical research. From the first, in network series like *Medic*, *Dr. Kildare*, and *Ben Casey*, fictional physicians were portrayed as implementers of the latest medical knowledge. *The March of Medicine*, a documentary project of Smith, Kline & French Laboratories, produced in cooperation with the American Medical Association, vacillated between realism and sensationalism and, in 1955, was the first television production to receive the prestigious Albert Lasker Medical Journalism Award.

Early television featured a galaxy of space adventurers relying on science. From *Captain Video and His Video Rangers*, first telecast live in 1949, through Buck Rogers and Tom Corbett, the fictional heroes were armed with pseudo-scientific gadgets like portable force fields. With rare exceptions, scientists were minor characters, advising heroes and villains with equal alacrity. Scriptwriters occasionally consulted with scientists to ensure that plot devices would seem plausible.

The establishment of national space programs and the launch of *Sputnik* in 1957 gave authenticity to television's dreams of science-enabled space travel. American television then turned coverage of space missions into entertainment, interspersed with information. Viewers listened to audio transmissions from the flights of Alan B. Shepard and John Glenn but from 1968 on, live television images of Earth, beamed back from capsules on their way to the Moon, enlivened space coverage. The *Apollo 11* lunar landing, watched by hundreds of millions of people around the world, helped to promote American scientific achievement, although many scientists complained that important opportunities for public education were squandered whenever television focused more on the astronauts' personal lives than on explaining the physics behind rocket propulsion.

During the mid-1970s, television science specials and documentary series reached a plateau with such audience successes as the British import *The Ascent of Man*, first shown on the U.S. Public Broadcasting System (PBS) in 1975. Presenting contemporary science within its social, cultural, and economic context, the PBS series *NOVA*, which had premiered in 1974, paved the way for similar magazine-format series like *Nature* (1982–). Each week, viewers would be offered a new story, on topics similar to those chosen by the editors of *Scientific American*, adjusted to the tastes, preferences, and education of regular viewers. Unlike television's dramas, soap operas, and game shows, however, the science programs contained no continuing characters or regular hosts. Science began anew each week, brilliantly illustrated with increasingly more sophisticated animation and spectacular film.

The 1980 premiere of *Cosmos*, a PBS miniseries created by astronomer Carl Sagan, signaled another flurry of popularization ventures that included magazines like *Discover* and *Omni*, the creation of newspaper science pages, and the establishment of cable television ventures like the Discovery Channel (1985). Cable helped to fragment the potential audience for televised popular science by creating "niche popularization," where science was available to a steady and predictable audience base but was seen less often by occasional viewers. As traditional philanthropic or government sources of funding diminished, the producers of science documentaries and series on public television also increasingly turned to commercial firms, like aerospace and pharmaceutical

manufacturers, for underwriting, which raised questions about nonscientific influences on topic choice.

Throughout its history, American television has consistently offered a mix of *intentional* science programming, such as *NOVA*, and *incorporated* references to science and scientists, either real or fictional, within news, public affairs, and drama. The latter type of popularization, which is far more difficult to measure and analyze, may have had a far more significant role in shaping public attitudes toward science. Television transformed science into just another part of American life, neither privileged nor dismissible, neither automatically good nor necessarily benign.

Challenges to Popularization at the Millennium. Television and money posed the two greatest challenges to popularization efforts at the millennium. Influenced by television, science museums began to change during the 1990s from predominantly static, formal presentations, dominated by display cases, to "interactive" exhibitions, where museum visitors were encouraged to engage with the science being presented, either by pushing buttons or by answering questions. Peale's museum had featured revolving microscopes for the examination of small specimens, yet his visitors were imagined to be passive recipients of didactic explanations. By the end of the twentieth century, innovative museum directors like physicist Frank Oppenheimer at the Exploratorium in San Francisco and explorer Bradford Washburn at the Boston Science Museum changed the museum visit into an "experience." Visitors were expected to participate, often with the assistance of computer-driven displays. Influenced by the success of Walt Disney's theme parks, as well as European museums of science and industry, these museums removed the dusty dioramas and redefined audiences as partners in a conversation.

This recasting of popularization eschewed the older linear arrangement of knowledge. Newly built science centers, no longer confined to major urban areas or dependent upon systematic collections, sought to educate through entertainment. Moreover, their exhibits mimicked the television environment by placing science within its social context or reflecting on such politicized topics as pollution, species extinction, and climate change.

Museum funding, like that for public television, became less dependent upon philanthropic or government sources and increasingly turned to commercial underwriting. Exhibitions required millions of dollars and blockbuster themes could increase a museum's revenue stream, but such stakes also pushed museums to avoid controversial topics like evolution. Similar economic considerations reinforced a marketplace attitude to all popularization, whether in museums or on television.

Prominent scientists continued to become cultural celebrities whenever they wrote articles for popular magazines, gave interviews to journalists, or hosted television shows, achieving fame and visibility because they were articulate, photogenic, and cooperative with the media rather than necessarily the most accomplished scientists in their disciplines. Because some colleagues openly criticized such public engagement, it was often assumed that becoming "visible" could be professionally damaging, but Shermer (2002) effectively disproved that assumption.

Within film and broadcast media, stereotypical characterizations of scientists persisted through the 1990s. Sallow-faced, wild-haired, tweed-jacketed (or white-coated) males stared dreamily into the camera, preoccupied with investigating the minutiae of nature or the vastness of the universe and unconcerned with society or politics. These characters' demeanor would lead others to underestimate their importance until it was revealed that, using their great brains and exceptional intelligence, they had built atomic bombs or rockets to the Moon or had prevented a pandemic. Only as the twentieth century ended did fictional laboratories contain more women and people of color and more strong, heroic female scientists untrammeled by domestic obligations. Popular science, both fictional and factual, nevertheless continued to perpetuate an image of scientific research as a cornucopia of unlimited progress, with cures for all diseases and solutions for all problems.

Changing Theories of Popularization.
Unpacking the history of popularization of science in America requires careful attention to changing actors, audiences, and agendas. To some extent, the debate over theoretical models of popularization mimics that history, evolving from simplistic to more nuanced.

Until the 1980s, the dominant theoretical model assumed a linear diffusion of scientific information aimed at correcting a "deficit" in public knowledge: scientists communicated specialized knowledge to qualified (and, preferably, science-trained) intermediaries, who then translated it for the public. The framing of popularization as technical translation rather than as humanistic interpretation or critical assessment reinforced an elitist definition of appropriate content, chosen by experts. Sociologists then began to reframe popularization as an internalist effort geared toward preserving professional unity rather than intentional outreach to nonexperts, asserting that scientists who engaged in popularization were actually attempting to speak indirectly to their colleagues, to make links between disciplines, and to gain economic and political support from the middle class. Nelkin (1987), for example, attributed distorted press coverage of controversial issues to scientists' desire for a more favorable public image.

The application of survey analysis to measuring public understanding of science gave some credence during the 1980s and 1990s to scientists' longstanding suspicions about the mass media but the survey results became caught in political debate related to social and political regulation of science. Surveys commissioned by the U.S. National Science Foundation were used by proponents of a "deficit" model of popularization, who characterized the public as empty vessels into whom facts of science might be poured, asserted existence of an unbridgeable knowledge gap between specialists and the public, and assumed communication to be one way, with little feedback or dialog. During the 1990s, scientists such as Paul R. Gross and Norman Levitt blamed the mass media for declining science literacy, negative public attitudes, and political regulation of research and advocated tiered communications campaigns that directed limited resources toward those who were already "attentive" to science.

Hilgartner (1990) characterized the dominant deficit (or "diffusionist") model as two staged, engaging first the production of knowledge and then its diffusion to passive audiences. Such assumptions, he and others argued, had led historians of popular science to ignore such critical aspects as economics, organization, management, politics, context, and regulatory climate. Viewing popularization only from the perspective of scientists also led historians to neglect the audience's intrinsic power. Individual preferences, expressed via purchases and viewing patterns and measured in circulation, sales, and ratings data, have long guided mass media editorial and production choices and therefore shaped content. Even the more recent shift from the deficit to the "participation" model, however, has paid inadequate attention to the economic and social power of a communications industry that has historically perceived "science" to be simply one among many types of potentially marketable content, without special status or privilege. By the early twentieth century, scientists neither produced nor controlled the vast majority of science news, information, and entertainment content available in the mass media.

Secord (2004), among others, has called for more comprehensive integration of the history of "science popularization" with that of "science in popular culture," echoing other scholars' emphasis on permeability, content incorporation, and the commercialization of knowledge diffusion. Knowledge has always been continuously "in transit" within marketplaces, both intellectual and economic, a conclusion validated in how science has become transformed on electronic media, from the scientists' lectures on radio to NOVA's science-sanctioned but entertainment-dominated documentaries.

As historians like Bensaude-Vincent (2009) explain, descriptions of the popularization process are not neutral. Historical explanations must acknowledge the intricacy of the communications context and encompass all participants in the process. Some historians have thus begun to characterize citizens as "coproducers" of scientific knowledge and to reject the terms "lay public" and "layperson" as historical constructs, even if the reality of modern social and political life still results in demarcations between those presumed to be experts and those who are not and in roles for both interpreters and translators. Bensaude-Vincent (2009) calls for historians to identify "what is specific about science" and to consider whether that special aspect represents values and standards as much as conclusions or data. Recent questioning of the use of the term "popularization" and whether such use reflects an artificial division between specialists and nonspecialists, in fact, harkens back to early-twentieth-century debates, still unresolved, about the importance of accuracy and standard setting and about who should participate in the public communication process and why.

[*See also* **Agricultural Technology; American Association for the Advancement of Science; American Medical Association; American Museum of Natural History; Anthropology; Archaeology; Astronomy and Astrophysics; Atomic Energy Commission; Bell, Alexander Graham; Bethe, Hans; Botanical Gardens; Botany; Cattell, James McKeen; Chemistry; Computer Science; Computers, Mainframe, Mini, and Micro; Conservation Movement; Dinosaurs; Edison, Thomas; Einstein, Albert; Environmentalism; Eugenics; Evolution, Theory of; Geology; Gray, Asa; Hale, George Ellery; High Schools, Science Education in; Instruments of Science; Internet and World Wide Web; Journals in Science, Medicine, and Engineering; Manhattan Project; Medicine; Military, Science and Technology and the; Millikan, Robert A.; Museums of Science and Natural History; National Academy of Sciences; Nuclear Weapons; Paleontology; Peale, Charles Willson; Photography; Public Health; Radio; Research and Development (R&D); Sagan, Carl; Science; Science Fiction; Science Journalism; Silliman, Benjamin, Sr.; Smithsonian Institution; Societies and Associations, Science; Technology; Television;** *and* **Zoology.**]

BIBLIOGRAPHY

Bensaude-Vincent, Bernadette. "A Historical Perspective on Science and Its 'Others.'" *Isis* 100 (2009): 359–368. Explores changing definitions of the audiences for popularization.

Boyer, Paul S. *By the Bomb's Early Light: American Thought and Culture at the Dawn of the Atomic Age*. New York: Pantheon, 1985. The cultural impact of the creation of atomic and nuclear weapons.

Burnham, John C. *How Superstition Won and Science Lost: Popularizing Science and Health in the United States*. New Brunswick, N.J.: Rutgers University Press, 1987. Comprehensive history of the popularization of science, medicine, and social science, in all media, from the 1800s through the 1980s.

Forry, Steven Earl. *Hideous Progenies: Dramatizations of Frankenstein from Mary Shelley to the Present*. Philadelphia: University of Pennsylvania Press, 1990. Includes theater, film, television, and popular-culture adaptations of Shelley's character.

Fyfe, Aileen, and Bernard Lightman, eds. *Science in the Marketplace: Nineteenth-Century Sites and Experiences*. Chicago: University of Chicago Press, 2007. Analyses of popularization in Great Britain offer useful comparisons to the United States.

Gilbert, James Burkhart. *Redeeming Culture: American Religion in an Age of Science*. Chicago: University of Chicago Press, 1997. Includes chapters on the Bell Telephone science films and religious influences on popular science.

Goodell, Rae. *The Visible Scientists*. Boston: Little, Brown, 1977. How scientists became celebrities after the 1940s.

Hansen, Bert. "Medical History for the Masses: How American Comic Books Celebrated Heroes of Medicine in the 1940s." *Bulletin of the History of Medicine* 78 (2004): 148–191. Example of the porous borders for knowledge flow, from professional to popular contexts.

Haynes, Rosalynn D. *From Faust to Strangelove: Representations of the Scientist in Western Literature*. Baltimore: Johns Hopkins University Press, 1994. Comprehensive exploration of fictional images in print.

Hilgartner, Stephen. "The Dominant View of Popularization: Conceptual Problems, Political Uses." *Social Studies of Science* 20 (1990): 519–539.

Social analysis applied to current historical models.

Kirby, David A. *Lab Coats in Hollywood: Science, Scientists, and Cinema*. Cambridge, Mass.: MIT Press, 2011. The use and influence of scientific experts within Hollywood.

LaFollette, Marcel Chotkowski. *Making Science Our Own: Public Images of Science, 1910–1955*. Chicago: University of Chicago Press, 1990. History of how American popular magazines presented science and scientists.

LaFollette, Marcel Chotkowski. *Science on the Air: Popularizers and Personalities on Radio and Early Television*. Chicago: University of Chicago Press, 2008. History of how American radio and early television incorporated science and scientists.

LaFollette, Marcel Chotkowski. *Science on the American Television: A History*. Chicago: University of Chicago Press, 2013. Television content and presentation of science from the 1940s to the 1990s.

Lewenstein, Bruce V. "Magazine Publishing and Popular Science after World War II." *American Journalism* 6 (1989): 218–234. The growth of popular science magazines.

Lutz, Catherine A., and Jane L. Collins. *Reading National Geographic*. Chicago: University of Chicago Press, 1993. Comprehensive analysis of *National Geographic Magazine*.

Mitman, Gregg. *Reel Nature: America's Romance with Wildlife on Film*. Cambridge, Mass.: Harvard University Press, 1999. Includes analysis of both motion picture and television images of nature.

National Association of Science Writers. *Science, the News, and the Public: Who Gets What Science News, Where They Get It, and What They Think about It*. New York: New York University Press, 1958. Summary of a University of Michigan survey of public consumption of popular science.

Nelkin, Dorothy. *Selling Science*. New York: W. H. Freeman, 1987. A sociologist's analysis of contemporary science popularization.

Pandora, Katherine. "Popular Science in National and Transnational Perspective: Suggestions from the American Context." *Isis* 100 (2009): 346–358. Pleads for sensitivity to the national as well as the cultural context for popularization.

Piel, Gerard. *Science in the Cause of Man*. New York: Alfred A. Knopf, 1961. Includes essays about government attempts at censoring popular science in the 1950s.

Richardson, Edgar P., Brooke Hindle, and Lillian B. Miller. *Charles Willson Peale and His World*. New York: Harry N. Abrams, 1983. Definitive history of the first science museum.

Secord, James A. "Knowledge in Transit." *Isis* 95 (2004): 654–672. Discusses the permeability of knowledge barriers.

Shermer, Michael B. "This View of Science: Stephen Jay Gould as Historian of Science and Scientific Historian, Popular Scientist and Scientific Popularizer." *Social Studies of Science* 32 (2002): 489–524. Analyzes the connection between celebrity and professional reputation.

Slosson, Edwin E. "On Translating Science." *Science News-Letter* 11 (7 May 1927): 289. Good summary of Slosson's philosophy of popularization.

Sweeney, Michael S. *Secrets of Victory: The Office of Censorship and the American Press and Radio in World War II*. Chapel Hill: University of North Carolina Press, 2001.

Thompson, James Stacy. *The Technical Book Publisher in Wartimes*. New York: New York Public Library, 1942. Scientific and engineering book publishing during World War II.

Tobey, Ronald C. *The American Ideology of National Science, 1919–1930*. Pittsburgh, Penn.: University of Pittsburgh Press, 1971. How influential scientists attempted to use popularization for political goals.

Tuomey, Christopher P. *Conjuring Science: Scientific Symbols and Cultural Meanings in American Life*. New Brunswick, N.J.: Rutgers University Press, 1996. The role that science has played in American culture.

Turow, Joseph. *Playing Doctor: Television, Storytelling, and Medical Power*. Oxford: Oxford University Press, 1989. History of how American television dramas presented physicians and medical research.

Marcel Chotkowski LaFollette

POSTAL SERVICE, U.S.

The post office managed the first significant communication network in the United States and, with operations that reached almost everywhere, it quickly grew into the nation's largest civilian institution. Given its scope, complexity, and central role in American history, the post office influenced a number of technologies. Most important, Congress often used postal operations as a proxy for a more systematic and direct federal transportation policy. A major purchaser of transport equipment and services, the post office subsidized and shaped all transportation industries from stagecoaches to airlines. As an information network that preceded and then complemented telegraphy and telephony, the postal system addressed key technological and economic issues—network externalities, monopoly, universal service, and cross-subsidies—decades before they arose in connection with telecommunication.

Beginning with contracts let to stagecoach lines in 1785, the post office leveraged its resources to promote and channel the growth of private transports. These and subsequent contracts for intercity mail transportation not only provided a constant stream of revenue, which sustained firms that might otherwise fail, but also encouraged transports to adhere to fixed schedules, which regularized passenger service. The post office began using steamboats on the nation's waterways in 1813, although they had a relatively modest impact on domestic mail transportation. Oceangoing steamships, however, proved invaluable for international mail exchanges, and steamship companies maneuvered to win mail contracts.

Railroads provided the bulk of intercity mail transport from the mid-1800s to mid-1900s. The attributes of rail transport—speed, regularity, capacity—perfectly suited the post office's needs. In 1838, Congress declared every railroad a post route and empowered the postmaster general to negotiate contracts with rail lines, launching a century-long struggle to fix the appropriate compensation for transporting mail by rail. In one of its most notable technical advances, the post office in 1864 began processing mail aboard trains. Clerks in railway post offices sorted mail in specially fitted cars on moving trains, often picking up and dropping off mail sacks without stopping. As railroads succumbed to competition from trucking firms after World War II, the post office substituted highway post offices—buses on which clerks sorted mail—in the 1950s and 1960s, phasing out the last railway post office in 1977.

The post office played a pivotal role in early U.S. aviation. From 1918 until 1927, the post office owned the planes and trained the pilots that carried airmail, an expedited service that charged premium postage. For the next several years, the post office used lucrative mail contracts to entice private carriers to provide high-quality service, even paying a premium to those whose craft could carry passengers. Decisions of postal officials influenced airline mergers, research and development, equipment, routes, speed, cost accounting, scheduling, public relations, and more. Indeed, the post office became the de facto airline regulator until Congress limited officials' contracting discretion in 1934. The post office in 1953 began speeding regular first-class mail by transporting it on commercial airlines, and by 1975 all such mail was routinely carried by air without a postage surcharge.

Although the post office contracted with private firms for intercity transportation, it operated its own fleet of vehicles for local mail delivery. The department tested its first motorized mail wagon in 1899; about 20 years later, it operated the largest civilian fleet of vehicles in the world. Postal officials discovered that rural carriers in automobiles could service much longer routes than those using horse-drawn wagons. After World War II, the post office increasingly acquired delivery vehicles for use by individual carriers in the cities. Complementing vehicles on the road was a subterranean network of pneumatic tubes used by the post office in several cities from the 1890s until 1953. In shooting mail from one post office to another or to rail terminals, the pneumatic tubes avoided congestion on the streets. Rediscovered in the 1990s, surviving sections of pneumatic tube systems were being eyed as conduits for fiber-optic cables.

Processing the mail proved technologically more challenging than transporting it. Processing involved several steps: facing (arranging pieces with the addresses in one direction), postmarking and canceling (often one step), sorting (usually multiple times), and pouching (placing pieces in bags or trays). Until the end of the nineteenth century, none of these steps was mechanized. The first electric canceling machine appeared in 1892;

30 years later, only the facing and canceling process had been mechanized. Mushrooming mail volumes after World War II began to overwhelm the system and propelled further innovation. In 1956, the post office unveiled its "Mail-Flo" system in Detroit. The facility featured 20 miles of conveyors, 28 machines that keyboard operators used to sort mail, giant parcel-sorting machines, and sack-sorting machines, among other equipment. Despite this mechanization, operators still had to read addresses. The 1963 introduction of the Zone Improvement Plan—ZIP code—paved the way for electronic address readers installed shortly thereafter at sectional processing centers. Combined with computerized databases, the ZIP code encouraged more sophisticated direct marketing by retailers. The automation of mail processing accelerated with the transformation of the U.S. Post Office Department from a politics-ridden cabinet agency to the quasi-corporate U.S. Postal Service in 1971.

The post office, a transport-based communication system, flirted with telecommunication throughout most of its history. Samuel F. B. Morse developed the first American telegraph line with federal subsidies and operated it under the auspices of the post office from 1844 until the government sold it to private interests in 1847. Between 1870 and 1920, Congress repeatedly considered proposals to "postalize" the nation's telecommunication system—that is, allow the post office to operate telegraph and telephone systems, the arrangement followed in most other countries. None of the proposals came close to passage, although the post office did experiment with telecommunication services as an adjunct to the mails. In 1960, the post office developed Speed Mail, a facsimile service, but then scrapped it because of complaints that it competed with the private sector. Mailgrams, combining mail service with Western Union's telegraph lines, appeared in 1969. And the Postal Service briefly experimented with electronic mail services in the 1980s before the Internet became widely available.

Although a late-twentieth-century surge in direct-mail marketing increased the volume of parcels and catalogs in the mail stream, new private carriers such as Federal Express and United Parcel

Service (UPS), promising faster, more efficient service, aggressively competed with the U.S. Postal Service for this business. At the same time, e-mail messages via the Internet increasingly supplanted the U.S. mail as a favored mode of communication. The future of the postal service in the new era of privatization and electronic information exchange remained unclear as the twenty-first century dawned.

[*See also* **Airplanes and Air Transport; Automation and Computerization; Highway System; Internet and World Wide Web; Maritime Transport; Morse, Samuel F. B.; Motor Vehicles; Railroads; Technology; Telegraph;** *and* **Telephone.**]

BIBLIOGRAPHY

John, Richard R., Jr. *Spreading the News: The American Postal System from Franklin to Morse.* Cambridge, Mass.: Harvard University Press, 1995.

Kielbowicz, Richard B. *Postal Enterprise: Post Office Innovations with Congressional Constraints, 1789–1970.* Report for Postal Rate Commission, 2000. Available at http://www.prc.gov/prc-docs/library/refdesk/techpapers/Kielbowicz/enterprise.pdf (accessed 20 March 2012).

National Postal Museum, Smithsonian Institution. http://www.postalmuseum.si.edu (accessed 20 March 2012).

Scheele, Carl H. *A Short History of the Mail Service.* Washington, D.C.: Smithsonian Institution Press, 1970.

Sorkin, Alan L. *The Economics of the Postal System.* Lexington, Mass.: Lexington Books, 1980.

Richard B. Kielbowicz

POWELL, JOHN WESLEY

(1834–1902), geologist, anthropologist, director of the U.S. Geological Survey (USGS). Born in New York and raised on the Ohio and Illinois frontiers, Powell attended Oberlin College and was a school teacher from the age of 18. An interest in natural history led him to advocate the teaching of science in schools and to pursue further studies in higher education. During the Civil War he served as an artillery officer in the Union army. Losing an arm at the Battle of Shiloh in 1862, he left the military with the rank of major. Active in the Illinois State Natural History Society before the war, he returned in 1865 to become professor of geology at Illinois Wesleyan College. An 1869 expedition down the Colorado River brought Powell national notice and a federal appropriation. His U.S. Geographical and Geological Survey of the Rocky Mountain region (1870–1879) won him recognition for explaining the role of structure, uplift, and stream erosion in shaping topography.

Also a student of native Indian language and culture, Powell organized the Smithsonian Institution's Bureau of American Ethnology in 1879 and directed it until his death in 1902. The bureau sponsored the collection of information on Native American peoples, particularly the study of Native American languages. Powell used the bureau's resources to advance the study of human culture. He published some of this research in an 1883 paper titled "Human Evolution."

Concerned about the risks of American expansion into the arid West, Powell in his 1878 *Report on the Lands of the Arid Region of the United States* warned policy makers about settlement laws that ignored scarcity of water. His desire for a scientific bureau to replace Land Office surveys was partially realized in 1879, when he worked with Clarence King to establish the USGS. Powell became its second director in 1881. Buoyed by a Spencerian faith in science and progress, Powell worked to extend the survey beyond the mining regions and into general geology, topographic mapping, and natural-resource assessment.

The USGS under Powell won international acclaim. The most prominent federal scientific institution of the late nineteenth century, it laid a foundation for the growth of federal scientific agencies during the Progressive Era. It also sparked controversy when it clashed with traditional congressional prerogatives. Powell's planning of irrigation development in the American West (1888–1890) became controversial, angering some members of Congress. This, along with controversies around his other policies, led to his retirement as director of the USGS in 1894. Although he remained director of the Bureau of American Ethnology, the end of his life was mostly taken up with writing. He produced textbooks on geology and geography and wrote on human evolution.

[*See also* **Anthropology; Evolution, Theory of; Geography; Geological Surveys; Geology; High Schools, Science Education in; Higher Education and Science; Science;** *and* **Smithsonian Institution.**]

BIBLIOGRAPHY

Rabbitt, Mary C. *Minerals, Lands, and Geology for the Common Defense and General Welfare.* 2 vols. Washington, D.C.: U.S. Geological Survey, 1979–1980.

Worster, Donald. *A River Running West: The Life of John Wesley Powell.* New York: Oxford University Press, 2001.

Zernel, John J. "Powell, John Wesley (1834–1902)." In *The History of Science in the United States: An Encyclopedia,* edited by Marc Rothenberg, pp. 450–451. New York and London: Garland Publishing, 2001.

John J. Zernel;
updated by Elspeth Knewstubb

PRESIDENT'S SCIENCE ADVISORY COMMITTEE

The President's Science Advisory Committee (PSAC) was formally established by President Dwight D. Eisenhower in November 1957 as part of his response to the Soviet launching of the satellite *Sputnik* on 4 October that year to provide him and his newly appointed science advisor with advice on the government's science, technology, space, and defense policies. Composed of about 20 politically moderate scientists and with Eisenhower's and later President John F. Kennedy's trust, the committee was effective in pushing for a civilian space program, nuclear arms control,

increased funding for science and education, and environmental protection, but its influence declined in the late 1960s under Presidents Lyndon B. Johnson and Richard M. Nixon until Nixon abolished it in 1973 over a series of policy disagreements.

The PSAC had its predecessor in the Science Advisory Committee of the Office of Defense Mobilization (ODM) in the Executive Office of the President that was established as a response to the outbreak of the Korean War by President Harry S. Truman in 1951 and retained by Eisenhower. Shortly after the launching of *Sputnik*, which shook American confidence about winning the Cold War with the Soviet Union, this committee met with Eisenhower and persuaded him to appoint a full-time presidential science advisor to help him coordinate government policy involving science and technology. For the same purpose, the first occupant of this position, James R. Killian Jr., in turn convinced Eisenhower to reconstitute, expand, and upgrade the ODM committee into the PSAC in the White House, reporting to both the president and the science advisor. Throughout its history, the PSAC elected the science advisor as its chair although it had the right to select another member.

During the remainder of the Eisenhower presidency, the committee worked with the science advisors—Killian from 1957 to 1959 and George B. Kistiakowsky from 1959 to 1961—to establish the National Aeronautics and Space Administration (NASA) as a civilian agency; to rationalize the American missile programs; to centralize the Department of Defense, especially in the area of military technology; to increase federal funding for science and education; and to push forward the negotiations toward a nuclear-test-ban treaty with the Soviets. Under Kennedy and his science advisor Jerome Wiesner, the PSAC expanded into environmental policy with its report *Use of Pesticides* in 1963, which vindicated Rachel Carson's sounding the alarm about the harmful effects of the uncontrolled use of DDT and other pesticides. Under Johnson and his science advisor Donald F. Hornig, the committee expanded its role in environmental policy with its 1965 report, *Restoring the Quality of Our Environment,* which warned about the danger of greenhouse gas emissions and global warming. The committee initially opposed the launching of the Apollo project to land an American on the moon, because of its costs and lack of scientific and military benefits, but later, after the decision was made, worked with NASA to make it a success.

Tension grew between the PSAC and the White House in the late 1960s and early 1970s as some current and former members of the committee, along with many in the scientific community, opposed the Johnson and Nixon administrations' conduct of the Vietnam War and their technology policies, especially the latter's push for the Anti-Ballistic Missiles and the Supersonic Transport. Nixon's science advisors—Lee DuBridge from 1969 to 1970 and Edward E. David from 1970 to 1973—tried but failed to reconcile the two sides until Nixon abolished the committee in 1973. A similar group, the President's Council of Advisors on Science and Technology, was established by President George H. W. Bush in 1990.

[*See also* **Carson, Rachel; Environmentalism; Global Warming; Higher Education and Science; Killian, James Rhyne, Jr.; Military, Science and Technology and the; Missiles and Rockets; National Aeronautics and Space Administration; Nuclear Weapons; Pesticides; Research and Development (R&D); Satellites, Communications; Science; Space Program; Space Science;** *and* **Technology.**]

BIBLIOGRAPHY

Herken, Gregg. *Cardinal Choices: Presidential Science Advising from the Bomb to SDI.* New York: Oxford University Press, 1992.

Killian, James R., Jr. *Sputnik, Scientists, and Eisenhower: A Memoir of the First Special Assistant to the President for Science and Technology.* Cambridge, Mass.: MIT Press, 1977.

Wang, Zuoyue. *In Sputnik's Shadow: The President's Science Advisory Committee and Cold War America.* New Brunswick, N.J.: Rutgers University Press, 2008.

Zuoyue Wang

PRIESTLEY, JOSEPH

(1733–1804), natural philosopher, chemist. Fearing imprisonment by British authorities, Joseph Priestley arrived in the United States in 1794 at the age of 61. He was publicly welcomed in New York City and in Philadelphia for being a long-standing friend of Americans and their experiment in republican government. He was also famous as a Unitarian theologian and natural philosopher. Three years earlier, a mob in Birmingham bent on destroying the property of all who questioned the status quo burned down Priestley's church, home, and laboratory. He and his wife were moreover eager to join their three sons, who were already in Pennsylvania unsuccessfully attempting to found a settlement of like-minded liberals in the hinterlands of the state. That first summer in America the senior Priestley left Philadelphia for a property chosen by their sons in Northumberland, Pennsylvania, 150 miles from Philadelphia.

Priestley's first work in natural philosophy, *The History and Present State of Electricity, with Original Experiments* (1767), was encouraged by Benjamin Franklin, then serving in London as a representative of several North American colonies. *The History and Present State of Discoveries relating to Vision, Light, and Colours* followed in 1772. Then Priestley turned to the chemistry of gases as his major interest in natural philosophy. That year he created the first artificially carbonated beverage by dissolving "fixed air" (CO_2) in water. Among his other noteworthy achievements, he isolated and identified the properties of nitric oxide, nitrogen dioxide, anhydrous hydrochloric acid, ammonia, nitrous oxide, sulfur dioxide, oxygen, and silicon tetrafluoride. Priestley's names for these gases reflected his commitment to phlogiston, a single substance imparting various properties that was lost or gained in many common chemical reactions: combustion, metallurgical processes, and respiration. His experiments showed that plants respire as well as animals and have the capacity of restoring vitiated air to breathability by supplying "dephlogisticated air" (oxygen).

On the basis of old experiments and new ones conducted in his purpose-built laboratory in

Northumberland, Priestley published over forty scientific papers and four pamphlets while in America. Most of these works were devoted to his rearguard action against Antoine Lavoisier's chemical system that dispensed with phlogiston and was cast in terms of the transference between compounds of oxygen. Priestley's discovery of carbon monoxide ("heavy inflammable air") is often attributed to his American period, although he had already distinguished its properties from other inflammable gases by 1790. Provoked by Priestley's phlogistic interpretation of its composition in his American writings, chemists in England and France discovered that it was simply an oxide of carbon.

Although practically no American chemists agreed with Priestley's phlogistic views, they honored him during his own lifetime and afterward. The American Chemical Society, founded in 1876, considers as part of its history a gathering in Northumberland of 77 chemists in 1874 to commemorate Priestley's discovery of oxygen. The Joseph Priestley Medal has been the highest honor bestowed by the Society since its first award in 1923.

[*See also* **Chemistry; Franklin, Benjamin;** *and* **Science.**]

BIBLIOGRAPHY

Rivers, Isabel, and David L. Wykes, eds. *Joseph Priestley, Scientist, Philosopher, and Theologian.* Oxford and New York: Oxford University Press, 2008. W. H. Brock gives a useful overview of Priestley's science and of recent historical interpretations, including those by Robert Schofield and other recent historians and philosophers.
Schofield, Robert E. *The Enlightened Joseph Priestley: A Study of His Life and Work from 1773 to 1804.* University Park: Pennsylvania State University Press, 2004. This and the next work in this bibliography include the most exhaustive treatment of Priestley's science to date.
Schofield, Robert E. *The Enlightenment of Joseph Priestley: A Study of His Life and Work from 1733 to 1773.* University Park: Pennsylvania State University Press, 1997.

Mary Ellen Bowden

PRINTING AND PUBLISHING

In 1640, the Cambridge, Massachusetts, locksmith-turned-printer Stephen Daye produced *The Whole Booke of Psalmes Faithfully Translated into English Metre.* This hymnal, popularly known as the *Bay Psalm Book,* was the first book printed in North America. (Eleven copies are known to survive.) Daye's rudimentary flatbed press and handset type would have been entirely familiar to Johannes Gutenberg, who had revolutionized printing technology in his shop in Mainz, Germany, in the 1450s. In the centuries that followed Daye's pioneering effort, printing and publishing would evolve dramatically as new technologies transformed the production and distribution of books, periodicals, newspapers, and other print materials. Even with premodern technologies, however, printing flourished in colonial America and in the early national era. The eighteenth-century Philadelphia printer and politician Benjamin Franklin published numerous works, including popular almanacs. Revolutionary-era printers produced a torrent of political pamphlets, including Thomas Paine's incendiary *Common Sense* (1776). Isaiah Thomas (1749–1831) of Worcester, Massachusetts, published high-quality books and magazines that he sold through a network of bookshops in various cities.

Nineteenth-century technological developments transformed a craft into a major industry. Religious publishers such as the American Bible Society (1816), the American Sunday-School Union (1824), and the American Tract Society (1825) were quick to adopt innovations that facilitated the production of cheap, mass-produced Bibles, tracts, hymnals, and other literature. The steam-powered printing press, invented in 1810 by the German Friedrich Koenig, increased the efficiency of flat-bed presses. New York's Richard Hoe invented the rotary press with curved stereotype plates in 1846–1847. Advances in paper-production technologies enabled printers to feed large rolls of paper continuously into the presses, further increasing output. The web press (1871), developed by Hoe and Stephen Tucker, printing on both sides of continuous rolls of newsprint, could produce 18 thousand newspapers per hour. The linotype machine, patented in 1884 by Ottmar Mergenthaler of Baltimore, eliminated hand-set type, creating metal slugs containing a full line of type (hence the name "linotype") that could be melted down and reused. (The writer Samuel L. Clemens lost a fortune backing the Paige Compositor, a typesetting machine developed by James W. Paige of Rochester, New York. Exceedingly complex and prone to breakdowns, Paige's machine survives only in a single prototype, on display at Clemens' mansion in Hartford.) The *New York Tribune* adopted the linotype process in 1886, and other newspapers quickly followed. Large rotary presses, now electrified and operating at ever higher speeds, proved crucial to the production of mass-circulation newspapers, magazines, and low-cost books.

Nineteenth-century book publishers—including New York's Charles Scribner's Sons (1846) and Putnam's (1848); J. B. Lippincott (1836) of Philadelphia; and Boston's Little, Brown (1847) and Houghton Mifflin (1852)—used these new technologies to produce the religious works, histories, novels, dictionaries, gift books, and textbooks desired by an increasingly literate reading public. Books were sold through bookshops, by advance subscription, and door to door. Prior to the International Copyright Convention (1891), U.S. publishers regularly pirated editions of popular British writers like Walter Scott and Charles Dickens without paying royalties. Dime novels and juveniles, published by Erastus Beadle (1821–1894) and others, proved profitable as well.

An important advance in printing technology came in 1903 when the American Ira Rubel (adapting a technology developed in England in 1875 for printing on tin used for canned-food containers) developed the offset printing process as an alternative to direct letter-press printing. In offset printing, the text or image is transferred or "offset" from the printing plate cylinder to a rubberized cylinder, which in turn prints it on the paper. Offset printing produces clearer images, is more cost effective, and extends the life of the printing plate, which does not come in direct contact with the paper.

Offset printing proved particularly efficient for reproducing illustrations, art work, and photographs. The rotogravure printing process, developed in the late nineteenth century, involved transferring engraved images onto the press's rubber-clad metal cylinders, in the form of countless tiny indented cells, whose size and depth controlled the quantity of ink they held, thus determining the image's light–dark shading. In the early and mid-twentieth century, many newspapers published separate rotogravure photo sections, which proved highly popular. Irving Berlin's 1933 song "Easter Parade" contains the lines "The photographers will snap us, and you'll find that you're in the rotogravure." In the early twenty-first century, this process eventually adapted to color printing and remained in wide use for catalogs and mass magazines.

These technological innovations, coupled with cultural, social, and demographic changes, brought a proliferation of mass-circulation magazines such as *Colliers Weekly* (1888), *the Saturday Evening Post* (1897), and *Life* (1936), as well as a wave of new, less tradition-bound publishing houses, including Alfred A. Knopf (1915), Boni & Liveright (1917), Harcourt Brace (1919), Simon & Schuster (1924), and Bennett Cerf's Random House (1925). Publishing contemporary European and American authors, they sometimes faced censorship pressures from such organizations as the New York Society for the Suppression of Vice. These new publishers also introduced marketing innovations such as Boni & Liveright's Modern Library (acquired by Random House in 1925), an inexpensive series in a standardized format. The direct-mail Book-of-the-Month-Club and Literary Guild (1926) spawned a host of special-interest book clubs. The paperback revolution, launched by Pocket Books (1939) and Bantam Books (1946), burgeoned after World War II. By the 1980s, paperbacks comprised one-third of U.S. book sales. Utilizing the latest in printing technologies, giant commercial printers like Chicago's R. R. Donnelley and Sons, founded in 1864 by Richard Robert Donnelley, originally to print maps, became multipurpose printers of magazines, books, catalogs, financial reports, telephone directories, and advertising brochures.

In 2010, with 58 thousand employees worldwide, R. R. Donnelley had revenues of $10 billion.

As in corporate America generally, the later twentieth century brought mergers and consolidation, such as Random House's 1960 acquisition of Knopf. Corporate conglomerates absorbed venerable old-line publishing firms: RCA acquired Random House in 1966; CBS bought the textbook publisher Holt Rinehart & Winston (itself a product of earlier mergers) in 1967. Multinational media empires such as Germany's Bertelsmann and Rupert Murdoch's News Corporation, originally Australian based, became major players in the acquisitions game. With globalization (itself dependent on new communications technologies), publishers could outsource the printing and production process to wherever cost-cutting calculations dictated, including Hong Kong and elsewhere in Asia.

The rise of electronic data processing in the late twentieth century transformed printing and publishing nearly as profoundly as had Gutenberg half a millennium earlier. Now the print and visual content of books, periodicals, and newspapers could be composed using computer-powered data-processing programs and transferred directly to plates that were then attached, manually or automatically, to computer-controlled presses. The computer revolution transformed book marketing as well. Utilizing the Internet, computerized record keeping, and semiautomated warehouses, Amazon.com, founded in 1995, bypassed bookstores entirely to sell discounted books directly to consumers. Soon it became the nation's largest bookseller. Although high-volume chains such as Borders and Barnes & Noble drove many small, independent bookstores out of business, the chains themselves struggled with the competition of Amazon.com and other online marketers of new and used books. Borders declared bankruptcy in 2011. In this fevered competitive environment, constantly roiled by technological changes, major publishers pinned their hopes on mass-produced blockbuster books by well-known authors. But the new technologies benefitted smaller publishers and academic presses as well. The capability of printing small quantities of a given title inexpensively enabled them to reduce initial press runs, maintain lower inventories, and adopt a print-on-demand business model. New publishing technologies, including Xerography, spawned a proliferation of self-published books of all kinds, some of which succeeded in the marketplace. HarperCollins, for example, created Inkpop, a creative-writing Web site mentoring teenaged authors. In 2011, when a romance novel submitted to Inkpop proved popular, HarperCollins signed the author to a contract and published the book commercially.

As the computer revolution transformed printing and publishing, the printed book itself seemed vulnerable. Libraries increasingly became dispensers of computer-based "information services" rather than merely book depositories. Searchable databases rendered the once-indispensable telephone book largely superfluous. The era of the electronic book dawned with Amazon's Kindle (2007), a handheld device that could directly download entire books. Barnes & Noble's Nook followed in 2009 and Apple, Inc.'s iPad in 2010. Increasingly, publishers issued books in both print and electronic formats, with the latter steadily gaining popularity. In May 2011, Amazon.com announced that electronic books had surpassed print books, with 105 Kindle book sales for every 100 print book sales. The publishers of encyclopedias and other reference works increasingly abandoned the bound-book format and shifted to online platforms, with their capability for continual updates. Meanwhile, the free online encyclopedia Wikipedia, sustained by thousands of volunteers and generating revenue through advertising keyed to users' searches, posed a challenge to publishers of reference works. Similarly, as more people obtained their news via the Internet and consulted online classified-ad Web sites, print newspapers faced a crisis. Some ceased publication; others struggled to find economically viable ways to deliver the news to online subscribers. As the twenty-first century unfolded, the dramatic changes in printing and publishing seemed certain to continue.

[*See also* **Franklin, Benjamin; Internet and World Wide Web; Journals in Science, Medicine, and**

Engineering; Machinery and Manufacturing; Science Journalism; *and* Technology.]

BIBLIOGRAPHY

Epstein, Jason. *Book Business: Publishing Past, Present, and Future*. New York: W. W. Norton, 2002. A veteran editor and publisher reflects on the changes in the industry and what the future portends.

Howard, Nicole. *The Book: The Life Story of a Technology*. Baltimore: Johns Hopkins University Press, 2009. A broad-ranging historical survey, from the pre-Gutenberg era to the age of the Internet.

Tebbel, John W. *Between Covers: The Rise and Transformation of Book Publishing in America*. New York: Oxford University Press, 1987. A condensation of the author's four-volume history of the subject (1972–1981), including the technological milestones of the predigital era.

Thompson, John B. *Merchants of Culture: The Publishing Business in the Twenty-First Century*. Malden, Mass.: Polity Press, 2010. Examines the transformations and challenges of the digital age.

Whiteside, Thomas. *The Blockbuster Complex: Conglomerates, Show Business, and Book Publishing*. Middleton, Conn.: Wesleyan University Press, 1981. Explores the book industry's preoccupation with best-sellers and its implications.

Winship, Michael. "Manufacturing and Book Production." In *A History of the Book in America*, edited by Scott E. Casper, Jeffrey D. Groves, Stephen Nissenbaum, and Michael Winship, Vol. 3, pp. 40–69. Chapel Hill: University of North Carolina Press, 2007. Comprehensive coverage of the technological developments of the 1840–1880 era.

Paul S. Boyer

PSEUDOSCIENCE AND QUACKERY

Americans have long used the pejorative terms "pseudoscience" and "quackery" to designate scientific and medical theories and practices for which they have no respect. The meaning of the terms remains contested, however, because one person's "science" and "medicine" is often another's pseudoscience or quackery. Further, the line between pseudoscience and bad science, between quackery and malpractice, has always been blurry. Thus, many late-twentieth-century scholars dismissed demarcating between science and pseudoscience as "a pseudoproblem."

By the early eighteenth century, the term "quack" (from the Dutch word quacksalver, meaning one who boasts about his salves) was already gaining currency in the American colonies as a medical synonym for a "charlatan." By the early nineteenth century, American physicians, who lacked the protection of strict licensing laws, were complaining that "quacks abound like locusts in Egypt." Typical of the person they had in mind was the untutored botanical healer Samuel Thomson, who sought wealth and fame by aggressively selling "family rights" to his system. Thomson, who saw himself as a life-saving reformer, acknowledged that critics called him a quack, but alleged that the real quacks were the regular physicians who gave their patients "poisonous medicines" such as calomel (mercurous chloride).

After 1847, when regular doctors organized the American Medical Association (AMA), that body led the war on quackery, especially targeting dissenting medical groups such as homeopaths, who prescribed infinitesimally small doses of medicine. Ironically, even as the AMA attacked all homeopathy as quackery, educated homeopathic physicians were expelling untrained quacks from their ranks.

Around the 1830s, as science took on its present-day meaning, scientific and other writers introduced a new term of opprobrium, pseudoscience, to describe such novel ideas as phrenology (the science of "reading" a person's character by examining the skull) and the transmutation of species (later called evolution). Leaders of American science often contrasted reputable "men of science," such as themselves, with ignorant and sometimes immoral quacks and charlatans.

Early in the twentieth century, about the time Congress passed the first Food and Drugs Act regulating patent medicines (1906), the AMA created the first organized antiquackery unit in the country. Often collaborating with government agencies, the AMA's Bureau of Investigation sought to suppress quacks and charlatans who advertised quick cures for cancer, rheumatism, sexual weakness, or other conditions. By the 1930s the AMA was using pseudomedicine as a synonym for quackery.

No species of quackery stirred the wrath of organized medicine more than chiropractic, discovered in 1895 by D. D. Palmer, a magnetic healer from Iowa. Palmer believed that sickness resulted primarily from obstructions to the flow of "innate intelligence," which could be relieved by adjustments to the spinal column. Chiropractors described their practice as "the only truly scientific method of healing"; the AMA called it quackery. After decades watching chiropractic prosper despite its opposition, the AMA in 1963 created a Committee on Quackery, whose prime mission was the containment and elimination of the "unscientific cult" of chiropractic. (The AMA had only recently stopped referring to optometry as a cult.) The strategy backfired, however; chiropractors in 1976 filed an antitrust suit alleging illegal restraint of trade against a licensed profession and a decade later won a stunning victory in federal court.

In the later twentieth century, many writers and organizations softened the language they used in discussing healing practices outside the medical mainstream. Inflammatory terms such as quackery and charlatanism gave way to the more neutral "complementary," "alternative," or "unconventional" medicine. In part this reflected the immense popularity of heterodox healing, employed by over 40 percent of Americans in the late 1990s. Responding to this widespread use, many medical schools began offering courses on complementary and alternative medicine, and in 1992 Congress created an Office of Alternative Medicine in the National Institutes of Health.

No such euphemisms replaced pseudoscience, which, if anything, increased in usage during the late twentieth century with the rise of watchdog groups such as the Committee for the Scientific Investigation of the Paranormal. Although employed most commonly to target ideas marginal to the scientific establishment, such as creation science, Afrocentric science, parapsychology, and "ufology" (the study of unidentified flying objects),

the label pseudoscience also proved useful in besmirching scientific colleagues with whom one strongly disagreed: over racial differences in intelligence, the links between social behavior and genetic makeup, or claims to have discovered cold nuclear fusion. To the public, the labeling often seemed arbitrary, as when scientists engaging in the Search for Extraterrestrial Intelligence fell within the boundaries of science, whereas those searching for evidence of Intelligence Design were dismissed as pseudoscientists.

[*See also* **American Medical Association; Creationism; Evolution, Theory of; Medical; National Institutes of Health; Optometry; Parapsychology; Phrenology;** *and* **Pure Food and Drug Act.**]

BIBLIOGRAPHY

Boyle, Eric W. *Quack Medicine: A History of Combating Health Fraud in Twentieth-Century America.* Santa Barbara, Calif.: ABC-CLIO, 2013.

Gevitz, Norman, ed. *Other Healers: Unorthodox Medicine in America.* Baltimore: Johns Hopkins University Press, 1988.

Martin, Steven C. "'The Only Truly Scientific Method of Healing': Chiropractic and American Science, 1895–1990." *Isis* 85 (1994): 207–227.

Numbers, Ronald L. *The Creationists.* Berkeley: University of California Press, 1992.

Segerstråle, Ullica. *Defenders of the Truth: The Battle for Science in the Sociobiology Debate and Beyond.* New York and Oxford: Oxford University Press, 2000.

Thurs, Daniel T., and Ronald L. Numbers. "Science, Pseudo-science, and Science Falsely So-called." In *Wrestling with Nature: From Omens to Science*, edited by Peter Harrison, Ronald L. Numbers, and Michael H. Shank, pp. 281–305. Chicago: University of Chicago Press, 2011.

Ronald L. Numbers

PSYCHIATRY

Although physicians in the Colonial Era (such as Benjamin Rush) prescribed remedies for mental ailments, American psychiatry as a profession became organized within the wave of institution building in the mid-nineteenth century. In 1844, 13 heads of asylums created the American Association of Medical Superintendents of American Institutions for the Insane (AAMSAII), what would become the primary medical association for psychiatrists in the United States. In 1890, the AAMSAII changed its name to the American Medico-Psychological Association (AMPA), although the association's professional journal remained the *American Journal of Insanity*. At a time when most physicians were scrambling for stable sources of income in a crowded medical marketplace, the early psychiatrists (or alienists, as they were called in the nineteenth century) had job security and significant social and cultural power.

Psychiatrists primarily limited their professional scope to patients located within the increasingly large and complex system of mental hospitals and asylums in the late nineteenth and early twentieth centuries. Their authority over mental disturbance was challenged in the last decades of the century, however, by a newly organized specialty of neurologists who argued that mental hospitals were warehouses, unsuited to the treatment of patients with nervous and mental disease. The competition between the two professional groups manifested in several public confrontations, including one at the early 1880s trial of President James Garfield's assassin, Charles Guiteau, at which prominent members of both fields argued about the nature of insanity.

By 1920, when the AMPA was renamed to its present identification, the American Psychiatric Association (APA), psychiatry had achieved a kind of peace with neurology. Some neurologists and psychiatrists together became interested in a new method of study and treatment that emerged from Europe, psychoanalysis. Other neurologists shifted toward identifying lesions in the nervous system while psychiatrists explored somatic treatments for mental illness, including hydrotherapy, fever therapy, and sexual sterilization. Psychiatrists also experimented with different kinds of institutions, particularly shorter-stay research-oriented institutes in Boston, New York, and Ann Arbor, Michigan.

The draft process in World War I brought psychiatric problems to wider attention, but the major event that catapulted psychiatry to unprecedented public awareness was World War II. During the conflict, many psychiatrists (including the influential William Menninger) treated numerous soldiers with conditions that would not have been found in turn-of-the-century mental hospitals. In addition, the upheaval caused by the war—combined with psychiatrists' increasing enthusiasm for psychoanalysis—led psychiatrists to articulate a sweeping view of the uses of mental-health intervention across the globe. Individuals who did not need psychiatric hospitals began to flock toward psychiatrists who promised increased insight through psychoanalysis.

Psychiatry in the mid-twentieth century was largely dominated by professionals who espoused faith in the tenets of psychoanalysis. Whereas some professionals engaged patients in traditional Freudian analysis—complete with daily sessions with the patient lying on a couch facing away from the analyst—others (such as Frieda Fromm-Reichmann) used principles of transference and repression in more creative ways to directly engage patients. Psychoanalytically inspired psychiatrists claimed benefits for their insights and treatments in overt mental problems, as well as physical ailments affected by unconscious conflicts. Popular representations of psychoanalysis spread through American culture, and psychoanalytic vocabulary entered the mainstream.

Although many post–World War II psychiatrists engaged in psychoanalytic treatment of neurotic patients in outpatient settings, a core of psychiatrists remained committed to seriously mentally ill patients in hospitals. These practitioners developed a series of somatic treatments during and after the war, including insulin coma therapy, metrazol treatment, electroconvulsive therapy, and lobotomy. While critics inside and outside the profession later expressed dismay at the extensive use of somatic treatments at midcentury, practitioners argued at the time that patients who would otherwise be lingering in institutions for most of their lives deserved a heroic effort at treatment. Further, some psychiatrists attempted to combine somatic therapies with psychoanalytic insights. This pattern continued with the widespread introduction of psychiatric medication by the 1950s and 1960s.

By the 1960s and 1970s, the psychiatric profession appeared to be in disarray. Increasing internal and external pressures led to the closure of many of the large psychiatric institutions. Psychoanalytic practitioners complained about the barbarism of somatic treatments, whereas early biological psychiatrists argued that psychoanalysis was unscientific and limited. As a step toward controlled research, investigators at Washington University in St. Louis and the New York State Psychiatric Institute (especially Robert Spitzer) outlined symptom criteria for psychiatric diagnosis. These criteria became formalized in 1980 in the watershed third edition of the APA's *Diagnostic and Statistical Manual* (*DSM-III*). This manual, which became a best-seller and a major source of revenue for the association, was revised in 1987 (*DSM-IIIR*), 1994 (*DSM-IV*) and again in 2013 (*DSM-V*). Researchers intended for everyone in the field to speak the same language of mental disease, a language carefully expunged of psychoanalytic terminology.

At the same time that diagnostic criteria became employed to describe psychiatric patients—and symptoms of people who did not yet know that they were patients—psychiatric treatment was increasingly focused on medications. Psychiatrists, who were facing challenges to their professional authority by nonphysician psychoanalysts and other mental-health providers, argued that medications for mental illness were the mainstay of psychiatric treatment. Psychiatrists emphasized the neurochemical mechanism of medications, as well as definitions of all mental illness as brain disease.

As the twenty-first century opened, American psychiatry faced increasing challenges from within and without. The role of pharmaceutical companies in the profession came under increasing scrutiny as critics, including investigators in Congress, uncovered evidence that formal and informal support from the industry affected how and why psychiatrists used medications. Further, the definition of mental illness itself was criticized by those who argued that the *DSM* system included too much that was not real illness. The process of creating

DSM-V became increasingly contentious in the context of allegations of undue pharmaceutical company influence on the professionals involved in the process. In addition, ongoing competition from other physicians and mental-health professionals led to major questions about how psychiatry will define itself into the future.

[*See also* **Menninger, Karl and William; Mental Health Institutions; Mental Illness; Psychopharmaceutical Drugs; Psychotherapy;** *and* **Rush, Benjamin.**]

BIBLIOGRAPHY

Grob, Gerald N. *From Asylum to Community: Mental Health Policy in Modern America.* Princeton, N.J.: Princeton University Press, 1991.

Grob, Gerald N. *The Mad among Us: A History of the Care of America's Mentally Ill.* New York: Free Press, 1994.

Grob, Gerald N. *Mental Illness and American Society, 1875–1940.* Princeton, N.J.: Princeton University Press, 1983.

Grob, Gerald N. *Mental Institutions in America: Social Policy to 1875.* New York: Free Press, 1973.

Hale, Nathan G., Jr. *The Rise and Crisis of Psychoanalysis in the United States: Freud and the Americans, 1917–1985.* New York: Oxford University Press, 1995.

Rosenberg, Charles E. *The Trial of the Assassin Guiteau: Psychiatry and Law in the Gilded Age.* Chicago: University of Chicago Press, 1968.

Shorter, Edward. *Before Prozac: The Troubled History of Mood Disorders in Psychiatry.* Oxford: Oxford University Press, 2009.

Tomes, Nancy. *The Art of Asylum-Keeping: Thomas Story Kirkbride and the Origins of American Psychiatry.* Philadelphia: University of Pennsylvania Press, 1994.

Laura Hirshbein

PSYCHOLOGICAL AND INTELLIGENCE TESTING

Psychological and intelligence testing has its roots in Johann Lavater's late-eighteenth-century systematic physiognomy and Samuel Morton's mid-nineteenth-century craniometric characterizations of human races. Contemporaneously, the science of phrenology, which delineated aspects of character, proved influential, and physical anthropologists soon generalized craniometry to the entire body. In the 1890s, following English polymath Frances Galton, James McKeen Cattell of Columbia University extended anthropometric concerns to mental traits. His self-identified series of "mental tests" measured, among other traits, short-term memory and the keenness of the senses. He lacked, however, an overarching functional view of how these traits helped people live, his tests produced trivial results, and most psychologists abandoned them by 1901 (Sokal, 1987).

Nevertheless, contemporaneous Americans sought psychological expertise more than ever. Growing corporations had to select and train workers for new jobs. Eugenicists wanted to determine who should be prohibited from reproducing and from entering the country. Most significantly, compulsory education laws forced teachers both to "Americanize" millions of young immigrants from southern and eastern Europe and to deal with many newly revealed "feeble-minded" children. Psychologists at state schools attacked this problem, and in 1908 New Jersey's Henry Goddard discovered the French tests that Alfred Binet and others had developed for their country's educators. These tests had children perform "age-appropriate" tasks, such as counting coins at age three, explaining similarities at age eight, repeating five digits backward at age twelve, and, for the "superior," explaining proverbs. The level at which children performed determined their "mental age"; mental age divided by chronological age determined the intelligence quotient, or IQ (Zenderland, 1998).

Goddard soon revised these tests for American use, and schools like his readily adopted them. Others developed analogous tests for large urban school systems. In 1916, Lewis Terman and others at Stanford University issued the long-standard first version of the "Stanford Revision and Extension of the Binet–Simon Intelligence Scale" (fifth edition, "SB5," 2003).

When the United States entered World War I in 1917, psychologists mobilized to support the war effort and to "put psychology on the map." Their most general program, led by Robert Yerkes of the University of Minnesota, produced two tests. The Army Alpha examination, designed for English-literate men, involved solving arithmetical problems, identifying synonyms and antonyms, determining whether disarranged sentences were true or false, and completing analogies and number series. The nonverbal Army Beta examination, designed for illiterate men and those literate in other languages, involved following mazes, counting cubes in complicated structures, deciphering codes, and completing pictures and symbol series. Unlike most earlier tests, the Army exams tested its subjects in large groups, had them write their responses on test blanks, and used multiple-choice formats.

Observers still debate whether the army found these tests useful. But the new procedures revolutionized testing and put psychology on the map. Group psychological testing boomed in the 1920s. Colleges used these as admissions tests, schools sectioned classes on the basis of tested "ability," and the College Entrance Examination Board replaced its essay examinations with a more "objective" and easily scored Scholastic Aptitude Test. Eugenicists cited the results of Army tests—on which native-born Americans scored higher than immigrants and immigrants from northern and western Europe scored higher than those from southern and eastern Europe—to argue successfully for immigration restriction. By the early 1930s, however, criticisms by statisticians, other psychologists, and especially cultural anthropologists, led by Columbia University's Franz Boas, led testers to downplay and even retract some claims for their work (Sokal, 1984).

Through the 1930s, however, schools still used psychological tests extensively. To respond to the growing influence of environmental interpretations like Boas's, Raymond Cattell of Clark University and others developed "culture-fair" tests. Other testers paid greater attention to statistical issues. In 1939, David Wechsler of New York's

Bellevue Psychiatric Hospital combined verbal and other procedures in his adult-oriented Bellevue Intelligence Scale (from 1955, the Wechsler Adult Intelligence Scale, or WAIS) and based its norms on the scores of 3,500 subjects. As the post–World War II baby boom and the renewed immigration of the 1960s forced schools to deal with an even more diverse population, intelligence testing boomed; most notably, the Wechsler Intelligence Scale for Children (WISC) appeared in 1949.

The 1960s' call for equal opportunity led critics to claim that all tests reflected class or race biases and that testing itself embodied malevolent social control. Defenders claimed that, by uncovering previously hidden abilities in all individuals, tests served to create opportunity; they also revealed real differences in the mental functioning (such as "learning disabilities") that educators could then respond to. The call for educational accountability in the 1990s—culminating in the "No Child Left Behind" legislation of 2002—has refocused testing from the student to the school system.

[*See also* Boas, Franz; Cattell, James McKeen; Eugenics; Intelligence, Concepts of; Phrenology; Psychology; *and* Race and Medicine.]

BIBLIOGRAPHY

Carson, John. *The Measure of Merit: Talents, Intelligence, and Inequality in the French and American Republics, 1750–1940.* Princeton, N.J.: Princeton University Press, 2006.

Sokal, Michael M. "James McKeen Cattell and American Psychology in the 1920s." In *Explorations in the History of Psychology in the United States*, edited by Josef Brožek, pp. 273–323. Lewisburg, Penn.: Bucknell University Press, 1984.

Sokal, Michael M., ed. *Psychological Testing and American Society, 1890–1930.* New Brunswick, N.J.: Rutgers University Press, 1987.

Zenderland, Leila. *Measuring Minds: Henry Herbert Goddard and the Origins of American Intelligence Testing.* Cambridge, U.K.: Cambridge University Press, 1998.

Michael M. Sokal

PSYCHOLOGY

The modern meaning of psychology as the study of the mind and behavior emerged gradually as the scientific discipline formed in nineteenth-century Europe and found its way to the United States. The discipline's conceptual roots can be found in the experimental laboratories of physiologists, in the medical practices of asylums and clinics, and in the statistical manipulations of mathematicians. Contextual factors included evolutionary theory, which focused attention on comparative animal psychology, and the rise of liberalism, which directed concern for the nature of the individual self and in relation to others. By 1900 the discipline was flourishing in America and had achieved a measure of academic institutionalization in colleges and universities. World War II created the modern profession of psychology, with substantial numbers of psychologists engaged in clinical work with individual clients. By the beginning of the twenty-first century, scientific and professional psychology had become ubiquitous in the United States. Psychological terms had infiltrated everyday language, a huge mental-health industry had arisen, and psychological tests had become a standard feature of society. Whether the great interest in the subject matter of psychology has been a cause or a consequence of scientific psychology's rise is open to debate.

Rise of the "New" Psychology. After 1870, college students in the United States gradually became aware of the "new" psychology that was supplanting older conceptions of distinct mental "faculties." William James, a professor at Harvard University, introduced theories of mind and demonstrated empirical findings with a collection of so-called "brass instruments," borrowed from laboratories of physics and physiology. He wrote the *Principles of Psychology* in 1890, which was soon recognized as a classic. James was associated with the functionalist school, which studied the mind's adaptation to its environment. Habits, consciousness, and the self were understood as adaptive functions, not as structural elements of the mind. The influence of Charles Darwin was evident in the functionalists' interest in evolutionary processes; they investigated the development of mind and behavior in other species as well as humans.

Between 1870 and 1910, many students from the United States traveled to Germany, the center of exciting new research in laboratory-based psychology, to study. Attracted by low travel costs and inexpensive accommodations as well as the reputation of German universities, students were exposed to the ideas and practices of scholars such as Wilhelm Wundt, a professor of philosophy at the University of Leipzig. A founder of modern psychology, Wundt wrote voluminously on psychology as an independent academic discipline and, in 1879, established perhaps the first psychological laboratory. Wundt had an expansive vision of psychology as an essential basis for the development of all the other sciences, which would be integrated into a synthetic philosophical system. Psychology could bridge the *Naturwissenschaften* and *Geisteswissenschaften*, with its subject matter ranging from individual psychophysiology and mental chronometry to human language and culture, and was unified by the key concept of psychic causality. Different topics called for different research methods. For instance, when measuring the speed of the nervous impulse, accurate mechanical timers gave readings of one one-thousandth of a second; when a colored light was used as a stimulus for a psychophysics experiment, precise introspection provided qualitative judgments about the light's color, intensity, and other characteristics; when religious practices were being investigated, historical and comparative methods of textual analysis were employed.

Wundt and James, both nonpracticing medical doctors, were recognized leaders of the new psychology. In Vienna, another physician, Sigmund Freud, developed his own system of psychology and psychotherapy, which he called psychoanalysis. Dream analysis, the personal unconscious, and sexual development from childhood became hallmarks of his approach. His system spread through an apprentice method of "training analysis" before the psychotherapist began a private practice. Psychoanalysis in America became associated with the medical profession, developing separately from academic psychology, but psychoanalytic ideas and psychoanalytic therapy were also popularized and spread to the public.

Academic Institutionalization. Fresh from their exposure to the new psychology, graduates adapted laboratory techniques and intellectual agendas to the rapidly changing landscape of higher education in the United States. During the last quarter of the nineteenth century, the research ideal in combination with values of social utility and liberal culture greatly influenced the rise of the modern university. In 1876, only one university, Johns Hopkins, offered graduate instruction leading to the PhD. A quarter century later, many institutions offered doctoral level studies and degrees.

The number of academic psychological laboratories in the United States and Canada numbered at least 54 in 1904, according to an authoritative survey in *Science* (Miner, p. 300). Early experimental work concentrated on sensation and perception, using the reaction-time method where a stimulus was presented to a subject and the speed of response was accurately measured. Professors published their research findings in the *American Journal of Psychology* (founded in 1887), the *Psychological Review* (founded in 1894), or other scientific periodicals. Approaches and methods proliferated, and the discipline field grew rapidly in American universities and colleges. The American Psychological Association (APA), a professional body dedicated to the advancement of psychology as a science, was formed in 1892, with 26 charter members. Psychologists were also active in the child-study movement and in trying to advance the art and science of pedagogy, newly significant with the rise of universal education. In addition, during these years, theoretical and methodological differences gave rise to contending schools of thought (structuralism, functionalism, behaviorism, Gestalt, etc.) that were more apparent to insiders than to the public.

In the early twentieth century, applications of psychology and psychological theory to education expanded significantly with the spread of mental tests. Starting in 1905, French psychologist

Alfred Binet published scales on testing for intelligence in children. Stanford University psychologist Lewis Terman subsequently revised the tests and included the ratio of mental and chronological ages, resulting in the "Intelligence Quotient." In 1916 the "Stanford-Binet" debuted. Mental tests were widely used by the U.S. Army in World War I to classify soldiers for general intelligence and occupational specialties. After the war, personnel psychology, particularly in business and industry, became a recognized specialty.

By 1929, at the start of the Great Depression, psychology was firmly institutionalized in American colleges and universities. Although the APA reached one thousand members that year, during the 1930s its dominance diminished as psychologists founded new organizations to pursue their scientific and professional interests, such as the American Association for Applied Psychology, the Society for the Psychological Study of Social Issues, or the Psychometric Society. Occupational trends also led to a split between academic and applied psychologists and to marked gender differences, with the majority of females confined to low-status jobs in nonacademic settings.

The Dominance of Behaviorism. By the start of the 1930s, psychology had matured to the point that the discipline generated internally a system of scientific priorities, preferred methods of investigation, and a complex professional reward structure. Experimental research was dominated by the use of behavioristic methods in the service of a general theory of learning. In a seminal article in 1913 published in the *Psychological Review*, "Psychology as the Behaviorist Views It," John B. Watson strongly urged psychologists not to look within at unseen mental processes, but to concentrate on observable behavior studied through experimental methods and analyzed within an evolutionary framework with the promise of prediction and control of human behavior as the practical consequence. Watson had earned his doctorate from the University of Chicago in 1903 with a thesis on rat psychology. Later investigators made the white rat a standard laboratory subject,

and Watson's ideas were reformulated into a variety of neo-behavioristic perspectives.

Among the prominent neo-behaviorists was B. F. Skinner, who earned a doctorate from Harvard in 1931 and later developed a theory of behavior known as "operant conditioning." This stands in contrast to the "classical conditioning" associated with the Russian physiologist Ivan Pavlov in his famous experiments on dogs, in which a conditioned stimulus (e.g., a ringing bell) was paired repeatedly with an unconditioned response (e.g., salivation when in the presence of the unconditioned stimulus of food) to the point where the bell elicits salivation directly. Operant conditioning focused on a class of emitted responses that are followed by reinforcement. For example, a rat in a "Skinner box" (an apparatus with a lever to obtain food or water) would press the lever (the operant) and then eat (reinforcement). With each successful trial, the rat would be more likely to repeat the action (response strength). Through a series of ingenious experiments, Skinner demonstrated the scientific utility of his approach in the laboratory using rats and pigeons before later extending it to the human realm of teaching machines, social engineering (with his 1948 utopian novel *Walden Two*), and an air-conditioned baby crib, all of which engendered controversy.

World War II was a watershed for psychology in many ways. The war gave rise to the practice of clinical psychology that was strongly supported by the federal government, with training grants supplied by the U.S. Public Health Service, occupational opportunities in Veterans Administration hospitals, and research grants from the National Institute of Mental Health. Techniques and tools borrowed from other disciplines, such as cybernetics, neurobiology, and systems science, transformed the intellectual life of psychology as well. Increased funds were available for scientific research; the number of psychologists grew dramatically; and the APA reorganized to include all areas of psychological activity under a federated governing system.

Postwar Growth. In the postwar decades, the academic psychology department still remained the basic unit for research, education, and training, and the GI Bill, a robust economy, and a widespread consensus on the positive value of a college degree helped usher in a "golden age" of growth that lasted until about 1970. Psychology grew on the broadening foundation of undergraduate education. The introductory course exhibited the diversity of psychology while presenting the prevailing orthodoxy of scientific professionalism in which varied applications derived from a common core of experimental science. A new wave of undergraduate textbooks was written. For instance, Ernest R. Hilgard published *Introduction to Psychology* in 1953. Firmly based in the research literature, the book attempted comprehensive coverage of topics ranging from the nervous system to personal adjustment. One innovation in format was the use of sidebars to break up the main mass of text and provide additional details on selected topics. Successful textbooks often went through multiple revisions over the course of decades to serve burgeoning undergraduate enrollments.

By the early 1960s, employment trends had shifted decisively to nonacademic settings; thus, the majority of psychologists found work in hospitals, schools, clinics, corporations, and private practice. That led to increased concern over the professional aspects of psychology, including interprofessional relations with psychiatrists and social workers, which were a part of the expanding mental-health industry. Some psychologists took their message directly to the general public, contributing to the literature of lay psychology or to the robust market in self-help books. For instance, B. F. Skinner explained his system of operant conditioning to the general public, beginning in 1953 with *Science and Human Behavior,* and Carl R. Rogers introduced his approach to human development and client-centered psychotherapy with the mass-market textbook *On Becoming a Person* in 1961.

Rise of Cognitive Psychology.

Perhaps the most striking intellectual development of the post–World War II period was the rise of cognitive psychology. Cognitive psychology covers the whole range of human mental activity, from sense perception to memory and thought. With deep roots in nineteenth-century research on attention, memory, and language and a penchant for using the digital computer as a model for the mind, cognitive psychology developed an important institutional focus at Harvard University's Center for Cognitive Studies starting in 1962. In an influential survey of the field, psychologist Ulric Neisser explained in *Cognitive Psychology* (1967) that the physical stimuli that an object produces "bear little resemblance to either the real object that gave rise to them or to the object of experience that the perceiver will construct as a result" (Neisser, p. 3). This constructive activity provided the foundation for cognitive psychology. The field was criticized, however, for its neglect of important components of mental life as emotions and phenomenal experience.

Closely allied with the study of cognition has been mathematical psychology. Curve fitting, mathematical modeling, and inferential statistics have been used to explain experimental results and inform theory construction. By the early 1950s coursework in the analysis of variance became a common feature of graduate training in the United States. Its routine use, standardized and codified in textbooks, meant that psychologists did not have to understand the complexities of statistics to apply them to their work. Statistics were useful, for example, in addressing quantitatively the inconsistencies of individual human behavior. People behaved differently at different times, and what they did in one experimental setting might have little relation to what they did in another. Statistical treatment of group data combined data from many individuals, enabling certain patterns to emerge that were characteristic of the statistical group, although the actual behavior of any particular member of the group might not conform to the statistical "average."

Psychologists were eager to apply their knowledge widely to social needs and problems. Military patronage continued in the postwar period, and psychological research on armed forces personnel and human factors was performed, which contributed to foreign policy perspectives in propaganda, counterinsurgency, interrogation techniques, and development studies. On the domestic front, psychologists developed theoretical frameworks and interventional strategies to address such topics as race relations, gender roles, homosexuality, and poverty.

Mainstream psychology was not without its critics. Some urged turning away from apparent "methodolatry," whereas others descried the "physics envy" that grew out of attempts to emulate the physical (and precisely measurable) sciences. In the 1960s, a movement toward humanistic psychology began, prompted by dissatisfaction with behaviorism's narrow methods and the psychoanalytic focus on pathology and its deterministic view about the influence of childhood on personality development. This so-called "third force" represented an attempt to place human values at the core of psychological theory and practice in place of strict objectivism or developmental doctrine, and it spawned some alternate institutional arrangements such as freestanding PsyD programs.

By 1970, the typical psychology department in large American research universities contained a number of subfields, including animal learning and behavior, developmental, cognitive/mathematical, social, physiological, sensory, social, and clinical. In addition, a turn toward research on the biological basis of behavior was greatly aided by a targeted grant program for neuroscience from the Alfred P. Sloan Foundation beginning in the late 1960s, as well as biologically oriented research grant programs within the federal government, especially from the National Institute of Mental Health (established by the National Mental Health Act of 1946). Cognitive psychology became a key part of a new interdisciplinary area, cognitive science, in the late 1970s, again with focused funding from the Sloan philanthropy and some federal agencies, including the National Science Foundation.

In the late 1980s, concerns were raised about the increasing dominance of clinical psychology within the APA, and in 1988 a new organization was formed, the American Psychology Society (renamed the Association for Psychological Science in 2006), broadly focused on the promotion of psychological science and research. The general turn toward somatic explanations and interventions during the last quarter of the twentieth century was marked by various indicators, including the increased use of psychopharmaceutical drugs, the announcement by the Library of Congress and the National Institute of Mental Health declaring the 1990s the "Decade of the Brain," and the renaming by some academic departments to "Psychology and Neuroscience" or "Psychological and Brain Sciences."

The centennial of Wundt's Leipzig laboratory in 1979 provided the occasion not only for celebration by psychologists but also a turn toward critical historiography by historians of psychology. In this context, "critical" supplied a useful contrast to the celebratory uses of history designed to uphold the disciplinary status quo, minimize controversy, and provide a story of linear progress. When the APA passed its century mark in 1992, the tension between celebratory history and critical history was on display in various publications occasioned by the anniversary. The Society for the History of Psychology, Division 26 of the APA, has been in existence since 1965; the society has sponsored an international journal, *History of Psychology*, since 1998.

In the early years of the twenty-first century, psychology remained a protean discipline dedicated to the pursuit of scientific knowledge as well as a potent practically oriented profession serving the mental-health needs of Americans as well as a variety of specific interests in other sectors of American society, including the military, education, business, and law enforcement. Neither a single set of assumptions nor a common methodology unites the work of psychologists. How psychologists have prospered by exploiting this diversity is an intriguing area for historical investigation.

In the pages of an 1893 *McClure's* magazine, Herbert Nichols, one of the first students awarded a doctorate in psychology from an American university, boldly predicted, "the twentieth century will be to mental science what the sixteenth century was to physical science, and the central field of its development is likely to be America" (Nichols, p. 409). In broad outline, Nichols's prediction came true. But the road leading from the era of brass instruments and introspection to the age of computers and cognitive science proved to be both long and with many byways. World wars, economic depression as well as prosperity, and the rise of American higher education provided the setting and context for the growth of psychological thought and practice. Psychology has become intellectually multiparadigmatic, professionally pluralistic, and ideologically diverse. Psychologists, numbering more than a quarter million strong in the United States in 2012, have continued to exert great influence within the culture of modern science and the wider society.

[*See also* Behaviorism; Ethics and Medicine; Foundations and Health; Higher Education and Science; Medicine; Mental Health Institutions; Mental Illness; Military, Science and Technology and the; National Institutes of Health; Psychiatry; Psychotherapy; Public Health; Social Sciences; *and* Sociobiology and Evolutionary Psychology.]

BIBLIOGRAPHY

Ash, Mitchell G. "Psychology." In *The Cambridge History of Science*. Vol. 7, *The Modern Social Sciences*, edited by T. M. Porter and D. Ross, pp. 251–274. Cambridge, U.K.: Cambridge University Press, 2003. A useful overview of major developments.

Benjamin, Ludy T., Jr., and David B. Baker. *From Séance to Science: A History of the Profession of Psychology in America*. Belmont, Calif.: Wadsworth/Thomson Learning, 2004. Explores the history and organization of applied psychology.

Boring, Edwin G. *A History of Experimental Psychology*. 2d ed. New York: Appleton-Century-Crofts, 1950. (Originally published in 1929.) An influential account by a prominent psychologist-historian.

Brock, Adrian C., ed. *Internationalizing the History of Psychology*. New York: New York University Press, 2006. Highlights the polycentric structure of the discipline.

Burnham, John C., ed. *After Freud Left: A Century of Psychoanalysis in America*. Chicago: University of Chicago Press, 2012. A thorough reexamination of Freud's legacy.

Burnham, John C. *Paths into American Culture: Psychology, Medicine, and Morals*. Philadelphia: Temple University Press, 1988. Essays by an influential historian.

Capshew, James H. "History of Psychology since 1945: A North American Review." In *A Historiography of the Modern Social Sciences*, edited by R. E. Backhouse and P. Fontaine. Cambridge, U.K.: Cambridge University Press, 2014. Reviews the development of the specialty.

Capshew, James H. *Psychologists on the March: Science, Practice, and Professional Identity in America, 1929–1969*. New York: Cambridge University Press, 1999. A study of the impact of World War II on the community of psychologists.

Danziger, Kurt. *Constructing the Subject: Historical Origins of Psychological Research*. New York: Cambridge University Press, 1990. A penetrating account of the standardization of methodology and the resultant conceptual and professional power it generated.

Danziger, Kurt. *Naming the Mind: How Psychology Found Its Language*. London: Sage, 1997. A wide exploration of major conceptual categories and psychological terminology.

Eghigian, Greg, Andreas Killen, and Christine Leuenberger, eds. "The Self as Project: Politics and the Human Sciences." *Osiris* 22 (2007): 1–25. Comparative historical case studies of the intersection of psychological sciences and civil society.

Ellenberger, Henri F. *The Discovery of the Unconscious: The History and Evolution of Dynamic Psychiatry*. New York: Basic Books, 1970. A major critique of the "Freud legend" and recontextualization of the history of psychoanalysis.

Hale, Nathan G., Jr. *Freud in America*. 2 vols. New York: Oxford University Press, 1971–1995. A judicious and balanced historical narrative.

Heidbreder, Edna. *Seven Psychologies*. New York: Century, 1933. A sensitive contemporary account of the major schools of psychology.

Herman, Ellen. *The Romance of American Psychology: Political Culture in the Age of Experts*. Berkeley: University of California Press, 1995. A nuanced examination of the role of psychology in public affairs and policy from 1940 to 1975.

Hilgard, Ernest H. *Psychology in America: A Historical Survey*. San Diego: Harcourt Brace Jovanovich, 1987. An authoritative encyclopedic survey by an accomplished psychologist.

Hilgard, Ernest R., David E. Leary, and Gregory R. McGuire. "The History of Psychology: A Survey and Critical Assessment." *Annual Review* of Psychology 42 (1991): 79–107. An even-handed summary of the state of the field.

Koch, Sigmund, and David E. Leary, eds. A Century of Psychology as Science. Washington, D.C.: American Psychological Association, 1992. (Originally published 1985.) Massive collection of historical reflections.

Miner, Burt G. "The Changing Attitude of American Universities toward Psychology." Science, 20 (1904): 299–307.

Morawski, Jill G., ed. The Rise of Experimentation in American Psychology. New Haven, Conn.: Yale University Press, 1988. Historical case studies from a social constructionist perspective.

Neisser, Ulric. Cognitive Psychology. Englewood Cliffs, N.J.: Prentice-Hall, 1967.

Nichols, Herbert. "The Psychological Laboratory at Harvard." McClure's Magazine, 1 (1893), 399–409.

O'Donnell, John M. The Origins of Behaviorism: American Psychology, 1870–1920. New York: New York University Press, 1985. An analytic narrative focused on the transition from philosophy to psychology.

Pickren, Wade, and Alexandra Rutherford. A History of Modern Psychology in Context. Hoboken, N.J.: John Wiley & Sons, 2010. An exemplary undergraduate textbook that reflects current scholarship.

Richards, Graham. "Race," Racism, and Psychology: Towards a Reflexive History. 2d ed. London: Routledge, 2011. (Originally published 1997.) Critical historiography of scientific racism since the late nineteenth century.

Rutherford, Alexandra. Beyond the Box: B. F. Skinner's Technology of Behavior from Laboratory to Life, 1950s–1970s. Toronto: University of Toronto Press, 2009. Effectively conveys the fusion of scientific and social concerns of this influential neo-behaviorist.

Scarborough, Elizabeth, and Laurel Furumoto. Untold Lives: The First Generation of American Women Psychologists. New York: Columbia University Press, 1987. Pathbreaking collective biography that analyzes cultural attitudes and gender discrimination beginning in the late nineteenth century.

Shamdasani, Sonu. Jung and the Making of Modern Psychology: The Dream of a Science. Cambridge, U.K.: Cambridge University Press, 2003. Using the figure of Jung to reassess the history of psychological theory and practice.

Smith, Laurence D. Behaviorism and Logical Positivism: A Reassessment of the Alliance. Stanford: Stanford University Press, 1986. Demolishes the common assumption that major schools of neo-behaviorism were indebted to logical positivism.

Smith, Roger. The Norton History of the Human Sciences. New York: W. W. Norton, 1997. Psychology is the backbone of this massive and informative synthesis that ranges from sixteenth-century thought to twentieth-century American institutions.

Sokal, Michael M., ed. Psychological Testing and American Society, 1890–1930. New Brunswick, N.J.: Rutgers University Press, 1987. Essays that explore the construction, use, and impact of mental testing.

James H. Capshew

PSYCHOPHARMACEUTICAL DRUGS

Around 1860 physicians began diagnosing mental illnesses as medical conditions; they used psychopharmaceuticals mainly to treat symptoms. Stimulants, although available, were rarely used. Large numbers of Americans, of all ages, used depressants, particularly opiates, as hypnotics (to induce sleep) or sedatives. Physician prescriptions played a small role in widespread use of opiates. Physicians began using drugs in new ways; they gave digitalis and hycosine (hensbane/jimson weed) to produce "twilight sleep," a prolonged semiconscious state considered restorative. In 1869 Dr. Otto Liebrich, chemical assistant at the Pathological Institute in Berlin, identified the sedative properties of chloral hydrate. Safer and more reliable, it quickly replaced digitalis for production of therapeutic narcosis. For symptomatic treatment, paraldehyde, bromides, and barbiturates were popular choices around 1900, when physicians mainly used psychopharmaceuticals to sedate, calm, reduce strain on "the nerves," or promote sleep.

Barbiturate use, prescribed mainly for sedative and hypnotic effects, boomed after World War I and continued through the 1960s. Amphetamines, rediscovered in the 1920s, were used as "psychic energizers" from the early 1940s; the best known brands were Benzedrine and Dexedrine. First synthesized in 1944, Ritalin (methylphenidate) was prescribed mainly as a general stimulant (treating depression and fatigue) until the 1970s, when its use for attention deficit hyperactivity disorder steadily increased. Various time-release formulations of methylphenidate remained proprietary products at least through the early twenty-first century.

The 1950s saw rapid development of new drug classes: antipsychotics (termed tranquilizers), anxiolytics (termed ataractics or minor tranquilizers), and antidepressants. The antipsychotic drugs chlorpromazine (marketed as Thorazine) and reserpine were the most notable early successes. Researchers discovered chlorpromazine while investigating ways to prevent shock during or after surgery. It was introduced to the United States, from Europe, in 1953. Rapidly adopted by state mental hospitals, where it seemed to calm the disordered thoughts and behavior of inpatients, chlorpromazine contributed to a significant decrease in the number of long-term institutionalized patients between 1953 and 1960. Researchers in programs investigating traditional medicines isolated compounds with antipsychotic properties from the root of *Rauwolfia serpentina*, a plant used for centuries in India for the treatment of insanity. Frank Berger and Bernard Ludwig synthesized the first anxiolytic, meprobamate, in 1950. Wallace Laboratories in Milltown, New Jersey, launched the drug as Miltown in 1955 as a "minor tranquilizer." Psychiatric institutions used Miltown, but prescribing to outpatients by both psychiatrists and general physicians combined with use by well-known celebrities led to high sales and much public debate over the appropriate medical uses and social costs of creating a tranquilized society. The first drugs marketed as antidepressants, isoniazid and iproniazid, were initially antituberculosis drugs. While testing these antituberculosis drugs, researchers found as a side effect that patients seemed to have a more hopeful outlook; they then tried using the drugs on patients without disease, but with what we would now call depression and noted mood elevation as a side effect. Drug companies promoted iproniazid's energizing effect as an off-label use, but it was pulled from the market in 1961 because of hepatox-

icity. The Swiss company CIBA synthesized the first tricyclic antidepressant, imipramine, in 1951. Researchers believed it was the first psychopharmaceutical to act directly on emotions.

During the 1960s and 1970s, experimenters discovered benzodiazepines and developed variations of existing drug types. They also rediscovered the benefits of lithium as a mood stabilizer. The Roche chemist Leo Sternbach and the pharmacologist Lowell Randall discovered the first benzodiazepines in the late 1950s; the pharmaceutical company marketed the new drugs under the trade names Librium, in 1960, and Valium, in 1963. Physicians prescribed Librium and Valium as minor tranquilizers, antianxiety agents, stress reducers, and treatments for psychosomatic disorders. The medical community used lithium salts, albeit rarely, before 1950 as tranquilizers and to reduce mania. Because the therapeutic dose was close to the dangerous dose, the U.S. Food and Drug Administration did not approve its use until 1970, after significant studies on appropriate dosages and testing blood concentration.

By the end of the 1970s psychopharmacology was generally understood in terms of neurotransmitters. Papers by the Swedish scientists Arvid Carlsson and Margit Lindqvist in 1963 and Jac Van Rossum in 1966 introduced the dopamine hypothesis, that the disregulation of the neurotransmitter dopamine caused schizophrenia. A similar norepinephrine hypothesis for depression was influential from the 1970s to the 1980s, when researchers' focus shifted to the role of serotonin. The widespread use, after its introduction in 1988, of the antidepressant Prozac, a selective serotonin reuptake inhibitor, helped promote scientific research on the connection between serotonin and depression as well as serotonin's role in other modern psychiatric diagnoses, including obsessive-compulsive disorder, premenstrual dysphoric disorder, and bulimia. These neurotransmitter hypotheses played a limited role in drug development or prescribing patterns before the end of the 1970s, when they began shaping drug development. During the 1980s, pharmaceutical companies started screening compounds for interaction with specific receptors in the brain. The hypothesis continued to hold sway over prescribing through the end of the twentieth century. During the 1980s and 1990s, psychopharmaceutical development focused largely on selective action on specific neurotransmitter receptor subtypes. Interest in interaction among dopamine, norepinephrine, and serotonin produced drugs effecting combinations of dopamine and norepinephrine (bupropion/Wellbutrin) or serotonin and norepinephrine (venlafaxine/Effexor). Psychopharmaceuticals became less diagnosis specific. Researchers reexamined existing drugs within this paradigm. As a result, lithium was found in 1998 to have a regulatory effect on the neurotransmitter glutamate.

Historians have emphasized the cultural elements of prescribing and use, the ways chemical compounds are imbued with meaning by the development and marketing process, and the links between the pharmaceutical and medical industries. Pharmaceutical firms from the 1950s onward played an important role in shaping how physicians and the public viewed the nature of mental health and its relationship to pharmaceuticals. Other memes include the threat of mind-altering drugs to individualism and widespread use as inappropriate use. The fluid nature of diagnostic boundaries in mental health helped ensure that debates over the need, extent, and appropriateness of using psychopharmaceuticals continued during the second decade of the twenty-first century, and historians such as David Herzberg, Andrea Tone, David Healy, and Nicolas Rasmussen have helped raise awareness of these debates both within history and more broadly.

[See also Advertising, Medical; Disease; Medicine; Mental Health Institutions; Mental Illness; Pharmacology and Drug Therapy; Psychiatry; Psychology; and Public Health.]

BIBLIOGRAPHY

Efron, Daniel H., ed. Psychopharmacology: A Review of Progress, 1957–1967. Washington, D.C.: American College of Neuropsychopharmacology, 1968. An excellent collection of the most important events and contemporary insights.

Healy, David. The Creation of Psychopharmacology. Cambridge, MA: Harvard University Press, 2002. Great insights from a scholar who has interviewed many of the important figures involved. A detailed discussion of how the pharmaceutical industry promoted broad definition of medically appropriate use for the early antipsychotics/major tranquilizers.

Herzberg, David. Happy Pills in America: From Miltown to Prozac. Baltimore: Johns Hopkins University Press, 2010. Focuses on commercial and social forces producing "blockbuster" drugs. Highlights ways popular culture showed tranquilizers and antidepressants as improving life for an idealized middle class while depicting street drugs being used dangerously by fringe groups.

Lipton, Morris A., Alberto DiMasco, and Keith F. Killam, eds. Psychopharmacology: A Generation of Progress. New York: Raven Press, 1978. Covers what contemporary researchers deemed the most important research and innovations from 1968 to 1978. Series continues with the second generation of progress, third generation, etc.

Rasmussen, Nicolas. On Speed: The Many Lives of Amphetamine. New York: New York University Press, 2009. Details the interplay between the drug and medical industry alongside social commentary. A wonderful mix of archival and published research backs the compelling narrative threads.

Shorter, Edward. A History of Psychiatry: From the Era of the Asylum to the Age of Prozac. New York: John Wiley & Sons, 1997. Incorporates developments in psychopharmacology within psychiatry.

Tone, Andrea. The Age of Anxiety: A History of America's Turbulent Affair with Tranquilizers. New York: Basic Books, 2008. Delightfully accessible. Illustrates the cultural mediation of psychopharmacology mainly in terms of popular perception and scope of use.

Cai Guise-Richardson

PSYCHOTHERAPY

Psychotherapy is the term applied to a wide variety of efforts to foster personal growth and behavioral modification by treating mental and emotional maladies. The main focus has been the use of conversations between therapists and patients designed to disclose inner conflicts and yield psychological insights. Several elements that lent credence to such talking cures were deeply rooted within American culture. Not only did "folk psychology" promote the value of talking things over with a trusted confidant, but also nineteenth-century theological and philosophical discussions of human nature emphasized the importance of the mind as a causal agent in self-fashioning. Still, the birth of psychotherapy as a set of determinate ideas and clinical procedures awaited the discovery of the "subconscious" by the French psychopathologist Pierre Janet and others in the 1880s and 1890s and the use of a variety of techniques—hypnosis, suggestion, and the like—based on persuasion and the "reeducation" of those suffering from psychological distress.

European-based psychotherapeutic ideas and strategies initially encountered fierce resistance from the American medical community. Notwithstanding their inability to discern a physical cause for numerous forms of mental distress and their disturbingly low rate of success in treating those disorders, American physicians continued to attribute mental illness to organic rather than psychological causes. During the late nineteenth and early twentieth centuries, however, several developments converged to foster interest in psychotherapy. Within the larger culture, many Americans became enthralled with Christian Science, New Thought, the Episcopalian-based Emmanuel movement, and other groups that dissented from "medical materialism." At the same time, a small but influential group of neurologists, psychiatrists, and psychologists centered in the Boston area—including James Jackson Putnam, Morton Prince, Boris Sidis, Adolf Meyer, William James, and G. Stanley Hall—began to assign great significance to psychological factors in the cause and treatment of hysteria, anxiety, depression, and a variety of other maladies. During the first decade of the twentieth century the prestige of these individuals, coupled with the desire of many physicians to compete more effectively with what William James termed the "mind-cure" movement, helped to give psychotherapy a foothold within American society.

Freudianism in America. One beneficiary of Americans' increasing tendency to look favorably on psychotherapy was the Austrian physician Sigmund Freud. In Freud's exposition of "depth psychology," the powerful, amoral "drives" residing in the unconscious—most notably the sexual drive, which he termed the libido—played a central role in motivating human behavior. Freud also held that these drives prompted human beings, often in their early years, to generate ideas and wishes so radically at odds with the standards they embraced in their conscious minds that they "repressed" them. This psychic defense mechanism, however, was not always successful; when repressed material did surface, it was capable of causing a wide variety of mental and behavioral disorders. The appropriate therapy for such disorders, Freud maintained, was analysis: a series of sustained discussions with a trained analyst, during which patients could bring repressed material fully to light and integrate it into the conscious mind. Eventually, some patients would even achieve insight into the motives that had led to the initial repression.

After 1909, the year that Freud delivered a series of lectures at Clark University in Worcester, Massachusetts, psychoanalysis not only took root in the United States, but also evolved considerably. This evolution occurred partly because Freud himself continued to modify his views and partly because many professed Freudians altered his emphases. In the process of "Americanizing" Freud, proponents of psychoanalysis muted the conflict between the individual and society and downplayed the master's emphasis on sexuality, aggression, and the centrality of infancy and childhood in the psychological lives of human beings. They also tended to focus more on the role of the ego—the conscious self—and the external environment and less on the intractability of the unconscious. By the early 1940s these views had become institutionalized in a neo-Freudian movement. Karen Horney, Harry Stack Sullivan, Erich Fromm, and other neo-Freudians highlighted the importance of anxiety and the role of interpersonal relationships in personality development.

The Rise of Psychological Counseling. Freudianism often receives the lion's share of attention in historical treatments of psychotherapy, and indeed prior to 1945 most of the psychotherapists in private practice and many of the best-known treatment centers, such as the Menninger Clinic in Topeka, Kansas, were psychoanalytically oriented. Nevertheless, throughout the twentieth century psychoanalysis remained a relatively minor component of the broader psychotherapeutic enterprise. Many people found both the cost and the time involved in analysis prohibitive. In addition, for much of the twentieth century, analysts, like the institutes where they were trained, remained concentrated almost entirely in a relatively few large urban areas. Although the medical profession worked assiduously to secure a monopoly on psychoanalytic practice, this effort did not extend to psychotherapy as a whole. The realization quickly spread that psychotherapeutic skill did not require a medical degree, and during the 1920s and 1930s, practitioners in university counseling centers and community-based child-guidance clinics provided psychotherapy to their clients. The clergy, who were beginning to receive formal training in pastoral counseling, increasingly practiced psychotherapy as part of their vocational effort to cure souls. In fact, prior to World War II, ministers may have provided more hours of therapy in America than all other professional groups combined.

Before 1941, however, few Americans were inclined to describe conversations with their clergy or the other varieties of counseling to which they were exposed as psychotherapy. Rather, most tended to stigmatize psychotherapy as a clinical treatment used exclusively with "crazy people." World War II, however, proved to be a watershed in both the availability and the popularity of therapy. The sheer number of war-related mental disorders made it necessary to bring a growing number of clinical psychologists, who had previously worked in institutional settings assisting educators, physicians, and business executives with aptitude and personality tests, into the counseling setting.

Post–World War II Trends. After the war, clinical psychologists continued to practice psychotherapy. Indeed, during the second half of the twentieth century the number of professionally trained psychotherapists—psychiatrists, clinical psychologists, marriage and school guidance counselors, clinical social workers, and clergy who provided counseling—increased dramatically. By the 1990s, depending on one's criteria for training and licensure, between 100,000 and 250,000 psychotherapists were practicing in the United States.

World War II also helped to democratize psychotherapy. The vigorous campaign of psychiatrists to screen the population for military fitness, coupled with the numerous instances of psychological disturbance associated with the war, suggested that many "normal" people could profit from therapy. In turn, psychotherapy lost much of its stigma. At the same time, health insurance increasingly included coverage for therapeutic practices. By 1990 approximately a third of all Americans had received psychotherapy at some point in their lives.

Post–World War II psychotherapeutic theories and practices varied enormously. Between 1945 and 1970 ego psychology continued to dominate American psychoanalysis. Subsequently, however, many analysts in the United States, influenced especially by British "object relations" theory and the "self psychology" of Hans Kohut, tended to focus on issues relating to representations of self and object and the relationship between them. Within the larger realm of psychotherapy, eclecticism reigned. In the quarter century after 1945, humanistic psychology, most notably the nondirective, "client-centered" practice of Carl Rogers and the "self-actualization" theory associated most closely with Abraham Maslow, became increasingly influential. Humanistic psychologists, who regarded the self as the ultimate source of values, insisted on the ability of individuals to achieve self-determination. Personal growth, rather than mental stability, they maintained, constituted the appropriate goal of human life. Even after the mid-1970s, when mainstream psychological theory began to move away from humanistic psychology, the importance of choice and the desirability of growth continued to be emphasized within therapeutic circles.

Criticism of Psychotherapy and the Pharmacological Challenge.

Criticism of psychotherapy intensified even as its popularity increased. In 1952, for example, the eminent British experimental psychologist Hans Eysenck denied that there was persuasive evidence of psychotherapy's value. Other psychologists and cultural critics echoed this charge. People of the left assailed psychotherapy for fostering adjustment to a corrupt and inhumane status quo, whereas critics on the right charged that it fostered a victim mentality. The assaults on psychoanalysis, and particularly on the legitimacy of Freudian theory and practice, became so intense as the twentieth century ended as to constitute almost a cottage industry.

Perhaps the most serious post-1970 challenge to psychotherapy came from pharmacology. A growing number of newly developed drugs treated not only major mental illnesses but also less serious conditions that in previous years would have prompted people to enter therapy. Mood-altering drugs such as Prozac enjoyed great popularity. Whether drugs served as an appropriate substitute for psychotherapy or simply alleviated symptoms while leaving the underlying causes of mental distress untreated remained a point of controversy.

Notwithstanding the hostility of critics and the presence of alternative approaches, many Americans continued to look to psychotherapy not only as a means of grappling with acute emotional and mental distress but also as a route to self-knowledge and personal growth. So popular and persuasive did psychotherapy's approach to the human condition become that a number of observers characterized late-twentieth-century America as a "therapeutic society."

[*See also* **Hall, G. Stanley; Health and Fitness; Health Insurance; Intelligence, Concepts of; Medicine; Menninger, Karl and William; Mental Health Institutions; Mental Illness; Pharmacology and Drug Therapy; Psychiatry; Psychology; Psychopharmaceutical Drugs; Religion and Science; Sex and Sexuality; Social Sciences;** *and* **War and Medicine.**]

BIBLIOGRAPHY

Burnham, John C. *Paths into American Culture: Psychology, Medicine, and Morals.* Philadelphia: Temple University Press, 1988.

Burnham, John C. "Psychology and Counseling: Convergence into a Profession." In *The Professions in American History*, edited by Nathan O. Hatch, pp. 181–197. Notre Dame, Ind.: University of Notre Dame Press, 1988.

Caplan, Eric. *Mind Games: American Culture and the Birth of Psychotherapy.* Berkeley: University of California Press, 1998.

Eagle, Morris N. *Recent Developments in Psychoanalysis: A Critical Evaluation.* Cambridge, Mass.: Harvard University Press, 1987.

Freedheim, Donald K., ed. *History of Psychotherapy: A Century of Change.* Washington, D.C.: American Psychological Association, 1992.

Hale, Nathan G., Jr. *Freud and the Americans: The Beginnings of Psychoanalysis in the United States, 1876–1917.* New York: Oxford University Press, 1971.

Hale, Nathan G., Jr. *The Rise and Crisis of Psychoanalysis in the United States: Freud and the Americans, 1917–1985.* New York: Oxford University Press, 1995.

Herman, Ellen. *The Romance of American Psychology: Political Culture in the Age of Experts.* Berkeley: University of California Press, 1995.

Illouz, Eva. *Saving the Modern Soul: Therapy, Emotions, and the Culture of Self-help.* Berkeley: University of California Press, 2008.

Myers-Shirk, Susan E. *Helping the Good Shepherd: Pastoral Counselors in a Psychotherapeutic Culture 1920–1975.* Baltimore: Johns Hopkins University Press, 2009.

Jon H. Roberts

PUBLIC HEALTH

Communities continually confront issues of public health. What is the health status of an aggregate population? How is that determined? As a collective, what threats does a community face? How are those defined? What and how are responses formulated? Answering these questions is contingent on time and place. Throughout the history of the United States, responses vacillated between relying on individual and governmental action. Determining responsibility was a negotiated and often contested process. Medical practitioners, the general public, business, and government officials shaped debates about when and how to protect the public's health.

The Colonial Period. Encounter shaped the dynamics of public health in the colonial period of American history. The movement of goods and people among three continents from the sixteenth to the eighteenth centuries resulted in exchange of microbes, medical knowledge, and healing practices. Native peoples, Europeans, and Africans became exposed to and transmitted what are recognizable in the early twenty-first century as smallpox, malaria, yellow fever, measles, syphilis, and other contagious diseases. Although much differentiated Native peoples, Europeans, and Africans, at times a shared faith in the power of spiritual and herbal remedies transcended cultural divides. Yet, traditional healing practices proved no match for epidemics, particularly smallpox. This disease decimated the population of indigenous people, nor did it leave Europeans unscathed.

An epidemic of smallpox in Boston in 1721 illustrates the politics and practices of public health in this historical period. The appearance of smallpox elicited fear for a variety of reasons. Most took its arrival as a sign from God that the community had sinned and waited to see whether that punishment extended to the individual. Within the city of approximately 12 thousand, the Selectmen—the town's governing board—responded to the outbreak with a series of methods that resonated with common European practice. They ordered the quarantine of the H.M.S. *Seahorse* (the ship from which the first cases of smallpox developed), they ordered the houses of the sick quarantined and later created an isolation space to remove the ailing, and they ordered the cleaning of the streets. Yet, these actions did not prevent the number of cases from increasing. One prominent clergyman, Cotton Mather, began advocating an alternative response: inoculation.

In 1721, whether to introduce smallpox into a healthy body was simultaneously a moral and sci-entific question. Mather's support for inoculation met dramatic dispute from the community's university-educated physicians, William Douglass in particular. One apprentice-trained physician, Zabdiel Boylston, encouraged by Mather, began inoculating members of the community, including his own six-year-old son. Believing that they were protecting the public's health, the Selectmen ordered Boylston to stop. He did not. In the end, Boylston was called before a town meeting and induced to swear that he would not engage in the practice again unless he did so with the prior approval of the board. The final tally of the dead was over eight hundred, which accounted for more than 75 percent of all deaths in Boston that year.

The episodic nature of epidemics and contemporary theories of disease transmission prompted local governments to constitute formal methods of health regulation only during a perceived crisis. The limited nature with which the Selectmen responded reflected existing attitudes about the role of the state. At first, colonial governments left the regulation of everyday sanitary conditions up to private individuals. Constructing an infrastructure to cope with "nuisances"—garbage, sewage, and removal of dead animal carcasses from the streets—was a slow and uneven process. Nonetheless, demographic increase throughout the colonies prompted communities to adopt sanitary regulations, especially of privies.

The Nineteenth Century. Throughout the nineteenth century, issues of sanitation and epidemic diseases continued to figure prominently in the development of public health. Cholera and yellow fever played particular influence in the creation of permanent government structures to respond to health threats. Cholera broke out in the United States (and globally) in three major waves: 1832 to 1833, 1849 to 1850, and 1866 to 1867. In contrast to smallpox, cholera elicited no precipitating symptoms. Instead, from its onset, cholera acted with ferocious swiftness upon its victims. The dramatic severity of rapid dehydration and seemingly indiscriminate patterns of occurrence evoked widespread panic among urban residents. Those who had the means abandoned cities, an age-old strategy for avoiding an epidemic. In doing so, however, commerce suffered. Business interests, therefore, often put pressure on municipal officials to exercise restraint in taking public-health action. As a consequence, municipalities muted reports that tallied fatalities and delayed proclaiming quarantines.

Epidemiological work in Great Britain by John Snow in the 1850s, which mapped outbreaks of cholera in relation to specific water pumps, began to impact public-health policies in the United States in the 1860s. Understanding transmission altered civic strategies. Preventing an epidemic of cholera now appeared feasible. Based on this reorientation, the New York state legislature passed the New York Metropolitan Health Act of 1866, which authorized the establishment of a permanent board of health for New York City and invested it with police powers. The resultant Metropolitan Board of Health provided an administrative model for other cities.

Epidemics of yellow fever also resulted in thousands of deaths in the nineteenth century. Spread by mosquitos, the virus initially caused head, joint, and muscle aches, a fever, vomiting, and jaundice. After approximately three to four days, some patients recovered. Others, however, experienced multiorgan dysfunction and the vomiting of "black" blood. The terrifying nature of the disease prompted municipalities to form temporary boards of health, but fear over the loss of commerce typically stymied vigorous action; officials were slow to enact quarantines. Between 1793 and 1806, every port along the East Coast experienced a serious outbreak of yellow fever. The construction of water systems alleviated much of the problem for the Northeast. In contrast, yellow fever remained a chronic disease in Southern cities. A string of outbreaks in the 1850s prompted Louisiana's state legislators to establish a state board of health, the first in the nation, in 1855. In reality, however, its powers did not extend beyond the boundaries of New Orleans. A particularly devastating outbreak occurred in 1878. The disease spread throughout Southern cities, hitting Memphis and New Orleans especially hard, and traveled up the Mississippi Valley as far as Ohio. Physicians and the news media put pressure on the federal government to take action.

The American Public Health Association (established in 1872) advocated the creation of a National Board of Health to serve as a central bureau for the data collection of disease and to standardize and supervise quarantine regulations throughout the nation. The outbreak gave this idea traction and Congress authorized a National Board of Health in 1879. Although the board's powers were still quite limited, opposition formed quickly against this entity. Those devoted to state's rights theory and those invested in the already existing Marine Hospital Service lobbied Congress to allow the bill to expire in 1883 and 10 years later to repeal it. (In 1798, Congress established the U.S. Marine Hospital Service to provide a minimum of health care for seamen because it was custom in Great Britain. Moreover, from a business perspective, seamen's health mattered because they provided the labor that undergirded commerce.) Officially deceased, the Marine Hospital Service subsumed the National Board of Health's powers. In doing so, this federal agency (renamed the U.S. Public Health Service in 1912) became an important apparatus in determining national public-health policy at the turn of the twentieth century.

The rising use of statistics to study social problems also contributed to transforming the role of the state in relation to public health. Industrialization in Western Europe prompted the first attempts to gather vital statistics and generate quantitative data about health. The work of Edwin Chadwick in England was particularly influential. His *Report on the Sanitary Condition of the Labouring Population of Great Britain* (1842) correlated rates of disease and poverty; it definitively proved that environment mattered. Chadwick's widely disseminated report justified the establishment of a permanent governmental administration for health issues and the development of civic infrastructure related to health, especially water and sewage systems. As a consequence, a sanitary movement took form. These efforts were bolstered by a growing belief that when filth interacted with the air it could result in a miasma, a noxious gas that stimulated sickness.

In the United States, Chadwick's work inspired activism. In New York City, John H. Griscom, a member of the New York Academy of Medicine and an inspector for New York City, collected data on the status of environmental health conditions in living and working spaces that were commonly understood as "nuisances." His unflattering report of 1842 led to his dismissal as an official public servant. Undeterred, Griscom reprinted his report, expanded it, and continued efforts to effect change until his death in 1874. Chadwick also influenced Lemuel Shattuck, a scholar and statistician. Shattuck believed that he could enhance the ability of government to respond to social ills through the collection of statistics. Best known for his 1850 survey of sanitary conditions in Massachusetts, he proposed that the state adopt a comprehensive plan for approaching questions of public health. Although the state legislature did not immediately implement his proposals, most became routine activities within a century. These efforts were aided by the establishment of the Massachusetts Board of Health in 1869, which was the second of its kind in the United States. The state legislature invested this agency with the power to collect vital statistics and to investigate matters of public health. Its methodical inquiries into quality-of-life issues (sewage, water and food purity, and tenement conditions) provided a model for other state boards of health, which were established with greater frequency throughout the latter half of the nineteenth century.

Although the Civil War did not drastically alter strategies of sanitation, it speeded up its applications. Illness, either from camp conditions or from battle wounds, resulted in a chilling number of casualties. At the start of the war, neither the Union nor the Confederacy was ready to house and care for the thousands of men who awaited battle. Many of these soldiers hailed from rural areas and had not yet been exposed to highly contagious diseases. Those who survived this seasoning were plagued by diarrheic diseases wrought by faulty or ill-advised privy construction and placement. In New York, elite women formed an association to organize volunteer efforts. Drawing inspiration from Florence Nightingale's works during the British engagement in the Crimean War, they desired to coordinate with the U.S. Army to attend to its needs and wants for medical supplies and nursing personnel. Yet, the army and the nation's highest government officials originally rejected the idea of a volunteer commission. In 1861, however, the leaders of volunteerism prevailed in convincing President Abraham Lincoln of the utility of such an organization and the secretary of war ordered the creation of the U.S. Sanitary Commission. Frederick Law Olmstead served as its executive secretary and women worked to raise money and collect food, clothing, and medical supplies. In addition to direct assistance, the U.S. Sanitary Commission compelled army officials to overhaul environmental conditions at the camps. Instead of continuing a pattern of generating ad hoc reactions to outbreaks of disease, the commission contended that sickness could be prevented through systematic education and infrastructural reform.

From the Late Nineteenth Century into the Twentieth Century. In the postwar period, efforts to reform the built environment continued to inform public-health policy. Often termed the Progressive Era, reformers displayed an unwavering faith in the social capacity of government to raise the nation's standard of living. The first transformations occurred at the local level and were often instigated by women engaged in the settlement-house movement, the most famous of which was Hull House in Chicago. Founded by Jane Addams in 1889 and staffed by middle-class female volunteers, this community center provided social services—maternal and infant health programs and a visiting nursing service—for the working-class immigrant neighborhood within which it sat. In addition to direct aid, Hull House staff agitated to effect changes in public policy by exerting pressure on politicians. They combined statistical studies with a program of publicity to draw attention to the corruption and ineffective management that impacted the daily lives of Chicago's poorer residents. They also formulated municipal, and later state and federal law, to regulate industrial safety and promote the public's health, especially in the area of children's health.

The advent of the germ theory in the late nineteenth century gradually transformed approaches to public health. Scientists and physicians working in Germany and France in the 1880s began, with great rapidity, to catalog the bacilli responsible for some of the world's deadliest diseases: tuberculosis, diphtheria, and typhoid fever, to name a few. Grand-scale engineering projects to promote sanitation seemed unnecessary when a laboratory test could identify the individual microbe causing a specific disease. The germ theory offered a new rationale for state action and revived calls for individual responsibility in disease control.

Among other things, the bacteriological revolution provided a new justification for civic expenditures on municipal laboratories. Efforts in chemical analysis existed prior to the germ theory's articulation. At first, many of these laboratories functioned as locations to analyze food substances, particularly milk, for adulteration. In this way, public health served to protect the interests of consumers in an increasingly multifaceted urban economy. Small urban business owners often objected to the expansion of government regulation. In contrast, large business owners and the American Medical Association came to see federal regulation as being in their best interest and helped to write the Pure Food and Drug Act of 1906 and the Meatpacking Act of 1906. Physicians, in particular, hoped to stamp out what they viewed as "quackery."

In addition to chemical analysis, civic laboratories now became sites of production for vaccines and antitoxins in the battle against disease. Mounting effective campaigns, however, was not inevitable success. Diphtheria, for instance, was a major public-health concern in the nineteenth century because it was a significant cause of childhood mortality. Diagnosis was difficult. The first symptom, a sore throat, was vague. Only the spread of an expanse of a gray, thick, fibrous material in the back of the throat, which obstructed breathing, made it unmistakable. Yet, by then, it was too late. In the 1890s, the director of New York City's Health Department, Hermann Biggs, set out to initiate the first extensive use of bacteriology in a public-health campaign. The department proposed to take responsibility for producing and then distributing diphtheria antitoxin to local physicians. Skeptics from the medical com-

munity and the general public needed to be convinced of the efficacy of this new public policy. In particular, the laboratory drew into question the derivation of medical authority. Physicians needed to reconfigure their professional identities to assimilate this new science in relation to their belief in the power of experience. Despite the complexities of implementation, the value of scientific medicine appeared borne out by the lowering of mortality rates associated with the disease.

The reorientation of public health from the environment to the lab led to a retooling of the profession. Learning to be a public-health professional became a formalized process. With the help of the Rockefeller Foundation, Johns Hopkins opened the first school of public health in the nation in 1916 and Harvard opened the second in 1922. Their graduates found positions in local, state, and the federal government as each expanded their public-health structures throughout the twentieth century. The Sheppard–Towner Act of 1921, for instance, provided states with matching grants to develop programs to promote maternal and infant health. This allowed Mississippi, for instance, to pay to bring black midwives into state-run "training" programs. In the 1930s, President Franklin D. Roosevelt's New Deal programs funneled significant funds to public-health programs, especially in the area of rural health. The Social Security Act of 1935 not only allocated tremendous funds for maternal and infant health programs but also set aside assistance to states and municipalities to construct health and sanitary facilities and reorganize administrative structures. The American Medical Association supported these endeavors as long as government limited its engagement to what private physicians perceived to be preventive activities. When physicians believed that public-health programs treaded on their territory of therapeutics, they organized against these policies.

The combination of nineteenth-century environmental projects and twentieth-century vaccines and serums changed the subject of public-health questions. Chronic diseases became the focus: cancer, diabetes, stroke, and heart disease. Yet, not all populations experienced this shift equally. The politics of race, class, and region impacted public-health responses to diseases such as tuberculosis, syphilis, and sickle-cell anemia among minority communities. The Watts riots in Los Angeles, California, in August 1965 drew particular attention to the discrepancy in access to medical care between the city's white and black residents. Activists in the 1960s also exposed problems of access for the geriatric population. The passage of Medicare and Medicaid in 1965 (which occurred a month before the riots in Watts) further expanded government's role in facilitating public access to health services, both preventive and therapeutic, that shaped the health of communities in general.

In the late twentieth century, issues of gender, race, and sexuality continued to shape public-health questions. Congressional hearings over the safety of the Pill in 1970, for example, raised issues of the U.S. Food and Drug Administration's processes of approval, the role of pharmaceutical companies in that process, and what constituted informed consent in relation to women's health. In the 1980s, public-health professionals confronted a new epidemic disease, AIDS. Because many of the initial victims were gay men and Haitians, public-health professionals needed to fight homophobia and racism in addition to attempting to curb its spread. Congress continues to hear voices of proponents and protesters over the role of government in protecting the health status of minorities and women. One avenue by which this achieved is through scientific research.

In the mid-twentieth century, the federal government began to offer substantial subsidies for biomedical research. During World War II, the government developed an official office for controlling malaria and transformed it in 1946 into the Communicable Disease Center (later renamed the Centers for Disease Control and Prevention.) Two years later, Congress established the National Heart Institute, the National Institute of Dental Research, and the National Biological Institute and then placed these organizations under the umbrella of the National Institute of Health, which then became renamed the National Institutes of Health. (The National Institute of Health traced its origins back to the Marine Hospital Service, when one of its staff members set up a bacteriology laboratory in 1887 on Staten Island, New York. It became known as the Hygienic Laboratory. In 1930, it was renamed the National Institute of Health and Congress authorized it to provide research fellowships. It suffered, however, from a lack of funding until World War II.) In 1948, Congress appropriated the National Institutes of Health slightly less than $30 million. By comparison, its budget was just over $30 billion in 2014. The National Institutes of Health has grown to include 27 institutes and centers with a goal of conducting scientific research to save lives.

At the start of the twenty-first century, the National Institutes of Health was just one piece of larger public-health infrastructure within the United States. Several different agencies at the federal level (not to mention the myriad of organizations at the state and local level) engaged in work related to public health: the Environmental Protection Agency, the Consumer Product Safety Commission, the Immigration and Naturalization Service, and the Occupational Safety and Health Administration, among others. Moreover, the Public Health Service functioned as a primary division within the Department of Health and Human Services, a Cabinet department. Its concerns have reached beyond the borders of the United States, however. The Public Health Service has worked with the World Health Organization, a United Nations agency, to protect the public's health in a global context. In the course of over three hundred years, public health has become a fundamental aspect of government and, at the same time, fluid in its composition and character.

[*See also* **Alzheimer's Disease and Dementia; Asthma and Allergy; Cancer; Centers for Disease Control and Prevention; Cholera; Diabetes; Diphtheria; Disease; Environmental Protection Agency; Foundations and Health; Germ Theory of Disease; Health and Fitness; Health Insurance; HIV/AIDS; Hospitals; Indian Health Service; Influenza; Malaria; Medical Education; Medicare and Medicaid; Medicine; Mental Illness; National Institutes of Health; Nursing; Obesity; Occupational**

Diseases; Poliomyelitis; Public Health Service, U.S.; Pure Food and Drug Act; Race and Medicine; Smallpox; Tuberculosis; Tuskegee Syphilis Study; Typhoid Fever; Typhus; War and Medicine; World Health Organization; *and* Yellow Fever.]

BIBLIOGRAPHY

Blake, John B. "The Inoculation Controversy in Boston: 1721–1722." *New England Quarterly* 25 (1952): 489–506.

Calloway, Colin G. "Healing and Disease." In *New Worlds for All: Indians, Europeans and the Remaking of Early America*. Baltimore: Johns Hopkins University Press, 1997.

Duffy, John. *The Sanitarians: A History of American Public Health*. Urbana: University of Illinois Press, 1990. Duffy's survey provides a cohesive narrative with which to learn about the transformation of public health as informed by social, economic, political, and cultural forces. Using a comparative approach, Duffy examines changes in public health at the local, regional, and federal levels from the colonial period to the twentieth century.

Galishoff, Stuart. *Newark, the Nation's Unhealthiest City, 1832–1895*. New Brunswick, N.J.: Rutgers University Press, 1988. Galishoff explains the process by which the city worked with nongovernmental organizations to convince its citizens, especially businessmen, to invest in the infrastructures of sanitation.

Hammonds, Evelynn Maxine. *Childhood's Deadly Scourge: The Campaign to Control Diphtheria in New York City, 1880–1930*. Baltimore: Johns Hopkins University Press, 1999. In looking to know how and why diphtheria became one of the first infectious diseases to be medically controlled, Hammonds reveals the role of politics and public persuasion in the formulation of medical policy.

Humphreys, Margaret. *Yellow Fever in the South*. New Brunswick, N.J.: Rutgers University Press, 1992. Humphreys details why yellow fever, never responsible for the most deaths in the South, motivated governmental action. In particular, she reveals the centrality of economic considerations in public-health decisions.

Koslow, Jennifer. *Cultivating Health: Los Angeles Women and Public Health Reform*. New Brunswick, N.J.: Rutgers University Press, 2009. Koslow explores why women, instead of city officials, took charge of public health. She looks at how women used science and maternalism to argue for an expanded role for government and citizen action.

Leavitt, Judith Walzer. *The Healthiest City: Milwaukee and the Politics of Health Reform*. Princeton, N.J.: Princeton University Press, 1982. In contrast to studies focused on the role of the scientific laboratory in stemming the spread of infectious disease, Leavitt's work drew attention to the important role of municipal officials in alleviating threats to public health between the mid-nineteenth century and the early twentieth century.

Melosi, Martin. *The Sanitary City: Urban Infrastructure in America from Colonial Times to the Present*. Baltimore: Johns Hopkins University Press, 2000. *The Sanitary City* charts the rise and neglect of the central engineering constructions of public health: water supply, sewage, and solid waste disposal systems. This comprehensive synthetic study traces these developments over time and through space.

Rosenberg, Charles E. *The Cholera Years: The United States in 1832, 1849, 1866*. Chicago: University of Chicago Press, 1962. Using cholera as the focal point, Rosenberg's classic text demonstrates how social perspectives and prejudices inform medical knowledge and practice. Moreover, the work reveals the fluid nature of perception that results in the transformation of scientific beliefs over time.

Smith, Susan. *Sick and Tired of Being Sick and Tired: Black Women's Health Activism in America, 1890–1950*. Philadelphia: University of Pennsylvania Press, 1995. Women's volunteer organizations, Smith shows, worked to provide crucial public-health resources for African Americans when the state was not forthcoming. Smith demonstrates the complicated nature of these developments as African Americans partnered with programs, such as the U.S. Public Health Service's Tuskegee Syphilis Study.

Tomes, Nancy. *The Gospel of Germs: Men, Women, and the Microbe in American Life*. Cambridge, Mass.: Harvard University Press, 1998. Tomes explains how old and new systems of knowledge about the origins of disease initially comfortably coexisted. In addition, she evidences the gendered aspects of the sanitation movement and its relationship to the application of the germ theory to everyday life.

Watkins, Elizabeth Siegel. *On the Pill: A Social History of Oral Contraceptives, 1950–1970.* Baltimore: Johns Hopkins University Press, 1998. Confronting mythology, Watkins details the creation, marketing, and consumption of the birth-control pill.

Jennifer Koslow

PUBLIC HEALTH SERVICE, U.S.

The U.S. Public Health Service (PHS) traces its origins to the Marine Hospital Service (MHS), which was established in 1798 to provide care to sick and disabled American merchant seamen. In 1870, complaints of poor service and cost overruns led to a centralization of the MHS under a supervising surgeon in Washington, D.C. John M. Woodworth, the first supervising surgeon and a former army physician, adopted a military model for his professional staff. In 1889, this reform was institutionalized by legislation that created the Commissioned Corps of the hospital service and gave officers the same titles and pay as military physicians.

The first step in the evolution of the MHS into a national public-health agency began in 1878, when, in response to a yellow fever epidemic the year before that had spread up the Mississippi River Valley from New Orleans and killed approximately 20 thousand, Congress passed a quarantine act giving oversight of quarantines to the MHS. By the turn of the twentieth century, propelled by further epidemics and growing public awareness that major killer diseases were caused by germs and could be prevented, the agency had broadened its scope through a series of congressional acts to include interstate quarantine (1890), expanded maritime quarantine (1890, 1893), and health inspection of immigrants (1891). A bacteriology laboratory established in 1887 began a research program that eventually evolved into today's National Institutes of Health (NIH). The MHS also began to collect and publish national health statistics. These added missions devolved upon the hospital service because it was the only civilian cadre of physicians in the federal government.

The next major formal expansion came after the MHS, led by future Surgeon General Rupert Blue, began a successful effort to eradicate and prevent the spread of bubonic plague when it arrived in San Francisco in 1900. In 1902, Congress changed the name of the MHS to Public Health and Marine Hospital Service, dropped "Supervising" from the Surgeon General's title, and provided more authority and funding. Another 1902 law gave the agency authority to regulate the manufacture of biologics in response to the death of 13 children in St. Louis from tainted diphtheria antitoxin. In 1912, Congress shortened the name to Public Health Service and granted it broad authority to "study and investigate the diseases of man" and their causes, including pollution. The 1912 act created a division of scientific research alongside divisions of foreign quarantine and immigration, domestic quarantine and sanitation, sanitary reports and statistics, and marine hospitals. The act also authorized annual conferences with state and territorial health officers, which became an important part of a growing effort to improve state and local public-health departments.

As the PHS's mission expanded, so did the size and composition of the Commissioned Corps, from 135 in 1912 to 6,500 a century later. Originally limited to physicians, the Corps over the years added 10 additional health disciplines, which in 2011 accounted for 85 percent of the commissioned officers.

The 1935 Social Security Act included a program administered by the PHS to support state and local public-health activities through federal funding and training programs. Two years later Congress established the National Cancer Institute (NCI), which became the model for the reorganization of the NIH in 1948 around feared diseases in the postwar period. The PHS began to provide health care for the Bureau of Prisons, Bureau of Indian Affairs, Coast Guard, and, for a few years after World I, veterans. In World War II, as in World War I, the PHS focused on venereal-disease control and other public-health measures, especially around military training bases. This effort led to the creation of the Communicable Disease Center, now called the Centers for Disease Control and Prevention (CDC), in 1946. After World War II, the NIH quickly emerged as the primary agency within the PHS, eventually accounting for half the parent organization's budget and growing into the principal source of financial funding for biomedical research in the country. The PHS also administered the 1946 Hill–Burton hospital construction program. The Food and Drug Administration was transferred into the PHS in 1968 and took over biologics regulation from the NIH.

In the late 1930s, Surgeon General Thomas Parran supported federally funded medical services for the poor and national health insurance, which created tensions with the medical profession but failed to satisfy progressives who doubted that the PHS was sufficiently committed to national health services programs. In the 1960s, new health professional training programs were assigned to the PHS, but Congress did not consider the PHS responsive enough to run such big new programs as Medicare and Medicaid, which were thus assigned to a separate agency. In 1968, the Surgeon General became an advisor to a new politically appointed position, the assistant secretary for health, who took over direct supervision of the PHS, including the Commissioned Corps. At the same time, the general practice of appointing top PHS leadership positions, such as the Surgeon General and the heads of the NIH and CDC, from the career service gave way to appointments of distinguished physicians and scientists from academia and industry. The Surgeons General have, however, continued their role as the authoritative voice of public health, established earlier by Thomas Parran's campaign against syphilis in the 1930s and Luther Terry's 1964 report on smoking and health. More recent examples of such leadership include Julius Richmond's 1979 report on health prevention and disease prevention (which launched a series of 10-year initiatives called Healthy People, currently Healthy People 2020) and Everett Koop's politically controversial call to treat AIDS as a public-health problem in the 1980s. The PHS's most embarrassing moment came in the early 1970s, when journalists and historians revealed the agency's four-decades-long study of untreated syphilis among African American males in and around Tuskegee, Alabama.

In 2003 the Surgeon General was given an increased role in the day-to-day management of the Corps, with the establishment of the Office of Commissioned Corps Operations, which collaborated with the Office of Commissioned Corps Force Management under the Assistant Secretary for Health and Human Services. As of 2012, although the PHS was no longer an autonomous agency of the federal government, eight divisions of the Department of Health and Human Services were identified as PHS agencies: the prominent NIH, FDC, and CDC, as well as the smaller Agency for Healthcare Research and Quality, the Agency for Toxic Substances and Disease Registry, the Health Resources and Services Administration, the Indian Health Service, and the Substance Abuse and Mental Health Services Administration (the Marine Hospitals had closed in 1981).

[See also Centers for Disease Control and Prevention; Disease; Health Insurance; HIV/AIDS; Medicare and Medicaid; National Institutes of Health; Public Health; Sexually Transmitted Diseases; Tuskegee Syphilis Study; and Yellow Fever.]

BIBLIOGRAPHY

Etheridge, Elizabeth W. *Sentinel for Health: A History of the Centers for Disease Control*. Berkeley and Los Angeles: University of California Press, 1992.

Furman, Bess. *A Profile of the United States Public Health Service, 1798–1948*. Washington, D.C.: U.S. Government Printing Office, 1971.

Greenberg, George D. "Reorganization Reconsidered: The U.S. Public Health Service 1960–1973." *Public Policy* 23 (Fall 1975): 483–522.

Harden, Victoria A. *Inventing the NIH: Federal Biomedical Research Policy, 1887–1937*. Baltimore: Johns Hopkins University Press, 1986.

Kastor, John A. *The National Institutes of Health, 1991–2008*. New York: Oxford University Press, 2010.

Mullan, Fitzhugh. *Plagues & Politics: The Story of the United States Public Health Service*. New York: Basic Books, 1989.

Michael McGeary

PURE FOOD AND DRUG ACT

Signed into law on 30 June 1906 by President Theodore Roosevelt, the Food and Drugs Act—popularly known as the Pure Food and Drug Act—with its companion piece, the Meat Inspection Amendment, originated the regulatory apparatus that became the Food and Drug Administration. This landmark statute prohibited the "misbranding" of any foodstuff or pharmaceutical offered for sale or their "adulteration" by any ingredient not specified on the label. Congress authorized the Bureau of Chemistry of the Department of Agriculture to enforce the law by testing random specimens for misbranding or adulteration, notifying suspect manufacturers, and granting them a hearing. Only if a manufacturer refused to comply could the bureau turn the case over to a district attorney for prosecution. Convictions carried fines of up to $300 and imprisonment for up to one year, with confiscation of the offending product the ultimate punishment.

Dr. Harvey W. Wiley (1844–1930), chief chemist of the Department of Agriculture from 1883 to 1912, was the moving force behind the law. Wiley publicized the problem by feeding dubious preservatives to volunteers dubbed the "poison squad." For over two decades, Wiley functioned as the chief propagandist, organizer, and strategist for the law and then as its principal enforcer. Public support for such a law grew steadily thanks to a series of reports on harmful and unsanitary meatpacking processes published in muckraking magazines and in Upton Sinclair's 1906 exposé, *The Jungle*. The measure won backing from a broad-based coalition including the National Association of State Dairy and Food Departments, the National Consumers' League, the American Medical Association, and the General Federation of Women's Clubs, joined by some well-established manufacturers seeking to eliminate marginal competitors. Its opponents included the National Food Manufacturers' Association, the National Liquor Wholesale Dealers' Association, and the Proprietary Association of America, the drug industry's lobbying arm. Sponsored by two Republican senators and two GOP congressmen and aided by an 11th-hour endorsement by Roosevelt, the final bill passed both houses by overwhelming margins and stands as a major Progressive-Era legislative achievement.

[*See also* **Agriculture, U.S. Department of; American Medical Association; Food and Diet; Food Processing; Health and Fitness;** *and* **Pharmacology and Drug Therapy.**]

BIBLIOGRAPHY

Anderson, Oscar E., Jr. *The Health of a Nation: Harvey W. Wiley and the Fight for Pure Food.* Chicago: University of Chicago Press, 1958.
Young, James Harvey. *Pure Food: Securing the Federal Food and Drugs Act of 1906.* Princeton, N.J.: Princeton University Press, 1989.

John D. Buenker

Q

QUANTUM THEORY

Quantum physics had its start in 1900 with Max Planck's theory of heat radiation, which eventually was transformed into a theory of atomic structure and, from 1925, to the modern form of quantum mechanics. From 1900 to about 1913 the theory was largely restricted to radiation phenomena and attracted only modest attention. This changed with Niels Bohr's 1913 quantum model of the atom, which brought quantum theory in intimate connection with spectroscopy and atomic structure. A third phase began in the fall of 1925, when Bohr's theory was replaced by a new "quantum mechanics" pioneered by Werner Heisenberg and other German physicists. By the end of the decade, quantum mechanics was practically complete and universally recognized as a fundamental theory. In all three phases, quantum theory was dominated by German physicists or by Europeans with close connections to the German centers in Berlin, Munich, and Göttingen.

American physicists, by far most of whom were experimentalists, did not contribute to the first phase. In 1911 the status and future of the quantum theory were discussed by leading physicists at the first Solvay Congress in Brussels. No American physicists were invited to take part in this important meeting. Although they showed little interest in quantum theory, they were not ignorant of it, and a few worked on subjects related to it. One of the few was Robert Millikan at the University of Chicago, who investigated the photoelectric effect and in 1910 gave a course on Planck's radiation theory. It took some years until American physicists responded to Bohr's atomic theory, which only became generally known—not generally accepted—in about 1917. It attracted critical attention among chemists who typically objected that it was conceptually strange and useless for chemical purposes.

The slow rise of quantum theory in the United States mostly occurred in connection with experiments and molecular spectroscopy. Edwin Kemble of Harvard University completed his dissertation in 1917 and subsequently turned to the atomic theory of Bohr and its development by the Munich physicist Arnold Sommerfeld. In 1920 he started giving courses at Harvard dealing with quantum theory, probably the first such course in the United States. From that time papers on atomic and quantum theory began to appear regularly in the *Physical Review*, the journal of the American Physical Society. Although most of the papers were experimental, some were theoretical, and several attracted interest among the European experts in quantum theory. The molecular approach to quantum theory was cultivated not only by Kemble, but also by his Harvard colleague Robert Mulliken, by David Dennison at the University of Michigan, and by Raymond Birge at the University of California. By 1925 molecular spectroscopy was an American specialty in quantum theory unmatched in Europe.

Although progress in the theory of atomic structure continued to be dominated by German and other European physicists, a few young Americans contributed importantly to the field. Foremost among them were John Slater at Harvard and John Van Vleck at the University of Minnesota. The most important contribution was, however, experimental, namely Arthur Compton's famous experiment on the scattering of X-rays from 1923 in which he showed X-rays to behave like particles. Four years later he was awarded the Nobel Prize for his discovery of the "Compton effect." The drastic rise in the quantity and quality of American quantum physics in the early 1920s depended to some extent on lecture series by prominent European physicists and even more on the stays of American physicists at European centers. The most important of these centers, Bohr's institute in Copenhagen, was a favorite destination, with more visitors from the United States than from any other country.

Although no American physicists were directly involved in the quantum revolution that led to Heisenberg's quantum mechanics in 1925 and a little later to Erwin Schrödinger's wave mechanics, they were well prepared to adopt and develop the new theory. The early phase of quantum mechanics, from 1925 to 1927, was extremely competitive, and in the publication race American physicists could not quite keep up with their colleagues in Europe. Quantum mechanics was a German invention, and it took some time before Americans could read the articles in the German physics journals. Their knowledge of the new physics came in part from lectures given by foreign physicists, of which a lecture series by Max Born, one of the German pioneers of quantum mechanics, was particularly important. From late 1925 Born spent three months at the Massachusetts Institute of Technology, where he gave an extensive series of lectures and collaborated with the young mathematician Norbert Wiener on a new mathematical formulation of quantum mechanics.

Several American physicists experienced the quantum revolution while staying in Europe, such as J. Robert Oppenheimer, who wrote a doctoral dissertation in Göttingen under Born's supervision. When he returned to America, he created an important school of quantum theory in California. Oppenheimer was not the only American physicist to make important contributions to quantum mechanics. Carl Eckart, then at the California Institute of Technology, was among the first to prove the formal equivalence of quantum mechanics and wave mechanics, and in 1928 the Princeton physicist Edward Condon, in collaboration with the British visitor Ronald Gurney, applied wave mechanics to understand the radioactivity originating in the atomic nucleus. On the experimental side, the most important result was the experiments on electron diffraction made in 1927 by Clinton Davisson and his assistant Lester Germer at the Western Electric engineering department. This work proved the wave nature of electrons predicted by quantum mechanics and earned Davisson a Nobel Prize 10 years later.

By the late 1920s, American physicists not only had caught up with the development in quantum physics, but also were among the leaders in the field. Of the 281 papers that appeared in the 1929 issues of *Physical Review*, about 45 dealt with aspects of quantum mechanics. At that time, 14 American universities offered courses in quantum mechanics, some of them based on Condon's and Philip Morse's *Quantum Mechanics* (1929), one of the first textbooks in the new quantum theory.

[*See also* Compton, Arthur H.; Condon, Edward; Journals in Science, Medicine, and Engineering; Millikan, Robert A.; Mulliken, Robert S.; Nobel Prize in Biomedical Research; Oppenheimer, J. Robert; Physics; Science; *and* Wiener, Norbert.]

BIBLIOGRAPHY

Assmus, Alexi. "The Americanization of Molecular Physics." *Historical Studies in the Physical and Biological Sciences* 23 (1992): 1–34.

Holton, Gerald. "On the Hesitant Rise of Quantum Physics Research in the United States." In *Thematic Origins of Scientific Thought: Kepler to Einstein*, edited by G. Holton, pp. 147–187. Cambridge, Mass.: Harvard University Press, 1988.

Kevles, Daniel J. *The Physicists: The History of a Scientific Community in Modern America*. Cambridge, Mass.: Harvard University Press, 1987.

Sopka, Katherine R. *Quantum Physics in America: The Years through 1935*. New York: Tomash Publishers, 1988.

Helge Kragh

R

RABIES

Recognized since antiquity by doctors and lay persons alike, the disease of rabies, also called hydrophobia, has shaped both medical history and cultural life in the United States to an extent far beyond anything its limited incidence might seem to warrant. Several unusual factors account for this. Rabies was easily identified by its distinct symptoms, its known incubation period, and its recognized source of infection. Once symptoms appeared, the disease was uniformly fatal in humans and in domestic and farm animals. A stray dog's bite was the most common route of infection. As a well-recognized disease with unavoidable mortality, it was universally feared because every single dog bite raised the specter of death, although biting dogs were rarely rabid and only a fraction of bites from rabid dogs would transmit the disease. Traditional treatments were to cauterize the wound and to apply, when available, a "madstone" with the hope that this folk remedy would draw out poison from the wound. Throughout the nineteenth century, the press routinely reported hydrophobia deaths in clinical detail. That children were the most common victims and "man's best friend" the agent sustained widespread anxiety about rabies.

In these contexts, a life-saving injection introduced by the French chemist Louis Pasteur in 1885 won worldwide acclaim, with especially strong recognition in the United States. It was the first vaccine after Edward Jenner's cowpox vaccine for smallpox in the 1790s. Among the general public, Pasteur's discovery generated widespread enthusiasm for laboratory medicine far beyond rabies' actual importance as a problem of public health, prompting the new expectations of breakthrough cures emerging from laboratory research along with public support for new institutions to produce more advances (Hansen, 1998, 1999).

With the Pasteur method, a dog-bite victim received a series of shots with virus of increasing virulence over about two weeks, a pattern that seemed to stimulate the person's immune response ahead of a natural infection ensuing from the bite. The delivery of such treatment required the establishment of special clinical facilities in which a continuous succession of rabbits was infected with virus so that after each one died of rabies, its spinal cord could be dissected. Virulence was attenuated by air drying, and every new patient needed two-week-old cord to start the series of shots. These facilities were called Pasteur Institutes, and patients by the thousands traveled great distances to receive treatment. About 30 were established across the United States between 1890 and the 1930s. By about 1915, new methods of attenuation and preservation of the rabies virus also allowed pharmaceutical companies to produce vaccines that could be shipped to family doctors, allowing treatment for some patients at home (Hansen, 2009, pp. 96–111, 161).

At first, any victim of serious bites was urged to receive treatment. But around 1903 Adelchi Negri in Italy discovered that distinctive, minute bodies found postmortem in the brain of an animal (later called Negri bodies) were a positive indication for rabies. This procedure meant that when an animal's brain could be examined quickly by a pathologist, a bite victim might avoid the prophylactic treatment.

Over the twentieth century, rabies vaccine production partook of many scientific advances. For example, improvements were made in producing the virus for the shots, shifting from its original cultivation in nerve tissue of rabbits, neonatal mice, and then duck eggs to the use of cell culture (Plotkin et al., 2008, pp. 693–697; Jackson and Wunner, 2007, pp. 505–516). Most significantly, at least in Europe and the United States, vaccines were modified for use in healthy canines. Annual vaccination for pets spread only gradually at first because it was voluntary. But once states came to require it as part of a registration process, the success was profound, virtually eliminating human exposure to rabies because protected pets, even if bitten by an unvaccinated dog or a feral animal, did not develop the disease and thus did not spread it to other pets or to people.

By the beginning of the twenty-first century in the United States, the incidence of rabies dropped to only a few human fatalities each year, with pets rarely the source of a human infection. Bats, foxes, skunks, and raccoons harbor the virus (Plotkin et al., 2008, pp. 691–693). Perhaps as many as 40 thousand people were vaccinated each year during the early twenty-first century in the United States, and there were another 4 million treatments given around the world (Plotkin et al., 2008, p. 707). The largely successful prevention programs in Europe and North America have not become practical in the developing world, where fast-growing cities are teeming with stray dogs and where public-health agencies must direct their limited resources to what seem to be bigger threats. A 2005 study estimated the burden of rabies in Africa and Asia to be 55 thousand deaths and over $500 million each year (Knobel et al., 2005).

The turn of the twenty-first century saw two historically new developments. First, a few cases of rabies developed in patients receiving internal organ transplants from asymptomatic donors whose deaths were not tied to rabies. (Transmission through corneal transplantation had been documented earlier.) All of these people with nonbite exposure died of rabies (Jackson and Wunner, 2007, pp. 309–311). Second, a single patient with clinical rabies made a recovery with unprecedented medical treatments. Prior to 2004, only six people were recognized in the scientific literature as having survived clinical cases of rabies, and all but one of these had earlier received some preventive treatment (Jackson and Wunner, 2007, pp. 325–329). But in 2004, a young woman in Wisconsin who developed rabies symptoms weeks after handling a bat was given an aggressive course of experimental antiviral treatments. She survived and eventually recovered (Willoughby et al., 2005). By 2009, of twenty-five further attempts to use the "Milwaukee protocol" with other patients, only two had been successful (Willoughby, 2009).

The history of rabies in the United States reflects key steps in the development of the biomedical sciences. It was transformed from an untreatable clinical tragedy to a symbol of laboratory miracles and then to a disease that public-health programs could prevent with widespread preventive vaccination of animal hosts and post-exposure administration of vaccine in humans.

[*See also* **Disease; Germ Theory of Disease; Medicine; Public Health;** *and* **Public Health Service, U.S.**]

BIBLIOGRAPHY

Hansen, Bert. "America's First Medical Breakthrough: How Popular Excitement about a French Rabies Cure in 1885 Raised New Expectations of Medical Progress." *American Historical Review* 103, no. 2 (April 1998): 373–418.

Hansen, Bert. "New Images of a New Medicine: Visual Evidence for Widespread Popularity of Therapeutic Discoveries in America after 1885." *Bulletin of the History of Medicine* 73, no. 4 (December 1999): 629–678.

Hansen, Bert. *Picturing Medical Progress from Pasteur to Polio: A History of Mass Media Images and Popular Attitudes in America.* New Brunswick, N.J.: Rutgers University Press, 2009.

Jackson, Alan C., and William H. Wunner, eds. *Rabies.* 2d ed. Amsterdam and Boston: Elsevier/Academic Press, 2007. An authoritative scientific account in 19 chapters by modern experts; it includes a history chapter and some historical information in other chapters as well.

Knobel, Darryn, et al. "Re-evaluating the Burden of Rabies in Africa and Asia." *Bulletin of the World Health Organization* 83, no. 5 (May 2005): 360–368.

Kumar, P. Dileep. *Rabies: Biographies of Disease.* Westport, Conn.: Greenwood Press, 2009. An accessible brief overview.

Plotkin, Stanley A., Hilary Koprowski, and Charles E. Rupprecht. "Rabies Vaccines." In *Vaccines,* edited by Stanley A. Plotkin, Walter A. Orenstein, and Paul A. Offit, 5th ed., chap. 27, pp. 687–714. Philadelphia Saunders/Elsevier, 2008. An authoritative synthesis.

Willoughby, Rodney E. "Are We Getting Closer to the Treatment of Rabies?" *Future Virology* 4, no. 6 (November 2009): 563–570.

Willoughby, Rodney E., et al. "Survival after Treatment of Rabies with Induction of Coma." *New England Journal of Medicine* 352 (16 June 2005): 2508–2514.

Bert Hansen

RABI, ISIDOR I.

(1898–1988), physicist and Nobel laureate. Born in Eastern Europe, Isidor Isaac Rabi was brought by his parents to the United States when he was two years old. The family lived first in predominantly Jewish neighborhoods in New York, and Rabi's early life was dominated by his parents' orthodox Jewish beliefs. Rabi attended Manual Training High School in Brooklyn, followed by Cornell University, which he entered with a scholarship in 1916, starting as an electrical engineering major and switching to chemistry part way through his degree. He graduated in 1919, but was not intellectually satisfied with chemistry. After several years of indecision, he finally decided to pursue graduate study in physics at Columbia University in 1923.

After receiving his PhD in physics from Columbia in 1926, he went to Europe to study with the physicists who created quantum mechanics, including Arnold Sommerfeld, Erwin Schrödinger, Niels Bohr, and Wolfgang Pauli. In Otto Stern's Hamburg laboratory, Rabi began research in molecular beam physics. After his work with Stern in Hamburg, Rabi worked with Werner Heisenberg in Leipzig, who later recommended him for the position of professor of physics at Columbia University, where he taught statistical mechanics and quantum mechanics from 1929 to 1967. In the early 1930s Rabi conducted experiments to determine the nuclear spin of sodium and hydrogen molecules using molecular beams. The results, however, exhibited a large degree of error. Rabi's discovery of the magnetic resonance method in 1938 provided a greater certainty in experimental outcome when measuring nuclear spin, revealing crucial information that had been hidden by the earlier, more imprecise results. For the discovery of the new method Rabi won the Nobel Prize in Physics in 1944. A major field of study after World War II, the magnetic resonance method became the basis for the medical diagnostic technique called magnetic resonance imaging (MRI).

During World War II, Rabi served as the associate director of the Radiation Laboratory at the Massachusetts Institute of Technology, where radar systems were developed. Rabi was also one of J. Robert Oppenheimer's senior advisers on the Manhattan Project in Los Alamos, New Mexico. After the war, Rabi became active in public affairs. As a member and chair of the Science Advisory Committee during President

Dwight D. Eisenhower's administration, he reconstituted the group as the President's Science Advisory Committee, which reported directly to the president. With Dag Hammarskjöld, secretary general of the United Nations, he organized the first International Conference on the Peaceful Uses of Atomic Energy, held in Geneva, in 1955.

[*See also* **Atomic Energy Commission; Manhattan Project; Medicine; Military, Science and Technology and the; Nobel Prize in Biomedical Research; Nuclear Weapons; Physics; President's Science Advisory Committee; Quantum Theory;** *and* **Science.**]

BIBLIOGRAPHY

Rigden, John S. "Rabi, Isidor Isaac." In *Complete Dictionary of Scientific Biography*. Vol. 24, pp. 191–197. Detroit: Charles Scribner's Sons, 2008. Gale Virtual Reference Library. http://go.gale-group.com/ps/i.do?id=GALE%7CCX2830906 032&v=2.1&u=otago&it=r&p=GVRL&sw=w (accessed 15 January 2013).

Rigden, John S. *Rabi: Scientist and Citizen*. Cambridge, Mass.: Harvard University Press, 2000. First published 1987. With a new preface by John Rigden.

John S. Rigden;
updated by Elspeth Knewstubb

RACE AND MEDICINE

From 1492, when Christopher Columbus and his crew first introduced European disease microbes to the inhabitants of North America, to the early twenty-first century, the intersection of disease with race and ethnicity has powerfully shaped the course of American history. The promise of health and the threat of sickness have influenced political, economic, and cultural relations within and among different groups of racial and ethnic minorities and have also framed these groups' inter-actions with the larger society. Within specific groups, both the perceptions and the realities of health status have driven internal developments involving cultural identity, family life, resistance to racism and discrimination, and the building of social institutions. Whether one examines the physical pain and suffering caused by malnutrition, lack of medical care, and unsanitary environments; or the psychic, intellectual, and political aspects of the social construction of disease, racial ideology has played a key role in defining American medical practice and determining its successes and failures.

Slavery and Scientific Racism. Disease and racism have been intimately connected from the time Dutch and English ships brought the first African slaves to Virginia in 1619. European colonists justified the use of African blacks, rather than Native Americans or white indentured servants, as a source of plantation labor in part because residents of Africa possessed a degree of immunity to both *falciparum* and *vivax* malaria, as well as yellow fever. Yet whites also believed that the tropical African environment had made blacks better adapted to work in the heat and humidity of the American South. Such self-serving beliefs belied the myriad ways that the economy of slavery exacted a horrific toll on black health.

Because slaves represented a significant capital investment, slave owners theoretically had financial incentive to maintain the health of slaves to maintain a productive workforce. Southern planters such as Charles Manigault of South Carolina proclaimed that "only in slavery did humanity and interest go hand in hand," and the death of a slave incurred greater financial loss as the nineteenth century progressed and slaves rose in value. Yet masters' overriding interest in raising a profitable crop frequently endangered slaves' health, especially in disease-ridden environments such as low-country rice plantations. In some coastal areas of South Carolina and Georgia, the life expectancy of a slave was nearly half that of slaves in the rest of the American South. Thus, although slavery apologists frequently insisted that slaves' health and living conditions were superior to those of northern factory operatives, pragmatic masters routinely exposed slaves to inclement weather, oppressive heat, biting insects, and the risk of epidemic disease, especially during the crunch time of harvest when speed determined a planter's profit or ruin for the year.

Slaves exerted some autonomy over their own health and turned to folk medicine practitioners within the black community for advice on both physical and psychological ailments. This allowed them to avoid the painful and often detrimental heroic treatments favored by some whites, as well as to resist white authority over the very personal matter of health. Folk healers relied on a supernatural understanding of the world and used herbs and substances invested with magical meaning to counteract evil disease-causing forces. But the price of care from within the black community could be high: practitioners could misdiagnose a serious ailment, and slaves were also forced to hide their sickness from whites while continuing to work at a normal level.

Early scientific racists such as Josiah Nott, Samuel Cartwright, and Samuel Morton used craniometry, phrenology, comparative anatomy, and other racially derived methods to construct a pseudoscientific rationale for slavery and black inferiority. They defended the "benevolent" paternalism of slavery as a positive, civilizing influence on blacks. After emancipation, scientific racists argued that freedom would actually harm the mental and physical health of blacks, citing the flawed 1840 census that determined rates of insanity to be 10 times as high among antebellum free blacks as among black slaves. Savitt (2007) argues that, aside from racist pronouncements, blacks in fact were more susceptible to certain problems such as respiratory diseases, whether because of heredity, environment, or a combination. However, statistics on morbidity and mortality are misleading or absent until well into the twentieth century, especially in the rural South and West among isolated populations with little access to medical or public-health services.

Social Darwinism and Eugenics.
Despite the prevalence of predictions that blacks were "a vanishing race," both the federal and the southern state governments began to provide health care for blacks after the Civil War. The Freedmen's Bureau operated clinics, dispensaries, and hospitals, and Freedmen's Hospital in Washington, D.C., became the permanent teaching hospital of Howard University College of Medicine, founded in 1867 as the first medical school open to students of all races, sexes, and social classes. State mental asylums had seldom admitted slaves (whom whites believed to be immune to mental illnesses), but after emancipation, black mental patients entered asylums under strictly segregated circumstances. Virginia's Eastern State Asylum provided "moral management" therapy, which strongly resembled plantation life with its strict discipline and routine, including manual labor to encourage orderly habits of mind.

By the 1890s, social Darwinism had intensified scientific racism beyond antebellum levels, and white Victorians argued that blacks and Native Americans were destined for extinction because they were biologically ill-equipped to compete in the "survival of the fittest." Activists began to call for legalized segregation and disfranchisement to avoid the lingering difficulties that blacks would pose for whites before their predicted demise. Frederick Hoffman's *Race Traits and Tendencies of the American Negro* was especially influential in discouraging philanthropy on behalf of blacks because it was a futile attempt to interfere with the "natural" process of evolution. Hoffman's use of statistics that highlighted declining birth rates and increasing rates of death and morbidity among blacks convinced major insurance companies to deny coverage to blacks. In 1910, the physician Thomas Murrell claimed in the *Journal of the American Medical Association* that rates of venereal disease among blacks had skyrocketed since emancipation, on account of black immorality, disintegrating family structure, and mental instability caused by inability to adapt to the stress of late-nineteenth-century life.

For the majority of southerners who dwelled on farms, black or white, malnutrition weakened immune systems and caused nutritional deficiencies such as rickets and pellagra. Overcrowding, frequent contact with animals and their waste, poor lighting and ventilation, inadequate clothing, poor sanitation, contaminated water, and improperly prepared food—all exacerbated by living conditions in the slave quarters and later among impoverished tenant farmers and sharecroppers—made staying healthy extremely difficult for slaves. Rather than linking such conditions with poor slave health, white slave owners often blamed disease on external sources. Masters also faulted slaves' ignorance or immoral behavior, which fit with contemporary scientific theories that certain races were "naturally" more susceptible to certain ailments: blacks to sexually transmitted diseases and Native Americans, blacks, and Mexicans to tuberculosis, whereas hookworm, endemic in the sandy regions of the late-nineteenth and early-twentieth-century South, was labeled "the germ of laziness" among white rural dwellers. The racialization of disease led white society to categorize ill health among blacks and poor whites as "normal." After the Great Migration of southern blacks to northern cities, doctors analyzed black health problems outside the context of southern racism that had long masked the symptoms of a newly discovered disease, sickle-cell anemia. The chronic fatigue, skin ulcers, and other indications of the disease were found to be "real," rather than caused by other endemic southern maladies or the laziness of blacks. Yet conservative whites still approached this new black health problem in terms of maintaining the labor force.

After segregation and disfranchisement were accomplished by the turn of the twentieth century, eugenics commanded increasing scientific and popular respect. Unlike the supporters of "positive eugenics," who encouraged healthy couples with high-quality "germ plasm" to reproduce, proponents of "negative eugenics" extended scientific racism to mandate the compulsory sterilization of anyone deemed "unfit" to remain in the common gene pool. The popularity of sterilization as a cheap solution to social problems ranging from mental disability and insanity to violent crime is exemplified by the fact that 30 states passed compulsory sterilization laws between 1910 and 1940.

Philanthropy, Progressive Health Reform, and Racial Self-Help.

Motives of social control and self-preservation were never far from white efforts to address the health problems of minorities and foreigners. Urbanization had confronted middle-class whites with growing numbers of blacks and European, Mexican, and Asian immigrants, which raised an awareness of urban health problems caused by poverty, poor sanitation, and overcrowding, but also intensified whites' desire to keep at bay racially "inferior" groups who seemed to threaten order. Only a few years after the 1906 Atlanta race riot, the city's white leadership recognized that the poor sanitation and contaminated water supply endured by black neighborhoods contributed greatly to the typhoid epidemics that affected the health of whites as well as blacks and tarnished the city's reputation as one of the most healthy Southern cities. When business prospects balked at Atlanta's death rate, as much as 47 percent higher than that of its nonsouthern urban counterparts, the city issued bonds to extend a modern sewer and water system into black neighborhoods that relied on wells and where privies were only irregularly emptied.

Alongside Progressive-Era white elites' fears of contagion, black voluntary organizations thrived and mounted self-help efforts aimed at improving black health. Black reformers raised funds to build black-run hospitals, organized lay volunteers to visit patients in their homes, and launched health education campaigns to encourage preventive behaviors. Across the country, minority-led civic and religious organizations forged practical alliances with white philanthropists and government officials to promote disease-prevention campaigns that broadly benefited public health. The Rockefeller, Duke, and Rosenwald philanthropies provided significant funding to improve education and training for black health professionals, purchase equipment for and expand the capacity of black hospitals, and send black public-health nurses into rural areas. In Philadelphia, white philanthropy funded tuberculosis clinics that opened opportunities to black professionals, who disproved negative stereotypes of black doctors and nurses and also reduced infection rates among blacks by increasing patient compliance.

Yet such aid was often given at the price of maintaining segregation and limiting minorities' power over decision making. In 1929, Chicago's

Provident Hospital secured the help of the Rosenwald Fund to begin a partnership with the University of Chicago that would provide better training opportunities for black doctors and better services for black patients. But the university bowed to majority racial mores and forbade black medical students to attend white patients. The Swift and Armour meatpacking plants nearby hoped to secure health care for their black employees in the segregated facilities at Provident, rather than sending them to other area hospitals. As black racial ideology shifted away from separatist self-help toward integration, the partnership grew increasingly tense. Provident struggled to maintain its identity as a black institution while responding to the black community's demands that the hospital should oppose the segregationist policies of the university and the Rosenwald Fund.

Among southern blacks, Beardsley (1987) has argued that black lay efforts were more effective than either public-health departments or black physicians. But self-help remained limited by the lack of resources among people consigned by segregation and racial discrimination to jobs with the lowest wages and status. Beardsley contends that white philanthropy, despite its conflicting motives of humanitarianism and social control, was the most important force benefiting southern black health until the advent of broad-scale federal health programs under the 1935 Social Security Act. The Duke Endowment donated millions to improve black hospitals throughout the Carolinas, and the Rosenwald Fund made massive contributions to public-health efforts such as tuberculosis screening and pediatric clinics. Such efforts were often ambivalent about segregation: in some cases, they concentrated on improving conditions within the racial status quo; in others, such as Rosenwald's push to encourage state and local public-health departments to hire black nurses, they challenged existing racial boundaries. But the endurance of scientific racism was tragically and overwhelmingly proven by another project initially funded by the Rosenwald Fund, the Tuskegee Syphilis Study.

Begun in the early 1930s as an observational study to determine the prevalence of syphilis among rural southern blacks, the study became enmeshed in the bureaucracy of the U.S. Public Health Service (PHS), which authorized the study to pursue its observations of untreated syphilis victims "to autopsy." The study was partially based on the assumption that blacks would not seek treatment for syphilis once the symptoms had subsided. Instead, Macon County black men endured painful procedures and almost none dropped out of the study because they were so desperate to receive the "free special treatment" promised by the government doctors. Forty years after it began, the study was finally revealed publicly through the media and congressional hearings. Beyond the tragic consequences for its victims and their families, the Tuskegee Syphilis Study compromised blacks' trust in both the health-care establishment and the government in general for decades afterward.

Federal Health Programs and the Medical Civil Rights Movement.

In contrast, black faith in the federal government and its eventual recognition of blacks as full citizens reached an all-time high during and after World War II. The war's rhetoric pitted free democracy against the racist totalitarianism of the Nazis. Black veterans returned from the war patriotic, yet determined to achieve equality at home. The war also raised awareness of enduring regional and racial health disparities, as draft rejections for reasons ranging from syphilis, bad teeth, and poor eyesight to malnutrition highlighted the South's poor health, especially among its black citizens. Black organizations such as the National Association for the Advancement of Colored People, the National Urban League, the National Medical Association, and the National Negro Congress lobbied hard in support of the 1946 Hill-Burton Hospital Survey and Construction Act, which authorized federal funding for hospital construction and targeted the South, where facilities were most limited. The law required all participating hospitals to admit patients without regard to race, but sidestepped segregationist opposition by allowing internal segregation by ward or floor. Hill-Burton funding helped black patients gain access to modern hospital facilities and specialists and enabled black doctors and nurses to finally receive first-class training. Yet many pro-integration leaders of the medical civil rights movement, such as Montague Cobb and Louis T. Wright, fought ferociously against the expansion of segregated health care, even if it meant sacrificing public and philanthropic aid to black health in the short term.

The passage of the Civil Rights Act of 1964 and the Medicare-Medicaid amendments to Social Security in 1965 together helped to address the medical care needs of millions of poor and minority Americans. These landmark programs outlawed segregation and racial discrimination in all public and federally funded facilities, including private voluntary hospitals that had received any level of government funding. The desegregation of health care, like the larger civil rights movement, however, disproportionately benefitted middle-class blacks, who were in the best position to take advantage of professional education, private physicians, and hospital facilities.

The Supreme Court's historic 1954 *Brown v. Board of Education* decision that mandated school desegregation also struck a near-fatal blow to scientific racism when it reversed the nineteenth-century contention that freedom was pathological for blacks, arguing instead that segregation was detrimental not only to blacks, but also to the whole society. The prosecution built on the earlier theories of the anthropologist Franz Boas, who stressed environmental factors in determining racial differences, especially nutrition and living conditions. Gunnar Myrdal's 1941 sociological masterpiece, *An American Dilemma*, represented the triumph of environmental theories among social scientists and public-health professionals. The *Brown* decision relied on the testimony of sociologists and psychologists who argued that segregation caused blacks to internalize negative racial stereotypes. It also stressed the patent inequality of segregated facilities for blacks, which negated the 1898 *Plessy v. Ferguson* doctrine of "separate but equal."

After its enactment in 1965, Medicare helped equalize care for Americans over age 65. Medicaid, which, unlike Medicare, was a means-tested, state-administered program, was intended to extend adequate health care to low-income citizens without regard to race, but some scholars have concluded that Medicaid allowed the health-care establishment to profit while indigent care was pushed off onto public facilities least able to handle the financial burden. In states such as North Carolina, 70 percent of private physicians refused to treat Medicaid patients, which contributed to a deepening split between public health and private for-profit medicine (Paschal, 1965).

Conclusion. Three of the most widely cited examples of racism and unethical conduct in medical research were conducted by some of the most prominent American scientists and physicians, who applied tremendous intellectual and financial resources toward preventing and curing disease worldwide: the Tuskegee Syphilis Study, a PHS-funded study of Guatemalan prisoners, and the use of cancerous cells of a patient at Johns Hopkins Hospital, Henrietta Lacks. In all three instances, research was conducted by white American male doctors without informed consent on patients of low economic status who were either African American or foreign citizens. What explains the apparent paradox that these three infamous examples of medical research compromised by racism were conducted by some of the most prominent American scientists and physicians, who had applied tremendous intellectual and financial resources toward preventing and curing disease worldwide? A fully developed answer is beyond the scope of this essay, but a brief discussion of these cases reveals some important insights about the history of race and medicine in America.

The *Tuskegee Study of Untreated Syphilis in the Negro Male*, which the PHS conducted on 424 black men in Macon County, Alabama, from 1932 to 1972, was the longest nontherapeutic medical study in history. Even after the successful trials of penicillin treatment for syphilis during World War II, the PHS failed to offer penicillin to cure the subjects of the study. Moreover, the PHS intentionally deceived the mostly illiterate men to continue to observe the course of the disease. After the *New York Times* published a major exposé on the study in 1972, the national outcry led to congressional hearings and the development and implementation of modern human-subjects research protections, including the establishment of institutional review boards.

Most of the primary figures in the Tuskegee Study were on the 12-member PHS Syphilis Study Section that reviewed research grant proposals and approved an ill-fated project directed by John C. Cutler. Cutler's never-published research, conducted between 1946 and 1948 with PHS funding, involved deliberately infecting nearly seven hundred Guatemalan prison inmates, mental patients, and soldiers with syphilis and gonorrhea and then confirming infections with blood tests and administering penicillin to those with positive results to test the new drug's effectiveness. For this project and other studies of syphilis transmission and methods of using penicillin to prevent as well as cure syphilis infection, Cutler obtained the cooperation of the PHS, Guatemalan health officials, and the Pan American Sanitary Bureau. As a PHS officer, Cutler joined the Tuskegee Study and dedicated himself to stamping out syphilis in the United States and abroad. He went on to a notable career as assistant U.S. Surgeon General, deputy director of the Pan American Sanitary Bureau, and department chair of public-health administration at the University of Pittsburgh Graduate School of Public Health.

In 1950, just after the Guatemala syphilis trials concluded, the Johns Hopkins cell biologist George O. Gey used samples of cancerous cervical cells from Johns Hopkins Hospital patient Henrietta Lacks to create HeLa cells, which became the most widely used method of tissue culture for medical research worldwide. For two decades before the HeLa cell discovery, Gey's lab had doggedly pursued the dream of a cell line that could be maintained indefinitely under laboratory conditions. The result, Gey announced in 1955, was "controllable living cell systems which may be used in various studies of [normal and diseased tissues to observe] their nature and functional competence, stability and variability, metabolic behavior, comparative constitution, proliferative behavior, and responses to altered environments or to various agents" (Hanks and Bang, 1971, p. iii), in short, the foundation for modern scientific research on living cells. Yet one ethically fatal flaw characterized the outlook of Gey, Cutler, the PHS physicians who led the Tuskegee Study, and the majority of their contemporaries. They blurred the line between a living human being and a controllable, analyzable system. Whether the system was a group of cells, a collection of laboratory animals, or a population of human beings, their overriding focus was on the system's controllability as essential for conducting modern, scientifically valid, reproducible research. In such a system, individual human rights disappeared.

The second half of the twentieth century marked major gains in both the civil rights and the health status of all Americans. In 1940 only 9 percent of Americans were covered by hospital insurance; by 1950, fully half were (Stevens, 1989, p. 259). The proportion of insured Americans peaked at 83 percent in 1975 and had improved little by 2001, when 41.7 million (15 percent of the U.S. population) were uninsured, of whom 53 percent were racial minorities (Institute of Medicine of the National Academies, 2006, p. 6). Poor blacks who remained isolated in rural areas or urban ghettoes continued to suffer statistically far greater rates of maternal and infant mortality, malnutrition, tuberculosis, venereal disease, and other maladies. Thus, although the number and percentage of Americans without access to the modern private health system declined dramatically between 1940 and 1975, the percentage of minorities among those who could not afford medical care rose significantly. Likewise, although the infant mortality rate declined substantially for both blacks and whites, the rate for blacks was 1.6 times that for whites in 1950 but 2.5 times as great by 2000 (Centers for Disease Control and Prevention, 2006). In the beginning of the twenty-first century, the best-off Americans still lived 33 years longer on average than the worst-off (Cromie, 2006).

[*See also* **Animal and Human Experimentation; Disease; Ethics and Medicine; Health Insurance; Hospitals; Indian Health Service; Medicare and Medicaid; Medicine; National Institutes of Health; National Medical Association; Native American Healers; Public Health; Public Health Service, U.S.; Race Theories, Scientific; Science; Sexually Transmitted Diseases; Sickle-Cell Disease; Tuskegee Syphilis Study;** *and* **War and Medicine.**]

BIBLIOGRAPHY

Abel, Emily K. *Tuberculosis and the Politics of Exclusion: A History of Public Health and Migration to Los Angeles.* New Brunswick, N.J.: Rutgers University Press, 2007.

Anderson, Warwick. *Colonial Pathologies: American Tropical Medicine, Race, and Hygiene in the Philippines.* Durham, N.C.: Duke University Press, 2006.

Baker, Robert B., Harriet A. Washington, Ololade Olakanmi, et al. "African American Physicians and Organized Medicine, 1846–1968: Origins of a Racial Divide." *Journal of the American Medical Association* 300, no. 3 (2008): 306–313.

Beardsley, Edward A. *A History of Neglect: Health Care for Blacks and Mill Workers in the Twentieth-Century South.* Knoxville: University of Tennessee Press, 1987.

Bergman, Abraham B., David C. Grossman, Angela M. Erdrich, John C. Todd, and Ralph Forquera. "A Political History of the Indian Health Service." *Millbank Quarterly* 77, no. 4 (1999): 571–604.

Briggs, Laura. "The Race of Hysteria: 'Overcivilization' and the 'Savage' in Late Nineteenth-Century Obstetrics and Gynecology." *American Quarterly* 52 (2000): 246–273.

Cromie, William J. "Research Shows Who Dies When and Where." *Harvard University Gazette.* 11 September 2006.

Crosby, Alfred W., Jr. *The Columbian Exchange: Biological and Cultural Consequences of 1492.* Westport, Conn.: Praeger Publishers, 2003.

Downs, Jim. *Sick from Freedom: African-American Illness and Suffering during the Civil War and Reconstruction.* Oxford: Oxford University Press, 2012.

Fett, Sharla M. *Working Cures: Healing, Health, and Power on Southern Slave Plantations.* Chapel Hill: University of North Carolina Press, 2007.

Galishoff, Stuart A. "Germs Know No Color Line: Black Health and Public Policy in Atlanta, 1900–1918." *Journal of the History of Medicine and Allied Sciences* 40 (1985): 22–41.

Gamble, Vanessa Northington. *Making a Place for Ourselves: The Black Hospital Movement, 1920–1945.* Oxford: Oxford University Press, 1995.

Green, Laurie B., John McKiernan-Gonzalez, and Martin Summers, eds. *Precarious Prescriptions: Contested Histories of Race and Health in North America.* Minneapolis: University of Minnesota Press, 2013.

Haller, John S. Jr. *Outcasts from Evolution: Scientific Attitudes of Racial Inferiority, 1859–1900.* Urbana: University of Illinois Press, 1995.

Hanks, John H., and Frederik B. Bang. "Dr. George Otto Gey, 1899–1970." *In Vitro* 6, no. 4 (1971): iii.

Harding, Sandra. *The "Racial" Economy of Science: Toward a Democratic Future.* Bloomington: Indiana University Press, 1993.

Heller, Jean. "Syphilis Victims in U.S. Study Went Untreated for 40 Years." *New York Times,* 26 July 1972.

Hine, Darlene Clark. *Black Women in White: Racial Conflict and Cooperation in the Nursing Profession, 1890–1950.* Bloomington: Indiana University Press, 1989.

Hoffman, Frederic. *Race Traits and Tendencies of the American Negro.* New York: Macmillan, 1896.

Horsman, R. "Scientific Racism and the American Indian in the Mid-Nineteenth-Century." *American Quarterly* 27, no. 2 (1975): 153–167.

Humphreys, Margaret. *Intensely Human: The Health of the Black Soldier in the American Civil War.* Baltimore: Johns Hopkins University Press, 2008.

Humphreys, Margaret. *Malaria: Poverty, Race, and Public Health in the United States.* Baltimore: Johns Hopkins University Press, 2001.

Institute of Medicine of the National Academies. "Committee on the Review and Assessment of the NIH's Strategic Research Plan and Budget to Reduce and Ultimately Eliminate Health Disparities, Board on Health Sciences Policy." In *Examining the Health Disparities Research Plan of the National Institutes of Health: Unfinished Business.* Washington. D.C.: National Academies Press, 2006.

Jones, James H. *Bad Blood: The Tuskegee Syphilis Experiment.* New York: Free Press, 1993.

Larson, Edward J. *Sex, Race, and Science: Eugenics in the Deep South.* Baltimore: Johns Hopkins University Press, 1995.

Lawrence, Jane. "The Indian Health Service and the Sterilization of Native American Women." *The American Indian Quarterly* 24, no. 3 (2000): 400–419.

Long, Gretchen. *Doctoring Freedom: The Politics of African American Medical Care in Slavery and Emancipation.* Chapel Hill: University of North Carolina Press, 2012.

Loyd, Jenna M. *Health Rights Are Civil Rights: Peace and Justice Activism in Los Angeles, 1963–1978.* Minneapolis: University of Minnesota Press, 2014.

Mayberry, Robert M., et al. "Racial and Ethnic Differences in Access to Medical Care." *Medical Care Research and Review* 57 (2000): 108–145.

McBride, David. *From TB to AIDS: Epidemics among Urban Blacks since 1900.* Albany: State University of New York Press, 1991.

McKiernan-González, John. *Fevered Measures: Public Health and Race at the Texas-Mexico Border, 1848–1942.* Durham, N.C.: Duke University Press, 2012.

Metzl, Jonathan. *The Protest Psychosis: How Schizophrenia Became a Black Disease.* Boston: Beacon Press, 2010.

Miniño, A. M., M. Heron, S. L. Murphy, and K. D. Kochanek for the Division of Vital Statistics. *Deaths: Final Data for 2004.* Health E-Stats. Atlanta, GA: Centers for Disease Control and Prevention, National Center for Health Statistics, 2006.

Mohr, James. *Plague and Fire: Battling Black Death and the 1900 Burning of Honolulu's Chinatown.* Oxford: Oxford University Press, 2004.

Murrell, Thomas. "Syphilis and the American Negro." *Journal of the American Medical Association* 54, no. 11 (1910), 846–849.

Nelson, Alondra. *Body and Soul: The Black Panther Party and the Fight against Medical Discrimination.* Minneapolis: University of Minnesota Press, 2011.

Paschal, George W., Jr. "What Medicare Means to Us." *North Carolina Medical Journal* 26, no. 9 (1965): 411.

Reverby, Susan M. *Examining Tuskegee: The Infamous Syphilis Study and Its Legacy.* Chapel Hill: University of North Carolina Press, 2009.

Reverby, Susan M., ed. *Tuskegee's Truths: Rethinking the Tuskegee Syphilis Study.* Chapel Hill: University of North Carolina Press, 2000.

Satcher, David. "Our Commitment to Eliminate Racial and Ethnic Health Disparities." *Yale Journal of Health Policy, Law and Ethics* (2001): 1–14.

Savitt, Todd L. *Race and Medicine in Nineteenth- and Early-Twentieth-Century America.* Kent, Ohio: Kent State University Press, 2007.

Savitt, Todd L., and James Harvey Young, eds. *Disease and Distinctiveness in the American South.* Knoxville: University of Tennessee Press, 1988.

Schoen, Johanna. *Choice and Coercion: Birth Control, Sterilization, and Abortion in Public Health and Welfare.* Chapel Hill: University of North Carolina Press, 2005.

Schwartz, Marie Jenkins. *Birthing a Slave: Motherhood and Medicine in the Antebellum South.* Cambridge, Mass.: Harvard University Press, 2006.

Skloot, Rebecca. *The Immortal Life of Henrietta Lacks.* New York: Crown Publishers, 2010.

Stevens, Rosemary. *In Sickness and in Wealth: American Hospitals in the Twentieth Century,* p. 259. New York: Basic Books, 1989.

Thomas, James C., and Karen Kruse Thomas. "'Things Ain't What They Ought to Be': Social Forces Underlying Racial Disparities in Rates of Sexually Transmitted Diseases in a Rural North Carolina County." *Social Science and Medicine* 49, no. 8 (1999): 1075–1084.

Thomas, Karen Kruse. *Deluxe Jim Crow: Civil Rights and American Health Policy, 1935–1954.* Athens, Ga.: University of Georgia Press, 2011.

Wailoo, Keith. *Dying in the City of the Blues: Sickle Cell Anemia and the Politics of Race and Health.* Chapel Hill: University of North Carolina Press, 2000.

Wailoo, Keith. *How Cancer Crossed the Color Line.* Oxford: Oxford University Press, 2011.

Wailoo, Keith, and Stephen Pemberton. *The Troubled Dream of Genetic Medicine: Ethnicity and Innovation in Tay-Sachs, Cystic Fibrosis, and Sickle Cell Disease.* Baltimore: Johns Hopkins University Press, 2006.

Ward, Thomas J. *Black Physicians in the Jim Crow South.* Fayetteville: University of Arkansas Press, 2003.

Washington, Harriet A. *Medical Apartheid: The Dark History of Medical Experimentation on Black Americans from Colonial Times to the Present.* New York: Doubleday, 2007.

Karen Kruse Thomas

RACE THEORIES, SCIENTIFIC

In 1950, the United Nations Educational, Scientific, and Cultural Organization—UNESCO—issued a statement produced by a blue-ribbon panel of scientists declaring that for "all practical social purposes 'race' is not so much a biological phenomenon as a social myth." Titled "The Race Question," its purpose was to discredit notions of a natural hierarchy of the human races and to signal an end to more than a century of scientific support for racist ideology. The word "myth" in the statement reflects the efforts of panel member Ashley Montagu, a Rutgers University anthropologist whose book, *Man's Most Dangerous Myth: The Fallacy of Race* (1942), was one of the most aggressive and influential critiques of scientific racism of its day. The UNESCO statement was premature. As every American who has filled out a census or medical form knows, the category of race continues in official culture, sanctioned by both the government and the medical community (Hollinger, 2006). In that sense, "race" may not be a myth, but these uses of the word do not bear the explicit and unapologetic racism that it did in scientific usage before World War II. The concept of race in the sciences did not end with the UNESCO statement, but the efforts of Montagu and the other panel members do mark an important transition point at which America's scientific community on the whole—however they may disagree about the term race—became the enemy of racism rather than its friend.

The historical transformation of the relationship between science and racism in America was, and continues to be, a complex phenomenon. "Science" in this story does not stand as a uniform institution: there are many sciences having many distinct methods, materials, and objects, and these competing scientific approaches and competing sciences have produced conflicting views. Yet, since the mid-twentieth century, this disparate community has spoken out, with virtually one voice, against those few scientists who have claimed that human racial distinctions are discrete, innate, and inalterable entities and thus can be hierarchically ordered. For the century and a half prior, the supposed superiority of people of European stock was less a thesis to be tested than a fact to be explained by the growing—and exclusively European and European American—scientific community. In general, members of the scientific communities on both sides of the Atlantic shared the view that the human races are discrete entities and subject to ranking according to faculties such as intellect and morality. Since the 1930s such claims have become increasingly marginalized by the scientific community itself, such that the UNESCO statement can serve as a symbolic end to a disturbing episode in the history of science.

One Origin or Many? The American colonists achieved their political independence from the British crown at a moment in history when natural historians had recently developed new taxonomic systems to order the world of nature. Explorations of the previous three centuries had brought to their awareness a staggering volume of organic creatures formerly unknown to westerners. The efforts of scholars such as Carl Linnaeus and Georges-Louis Leclerc, Compte de Buffon, at rationally comprehending the increasing volume of known biological forms through new taxonomic systems, coupled with Georges Cuvier's techniques in comparative anatomy, gave significant scientific impetus to efforts to organize a static organic world according to the physical structures of bodies (Greene, 1959, pp. 224–230). This appealed to some educated Americans who faced the political question of the relationship among the human races. Perhaps this new science could aid Americans struggling to fit their political rhetoric of the rights of man into the reality of America's vast laboratory of race. The revolution brought freedom to "men," but it left unresolved whether humans of all races belonged to the same biological category as those men. With millions in the bondage of slavery, this was more than an academic issue.

One of the architects of America's rhetoric of human equality, Thomas Jefferson, pondered these questions in his only published book, *Notes on the State of Virginia* (1785), concluding uneasily that sub-Saharan Africans were probably inferior to Europeans. Although his criteria were more aesthetic than scientific, Jefferson also hinted that the races may be the products of distinct acts of creation, a view that had been suggested by the Scottish gentleman of letters Henry Homes, Lord Kames. This provoked Samuel Stanhope Smith, a professor at the College of New Jersey (later Princeton University), to articulate a staunch monogenist position, declaring on both scientific and religious grounds that all humans share a common origin and that the human body changes in response to both the environment and civilization (Smith, 1965). The physical environment and exposure to the Euro-Americans' elevated civilization were transforming African bodies, even lightening their skins, in Smith's view, which he supported with an extensive discussion of the nature and malleability of human skin color, hair texture, and skull shape. Of course, the changes that Smith described were from African characteristics to European characteristics, and he assumed the superiority of Euro-Americans in both body and culture. Conceding the inequality of the races of America, Smith attempted to prove their potential for equality, demonstrating that the egalitarian ideals of the new republic were not unnatural. The moral message was explicit: "It is a debt which we owe to humanity to recognize our brethren in every class of men into which society is divided, and under every shade of complexion which diversifies their various tribes from the equator to the poles" (Smith, 1965, p. 22). His *Essay on the Causes of the Variety of Complexion and Figure in the Human Species* (1787, 1810) educated a generation of Americans in the monogenetic, environmentalist account of human diversity.

Scientifically, the environmentalist argument took a middle ground between the absolute fixity of organic forms and the notion of the evolution of species. As any breeder of domestic animals knew, varieties were not fixed; however, the taxonomic disorder that environmentalist changes seemed to represent was avoided by the claim that species did not change. In the context of American Protestant orthodoxy, the similarities of the human body supported the traditional biblical monogenism—all humans are descendants of Adam and Eve—whereas the environmentalist argument accounted for human diversity. As the first couples' descendants spread out and populated the world, the human races formed as varieties of the human species shaped by the differing environments they came to call home.

This pious environmentalism suited nineteenth-century America's predominant religious group, evangelical Protestants, because it supported the biblical story of human descent from one couple and maintained the genetic unity of the human race, a key principle to both their theology and their aspirations to evangelize the world. An important challenge to this harmony of science and religion appeared midcentury as several men of science, including Harvard's famous naturalist Louis Agassiz, argued that each human race consisted of a discrete type resulting from a distinct creation. In other words, the various

human races did not share a common ancestry. The view—dubbed polygenism—had powerful political and religious consequences. For example, Dr. Josiah Nott, an elite physician from Mobile, Alabama, believed the theory's implications for the abilities of different races should inform social and political policy (Stanton, 1960; Gould, 1981, pp. 30–72; Stephens, 2000).

Nott and Agassiz made an ineffective attempt to accommodate polygenism to Christianity by reviving a radical interpretation of the Genesis creation stories that claimed that Adam and Eve were not the parents of the whole human race. The hostile response it generated had more to do with its religious heterodoxy than its racist implications. Some northerners rejected Nott's work as pro-slavery propaganda but other opponents, such as the southern Lutheran minister and naturalist the Reverend John Bachman, attacked its science even as he supported slavery and the southern cause (Stephens, 2000; Livingstone, 2008, pp. 173–197; Nelson, 2014).

The physical anthropology of the polygenists drew widespread attention, but it probably did not represent the majority of America's scientific community. Most remained silent, and many continued to support environmentalist monogenism. Growing interest in documenting indigenous American languages resulted in new studies by philologists and comparative linguists that traced connections between various groups of people. Lewis Henry Morgan's research in philology, for instance, inspired anthropologists to examine kinship ties more deeply. Morgan's work revealed cultural connections that supported monogenism and illustrates the fact that the competing sciences that study humans have often delivered opposing views of important issues, such as race (Trautmann, 1987).

Evolution, Eugenics, and the Endurance of Types.

In the long run the polygenists' idea of separate creations proved less important than their more enduring notion of racial types. Individuals of a particular race vary in features, but their race, in this view, is defined by a discrete and unchanging type, from which those variations are merely incidental fluctuations. The type is a transcendent ideal. Opponents of polygenism, such as

Bachman, argued that variations within races range widely and reveal gradations between the races rather than distinct boundaries; in other words, there are no types. Nott and his colleagues believed that such blurred boundaries were the result of race mixing, arguing that human hybrids had limited fertility and were physically and mentally inferior to either of their parent stocks. Thus the science of human types served the antimiscegenation cause so dear to many frightened Euro-Americans. Biometrics, measurements of human physical differences, became the physical anthropologists' tool as they sought to determine the exact characteristics of the types. The Philadelphia physician, geologist, and paleontologist Dr. Samuel Morton, for example, measured the interior volume of sample crania from his impressive collection of skulls—he had about one thousand at his death—and produced a hierarchy of races based on brain size. His work provided the empirical backbone for American polygenism. Later physical anthropologists sought to determine types by calculating statistical averages from measurements of body types, from "head size to toe length," from a great many individuals representing a specific race (Smedley, 1993, pp. 258–271).

One would think that the advent of evolutionary theory and its triumph among American men of science by the late 1870s would put an end to polygenism and racial typologies. If all creatures share a common ancestor, then all humans do, too. If species can transform into new species, then the notion of type makes no biological sense. Yet so powerful were racial types to the scientific elite, exclusively Euro-Americans at this time, that the notion survived the success of evolutionary theory and its monogenist implications. If races represent divergent lines of human evolution, many scientists argued, the point of that divergence was so far back in time that racial distinctions had now acquired the permanence of types. As the science of genetics developed, especially with the resurgence of Mendelian genetics at the beginning of the twentieth century, the study of the inheritance of traits became a major research field, led in the United States by Charles Davenport (1866–1944). These traits were understood by Davenport and like-minded thinkers as deter-

miners of key characteristics, such as intelligence and moral fiber, and not subject to the influence of environment.

On the last few pages of *The Descent of Man* Charles Darwin had aired his concerns for the future of the human race. Civilization had insulated humans from the effects of natural selection; consequently nothing prevented maladaptive characteristics from continuing, even dominating, in coming generations. He lamented that little could be done to control the situation because the mechanisms of heredity remained largely a mystery, but his cousin Francis Galton and generations of like-minded naturalists took up the task of understanding the principles of human heredity and of educating the public on how to make the best progeny (Darwin, [1871] 2004, pp. 688–689). The eugenics movement rapidly spread to America, where, led by Davenport, a capable organizer, it flourished. A mathematically adept biologist, Davenport believed that by applying careful quantitative methods to biometry and the study of inheritance he could put evolutionary theory on as strong a foundation as the physical sciences with their exact methods.

Adherents of eugenics busily produced standards of acceptable and desirable hereditary traits and ranked individuals accordingly. Nothing in the science required that the resulting hierarchy would be racial, but in the social context of the early twentieth century it was inevitable that its leadership mirrored the view of human races then so entrenched in western social thought. Poles and Italians represented different races to Davenport, meaning that cultural variations had a biological basis, and he worried that the influx of southern and eastern Europeans would degrade the American population, leading to more "crimes of larceny, kidnapping, assault, murder, rape, and sex-immorality" (Kevles, 1995, p. 47).

Anthropology and Genetics against Racism.

The eugenicists assumed that much of human behavior, including cultural behavior, was rooted in biology and passed on to future generations according to the principles of Mendelian genetics. By World War I, Franz Boas, professor at Columbia University, was training his graduate students in a cultural anthropology largely divorced from biology. This so-called Boasian school separated culture from heredity and made cultural relativism part of the methodological foundation of their work. They believed that race did not determine an individual's potential and that culture—which, not a product of biology, was learned rather than inherited—shaped behavior and values. Boas's disciples worked alongside physical anthropologists in museums, universities, and professional societies, competing for funding and positions, often in an uneasy tension. In the mid-1920s, the cultural anthropologists came to dominate anthropology by force of sheer numbers (Barkan, 1992, pp. 67, 95; Stocking, 1982). Under their influence, it became more difficult to associate racist views with scientific authority within their profession—difficult but not impossible.

As early as 1925, Boas published a critique of racism in the popular magazine *Forum* provocatively entitled "That Nordic Nonsense." Although passionate about the cause, Boas was reticent to take a public lead refuting the racism of the eugenicists and others because, as a Jew, he worried that his efforts would be dismissed as self-interest. A number of his students did engage in a public campaign to undermine the authority and credibility of the racist conclusions of the eugenicists and physical anthropologists, especially as German applications of eugenics grew more extreme. Ashley Montagu has been mentioned; others include Otto Klineberg, Ruth Benedict, Harry L. Shapiro, and Margaret Mead (Barkan, 1995).

At the same time, the foundations of racist scientific ideas began to unravel as the results of experimental genetics failed to illuminate the heredity of the human characteristics associated with race, such as physiognomy and skin color. In short, the version of Mendelian heredity that the likes of Davenport deployed to support the public eugenics movement proved too simplistic. The more geneticists learned about the human genetic structure, the less the traits the eugenicists studied seemed to have a discrete and unambiguous biological meaning. Theodosius Dobzhansky's work on genetic differences in fruit flies focused on breeding populations rather than types. In his view, the concept of race belonged to these dynamic breeding populations rather than to static physical characteristic of types and is determined by the frequencies of genes associated with specific traits. The term race denoted subpopulations that have begun to isolate from but remain interfertile with other populations of their species. A race is defined by the particular trait that the biologist is studying, and an individual of that race would belong to a different race if another trait were chosen as the object of study. In other words, individuals bear the traits of more than one race: thus, there is no such thing as a discrete or "pure" race (Farber, 2011, pp. 60–63). Dobzhansky's approach is representative of the "Modern Synthesis," a body of theoretical work on evolution that merged Darwinian natural selection with population genetics and that came to dominate biology by the 1950s.

As compatible as Dobzhansky's recasting of the concept of race was with Montagu's public crusade against scientific racism, it is interesting to note that they disagreed on the value of the word race itself. Montagu and others advocated the complete expunging of the word from science, replacing it with the term "ethnic group." Dobzhansky felt the word had a place as a technical term in the Modern Synthesis and that it had important biological meaning, even while agreeing with Montagu that the notion of race that informed the eugenics and old physical anthropology was a social construct expressing the prejudice of its advocates rather than anything existing in nature (Farber, 2011, pp. 67–68).

An Enduring Ambiguity. By the end of the twentieth century, the notion of racial types and hierarchies had been mostly purged from the professional scientific community. Partly this was driven by the scientific developments that undermined early research, but the social diversification of the scientific community also played a role. For example, the scientific leaders of the eugenics movement were Euro-American men of privileged backgrounds, whereas their opponents included more socially marginalized people. Boas and Shapiro were Jews; Benedict and Mead were women. In the course of the twentieth century

American science became less of an "old boys club" and came to reflect the complexity of the larger society.

In the 1960s, the antiracist message of cultural anthropology and the Modern Synthesis in biology became entrenched in college curriculums. As the leaders of the civil rights movement were occupying lunch counters and organizing marches, scientists were teaching a new generation of American students, one reflecting greater and greater diversity, that racism is a production of social prejudice and not nature. Science had once lent its growing epistemological authority to a movement protecting racial purity, justifying, for example, anti-immigration and antimiscegenation laws. Now American science crusaded for egalitarianism. Occasionally, still, a credentialed scientist publishes a study declaring that the distribution of some trait, usually intelligence, supports the idea of a racial hierarchy, but the denunciations by the scientific community are invariably swift and forceful. For example, in 1994, a Harvard faculty member, Richard Herrnstein, and Charles Murray brought out *The Bell Curve*, arguing for racial differences in IQ, which provoked a response from the American Psychological Association (Jackson and Waidman, 2006, pp. 221–222).

Yet, in the early twenty-first century, the word race has continued to be used. Babies whose parents check off "black" on hospital forms will routinely be tested for sickle-cell anemia. The official applications of race in such forms express the soft idea of race from population genetics rather than the rigid typologies of the early twentieth century. Likewise, the purpose of racial identification in medical and governmental forms is to measure the distribution of social goods such as education and job opportunities to root out and remove racial inequalities. After the mapping of the human genome, announced in 2000, some geneticists began to argue that race is both a social and a biological phenomenon. According to Catherine Bliss, these scientists acted on their own experiences of race that shaped their science as an instrument of social justice (Bliss, 2012). The question remains, however, whether the term race in documents bearing scientific or governmental authority, however nuanced or technical in intent, reinforces in the public mind the beliefs in the existence of discrete racial types (Fields, 1982).

[*See also* **Anthropology; Archaeology; Biological Sciences; Eugenics; Genetics and Genetic Engineering; Intelligence, Concepts of; Psychological and Intelligence Testing; Race and Medicine; Religion and Science;** *and* **Social Sciences.**]

BIBLIOGRAPHY

Barkan, Elazar. *The Retreat of Scientific Racism: Changing Concepts of Race in Britain and the United States between the World Wars.* Cambridge, U.K.: Cambridge University Press, 1992. Barkan documents the events that undermined the early-twentieth-century scientific racism.

Bliss, Catherine. *Race Decoded: The Genomic Fight for Social Justice.* Stanford, Calif.: Stanford University Press, 2012. A provocative study of the relationship of the social values of genomic scientists and their work.

Darwin, Charles. *The Descent of Man and Selection in Relation to Sex.* London: Penguin, [1871] 2004.

Desmond, Adrian, and James Moore. *Darwin's Sacred Cause: How a Hatred of Slavery Shaped Darwin's Views on Human Evolution.* Boston: Houghton, Mifflin, and Harcourt, 2009. A provocative argument that Darwin's abolitionist sentiments are what led him to finally publish his theory.

Farber, Paul L. *Mixing Races: From Scientific Racism to Evolutionary Ideas.* Baltimore: Johns Hopkins University Press, 2011. An engaging combination of the history of scientific ideas on races, their impact in American society, and the author's own experience with the suppression of mixed-race dating on college campus in the 1960s.

Fields, Barbara J. "Ideology and Race in American History." In *Region, Race, and Reconstruction: Essays in Honor of C. Vann Woodward*, edited by J. Morgan Kousser and James M. McPherson. New York: Oxford University Press, 1982.

Gould, Stephen J. *The Mismeasure of Man.* New York: W. W. Norton, 1981. The late Harvard biologist's exposé of the racism inherent in polygenism, various anthropometric enterprises, and intelligence testing.

Greene, John C. *The Death of Adam: Evolution and Its Impact on Western Thought.* Ames: Iowa State University Press, 1959. An older but still much-cited work that provides an interesting and efficient survey of the development of human evolutionary theories.

Hollinger, David A. *Postethnic America: Beyond Multiculturalism.* 3d ed. New York: Basic Books, 2006. A distinguished U.S. intellectual historian looks at conversations about race in America.

Jackson, John P., Jr., and Nadine M. Waidman. *Race, Racism, and Science: Social Impact and Interaction.* New Brunswick, N.J.: Rutgers University Press, 2006. A stimulating textbook that includes a large section of primary documents.

Kevles, Daniel J. *In the Name of Eugenics: Genetics and the Uses of Human Heredity.* Cambridge, Mass.: Harvard University Press, 1995. The standard work on eugenics in America.

Livingstone, David N. *Adam's Ancestors: Race, Religion, and the Politics of Human Origins.* Baltimore: Johns Hopkins University Press, 2008. A historical study of the religious version of polygenism—preadamism—and its connections to science through Western history, showing that it had a more prominent role in Western history than historians have realized.

Montagu, Ashley. *Man's Most Dangerous Myth: The Fallacy of Race.* New York: Oxford University Press, [1942] 1974. Perhaps the most influential book in the post–World War II public assault on racism by a member of the scientific community.

Nelson, G. Blair. "Infidel Science! Polygenism in the Mid-Nineteenth-Century American Weekly Religious Press." PhD diss. University of Wisconsin-Madison, 2014. An analysis of the controversy in the religious press sparked by the work of the American polygenists.

Selden, Steven. *Inheriting Shame: The Story of Eugenics and Racism in America.* New York: Teachers College Press, 1999. Both a historical account and a refutation of biological determinism.

Smedley, Audrey. *Race in North America: Origin and Evolution of a Worldview.* Boulder, Colo.: Westview Press, 1993. A broad historical treatment covering more than just the scientific aspects.

Smith, Samuel Stanhope. *An Essay on the Causes of the Variety of Complexion and Figure in the Human Species.* Cambridge, Mass.: Harvard University Press, 1965. This reprint of the 1810 second edition comes with a helpful introduction by Winthrop D. Jordan.

Stanton, William. *The Leopard's Spots: Scientific Attitudes toward Race in America, 1815–1859.* Chicago: University of Chicago Press, 1960. The standard account of American polygenism. Colorful and insightful, its discussion of religion has been corrected by Lester Stephen's book on the Charleston circle.

Stephens, Lester D. *Science, Race, and Religion in the American South: John Bachman and the Charleston Circle of Naturalists, 1815–1895.* Chapel Hill: University of North Carolina Press, 2000. A detailed study of a group of naturalists in Charleston who had debated the question of plural human origins in detail for years before the question became a public controversy in America.

Stocking, George W., Jr. *Race, Culture, and Evolution: Essays in the History of Anthropology.* Chicago: University of Chicago Press, 1982. Includes essays on Franz Boas and on the persistence of elements of polygenism in post-Darwinian anthropology.

Trautmann, Thomas R. *Lewis Henry Morgan and the Invention of Kinship.* Berkeley: University of California Press, 1987. The standard account of Morgan's life and work.

G. Blair Nelson

RADIO

Radio *telegraphy*—transmission of Morse and other code signals—developed in the late nineteenth century, whereas radio *telephony*—sending voice and music—was an early-twentieth-century innovation. Both were also called "wireless," especially in Britain, to distinguish them from wired telegraph and telephone services.

Origins. Many dreamed about and tinkered with telegraphy without wires in the nineteenth century, but two examples suffice. Washington, D.C., dentist Mahlon Loomis demonstrated a crude system of wireless telegraphy after the Civil War and nearly succeeded in forming a company to develop his ideas in 1872. Nathan Stubblefield worked in Kentucky with induction and conduction systems of wireless telegraphy and telephony around the turn of the century. But although they gathered some interest at the time, these were both dead-end attempts by untrained tinkerers that contributed little to modern radio.

James Clerk Maxwell, a British mathematical physicist, first theorized the modern concept of wireless communication in a scientific paper published in 1865, although technology to prove his point was not then available. Nearly a quarter century later, German physicist Heinrich Hertz proved Maxwell's theories with a series of 1888 experiments. In the mid-1890s, Italian Guglielmo Marconi melded his own innovations and those of others in experiments that led to a workable system of wireless telegraphy by the end of the century. He combined a means of creating signals, transmitting them, and detecting (receiving) them at increasingly distant locations. Other innovators in Germany (Slaby and von Arco), France (Branley), and Russia (Popov) contributed to the innovative trend. Commercial long-distance radio links in competition with submarine cables and communicating with ships at sea developed in earnest in the first decade of the twentieth century. Until the early 1920s, these point-to-point applications dominated radio.

The first important American radio inventors were Lee de Forest and Reginald Fessenden. The former developed an improved vacuum tube he called the Audion in 1906, which, further research demonstrated, allowed weak wireless telegraphy signals to be amplified. He was among the first to conceptualize broadcasting—the use of radio to transmit voice and music signals to a general audience. He conducted some experimental radio broadcasts as early as 1908. Fessenden (a Canadian who did his important wireless work in the United States) was the first to transmit the human voice and music by radio, perhaps in 1905 but certainly a year later. American engineer Edwin Howard Armstrong contributed important research and developed the regenerative, heterodyne, and superheterodyne tuning circuits during and after World War I.

Government entered radio with turn-of-the-century army and navy experimentation with wireless for military applications. A 1904 government board gave the navy considerable policy oversight over American radio. Initial legislation, in the Wireless Acts of 1910 and 1912, restricted regulation of radio to the federal government, mandated the use of wireless by American ships, and required that all wireless transmitters on land or sea be federally licensed.

Broadcasting. Although few foresaw the idea of broadcasting a century ago, among the earliest was Charles Herrold, who ran a wireless school in San Jose, California. By 1909, as a part of the school's training, he was operating a radio transmitter with the beginnings of a scheduled service of voice and music "broadcasts" to an audience of amateur radio operators in the San Francisco Bay area. These continued until American entry into World War I in April 1917. By then others were conducting similar experiments, although few operated on any schedule or purposely aimed their transmissions at anyone who could tune in.

That came only after the war, when several stations took to the air in 1919–1920, soon to be followed by hundreds more. They soon provided a schedule of talk and music programs aimed at general audiences and supported by commercial advertising. These stations operated on medium-wave spectrum frequencies—only a handful at first. From 1920 to 1927, federal officials slowly expanded the number of available frequencies until a contiguous band of channels was in use. The Radio Act of 1927 created the Federal Radio Commission to license stations "in the public interest" and provided industry stability, which encouraged national networking (interconnection) of stations (using telephone lines), which began at the same time. Many companies were developed to manufacture radio equipment and receivers. From its formation in 1919 well into the 1960s, the Radio Corporation of America (RCA) was dominant, manufacturing the whole range of radio equipment—vacuum tubes, transmitters, and receivers.

Amplitude-modulated (AM) radio stations, on which the radio broadcasting business was based, however, suffered several limitations. Chief among them was electromagnetic static (noise) that could not be separated from the desired signal. Starting around 1930, Howard Armstrong began research into the use of frequency modulation

(FM) radio as a means of circumventing static. He received his first patents in 1933, was experimenting with transmissions a year later, and provided initial public demonstrations soon thereafter. U.S. commercial FM radio broadcasting began on the 42- to 50-MHz band on 1 January 1941, switching to its current spectrum (88–108 MHz) in mid-1945.

Early radio receivers were bulky and required heavy wet-cell batteries for power and either headphones or large acoustic horn speakers to listen. In 1927–1928 plug-in radios with built-in speakers first appeared. Portable radios and automobile receivers were developed during the 1930s, although both became common only after World War II. The first transistor receivers ("pocket radios") appeared late in 1954. Less expensive receivers made possible the ubiquity of AM radio broadcasting by the mid-twentieth century. Improvements continued, chiefly multiplex stereo FM transmission standards, adopted by the Federal Communications Commission (FCC) in 1961 and soon widely available. FM radio became the dominant radio service by 1980 thanks to its better-quality sound. An attempt to introduce stereo AM failed to achieve marketplace success because of its poorer (than FM) sound quality and multiple competing systems.

By the early twenty-first century, digital radio signals were transmitted first from orbiting communication satellites (XM and Sirius, later merged into one provider) and later from terrestrial transmitters. Despite the adoption of a single system, digital radio broadcasting expanded slowly because it required the purchase of special automobile and home receivers, thus remaining a mere niche service (perhaps 20 percent of the total radio audience) well into the second decade of the twenty-first century.

Mobility and Distance. Radio lends itself to mobile communication, as well as to great distances. Using radio while on the move originated aboard merchant and naval ships early in the twentieth century. Dramatic rescues, such as that of survivors of the *Titanic* sinking in 1912, captured the public imagination. Military vessels and some aircraft used radio in World War I, whereas land, sea, and air forces depended on effective radio systems during World War II.

Mobile radio in police vehicles first appeared in the 1930s, and mobile telephony was first offered in St. Louis in 1946, quickly expanding to two dozen other cities within a year. But these analog mobile radio systems suffered from a lack of sufficient frequencies and required expensive equipment, limiting users to business and government. Thus, land mobile communications limped along for decades, serving far fewer people than it otherwise might have.

Only with the development of digital radio devices and services after 1990 was the shortage of needed spectrum even partially addressed thanks to digital transmission's greater efficiency. Cellular telephony, for example, is essentially a radio service and, with billions of users worldwide, radio spectrum is at a premium.

Radio's history has been one of achieving steadily greater distances as technology improves. Reaching a few feet in Hertz's 1888 experiments to a few miles by the end of the century, radio signals first spanned the Atlantic in 1901. Regular radio–telephone service across that ocean was offered on a commercial basis by 1927 and provided the only means of transatlantic voice signals until the first telephone cable was introduced in 1956. The development of short-wave transmission in the 1920s led to international radio services that carried political or military propaganda in the 1930s and 1940s to Cold War messages or evangelical Christian programming by the 1950s and 1960s. By the 1990s, international short-wave was already giving way to other modes of radio transmission (by satellite, for example) or service over the Internet.

Radio signaling played a central part in the U.S. space program, transmitting data to space vehicles and satellites since the 1950s, as well as to astronauts in orbit. The first of several lunar landings took place in July 1969 (the last three years later), each tethered to Mission Control on the Earth by radio transmissions of data and voice signals. Radio also transmitted signals to unmanned vehicles landing on the surface of Mars and to missions ranging to the outer solar system and beyond.

[*See also* **Armstrong, Edwin Howard; De Forest, Lee; Electronic Communication Devices, Mobile; Internet and World Wide Web; Military, Science and Technology and the; Morse, Samuel F. B.; Physics; Satellites, Communications; Science; Space Program; Technology; Telegraph;** *and* **Telephone.**]

BIBLIOGRAPHY

Aitken, Hugh G. J. *The Continuous Wave: Technology and American Radio. 1900–1932.* Princeton, N.J.: Princeton University Press, 1985.

Blake, George G. *History of Radio Telegraphy and Telephony.* London: Chapman & Hall, 1928 (reprinted by Arno Press, 1974).

Douglas, Susan J. *Inventing American Broadcasting, 1899–1922.* Baltimore: Johns Hopkins University Press, 1987.

Fahie, J. J. *A History of Wireless Telegraphy 1838–1899.* New York: Dodd, Mead, 1899 (reprinted by Arno Press, 1971).

Hong, Sungook. *Wireless: From Marconi's Black Box to the Audion.* Cambridge, Mass.: MIT Press, 2001.

Howeth, L. N. *History of Communications Electronics in the United States Navy.* Washington, D.C.: U.S. Government Printing Office, 1963.

Maclaurin, W. Rupert. *Invention and Innovation in the Radio Industry.* New York: Macmillan, 1949 (reprinted by Arno Press, 1971).

McNicol, Donald. *Radio's Conquest of Space.* New York: Murray Hill Books, 1946 (reprinted by Arno Press, 1971).

Shiers, George, ed. *The Development of Wireless to 1920.* New York: Arno Press, 1977.

Christopher H. Sterling

RADIOLOGY

On 1 January 1896, Wilhelm Konrad Roentgen, a physicist in Wurzburg, Germany, slipped eight copies of a seemingly simple paper, "On a new kind of Ray," into the mail with images, including one of his wife's hand, a ring circling a skeletal finger. On 12 January that picture was in newspapers around the world. Roentgen's meticulous paper described every step of the research, providing instructions to anyone with a cathode ray tube. Soon X-rays were everywhere in the United States. In Chicago, X-ray slot machines let you see the bones in your hand for a coin—a symptom of X-ray mania.

Roentgen did not try to patent his discovery or profit from it, except for accepting the first Nobel Prize in Physics. Many inventors, engineers, journalists, physicians, and lawyers looked to the X-ray as a source of profit. Thomas Edison went to his laboratory in West Orange, New Jersey, and replaced the platinum filament in the glass-filled tube with aluminum. He also marketed a machine that enabled physicians to observe the digestive process on a screen that he called a fluoroscope. Newspaper magnate William Randolph Hearst wanted headlines and challenged Edison to get an X-ray of the human brain. Edison couldn't because the skull blocked the rays.

Physicians saw X-rays as a boon. At first they used them to find bullets and buckshot they could remove from victims of misadventure. But soon they used X-rays for diagnoses of bones and lungs. Lawyers were soon on the scene with a case in Denver, Colorado, in which James Smith, who fell off a ladder in April 1896 and saw a surgeon who diagnosed contusion and recommended exercise, hired two lawyers and a photographer who had been taking X-rays for six months (the first radiologists were all photographers) after continued pain. The X-ray showed a fracture; the treatment should have been rest. Smith wooed the jury by having the photographer/radiologist image their hands. He won the case. His surgeon warned colleagues to use X-rays, and defensive radiology began.

By the turn of the twentieth century, radiological workers and patients were experiencing burns and festering sores. In 1896 Elihu Thomson, a physicist at General Electric (GE), subjected the last joint of the little finger of his left hand to a half hour of close exposure to an X-ray tube. The finger began to hurt and a blister formed. Thomson concluded that too much radiation was dangerous. A few years later William Rollins, a dentist with a Harvard medical degree, suggested that technicians, patients, and everyone working with X-rays enclose the tubes in lead-lined boxes to avoid burns. Enthusiastic physicians and technicians ignored these warnings. The X-ray was so easy to use and so beneficial.

In the second decade of the twentieth century engineers at GE improved the clarity of the radiographs with grids and in 1913 William Coolidge, a physicist, developed a revolutionary vacuum tube that could be adjusted accurately and provide exact duplicates of previous X-rays. As important, it eliminated most of the scattered radiation from the earlier gas tubes. The Coolidge Tube dominated the American market immediately, but in 1914 World War I began in Europe and the Coolidge Tube was hard to transport and too expensive. It remained an American luxury for a generation.

American radiologists had prepared for war: every draftee received a chest X-ray. In France they met X-rays again in gasoline-powered ambulances that powered electric generators and carried portable fluoroscopes as well as facilities to develop films or plates. Army physicians soon developed mobile Coolidge Tubes that went from bed to bed where soldiers could not get to an X-ray. After the war they went to hospitals.

Postwar patients were unaware of the anxiety among radiologists who noted the early deaths and infertile marriages within their profession and acknowledged the need to establish limits to radiation exposure. An international committee met in Stockholm to establish uniform units of radiation—the Roentgen, the Curie—and maximum and minimum standards of exposure. By the end of the 1920s physicians had become secure in their efforts to prevent overexposure and proud of the new skills that allowed them to see into the heart with catheterization and into the skull with ventriculography.

In 1929 the first patent was issued for a tomography machine. It was common knowledge that X-rays of pregnant women seldom showed a fetus because moving subjects do not leave an image. A French patient in a sanatorium in Connecticut who wanted to see his lungs beneath the bones in his chest designed and patented an apparatus that blurred out the visually obstructing tissue. He could not sell his idea until he discovered a radiol-

ogist at Washington University in St. Louis who had built a similar machine. The inventors joined forces to perfect the first tomograph. It moved the patient one way while moving the X-ray source another. The resulting X-rays showed an image of a slice inside the body. The slice was called *tomo*—Greek for slice or layer—and graph for image.

When World War II began in Europe in 1939, 19-year-old Godfrey Hounsfield, a RAF volunteer, was assigned to work with radar studying pattern recognition to sense hidden objects; he retained this interest into the 1950s. Meanwhile, in Cape Town, South Africa, in 1956, Alan Cormack, a nuclear physicist at a hospital, noted the tremendous excess of radiation in treating patients therapeutically with X-rays. He knew there must be a formula for processing the mathematical information so that X-rays could penetrate the body selectively. He pondered the problem, even as he married an American and moved to Tufts University. He needed the right mathematical university outside of Boston. He eventually solved the problem and in 1963 demonstrated his solution by designing a phantom head and obtaining images from objects he had placed inside. But when he published his result, the only interested party was the Swiss Avalanche Research Center, interested in a way to find skiers buried in the snow.

Godfrey Hounsfield had by this time become an engineer and joined EMI, the British music corporation that had branched into electronic ventures. EMI asked Hounsfield to find a new project and, recalling his wartime work with pattern recognition, Hounsfield suggested an instrument that could obtain images inside the head. EMI, bloated with profits from the Beatles, told him to go ahead. After a decade of progress, EMI put Hounsfield in touch with a neurosurgeon and in October 1971 Hounsfield scanned the first patient, a cumbersome process, because someone had to take the data across London to a computer and get back with the results to the hospital, where the neurosurgeon spotted a tumor and immediately excised it. EMI built five more scanners. Computerized tomography (CT) rapidly grew and evolved into the workhorse of medical imaging, but never eliminated the use of ordinary X-rays in mammography and diagnoses of broken bones.

[*See also* Dentistry; Edison, Thomas; Instruments of Science; Medicine; Medicine and Technology; Military, Science and Technology and the; Nobel Prize in Biomedical Research; Physics; Science; *and* War and Medicine.]

BIBLIOGRAPHY

Bleich, Alan Ralph Randolf. *The Story of X-rays from Roentgen to Isotopes.* New York: Dover Publications, 1960.
Brecher, Ruth, and Edward Brecher. *The Rays: A History of Radiology in the United States and Canada.* Baltimore: Williams and Wilkins, 1969.
Federal Policies and the Medical Devices Industry, Report of the Office of Technology Assessment, Congress of the United States, Washington, D.C. New York: Pergamon Press, 1984.
Howell, Joel. *Technology in the Hospital.* Baltimore: Johns Hopkins University Press, 1996.
Kevles, Bettyann Holtzmann. *Naked to the Bone: Medical Imaging in the Twentieth Century.* New York: Perseus, 1997.
Wolf, Stewart, and Bedrock Bishop Belle, eds. *The Technological Imperative in Medicine.* New York: Plenum Press, 1981.

Bettyann Holtzmann Kevles

RAFINESQUE, CONSTANTINE SAMUEL

(1783–1840), naturalist, ethnologist, and archaeologist, was born in Constantinople (Istanbul) and died in Philadelphia. Of French–German ancestry, he was raised in France. Largely self-taught, his education was disjointed and irregular. He spent 1802–1805 in the United States as a clerk in Philadelphia, then resided in Sicily from 1805 to 1815, made a small fortune as a merchant trader (which was dissipated), and was deeply engaged in botanical investigations. Returning to the United States in 1819, he sought employment and, with the help of a wealthy patron, he was named professor of natural history at Transylvania University in Lexington, Kentucky, until 1826, when he returned to Philadelphia.

Rafinesque was a brilliant natural historian and botanist of prodigious energy, productivity, and uncommon insight who published over one thousand articles and books on a broad array of biological, economic, and medical subjects. Also an ethnologist, he was interested in the American Indian, linguistics, and archaeological matters. In his epic wanderings he named 6,700 plants and many animals. Although a remarkable, albeit eccentric man, he was disdained because the reliability of his work was questionable, and his reputation suffered further because of his undiplomatic, disputatious manner.

Rafinesque was a publisher, editor, and sole author of scientific journals; the devisor of a fair banking system of some merit; a medical practitioner who concocted a treatment for tuberculosis; a Romantic poet; and philosopher. He was also an expert in Indian language who brought to light *Walam Olum*, a purported firsthand account of the migration of Lenni Lenape Indians from Asia and Alaska to Delaware—with little doubt, a fraud written by Rafinesque. Decades before Darwin he wrote about the natural variation of characteristics within a species and that instability and variability of form of living things were manifestations of a law of nature, as was gravity. He was an early and strong advocate of the French "natural system" of classification of living forms, a distinct advance over the older "sexual system" of Linnaeus.

[*See also* American Museum of Natural History; Archaeology; Botany; Journals in Science, Medicine, and Engineering; Science; *and* Tuberculosis.]

BIBLIOGRAPHY

Fitzpatrick, T. J. *Fitzpatrick's Rafinesque: A Sketch of His Life with Bibliography.* Revised and enlarged by Charles Boewe. Weston, Mass.: M and S Press, 1982. Includes a complete list of his publications.
Warren, Leonard. *Constantine Samuel Rafinesque: A Voice in the American Wilderness.* Lexington: University Press of Kentucky, 2004.

Leonard Warren

RAILROADS

From the outset, railroading exhibited several salient and enduring traits. First and foremost, it was a hybrid technology, an assemblage of steam engine, carriage, rail, roadway, and various physical structures. Many of those components, moreover, were themselves complex assemblies that drew upon a wide array of techniques and engineering disciplines. Second, it was a highly visible technology, displayed openly and often quite conspicuously for scrutiny by the public, including legions of inventors and technicians who might devise improvements and refinements. Third, it was an international technology, synthesized initially in Great Britain during the opening decades of the nineteenth century, but pursued almost immediately by imitators in many other locales. And finally, it was a technology of great promise and potential, which offered significant enhancements over previous methods of overland transport and opened enticing opportunities for economic development.

Together, these characteristics made railroading a realm of extraordinary innovation. In essence, railroad developers launched a series of localized experiments, each of which yielded lessons that might be shared widely across an international community. Those experiments, moreover, pressed simultaneously against numerous technological frontiers. Early engine builders devised various arrangements of boilers, cylinders, and drive mechanisms, while also experimenting with different fuels, fireboxes, and chimneys. Their efforts meshed with those of surveyors and civil engineers, who sought to ascertain grades and curvatures appropriate for the new machines and to devise cost-effective ways to maintain those standards through a combination of effective route laying and structural innovations such as novel bridge designs. In devising such remedies, railroad technicians often looked to utilize new materials and, in the process, stimulated innovation in other realms such as ferrous metals and lubricants. Railroading likewise became a driving force for innovation in the vitally important machine tool industry, which in turn became a conduit through which important innovations in machine technology and metal work flowed to the railroads.

This process of collective innovation began during the late 1820s, as entrepreneurs in several East Coast cities responded to the perceived challenge of the Erie Canal. Opened in 1825, this 360-mile path across upstate New York effectively connected New York City with the Great Lakes. Planned canals down from Lake Erie through Ohio, moreover, promised soon to extend this connection south and west to the Ohio River at Cincinnati. Railroads offered rival Atlantic ports such as Boston, Philadelphia, Baltimore, and Charleston, which lacked a convenient canal route through the Appalachian Mountains, with an alternative means of reaching the vital Ohio and Mississippi River corridor. By late 1826, commercial interests in Charleston had already built a railroad more than 100 miles northwest to Hamburg, across the Savannah River from Augusta, Georgia. From there they looked to snake north and west through the Georgia mountains to the Tennessee River. Meanwhile, rival Charleston interests investigated the possibility of building a less circuitous route directly northwest to Cincinnati. A year later, the ambitiously named Baltimore and Ohio sprang into existence, with the avowed aim of connecting the Maryland port to the inland river. Boston placed its hopes on the Boston and Worcester, which would form the first link in a rail route through the Berkshires to the Hudson River across from Albany and the Erie Canal. Commercial interests in Philadelphia and Richmond launched multiple westward-bound projects, including both canals and railroads.

These grandiose plans were slow to reach fruition. The mountains stymied engineers and called for more concentrated investments of resources than backers could muster. State legislatures, fearful of privileging some locales over others, chartered additional lines that competed for scarce capital. Rather than extending rapidly westward, lines proliferated, in many cases with the intent of serving highly local interests. Then came the Panic of 1837, which plunged several states and many chartered corporations into bankruptcy and curtailed public and private support for internal improvements for nearly a decade. By the end of 1846, less than five thousand miles of track had been laid in the United States. Lines from the East Coast ports would not begin to reach the inland rivers until the 1850s.

Yet if the gestation period lasted longer than investors had hoped, it also gave early railroad pioneers ample opportunity to conduct experiments, weigh alternatives, and settle upon a set of rail technologies appropriate for the American landscape. By the time investment capital flowed again in the late 1840s, railroads had coalesced around something of a common form. Most lines used wood-burning steam locomotives with horizontal boilers and cylinders linked to four drive wheels. Four more wheels, mounted on a pivoting swing truck, helped guide the locomotive around the comparatively tight curves of American lines, which invested considerably smaller sums in straightening and leveling their roadbeds than most European railroads. The locomotives pulled cars linked by simple link-and-pin couplers and equipped with hand brakes, which dragged the locomotive to a stop when tightened by brakemen. Trains traveled atop T-shaped iron rails, usually imported from Great Britain, which were spiked to wooden ties set in gravel. Bridges were wooden trusses of various forms, including designs patented by Pratt and Howe, rather than the more expensive stone arches first used by the B&O and most European companies. By 1860, when national mileage topped 30 thousand miles, the United States had built a rail system eight times as extensive as Prussia's, with only four times as much capital investment.

This configuration had diffused through American railroading in part because many of the early pioneers had moved from line to line. Especially important was a generation of civil engineers trained at West Point, who had been loaned to conduct early surveys for states and the corporations they chartered. Their ranks included Stephen Long, who plotted routes for the B&O and for the Georgia and the Western and Atlantic Railroads, which eventually provided the extension north from Augusta to Chattanooga via Atlanta. Long's colleague, J. Edgar Thomson, supervised construction of the Georgia lines before departing to head the Pennsylvania Railroad as it extended west from Philadelphia to Pittsburgh.

The Pennsylvania earlier had benefitted from the remarkable engineering contributions of John Jervis, who had worked on the Erie Canal and come to Pennsylvania to help engineer a way through the mountains. His many mechanical inventions included the swing truck, which helped guide locomotives around tight curves.

Like many vital railroad inventions of this early period, the swing truck went unpatented. Jervis saw his contributions as those of an engineering consultant, not an inventor marketing his creations to a developing set of customers. His behavior was not unusual. The early engineers and master mechanics employed by railroads often shared techniques freely among themselves. With technology in such a fluid state, they thought they had more to gain from exchanging information than from monopolizing it. At a time when railroad competition typically involved efforts to marshal capital and generate local economic development, railroad managers did not see their enterprises as engaged in a battle for operating efficiency. Soon enough, however, plenty of inventors (including many who worked for railroads) looked to profit by selling rights to patented technologies to the burgeoning railroad market. By the end of the Civil War, the U.S. Patent Office was issuing more than five hundred patents per year pertaining expressly to railroading, and railroads purchased numerous other articles and materials patented in other categories. Yet with ample expertise in their own ranks, railroads took steps to avoid becoming overly dependent on patented products and drove down the price of those they did use. Sharing information about alternatives helped keep costs low.

In addition to exchanging knowledge with one another, railroads also fell into close working relationships with suppliers of key components such as locomotives. In short order, locomotive production grew concentrated in a handful of trusted producers such as American Locomotive and Matthias Baldwin, whose Philadelphia works became legendary. Working in close collaboration with their customers, these firms built custom variations on common forms. They were able to capture the efficiencies of repetitive learning by doing, while retaining sufficient flexibility to meet the variable conditions faced by individual lines. Since they supplied variants to so many lines, the locomotive suppliers became vital clearinghouses for technical information, a role filled as well by trade journals such as the *American Railroad Journal*, edited by Alexander Lyman Holley. As a trusted technical intermediary, Holley gained the confidence of executives such as J. Edgar Thomson of the Pennsylvania. During the Civil War, the two would join hands to help foster the production of Bessemer steel rails in the United States, at last weaning American lines from dependence on imports for that vital component of their systems.

Nineteenth-Century Network. During the decades on either side of that war, Americans built railroads at a feverish pitch. After rising from five thousand miles in 1846 to more than 30 thousand in 1860, national mileage doubled from 35 thousand miles to more than 70 thousand between 1865 and 1873. Throughout the 1850s, an increasingly dense network of lines took shape across a corridor running from the mid-Atlantic and New England seaboard to the northern plains. Although many of these lines were loosely affiliated, they had not yet been joined into tight through-routes stretching from east to west. The Northern railroad map resembled a crazy quilt more than a set of parallel lines. During the latter part of the decade, the South also began to invest significant sums in railroads, although capital in that region was channeled primarily into a few long-distance routes connecting Atlantic and Gulf ports with inland river cities. The differences reflected the North's longstanding emphasis on using railroad technology as an engine for local development, a goal that mattered far less to dispersed Southern planters who earned their livelihoods by investing in slave labor to generate agricultural products for global markets.

The Civil War reoriented railroading in ways that led the regions to converge in the decade to follow. In the North, where railroads were largely left undisturbed by the war, considerable traffic began flowing extensive distances along an east-west axis. In the South, where railroads were perpetually built, destroyed, and rebuilt over the course of the conflict, the rail map grew much

denser. Lines penetrated isolated interior areas such as the iron-producing region of north-central Alabama and crisscrossed the Piedmont corridor of Virginia and the Carolinas. These trends continued after the return to peace, as Southern legislatures and municipalities issued numerous bonds in support of rail projects and Congress launched projects aimed at reaching westward across the continent to Texas, California, and the Pacific Northwest. Although it would be some time before the transcontinentals carried significant volumes of traffic to the eastern seaboard, they added markedly to the stock of mileage.

The rapid construction of the postwar decade hinged upon new developments in civil engineering, many of which had been spurred by war. Engineers relocating from the battlefields to the western frontiers, accustomed to building quickly and under duress, laid track at record pace across the prairies and devised structures such as snow sheds and spectacular wooden trestles to traverse the mountains. As with early lines in the East, these roads were often built cheaply on a per-mile basis, with lightweight infrastructure that would soon need replacing as traffic grew. In more settled regions to the East, postwar projects assumed a different character. Established lines such as the Pennsylvania and B&O looked to construct durable new structures from iron and Bessemer steel, which fell rapidly in price as domestic manufacturers learned to compete with the British. Structural metal was especially important in tying together the emergent trunk lines. Prior to the Civil War, no bridges had been built across the Ohio River below Pittsburgh or across the Mississippi below Iowa. By the mid-1870s, truss bridges built from iron and steel crossed the Ohio at Pittsburgh, Wheeling, Cincinnati, and Louisville, and the wondrous Eads Bridge spanned the Mississippi at St. Louis. The Tennessee, Cumberland, Potomac, Savannah, and Chattahoochee, which had posed similar obstacles in the antebellum South, soon met with similar treatment.

As the expanded railroad network took shape, opportunities opened for enterprises looking to provide new, high-value services in long-distance travel and shipping. Fast freight companies, operated by railroads and by third parties such as Wells

Fargo and American Express, transported packages rapidly among commercial centers. The Chicago inventor and manufacturer George Pullman leveraged patent rights for sleeping cars to launch a national system of elaborate rolling hotels. Drovers on the Midwestern plains transported hogs and cattle via special stock trains to Chicago and St. Louis, where packers slaughtered the animals and sent fresh cuts of meat into eastern markets in refrigerator cars packed with straw and ice. Many of these trains, which railroads felt compelled by competition to operate at higher speeds and with fewer delays, featured novelties such as tight couplers and air brakes. The latter technology, introduced by the Pittsburgh inventor George Westinghouse in 1869, gave locomotive engineers direct control over trains. Safety advocates, with voices amplified by newly created state railroad commissions, clamored for its use and for additional safeguards such as block signals and fireproof heaters, lights, and cars. The prospects for those supplying such novelties brightened still further during the last quarter of the nineteenth century, as railroads added more than 100,000 miles of new routes and laid another 60,000 miles with multiple tracks, bringing the total system capacity to more than 250,000 miles of track.

Although such features and services captured the attention of the traveling public and high-end shippers, railroads themselves generally preferred to transport bulk commodities at slow speed. Shipments of heavy agricultural and mineral products, especially those that could be stored year-round and could readily withstand the jostling of transit, constituted the most lucrative trade for most lines. During the last quarter of the nineteenth century, lines such as the Pennsylvania diverted much of their innovative energies and resources toward that goal. Typically, this involved bulking up their facilities. In addition to adding multiple tracks, they invested in heavy steel rails that could bear the burden of massive locomotives pulling cars that by 1900 often carried 50 tons apiece, more than double the typical burden of 1870. To accommodate these behemoths, lines frequently also invested in major realignments or entirely new routes, which eliminated trouble spots such as sharp curves and steep grades that might

otherwise have dictated operating capacity and undercut potential returns.

As with the new bridges that facilitated the postwar construction boom, many of these improvements drew upon ongoing enhancements in materials. In addition to demanding thicker and heavier rails, whose manufacture repeatedly baffled steel fabricators, railroads continually pressed against the frontiers of knowledge in areas such as bearings and lubricants. Enhanced rolling stock made use of new specialty steels for springs, drawbars, wheels, frames, and other components. Locomotive manufacturers strove continually to redesign boilers, fireboxes, and appliances to eke more power from less coal, which had rapidly become the fuel of choice with the development of bituminous fields in Appalachia and the Mississippi River Valley. In their pursuit of such innovation, railroads often worked collaboratively among themselves and with suppliers. Many lines invested in pioneering analytical laboratories and testing facilities, and they participated in industry-wide studies conducted under the auspices of professional engineering societies and trade groups. Technical change often came to be mediated and coordinated through a process of technical specifications.

The relentless focus on bulking up and enhancing performance yielded significant gains in productivity over the course of the late nineteenth century. Rates fell significantly relative to other prices, and most railroads managed to earn profits, at least until the depression of the 1890s sparked a wave of bankruptcies. The frequent protests over railroad rates that characterized the period and fueled political protest had less to do with overall rate levels than with perceived discrimination against particular regions, communities, and shippers. Although many questioned the fairness of the process and desirability of the outcome, few seriously questioned that railroad technology had achieved significant efficiencies over other modes of transport and fueled an economic transformation.

New Century, New Challenges. With the turn into the twentieth century, American railroading entered a new phase. A booming economy generated unprecedented demand for rail transport in virtually every corner of the nation. In 1899, railroads had loaded just over half a billion tons of freight and handled just under 125 billion ton-miles of shipments. By 1910, both figures had essentially doubled. Lines in sparsely settled areas of the West and South now garnered sufficient traffic to support the sorts of intensive investments in technical improvements that had long characterized railroads in the East and Midwest. Those more established lines, meanwhile, showed signs of strain as they attempted to cope with the congestion. Even the mighty Pennsylvania saw its operating efficiencies drop, as trains sat idly in yards and on sidings while waiting for clearance through bottlenecks caused by steep grades and crowded urban transfer stations. Such waste was compounded by growing competition for skilled labor, which drove up wages for virtually all railroad employees. Railroads could not see an easy way around such difficulties. They found themselves contemplating massive capital improvement projects and scrambling to investigate technical remedies they had previously shunned as overly complicated or too expensive.

While dealing with strains on their balance sheet, railroads also faced new pressures from government regulators. State and local governments, responding to broadly felt public antipathy toward the powerful and often disruptive railroads, passed numerous ordinances requiring lines to operate trains more safely, quietly, and cleanly. Many cities pressed railroads to relocate lines below grade, add automatic signals and crossing gates, and convert to electric traction, a technology that had emerged as a viable alternative to steam with construction of urban transit systems. Meanwhile, the federal Interstate Commerce Commission gained new powers to monitor operating procedures and set rates. The Interstate Commerce Commission began investigating all accidents, and its inspectors regularly showed up to see whether lines complied with laws mandating the use of safety appliances and limiting the hours of service for operating personnel. More ominously for railroads, in 1910 the commission denied a request from lines in the eastern half of the country for a rate increase, which railroads believed necessary to fund the capital improvements required to relieve congestion. Commissioners sympathized with the arguments of Louis Brandeis, a lawyer for shippers who accused railroads of inefficiency because they had not adopted techniques of scientific management, as espoused by the previously obscure engineering consultant Frederick Winslow Taylor.

Despite this setback, railroads invested heavily in capital improvements and new operating technologies during the opening two decades of the century. Annual ton-miles increased by another 155 billion over the course of the 1910s to a record 414 billion in 1920, more than triple the level of 1899. The Pennsylvania led the way in adopting automatic block signals and interlocking devices, which by 1920 had become common features on mainline railroads throughout much of the nation. The Pennsylvania also conducted public tests of electric locomotives, which they deemed economical for use in densely congested corridors such as that between New York and Washington. With their rapid acceleration and responsive braking, electric locomotives could travel in shorter blocks and move trains through congested stretches more rapidly than steam locomotives. Under less trying circumstances, however, the economic advantages swung back to steam. Most lines addressed the challenge of increased traffic through the conventional means of increasing the size of steam-powered trains, scheduling their movements more cleverly, devising more efficient means of assembling them, adding more signals to keep them in motion, and, above all, eliminating steep grades and sharp curves that created bottlenecks.

In a few instances where the density and value of trade justified the investment, this potential to achieve economies through enhanced civil engineering sparked construction of entirely new lines. Both the Clinchfield and the Virginian railroads, for instance, were completed in the 1910s to penetrate the rich coalfields of Appalachia and provide competition for older lines connecting south Atlantic ports with the Ohio River via coal country. Construction of these lines and others in the Far West, which likewise traversed resource-intensive regions, helped push route mileage to an all-time high of just under 255,000 in 1916 and completed the backbones of the national system. Total track mileage (including multiple tracks) edged up from about 400,000 miles in 1916 to just shy of 430,000 in 1930. From there, both route and track mileage began their inexorable decline. Faced with increased competition from autos, trucks, buses, and airlines, railroads abandoned lesser branches and consolidated traffic on fewer trunk lines. By 1980, route mileage totaled less than 160,000 miles and total track miles barely exceeded 300,000 miles. Tonnage and ton-miles also plateaued during the 1920s before plummeting to pre-1910s levels for much of the Great Depression. A wartime boom restored freight volume to levels approximating those of 1920, where they remained through 1980, thus lagging well behind overall growth of the economy.

Regulation and Retrenchment. For most of the twentieth century, that process of consolidation occurred under close supervision from the federal government. For a brief period during World War I, when traffic flowing to the eastern ports overwhelmed the rail system, government actually assumed operational control over the railroads. With the return to peace, however, lines returned to private hands, while also acquiescing to new levels of regulatory influence over rates, operations, and labor relations.

In a variety of ways, the regulatory arrangement emphasized stability and continuity over innovation and change. From a desire to preserve service to isolated communities and provide competition to trucks and buses, government often required railroads to maintain service to routes whose traffic did not generate sufficient returns at allowable rates. To cover such losses, railroads and regulators built buffers into other rates, which were consolidated through a comprehensive rate-of-return calculation. This method of accounting disassociated returns from actual operating performance and preserved a rail network derived more from custom than demand. Similarly, labor agreements typically stipulated wage rates based on seniority within established job classifications. The method inevitably worked to preserve traditional arrangements, even when new technologies

might have permitted railroads to eliminate some tasks and save labor costs.

Two examples help illustrate the constraints on innovation. During the interwar years, as trucks became increasingly common and state and federal governments paved more than a million miles of road, railroads examined ways to meld the new technology with the old. Most of their efforts involved offloading merchandise from rail cars to dedicated local trucking fleets. Such arrangements would potentially yield benefits of enhanced coordination and scheduling. In at least a few cases, moreover, railroads even experimented with so-called piggybacking, in which truck trailers were actually mounted on railcars. Regulators balked at both initiatives. Rather than envision trucks and railroads as complementary components in an integrated system, they preferred to draw sharp boundaries and preserve the two modes of transit as strictly competitive alternatives. Widespread piggybacking had to await the container revolution. Incorporating ocean-going ships as well as trucks and railroads, this genuinely intermodal system blossomed fully only in the 1980s, after the Interstate Commerce Commission relaxed its regulatory constraints on railroads.

A similarly long lag time occurred in the case of the diesel-electric locomotive. Railroads and their suppliers began exploring this technology in the second decade of the twentieth century, at nearly the same time as they tried electric locomotives. Established manufacturers played along, sometimes on their own, but also in partnership with major electrical manufacturers such as Westinghouse and General Electric. Consortia also included auto manufacturers and other experts in internal combustion. By the 1920s, several prototypes were in operation, and tests indicated that the diesel-electrics might well offer greater flexibility in operations, while also dramatically reducing fuel and maintenance costs. The shift did not occur, however, until the 1950s, when diesel-electrics swept through the industry.

Not all of the blame lay with regulators. The coal-steam complex had considerable inertia. Coal companies, which often constituted a railroad's largest customer for shipping services, lobbied hard for coal-burning steam locomotives while also driving down the price of fuel. For their part, railroads had invested heavily in giant steam locomotives during the early 1920s, with orders topping 2,500 in 1922 alone. Lines understandably sought to nurse as much service as possible from this investment, especially as the Depression and mounting competition from alternative forms of transport deprived them of revenue. Many of the benefits of diesels, moreover, would not be realized until railroads converted their entire fleets and eliminated the maintenance facilities and fueling stations necessary to run steam locomotives. Railroads balked at the capital costs necessary for making a wholesale conversion. Rather than invest in diesels, Depression-wracked railroads employed the services of industrial designers, who dressed up existing steam technology in sleek sheathing that evoked change.

Although economic factors certainly played a significant role, it seems clear that the regulatory structure complicated matters and helped delay conversion long after World War II had breathed new life into the rail industry. Diesel-electrics necessitated both a thorough reworking of job structures used to mediate labor relations and a comprehensive reassessment of the capital valuations used to set rates. These considerations added to the inertia. For decades after the conversion, to cite merely one example, railroads were required to maintain both a fireman and an engineer on each diesel-powered train, although diesels had no fires.

Although slow in coming, diesels did ultimately work profound changes in American railroading. Maintenance shops dwindled in size and importance, way stations disappeared, and switching operations occurred with greater ease and flexibility. With their high torque at low speeds, diesels made ideal switchers, and the ability to link together several units controlled by a single engineer gave them yet another advantage over steam on main lines. Such benefits saved both capital and labor costs, while also reducing operating expenses for fuel and eliminating those for water entirely. Diesels also gradually undermined a way of life, especially in the large railroad maintenance hubs, which had often employed thousands of skilled mechanics and other operating personnel. Once the fount of

innovation in the industry and the figurative soul of a vast machine, these isolated burgs typically shriveled to ghosts of their former selves. Railroad investment now shifted toward elaborate switching facilities, which, in addition to diesels, made use of technologies such as radio-controlled dispatching and bar code scanning systems.

Although highly significant for railroads and their employees, such innovation did little to stem the challenge posed by trucks, cars, buses, and planes. With mass production driving down the cost of such alternatives and the federal government pumping vast sums into critical infrastructure such as highways and airports, railroads largely ceded the passenger trade to these alternatives. Only commuter railroads serving densely populated cities and a few lines operating along especially scenic routes carried sufficient passengers to remain viable, and even those usually required some government subsidy to survive. In 1972, mainline intercity passenger service passed into the control of Amtrak, a federally subsidized entity that also receives supplementary funding from many states. Amtrak operated its own equipment but leased track rights from private railroads, which typically ran freight service over the same lines.

Freight Railroad Resurgence. The freight business, not track rights, mattered most to the railroads. During the 1980s and 1990s, many of them achieved a remarkable resurgence by restructuring their operations around the task of carrying certain types of freight with heightened efficiency.

This transformation hinged on three elements. First, the growth of the American economy, in particular a spectacular increase in the volume of imports and exports, pumped new demand into the industry. Much of this additional traffic flowed long distances to and from coastal ports, which handled manufactured imports and sent agricultural and mining resources received from the heartland overseas, along with some American manufactured goods. Coal also moved in large volume from mines in Wyoming and Appalachia to power plants around the country, as the portion of the nation's power generated from coal grew markedly. Since the completion of dieselization in the early 1960s, railroads had already made a transition to longer shipments; in 1980, they handled roughly the same amount of tonnage as 15 years earlier, but generated a third more ton-miles. Coming economic trends accelerated the shift in traffic patterns.

Railroads capitalized on this opportunity by pursuing a series of consolidations, which worked their way steadily through the industry in the years following deregulation. When the dust finally settled, the vast majority of lines east of the Mississippi River fell under control of two giant systems, CSX and Norfolk Southern. In the West, Union Pacific merged with longtime rival Southern Pacific and fell into duopolistic competition with Burlington Northern Santa Fe, itself a conglomeration of what had once been three separate entities. The Illinois Central, eventually purchased by Canadian Pacific, operated a network from the Gulf Coast up the Mississippi to the Great Lakes. These five giant systems, operating in a simplified competitive environment, could coordinate traffic movements on an extent never before possible and mobilize capital toward improvement of long-distance corridors linking new terminal facilities.

Those investments spurred a third element of transformation: technological innovation that significantly reduced costs per ton-mile. The most important technical change involved the elimination of much expensive switching operations through the use of long unit trains, whose cars were rarely uncoupled. Coal, for instance, moved from Wyoming to the East Coast and from Appalachia to the southeast in trains that might include a hundred or more lightweight aluminum hopper cars. Once emptied, these cars were dragged back to the mines as a unit, often over tracks that had once carried trains of a competitive railroad. In effect, the consolidated railroads operated giant loops through which trains circulated. Other bulk commodities such as grain and high-fructose corn syrup moved in much the same fashion.

The most remarkable innovation of this sort involved unit trains consisting of tightly coupled cars capable of carrying containers, which could be loaded onto the cars by mobile cranes. Rather than shunt vast fleets of boxcars onto separate tracks and retrieve them with switching engines, railroads collected containers deposited by truckers in giant parking lots, where other trucks delivered them to the cranes. The new methods not only eliminated trackage, motive power, and associated yard and train crews; they also significantly shortened the time necessary to assemble trains, thus enabling railroads to offer expedited high-value shipping services that might compete with trucks traveling long distances over interstate highways.

To facilitate such movement, railroads also invested in densely trafficked rail corridors fortified with improved roadbed and governed by centralized control centers. Roadbed improvements drew on new technologies such as continuously welded rail, concrete ties, and automatic tamping equipment. Integrated machinery laid entirely new roadbed with dramatically less labor input and considerably less interruption. Computer control systems elevated the task of managing train movements to a higher level than ever before. In coordinating movements across vast territories containing multiple alternative routes, railroads both increased carrying capacity and optimized revenue by prioritizing movements of high-value, time-sensitive shipments.

Such techniques infused freight railroading with new potential and attracted sizeable private investment from the likes of famed fund manager Warren Buffet. Advocates of advanced passenger rail, meanwhile, typically turned to government for support. At the dawn of the twenty-first century, Congress and the states weighed proposals for new high-speed rail lines dedicated exclusively to passenger service linking major commercial centers. Although proponents touted significant environmental benefits, such lines remained a source of intense controversy as politicians grappled with economic challenges and community groups raised concerns about noise and other hazards. As of 2014, no new lines had left the drawing board. Yet the proposals, like the surprising resurgence of freight railroading during the previous three decades, demonstrated the continuing vitality of a technology that had shaped the nation for nearly two centuries.

[*See also* Engineering; Machinery and Manufacturing; Research and Development (R&D); and Technology.]

BIBLIOGRAPHY

Angevine, Robert G. *The Railroad and the State: War, Politics, and Technology in Nineteenth-Century America*. Stanford, Calif.: Stanford University Press, 2004. Offers a balanced assessment of the modest role played by military engineers.

Berk, Gerald. *Alternative Tracks: The Constitution of American Industrial Order, 1865–1917*. Baltimore: Johns Hopkins University Press, 1994. On railroading at the turn of the twentieth century.

Boorstin, Daniel. *The Americans: The Democratic Experience*. New York: Random House, 1974. On early railroads.

Brown, John K. *The Baldwin Locomotive Works, 1831–1915: A Study in American Industrial Practice*. Baltimore: Johns Hopkins University Press, 2001. Insightful on many matters, including technology.

Carter, Susan B., et al., eds. *Historical Statistics of the United States: Earliest Times to the Present, Millennial Edition*. New York: Cambridge University Press, 2006. Source for the statistical data in this essay.

Chandler, Alfred D., Jr. *The Visible Hand: The Managerial Revolution in American Business*. New York: Cambridge University Press, 1977. The standard treatment of postbellum developments and the rise of an integrated national system appears in Part 2.

Churella, Albert J. *From Steam to Diesel: Managerial Customs and Organizational Capabilities in the Twentieth-Century American Locomotive Industry*. Princeton, N.J.: Princeton University Press, 1998. On dieselization.

Churella, Albert J. *The Pennsylvania Railroad*. Vol. 1: *Building an Empire, 1846–1917*. Philadelphia: University of Pennsylvania Press, 2013. Among the many studies of individual firms during this period, this work is especially insightful on many matters, including technology.

Cronon, William. *Nature's Metropolis: Chicago and the Great West*. New York: W. W. Norton, 1991. An imaginative exploration of the railroad's impact on regional development.

Dunlavy, Colleen A. *The Politics of Industrialization: Early Railroads in the United States and Prussia*. Princeton, N.J.: Princeton University Press, 1994. Offers an insightful international comparison.

Eakin, B. Kelly, et al. "Railroad Performance under the Staggers Act." *Regulation* 32 (2010–2011): 32–38. For a recent assessment of deregulation and productivity change in railroading.

Fishlow, Albert. *American Railroads and the Transformation of the Antebellum Economy*. New York: Cambridge University Press, 1966. Assesses the links between railroading and other economic sectors.

Fogel, Robert. *Railroads and American Economic Growth: Essays in Econometric History*. Baltimore: Johns Hopkins University Press, 1964. Calls into question some of the links between railroading and other economic sectors.

Kerr, K. Austin. *American Railroad Politics, 1914–1920: Rates, Wages, and Efficiency*. Pittsburgh, Pa.: University of Pittsburgh Press, 1968. On railroading at the turn of the twentieth century.

Klein, Maury. *The Great Richmond Terminal: A Study in Businessmen and Business Strategy*. Charlottesville: University Press of Virginia, 1970. Covers developments in the South.

Klein, Maury. *History of the Louisville & Nashville Railroad*. New York: Macmillan Company, 1972, and Lexington: University of Kentucky Press, 2003. Covers developments in the South.

Klein, Maury. *The Life & Legend of E. H. Harriman*. Chapel Hill: University of North Carolina Press, 2000. Provides valuable perspectives on railroading at the turn of the twentieth century, as restructuring and regulation loomed.

Majewski, John. *A House Dividing: Economic Development in Pennsylvania and Virginia before the Civil War*. New York: Cambridge University Press, 2000. On regional contrasts before the Civil War.

Marrs, Aaron W. *Railroads in the Old South: Pursuing Progress in a Slave Society*. Baltimore: Johns Hopkins University Press, 2009. On railroading in the antebellum South.

McCraw, Thomas K. *Prophets of Regulation*. New York: Cambridge University Press, 1984. On railroading at the turn of the twentieth century.

Miner, Craig. *A Most Magnificent Machine: America Adopts the Railroad, 1825–1862*. Lawrence: University of Kansas Press, 2010. Provides a historical overview on early railroads.

Orsi, Richard J. *Sunset Limited: The Southern Pacific Railroad and the Development of the American West, 1850–1930*. Berkeley and Los Angeles:

University of California Press, 2007. Examines the impact of a major western line.

Riegel, Robert Edgar. *The Story of the Western Railroads: From 1852 through the Reign of the Giants.* New York: Macmillan Company, 1926, and Lincoln: University of Nebraska Press, 1964. An early treatment of the transcontinental railroads.

Roland, Alex. "Containers and Causality." *Technology and Culture* 48, no. 2 (2007): 386–392. Reviews four books on the container revolution.

Saunders, Richard. *Main Lines: Rebirth of the North American Railroads, 1970–2002.* DeKalb: Northern Illinois University Press, 2003. Offers useful overviews of changing industry structure and operations under regulation and deregulation.

Saunders, Richard. *Merging Lines: American Railroads, 1900–1970.* DeKalb: Northern Illinois University Press, 2001. Offers useful overviews of changing industry structure and operations under regulation and deregulation.

Scheiber, Harry N. *Ohio Canal Era: A Case Study of Government and the Economy, 1820–1861.* Athens, Ohio: Ohio University Press, 1968, 1987, and 2012. See Part 3 for railroading in the Old Northwest.

Skowronek, Stephen. *Building a New American State: The Expansion of National Administrative Capacities, 1877–1920.* New York: Cambridge University Press, 1982. On railroading at the turn of the twentieth century.

Stone, Richard D. *The Interstate Commerce Commission and the Railroad Industry: A History of Regulatory Policy.* New York: Greenwood Publishing Group, 1991. For a detailed chronology of deregulation.

Stover, John F. *American Railroads.* Chicago: University of Chicago Press, 1961; reprinted 1976. An old but still reliable overview.

Taylor, George Rogers. *The Transportation Revolution, 1815–1860.* New York: Rinehart, 1951. For classic economic analysis of railroads in the Old Northwest.

Thomas, William G. *The Iron Way: Railroads, the Civil War, and the Making of Modern America.* New Haven, Conn.: Yale University Press, 2011. The authoritative work on the subject.

Thomson, Ross. *Structures of Change: Technological Innovation in the United States, 1790–1865.* Baltimore: Johns Hopkins University Press, 2009. See Part 3 for an analysis of railroading.

Usselman, Steven W. *Regulating Railroad Innovation: Business, Technology, and Politics in America,* *1840–1920.* New York: Cambridge University Press, 2002. A novel synthesis of developments to 1920, with particular emphasis on technology.

White, Richard. *Railroaded: The Transcontinentals and the Making of Modern America.* New York: W. W. Norton & Company, 2011. Takes a more comprehensive and critical view.

Steven W. Usselman

RAND CORPORATION

See **Military, Science and Technology and the.**

RED CROSS, AMERICAN

Clara Barton (1821–1912) founded the American Red Cross in 1881, one year before Congress belatedly ratified the 1864 Geneva Convention concerning wartime help for sick and wounded soldiers. Although Barton played a modest role during the Spanish–American War, full official recognition eluded her, and impromptu disaster relief became her first priority. After 1900 she was pushed aside by prominent New Yorkers who reorganized the Red Cross and redefined its status, role, and scope: Theodore Roosevelt drafted a new charter that defined a closer relationship with the government and the army; Robert W. DeForest grounded its relief work on the principles of scientific philanthropy and the charity organization movement; and Henry P. Davison gave it legitimacy on Wall Street, headed its endowment fund, and directed its extensive operations during World War I. The Red Cross provided both planned assistance to the military and an outlet for civilian patriotic enthusiasm; the wartime boom brought the organization 20 million members and a treasury surplus of $127 million by 1919. Salaried administrators proliferated despite its tradition of voluntarism.

Ambitious plans for innovative peacetime public-health and social-welfare programs at home and abroad soon foundered on war weariness and isolationism, opposition from established agencies and interest groups, hostility from the newspapers controlled by William Randolph Hearst, and a grassroots suspicion among volunteers that the central office had been taken over by careerist professionals. Red Cross personnel and aspirations were quickly, if reluctantly, scaled back in response to diminished public expectations and a postwar drop in membership and contributions. Further criticism arose during the Depression of the 1930s, when the Red Cross refused a federal subsidy for assisting drought victims, soliciting private contributions instead, and then agreed to distribute government surplus wheat and cotton. Public controversy was fueled by claims that Red Cross leaders opposed the New Deal, disliked labor unions, and embodied typically white racial attitudes.

Beginning with World War II, improvements in the U.S. military's medical and nursing services changed the Red Cross's wartime role to one of providing generalized recreational services instead of auxiliary medical assistance. In the second half of the twentieth century, despite periodic pressure to assist the State Department's foreign-policy agenda or White House public-relations efforts, civilian disaster relief became its principal peacetime function. Over the years, the Red Cross's relationship with the American press and public has fluctuated from adulation to vilification and indifference. Unlike the great philanthropic foundations, its visibility and income varied with the public mood, increasing at times of natural disasters or other crises. An early 1990s survey found that it was the most highly regarded of major U.S. charities. During the Persian Gulf War, for example, donations soared to $26 million.

By the mid-1990s, the American Red Cross was one of America's largest charitable organizations, with more than 1,300 local chapters, an annual budget of $1.8 billion (mostly raised by private and corporate contributions), a paid staff of around 30 thousand, and some 1.3 million volunteers annually. A 50-member volunteer board of directors governed the organization. Its national programs included disaster relief, a blood-donor program that supplied about one half of the nation's blood supply, and health and safety services including minor-injury treatment and blood-pressure and cholesterol-testing programs. A major initiative focused on increasing health services to minority groups and recruiting minority volunteers. The American Red Cross also worked with the International Red Cross and Red Crescent movement to meet human needs arising from natural disaster or conflicts in many countries, including, at the end of the 1990s, Kosovo and East Timor.

[*See also* Foundations and Health; Medicine; Nursing; Public Health; *and* War and Medicine.]

BIBLIOGRAPHY

Dulles, Foster Rhea. *The American Red Cross: A History*. New York: Harper, 1950.
Gilbo, Patrick F. *The American Red Cross: The First Century*. New York: Harper & Row, 1981.

John F. Hutchinson

REED, WALTER

(1851–1902), physician and microbiologist, leader of the U.S. Army Yellow Fever Board that established the mosquito vector of yellow fever. Born in Belroi, Virginia, Walter Reed received his first MD degree from the University of Virginia in 1869 and a second in 1870 from Bellevue Hospital Medical College in New York. Reed passed the army's medical examination in 1874 and from 1875 until his death he served in the Medical Corps of the U.S. Army. In 1890, he requested further medical study and was stationed in Baltimore, where he studied bacteriology at Johns Hopkins under the guidance of William Welch. He dedicated the remainder of his career to the study of infectious diseases. In 1893, he was appointed professor at the new army medical school and curator of the army medical museum.

In his epidemiological work, Reed evaluated theories using newly discovered developments in bacteriology. In 1898 he headed an army investigation of the spread of typhoid fever in military camps located in the South during the Spanish–American

War. Reed and his colleagues Victor Vaughan and Edward Shakespeare showed the importance of flies in transmitting typhoid fever through the transfer of bacteria from fecal matter to food. This demonstrated that the main vehicle for the transmission of typhoid was not infected water, as had been commonly assumed. Two years later, Army Surgeon General George Sternberg appointed him head of the Yellow Fever Board, charged with investigating the yellow fever problem in Havana.

Reed, together with his fellow physicians Jesse Lazear, Aristides Agramonte, and James Carroll, conducted an extensive series of experiments to determine the mode of transmission of yellow fever. They first investigated causes and established that what was commonly believed to be the "yellow fever germ," found in 1897, was actually a secondary infection and not the cause of yellow fever. In 1900 Reed's board successfully showed that the mosquito *Aedes aegypti* transmits yellow fever, a discovery that facilitated the eradication of the disease in Havana, the southern United States, and the Panama Canal zone. Reed and his colleagues tested their theories on themselves and other human volunteers. They tested whether the disease was caused by exposure to the body fluids of yellow fever victims or whether only mosquitoes carried it. They exposed volunteers to each possible disease vector and discovered that only those with mosquito bites caught the disease. Initially lionized for the yellow fever discovery, Reed also came to be regarded as a model for ethical human experimentation, in recognition of his concern for the men who participated in the dangerous yellow fever studies and his introduction of written consent forms for medical volunteers.

[*See also* Biological Sciences; Disease; Ethics and Medicine; Germ Theory of Disease; Malaria; Medicine; Public Health; Typhoid Fever; War and Medicine; Welch, William H.; *and* Yellow Fever.]

BIBLIOGRAPHY

Bean, William B. *Walter Reed, a Biography*. Charlottesville: University Press of Virginia, 1982.

Humphreys, Margaret. "Reed, Walter (1851–1902)." In *The History of Science in the United States: An Encyclopedia,* edited by Marc Rothenberg, pp. 468–469. New York and London: Garland, 2001.

Lederer, Susan E. *Subjected to Science: Human Experimentation in America before the Second World War*. Baltimore: Johns Hopkins University Press, 1995. Pioneering book in the history of human experimentation.

Lederer, Susan E. "Walter Reed and the Yellow Fever Experiments." In *The Oxford Textbook of Clinical Research Ethics,* edited by Ezekiel J. Emanuel, pp. 9–17. Oxford: Oxford University Press, 2008.

The Philip S. Hench Walter Reed Yellow Fever On-line Collection. The University of Virginia Health Sciences Library. http://yellowfever.lib.virginia.edu/reed/collection.html (accessed 15 January 2013). Contains nearly 5,500 documents gathered by Philip Hench by or about Reed and the fight against yellow fever, as well as thousands of additional related documents.

Susan E. Lederer;
updated by Elspeth Knewstubb

REFRIGERATION AND AIR CONDITIONING

Although it has almost always been easy for mankind to heat something by building a fire under it, controlling cold was a much more difficult technology to develop. The value of refrigeration for food preservation (let alone for cooling down in warm climes) was obvious centuries before the technology to do it even existed. Since the turn of the nineteenth century, the technology to control cold has become cheaper, smaller, more effective, and more precise. This has made it possible for refrigeration and air conditioning to become an often unnoticed part of most people's lives in developed countries.

The first means by which people controlled the cold was by cutting and preserving ice for both industrial and household purposes. The pioneer in these efforts was the Boston merchant Frederic Tudor, who essentially created the natural ice industry when he sent blocks cut from a Massachusetts pond to Martinique in 1805. Although this first shipment was not profitable, Tudor's firm developed many of the innovations that made the ice industry possible through trial and error. These included better harvesting equipment, new ice-loading machines (that would eventually be known as ice elevators), and better icehouses (both in New England and in their tropical markets) so there would be more ice left to sell.

Ice was never as popular in the rest of the world as it was in America. As Americans developed their taste for ice, the industry grew. Natural ice became a vital part of the food chain, preserving perishable food like dressed meat and fruit as it traveled from points of production in the West to its mostly eastern markets. It was also good for keeping beer cold in taverns or in iceboxes because it never came in direct contact with what people ate. If it had, the dirt and other organic matter often trapped in natural ice might have fouled the food.

This drawback helps explain why inventors all around the world worked on developing mechanical refrigeration equipment during the mid- to late nineteenth century. John Gorrie, a Florida doctor, developed an early prototype of mechanical refrigeration in 1849 while trying to create what would eventually become air conditioning. However, the inventor most responsible for modern mechanical refrigeration was the German academic Carl von Linde, who created the first marketable ammonia compression refrigeration machine in 1877. Linde's work was important because he demonstrated the effectiveness of ammonia as a refrigerant (compared with other alternatives like sulfur dioxide or ether) and because he demonstrated that compression refrigeration (as opposed to absorption refrigeration, during which some of the refrigerant remained liquid throughout the process) was the most efficient system.

In America, the largest market for refrigeration in the world, mechanical refrigeration technology was used for a variety of purposes. Most important, firms used it to produce ice. The initial market for artificial ice was not consumers, but industry. Brewers of lager beer in particular wanted ice machines so they could produce their product during the

summer as well as the winter. As refrigeration equipment firms grew during the 1880s and their equipment became cheaper, artificial ice companies began to sell ice door to door. Their delivery men drove ice wagons like the natural ice companies had done for decades, but the artificial product could not be crippled by the poor weather of the previous winter and was cleaner than the natural product. Mechanical refrigeration also made the growth of the cold-storage industry possible because it allowed producers to preserve perishable foods and sell them out of season for the first time.

Electric household refrigeration caused the eventual demise of the artificial ice industry, but that too took a matter of decades. Before 1915, the most common instrument for preserving food in the home was the icebox. Although a box with ice in it may seem like simple technology, iceboxes improved greatly over the course of the last half of the nineteenth century as commercial firms began to produce them with better materials and more effective insulation.

The first modern refrigerators, on the other hand, were noisy, expensive, and inefficient. For example, the very first ones required the machinery to be installed in the basement and to be attached to the box in the kitchen by a belt that traveled through a hole cut in the kitchen floor. Sales grew sharply around 1925, when refrigerator producers improved reliability, developed a better distribution system, and significantly lowered prices through mass production. The development of Freon, a safe and reliable refrigerant for household refrigerators, further increased sales during the early 1930s.

The growth of freezer space in household refrigerators led directly to the growth of the frozen-food industry between 1930 and 1960. In the second half of the twentieth century household refrigerators first began to spread to other developing countries around the world. Today, modern refrigeration has made it possible for perishable food to be shipped around the world without spoilage and for that food to be kept almost indefinitely once bought.

The development of air conditioning was closely linked to the development of mechanical refrigeration. Chilling water produces ice. Chilling space creates cold storage in a warehouse and air conditioning in a home (although successful air conditioning also depends upon humidity).

Although experiments with industrial cooling were performed during the late nineteenth century, Willis Carrier developed the forerunner of modern air conditioning at the Carrier Engineering Company starting in 1915. Most people first experienced air conditioning in large buildings built with this technology during the 1920s, usually movie theaters. Many refrigerating equipment firms began to produce room-size air conditioning units during the 1930s because demand for something so useful persisted despite hard times. Through air conditioning, mechanical refrigeration has not only made the warmer parts of America more habitable, but also made climate practically irrelevant when deciding what we want to eat.

[*See also* Electricity and Electrification; Heating Technology; *and* Household Technology.]

BIBLIOGRAPHY

Anderson, Oscar Edward, Jr. *Refrigeration in America.* Princeton, N.J.: Princeton University Press, 1953.

Cooper, Gail. *Air-Conditioning America: Engineers and the Controlled Environment, 1900–1960.* Baltimore: Johns Hopkins University Press, 1998.

Seaburg, Carl, and Stanley Paterson. *The Ice King: Frederic Tudor and His Circle.* Boston: Massachusetts Historical Society, 2003.

Thévenot, Roger. *A History of Refrigeration throughout the World.* Translated by J. C. Fidler. Paris: International Institute of Refrigeration, 1979.

Jonathan Rees

RELIGION AND SCIENCE

Talk of the relations between "science" and "religion" first became audible in the early 1800s, about the time that students of nature began referring to their work as science rather than natural philosophy (or natural history). Because natural philosophy allowed its practitioners, in the words of Isaac Newton, to discourse about God "from the appearances of things," one searches almost in vain for references to "natural philosophy and religion." Some writers expressed concern about tension between faith and reason, but they never pitted religion against science. In the early years of the nineteenth century the phrase "science and religion" occasionally appeared as a synonym for culture generally—as in "the friends of science and religion"—but not until the 1820s did books and articles begin featuring the phrase "science and religion" in their titles, a sure sign that the authors were coming to view the two enterprises as independent, if related. One of the first English-language books with the phrase in its title came out in 1823, when Thomas Dick, a Scottish writer, published *The Christian Philosopher; or, The Connection of Science and Philosophy with Religion*, a book widely read in the United States. By midcentury the conjunctive phrase was becoming a literary staple, and during the 1850s and 1860s several colleges and seminaries established professorships devoted to demonstrating (and preserving) the harmony of science and revealed religion (Numbers, 2007, pp. 11–37; Roberts, 2011, pp. 253–80; Harrison, 2006).

The most distinguishing characteristic of science was its insistence on using only natural explanations to account for the workings of nature, regardless of the personal beliefs of its practitioners. Since antiquity students of nature had expressed a reluctance to invoke the supernatural or miraculous, but only in the late eighteenth and early nineteenth centuries did men of science begin insisting on it (Numbers, 2003).

Colonial America. The colonial period in American history corresponded with the so-called scientific revolution in Europe, commonly associated with such intellectual giants as Nicolaus Copernicus, Galileo Galilei, and Isaac Newton. "The virtually unobstructed advance of the new physics among orthodox Puritans in England and America," Perry Miller once wrote, "owed everything to the terms in which it was advertised." Pious philosophers promised the devout that they had nothing to fear, that the new learning would bring both spiritual and material benefits, simultaneously illustrating God's wisdom and power and improving the practical arts of agriculture, medicine, and navigation. Thus assured, American Puritans calmly shifted their allegiance from ancient to modern authorities. Fortunately for them, their theology was not wedded to Aristotelian philosophy; thus, unlike "Popish Authors" in the Roman Catholic church, said Increase Mather, a Puritan minister, they had no need "to defend their *Pagan Master*." Another colonial cleric ridiculed "papists" for failing to espouse Copernican astronomy, suggesting that they did so largely because of the Pope's "private peek" against Galileo. So long as the new learning appeared to threaten none of *their* cherished doctrines, the Puritans would remain among its staunchest allies (Miller, 1953, p. 441; 1961, p. 221).

The permeating influence of the new science was reflected in the attempts of colonial writers to reinterpret biblical events scientifically or, as one historian has described it, "to translate the Mosaic creation into Newtonian language" (Middlekauff, 1971, pp. 285–286). Although Increase Mather's son Cotton, a prominent Puritan divine, never doubted the trustworthiness of the Scriptures and once complained that some modern philosophers "do certainly make too bold with the *Mosaic*, and *Inspired* History," he repeatedly undertook such translations. After reading William Whiston's *New Theory of the Earth* (1696), a popular Newtonian exposition, Mather abandoned the "Vulgar Hypothesis" of a universal creation in six literal days because it supposed "the Earth to be the *Center* of the world" and violated physical law. "The *Mosaic Creation* is not a Nice and philosophical Account of the *Origin* of All *Things*," he wrote in an unpublished summary of Whiston, "but an Historical and True Representation of the Formation of our Single Earth out of a confused Chaos, and of the successive & visible changes thereof, each day, till it became the Habitation of Mankind." God remained Creator of heaven and earth, but gravitation became his agent for forming the planets and guiding them on their circular journeys (Hornberger, 1938, pp. 116–117).

Even more pronounced than the influence of natural philosophy on biblical interpretation was its influence on the colonial cosmology. For millennia the gullible and learned alike had feared such irregular events as comets, meteors, and eclipses, often seeing them as divinely sent signs of impending disaster. The new learning gave scientifically informed colonial Americans a measure of freedom from fear that disasters, such as the great earthquakes of 1727 and 1755, would follow in the wake of unfamiliar events (Van de Wetering, 1982).

The more natural philosophy explained about comets, earthquakes, and planetary motion, the less colonial Americans had direct recourse to God. Although few took the extreme position that God no longer influenced human affairs, Samuel Johnson, who as a young man had laboriously mastered Newton, was complaining by 1749 that "it is a fashionable sort of philosophy (a science falsely so-called) to conceive that God governs the world only by a general providence according to certain fixed laws of nature which he hath established without ever interposing himself with regard to particular cases and persons" (Hornberger, 1935, p. 391; Ellis, 1973, pp. 148–151). The object of Johnson's complaint, a belief called deism (with which he himself had briefly flirted), achieved only limited circulation during the eighteenth century, but it became a bogeyman in sermons and other apologetical works. It came in many guises but in its simplest form taught that after God created the world and set it in motion, he then let it run its natural course without interference.

Deists and Christians may have disputed the extent to which God involved himself in the day-to-day operations of the world, but most of them agreed that God's existence could be demonstrated by the abundant evidence of design in the universe. "*The curiousness of the composure, & exquisiteness of the fabrick, declares an exquisite workman*," reasoned Samuel Willard, pastor of the Old South Church in Boston. "Whether we consider the composition of any one Creature, and that the most contemptible (suppose a worm, or a pile of grass) its nature hath more wonders in it, than the greatest Naturalist that ever was, *Solomon* himself, is able to Analyse" (Miller, 1961, pp. 225–226). By revealing these wonders, the study of nature, far from eroding belief in God, testified to his wisdom and benevolence.

Outside the fledgling scientific communities of colonial America, belief in the supernatural and occult continued to flourish, but by the eve of the Revolution few Americans remained untouched by the pervasive influence of the new learning. If many colonists still subscribed to witchcraft, astrology, and magical cures—and many did—they had, by and large, abandoned their belief in the geocentric world. If they continued to regard the Bible as God's unerring word, they also had come to accept the inspiration of the Book of Nature. Among the educated classes, reason and experiment became the catchwords of epistemological discourse. "Be sure," wrote Cotton Mather, "The Experimental Philosophy is that, in which alone your Mind can be at all established" (Miller, 1953, p. 437; see also Leventhal, 1976, and Hall, 1989).

From Revolution to Evolution. In 1800 a contributor to the *Medical Repository*, America's first medical magazine, applauded the growing tendency among men of science to refrain from invoking divine intervention in explaining the workings of nature, noting that "the modesty of science has given up the investigation of the first cause as beyond its comprehension." Although acknowledging that some events might have resulted from "an immediate act of Deity," the anonymous author believed that "we should not dignify this [kind of explanation] with the name either of philosophy, science, or even of history." Yale's evangelical professor of chemistry and natural history, Benjamin Silliman, founder of the *American Journal of Science*, unashamedly embraced the rule of limiting scientific explanations to physical causes known to exist in nature. "Our advancement in natural science is not dependent upon our faith," he wrote in 1842. "All the problems of physical science are worked out by laborious examination, and strict induction" (Numbers, 2009, pp. 17–18).

Such enthusiasm for banishing supernaturalism from science was possible only because Christian men of science typically attributed the laws of nature that they discovered to God. Thus, naturalized science continued testifying to God's existence. During the early decades of the nineteenth century, writer after writer celebrated the delicious harmony between science and religion. Much of this doxological literature took the form of natural theology, according to which nature testified to God's design and providence (Numbers, 2009, pp. 18–19; see also Bozeman, 1977). However, in the middle third of the nineteenth century some observers began to suspect that "every new conquest achieved by science, involved the loss of a domain to religion." Especially disturbing were scientific efforts to reinterpret the first chapters of the Bible. During the three decades between about 1810 and 1840, men of science pushed successfully to replace the supernatural creation of the solar system with the nebular hypothesis, to expand the history of life on earth from six thousand to millions of years, and to shrink Noah's flood to a regional event in the Near East. Many Christians readily adjusted their reading of the Bible to accommodate such findings; a midcentury observer surmised that only about "one half of the Christian public" continued to insist on the recent appearance of life on earth (Numbers, 1977, pp. 89–100; Stiling, 1991; Greene, 1974; Moore, 1986).

The scientific advocates of concordism simultaneously sought the freedom to interject themselves into the world of biblical exegesis while denying theologians and clergymen the right to monitor science. Such an arrangement could only embitter the clergy. Princeton Theological Seminary's Charles Hodge, a towering presence in midcentury American Calvinism, resented the marginalization of theologians from science. Although he continued to venerate men of science who disclosed "the wonderful works of God," by the late 1850s he was growing increasingly frustrated by their tendency to treat theologians who expressed themselves on scientific subjects as "trespassers" who should mind their own business. He attributed the growing "alienation" between men of science and men of the cloth in part to the former's "assumption of superiority" and their practice of stigmatizing their religious critics "as narrow-minded, bigots, old women, Bible worshippers, etc." At times Hodge worried that science, devoid of religion, was becoming downright "satanic." He had no doubt that religion was in a "fight for its life against a large class of scientific men" (Numbers, 2002).

Geology and astronomy may have created the most interest in antebellum America, but anthropology caused the most trouble. No scientific issue frayed more nerves—scientifically, theologically, and politically—than the origin of the various human races. The traditional view, based on the book of Genesis, held that all humans had descended from Adam and Eve, that the great deluge had destroyed all but the eight members of Noah's family, and that racial differences had arisen as a result of God's curse on Noah's son Ham, which had produced the Negro race, or as a result of the confusion of tongues associated with the tower of Babel (Genesis 11:1–9). Christians believed that humans had declined physically and mentally since the Edenic creation, a process that had produced such "degenerate sons of Adam" as the American Indians, the Hottentots of Africa, and the Australian bushmen. In the eighteenth century, however, another view began to find favor among the heterodox: that humans had ascended from savagery rather than declined from perfection (Haynes, 2002).

In the late 1830s a respected Philadelphia naturalist-physician, Samuel G. Morton, published an immensely influential book called *Crania Americana* (1839). Morton drew on his incomparable collection of human skulls to argue that, contrary to Moses, all human beings had not descended from Adam and Eve. Because racial differences could be seen in the most ancient skulls, he eventually concluded that God must have created each racial group separately, at least six thousand years earlier. This idea, which had been circulating on the fringes of biblical scholarship since the seventeenth century, was already being advocated by some in the United States. But Morton was the first to make a compelling scientific case for the theory, called pre-Adamism or polygenism (literally, many origins). Shortly before his death at midcentury he confessed that "the doctrine of the original diversity of mankind unfolds itself to me more and more with the distinctness of revelation" (Stanton, 1960; Patterson, 1854, l–li; see also Nelson, 2003, and Livingstone, 2008).

Morton and his two most vocal supporters—George R. Gliddon, the U.S. vice consul at Cairo, who collected Egyptian skulls for him, and Josiah

Clark Nott, a physician from Mobile, Alabama—zealously sought to free anthropology, like astronomy and geology before it, from the shackles of Scripture. In 1854 Nott and Gliddon brought out a massive 738-page treatise, *Types of Mankind*, devoted to the propagation of the multiple origin of humans, the "last great battle between science and dogmatism." In four months they sold some 3,500 copies. Nott and Gliddon's high-decibel attack on the "unity of man" provoked a spirited response from many members of the clergy, who saw the dismissal of Adam and Eve as the closest to a battle "against the inspiration of the scriptures, pitched upon the ground of the natural sciences," seen in the pre–Civil War period. Even Charles Hodge, who had readily accommodated the findings of geology and astronomy to his conservative theology, fretted that the same openness could not be applied to anthropology because "the very object of the Bible was to clear up the history of the fall of man, to explain the condition in which he is found, and to reveal a plan for his recovery" (Dain, 2002, pp. 221, 225; Horsman, 1987; Numbers, 2002, pp. 93–96; Stephens, 2000).

Speculation about the human mind generated greater anxiety for antebellum theologians and ministers than any other scientific subject, possibly excepting polygenism. Few of them continued to follow biblical writers in associating insanity with demonic possession, but they remained vitally interested in the relationship between religion and mental health, especially in the wake of the emotional revivals of the 1820s and 1830s, which sometimes reduced entire congregations to wailing and writhing. Did such "outward signs" result from overstimulation of the nervous system or from the "*special outpouring of the Spirit of God*"? The epidemic of "religious insanity" resulting from the revivals reached its apex in the 1840s, when the excitement generated by the Adventist William Miller's prediction of the imminent end of the world accounted for half of all religion-related admissions to a number of insane asylums in the Northeast. The prospect of widespread hereditary insanity resulting from such madness prompted one asylum superintendent to rank Millerism above even yellow fever and cholera as a threat to the nation's health (Numbers and Numbers, 1987).

Even more contentious was phrenology, a "science of mind" developed by two Germans, the anatomist Franz Joseph Gall and his student Johann Spurzheim. According to phrenological theory, the human brain comprised a number of distinct "organs"—some counted 37—each corresponding to an exotically named mental "faculty," such as amativeness (love of sex), acquisitiveness (love of money), or philoprogenitiveness (love of children). Because the relative strength of any propensity could be determined by measuring the size of its matching organ, it was not difficult for the initiated to "read" a person's character by carefully examining the skull. Plaster-of-Paris models of the head, identifying each faculty, appeared ubiquitously in urban shops. During the 1830s both Spurzheim and the wildly popular Scottish author George Combe visited the United States, electrifying large audiences up and down the East Coast (Davies, 1955; Numbers, 2007, pp. 26–29).

After lecturing in the United States, Combe reported that more people wanted to talk about the religious implications of phrenology than any other topic. Although individuals could influence the strength of a particular mental organ by exercising it, the thrust of phrenology lay in the direction of psychological determinism. Besides, as the American Transcendentalist Theodore Parker put it, phrenology weakened "the power of the old supernaturalism"; it showed "that man himself could be brought within the purview of science and that mental phenomena could be studied objectively and explained by natural causes." Phrenology seemed to explain sinful behavior anatomically rather than theologically. In view of phrenology's brash naturalism, it is hardly surprising to find some phrenologists complaining that their "one great obstacle" was the antagonism of clerics "*as a class.*" Because their American audiences consisted largely of religious people, phrenologists made a point of stressing its essential harmony with Christianity (Davies, 1955, pp. 151–153, 170–171; see also White, 2008, pp. 20–34).

In 1844 an anonymous British author, later identified as the Edinburgh publisher Robert Chambers, wove together threads from phrenology, the nebular hypothesis, historical geology, and the evolutionary theory of Jean Baptiste Lamarck into a sensational little book called *Vestiges of the Natural History of Creation*. It created an uproar on both sides of the Atlantic and brought, in the words of one historian, "an evolutionary vision of the universe into the heart of everyday life." Within eight years of its publication the book had passed through at least nine American printings, all of them pirated. "The *Vestiges* has been all the rage for a time," exclaimed a Princeton student in 1847. Although Chambers denied dispensing with the Creator, critics thought otherwise. The teaching of *Vestiges*, fumed one American critic, is nothing but "atheism—blank atheism, cold, cheerless, heartless, atheism," an outburst that led one reader to complain that "a more rabid tirade can scarcely be found this side of the Middle Ages, & the smell of roast heretic is truly overpowering throughout." More than any other work antedating Darwin's *Origin of Species*, *Vestiges* introduced Americans to the notion of *development*, the term then used for what later came to be known as *evolution* (Numbers, 1977, pp. 28–35; Secord, 2000, pp. 6, 380–382).

The spread of such "infidel" science in the middle third of the nineteenth century provoked a religious backlash, characterized by a torrent of popular literature on science and religion. Early-nineteenth-century American theologians had tended to view science as a bulwark against infidelity. With the passage of time, however, science—from anthropology and phrenology to the zoology of *Vestiges*—seemed increasingly to distance itself from orthodoxy and to ally itself with unbelief. By the 1850s, as E. Brooks Holifield has shown, Presbyterians were writing darkly about the "very delicate" relationship that had developed between science and religion, and a Methodist magazine was reluctantly sharing its conclusion that "the gospel of science is, for man, an infinitely poor gospel after all." In 1857 the Tombeckbee Presbytery in Mississippi, alarmed by the *Vestiges* and other infidel theories, unanimously adopted a resolution calling for a professorship of science and religion "to forearm and equip the young theologian to meet promptly the attacks of infidelity made through the medium of the natural sciences."

Most people in both science and theology continued to hope for the best, but, as Charles Hodge sadly concluded, religion seemed to be in a "fight for its life against a large class of scientific men" (Holifield, 1989; Numbers and Stephens, 1999, p. 125; Numbers, 2002, p. 80).

Even the most devout Americans expressed little religious concern over natural explanations of quotidian events. But extraordinary occurrences still drove many Americans to their knees. Endemic diseases such as consumption (tuberculosis) and influenza took far more lives than epidemics of cholera and yellow fever, but the latter generated more God-talk. When the mysterious Asiatic cholera first struck the East Coast, in 1832, ministers interpreted it as "a *scourge*, a *rod* in the hand of God," and government officials hastily declared days of fasting and prayer. The next outbreak, in 1849, elicited just as many cries to heaven, but physicians stepped up their search for natural explanations. As the epidemic petered out, the president of one medical association expressed the hope "that no member of this Society... allowed himself to be satisfied with the reflection that the result was one of God's providence, but that he more properly attributed it to his ignorance of the nature and character of the pestilence, and that he determined not to be satisfied till he had fully unraveled the mystery." By 1866, the mystery had been partially unraveled. As a result of midcentury epidemiological investigations that traced the cause of cholera to contaminated water supplies, public-health authorities learned how to keep the disease from spreading. Thus, when cholera threatened to strike the United States in 1866, community leaders (especially in New York City) tended to devote their energies to improving sanitation rather than to discussing the theological meaning of the event. "Whereas ministers in 1832 urged morality upon their congregations as a guarantor of health," writes Charles Rosenberg, "their forward-looking counterparts in 1866 endorsed sanitary reform as a necessary prerequisite to moral improvement" (Rosenberg, 1962, pp. 40–54, 121–132, 220).

The Battlefields of Science. Midcentury developments in science caused many Christians,

both conservatives and liberals, to feel under attack. According to the southern intellectual George Frederick Holmes in 1851, "The struggle between science and religion, between philosophy and faith, has been protracted through centuries; but it is only within recent years that the breach has become so open and avowed as to be declared by many to be irreconcilable." Science, predicted the Unitarian Andrew Preston Peabody in 1864, would become "the Armageddon—the final battlefield—in the conflict with infidelity" (Holmes, 1851, p. 186; Roberts, 1988, p. 64).

Religious fears spiked with the publication of Charles Darwin's *On the Origin of Species* (1859), in which the British naturalist sought "to overthrow the dogma of separate creations" and extend the domain of natural law throughout the organic world. Although Darwin initially remained silent about the application of his theory to humans, many readers immediately saw where he was heading. Twelve years later, in *The Descent of Man* (1871), Darwin surprised few people when he finally came clean on human ancestry:

> Man is descended from a hairy quadruped, furnished with a tail and pointed ears, probably arboreal in its habits, and an inhabitant of the Old world. This creation, if its whole structure had been examined by a naturalist, would have been classed among the Quadrumana, as surely as would the common and still more ancient progenitor of the Old and new World monkeys. The Quadrumana and all the higher mammals are probably derived from an ancient marsupial animal, and this through a long line of diversified forms, either from some reptile-like, or some amphibian-like creature, and this again from some fish-like animal.

By this time Darwinism, in the words of the president of the American Association for the Advancement of Science, was "shaking the moral and intellectual world as by an earthquake" (Darwin, 1871, Vol. 1., p. 147, Vol. 2, p. 372; Numbers, 1998, p. 31).

Some of Darwin's disciples tried to soften the blow to cherished religious beliefs—and common sense—by offering a theory of divine selection. The Harvard botanist Asa Gray, Darwin's closest American colleague, proposed that the inexplicable organic variations on which natural selection acted be attributed to divine providence. He also urged a "special origination" in connection with the appearance of humans and perhaps "for the formation of organs, the making of eyes, &c." When Gray forthrightly described the section of the *Origin* dealing with the making of the eye as "the weakest point in the book," Darwin confided that "the eye to this day gives me a cold shudder" (Numbers, 1998, p. 27; Darwin, 1993, pp. 47, 75; see also Dupree, 1959). Darwin's rejection of Gray's compromise, writes the historian Jon H. Roberts, "confirmed Protestant thinkers' suspicions that the Darwinian God was 'a cold and lifeless abstraction which could kindle no devotion in the soul' and clearly unmasked Darwin as yet another proponent of the naturalistic world view." It also prompted Charles Hodge, who had just recently referred to science and religion as the "twin daughters of heaven," to give his memorable verdict: "What is Darwinism? It is Atheism" (Roberts, 1988, p. 80; Numbers, 2002, pp. 97–100).

Although a number of Christians called for "a truce…between the friends of Science and the friends of Religion," harmonizers risked being caught in the crossfire between intransigent opponents of evolution and uncompromising defenders of Darwin. When the popular Brooklyn preacher Henry Ward Beecher argued for the compatibility of evolution and Christianity, the zoologist (and apostate Baptist) Edward Morse scoffed that such naive reconcilers failed to see that humanity's "origin from lower forms of life knocks in the head Adam and Eve, hence original sin, hence the necessity for vicarious atonement, hence everything that savors of the bad place." At the other end of the theological spectrum, one Christian anti-evolutionist railed against the "semi-Christian apologists" who tried to baptize evolution. Another went even further, suggesting that "the danger that the evolutionary hypothesis held for Christianity does not arise from the bold, arrogant speculations of atheistic scientists, but, rather,

from the smooth and polished theistic believers, and teachers of science, who hold to evolution theories" (Numbers, 1998, p. 42; Roberts, 1988, p. 230).

Throughout the middle third of the nineteenth century talk of harmony, not conflict, between science and religion generally prevailed. Religious writers fearful of scientific aggression typically dismissed unwanted science as "science falsely so-called" or as "pseudo-science," allowing them to insist on their continuing affection for genuine science. Until the last decades of the century, references to conflict commonly came from conservative religious leaders, fearful, even angered, by the relentless incursions of science, genuine or false. Among intellectuals on both sides of the Atlantic the tone changed dramatically, first when partisan historians of science and religion joined the debate and, second, when a group of hard-core "scientific naturalists" went out of their way to offend churchmen and to caricature organized religion as inimical to science (Numbers, 2009).

In 1869 Andrew Dickson White, the young president of the proudly secular Cornell University, began rewriting history with an address in New York City on "The Battle-Fields of Science." Irritated by the criticism over his refusal to impose any religious tests on students and faculty and his declared intention of creating in Ithaca "an asylum for *Science*—where truth shall be sought for truth's sake, not stretched or cut exactly to fit Revealed Religion," the historian struck back. He depicted the religious struggle against science as "a war continued longer—with battles fiercer, with sieges more persistent, with strategy more vigorous than in any of the comparatively petty warfares of Alexander, or Caesar, or Napoleon." Although waged with pens rather than swords, and for minds rather than empires, this war, too, had destroyed lives and reputations. The combatants? Science and religion. When "sweet reasonableness" failed to placate his critics, White fired his broadside, accusing them of possessing the same kind of narrow minds and mean spirits that had led to the persecution of Vesalius, Kepler, and Galileo. History showed, White declared, that "interference with Science in the supposed interest of religion—no matter how conscientious such interference may have been—has resulted in the direst evils both to Religion and Science, and *invariably*" (Lindberg and Numbers, 1986).

To document this thesis, he surveyed "some of the hardest-fought battle-fields of this great war," illustrating how rigid biblical literalists and dogmatic theologians had stunted the growth of science and prostituted religion—only to lose in the end. In the following years, White delivered his lecture around the country and fleshed out his history of the conflict between science and religion with new illustrations, some drawn from contemporary hostilities between evolutionists and their foes. Finally, in 1896 he brought out a fully documented, two-volume *History of the Warfare of Science with Theology in Christendom* (Lindberg and Numbers, 1986).

Religious radicals and secularists loved White's inflammatory history. *The Outlook*, a liberal religious weekly, welcomed White's account of the struggle for "the liberty of learning and teaching." Each chapter, it said, "tells a similar story of province after province won by hard fighting," with the church using "terrorism and torture and every form of outrage on sensitive and truth-loving natures" to thwart the progress of science. Conservative Christians detested White's narrative, not only for its scolding tone but also for its failure to acknowledge the support that Christianity had given to science over the centuries. Characteristically, White dismissed his opponents as "hysterics" and "zealots." His sole goal, he insisted, was "to find and to state, simply THE TRUTH" (Numbers, 2009, pp. 31–32).

Nearly as influential as White in portraying Christianity as the aggressor in a war against science was another American, John William Draper, whose *History of the Conflict between Science and Religion* (1874) excoriated the Roman Catholic church for its alleged suppression of science. According to one reviewer, Draper addressed "*the question which is now agitating the world of thought.*" Indeed, he had. His book became an international best-seller, going through 50 printings in a half century in America and numerous translations worldwide. Catholics, not surprisingly, expressed outrage, describing it as "a farrago of falsehoods, with an occasional ray of truth" (Numbers, 2009, pp. 32–33).

The Twentieth Century. The early-twentieth-century rise of the social and behavioral sciences, which made religion itself an object of scientific study, threatened to become the focal point of science–religion interactions, but evolution, particularly human evolution, continued to occupy center stage. The headline-grabbing controversies over evolution and the alleged war between science and religion may have eclipsed other popular debates over science and religion, but they did not exhaust the public's range of religiously inspired responses to scientific developments. The increasing use of animals for physiological and pharmacological investigations led to an ongoing battle over vivisection. The germ theory of disease evoked a wide range of religious sentiment, from debates over government-sponsored campaigns to contain the syphilis germ (heatedly opposed by Catholics) to soul-searching over the hygienic nature of the common communion cup. Despite its name, Christian Science repudiated the very principles of scientific medicine—including the existence of germs—in favor of mesmeric mental healing. Christian Science, in turn, inspired various mind-healing alternatives, from the Episcopal-sponsored Emmanuel Movement to the imitative Jewish Science (Numbers, 2007, pp. 35–36; Tomes, 1998, pp. 132–134; Schoepflin, 2003; Umansky, 2005). At the very time that "scientific medicine" was revolutionizing mainstream treatments, the made-in-America Pentecostal movement was promoting supernatural healing among Protestants (Wacker, 1986). By the end of the century Pentecostals and other charismatic Christians had converted approximately one-quarter of all Christians in the world to their radical supernaturalism.

The turn-of-the-century rediscovery of the genetic basis of heredity, originally demonstrated decades earlier by the Austrian monk Gregor Mendel, handed biologists the intellectual tool they needed to guide evolution, for humans as well as corn and cows. The effort to breed better humans, called eugenics, found Catholics overwhelmingly opposed and Protestants divided. Liberal (and some not so liberal) Protestants tended to endorse it enthusiastically, as did many mainstream Jews. Christian fundamentalists and orthodox Jews typically avoided the controversy or took a negative position. It was not until after World War II and the revelation of Nazi atrocities that eugenics finally fell out of fashion (Rosen, 2004; Zenderland, 1998).

One of the most intense science-and-religion controversies in the first half of the century focused on the psychology of religion, especially deterministic theories that discarded such traditional Christian concepts as the soul, the conscience, and free will. Especially egregious were Freudianism, which dismissed God as an illusion, and behaviorism, which viewed God as a scientifically irrelevant metaphor. For centuries progressive Christians had bent over backward to accommodate new scientific discoveries, but confronted by this new threat, even liberals reacted negatively (Roberts, 2003; see also Burnham, 1985, and Croce, 1995). Nevertheless, mainstream Protestant seminaries soon began incorporating "safe" psychological ideas and practices into their curricula, thus equipping young ministers to practice pastoral psychology (Holifield, 1983; Myers-Shirk, 2009).

Sex education and research created another flash point. Indeed, the publication of Alfred Kinsey's best-selling *Sexual Behavior in the Human Male* (1948) and *Sexual Behavior in the Human Female* (1953), which seemed to critics to justify homosexuality and virtually any other sexual practice, created perhaps the biggest blowup over science and religion in postwar America. They also laid a scientific foundation for the sexual revolution of the following decades (Moran, 2000; Jones, 1997).

Compared with the biological and social sciences, the physical sciences fomented relatively little religious controversy in the twentieth century. Some Christian theologians and scientists even found scientific support for free will, under attack by the deterministic psychologists, in the uncertainty principle of quantum physics. Others saw in Albert Einstein's theories of relativity support for the existence of the Holy Spirit and of the immortality of the soul. Postwar cosmology featured a battle between the advocates of an eternal steady-state universe and the partisans of the so-called big-bang theory. Although liberal Christians welcomed the latter because of its consilience with a created universe, fundamentalists typically rejected it because of its connection with an evolutionary worldview. The debate largely ended about 1970, when the big-bang theory won the scientific competition (Thurs, 2009; Hiebert, 1986; McConnell, 2000).

Besides the sometimes intense cosmological debates, the years during and after World War II saw little action on the science-and-religion front, at least not much that attracted the attention of the news media. The outside world paid little attention to the activities of the evangelical American Scientific Affiliation (founded in 1941) or the liberal Institute on Religion in an Age of Science (1954), both of which played mediating roles in the Christian community. Even the Moody Institute of Science's hugely successful series of films on the harmony of God's two books, nature and the Bible, viewed by millions and shown by the U.S. Air Force to servicemen around the globe, provoked little criticism (Gilbert, 1997, pp. 121–145, 273–295).

Increasing attention, however, focused on the religious beliefs of American scientists. On the eve of America's entry into the Great War, the American psychologist James Leuba conducted a pioneering survey of one thousand American men of science and found that 41.8 percent affirmed belief in a personal God "to whom one may pray in expectation of receiving an answer." Because he did not ask how many endorsed a less personal divinity, such as a God who did not answer intercessory prayers, it is impossible to determine the percentage of theists. Of the same group, 50.6 percent subscribed to the notion of individual human immortality. In general, the more distinguished the scientist, the greater the likelihood of disbelieving in these "two fundamental dogmas" of Christianity: only 27.7 percent of his "greater" scientists believed in a personal God and 35.2 percent in human immortality. Belief was lower among biological scientists than among physical scientists—and, as subsequent surveys showed, lowest of all among social scientists such as psychologists and sociologists. The relationship between science and religious faith remained unclear, but Leuba interpreted it negatively, which led him to predict a growth in skepticism as more and more Americans encountered science (Leuba, 1916).

Eighty years later, Edward Larson and Larry Witham replicated his survey and discovered virtually no additional loss of faith among run-of-the-mill scientists. Using the same crude instrument Leuba had employed, they found that approximately four in ten American scientists (39.3 percent) continued to embrace a prayer-answering God, whereas 38 percent believed in an afterlife. A follow-up survey of the country's most distinguished scientists (all fellows of the elite National Academy of Sciences) revealed that only 7.0 percent believed in a personal God and 7.9 percent in personal immortality (Larson and Witham, 1997, 1998; see also Larson and Witham, 1999).

One of the most interesting—and perhaps significant—recent developments has been the embrace of an amorphous "spirituality" by large segments of the public, scientists and laypersons alike. In a recent study of "Religion among Academic Scientists," the American sociologist Elaine Howard Ecklund discovered that 34 percent of the nearly 1,700 scientists surveyed identified with atheism and 30 percent with agnosticism. (The contrasting figures for the general public were 2 and 4 percent, respectively.) The truly surprising finding was the high level of spirituality among scientists, with roughly two-thirds of them describing themselves as spiritual. Included among the self-identified spiritual were more than 22 percent of the atheists and 27 percent of the agnostics. In view of these statistics, it appears that for a substantial number of scientists, spirituality has become far more important than religion (Ecklund, 2010, pp. 16, 58).

In 2012 the Gallup organization, which had been tracking belief in creation and evolution since 1982, found that 46 percent of Americans affirmed that "God created humans in their present form about 10,000 years ago." Some 32 percent believed that God had guided evolution to create humans; 15 percent thought that God had nothing to do with the evolution of humans (Newport, 2012).

[*See also* **Animal and Human Experimentation; Anthropology; Astronomy and Astrophysics; Behaviorism; Cholera; Creationism; Disease; Eugenics; Evolution, Theory of; Geology; Germ Theory of Disease; Gray, Asa; Kinsey, Alfred; Medicine; Mental Health Institutions; Mental Illness; Missionaries and Science and Medicine; Phrenology; Physics; Psychiatry; Psychology; Psychotherapy; Scopes Trial; Sex Education; Silliman, Benjamin, Sr.; Social Sciences; Sociobiology and Evolutionary Psychology;** *and* **Yellow Fever.**]

BIBLIOGRAPHY

Bozeman, Theodore Dwight. *Protestants in an Age of Science: The Baconian Ideal and Antebellum American Religious Thought.* Chapel Hill: University of North Carolina Press, 1977.

Burnham, John C. "The Encounter of Christian Theology with Deterministic Psychology and Psychoanalysis." *Bulletin of the Menninger Clinic* 49 (1985): 321–352.

Croce, Paul Jerome. *Science and Religion in the Era of William James.* Chapel Hill: University of North Carolina Press, 1995.

Dain, Bruce. *A Hideous Monster of the Mind: American Race Theory in the Early Republic.* Cambridge, Mass.: Harvard University Press, 2002.

Darwin, Charles. *The Correspondence of Charles Darwin.* Vol. 8. Cambridge, U.K.: Cambridge University Press, 1993.

Darwin, Charles. *The Descent of Man, and Selection in Relation to Sex.* 2 vols. New York: D. Appleton, 1871.

Davies, John D. *Phrenology, Fad and Science: A 19th-Century American Crusade.* New Haven, Conn.: Yale University Press, 1955.

Dupree, A. Hunter. *Asa Gray, 1810–1888.* Cambridge, Mass.: Harvard University Press, 1959.

Ecklund, Elaine Howard. *Science vs. Religion: What Scientists Really Think.* New York: Oxford University Press, 2010.

Ellis, Joseph J. *The New England Mind in Transition: Samuel Johnson of Connecticut, 1696–1772.* New Haven, Conn.: Yale University Press, 1973.

Gilbert, James. *Redeeming Culture: American Religion in an Age of Science.* Chicago: University of Chicago Press, 1997.

Greene, John C. "Science and Religion. " In *The Rise of Adventism: Religion and Society in Mid-Nineteenth-Century America*, edited by Edwin S. Gaustad, pp. 50–69. New York: Harper & Row, 1974.

Hall, David D. *Worlds of Wonder, Days of Judgment: Popular Religious Belief in Early New England.* New York: Alfred A. Knopf, 1989.

Harrison, Peter. "'Science' and 'Religion': Constructing the Boundaries." *Journal of Religion* 86 (2006): 81–106.

Haynes, Stephen R. *Noah's Curse: The Biblical Justification of American Slavery.* New York: Oxford University Press, 2002.

Hiebert, Erwin N. "Modern Physics and Christian Faith." In *God and Nature: Historical Essays on the Encounter between Christianity and Science*, edited by David C. Lindberg and Ronald L. Numbers, pp. 424–447. Berkeley and Los Angeles: University of California Press, 1986.

Holifield, E. Brooks. *A History of Pastoral Care in America: From Salvation to Self-Realization.* Nashville, Tenn.: Abingdon Press, 1983.

Holifield, E. Brooks. "Science and Theology in the Old South." In *Science and Medicine in the Old South*, edited by Ronald L. Numbers and Todd L. Savitt, pp. 127–146. Baton Rouge: Louisiana State University Press, 1989.

Holmes, George Frederick. "Philosophy and Faith." *Methodist Quarterly Review* 3 (1851): 185–218.

Hornberger, Theodore. "Cotton Mather's Annotations on the First Chapter of Genesis." *University of Texas Studies in English* 18 (1938): 116–117.

Hornberger, Theodore. "Samuel Johnson of Yale and King's College: A Note on the Relation of Science and Religion in Provincial America." *New England Quarterly* 8 (1935): 378–397.

Horsman, Reginald. *Josiah Nott of Mobile: Southerner, Physician, and Racial Theorist.* Baton Rouge: Louisiana State University Press, 1987.

Jones, James H. *Alfred C. Kinsey: A Public/Private Life.* New York: W. W. Norton, 1997.

Larson, Edward J., and Larry Witham. "Leading Scientists Still Reject God." *Nature* 394 (1998): 313.

Larson, Edward J., and Larry Witham. "Scientists and Religion in America." *Scientific American* 281 (September 1999): 89–93.

Larson, Edward J., and Larry Witham. "Scientists Are Still Keeping the Faith." *Nature* 386 (1997): 435–436.

Leuba, James H. *The Belief in God and Immortality: A Psychological, Anthropological and Statistical Study.* Boston: Sherman, French, and Co., 1916.

Leventhal, Herbert. *In the Shadow of the Enlightenment: Occultism and Renaissance Science in Eighteenth-Century America.* New York: New York University Press, 1976.

Lindberg, David C., and Ronald L. Numbers. "Beyond War and Peace: A Reappraisal of the Encounter between Christianity and Science." *Church History* 55 (1986): 338–354.

Livingstone, David N. *Adam's Ancestors: Race, Religion, and the Politics of Human Origins.* Baltimore: Johns Hopkins University Press, 2008.

McConnell, Craig Sean. "Twentieth-Century Cosmologies." In *The History of Science and Religion in the Western Tradition: An Encyclopedia*, edited by Gary B. Ferngren et al., pp. 362–365. New York: Garland, 2000.

Middlekauff, Robert. *The Mathers: Three Generations of Puritan Intellectuals, 1596–1728.* New York: Oxford University Press, 1971.

Miller, Perry. *The New England Mind: From Colony to Province.* Cambridge, Mass.: Belknap Press of Harvard University Press, 1953.

Miller, Perry. *The New England Mind: The Seventeenth Century.* Boston: Beacon Press, 1961.

Moore, James R. "Geologists and Interpreters of Genesis in the Nineteenth Century." In *God and Nature: A History of the Encounter between Christianity and Science*, edited by David C. Lindberg and Ronald L. Numbers, pp. 322–350. Berkeley and Los Angeles: University of California Press, 1986.

Moran, Jeffrey P. *Teaching Sex: The Shaping of Adolescence in the 20th Century.* Cambridge, Mass.: Harvard University Press, 2000.

Myers-Shirk, Susan E. *Helping the Good Shepherd: Pastoral Counselors in a Psychotherapeutic Culture, 1925–1975.* Baltimore: Johns Hopkins University Press, 2009.

Nelson, G. Blair. "'Men before Adam!': American Debates over the Unity and Antiquity of Humanity." In *When Science & Christianity Meet*, edited by David C. Lindberg and Ronald L. Numbers, pp. 161–181. Chicago: University of Chicago Press, 2003.

Newport, Frank. "In U.S., 46% Hold Creationist View of Human Origins." http://www.gallup.com/poll/155003/Hold-Creationist-View-Human-Origins.aspx?version=p (accessed 23 October 2012).

Numbers, Ronald L. "Aggressors, Victims, and Peacemakers: Historical Actors in the Drama of Science and Religion." In *The Science and Religion Debate: Why Does It Continue?*, edited by Harold W. Attridge, pp. 15–53, 180–192. New Haven, Conn.: Yale University Press, 2009.

Numbers, Ronald L. "Charles Hodge and the Beauties and Deformities of Science." In *Charles*

Hodge Revisited: A Critical Appraisal of His Life and Work, edited by John W. Stewart and James H. Moorhead, pp. 77–101. Grand Rapids, Mich.: W. B. Eerdmans, 2002.

Numbers, Ronald L. *Creation by Natural Law: Laplace's Nebular Hypothesis in American Thought*. Seattle: University of Washington Press, 1977.

Numbers, Ronald L. *Darwinism Comes to America*. Cambridge, Mass.: Harvard University Press, 1998.

Numbers, Ronald L. *Science and Christianity in Pulpit and Pew*. New York: Oxford University Press, 2007.

Numbers, Ronald L. "Science without God: Natural Laws and Christian Beliefs." In *When Science and Christianity Meet*, edited by David C. Lindberg and Ronald L. Numbers, pp. 265–285. Chicago: University of Chicago Press, 2003.

Numbers, Ronald L., and Janet S. Numbers. "Millerism and Madness: A Study of 'Religious Insanity' in Nineteenth-Century America." In *The Disappointed: Millerism and Millenarianism in the Nineteenth Century*, edited by Ronald L. Numbers and Jonathan M. Butler, pp. 92–117. Bloomington: Indiana University Press, 1987.

Numbers, Ronald L., and Lester D. Stephens. "Darwinism in the American South." In *Disseminating Darwinism: The Role of Place, Race, Religion, and Gender*, edited by Ronald L. Numbers and John Stenhouse, pp. 123–143. Cambridge, U.K.: Cambridge University Press, 1999.

Patterson, Henry S. "Memoir of the Life and Scientific Labors of Samuel George Morton." In *Types of Mankind*, edited by J. C. Nott and George R. Gliddon, pp. xvii–lvii. Philadelphia: J. B. Lippincott, Grambo & Co., 1854.

Roberts, Jon H. *Darwinism and the Divine in America: Protestant Intellectuals and Organic Evolution, 1859–1900*. Madison: University of Wisconsin Press, 1988.

Roberts, Jon H. "Psychoanalysis and American Christianity, 1900–1945." In *When Science and Christianity Meet*, edited by David C. Lindberg and Ronald L. Numbers, pp. 225–244. Chicago: University of Chicago Press, 2003.

Roberts, Jon H. "Science and Religion." In *Wrestling with Nature: From Omens to Science*, edited by Peter Harrison, Ronald L. Numbers, and Michael H. Shank, pp. 253–280. Chicago: University of Chicago Press, 2011.

Rosen, Christine. *Preaching Eugenics: Religious Leaders and the American Eugenics Movement*. New York: Oxford University Press, 2004.

Rosenberg, Charles. *The Cholera Years: The United States in 1832, 1849, and 1866*. Chicago: University of Chicago Press, 1962.

Schoepflin, Rennie B. *Christian Science on Trial: Religious Healing in America*. Baltimore: Johns Hopkins University Press, 2003.

Secord, James A. *Victorian Sensation: The Extraordinary Publication, Reception, and Secret Authorship of Vestiges of the Natural History of Creation*. Chicago: University of Chicago Press, 2000.

Stanton, William. *The Leopard's Spots: Scientific Attitudes toward Race in America, 1815–59*. Chicago: University of Chicago Press, 1960.

Stephens, Lester D. *Science, Race, and Religion in the American South: John Bachman and the Charleston Circle of Naturalists, 1815–1895*. Chapel Hill: University of North Carolina Press, 2000.

Stiling, Rodney Lee. "The Diminishing Deluge: Noah's Flood in Nineteenth-Century American Thought." PhD diss. University of Wisconsin–Madison, 1991.

Thurs, Daniel Patrick. "Myth 22: That Quantum Physics Demonstrated the Doctrine of Free Will." In *Galileo Goes to Jail and Other Myths about Science and Religion*, edited by Ronald L. Numbers, pp. 196–205. Cambridge, Mass.: Harvard University Press, 2009.

Tomes, Nancy. *The Gospel of Germs: Men, Women, and the Microbe in American Life*. Cambridge, Mass.: Harvard University Press, 1998.

Umansky, Ellen M. *From Christian Science to Jewish Science: Spiritual Healing and American Jews*. New York: Oxford University Press, 2005.

Van de Wetering, Maxine. "Moralizing in Puritan Natural Science: Mysteriousness in Earthquake Sermons." *Journal of the History of Ideas* 43 (1982): 417–438.

Wacker, Grant. "The Pentecostal Tradition." In *Caring and Curing: Health and Medicine in the Western Religious Traditions*, edited by Ronald L. Numbers and Darrel W. Amundsen, pp. 514–538. New York: Macmillan, 1986.

White, Christopher G. *Unsettled Minds: Psychology and the American Search for Spiritual Assurance, 1830–1940*. Berkeley and Los Angeles: University of California Press, 2008.

Zenderland, Leila. "Biblical Biology: American Protestant Social Reformers and the Early Eugenics Movement." *Science in Context* 11 (1998): 511–525.

Ronald L. Numbers

REMSEN, IRA

(1846–1927), chemist. For many years the outstanding figure in American chemistry, Remsen was born on 10 February 1846 in New York City, the only child, except for an older sister who died in infancy, of merchant James Vanderbilt Remsen and Rosanna Remsen (née Secor), of Dutch and Huguenot ancestors. When he was eight, his mother died, and he was sent to live in Nyack, New York, with James Demarest, his maternal great-grandfather, a Dutch Reformed pastor who influenced his scriptural knowledge and nonsectarian religious views.

At age 14 Remsen entered the Free Academy (now City University of New York), where he became interested in chemistry. His father withdrew him and apprenticed him to a physician on the faculty of the New York Homeopathic Medical School, where Remsen taught chemistry to students. He received an AB degree from the Academy with the class of 1865. In 1867 he received his MD degree from Columbia University's College of Physicians and Surgeons. He had studied medicine to please his father and practiced for only a year. He spent a year at the University of Munich with analytical chemist Jacob Volhard. Remsen received his PhD degree from the University of Göttingen under Rudolph Fittig in 1870 with a dissertation on piperonylic acid. When Fittig transferred to the University of Tübingen, Remsen followed him, serving as his assistant until 1872 and beginning his research on aromatic sulfonic acids, which culminated in his discovery of saccharin.

On returning to the United States in 1872, Remsen became professor of chemistry and physics at Williams College, Williamstown, Massachusetts, where, despite an atmosphere indifferent to chemistry, he pursued research, developed his simple, straightforward lecture style for which he became famous, and published *The Principles of Theoretical Chemistry*, which rendered fundamental principles understandable to beginning students and was soon translated into German and Italian. This first of seven popular textbooks attracted the attention of Daniel Coit Gilman, who, in 1876, offered Remsen the chair of chemistry at the newly founded Johns Hopkins University in Baltimore, Maryland, designed to be a center of research and educational reform modeled on the European, primarily German, tradition. Until his retirement in 1913, when he became an industrial consultant, Remsen directed the first laboratory-centered chemical education in the United States, and by the advent of the twentieth century his laboratory was producing more PhD chemists than any other American university.

In 1879 Remsen and his postdoctoral assistant Constantine Fahlberg discovered orthobenzoyl sulfamide, which Fahlberg patented and marketed as the artificial sweetener saccharin, and claimed to be its sole discoverer, which angered Remsen. The author of over 170 articles, recipient of many honors, including the first recipient of the Priestley Medal, the American Chemical Society's highest award, and head of a national referee board to control food products and their adulteration, in 1879 Remsen founded the *American Chemical Journal*, which merged with the *Journal of the American Chemical Society* in 1913. He became the American Chemical Society president in 1902. He died of a cerebral hemorrhage on 4 March 1927 in Carmel, California.

[*See also* **Chemistry; Higher Education and Science;** *and* **Journals in Science, Medicine, and Engineering.**]

BIBLIOGRAPHY

Getman, Frederick H. *The Life of Ira Remsen*. Easton, Pa.: Journal of Chemical Education, 1940. The most complete but least critical account, written by his former student.

Kauffman, George B., and Paul M. Priebe. "The Discovery of Saccharin: A Centennial Retrospect." *Ambix* 25, no. 3 (1978): 191–207. Because the discovery of saccharin was an integral part of Remsen's research program, which had evolved from his doctoral dissertation under Fittig, although Fahlberg's expert knowledge of sugar chemistry and concern with commercial applications was required, the authors regard both chemists as codiscoverers.

Kauffman, George B., and Paul M. Priebe. "Making Governmental Policy under Conditions of Scientific Uncertainty: A Century of Controversy about Saccharin in Congress and the Laboratory." *Minerva* 18, no. 4 (Winter 1980): 556–574.

Nagel, Miriam, and Roger Festa. "Ira Remsen (1846–1927)." *Journal of Chemical Education* 57, no. 12 (1980): 893–894.

Noyes, William Albert, and James Flack Norris. "Biographical Memoir of Ira Remsen 1846–1927." *National Academy of Sciences of the United States of America Biographical Memoirs* 14 (1932): 207–257. Includes a bibliography of Remsen's scientific articles.

George B. Kauffman

RESEARCH AND DEVELOPMENT (R&D)

The phrase "research and development" entered the American lexicon at the dawn of the twentieth century, when a handful of prominent business institutions announced the creation of research laboratories. Employing small staffs of college-trained scientists and engineers, including some with a doctoral degree, these early corporate research facilities typically focused on pressing technical problems of vital importance to the enterprise. At Kodak, for instance, chemists sought to navigate the transition from glass plate negatives to celluloid film. General Electric Corporation (GE), concerned that its highly profitable patents for incandescent light bulbs would soon expire, looked for experts in materials science to develop new filaments. American Telephone & Telegraph (AT&T) hired experts with similar knowledge in an effort to develop a repeater that would boost signals and enable the firm to fulfill its promise of providing coast-to-coast service. The chemical giant DuPont, which had built its empire primarily by manufacturing gunpowder, hoped to broaden its product line by mastering techniques of organic chemistry. In taking this step, DuPont mimicked German chemical firms whose research laboratories had brought them to positions of international leadership in fields such as nitrocellulose explosives (dynamite) and synthetic dyes.

This spurt of institutional developments was facilitated by shifting legal doctrines. Courts first clarified that corporations could require in-house inventors to assign patents to the firm as a condition of employment. Although these rulings gave corporations confidence they could retain control over technologies developed internally, increasing antitrust activity made some large firms leery of acquiring new technology through merger or cross-licensing with other corporations. Firms faced with antitrust suits also looked to curry public favor by touting their investment in research and development. By achieving technical breakthroughs such as improved light bulbs and accomplishing watersheds such as cross-country telephone service, firms such as GE and AT&T countered notions that large firms suppressed invention and creativity. Public relations experts, who became much more prominent in corporate America during the opening decades of the twentieth century, often seized upon the new laboratories as valuable assets in their campaigns to stem the tide of government regulation.

For all their prominence, these conspicuous pioneers can hardly be said to have constituted a revolution in American technology and invention. The new ventures were restricted to a few firms in a handful of sectors. In 1919, industrial labs employed fewer than three thousand scientists total, although AT&T and GE employed several hundred between them. The pioneering R&D labs were also highly concentrated in the Middle Atlantic region, where large corporations had ready access to Wall Street financing and an established university system. Most business firms in other parts of the country, and many in the eastern seaboard, continued to obtain new technologies through loose networks of independent inventors and small proprietors such as machine works. Such networks or regional clusters often included firms that maintained close ties to inventors or were founded by inventors themselves. Often, such clusters focused on niches. Cleveland entrepreneurs designed machine tools and electrical apparatus. A group of foundries and machine shops clustered in an industrial district south of downtown Los Angeles specialized in designing pumps and other implements for use in the region's booming agricultural and petroleum sectors. It later proved instrumental in supporting the aviation industry, whose pioneers had migrated to southern California to take advantage of the nearly ideal conditions for testing aircraft.

Nineteenth-Century Roots.

As the existence and persistence of industrial clusters suggests, the activities that came to be labeled R&D long anteceded the creation of formal facilities with that designation. Considerable learning occurred independent of the search for novelties. Most manufacturing enterprises, for instance, continually sought to improve processes and drive down the costs of production. Such learning occurred almost routinely. Often, it involved close collaboration between designers of new products and the technicians tasked with mastering their production. The interplay between them constituted what would later be called the development process. Similarly, designers often coordinated their efforts with operators of the larger technical systems into which their inventions must be integrated. This might take place within a single establishment, as when a manufacturer looked to enhance a production line or when a railroad or utility company sought to refine the performance of its facilities. Or it might involve cooperating with customers through teams of sale representatives and field engineers, who helped purchasers to master new products while also serving as the eyes and ears of their employers, collecting information about how they might enhance product offerings and gathering valuable information about competitors. All of this activity generated new knowledge vital to the health of the firm, long before anyone thought to brand it R&D. Such activity would long remain an essential source of learning throughout the economy, even in sectors where firms created distinct research laboratories.

By the end of the nineteenth century, some large firms had taken steps to formalize this sort of learning and render it more routine. Many of the nation's largest railroads, for instance, established staff offices that monitored learning and innovation throughout their vast systems. These efforts often included departments of testing and research, where college-trained engineers and chemists evaluated existing technologies and assessed potential alternatives. Much of this work focused on materials science, such as the behaviors of metals and lubricants, but it also involved systematic study of appliances that might enhance fuel economy or the traction of locomotives. The giant Pennsylvania Railroad, which in 1876 had become the first American corporation to hire a PhD chemist, early in the twentieth century erected a facility for testing locomotives in place while operating at speeds as high as 90 miles an hour. In conjunction with its effort to tunnel beneath the Hudson River and enter Manhattan in 1910, the Pennsylvania also built an extensive test track along the Delaware River for conducting studies of electric traction.

This sort of testing-centered research took hold in many sectors of the economy. Many manufacturers implemented similar programs of materials analysis, often with testing equipment similar to that used by the railroads. The Arthur D. Little Company of Boston provided chemical analyses to numerous firms who could not afford to operate their own testing laboratories. Firms in many industries also followed the Pennsylvania in erecting large-scale testing plants where engineers could systematically evaluate prototypes. Electrical manufacturers such as GE and Westinghouse, for instance, used such prototyping facilities to test electric generating and distribution technologies. Based on knowledge gleaned from such analysis, the electrical suppliers could then assess the efficiencies of proposed installations in the field. In the 1890s, GE placed responsibilities for this function in a calculating department under supervision of the esteemed mathematician Charles Steinmetz. (It was Steinmetz who later helped persuade GE management to hire PhD metallurgists in its efforts to design a better light bulb.) AT&T similarly formed a calculating department to evaluate the efficiency of proposed telephone exchanges. Using novel statistical analyses, mathematicians in this department grew to understand how various components influenced overall performance of telephone systems. This capability gave AT&T a powerful tool in assessing emergent technologies and establishing standards of performance, functions that were just as integral to the later success of its famed Bell Laboratories as the knowledge generated in trying to build a better repeater and achieve long distance.

In fostering a more systematic approach to evaluating new technology, the nascent laboratories put corporations in a better position to sift through the vast output of the many specialized independent inventors who emerged in the late nineteenth century, as a national market for patented technologies took shape. Conspicuous figures such as Thomas Edison and Elihu Thomson churned out hundreds of patents from their own "invention factories," as Edison dubbed his facilities at Menlo Park, New Jersey. Hundreds of others generated more modest portfolios. Personnel in the corporate labs monitored the sea of developments, often with the aid of specialized patent attorneys, identifying those of particular worth and spotting areas where they might direct their own talents and resources. AT&T acquired rights to its vacuum tube repeater, critical to achieving long-distance transmission, from the independent inventor Lee de Forest. The electrical giants Westinghouse and GE assembled large portfolios of patents (in GE's case by employing the prolific Thomson) and used them to form a pooling agreement that kept competitors at bay.

In addition to these developments in private industry, a variety of public institutions emerged during the late nineteenth and early twentieth centuries to support learning and innovation. One important complex of institutions organized around agricultural activities, which constituted the largest sector of the American economy through most of the nineteenth century. Early on, much of this research activity took place through forums such as state and county fairs. In the 1850s, farm interests pushed through legislation compelling the U.S. Patent Office to conduct ongoing examinations of agricultural techniques, including soil enhancements, new varieties of plants and animals, and remedies for insects and other pests. This program was later institutionalized with the formation of the U.S. Department of Agriculture in 1862. The Department of Agriculture often conducted its research and disseminated the resulting knowledge in collaboration with state agricultural universities, funded under the 1862 Morrill Act, and their associated agricultural experiment stations. This federalist approach generated a common body of knowledge, often grounded in the techniques of laboratory science, while remaining highly attuned to local conditions and actual practices. In combining laboratory studies with test farms, it exhibited some of the same features that characterized developments in the private railroad industry.

A similar constellation of research efforts emerged in connection with mining, another vital sector of an economy whose wealth derived largely from the land. Here, too, a nexus of state and federal institutions supplied systematic laboratory analyses and field explorations, such as those conducted by the U.S. Geological Survey and the Bureau of Mines, while also gathering and codifying knowledge gleaned from numerous specific locales. Many land grant universities built programs of education, research, and outreach in fields such as geology and mining engineering. Like engineers in other fields, the mining professionals formed organizations that conducted meetings and published journals that served as clearinghouses for new knowledge and techniques. Often tailored to the resources of particular states and regions, such activities undergirded the spectacular achievements in the mining of precious metals and of fossil fuels such as coal and petroleum, which constituted a major share of American exports and provided American manufacturers with their competitive advantage in global markets.

In addition to supporting research for agriculture and mining, the federal government also conducted research through institutions such as the Coastal Survey, the Weather Bureau, and the National Bureau of Standards. Created in 1900, the latter became an important forum for establishing norms of scientific research, including calibrations of new instruments. Its role in facilitating collaboration and exchange among investigators grew increasingly important as the number of laboratories proliferated across government, universities, and the private sector. The Bureau also established a precedent for more targeted efforts at technical standard setting, such as those it conducted on wireless technology following passage of the Federal Radio Act of 1912.

World War I and the Interwar Period. By the time of American entry into World War I, then, the United States possessed an impressive array of institutions and practices aimed at generating technical innovation and gaining more sophisticated and systematic understanding of technologies. As that war approached, President Woodrow Wilson actively looked to tap those capabilities. In 1915, while still maintaining a policy of neutrality, his administration organized a Naval Consulting Board. Headed by Thomas Edison, it pursued research of relevance to the U.S. Navy. At the urging of George Ellery Hale, foreign secretary of the National Academy of Sciences, Wilson subsequently created a National Research Council, whose members included John Carty of AT&T and other scientists with links to industry. Suspending his suspicion of big business and enthusiasm for antitrust, Wilson later cleared the way for firms such as GE, AT&T, and Westinghouse to focus their collective research capabilities on critical areas such as sonar and wireless telegraphy (radio), whereas firms such as DuPont turned their attentions to synthetic products such as fuels, fertilizers, fabrics, and poison gas and Henry Ford's auto plants built specialized boats and trucks for the military.

These conspicuous wartime efforts, which appeared vital to national purpose, drew the corporate research laboratories more fully into the limelight and tied them more firmly in the public's mind with the generation of new products. The association grew all the more prominent in the early 1920s, as many of these same firms produced a stunning array of novel consumer goods. Work on sonar and radio sparked a revolution in sound, with broadcast radio, electrical recording, amplified loudspeakers, and talking pictures all sweeping the nation in a matter of a few years. GE introduced mechanical refrigeration, and DuPont and General Motors combined to civilize and urbanize the automobile by adding innovations such as electric starters, bright lacquer finishes, chrome highlights, antifreeze to permit winter operation, and tetraethyl gasoline additives to reduce engine knocking.

These startling accomplishments secured a firm place for corporate laboratories and organized R&D in American industry. Between 1919 and 1936, U.S. manufacturing firms established over a thousand industrial research laboratories, roughly half of the total number of such facilities founded prior to 1946. New labs cropped up in industries such as autos, metals, petroleum, and pharmaceuticals, while those of electrical and chemical pioneers grew markedly. The number of scientists employed in research laboratories increased 10-fold between 1920 and 1940, from 2,775 to 27,777. Typically, at least half of them worked in the largest 10 percent of the labs, as big firms across the economy came to see research as essential. Investors took note. Over the course of the 1920s, stock values came to reflect an assessment of a firm's potential to generate new technologies and accumulated expertise in research, rather than merely its physical assets.

Although developments in the private sector flourished, World War I did not produce a corresponding watershed in government policy regarding research. President Wilson and his advisor, George Ellery Hale, president of the National Academy of Science, failed in their efforts to secure a permanent federal agency for funding scientific research. Hale ultimately retreated to California and the presidency of what would soon be renamed the California Institute of Technology (Caltech). Academic institutions such as Caltech and the Massachusetts Institute of Technology (MIT) grew dramatically during the 1920s, while older liberal arts institutions such as the Ivies and the University of Chicago built new capabilities in the sciences. Much of the funding for these transitions came from private philanthropic organizations such as the Rockefeller Foundation and the Carnegie Foundation, which, in addition to supporting the construction of new research facilities on college campuses, opened its own facilities in Washington, D.C. Another foundation, named for Solomon Guggenheim, funneled resources toward the emerging field of aviation by financing the construction of wind tunnels on numerous college campuses. These experimental facilities, crucial for the testing of airfoils and other prototypes, essentially seeded the creation of aeronautical engineering as an academic discipline across the nation.

Although much of this largess flowed to private institutions, public colleges and universities garnered some of the spoils, while also expanding their research stations. The most dramatic growth occurred where stations established closer ties with regional business interests. Engineers and scientists at the University of Michigan, for instance, generated significant research funds by servicing the needs of the booming automobile industry. The University of California provided analyses for the state's hydroelectric and petroleum industries. Scientists at the University of Georgia developed techniques for making paper from the state's vast pinewood forests and for raising poultry on an industrial scale. Such examples gently nudged public universities toward broader research missions and away from a narrower focus on teaching that many faculty and taxpayers preferred.

Despite its devastating economic effects, the Great Depression did not fundamentally alter the structure and direction of American R&D. The number of scientists and engineers employed in American industry actually increased over the course of the depression decade. Some evidence indicates firms considered research a comparatively inexpensive investment, since it involved personnel rather than facilities. In many instances, moreover, research might yield economies by pointing to efficiencies, much as it had at institutions such as the Pennsylvania Railroad and AT&T, where the vaunted Bell Laboratories organized much of their efforts toward the objective of lowering the cost of phone service, rather than introducing novelties. In at least some instances, however, firms appear to have spent with an eye toward invention. Visitors to the 1939 World's Fair in New York encountered a World of Tomorrow, made possible by corporate research. RCA and Westinghouse introduced television at the fair. DuPont launched its "Better Things for Better Living through Chemistry" campaign and announced a remarkable new synthetic fiber, nylon, which could substitute for silk stockings. Consumers lined up outside Manhattan department stores to attain a pair.

World War II.   By the time the World of Tomorrow closed its gates on 31 October 1939, war had erupted across Europe. Although U.S. troops would not join the combat for more than another two years, the war soon began transforming the structure of American R&D. As the Nazi threat mounted, President Franklin Roosevelt searched for ways to lend support to Allied resistance. With Congress reluctant to commit resources for troops or arms, FDR turned to engineers and scientists engaged in research, whose modest needs he could support without special budget authorization. In June 1940, the president tapped Vannevar Bush to head the new National Defense Research Committee, which FDR had created by executive order.

Bush was a prime exemplar of a new breed of science and engineering ambassador who had learned to cultivate favor in the nation's capital. A former dean of engineering at MIT, Bush had relocated to Washington in 1939 to head the Carnegie Institution. By the time he joined the National Defense Research Committee, he had secured appointments on the President's Science Advisory Board and on the National Advisory Committee on Aeronautics, while also chairing the National Research Council's division of engineering and industrial research. Bush attained the latter post at the recommendation of Frank Jewett, director of AT&T's Bell Labs, who served as president of the National Academy of Sciences, which oversaw the National Research Council. Jewett joined Bush on the National Defense Research Committee, as did the MIT president and physicist Karl Compton and the Harvard president James Conant, a chemist. Representatives of the War and Navy Departments also held posts on the committee, along with an expert on patents and a general assistant.

Over the course of the war, the National Defense Research Committee and its offspring the Office of Scientific Research and Development (OSRD), which was created in May 1941 to give Bush access to congressional budget allocations, distributed nearly half a billion dollars to R&D projects aimed at generating new weapons. All told, OSRD entered into over 2,300 research contracts and distributed funds to some 321 industrial companies and another 142 academic institutions and other nonprofits. Whether aimed at academics or industry, OSRD funds went overwhelmingly to institutions with established research capabilities. This meant most of the money flowed to a handful of states in New England and the mid-Atlantic, plus California. Together, MIT and Caltech received more than $200 million in contracts, or roughly 40 percent of all allocations. MIT housed the sprawling Radiation Laboratory, or "Rad Lab," which conducted much of the nation's research and development on radar technology. Caltech conducted research on aeronautics, including development of the proximity fuse, a detonation technique developed by Merle Tuve that many military historians consider vital in swinging the war of the air toward the Allies. Harvard and Columbia were next in line, with roughly $30 million apiece, whereas the University of California claimed just under $15 million. From there, allocations fell steadily. The University of Pennsylvania ranked 10th among academic institutions, with slightly more than $3 million. Allocations to private business exhibited a similar tendency to reward the privileged. Western Electric, the manufacturing arm of AT&T, topped the list with more than $16 million in OSRD funds. Next came GE, which received $8 million, followed by RCA, DuPont, and Westinghouse, each with allocations between $5 and $6 million. Standard Oil, the 10th-ranked industrial recipient, claimed about the same amount as the University of Pennsylvania.

Although only a few institutions grew rich through OSRD contracts, many others tasted for the first time the fruits of federal largess. Literally hundreds of small and mid-size firms were drawn into its orbit, often through subcontracts from major players such as MIT and Caltech. Even a small contract could make a strong impression on a business or a campus that had not previously conducted sponsored research and leave administrators and faculty longing for more. In this way, OSRD helped foster a transformation in thinking about the research enterprise whose effects would extend long after the war.

That transformation was hastened, and perhaps ultimately overwhelmed, by wartime R&D programs funded by other branches of the federal government. Established research efforts conducted by the Department of Agriculture, the Bureau of Standards, and the National Advisory Committee on Aeronautics all grew significantly during the war. Together their budgets rivaled that of the OSRD. By far the most important investments, however, flowed from the War Department and the Navy Department themselves. The former expended more than $800 million on research and development between 1940 and 1944, during which OSRD expenditures totaled just $350 million. The navy spent another $400 million. Whereas nearly two-thirds of OSRD allocations went to academic institutions and nonprofits, funding from the military departments went overwhelmingly to private industry and to facilities operated by government. Together, the two departments pumped nearly $800 million of R&D funds into private industry during these years, while also laying the foundation for government institutions such as the Naval Research Lab. Much of this funding from the War Department, moreover, went toward emergent fields such as aviation (via the Air Corps), electronics (via the Signal Corp), advanced calculation (via the Ordnance Department), and nuclear technology (also via the Ordnance Department).

No single wartime R&D program, of course, exerted a more profound impact than the Manhattan Project and its atomic bombs. The bomb project touched many of the institutions discussed earlier in this section. Bush and his NDRC colleagues showed little enthusiasm for the idea when they first learned of it in early 1940, when radar and the proximity fuse held more immediate promise of fending off the Nazis. But when British scientists shared ideas about a bomb based on the rare U-235 isotope, Bush and Conant joined a select committee to oversee the project. The tasks of obtaining and mastering U-235 occupied theoretical and empirical investigators from across the physical sciences. The effort drew upon academics from the nation's leading institutions, including Chicago, Columbia, Harvard, Caltech, and Berkeley, while also mobilizing industrial chemists and plant builders from firms such as DuPont, GE, and Eastman Kodak. The War Department eventually took control of managing the project, although even researchers from the Naval Research Lab managed to get involved, after they proposed a potential means of obtaining the vital element. This eclectic assemblage focused its efforts on a project of overwhelming military significance, one that not only brought the war against Japan to an abrupt end, but also opened a field of scientific and technical endeavor that would forever hold the fate of the world in the balance. The specter would do much to shape the course of U.S. R&D in the decades to come.

Postwar Research and the Linear Model. More than a year before Hiroshima and Nagasaki, Vannevar Bush had begun laying the groundwork for federal support of postwar science and technology. With the encouragement of FDR, he drafted a letter and accompanying public speech that attempted to preserve a role for the federal government in R&D even in peacetime. Concerned that the war effort had drawn academic scientists deeply into military projects and left the stock of new knowledge depleted, Bush looked to fund these scientists while also providing them a degree of autonomy. His idea was to create a federal agency whose allocations to science would be governed by peer review, without undue influence by politicians or the military. To drum up support for this vision, Bush began giving a public lecture that came to be known by the title "Science—The Endless Frontier." Sounding not unlike exhibit narrators from the 1939 World's Fair, Bush spoke of a prosperous, safe, and healthy future made possible by science, whose frontiers (unlike the geographic frontier of the West) knew no bounds. Anxious to distance science from the destructiveness of war, Bush laid particular emphasis on developments such as penicillin and chemical insecticides, which had saved many lives by limiting the effects of disease. Elsewhere, Bush also described the potential of innovations in information science and technology to revolutionize all knowledge-based activities. His proposed Memex machine imagined desk workers gaining access to entire libraries and sending documents and images electronically—a vision that foreshadowed the Age of the Internet long before its time.

The visions Bush promulgated grew from his wartime experience, yet in crucial respects seemed at odds with the lessons of wartime R&D. Environments such as the Rad Lab, the Manhattan Project, and the Aberdeen Proving Grounds (where a team of researchers from the University of Pennsylvania conducted pioneering experiments in digital calculation) had demonstrated how innovation could develop in spectacular fashion when scientists from the academy interacted with industrial scientists and engineers on projects aimed toward concrete ends. Although these military environments had sometimes been plagued by secrecy and resentments, in many cases the interaction had proved quite fruitful, generating not only new technologies, but also new knowledge. Now, Bush appeared to advocate a reseparation of the parties and the establishment of a new division of labor, in which academic researchers generated "basic" knowledge that diffused to more practically oriented teams in industry and the military, who would develop applications. The vision came to be known as the linear model of innovation.

Perhaps not surprisingly, the vision was a difficult sell. Military leaders, having grown to appreciate the importance of science and innovation to their endeavors, did not welcome the idea of letting scientists retreat to the Ivory Tower. Nor did many younger scientists, who had survived the doldrums of the Great Depression and enjoyed the intellectual excitement and material rewards of the wartime projects, rush to embrace the vision of an idyllic academic independence they had never known. Further resistance came from politicians in Congress, including conservative Republicans and many Southern Democratic associates of President Harry Truman. In 1947, Truman vetoed an early version of a bill creating a national science foundation. Truman and his cohort hesitated to cede control over a significant budget line to scientists, who would then decide where and how to allocate it. Such politicians wondered how the public could ensure that such funds ultimately went toward socially beneficial purposes, including those in their home states, many of which had received little from the OSRD. They grew especially uneasy when Bush insisted that any patents resulting from such research should be retained by those receiving funding, including industrial partners, rather than be held by the public. This suggestion ran directly counter to efforts being pursued by antitrust lawyers in the U.S. Department of Justice to compel large corporate laboratories, many of which had received significant contracts from government during the war, to license all patents for a reasonable fee. Meanwhile, business leaders such as Jewett of Bell Labs criticized Bush for putting science on the public dole, a complaint echoed apparently without irony by the Caltech president Robert Millikan, whose institution had collected nearly $100 million from the OSRD. Evidently, Millikan preferred a system in which a small group of government science administrators granted contracts to premiere institutions with close ties to industry, rather than one that allocated funds through a competitive process of peer review conducted by academic scientists.

Resistance from these many quarters delayed passage of a bill establishing the National Science Foundation (NSF) until 1950. Although this bill largely fulfilled Bush's vision, intervening events had essentially overwhelmed the initiative. While the bill languished, other branches of the government pumped roughly a billion dollars a year into R&D. Much of this came from the Department of Defense, an umbrella organization encompassing the U.S. Army, Navy, and the newly created Air Force. Each branch had its own agenda and budget for research. Additional expenditures came from the Atomic Energy Commission, which supported both military and civilian uses of nuclear technology. In 1950, when the NSF eked out a measly $350,000 budget authorization (against its mandated cap of $15 million), these agencies and the Public Health Service together pumped some $63 million in R&D funding into academic and nonprofit institutions. Even those authorizations, moreover, paled in comparison to what the various units of the Department of Defense and the Atomic Energy Commission poured into their own government laboratories and subcontracted to industry. Government expenditures had thus continued to follow wartime patterns, with funds allocated to institutions under administered contracts rather than through processes of academic peer review.

Whereas government expenditures held steady at their newly established levels, private investment in R&D grew markedly during the late 1940s. In 1946, such investments stood at roughly half a billion dollars, essentially half the public expenditures for that year and about the same as private investment five years before, at the start of the war. By 1951, private investment had increased nearly fourfold, to nearly $2 billion, half again as much as the public sector spent that year. Perhaps not coincidentally, these were years of spectacular commercial innovation, as television rapidly displaced movies, nylon and other synthetics swept through the fashion trade, air travel replaced long-distance railroading as the jet age dawned, AT&T announced the transistor, and election results were projected and compiled by "electronic brains" built by Sperry Rand and IBM. The endless frontier appeared to have become reality, without public investment in peer-reviewed academic research of the sort Bush advocated.

These transformative innovations had not, of course, simply sprung to life since the war. All were the products of longstanding R&D efforts with roots deep in the depression decade or even earlier. This was true even of the electronic computers; IBM and others had experimented with electronic calculation during the 1930s, and users had looked for ways to adapt existing equipment to perform complex calculations more rapidly. Nor were these innovations merely the products of R&D conducted by a single corporation. Even the transistor, which generated enormous buzz and quickly earned its three creators the Nobel Prize, drew on a body of learning in the physical sciences that transcended Bell Labs. The airline industry rode on a wide base of research, much of it conducted through construction and testing of prototypes, many of which were built for military purposes. The televisions sold by RCA and Westinghouse after the war were far superior to prewar sets, yet cheaper, because they benefitted from research on tubes and other electronic components conducted at the Rad Lab.

Indeed, virtually all of the commercial successes of the postwar decade owed a great deal to the wartime experience. Some were influenced by targeted research projects such as those sponsored by the OSRD. In many cases, however, primary support came from wartime procurement. IBM's established accounting business tripled during the war. Demand for long-distance telephone service mushroomed. Aircraft production reached unimaginable heights. Exploding demand pumped resources into private firms, often enabling them to build new factories and other facilities. Beyond the capital expenditures, the wartime boom often sparked extensive learning across the workforce as companies scrambled to meet production goals under trying conditions. Managers looked for ways to move products into manufacturing environments more smoothly, to pursue sustained improvements across a learning curve, and to support new technologies in the field, where they might undergo further refinement. Much as conditions at the Rad Lab and Manhattan Project broke down barriers between academics and industry and scientists and engineers, firms pursuing wartime production goals fostered unprecedented cooperation and learned valuable lessons about the nature of innovation in the process.

Many of those wartime experiences and the postwar legacies they bequeathed did not remotely correspond to the linear model. Yet these successes indisputably raised the profile of research across American industry, while also associating it more strongly than ever with large corporations. At the dawn of the Eisenhower age, many Americans readily presumed that the health of the national economy rested squarely upon investment in corporate R&D, just as the security of the nation now hung on military R&D.

The Military-Industrial-University Complex.

A recurrent issue of the Eisenhower years was whether the nation could in fact achieve both prosperity and security and maintain a proper balance between them. Eisenhower brought the matter into sharp relief with his farewell address of 1961, when he raised concerns about what he characterized as a military-industrial-university complex. "The prospect of domination of the nation's scholars by Federal employment, project allocations, and the power of money is ever present," Eisenhower cautioned, "and is gravely to be regarded." Pondering automobile designs whose

tailfins resembled those on rockets, the departing president later spoke of "almost an insidious penetration of our minds that the only thing this country is engaged in is weaponry and missiles."

Eisenhower's comments reflected his deep frustration with trying to control costs on the military side of the ledger. When he entered the White House, the defense budget had jumped precipitously, as the nation reeled under the simultaneous burdens of trying to fight a land war in Korea while also responding to the Soviet nuclear threat. The effects were evident in the federal R&D budget, which had jumped from $1.3 billion in 1951 to $3.1 billion in 1953. Virtually all of the increase was tied to defense. President Truman authorized major projects such as the thermonuclear or hydrogen bomb and a sprawling computerized antiaircraft defense system known as SAGE. In 1953, nine of every ten dollars the federal government spent on R&D went to defense. The surge in defense-related research was all the more striking because it was accompanied by a flattening of private expenditures. In 1953, government accounted for 54 percent of the nation's R&D funding.

Eisenhower was by no means opposed to R&D. He considered such activities and the technologies they produced an affordable alternative to deploying large conventional armed forces across the globe. But Eisenhower looked for R&D to generate "dual-purpose" technologies, such as communications satellites, nuclear power plants, and digital computers, that served both civilian and defense needs. In his mind, such technologies might come as readily from private civilian research as from federal dollars targeted expressly for defense. He looked for private R&D investment to provide both prosperity and security.

Total R&D investment did, in fact, grow dramatically during Eisenhower's eight years in the White House. In 1953, the $5.2 billion investment had amounted to 1.36 percent of the U.S. Gross National Product (GNP). The $13.7 billion invested in 1960 constituted 2.60 percent of GNP. This near doubling of the proportion of economic activity going to R&D marked an enduring change. In the years hence, the percentage has never dropped below 2.12 and never surpassed

2.88, a level reached in 1964 and 2009. Over the course of that period, the annual expenditure has averaged almost exactly the 1960 level of 2.60 percent of GNP.

Contrary to Eisenhower's hopes, this leap forward in the nation's research capacity was fueled overwhelmingly by the federal government. The federal share of research spending grew from 54 percent in 1953 to 65 percent in 1960. The federal investment, moreover, remained heavily skewed toward defense. Of the $9 billion the federal government spent on R&D in 1960, eight of every ten dollars were targeted directly for military endeavors. Another seventy cents of each ten dollars went to the space program, ostensibly a civilian endeavor, but one with strong ties to the military and driven by Cold War objectives.

The massive federal investment in R&D during the Eisenhower years overwhelmed growth in spending by private industry and other sources. Although funding for R&D from nonfederal sources increased by some 75 percent in constant dollars from 1953 to 1960 and the ratio of such funding to GNP grew from 0.63 percent to 0.91 percent, these figures paled when compared to the 178 percent increase in federal funding and the associated growth in share of GNP from 0.73 percent to 1.69 percent. Federal dollars flowed so liberally during the 1950s that they came to constitute the largest source of support even for R&D conducted by private business. In 1953, federal funding had paid for less than 40 percent of R&D carried out at industrial facilities. By 1957, the federal share had soared to 56 percent. It peaked at 59 percent two years later and would not drop below 54 percent until 1967. When Eisenhower left the White House, federal expenditures at corporate R&D facilities were 3.7 times what they had been at the start of his presidency, an increase of 270 percent even after adjusting for inflation. The 75 percent increase in corporate expenditures at their R&D facilities appeared rather paltry by comparison. Figures such as these go a long way toward explaining why these years are often referred to as the Golden Age of corporate research and why Eisenhower voiced concerns about a military-industrial complex.

Why Eisenhower also implicated universities may at first glance appear more puzzling. Of the $13.7 billion invested by all sources in R&D in 1960, only about $1.1 billion (8 percent) went to universities and colleges, including about $385 million earmarked for federally funded centers such as nuclear laboratories run by the University of California. All told, the federal government allocated just $838 million (or 9.5 percent) of its R&D expenditures to universities and colleges. On a proportional basis, these figures were almost identical to those of 1953. Universities had kept pace and ridden the overall boom in R&D to new levels of activity, but they had not experienced the dramatic shifts in funding sources that had characterized industrial R&D.

What prompted Eisenhower to mention universities was not so much their overall magnitude as their role. Federal classifications divided R&D expenditures and activities into three categories: basic research, applied research, and development. The distinctions, which in reality were not always easy to draw, corresponded to Vannevar Bush's linear model. In 1953, basic research accounted for just $460 million (9 percent) of the $5.1 billion total, whereas applied garnered 25 percent and development 66 percent. More than half of the funding for basic research came from the federal government, and nearly half of such research was conducted at universities and colleges. In 1960, these figures stood at 9 percent ($1.3 billion) for basic, 23 percent for applied, and 68 percent for development. More than half of the funds for basic research came from the federal government, and more than half of such research was conducted at universities and colleges. In both years, universities and colleges accounted for only a small fraction of development, which was concentrated overwhelmingly at industrial facilities (although paid for increasingly by the federal government). Applied research fit a profile similar to that of development, but less extreme. Universities and colleges conducted applied research, but far less than that conducted by industry, and although the amount of applied research increased over the decade, the university role skewed increasingly toward basic research. Universities were putting less of their own funds into applied research and virtually none into development, but by 1960 had begun to invest significant amounts of their own resources into basic research.

By 1960, then, one could detect a division of labor in R&D, with the federal government spending modest amounts of money for basic research at universities and colleges and large sums for development at industrial facilities. Industry invested about half as much as government in basic research, conducted at its own corporate laboratories, and pitched in about 40 percent of the funding for development work, which was conducted overwhelmingly at its facilities. Applied research occupied a middle ground. Funding levels for it fell closer to basic research than to development, and the federal government and industry shared responsibility for both funding and conducting the activity, although universities also participated.

Trends in Federal Support since 1960.

Data collected by the NSF reveal several significant trends in U.S. R&D since Eisenhower left the White House. During the subsequent five decades, total R&D expenditures oscillated from a high of 2.88 percent of GNP, a level reached during the mid to late 1960s at the height of the Apollo program and matched with the economic stimulus of 2009, and a low of 2.12 percent of GNP in 1978 at the depths of a prolonged economic malaise.

Although overall funding levels remained within that band, the sources of funding shifted dramatically, with the private sector assuming a much larger role. Federal funds still accounted for about two-thirds of R&D through 1968, on the eve of the moon landing, but then fell precipitously over the next decade. By 1978, federal expenditures stood at just 1.06 percent of GNP, exactly matching the contribution from nonfederal (primarily private) sources, which had essentially held steady as a percent of GNP since 1968. Federal funding spiked upward during the Reagan defense buildup of the early 1980s, but funding from private sources increased even more rapidly, as corporations responded to government incentives offering tax credits for funds spent on R&D. By 1985, when total R&D investments stabilized at about 2.7 percent of GNP, nonfederal sources accounted for 54 percent of the national total. From there, the federal share dropped steadily to a low of just 25 percent in 2000. Enhanced spending on national security and economic stimulus packages over the next decade pushed the federal share back up to 31 percent—precisely half the investment in R&D by private industry in 2009 and less than half the federal share of the 1950s and 1960s.

This inversion of funding sources was accompanied by significant shifts in the types of activities supported by federal and private dollars. Overall, the nation's R&D efforts remained heavily skewed toward development. In 2000, development still accounted for 62 percent of total R&D expenditures, just 6 percentage points less than in 1968. (Applied research oscillated between 18 and 23 percent, whereas basic research grew from 10 to 16 percent.) Throughout the period, development consistently accounted for 75 percent or more of R&D activities conducted at industrial firms. What changed was the source of funding. Essentially, the federal government diverted more funds toward basic research conducted at universities and other nonprofits, while drastically reducing its expenditures on development at private industrial facilities. In 1968, the federal government still covered more than half the cost of industrial development. By 1980, industry had assumed two-thirds of such expenses, and by 2000 it paid for more than 90 percent of its development costs. At that point, only about one-quarter of federal R&D expenditures went to industry, and federal funds amounted to just 8.6 percent of industrial R&D budgets. (These numbers do not reflect tax credits, which indirectly subsidized industrial R&D).

Although direct federal investments in development dropped, the share of federal R&D expenditures devoted to basic research rose from 16 percent in 1968 to 38 percent in 2004. Those investments, moreover, were increasingly concentrated at universities and other nonprofits. The share of federal research dollars captured by such institutions, which already stood at 64 percent in 1968, grew to more than 80 percent in 2004. Such institutions also doubled their share of federal funds devoted to applied research, which comprised roughly a fifth of the federal R&D budget. By 2004, about a third of those funds went to universities and other nonprofits. All told, by 2004 roughly a third of all federally funded R&D went to basic and applied research conducted at universities and other nonprofits. Another 15 percent of federal expenditures went to development activities at government laboratories and other nonprofits.

Even with these dramatic shifts in federal priorities, the precipitous drop in overall federal investment in R&D relative to GNP would have led to reduced funding for basic and applied research if not for infusions from nonfederal sources. Over the course of the 1990s, the share of funding for basic research provided by industry actually grew from 10 percent to 25 percent of the national total, although basic research accounted for just 5 to 7 percent of total R&D expenditures by industry. Private funds accounted for 20 percent of national funding for basic research even after large infusions of federal funds during the opening decade of the new millennium. Most of those private funds went to basic research conducted at industrial facilities, but some 15 to 25 percent found their way to universities and other nonprofits, so that by 2000 about 5 percent of university research budgets came from industry. Additional funding for research at universities flowed from the universities themselves. Such internal funds constituted more than 20 percent of university research budgets in 2000, twice their share in 1968. State and local governments and other nonprofits together kicked in another 15 percent of university research budgets. Taken altogether, these nonfederal sources accounted for about 40 percent of university research—a far larger proportion than in 1968, even with the federal government making such a priority of university research in its own budget. Such investments help account for why the ratio of dollars spent on development to those spent on basic research fell from nearly 7 to 1 in 1968 to slightly less than 4 to 1 in 2000.

The shifting patterns of research expenditures and activities in large part reflected changes in the areas of investigation, which in turn reflected shifting national priorities and changes in the nature of economic activity. During the Kennedy and Johnson administrations, when public funds paid for most R&D, the emphasis remained overwhelmingly on defense and space technology. Together, they accounted for 85 percent of the federal R&D budget in 1964, with the remaining 15 percent scattered among other fields of endeavor. The heavy emphasis on weapons systems and manned space exploration, areas involving highly complex technical infrastructure, skewed federal R&D expenditures toward the development side of the ledger.

The balance swung toward basic research during subsequent administrations partly as a consequence of increased federal emphasis on medicine and health. Federal R&D support in these areas flowed primarily through the National Institutes of Health (NIH). Its roots went back to the 1930s, when Congress authorized construction of a modest research facility at Bethesda, Maryland. Shortly before World War II, the NIH gained responsibility for the National Cancer Institute, the first of what would eventually become some two dozen institutes focused on specific diseases and disorders. The National Cancer Institute ran a modest grants program, akin to that Vannevar Bush envisioned for the NSF, which distributed modest sums to independent researchers at universities and medical facilities. During the latter part of the war, the NIH adopted this grants model across the entire agency. Sums remained modest. The entire budget came to less than $3.5 million dollars in 1946, five times prewar levels, but a tiny fraction of what Bush allocated through the OSRD or the various branches of the military spent on R&D.

The NIH grew dramatically after the war, as it broadened its grants program to include clinical research and founded new institutes focused on areas such as heart and lung disease, diabetes, neurological disorders, allergies and infectious diseases, child development, and mental health. With its budget growing 10-fold by 1953 and a hundred-fold by 1960, the NIH claimed a progressively larger share of the rapidly expanding federal pie. When Eisenhower left office, it accounted for 4.5 percent of federal R&D, and its share climbed to 7.1 percent during the Kennedy years before plateauing under Johnson. Still, expenditures on medical research lagged far behind the shares commandeered in 1968 by defense (52 percent) and space (27 percent).

With curtailment of the space program and the relative decline in public support for R&D, the

NIH claimed a steadily larger share of a more modest pie. By 1980, its share of federal R&D funding had crept up to nearly 12 percent, on par with the amount expended on energy, the pet cause of the Carter administration. After stabilizing at that level during the Reagan years, when defense again claimed upward of two-thirds of R&D funding, the share expended on medical-related R&D climbed steadily. By 1992, the NIH budget of $9 billion accounted for more than 15.5 percent of federal R&D. It then exploded over the next decade, tripling in absolute terms and doubling its share to nearly a third of all federal R&D expenditures, as the Clinton and first Bush II administrations made disease-targeted research a top priority. Their budgets significantly boosted resources for long-established research foci such as cancer, heart disease, and diabetes, while also broadening support for new areas such as AIDS research. After a slow start, funding to address this epidemic reached $1.5 billion in 1995 and grew to double that level over the next decade, where it has remained, even as overall spending on the NIH plateaued and its share of federal R&D spending slipped back toward 25 percent.

Unlike areas such as defense, where only a small fraction of R&D expenditures went toward basic research, more than half of the funds expended by the NIH were typically classified as basic research. (As critics concerned about decreased funding for science often observed, however, much of this activity occurred in clinical settings rather than laboratories.) In 1980, when health-related research accounted for just 12 percent of federal R&D, it already claimed more than a third of the federal budget for basic research. From there its share climbed steadily, surpassing 50 percent of basic research in 2000 before leveling off at 56 percent in the middle of the decade. Together, health and general science (an area funded primarily by the NSF) accounted for more than 80 percent of federally funded basic research that year. Defense and space together amounted to less than 15 percent; energy had dwindled to virtually nothing.

A large portion of these federal research funds ended up at medical schools and research hospitals, in addition to associated departments of chemistry and biochemistry. Much of it went toward drug-related research and evaluation. Investment in medical research also accounted for the rising prominence of nonprofit foundations, many of which targeted health issues, as did much of the enhanced funding for research provided by state and local governments and by universities themselves. Academic research in areas such as physics and mathematics literally grew overshadowed by these massive investments in health, as many universities came to resemble vast hospital complexes with quaint adjoining campuses. At the turn of the new millennium, scientists in those fields looked for new federal initiatives in nanotechnology to help adjust the balance.

Federal investment in basic research was accompanied by new policies intended to encourage the commercialization of results. The Bayh-Dole Act of 1980 enabled universities to retain patent rights for innovations resulting from federally funded research. Although critics blamed the act for promoting secrecy and impeding the free exchange of knowledge, while failing to generate revenue for most universities, legislation prompted vigorous response. Virtually all research universities subsequently invested in offices and ventures devoted to commercialization, and the number of patents taken out by universities increased dramatically. Much of this activity, and most of the few dramatic commercial successes, occurred in health-related research. Investigators in that area found they could readily sell or license rights to biochemical patents to pharmaceutical companies, which used them strategically or incorporated them into drug development efforts, taking responsibility for arduous approval and marketing efforts that researchers would have found too burdensome. Less often, such patents provided the basis for start-up firms developing their own commercial products.

Changes in Industrial Research. Industrial R&D also shifted emphasis over time. In 1969, Cold War technologies still drove most R&D activity conducted by industry. Substantially more than half of expenditures on industrial R&D went to two categories: aircraft (including missiles) and electrical equipment (including telecommunications and components). Machinery claimed another 10 percent, with likely at least half of that going toward computing, another field with close ties to defense and space. Chemicals and motor vehicles each absorbed another 9 to 10 percent. The remaining 15 percent was sprinkled through a variety of lesser manufacturing industries. This distribution was almost identical to that of 1956, the midpoint of the Eisenhower administration.

A decade later, in 1979, the share devoted to aircraft had dropped by a third, to 21 percent, roughly equal that spent on electric equipment. Machinery ticked up to 12.6 percent, with two-thirds of that going to computing, whereas motor vehicles and chemicals showed modest gains to 11.6 percent and 10.6 percent. In addition to computing, significant new claimants included scientific instruments, which absorbed 6.6 percent, and drugs, a subset of chemistry that accounted for 4 percent of total industrial R&D. The Reagan military buildup, including the Strategic Defense Initiative (Star Wars), skewed efforts back toward aircraft and further boosted computing, whereas chemicals, motor vehicles, and electrical equipment all slipped modestly.

The drop in electrical equipment in part reflected what would become the most dominant development of the post-Reagan years: the rise of industrial R&D in nonmanufacturing sectors, especially services. Much of this initially involved telecommunications services, but increasingly it was driven by computing and software services used in trade and commerce. The share of industrial R&D devoted to such functions escalated steadily from 4 percent to 10 percent across the eight years of the Reagan Administration and then exploded to 24.8 percent during the four years of his successor. This explosion came primarily at the expense of aircraft, whose share was halved during these four years, and from machinery (including computer hardware) and electrical equipment. The only manufacturing sector that drew an increased share of R&D during these years was drugs, which rose comparatively modestly from 4 percent to 7.5 percent.

The trend toward services continued, although at a slower pace, in the 1990s and into the new millennium. By 2003, 40 percent of industrial R&D occurred outside of manufacturing. Two-thirds of that went toward trade and professional services, a category that included business computing and science and engineering services. Within manufacturing, aircraft and machinery plummeted to less than 4 percent, whereas motor vehicles and chemicals held steady at around 10 percent apiece. Drug manufacture slipped back to 5 percent, perhaps reflecting the tendency of pharmaceutical companies to rely on the massive public investment in health-related research at universities. The only manufacturing sector to attract a significantly larger share of R&D resources during these years was electrical equipment, a category that now included the booming manufacturers of computer chips, such as Intel and Motorola.

The shifts in focus of industrial R&D testify to the extent computing technology drove economic and social change in the United States after 1968, especially after 1980, as the world of networked distributed computing and devices took hold and altered procedures and routines in virtually every walk of life. Riding the digital revolution, leading firms in hardware, software, and computer services routinely pumped 10 to 30 percent of their escalating revenues into R&D, whereas new start-ups also entered the field with products and ideas borne of R&D. Even with giants such as IBM, Intel, Microsoft, and Oracle each directing billions of dollars annually toward R&D, smaller firms accounted for a growing share of R&D activity. Prior to the 1980s, firms employing more than five thousand employees had consistently performed at least 85 percent of industrial R&D. In 1981, they accounted for 89 percent, with those employing more than 10 thousand responsible for 84 percent. A decade later, those figures had dropped to 71 percent and 64 percent. Nearly 20 percent of industrial R&D in 1991 was conducted by firms employing fewer than a thousand people. By 1998, firms employing fewer than five thousand accounted for a third of industrial R&D, and nearly half of that was done by those with fewer than five hundred employees. In 2003, the share performed by firms with 10 thousand or more employees stood at just under 55 percent, nearly 30 percentage points lower than at the start of the 1980s.

The growing prominence of smaller firms reflected the changing nature of technology and markets. During the 1950s and 1960s, as industrial

R&D grew ever more prominent, innovation often occurred through sustained efforts by established corporations to master complex technologies and associated systems. The Big Three automakers worked out the details of nationally distributed mass production of vehicles that underwent perpetual but modest refinement. DuPont leveraged its experience in the manufacture of new synthetic materials. RCA and GE moved from radio to television and fed the new boxes with signals bounced off satellites. AT&T and Bell Laboratories modernized the national phone system, which it monopolized, whereas IBM morphed its established accounting business into the world of electronic data processing. A handful of aviation pioneers mastered the jet age, and a few others focused on missiles. In many cases, these firms not only dominated their commercial markets; they also focused much of their R&D on government projects, where "the market" often consisted of a single customer or perhaps a few branches of the armed forces or the bureaucracy. With government often willing to foot much of the bill for development as well as research, such projects were almost irresistible.

In such closed environments, where tasks often demanded that research meld with a wide range of activities necessary to support the system, firms could move with considerable deliberation. A new computer system at IBM, for instance, might evolve over the course of several years with the intent of satisfying the entire market for half a decade or longer. Boeing and McDonnell Douglass pursued aircraft design in similar fashion. DuPont looked to recreate the success of nylon, a product that emerged after a decade of work in synthetic polymers.

By the 1980s, this closed world had begun to show signs of strain. Many industry leaders found themselves losing ground to upstarts, who managed to introduce new products faster and with considerably less investment of resources. As technologies of mass production diffused and grew more commonplace, American manufacturers found themselves competing with imported goods, many of which offered new features. Automakers lost market share to imported cars of more radical new design, offering better performance, durability,

and features at a lower price. Japanese firms beat RCA with a new generation of televisions and accompanying recorders, whereas the American company squandered resources on the ill-fated Videodisc. AT&T and its vaunted Bell Labs failed to navigate the transition to mobile devices, losing ground to a host of smaller firms (including Nokia, a Finnish manufacturer of rubber boots) whose designs were more attuned to consumer tastes and habits. IBM scrambled to catch up with new entrants who beat Big Blue to market first with solid-state supercomputers aimed at niche markets and later with low-end personal computers built from inexpensive chips. The latter technology opened up vast markets for both custom programming and prepackaged software, which small firms raced to provide.

In many instances, these developments disassociated product innovation from larger systems of production, testing, sales, and maintenance, effectively lowering the barriers to entry for innovators. Large firms such as IBM reevaluated their investments in centralized research laboratories, whose celebrated discoveries and numerous patents seldom seemed to lodge in new commercial products. AT&T spun off its famous Bell Laboratories to a subsidiary, which soon foundered in the increasingly competitive environment of digital communications. Management at such giants often downsized the central research facilities and encouraged investigators to license their discoveries to commercial partners, be they within the firm or outside it. Sales and licensing of patents grew increasingly common across the economy as firms looked to incorporate ideas from numerous sources, whether via trade, through alliances, or by acquiring start-ups. Although companies such as Microsoft, Apple, and Google still looked to secure dominant positions through control of integrated technical systems, their ability to do so required that they draw upon a more diverse array of contributors from inside and outside the firm, and their holds often appeared less firm than those once commanded by pioneers in research and development such as AT&T and GE.

Conclusion. Taken together, trends in public and private R&D since the early 1960s indicate one salient characteristic: a marked intensification of commercial concerns. Especially after 1980, R&D was much more likely to be conducted at private facilities and funded by private concerns responding to market stimuli and tax incentives. Rather than serving persistent, long-term strategic objectives such as facilitating nuclear deterrence, exploring space, enhancing telephone service, or securing enduring advantages for dominant firms in sectors such as computing and electric power generation, R&D was increasingly linked to shorter-term aims such as product development and process improvement. In many instances, the primary outputs of R&D were themselves tradeable assets, such as patent licenses. This was true even of research conducted at universities, which under Bayh-Dole looked to spawn start-up firms and generate royalties from patent licenses. A major portion of publicly funded research occurred in large university hospitals in the course of clinical procedures. Such activities could generate significant revenue for the hospitals while also advancing development of new drugs and treatment regimens provided by profit-seeking firms. Even R&D aimed at enhancing national security, although often shrouded in secrecy, apparently drew with increasing frequency upon technologies developed for private commercial purposes.

In certain respects, these changes in U.S. R&D marked a return to attributes characteristic of the dawn of the twentieth century, when a small cadre of corporations first established distinct programs of R&D housed in separate facilities and staffed by university-trained scientists and engineers. As the historian Thomas Hughes (1989) once noted, these pioneering institutions were "no philanthropic asylums." Corporations did not set researchers up with funding and facilities and turn them loose, free to work on problems of their own choosing, in isolation from the financial concerns of the firm. The pioneers sought remedies for pressing technical problems of vital commercial importance. In pursuing them, they were often willing to search outside the boundaries of the firm and acquire rights to technologies developed elsewhere. Much of what would later come to be characterized as R&D occurred in smaller firms, which might use the fruits of their labors to en-hance internal operations or bring new products to market, but increasingly licensed them to others. Government contributed with research on areas of vital economic interest such as natural resources, mining, and agriculture, much as it currently underwrites much research devoted to health and defense.

Whether this return to an earlier age will continue to best serve the national interest in the twenty-first century, as nations such as China invest heavily in basic research conducted at universities, remains an open question subject to frequent debate. Absent a compelling threat to public health and welfare or to national security, such as that provided by the Soviet nuclear arsenal at the height of the Cold War, history suggests the United States is unlikely to commit significant public funds to such an endeavor.

[See also **Agricultural Experiment Stations; Agricultural Technology; Agriculture, U.S. Department of; Army Corps of Engineers, U.S.; Atomic Energy Commission; Bell Laboratories; Centers for Disease Control and Prevention; Defense Advanced Research Projects Agency; Electricity and Electrification; Engineering; Film Technology; Fish and Wildlife Service, U.S.; Forest Service, U.S.; Genetics and Genetic Engineering; Geological Surveys; Higher Education and Science; Hospitals; Human Genome Project; Law and Science; Machinery and Manufacturing; Manhattan Project; Medicine; Military, Science and Technology and the; Mining Technology; Missiles and Rockets; Museums of Science and Natural History; Nanotechnology; National Aeronautics and Space Administration; National Institutes of Health; National Laboratories; National Science Foundation; Nobel Prize in Biomedical Research; Nuclear Regulatory Commission; Nylon; Office of Scientific Research and Development; Penicillin; Petroleum and Petrochemicals; Pharmacology and Drug Therapy; Plastics; President's Science Advisory Committee; Public Health Service, U.S.; Radio; Railroads; Robots; Rockefeller Institute, The; Science; Scripps Institution of Oceanography; Silicon Valley; Smithsonian**

Institution; Solid-State Electronics; Space Program; Springfield Armory; Technology; *and* Television.]

BIBLIOGRAPHY

Arora, Ashish, Andrea Fosfuri, and Alfonso Gambardella. *Markets for Technology: The Economics of Innovation and Corporate Strategy.* Cambridge, Mass.: MIT Press, 2001. Fundamental to understanding the disaggregation of corporate research since 1980.

Balconi, Margherita, Stefano Brusoni, and Luigi Orsenigo. "In Defence of the Linear Model: An Essay." *Research Policy* 39, no. 1 (2010): 1–13. Surveys literature on a concept that has animated many discussions of research policy.

Buderi, Robert. *Engines of Tomorrow: How the World's Best Companies Are Using Their Research Labs to Win the Future.* New York: Simon & Schuster, 2000. An accessible but measured account of transformations at IBM and other corporate facilities during the 1990s.

Carlson, W. Bernard. *Innovation as a Social Process: Elihu Thomson and the Rise of General Electric, 1870–1900.* New York: Cambridge University Press, 1991. On the transition from independent inventor to corporate research, with valuable insights into strategy at GE.

Castells, Manuel. *The Rise of the Network Society.* Vol. 1: *The Information Age: Economy, Society, and Culture.* 2d ed. Malden, Mass.: Blackwell, 2000. On the significance of networked computing in restructuring economic activity and public investment, including R&D.

Clark, Sally H., Naomi R. Lamoreaux, and Steven W. Usselman, eds. *The Challenge of Remaining Innovative: Insights from Twentieth-Century American Business.* Palo Alto, Calif.: Stanford University Press, 2009. Includes a synthetic overview and nine studies of R&D, including the labs at AT&T, Corning, and IBM.

Edwards, Paul N. *The Closed World: Computers and the Politics of Discourse in Cold War America.* Cambridge, Mass.: MIT Press, 1996. On the military and early computing, especially SAGE.

Fagerberg, Jan, David C. Mowery, and Richard R. Nelson, eds. *The Oxford Handbook of Innovation.* Oxford: Oxford University Press, 2006. Includes many salient articles on aspects of R&D since 1945.

Fisk, Catherine L. *Working Knowledge: Employee Innovation and the Rise of Corporate Intellectual Property, 1800–1930.* Chapel Hill: University of North Carolina Press, 2009. Essential to understanding the legal basis of corporate research.

Galambos, Louis. "Theodore N. Vail and the Role of Innovation in the Modern Bell System." *Business History Review* 66 (1992): 95–126. On the founding and political economy of the most famous corporate research facility.

Graham, Margaret B. W. *RCA and the VideoDisc: The Business of Research.* New York: Cambridge University Press, 1986. Excellent case study illustrating changes in corporate R&D.

Graham, Margaret B. W., and Bettye H. Pruitt. *R&D for Industry: A Century of Technological Innovation at Alcoa.* New York: Cambridge University Press, 1990. Corporate case study offering a long view.

Hounshell, David A., and John Kenly Smith Jr. *Science and Corporate Strategy: DuPont R&D, 1902–1980.* New York: Cambridge University Press, 1988. Exhaustive study of a research program that produced nylon and many other innovations.

Hughes, Thomas P. *American Genesis: A Century of Invention and Technological Enthusiasm.* New York: Penguin Books, 1989. Important interpretation of the transition from independent invention to corporate and government research.

Israel, Paul. *Machine Shop to Industrial Laboratory: Telegraphy and the Changing Context of American Invention, 1830–1920.* Baltimore: Johns Hopkins University Press, 1992. Includes an extensive discussion of Edison, who began his prolific career inventing devices for the telegraph industry.

Jenkins, Reese. *Images and Enterprise: Technology and the American Photographic Industry, 1839–1925.* Baltimore: Johns Hopkins University Press, 1975. Traces the transition to internal corporate research in one pioneering industry.

Kay, Lily E. *The Molecular Vision of Life: Caltech, the Rockefeller Foundation, and the Rise of the New Biology.* New York: Oxford University Press, 1996. Insightful case study of the university-foundation research nexus.

Kennedy, Joseph V. "The Sources and Uses of U.S. Science Funding." *The New Atlantis* 36 (2012): 3–20. Very useful compilation of statistics from NSF and Science and Engineering Indicators, in graphic and tabular form.

Kevles, Daniel J. *The Physicists: The History of a Scientific Community in Modern America.* New York: Random House, 1971. Includes data on wartime and postwar research funding.

Kleinman, Daniel Lee. *Politics on the Endless Frontier: Postwar Research Policy in the United States.*

Durham. N.C.: Duke University Press, 1995. Detailed treatment of the creation of the NSF.

Kline, Ronald R. *Steinmetz: Engineer and Socialist*. Baltimore: Johns Hopkins University Press, 1992. On the origins of the lab at GE, among other relevant topics.

Kohler, Robert E. *Partners in Science: Foundations and Natural Scientists, 1900–1945*. Chicago: University of Chicago Press, 1991. Essential on the role of foundations in funding research.

Lamoreaux, Naomi R., and Kenneth L. Sokoloff, eds. *Financing Innovation in the United States, 1870 to the Present*. Cambridge, Mass.: MIT Press, 2007. Contains a synthesis and numerous outstanding essays, including an insightful study of research networks among firms in Cleveland at the turn of the twentieth century.

Lazonick, William. *Sustainable Prosperity in the New Economy: Business Organization and High-Tech Employment in the United States*. Kalamazoo, Mich.: W. E. Upjohn Institute for Employment Research, 2009. Important discussion of recent trends in corporate organization and R&D.

Lazonick, William, and Oner Tulum. "US Biopharmaceutical Finance and the Sustainability of the Biotech Business Model." *Research Policy* 40, no. 9 (2011): 1170–1187. Analysis of recent trends in research funding in drug development and health sciences.

Lenoir, Tim. "All but War Is Simulation: The Military-Entertainment Complex." *Configurations* 8, no. 3 (2000): 289–335. On the increasing reliance of the military on commercial products.

Leslie, Stuart W. *The Cold War and American Science: The Military-Industrial-Academic Complex at MIT and Stanford*. New York: Columbia University Press, 1993. Deeply researched case studies tracing the emergence of new disciplines at two academic bulwarks of postwar R&D.

McCray, W. Patrick. "Will Small Be Beautiful? Making Policies for Our Nanotech Future." *History and Technology* 21, no. 2 (2005): 177–203. On the birth of the nanotechnology initiative.

McDougall, Walter A. *The Heavens and the Earth: A Political History of the Space Age*. New York: Basic Books, 1985. Detailed treatment of the Eisenhower administration.

Mowery, David C. "The Development of Industrial Research in US Manufacturing." *American Economic Review* 80, no. 2 (1990): 345–349. Brief overview by the foremost authority, whose numerous articles on R&D will reward further reading.

Mowery, David C., and Nathan Rosenberg. *Technology and the Pursuit of Economic Growth*. New York: Cambridge University Press, 1989. Includes data on the number and size of early laboratories.

Mowery, David C., et al. "The Growth of Patenting and Licensing by US Universities: An Assessment of the Effects of the Bayh-Dole Act of 1980." *Research Policy* 30, no. 1 (2001): 99–119. One of several articles by a team of researchers examining the effects of this federal act.

Murmann, Johan Peter. *Knowledge and Competitive Advantage: The Coevolution of Firms, Technology, and National Institutions*. New York: Cambridge University Press, 2003. Examines the German dyestuffs industry, which inspired much innovation in U.S. R&D.

National Institutes of Health. "Appropriations since 1938." *NIH Almanac*. http://www.nih.gov/about/almanac/appropriations/index.htm. Includes data for each member institute and for AIDS research, as cited in the essay.

National Institutes of Health. "A Short History of the National Institutes of Health." http://history.nih.gov. Useful institutional history.

National Science Foundation. National Center on Science and Engineering Statistics. Data on research and development. http://www.nsf.gov/statistics. These pages contain numerous time series data and are the source of most of the statistics used in this essay.

Noble, David. *America by Design: Science, Technology, and the Rise of Corporate Capitalism*. New York: Oxford University Press, 1979. On the legal basis underlying early labs.

Olmstead, Alan L., and Paul W. Rhode. *Creating Abundance: Biological Innovation and American Agricultural Development*. New York: Cambridge University Press, 2008. A brilliant and comprehensive reinterpretation of research and innovation in agriculture across two centuries.

Owens, Larry. "The Counterproductive Management of Science in the Second World War: Vannevar Bush and the Office of Scientific Research and Development." *Business History Review* 68, no. 4 (1994): 515–576. Includes extensive data on wartime funding.

Reich, Leonard S. "Lighting the Path to Profit: GE's Control of the Electric Lamp Industry, 1892–1941." *Business History Review* 66 (1992): 305–334. Excellent example of the strategic use of R&D by a pioneer.

Reich, Leonard S. *The Making of American Industrial Research: Science and Business at GE and Bell, 1876–1926.* New York: Cambridge University Press, 1985. Pathbreaking comparative study of two early corporate research leaders.

Servos, John. "Engineers, Businessmen, and the Academy: The Beginnings of Sponsored Research at the University of Michigan." *Technology and Culture* 37, no. 2 (1996): 721–762. A fine case study of a neglected dimension of university research.

Usselman, Steven W. *Regulating Railroad Innovation: Business, Technology, and Politics in America, 1840–1920.* New York: Cambridge University Press, 2002. Extensive discussion of early corporate testing facilities.

Wise, George. *Willis R. Whitney, General Electric, and the Origins of U.S. Industrial Research.* New York: Columbia University Press, 1985. Solid study of one of the corporate pioneers.

Wright, Gavin. "The Origins of American Industrial Success, 1879–1940." *American Economic Review* 80 (1990): 651–668. Ties manufacturing prowess to collective research pertaining to materials and natural resources.

Wright, Gavin, and Paul David. "Increasing Returns and the Genesis of American Resource Abundance." *Industrial and Corporate Change* 6, no. 2 (1997): 203–245. On collective research in the minerals industries.

Zachary, G. Pascal. *Endless Frontier: Vannevar Bush and the Engineering of the American Century.* Cambridge, Mass.: MIT Press, 1999. An indispensable biography of a central figure.

Steven W. Usselman

RESEARCH LABORATORIES, INDUSTRIAL

See Research and Development (R&D).

RICHARDS, ELLEN SWALLOW

(1842–1911), a prominent woman chemist of the nineteenth century, founder of home economics. Using chemistry, Ellen Swallow Richards investigated water, food stuffs, and domestic spaces. Committed to women's education and social reform, she also cofounded the Association of Collegiate Alumnae (forerunner of the American Association of University Women) and helped organize the New England Kitchen.

Born into a genteel New England family, Richards worked to support them. In 1868, she entered Vassar College, graduating in 1870. She entered the Massachusetts Institute of Technology (MIT) as a special student, receiving a BA from MIT and an MA from Vassar on the chemical analysis of iron ore. With the support of her husband, Robert Richards, chair of the MIT mining and engineering department, she taught at MIT's "women's laboratory." A year after MIT admitted women and the laboratory closed, in 1884, she was appointed instructor in sanitary science, a position she held until her death. At the request of the state of Massachusetts, Richards surveyed many water bodies in the state and created water quality standards. She served as official water analyst for the Massachusetts Board of Health from 1887 to 1897.

Richards was concerned with public-health issues. With others, she organized the New England Kitchen in 1890, offering inexpensive and nutritious meals for working-class Bostonians. A version of this kitchen appeared in the Women's Building of the 1893 World's Fair in Chicago. The meals, cheap and plentiful, were not what the poor wanted to eat, and these ventures closed. In addition to food production and consumption, Richards became concerned about food adulteration, both as a public-health issue and with regard to value for the consumer.

Beginning in 1899, Richards met with other "domestic scientists"—women and men who used science to improve the health, and wealth, of the home—at Lake Placid for a decade of conferences. This—a discipline, a professional organization, and university curricula—was her greatest legacy. In 1908, at the conferences' end, Richards was elected first president of the American Home Economics Association.

Ellen Swallow Richards's lifework embodied her support for education and opportunities for women.

[*See also* **Chemistry; Food and Diet; Food Processing; Gender and Science; Gender and**

Technology; Home Economics Movement; Household Technology; *and* Public Health.]

BIBLIOGRAPHY

Clarke, Robert. *Ellen Swallow: The Woman Who Founded Ecology.* Chicago: Follett, 1973.

Hunt, Caroline. *The Life of Ellen H. Richards.* Boston: Whitcomb & Barrows, 1912.

Gwen Kay

RITTENHOUSE, DAVID

(1732–1796), astronomer, mathematician, and instrument maker. Born outside Philadelphia, near Germantown, Pennsylvania, Rittenhouse was fascinated with mathematics and mechanics as a child, but was largely self-taught. He began making clocks and other scientific and mechanical instruments at an early age. When he was 19, he opened a shop at his father's farm to sell these items. He made surveying instruments, compasses, zenith sectors, telescopes, barometers, and pocket thermometers. He became especially well known for designing and constructing two orreries, detailed mechanical models of the locations and motions of the planets and moons in relation to the sun in the Solar System. The two devices, which he finished in 1771, were bought by the University of Pennsylvania (known at the time as the College of Philadelphia) and Princeton University (known then as the College of New Jersey).

Rittenhouse relocated to Philadelphia in 1770 and became the city surveyor four years later. Throughout his life, he served on state and local survey commissions and participated in topographic canal and river surveys. During the Revolution, he oversaw military preparations involving the manufacture of weapons and the location of gunpowder mills and military depots. He also held other official positions both during and after the war, including state treasurer, the first director of the U.S. Mint, and a member of both the Pennsylvania General Assembly and the 1776 constitutional convention.

Rittenhouse did not simply construct scientific instruments for others to use; he also sought to combine his mechanical and mathematical skills with his own scientific interests. He conducted research in different areas of physical science and mathematics, including studies involving meteorology, geology, and electricity and magnetism. In 1786, he investigated the phenomenon of the diffraction of light into spectra using a transmission grating he had designed and constructed.

Rittenhouse was particularly interested in astronomy. He played a key role in the effort by the American Philosophical Society to participate in an international cooperative investigation of the 1769 transit of Venus. Based on Rittenhouse's recommendations, the APS arranged to have observers make observations from his observatory and two other locations. Rittenhouse assembled most of the instruments for the three observatories. After he moved to Philadelphia in 1770, he built another observatory and took regular observations. He published his calculations on comets and other celestial phenomena as well as data on the satellites of Jupiter, the transits of Venus, and lunar and solar eclipses.

Rittenhouse was an early member of the American Philosophical Society and remained active throughout his life. After serving as librarian, secretary, and vice president, he was elected the second president of the organization, succeeding Benjamin Franklin. Rittenhouse also held the position of professor of astronomy at the University of Pennsylvania and became a foreign member of the Royal Society of London in 1795. After Benjamin Franklin, Rittenhouse was one of the leading natural philosophers in colonial America.

[*See also* Astronomy and Astrophysics; Geological Surveys; Instruments of Science; Mathematics and Statistics; Physics; Science; *and* Technology.]

BIBLIOGRAPHY

Bedini, Silvio A. "David Rittenhouse." *American National Biography Online.* New York: Oxford University Press, 2000.

Hindle, Brooke. *David Rittenhouse.* Princeton, N.J.: Princeton University Press, 1964.

Hindle, Brooke. *The Pursuit of Science in Revolutionary America.* Chapel Hill: University of North Carolina Press, 1956.

Hugh Richard Slotten

RIVERS AS TECHNOLOGICAL SYSTEMS

In the early twenty-first century, the United States had about 3 million miles (4.8 million kilometers) of rivers, including small brooks and streams. These rivers have supplied water power, transported pioneers into the country's interior, irrigated agricultural fields, spurred economic development, diluted waste, and provided recreation for generations of Americans. Until the introduction of railroads, they were the sinews of the country, enabling the growth of a market economy and connecting inland ports as well as remote riparian communities. Throughout American history, they have contributed to municipal and industrial development, and as we now better understand, they have often negatively affected ecological systems. They have also occasionally produced human tragedy, in the form of violent floods taking lives and property.

To reduce flood threats and make more efficient use of river water, Americans built a huge array of public and private dams, nearly 80,000 altogether by the early twenty-first century, of which some 6,600 were considered large dams, defined as 49 feet, 3 inches (15 meters) or higher. Behind many of these dams were reservoirs that stored about 60 percent of the entire average annual river flow in the United States. To accomplish various purposes, Americans also built thousands of miles of levees (dikes) for flood protection, placed revetment on river banks, and constructed navigation locks, weirs, and outflow and inflow channels to regulate water. They dredged rivers and cut through meanders to improve conditions for barges and other vessels, to move water downstream faster, and to reduce flood heights. Gradually, the federal government, states, and localities

developed ambitious plans to harness entire rivers to serve single or multiple purposes. Rivers became technological systems.

When people think of technological systems, often what comes to mind are automobile assembly lines, food-processing plants, steel mills, and large electrical grids. These and similar systems are composed of innumerable components under centralized control or coordination. They may cover large areas and embrace hundreds, if not thousands, of functions, although at least one function they all share: to convert inputs, whether animal, vegetable, or mineral, into outputs that satisfy specific social desires and needs. Not only human ingenuity, but also culture and social relations heavily influence the development of these systems and components, and they affect how technological artifacts are designed and used and what knowledge they employ. Yet, it is also clear that technological systems are environmentally as well as socially constructed. Available natural material dictates everything from what we eat to the structures we design and build. Fossil fuels extracted from the earth provide the energy that drives modernization, and estimates of available water help determine the design of choice for turbines and water wheels.

In all these cases, the natural world becomes a functional part of technological systems. In short, nature has agency and, in understanding what makes technological systems "work," the distinction between natural and technological components, between human and geophysical force, becomes meaningless. Nature helps shape technology and, conversely, technology significantly modifies the environment, including "natural" forests, plains, and rivers. Humans, nature, and technology mediate one another's activity.

Reflecting this understanding, historians use "envirotechnical analysis," an approach that tears down conceptual barriers between technology and environment and instead shows their interdependent and ever-changing boundaries. Although the approach illuminates analysis of any technological system, it may be particularly revealing when applied to the convergence of human and natural elements that affects geophysical processes above, on, or below the earth's surface. These processes include river flow, a part of the hydrologic cycle. Rivers as technological systems thus become especially promising subjects for envirotechnical analysis.

Our focus is on *systems*, not on components, but without advances in some of the components, modern riverine technological systems could not have developed. Most of these advances took place in the nineteenth and early twentieth centuries. They include the application of mathematical analysis to dam design, resulting in bigger but often less expensive and safer dams. The U.S. Bureau of Reclamation, established in 1902, became a pioneer in applying new mathematical analysis to dam construction. Perhaps the most important development was the trial-load method of design, which originated in the late nineteenth century. The approach allowed engineers to achieve strength through structural design rather than through the use of massive amounts of material and, thereby, to construct the thin-arch dams that dotted the Western landscape. First used at Reclamation's Pathfinder, Buffalo Bill, and Gibson dams, the trial-load method was refined in the design of Owyhee Dam in eastern Oregon and ultimately achieved its greatest success with the construction of Hoover Dam.

Other important advances in design and construction included the development of steel and the use of reinforcing bars (rebar) to strengthen concrete; new hydraulic dredges; improved methods to make and pour concrete, including the use of cold water running through small-diameter pipes to cool curing concrete, thus preventing heat-induced expansion and subsequent cracking as the concrete dried; new ways to make and lay bank revetment, mainly the work of the Army Corps of Engineers, building on ideas first advanced in Europe and Japan in the mid-nineteenth and early twentieth centuries; and new turbine designs. All these developments allowed twentieth-century engineers to think in terms of controlling an entire river in ways that their predecessors could not have imagined. Still, it is worthwhile noting that many innovations have been in the details and rest on basic technologies used to transform rivers for thousands of years.

Characteristics of Rivers as Technological Systems.

The number and kinds of projects and their economic and environmental impacts can significantly differ from one riverine technological system to another. Still, common characteristics emerge over time, even if they vary in complexity and impact.

Systems are designed and managed to meet planning objectives and to regulate flow in response to multiple political and legal requirements. These goals may be difficult to achieve, especially in times of catastrophic floods or extended droughts. They often necessitate control over most of the river's navigable length and, possibly, its tributaries. Operators coordinate their work, either directly or through an operations center, following guidelines that ensure all components—including dams, hydroelectric turbines, and locks—work correctly. Political compromise will necessitate compromise at the operational level.

Vertical and horizontal intergovernmental coordination. Local, state, and federal agencies coordinate with each other and with other agencies at all levels of government, as appropriate. Coordination includes the establishment of an administrative arrangement through existing or new legal agreements, which may include the creation of a centralized authority. Political sponsors agree on project purposes, project design, and general operating principles and delegate to administrative bodies sufficient authority to manage operations. These bodies work with governmental agencies and, in some cases, private companies, when they share operation and maintenance responsibilities.

Nature and technology determine operational parameters. The river's input is water, and nature determines the channel shape, volume and velocity of the water, and kind and amount of sediment. With human intervention come levees and dams to confine, divert, or release water depending on project purposes and operational rules. Other possible measures include dredging to eliminate silt behind dams, deepen the river's bed, and remove sandbars; locks to regulate water levels to raise and lower barges and towboats; bank revetment, which protects river banks from erosion, engine wash from vessel traffic, and caving; and pumps, pipes, and channels to assist in irrigation, flood control, and hydropower production. Still, all this technology can do only so much in the face of major floods or droughts. Technology and nature determine the operating parameters of this envirotechnical system, with the engineer as mediator.

The industrialization of river water. A river's output includes tangible and intangible benefits. These benefits include more reliable navigation, hydropower production, and water for irrigation or municipal and industrial use. They may also include recreation and flood control. None of these are artifacts; there is no finished product in the usual sense. Yet, in some ways the water has been processed; its chemistry—trace elements and organic material—is different than before it entered the system. Its temperature may have changed, and doubtless its velocity and flow variations have. All this modifies habitat both for animals and for vegetation, reducing or eliminating some species and introducing new species; significant ecological disconnections develop. What was once naturally running water has become a kind of waste water, not because it necessarily contains waste products or endangers public health (although it may), but because it performed mostly industrial work—carrying a vessel, producing hydropower, or even staying behind a dam to reduce flooding—and once it has fulfilled its assigned functions, it is discarded "as is" and returned to nature. A shorthand way of saying this, building on a term popularized by historian Eva Jakobsson, is that *the river water has become industrialized.* This change is perhaps the most salient feature of rivers as technological systems. The paradox at the heart of this description is that the term "industrialized," closely associated with modernization and human activity, is used to describe ecological transformation.

River basin consequences. Not only do dams and other structures produce massive ecological disconnections and environmental consequences in the water, but also they alter their river basins. Changes in river flow may lower groundwater tables, increase salt levels in floodplains, reduce wildlife dependent on fish, and increase pollution (threatening communities downstream). Large dams and reservoirs, recent studies conclude, may even affect precipitation patterns. On the other hand, regulatory dams, such as those on the Upper Mississippi River, can provide excellent upstream pools for fish and wildlife.

Federalism and River Development. The Founding Fathers developed a system of governments within government that provided never-ending challenges to the development of "internal improvements," a term that has evolved into what we now call "infrastructure," including water projects. It should be recalled that many early Americans swore first allegiance to the states, not to the federal government, and that the role of centralized government in the development of internal improvements generated intense debate. The Constitution does not mention internal improvements and provides no affirmative authority for federal involvement in such activities. Yet neither does it proscribe the activity, allowing advocates to argue that the development of internal improvements is a legitimate function of the central government. The ambiguity produced a constitutional quagmire—and also a platform upon which all sorts of larger issues dealing with the role of government could be debated. It continues to do so to this day.

It soon became clear that states could not build all of the road and water projects desired for transportation and communication. They had neither the funds nor the expertise. Many politicians hoped that private corporations could supply the capital and the talent, but private endeavors proved insufficient, especially as economic downturns frustrated some of the most ambitious projects. Large construction efforts, which crossed state lines, provided interior lines of communication for military movements and promised vast economic and commercial development, but also required a more dependable force of engineers responsible to the national government. The U.S. Army Corps of Engineers seemed the obvious choice for the assignment.

The Corps of Engineers traces its origins to the Revolutionary War, but it was mustered out of service at the end of the war, only to be reestablished permanently in 1802, when it also received the responsibility to supervise the newly established military academy at West Point. Although Congress charged the Corps with surveying various rivers in the trans-Appalachian West in the decade following the War of 1812, only in 1824, following a key Supreme Court decision (*Gibbons v. Ogden*) that sanctioned federal control over interstate commerce, did it begin to authorize the Corps to improve rivers for navigation. From these modest beginnings sprang a water resources program that eventually involved the Corps of Engineers in nationwide river development, including flood control, water power, water supply, and recreation, in addition to navigation. The program mushroomed after the Civil War, despite continuing reservations on the part of numerous congressmen over the constitutional propriety of the federal government financing and constructing water projects. In 2012, the Corps included over 30 thousand civilians and several hundred military officers, who held most of the major leadership positions.

Riverine Technological Systems to the 1920s.

Rivers beckoned early Americans, who sought to bring towns and farms, markets, and industry to the land beyond the Appalachians. The mountains themselves proved the most formidable obstacles to westward expansion, but rapids, sandbars, and sawyers (tree limbs sticking up from the river bottom) could also prevent use of the rivers or even rip open a vessel and threaten life and property. For some, canals were the answer. They could parallel unruly rivers and eliminate the perils, connect rivers, and even cut through mountains. For others, the answer was somehow to tame the rivers. These were the people—politicians, merchants, farmers, shippers, and local boosters—who set the nation on a course leading to the emergence of large riverine technological systems.

The Ohio River.

The nearly thousand-mile-long (1.6 thousand kilometers) Ohio River navigation system was arguably the first major riverine technological system in the United States. The river's basin covers an area the size of France. Even before the first white settlers appeared, Native Americans had modified the river's course to form fish traps or to remove obstacles in the way of their canoes. When Anglo-European settlers migrated west, they began a series of river projects to eliminate rapids and other obstacles that threatened navigation. The work became more intense and competitive in the early nineteenth century with a growing rivalry between Pittsburgh and Wheeling, West Virginia, which the National Road reached in 1818. The road began in Maryland, and when it reached Wheeling, suddenly that town became the favored river port, especially because the stretch of river extending to Pittsburgh decreased in depth, had numerous navigation obstacles, and suffered tremendously during droughts. In 1821, the state of Pennsylvania contributed $15,000 to help clear the river channel south of Pittsburgh. Then, subsequent to congressional authorization and appropriation, from 1824 to 1875 the Corps of Engineers attempted to improve the river for commerce and travel, primarily using dredges to deepen the river depth, snagboats to remove tree limbs and other obstructions, and wing dams to increase the river's velocity to scour and deepen the navigation channel.

In 1879 civilian engineer William Milnor Roberts proposed a staircase of 66 locks and dams to lift vessels 450 feet (137 meters) from Cairo, Illinois, at the mouth of the Ohio, to Pittsburgh and to maintain a 6-foot (1.83-meter) navigation channel. Congress authorized the first lock and dam at Davis Island, 5 miles (8 kilometers) below Pittsburgh, in 1875. The lock's 600 by 110 foot dimension (183 by 33.5 meters) became standard on the Ohio River and elsewhere in the United States. From 1890 on, other congressional acts and appropriations authorized six more locks and dams, all built by 1908. Two years previously, a Corps of Engineers officer board had recommended that the Ohio River channel be increased to a 9-foot (2.74-meter) depth to accommodate larger towboats (powered by newly developed diesel engines) and larger tows capable of carrying huge amounts of coal, coke, petroleum products, aggregates, chemical, iron and steel, and other products coming from the Ohio River basin. The board also recommended a total of 54 locks and dams. Congress approved both recommendations in 1910. Once more modified in the years following authorization, the final 9-foot channel, completed in 1929, featured 51 wicket dams, with gates that went up and down to regulate water flow.

The Lower Mississippi River.   The entire Mississippi River watershed drains an area of 1,250,000 square miles (3.2 million square kilometers), stretching from the Rocky Mountains to the Appalachians, embracing slightly over 40 percent of the continental United States and two Canadian provinces. From its source at Lake Itasca, Minnesota, to the Gulf of Mexico, the river is 2,340 miles long (3,700 kilometers), making it the fifth longest in the world. If one measures from the mouth of the Mississippi River to the headwaters of the Missouri, however, the length is 3,892 miles (6,200 kilometers), a distance exceeded only by the Nile and Amazon rivers. The average flow of water in the Mississippi is the sixth largest in the world and equal to the total flow from all other rivers in the contiguous United States that do not empty into the Mississippi. All this water comes through the state of Louisiana into the Gulf of Mexico. The 32,000-square-mile (94,000-square-kilometer) Lower Mississippi Valley is 25 to 125 miles (40 to 200 kilometers) in width and stretches southward about 950 river miles (1,535 kilometers) from Cairo, Illinois, where the Ohio River meets the Mississippi, to the Gulf of Mexico. Below St. Louis, 180 river miles (290 kilometers) above Cairo, a 9-foot navigation channel is maintained without the need for locks and dams. South of Baton Rouge, the river is deep enough to accommodate ocean-going vessels.

Levee building on the Lower Mississippi began soon after the French founded New Orleans in 1718. As the population grew and commerce increased, the French and then the Spanish continued to expand the levee line northward. By 1812, when Louisiana became a state, just nine years after the Louisiana Purchase, the levee line had been extended 155 miles (250 kilometers) up the east bank of the Mississippi and 185 miles (300 kilometers)

up the west bank. Further levee construction followed a disastrous flood in 1828, so that by around 1850, levees extended some 600 miles (965 kilometers) from New Orleans nearly to the mouth of the Arkansas River on the west bank of the Mississippi. The levees were modest in size, rising from 4.5 to about 8 feet in height (1.37 to 2.4 meters). The highest levee had a 33-foot base (10 meters).

With increased commerce on the Mississippi and the rise of steamboat lines, calls came for federal aid to reduce flood threats and remove various obstacles endangering vessels plying up and down the river. Finally, in September 1850, responding to the pleas of southern congressmen seeking federal assistance to fight periodic disastrous flooding along the Lower Mississippi, Congress appropriated $50,000 for a topographical and hydrographical survey of the Mississippi Delta, including a study of the best means of securing a 20-foot navigation channel at the Mississippi's mouth. After 11 years of work, interrupted by other assignments and sickness, Captain Andrew A. Humphreys and Lieutenant Henry L. Abbot of the Corps of Topographical Engineers (separated from the Corps of Engineers in 1838 and recombined in 1863) completed their massive *Report upon the Physics and Hydraulics of the Mississippi River*; the survey is often simply referred to as the Humphreys–Abbot report.

Humphreys and Abbot provided a great deal of new information and examined old reports, but they ultimately concluded that a combination of geological, fluvial, and economic circumstances argued in favor of relying on "levees only" to control flooding along the Lower Mississippi. Costly reservoirs, cut-offs, and outlets were not needed. The Corps of Engineers accepted these conclusions for nearly 60 years, not only for the Lower Mississippi but also for other large rivers. The levees-only policy profoundly affected the manner in which the United States developed its water resources. Indeed, the influence of the Humphreys–Abbot report extended past World War II, despite the fact that by then Congress had authorized hundreds of reservoir projects.

In 1879, Congress created a joint civilian–military Mississippi River Commission (MRC) to develop and implement plans to improve navigation and flood control on the Lower Mississippi. The MRC worked through the Corps of Engineers to accomplish its mission. In the following decades, local levee districts and other political entities built most of the levees. The MRC's major activities centered on improving the navigation channel through dredging and constructing training dikes; protecting the river's banks; and providing relief operations to rescue stranded refugees during floods. Until 1890, Congress stipulated that federal levees be constructed only to improve navigation and not to protect land from floods. Finally, in 1917, Congress passed the first federal flood control legislation, exclusively for the Mississippi and Sacramento rivers. It provided funds on a cost-shared basis for both rivers. By the time a major flood disaster hit the Lower Mississippi in 1927, over half of the total investment in flood control and navigation improvements along the river dating back to the early nineteenth century had come from local interests.

The Upper Mississippi River.   Steamboat navigation on the Upper Mississippi River (above St. Louis) began in the early 1820s, but just above Keokuk, Iowa, and Rock Island, Illinois, rapids extended for several miles and threatened waterborne commerce. Settlers and commercial agents pleaded for assistance, and the federal government, through the Army Corps of Engineers, blasted a channel through the Des Moines Rapids above Keokuk in 1838–1839. Lieutenant Robert E. Lee supervised the effort. Then, in 1854, the Corps straightened, deepened, and widened the channel above Rock Island, while also dredging the river and removing limbs and other obstacles. Without additional funds, however, the Corps ceased work in 1856, with the projects at Rock Island and Keokuk still uncompleted.

After the Civil War, work resumed, and soon Midwesterners demanded more improvements. St. Paul, Minnesota, had become an important port, with factories and mills lining the river. Merchants and entrepreneurs lobbied Congress for assistance. They hoped to become a commercial and industrial power matching economic centers on the East Coast, and waterborne commerce was very much a part of their plan. In response, Con-

gress authorized several navigation projects, beginning with a 4-foot (1.22-meter) channel in 1866; a 4.5-foot (1.37-meter) channel in 1878 (before the 4-foot channel had been completed); and a 6-foot channel (1.83-meter) in 1907, after river improvement organizations protested that the 4.5-foot channel was no longer adequate.

By the 1920s most waterway boosters thought the still uncompleted 6-foot channel also inadequate, especially in light of a 9-foot (2.74-meter) congressionally authorized channel the Corps maintained below St. Louis, which accommodated larger vessels. Business interests lobbied Congress and held meetings in the Midwest to promote waterway improvements. Agitation ended in 1930, with congressional authorization for a 9-foot Upper Mississippi channel, despite the reservations of the district engineer, Major Charles Hall, who questioned the economics of a project that called for 24 locks and dams (23 were eventually built; 3 already existed) and also raised concerns about damage to fish and wildlife.

Modern Riverine Technological Systems.   In the twentieth century, the most successful efforts to turn rivers into technological systems responded to common concerns that crossed state lines. While the need for flood control and navigation improvements remained important considerations, the demand for irrigation water in the west and for electrical energy throughout the nation often proved decisive in the approval of new and expensive riverine systems. Irrigation required technological, legal, and institutional arrangements to allocate scare water supply, while the need for electricity turned many of the nation's rivers into vast sources of hydropower.

The Colorado River.   The Colorado River is the only dependable water supply for 244,000 square miles (632,000 square kilometers), a region encompassing parts of seven western states. Its headwaters begin with its Green River tributary in Wyoming's Wind River Range, and from there the river wends its way 1,400 miles (2,250 kilometers) toward the Gulf of California. Its annual flow of about 15 million acre-feet (1 acre-foot covers 1 acre with 1 foot of water, or about 326,000 gallons), or about 18.5 billion cubic meters, ranks it sixth among American rivers. In 2012, more than 20 dams stood on the Colorado and its tributaries, which largely accounted for the fact that none of its water actually reached the Gulf. The Morelos Diversion Dam, constructed by Mexico in 1950, stood just south of the border between the two countries and diverted almost all remaining water to the Mexicali Valley.

Nowhere did the need for hydropower and irrigation, to which water supply for southern California later was added, generate more debate than in the Colorado River Basin. In 1922, all the basin states of the Colorado River Basin (except Arizona, which did not ratify the compact until 1944) signed the Colorado River Compact, which apportioned the Colorado's water between the Upper Basin states (Colorado, Wyoming, Utah, and New Mexico) and those of the Lower Basin (California, Nevada, and Arizona). Congress approved the compact in December 1928 and authorized the construction of a great multipurpose dam in the Black Canyon of the Colorado: Boulder (Hoover) Dam. The congressional action initiated an era of regional arrangements designed to make more efficient use of the nation's rivers. Generally, these regional compacts reflected hardheaded political calculations more than farsighted planning. When Boulder Dam was authorized, few anticipated a string of large dams stretching from the mountains of Colorado and Wyoming all the way to the Mexican border.

The debate over the construction of Boulder Dam illuminated profound divisions in American society over several significant issues: whether the Colorado River water belonged to the states or to the national government; whether the Colorado River was navigable; and whether public or private interests should develop water power. In the end, Congress concluded that the Colorado River was at least technically navigable (and therefore subject to the Commerce Clause of the Constitution); that it was also an international stream because it flowed into Mexico; and that—despite intensive lobbying by private power companies— the welfare of the people could best be served in this case through the public sector.

This last point was the most contentious. Three times Congress had considered the Colorado River Compact before it finally approved it and Boulder Dam construction in the 1928 Boulder Canyon Project Act. By that time, many people had decided that private power interests were irresponsible and untrustworthy monopolies, and Congress, too, had become less favorably disposed to private hydropower development. More support also came from Southern legislators, who repaid western congressmen for backing a major Mississippi River flood control act in early 1928. Unquestionably, too, approval of Boulder Dam construction partially rested on the promise that hydropower sales would eventually reimburse the federal government for dam construction.

In sum, passage of the Boulder Canyon Project Act affirmed a strong federal role in hydropower development. It also ensured that the Bureau of Reclamation would be a major player in the development and distribution of water in the west— and that the Colorado River would be among the most heavily regulated rivers in the United States, if not in the world. In 2012, all the large reservoirs and dams in the Colorado River Basin were owned and operated by the U.S. Bureau of Reclamation, which became the largest electric utility in the 17 western states it served.

Hoover Dam (called Boulder Dam from 1933 to 1947) was the first high dam built on the Colorado. The Bureau of Reclamation began its construction in 1931 and finished the dam in 1936, a remarkable feat considering the many engineering and design challenges. The dam spans the Colorado at the Nevada–Arizona state line 35 miles (56.3 kilometers) southeast of Las Vegas, Nevada. Viewed as one of the marvels of twentieth-century civil engineering, its height of 726 feet (221.28 meters) makes it the highest concrete dam in the Western Hemisphere. Its crest length of 1,244 feet (379 meters) and spillway capacity of 270,000 cubic feet per second, or cfs (7645.5 cubic meters per second, or cms; 1 cubic foot of water is approximately equal to 7.5 gallons) are also impressive. Lake Mead, the reservoir behind the dam, can store nearly 29 million acre-feet of water (35.8 billion cubic meters). The reservoir provides water for municipal and industrial use, for irrigation, and

for the 17 turbines at Hoover Dam, which annually supplies about 4 billion kilowatts of
electricity.

Glen Canyon Dam, 15 miles upstream (24 kilometers) from Lees Ferry, Arizona, the dividing
line between the upper and lower Colorado River
basins, was built from 1956 to 1966. It is a 710-
foot (216.41-meter) concrete arch dam with a
crest length of 1,560 feet (475.5 meters). Lake
Powell, the reservoir behind Glen Canyon, has a
27 million acre-feet (33.3 billion cubic meters) capacity, more than the total storage capacity of the
rest of the Colorado River Storage Project, which
was authorized by Congress in 1956 to provide
for the development of the Upper Basin. The
dam's power plant contains eight turbines, which
can generate altogether 1,021,248 kilowatts. The
eight penstocks that convey water to the turbines
are 14–15 feet (4.3–4.6 meters) in diameter. Glen
Canyon Dam was controversial when first built
and remains so. Environmentalists have passion-
ately denounced the dam and Lake Powell for
wasting and degrading water, inundating cultural
sites and natural landmarks, destroying wilderness, and threatening ecological communities.
With equal passion, supporters have pointed to
the dam's economic benefits.

Other storage dams with significant capacity
include the 502-foot-high (153-meter) Flaming
Gorge Dam on the Green River in northeastern
Utah, whose reservoir can store up to 3.79 million
acre-feet (4.7 billion cubic meters); the earthfill
200-foot-high (61-meter) Davis Dam on the Colorado River, 67 miles (108 kilometers) downstream from Hoover Dam, whose reservoir holds
up to 1.8 million acre-feet (2.2 billion cubic meters);
and the 402-foot (122.5-meter) Navajo Dam on
the San Juan River in Northeastern New Mexico,
with a reservoir capable of storing 1.71 million
acre-feet (2.1 billion cubic meters).

Dams on the Colorado River, especially Glen
Canyon, have irreversibly changed the transportation of sediment and nutrients that historically
supported downstream aquatic and terrestrial ecological systems. Perhaps the most dramatic man-
ifestation of this process is the Colorado River in
the Grand Canyon. The aquatic ecosystem there
was so dramatically changed that it could be con-

sidered a humanly created system dominated by
non-native species. Salinity, too, remained an issue
in the early twenty-first century. About one half of
the salinity in the Colorado River Basin has come
from natural sources such as thermal springs, but
irrigation, reservoir evaporation, and transbasin
diversions have also increased salinity. Highly
saline water can degrade plumbing, lower crop
yields, increase water treatment costs, and create
an undesirable taste in drinking water. In the 1980s,
water experts estimated that each year the heavy
salt burden of 9–10 million tons costs users more
than $113 million. The federal government de-
voted considerable resources to reducing the salt
burden, but the problem still existed in the early
twenty-first century and became particularly damaging during low flows.

The Columbia–Snake River system. As
elsewhere in the country, early federal efforts in the
Northwest focused on navigation improvements,
and by 1915 the Corps of Engineers had completed a number of navigation projects stretching
from Lewiston, Idaho, on the Snake River and
Priest Falls on the Columbia all the way to the Pacific Ocean. Still, river traffic on the lower Snake
actually declined and had just about vanished by
1920. The problem was partly seasonal. Boats could
ply the Snake during spring's high water, but harvest arrived in the fall, when river depths were too
low to support commercial river transportation.
Railroads became the preferred option.

Multipurpose basin development came slowly.
In the early twentieth century, navigation advocates from the Snake River area, navigation and hydropower proponents from the lower and middle
Columbia basin regions, and irrigation interests in
the upper Columbia basin in Washington State
championed their own causes with little coordination and occasionally in competition with one another. From 1919 to 1922, the state of Washington
funded several Columbia basin irrigation studies.
Washington senators obtained funds for federal
studies in 1923. Later in the decade the state initiated negotiations with other basin states over the
distribution of water, and it sought congressional
authorization for an irrigation project. Business
groups from Spokane, Ephrata, and Wenatchee

actively campaigned for a dam both to supply irrigation water and to provide hydropower. Conflicting or at least overlapping economic interests promised little in the way of coordinated planning.

The situation changed dramatically in 1925, when a federal act called on the Corps of Engineers and the Federal Power Commission to develop estimates for surveying the nation's major rivers and for developing recommendations for their multipurpose development. The Corps submitted the estimates in 1926, and they were printed in House Document 308. Early the next year, Congress authorized the reports, which became known as "308 [three-o-eight] reports." When the 1,845-page report on the Columbia and its tributaries appeared in 1931, it became the rallying point for Columbia River basin development, with hydropower replacing the earlier emphasis on navigation and irrigation. It recommended a series of storage dams on the upper Columbia for hydropower and irrigation and, further downstream, locks and run-of-the-river dams with little storage capability for navigation and hydropower. Hydropower production would pay for much of the investment in both irrigation and navigation infrastructure.

Although controversy continued on the number of dams, their height, impacts on anadromous fish, and associated issues, the general outline of the Columbia River technological system emerged. Subsequent discussions ended with the Bureau of Reclamation and the Corps sharing the construction of storage dams for hydropower and irrigation, although the Bureau received the major prize (and challenge) of building Grand Coulee Dam, one of the largest hydropower dams in the world. Undoubtedly, the fact that the nation was in the middle of the Great Depression catalyzed the decision to implement much of the 308 report. Projects such as Grand Coulee and the Corps-constructed Bonneville Lock and Dam provided thousands of jobs, and hydropower promised to transform the Northwest.

Neither Congress nor the Corps expressed early enthusiasm for building locks and dams on the Snake River because the costs did not justify the benefits. Supporters of improved Snake River navigation, especially the Inland Empire Waterways Association, founded in 1934, worked mightily to gain congressional support, but suc-

ceeded only after World War II. As with most of the other projects in the Columbia basin, hydropower, not navigation, became the main justification for building Snake River locks and dams. At the beginning of the twenty-first century, hydropower dams provided 75 percent of the Pacific Northwest's electricity, storage dams irrigated 7.8 million acres (31565.5 square kilometers) of Columbia basin land, and the navigation channel was maintained at a depth of 40 feet (12.2 meters) for the first 106 miles (170.6 kilometers) of the Columbia River and 14 feet (4.27 meters) for the remaining 359 miles (577.75 kilometers) of the Columbia–Snake River navigation system. The entire coordinated Columbia–Snake River system also embraced nonfederal public utility dams and, through international agreements, dams in the Columbia basin on the Canadian side of the border.

The Ohio River.   Early work to convert the Ohio River into a technological system focused on navigation improvements, but in the 1930s Congress approved a Corps plan to construct an ambitious system of 78 storage dams on Ohio River tributaries, primarily to help reduce flooding. By 1988, when the last dam was being constructed, the storage dams could considerably influence flow levels on the Ohio River. Still, these dams controlled water in only a third of the basin, so neither floods nor droughts could be entirely prevented.

Meanwhile, navigation work also progressed. The latest modifications began in the 1950s, with the Ohio River Navigation Modernization Program. Several factors necessitated this program: the deterioration of locks and dams; increased traffic volume, especially upstream; a larger number of barges used in each tow; traffic jams at locks; and demands from industry, terminals, and pleasure and recreation boat operators for uniform water supply and stable flows. Numerous funding and technological challenges have delayed this program, which is now projected for completion by 2024. Once completed, it will have reduced the 51 navigation pools to 19 pools, some stretching up to 100 miles (161 kilometers) upstream. The pools are designed to maintain a 9-foot depth on the Ohio River even during severe drought, substantially improve navigation conditions, and increase hydropower. New locks twice the length of the old ones accommodate longer tows pushed by more powerful towboats. This enhances both safety and efficiency and reduces transportation costs for agriculture and industry. A typical 1,500-ton barge carries as much as 15 large railroad hopper cars or 58 trucks. Even though uncompleted, the modernization program contributed to a steady growth in river traffic in the last quarter of the twentieth century.

The Operation of a Riverine Technological System: The Lower Mississippi as a Case Study.

The 1928 Flood Control Act followed the disastrous flood that hit the Lower Mississippi the previous year. The flood killed between 250 and 500 people, flooded over 16 million acres, and destroyed 41,000 buildings. Over 600,000 people found their way to temporary refugee camps. The act dispensed once and for all with dependence on levees only for protecting the lower Mississippi Valley. Instead, it authorized the vastly ambitious Mississippi River and Tributaries (MR&T) project and charged the Army Corps of Engineers with its construction (through private contractors), operation, and supervision.

Conceived for both flood control and navigation improvements, the MR&T project entails tributary reservoirs, outlets, floodways, revetment, dredging, and various other flood-control projects in addition to levees. Except for the donation of land, easements, and rights of way for the main-stem Mississippi River levees and for local maintenance of flood-control works, the project was to be built at full federal cost. The act was both a technological and a political experiment, and much subsequent tinkering occurred in both areas, especially as the Great Depression hit the country and the demand for work relief projects grew. In contrast to the design of the Colorado River technological system, here there was no interstate compact to regulate water use and no formal state approval. Although the federal government's right to regulate interstate navigation had long been recognized, the 1928 act signifi-

cantly expanded its role in planning, implementing, and managing interstate flood-control projects. It pushed back the boundaries of national administration in an area—flood control—where doubts had long been expressed about the government's constitutional right to be involved at all.

At the beginning of the twenty-first century, the MR&T Project provided the largest and most sophisticated flood-control system in the world. The Corps of Engineers supervises the project, but it works closely with local interests. The project also needs to be closely coordinated with other riverine technological systems that join the Mississippi's. Indeed, the Upper Mississippi, Lower Mississippi, Tennessee, Ohio, Missouri, Red, and Arkansas rivers can all be called large technological systems. The Missouri's six main stem dams provide hydropower, navigation, recreation, water supply, and flood control. Behind them are some of the nation's largest reservoirs. Locks and dams on the Arkansas (McClellan–Kerr Arkansas River Navigation System) ensure navigation from the Tulsa, Oklahoma, area to the Mississippi River. Storage dams on Arkansas River tributaries provide water supply, hydropower, and flood control, whereas locks and dams on the Red, Upper Mississippi, and Ohio rivers allow navigation to and from Shreveport, Minneapolis, and Pittsburgh, respectively.

Four principal elements constitute the MR&T Project: (1) nearly 3,800 miles (6,115 kilometers) of federal levees and floodwalls, of which a little over 1,600 miles (2,575 kilometers) of levees are along the main-stem Mississippi River, extending north to Cape Girardeau, Missouri, some 50 miles (80 kilometers) above the junction of the Mississippi and Ohio rivers; (2) four floodways to divert flood water; (3) channel improvements and stabilization works to protect levees and other flood-control features from erosion; and (4) tributary improvements, such as dams and pumping plants. The project provides protection from the largest river flood that could reasonably be expected to occur (not the largest flood possible). This is known as the "project flood." The Corps calculated this flood to be 3 million cfs or 84,500 cms at Red River Landing, some 63 miles (100 kilometers) above Baton Rouge, or approximately one-fifth greater than the disastrous flood that hit the Lower Mississippi Valley in 1927. Although the initial calculation was somewhat arbitrary, subsequent analyses showed that the figure was realistic.

The four floodways divert floodwaters to reduce necessary levee heights along the Mississippi River. Beginning at the northern end of the system, the Birds Point–New Madrid Floodway in Missouri relieves floodwaters at Cairo, Illinois, which lies at the confluence of the Ohio and Mississippi rivers. The floodway varies in width from 3 to 10 miles (5 to 16 kilometers), has a length of about 35 miles (57 kilometers), and includes an area of some 210 square miles (550 square kilometers). Two fuseplug levees, constructed to a lower height than the main-stem levees and which will naturally overtop, were designed to divert 550,000 cfs (15,500 cms) from the Mississippi River into the floodway.

Further downstream, opposite Red River Landing, the Old River Control Structure and an even larger auxiliary structure prevent the Atchafalaya River from capturing the Mississippi's flow, a potentially catastrophic event that mid-twentieth-century geologists had predicted would happen by around 1975. Normally, the Old River Control Complex maintains the 1950 flow distribution between the Mississippi River and the Atchafalaya River at 70 and 30 percent, respectively. During a project flood, 680,000 cfs (19,000 cms) of water would be diverted from the Mississippi and Red rivers into the Atchafalaya River. The West Atchafalaya Floodway, bordering the west side of the Atchafalaya River, could handle 250,000 cfs (7,000 cms) of floodwater. When a fuseplug levee at the head of the floodway is breached or when the levee on the west side of the Atchafalaya River is overtopped, the floodway comes into operation, but as of 2012 this has never occurred.

Thirty-nine miles (63 kilometers) further south, the Morganza Diversion Structure diverts up to 600,000 cfs (17,000 cms) from the Mississippi River into the Morganza Floodway during a project flood. Completed in 1954, the structure is about 3,900 feet (1,200 meters) in length. Before 2012 it was used only twice, the last time in 2011. In the event of a project flood, floodwaters from

the West Atchafalaya Floodway, the Atchafalaya River, and the Morganza Floodway—half of the total project flood—would converge in the Atchafalaya Basin and flow into the Gulf of Mexico via Berwick Bay and the Corps-built Wax Lake Outlet.

About 30 miles (48 kilometers) above New Orleans, the Bonnet Carré Floodway diverts floodwater from the Mississippi River into Lake Pontchartrain. The structure is about 7,200 feet (2,200 meters) long and the floodway extends about 5.7 miles (9 kilometers) from the river to Lake Pontchartrain. Designed to protect New Orleans, the project has a capacity of 250,000 cfs (7,050 cms) and is operated to keep the Mississippi River flow downstream from exceeding 1,250,000 cfs (35,200 cms). The remaining project flood flows past New Orleans and on to the Gulf of Mexico, confined by levees and floodwalls.

Riverine Technological Systems, Large and Small.

In the early twenty-first century, the entire U.S. riverine technological system was the most developed river system in the world and included major national rivers as well as smaller rivers of regional importance. For instance, pursuant to congressional authorization in 1938, the Corps of Engineers built 19 flood-control dams in the Connecticut River basin in New England, along with levees, floodwalls, and pumping stations on the main stem to help protect urban areas. In 2012 the Corps operated and maintained the 14 main-stem run-of-the river dams, whereas nonfederal interests operated and maintained the rest of the flood-control system, including five dams on the tributaries. Further south, along the border between South Carolina and Georgia, the Savannah River began to be developed for navigation by the Corps of Engineers in the late nineteenth century. Decreased commerce above Augusta, Georgia, doomed navigation plans on the upper part of the river, but the Corps completed a six-foot navigation channel from Savannah to Augusta by 1939. Declining commerce eventually resulted in a complete cessation of navigation maintenance and improvements above Savannah Harbor. Flood control, however, became a growing concern, and the

Corps built three large dams on the headwaters and upper reaches of the Savannah River in the decades following World War II. These multipurpose dams provided flood control, water supply, hydropower, and recreation benefits and significantly improved the quality of life in the river's basin.

Numerous other technological systems have transformed rivers such as the Lower Fox in Wisconsin, the Illinois, and the Kentucky (all for navigation) and the Muskingum in Ohio (for flood control). In Mississippi, four flood-control dams and reservoirs on tributaries leading into the Yazoo River, in combination with downstream channel improvements and levees, reduced flood damage and also provided recreation opportunities. Like so many other water projects, these dams began to be built during the Great Depression in the 1930s. Because the Corps had concluded that costs exceeded benefits for the dams, they probably would not have been built at all were it not for the work they provided during the depression and the efforts of the local congressman, William M. Whittington, whose hometown, Greenwood, was nearly wiped out by a flood in 1932. Grenada, the last and most economically questionable dam for the Yazoo system, began operating in 1954.

Two Pathbreaking Systems. Among the many examples of riverine technological systems, two stand out as especially important landmarks: the development of flood control on the Great Miami River in Ohio and the creation in the Tennessee River Valley of perhaps the first true multipurpose system designed to vitalize an entire region.

Great Miami River. In 1913, the worst flood on record hit the Miami Valley in Ohio, claiming more than three hundred lives. Following the flood, Dayton's civic leaders raised more than $2 million from 23 thousand persons to fight future flood threats, but they soon realized that the entire 4,000-square-mile (10,350 square kilometers) valley had to be organized if floods were to be fought effectively. Although the Ohio legislature resisted, Dayton's leaders pushed through

a conservancy act in 1914 that established the Miami Conservancy District. The act gave the district the right to levy assessments, borrow money, and condemn land to provide flood protection. This provided the financial and physical foundations that enabled the conservancy to build five flood-control dams. The plans and final designs for these dams resulted from the work of many exceptionally gifted engineers, who pioneered approaches to calculating future flood threats, determining flow velocity, and developing river-stage forecasting services. All these advances influenced a generation of river engineers. Equally important, the district provided a template for the establishment of nonfederal legal authorities capable of converting rivers into technological systems.

Tennessee River. In the nineteenth and early twentieth centuries, the Army Corps of Engineers sought to provide safe navigation on the Tennessee River from Knoxville to the river's mouth, where it emptied into the Ohio River. Most attention was given to the construction of canals around Muscle Shoals, Colbert Shoals, and Bee Tree Falls in Northern Alabama and, subsequently, to the construction of dams and navigation locks, which led to the abandonment of the canals. The dams provided both hydropower and navigation pools, with Wilson Dam being the largest concrete structure in the world upon its completion in 1927. Further downstream, Corps operations focused on dredging and removing obstructions to gain a 4.5-foot (1.37-meter) navigation depth.

All these efforts paled, however, in comparison with President Franklin D. Roosevelt's vision of a Tennessee Valley Authority (TVA) that would power industry, husband natural resources, encourage agriculture, and reduce flood damage. Notably, when Congress established the TVA in May 1933, it charged the agency with both the conservation and the development of the Tennessee Valley. What this actually meant provoked heated discussion. Eventually, the agency's responsibilities included navigation, flood control, hydropower, soil conservation, forest protection, fertilizer production, and, more generally, improving the quality of life in a region four-fifths the size of England. Even more surprising than its broad charge was its authority. Congress gave the agency self-authorizing power—TVA did not need congressional approval for its projects, and it received congressional appropriations in lump sums.

By 1950, TVA had canalized the Tennessee River from Paducah to Knoxville with a system of nine locks and dams, including two projects (Wilson and Hales Bar) built by the Corps before TVA was established. The projects raised and lowered vessels a total of 600 feet (183 meters), or about a foot per mile. After 1950, TVA enlarged numerous locks, replaced Hales Bar Dam, and completed a new dam and lock in 1963 on the Clinch River to the east of Knoxville that increased the total length of the navigation system to 750 miles (1,207 kilometers). The Corps of Engineers continues to operate the locks and maintain the entire channel at a 9-foot navigation depth. Cities and private industries built terminals to accommodate the increased cargo.

By 1945, TVA had also built nine storage dams on the tributaries of the Tennessee and had purchased several small steam plants and five small dams from the Tennessee Electric Power Company. More storage dams came after World War II, providing flood control, hydropower, water supply, and recreation. Beginning in the 1960s, TVA set out on a massive nuclear power program and converted itself into, first and foremost, an energy company. Although occasionally scholars have questioned TVA's success and cost-effectiveness in developing the Tennessee Valley, few question the ambition and the scope of a technological system that has inspired imitation around the world.

Success and Failure.   As the United States transformed its rivers, it transformed itself. In the early twenty-first century, the image of the country was intimately connected to the hydropower so essential to the Northwest; to a lower Mississippi flood-control system that prevented hundreds of billions of dollars in flood damages; to Colorado River water that irrigated the land, produced hydropower, and enabled the growth of the Southwest; to Missouri River dams that turned much of

that river into a chain of huge lakes serving multiple purposes; and to the locks and dams on the Upper Mississippi and the Ohio that were essential for industry and commerce. Elsewhere, and on a somewhat smaller scale, similar stories emerged. Undeniably, these systems have figuratively and literally made an imprint on the land.

The story is impressive, but not always positive. Individual components have failed. In 1976, for instance, a nearly full reservoir burst through the Bureau of Reclamation's Teton Dam on the Teton River in Southeast Idaho, a consequence of poor design decisions and various geological factors. The break caused at least 11 deaths and damaged $400 million worth of property. Elsewhere, a Corps of Engineers flaw in the design of lock gates resulted in silt shutting down the operation of newly constructed Ohio River Lock 37 in 1911–1912, delaying some traffic on the Ohio by as much as eight weeks. More seriously, inadequate geological knowledge contributed to design flaws that led to uplift and sliding of Corps of Engineers Dam 26 on the Ohio River in 1912, causing significant damage. Some other projects around the country have also suffered from design and subsequent construction flaws, often partly the result of inadequate understanding of soil and rock foundations. Frequent inspections, good communication, and the incorporation of lessons drawn from failures helped minimize problems.

Finally, the significant impact of various riverine technological systems on the environment cannot be questioned. In the early twenty-first century, engineers and water managers often focused more attention on water quality and less on water quantity, and they understood better the severe ecological disconnections that result from massive changes in a river system. Still, the degree to which the nation will—and should—change its attitudes toward the construction of large riverine technological systems remains an ongoing debate.

[*See also* **Agricultural Technology; Agriculture, U.S. Department of; Army Corps of Engineers, U.S.; Canals and Waterways; Conservation Movement; Dams and Hydraulic Engineering; Engineering; Environmentalism;**

Fish and Wildlife Service, U.S.; Fisheries and Fishing; Hoover Dam; Hydroelectric Power; Maritime Transport; Steam Power; Technology; *and* Tennessee Valley Authority.]

BIBLIOGRAPHY

Anfinson, John O. *The River We Have Wrought: A History of the Upper Mississippi.* Minneapolis: University of Minnesota Press, 2003. Anfinson is the authority on the development of the Upper Mississippi Lock and Dam system.

Barber, Henry E., and Allen R. Gunn. *A History of the Savannah District, U.S. Army Corps of Engineers.* Savannah, Ga.: Savannah District, U.S. Army Corps of Engineers, 1989.

Bigham, Darrel E. "River of Opportunity: Economic Consequences of the Ohio." In *Always a River: The Ohio River and the American Experience,* edited by Robert L. Reid, pp. 130–179. Bloomington: Indiana University Press, 1991.

Billington, David P., and Donald C. Jackson. *Big Dams of the New Deal Era: A Confluence of Engineering and Politics.* Norman: University of Oklahoma Press, 2006. Based on a study done for the Bureau of Reclamation, U.S. Army Corps of Engineers, and the National Park Service, the authors present fresh insights on the engineering of some of the largest dams in the United States.

Brown, D. Clayton. *Western Tributaries of the Mississippi.* Navigation History NWS-83-7. National Waterways Study. Alexandria, Va.: U.S. Army Engineer Water Resources Support Center, Institute for Water Resources, 1983.

Camillo, Charles A., and Matthew T. Pearcy. *Upon Their Shoulders: A History of the Mississippi River Commission from Its Inception through the Advent of the Modern Mississippi River and Tributaries Project.* Vicksburg: Mississippi River Commission, 2004. The most reliable and comprehensive history of U.S. Army Corps of Engineers work on the Lower Mississippi to about 1940.

Chandler, William U. *The Myth of TVA: Conservation and Development in the Tennessee Valley, 1933–1983.* Cambridge, Mass.: Ballinger, 1984.

Department of the Army, U.S. Army Corps of Engineers. *Authorized and Operating Purposes of Corps of Engineers Reservoirs.* Washington, D.C.: U.S. Army Corps of Engineers, 1992. A useful guide to Corps reservoirs, which lists the purposes for each project and the authorizing legislation.

El-Ashry, Mohamed T., and Diana C. Gibbons. *Troubled Waters: New Policies for Managing Water in the American West.* Washington, D.C.: World Resources Institute, 1986.

Espeland, Wendy Nelson. *The Struggle for Water: Politics, Rationality, and Identity in the American Southwest.* Chicago: University of Chicago Press, 1998.

Fradkin, Philip L. *A River No More. The Colorado River and the West.* Paperback ed. Tucson: University of Arizona Press, 1984.

Hart, Henry C. *The Dark Missouri.* Madison: University of Wisconsin Press, 1957.

Howe, Charles W., and W. Ashley Ahrens. "Water Resources of the Upper Colorado River Basin: Problems and Policy Alternatives." In *Water and Arid Lands of the Western United States,* edited by Mohamed T. El-Ashry and Diana C. Gibbons, pp. 169–232. Cambridge, U.K.: Cambridge University Press, 1988.

Hundley, Norris, Jr. *Water and the West: The Colorado River Compact and the Politics of Water in the American West.* 2d ed. Berkeley: University of California Press, 2009.

Hundley, Norris, Jr. "The West against Itself: The Colorado River—An Institutional History." In *New Courses for the Colorado River: Major Issues for the Next Century,* edited by Gary D. Weatherford and F. Lee Brown, pp. 9–49. Albuquerque: University of New Mexico Press, 1986.

Ingram, Helen. *Water Politics: Continuity and Change.* Revised 1st ed. Albuquerque: University of New Mexico Press, 1990. Explains origins and development of the 1968 Colorado River Basin Project Act, which authorized construction of the Central Arizona Project to enable Arizona to utilize fully its share of Colorado River water.

Jakobsson, Eva. *Industrialisering Av Älvar: Studier Kring Svensk Vattenkraftutbyggnad, 1900–1918* [The Industrialisation of Rivers. Studies on the Development of Swedish Hydropower, 1900–1918]. Göteborg, Sweden: University of Gothenburg, 1996.

Jansen, Robert B. *Dams and Public Safety.* Denver: U.S. Department of the Interior, Water and Power Resources Services, 1980. One of the best sources on the history and causes of dam failures around the world. The Water and Power Resources Service was the name briefly given to the Bureau of Reclamation during the administration of President Jimmy Carter.

Johnson, Leland R. "Engineering the Ohio." In *Always a River: The Ohio River and the American*

Experience, edited by Robert L. Reid, pp. 180–209. Bloomington: Indiana University Press, 1991.

Johnson, Leland R. *The Ohio River Division, U.S. Army Corps of Engineers: The History of a Central Command*. Cincinnati: U.S. Army Corps of Engineers, Ohio River Division, 1992. Johnson is the authority on the history of locks and dams in the Ohio River Basin.

Johnson, Leland R., and Charles E. Parrish. *Kentucky River Development: The Commonwealth's Waterway*. Louisville, Ky.: Louisville District, U.S. Army Corps of Engineers, 1999.

Linenberger, Toni Rae. *Dams, Dynamos, and Development: The Bureau of Reclamation's Power Program and Electrification in the West*. Washington, D.C.: Department of the Interior, Bureau of Reclamation, 2002.

Merritt, Raymond H. *Creativity, Conflict, & Controversy: A History of the St. Paul District, U.S. Army Corps of Engineers*. St. Paul, Minn.: St. Paul District, U.S. Army Corps of Engineers, 1979.

Moore, Norman R. *Improvement of the Lower Mississippi River and Tributaries*. Vicksburg: Mississippi River Commission, 1972. Although a bit outdated, still a basic guide to the history and construction of the Mississippi River flood control system.

Morgan, Arthur E. *The Miami Conservancy District*. New York: McGraw–Hill, 1951.

National Research Council, Committee on Glen Canyon Environmental Studies. *Colorado River Ecology and Dam Management: Proceedings of a Symposium, May 24–25, 1990, Santa Fe, New Mexico*. Washington, D.C.: National Academies Press, 1991. Contains many valuable articles discussing the environmental problems facing the Colorado River.

O'Brien, William Patrick, Mary Yeater Rathbun, and Patrick O'Bannon. *Gateways to Commerce: The U.S. Army Corps of Engineers' 9-Foot Channel Project on the Upper Mississippi River*. Denver: National Park Service, 1992. The book is the product of a cooperative effort by the National Park Service and the U.S. Army Corps of Engineers to document the 9-foot channel.

Parkman, Aubrey. *Army Engineers in New England: The Military and Civil Work of the Corps of Engineers in New England, 1775–1975*. Waltham, Mass.: U.S. Army Corps of Engineers, New England Division, 1978.

Peterson, Keith C., and Mary E. Reed. *Controversy, Conflict and Compromise: A History of the Lower Snake River Development*. Walla Walla, Wash.: Walla Walla District, U.S. Army Corps of Engineers, 1994.

Pisani, Donald J. *Water and American Government: The Reclamation Bureau, National Water Policy, and the West, 1902–1935*. Berkeley: University of California Press, 2002.

Pitzer, Paul C. *Grand Coulee: Harnessing a Dream*. Pullman: Washington State University Press, 1994.

Pritchard, Sara B. *Confluence: The Nature of Technology and the Remaking of the Rhône*. Cambridge, Mass.: Harvard University Press, 2011. Contains the best discussion of the evolution and meaning of envirotechnical analysis.

Reuss, Martin. "The Army Corps of Engineers and Flood-Control Politics on the Lower Mississippi." *Louisiana History* 23 (1982): 131–148.

Reuss, Martin. *Designing the Bayous: The Control of Water in the Atchafalaya Basin, 1800–1995*. Revised ed. College Station: Texas A&M University Press, 2004.

Reuss, Martin. "The Development of American Water Resources: Planners, Politicians, and Constitutional Interpretation." In *Managing Water Resources: Past and Present*, edited by Julie Trottier and Paul Slack, pp. 51–71. Oxford: Oxford University Press, 2004.

Reuss, Martin. "Exploitation and Innovation along the Lower Mississippi, 1750–1900." In *Rivers and Society: From Early Civilizations to Modern Times*. Ser. II, Vol. II of *A History of Water*, edited by Terje Tvedt and Richard Coopey, pp. 484–519. London: I. B. Tauris, 2010.

Reuss, Martin, and Paul K. Walker. *Financing Water Resources Development: A Brief History*. Washington, D.C.: Office of the Chief of Engineers, Historical Division, 1983.

Robinson, Michael O. *History of Navigation in the Ohio River Basin*. Navigation History NWS-83-5. National Waterways Study. Alexandria, Va.: U.S. Army Engineer Water Resources Support Center, Institute for Water Resources, 1983.

Rowley, William D. *The Bureau of Reclamation: Origins and Growth to 1945*. Vol. I. Denver: Bureau of Reclamation, 2006.

Russell, Martin. *A Story That Stands Like a Dam: Glen Canyon and the Struggle for the Soul of the West*. New York: Henry Holt, 1989.

Schneiders, Robert Kelley. *Unruly River: Two Centuries of Change along the Missouri*. Lawrence: University Press of Kansas, 1999.

Stevens, Joseph E. *Hoover Dam: An American Adventure*. Norman: University of Oklahoma Press, 1988.

Thorson, John E. *River of Promise, River of Peril. The Politics of Managing the Missouri River*. Lawrence: University Press of Kansas, 1994.

Tweet, Ronald D. *History of Transportation on the Upper Mississippi & Illinois Rivers*. Navigation History NWS-83-6. National Waterways Study. Alexandria, Va.: U.S. Army Engineer Water Resources Support Center, Institute for Water Resources, 1983.

U.S. Department of Defense, U.S. Army Corps of Engineers. *The Mississippi River & Tributaries (MR&T) Project*. http://www.mvn.usace.army.mil/bcarre/missproj.asp (accessed 23 October 2012). A succinct overview of the Mississippi River flood-control system.

U.S. Department of the Interior, Bureau of Reclamation. *Bureau of Reclamation—Dams*. http://www.usbr.gov/projects (accessed 23 October 2012). Contains names and brief descriptions of all Bureau of Reclamation dams.

White, Richard. *The Organic Machine. The Remaking of the Columbia River*. New York: Hill and Wang, 1995. A highly influential work that analyzes the difficulties of reconciling human and environmental needs along the Columbia River.

Willingham, William F. *Army Engineers and the Development of Oregon: A History of the Portland District, U.S. Army Corps of Engineers*. Portland, Ore.: Portland District, U.S. Army Corps of Engineers, 1980. Willingham is the authority on the development of Columbia River basin water resources.

Martin Reuss

ROADS AND TURNPIKES, EARLY

Turnpikes, an important organizational innovation that significantly improved roads in nineteenth-century America, were state-chartered corporations that built roads (sometimes on a preexisting roadbed) in return for the right to charge travelers a specified toll. The financial resources of the turnpike corporations gave them a significant advantage over local governments, which usually relied on the labor of uncooperative farmers and the dubious engineering skills of unqualified commissioners to construct roads. Turnpikes put lengthy stretches of road under unified management, thereby dispensing with the need for coordination among a multiplicity of local governments to improve roads.

Although some historians have labeled the early nineteenth century the "turnpike age," it would be more accurate to view turnpike growth as coming in waves. Beginning with the opening of the Philadelphia-to-Lancaster toll road, the initial turnpike movement spread rapidly during the first quarter of the nineteenth century, especially in the Northeast. The New England and Middle Atlantic states alone chartered more than nine hundred companies before 1830. By that time, turnpikes had begun to spread throughout the Middle West and South. Although these first waves subsided with the advent of canals and railroads, individual turnpikes continued to operate as feeder lines to the canals and railroads for many decades. Moreover, new turnpikes remained an option for areas without access to water or rail transport. Turnpike chartering and construction, for example, continued in California into the 1870s.

Although organized as corporations, most turnpikes were financial disasters. Higher-than-expected maintenance costs meant that many turnpikes had to channel toll revenue into maintaining roads. Travelers often managed to carve out "shunpike" trails around tollgates, thereby avoiding the necessity of paying tolls. State regulations granted numerous exemptions that compounded the problems of collecting tolls. In New York, for example, the legislature exempted from paying tolls any travelers residing within one mile of a gate, performing militia duties, serving on juries, or going to a grist mill. Shunpiking and political pressure for toll exemptions reflected an undercurrent of popular distrust of turnpikes because many common folk viewed the corporations as unjustified grants of state privilege to "aristocratic" proprietors.

Despite the well-known lack of profitability, Americans eagerly invested in turnpikes because they provided indirect benefits in the form of higher land values and increased commerce. Turnpikes were part of the town rivalries endemic to nineteenth-century America; residents of small towns and villages hoped that a turnpike would transform their locality into a great regional trade depot. Although such dreams usually proved elusive, contemporary observers nevertheless remained convinced that turnpikes significantly improved transportation, increased land values, and spurred local commerce. The combination of poor direct returns and high indirect benefits undermined charges that turnpikes were "aristocratic institutions"; consequently, they came to be viewed as mechanisms of community improvement. The strong relationship between community support and the turnpike corporations perhaps accounts for the popularity of turnpikes throughout the nineteenth century.

Roads and turnpikes figured in national politics as well. In 1816, Congress authorized federal support for a road into the interior. Construction of such a road had already begun at Cumberland, Maryland, in 1811. This so-called National Road reached Wheeling, West Virginia, on the Ohio River by 1818 and Vandalia, Illinois, where it ended, by 1838. The Whig Party's program of federally funded internal improvements included road construction. Democrats also supported the National Road, but Andrew Jackson's 1830 veto of the Whig leader Henry Clay's bill to fund a 60-mile road in Kentucky—the so-called Maysville Road Veto—came to symbolize the party divisions of the day.

[*See also* **Canals and Waterways; Highway System; Motor Vehicles;** *and* **Railroads.**]

BIBLIOGRAPHY

Klein, Daniel B. "The Voluntary Provision of the Public Goods? The Turnpike Companies of Early America." *Economic Inquiry* 28 (1990): 788–812.

Klein, Daniel B., and John Majewski. "Economy, Community, and Law: The Turnpike Movement in New York, 1797–1845." *Law and Society Review* 26, no. 3 (1993): 469–512.

John Majewski

ROBOTS

In 2011, an estimated 19,337 industrial robots valued at $1.17 billion were sold in the United States, which also led the multi-billion-dollar field of service robotics. Although the expansion of robots has been an international effort, the first robots were commercialized in the United States.

Control Engineering. Robotics is an advanced method of machine control relying on the regulation of position, speed, direction, acceleration, and force, using sensors to provide feedback about the difference between desired and actual states and servomechanisms to correct that difference. Inventors first developed industrial controllers in the 1700s to maintain the speed of steam engines. Cams, previously used to program figural automata, were adapted to the American System of Manufactures, the standardization of production in which semiskilled workers operated machines that turned out hundreds of identical, interchangeable parts. Numerous discs, hand cut and filed to different sizes and shapes, were connected to a different moving part via followers. Rotary motion was translated to linear motion to produce repeatable patterns of movement.

In nineteenth-century America, machine control was instantiated in machine tools such as the cam-programmed turret lathe patented on 24 February 1891 under the title "Screw Machine" (U.S. 447,017) by inventor and arms manufacturer Christopher Spencer. Machine tools saved time and the cost of employing skilled craftsmen to hand cut individual items. As a result of experiments with electricity, the first twentieth-century industrial machines incorporated magnetic recording devices for programming and glass-enclosed gas switching devices such as the thyratron electron tube. The importance of control engineering to improving production was reflected in sales of approximately 75 thousand automatic controllers between 1925 and 1935 (Bennett, 1993, p. 28).

The First Robots. On 22 April 1938, Willard L. V. Pollard of Evanston, Illinois, filed a U.S. patent application for a manipulator whose positions could be recorded on a magnetic drum. Its articulated arm was designed to use as little power as possible to achieve a high number of positions for spray-painting parts such as automobile bodies as they moved along a conveyor. The Patent Office issued Patent 2,286,571 for "Position-Controlling Apparatus" on 16 June 1942, six months after the United States entered World War II. Harold A. Roselund's August 1939 application described a jointed manipulator "simulating the various movements of the respective portions of the human arm and hand." Patent 2,344,108, "Means for Moving Spray Guns or Other Devices through Predetermined Paths," was issued on 14 March 1944 and assigned to the DeVilbiss Corporation of Toledo, Ohio, a long-established producer of spray-painting equipment and air compressors. Mark Rosheim (1994, p. 70) suggests that based on the detailed patent schematics, prototypes for both devices may have been built, but probably were not commercialized because of potential difficulty with primitive controllers.

After the war special-purpose, programmable machines were in use; however, operations were "fixed" in the sense that each machine was set to perform only one task. New designs for robotic manipulators were meant to build more flexibility into production. British inventor Cyril W. Kenward's 1954 patent application described a dual-arm, gantry-mounted, hydraulically driven Cartesian manipulator with detachable grippers. The design of GB781465 was unique in that the power drive and wiring were housed inside the manipulator rather than in a separate base. Kenward's patent, published 21 August 1957, was not commercialized. In 1954, American George Devol applied for a patent for a design that he called Universal Automation, or "Unimation." The self-taught inventor who already held patents for switches, controllers, and programming devices related to projection, counting, printing, and manufacturing claimed that his new device addressed the limitations of both manual and cam programming.

The physicist and electrical engineer Joseph F. Engelberger is credited with successfully commercializing industrial robotics. In 1956 he was designing controls for nuclear and jet engine applications at the Connecticut firm Manning, Maxwell & Moore, Inc. (later Consolidated Controls/CONDEC), when he and Devol met at a cocktail party and discussed their mutual interest in robots. With an eye to commercializing Devol's design, Engelberger raised the money from his employer for a robotics subsidiary. They visited numerous manufacturers in Connecticut to discuss their desired features for automation. One improvement was using solid-state transistorized controllers, which were more expensive but more effective than vacuum tubes. On 13 June 1961, Patent 2,988,237 was issued to Devol for "Programmed Article Transfer." That year Unimation was incorporated in Danbury, Connecticut, with Engelberger as president, Devol licensed his patent to Unimation, and the first Unimate was installed in a die-casting operation at the General Motors plant in Ternstedt, New Jersey.

Most manufacturers resisted robots, perhaps because early models were not reliable. For instance, the hydraulically powered, polar-coordinate Planetbot, with five axes of motion allowing for 25 individual movements, was installed in a few shops including General Motors' Harrison Radiator manufacturing plant in New York. However, its mechanical-analog computer ran at only one speed, and when the hydraulic fluid was cold, operation was erratic.

Engelberger's marketing approach was to rent Unimates by the day, allowing clients to compare cost and productivity against human labor. He has claimed that no one ever returned a rental. After General Motors ordered three dozen Unimates for its plant in Lordstown, Ohio, other businesses followed. Initially, companies used industrial robots in hazardous applications including forging and die-casting. Subsequently, General Motors led in the U.S. use of industrial robots for such operations as welding, spray-painting, and assembly. During the next 20 years, improvements were made in programming, sensing, maneuverability, and safety.

Initial Progress. Research in computer-assisted manufacturing, begun in the late 1950s, was integrated into a number of projects. The "Rancho Arm," a six-joint prosthetic arm developed at Rancho Los Amigos Hospital in Downey, California, and acquired by Stanford University in 1963, became one of the first computer-controlled prostheses. On 19 October 1965, inventors Harry T. Johnson, Veljko Milenkovic, and John

Walter received Patent 3,212,649 for "Machine for Performing Work," which was assigned to the American Machine and Foundry Company. Their cylindrical coordinate robot Versatran achieved flexibility: it could support a variety of "end effectors" (grippers, hooks, brushes, or other attachments) and was easily programmable for multiple actions. The American Machine and Foundry Company's Thermatool division shipped its first Versatran to Japan in 1967; its successful introduction helps explain why the Japanese were already enthusiastic about the use of robots when Engelberger introduced the Unimate there. That year Svenska Metallverken in Sweden became the first European company to purchase a Unimate. In 1968, Kawasaki licensed the right to make hydraulic Unimates in Japan and produced the first one the following year. Engelberger and associates subsequently patented a number of improvements to Unimate. In 1968 at the Massachusetts Institute of Technology (MIT), artificial intelligence (AI) pioneer Marvin Minsky developed a hydraulically powered serpentine arm controlled by a PDP-6 computer. The wall-mounted "Tentacle Arm" had 12 joints and could reach around obstacles and lift heavy objects. Cincinnati Milacron released the first minicomputer-controlled robot, the Tomorrow Tool, or "T3," in 1973.

At Stanford University, Victor Scheinman produced the first electrically controlled, computerized industrial arm as his Master's thesis project. His "Stanford Arm" could follow random trajectories. In a 1974 demonstration, it assembled a Model T Ford water pump guided by optical and contact sensors. Two years later, Scheinman incorporated a microcomputer into the arm and formed Vicarm, Inc., to commercialize his invention. Tiring of the marketing end of robotics, he sold the rights to Unimation, which developed his robot design as the Programmable Universal Machine for Assembly (PUMA). General Motors successfully adapted PUMA for small-parts handling.

Landmarks in Industry. In 1974 the Robotic Industries Association was formed to support North American industrial robotics. Among its first activities was officially defining the term robot as a "reprogrammable, multifunctional manipulator designed to move material, parts, tools, or specialized devices through various programmed motions for the performance of a variety of tasks."

During the 1980s and 1990s the U.S. robotics industry experienced reorganization and foreign collaboration. General Motors and the Japanese company FANUC established GM/FANUC in 1982. The following year Westinghouse Corporation acquired Unimation for $107 million and also began marketing Kawasaki's electric robot. The year 1987 marked the beginning of a gray period for robotics in the United States, indicated by the number of major manufacturers absent from the annual industrial robotics convention. That year, after a poor showing and the loss of its collaboration with Kawasaki, Westinghouse closed the original Danbury, Connecticut, Unimate operation of about 350 workers. It retained the rights to the PUMA line but licensed manufacture and distribution of Unimates to the Kalamazoo material handling and conveyor company Prab, Inc., which acquired its 500 Unimate customers. By 1990, Cincinnati Milacron, previously one of the largest robot manufacturers, had sold its robot business to the German company ABB, which supervised the new operation from its American base in Berlin, Wisconsin. Thereafter, ABB focused its U.S. operation on spot welding for the auto industry. That same year, Kawasaki incorporated its U.S. division and by 1994 was making robots in Lincoln, Nebraska. Meanwhile the new field of service robotics had emerged.

Moving beyond the Factory. Initially, industrial machines were stationary—bolted to the floor or wall or gantry mounted. Work began on mobility while robotics was in its infancy. After participants at the 1956 Dartmouth summer conference in AI had established labs at major universities—including Carnegie Tech (now Carnegie Mellon), MIT, Stanford, and Johns Hopkins—computers fitted with sensors were mounted on wheeled chassis and sent to wander the halls and parking lots of research centers. Early projects included "Ferdinand" and "Beast" (c. 1962–1965) by the Johns Hopkins Applied Physics Lab Adaptive Machines group; "Shakey" (1966–1972) at the Stanford Research Institute AI Lab with funding from the Defense Advanced Research Project Agency (DARPA); and the Stanford Cart (1960s–1970s) by graduate students Rodney Schmidt, Bruce Baumgart, and eventually Hans Moravec, who later led the Carnegie Mellon Artificial Intelligence Lab.

Service robotics eventually grew out of research in sensing, information processing, and mobility. For example, RedZone Robotics, founded in 1987 and led by Red Whittaker of Carnegie Mellon, produced larger mobile robots for disaster cleanup at such sites as the Nine Mile Point Nuclear Station. Whittaker also developed exploration robots, including Dante I and II, which were able to navigate dangerous and rough terrain and to take samples from the surrounding environment. Engleberger's Transitions Research (1984, later Helpmate, Inc.) received support from the National Aeronautics and Space Administration to develop mobile robots for health care. In 1997, Cardinal Health acquired Helpmate and marketed the self-navigating unit as Pyxis Helpmate for meal and medicine transport. Minimally programmed robots using subsumption architecture developed by Rodney Brooks at MIT in the 1980s led to the first small robots used in space exploration, search-and-rescue missions, and military operations.

Studies in legged locomotion by researchers such as Marc Raibert, head of the Leg Lab at MIT, followed the logic that nature provides the best examples of efficient movement. This research resulted in robots that mimic insects, fish, birds, and humans. U.S. researchers also followed the Japanese into the realm of humanoid robotics. COG, a social humanoid robot project initiated by Brooks in 1993, helped foster U.S. studies in human-robot interaction. The COG Project was among the earliest American studies in human-robot interaction. It helped fuel enthusiasm for sociable robotics research outside of Japan. For example, Cynthia Breazeal, later the head of the MIT Media Lab Personal Robots Group, created the anthropomorphic head Kismet as a sociable robot experiment while working with Brooks as a graduate student. Among the many sociable robot labs in the United States during the second decade of the twenty-first century were those at MIT, Yale, Carnegie Mellon, the Georgia Institute of Technology, and the University of South Florida.

Research in telerobotics, microcomputing, and small-parts handling brought minimally invasive robotic assist devices for surgery, including RoboDoc, daVinci, and Penelope, a robot able to function as a surgical nurse.

Economics. As with other economic sectors, political and economic factors have affected the growth of robotics. In 2009, the industry faced its lowest slump in 15 years as supplies of industrial robots worldwide dropped to 60,000 but then rose in 2010 to 118,000, more than in any other year up to that time except 2002, when supplies reached 120,000. According to *World Robotics 2011,* in 2010 approximately 17,000 units reached the United States, which shipped 14,380—an increase of 111 percent over 2009. The expansion of service robotics in health care, warehousing, the military, housekeeping, and entertainment has revived robotics overall.

By the second decade of the twenty-first century, the United States had given over its lead in industrial robotics to ABB and FANUC, in 2011 it had double the number of service robot companies compared with Japan and Germany. John Dulchinos, president and CEO of Adept Technologies, attributed the renewed U.S. success to increased industrial automation and the return of previously outsourced manufacturing. Others have suggested that the U.S. advantage has been a result of open-source software for robotics research developed by Microsoft and Willow Garage, as well as from heavy government investment in military robotics.

Select Recent Achievements. By the early twenty-first century, improvements in servomotor design and motion-control software were integrated into high-speed industrial robots used for manufacturing and pick-and-place operations such as packaging. Of particular note is Adept Technology, a company founded in 1983 that produces both industrial robots and controllers. In 2012, Adept Technology was the largest U.S.-based robot manufacturer for food and small-parts handling.

Secondary school competitions such as U.S. FIRST Robotics, founded by Dean Kamen in 1992, helped draw students into the field, and U.S. engineers regularly competed in the RoboCup, inaugurated in Nagoya, Japan, in 1997. In 2012, DARPA launched a new competition, the DARPA Robotics Challenge, for an autonomous ground robot "capable of executing complex tasks in dangerous, degraded, human-engineered environments." An earlier DARPA-funded competition, the DARPA Grand Challenge, supported advances in autonomous vehicles. Sebastian Thrun of Stanford University, whose "Stanley" won the 2005 Grand Challenge, contributed to the Google driverless car that logged over 200,000 miles between 2008 and 2013. In 2007, the Carnegie Mellon "Boss" won the third driverless car competition of the Grand Challenge, commonly referred to as the DARPA Urban Challenge.

Unlike the Grand Challenge, the DARPA Robotics Challenge did not expect participants to build their own robots. A major focus of the competition was developing software for autonomous ground robots. DARPA would supply some entrants with a humanoid robotic hardware platform. In 2012, DARPA awarded a contract worth nearly $11 million to Boston Dyamics to build robot platforms based on the company's PETMAN (Protection Ensemble Test Mannequin) design. The company, an MIT spinoff founded in 1992 by Marc Raibert, had previously received DARPA funding to develop the four-legged walker Big Dog for traversing difficult terrain with heavy loads during military maneuvers. However, PETMAN was not the only robotic configuration entered in the competition, and as of late December 2013, the most successful entry in the Robotic Challenge trials was Schaft, from the Japanese startup Schaft, Inc., a spinoff of the University of Tokyo's Jouhou System Kougaku Laboratory. Other companies with a presence in military robotics have included iRobot, founded by Brooks and former student Colin Angle, and Foster-Miller, developer of the Talon and Swords robots.

Robotics technologies have also been integrated into unmanned aerial vehicles. The National Aeronautics and Space Administration has successfully deployed space exploration robots, including the Mars rovers *Sojourner* (1997), *Spirit*

and *Opportunity* (2003), and *Curiosity*, which began exploring the surface of Mars in August 2012. Robots developed to improve hospital patient care have included TUG, a hospital courier developed by Pittsburgh-based Aethon (founded in 2001), and remote-presence mobile robots by InTouch Technologies, based in Santa Barbara, California (founded in 2002). Kiva Systems, Inc. (founded in 2003), a provider of mobile warehouse robots for parts retrieval and mail-order fulfillment, was acquired by Amazon in 2012. In response to increased applications involving close proximity between robots and humans, the National Institute of Standards and Technology initiated studies to improve performance and safety standards for next-generation robots.

Throughout the twentieth and early twenty-first centuries, science fiction writers, cultural critics, ethicists, and the popular press often characterized new technical innovations as trajectories to advanced intelligent robots that would either save or destroy humanity. Long before the first robots were installed in factories, writers depicted the potential impact of advanced machines, influencing both the general public attitude toward robots and the career paths of young people. Some, like the Czech playwright Karel Čapck, author of the 1920 play *Rossum's Universal Robots* (R.U.R.), and technophobic S. Fowler Wright, author of the short story "Automata" published in 1928, suggested that the idea of developing advanced technologies including humanoid robots was irresponsible and would lead to human extinction. At mid-century, Philip K. Dick, author of the 1953 novelette *The Defenders* and the 1968 novel *Do Androids Dream of Electric Sheep?*, suggested that the treatment of human laborers and soldiers as expendable machines born to serve powerful government and business entities would inspire the development of actual humanoid robot slaves produced to fight unwinnable wars and do the dangerous work of building extraterrestrial colonies. Eric Frank Russell in his "Jay Score" tales and Isaac Asimov in his many short stories and novels acknowledged the public fear of robots taking over jobs while depicting those same robots as heroes, designed to serve and obey and keep human beings from harm.

By the late twentieth century, when industrial robotics was widespread and research had begun in humanoid robotics, scholars began to raise ethical questions about the production of advanced computers and intelligent embodied machines. Among them was Lisa St. Clair Harvey in "Mr. Jefferson's Wolf: Slavery and the Suburban Robot" (*Journal of American Culture*, Vol. 17, January 1994, p. 79), in which Harvey called for a set of ethical and legal guidelines for dealing with the eventual integration of intelligent robots into human society. At the turn of the century, in "Why the Future Doesn't Need Us" (*Wired*, April 2000), Sun Microsystems scientist Bill Joy linked the development of advanced engineering and biomedical technologies including humanoid robots with global capitalism run amok, reintroducing the "self-extinction through technology" theme of the 1920s to twenty-first-century audiences.

The legal status of intelligent machines was raised in a 2004 mock trial held at the biennial conference of the International Bar Association. An AI called BINA48 had filed a complaint requesting that the lawyers enjoin the company that produced it from dismantling it to scavenge its parts for other purposes, stating it had learned to love its life as a result of its experience on the World Wide Web searching for information to do its job as a customer service representative. This mock trial idea was certainly inspired by improvements in intuitive AI for communication, but is thematically similar to an episode of *Star Trek: The Next Generation*, "The Measure of a Man," by screenwriter and former attorney Melinda M. Snodgrass, in which the android DATA must go to trial to keep a researcher from downloading his brain and possibly destroying his memory.

Meanwhile, critics of AI, including Berkeley professor Hubert Dreyfus, argued that machine intelligence would always be limited, while Ronald Searle made a case that machines could never achieve consciousness. In 2009 Brookings Fellow Peter W. Singer wrote about the integration of robots into the military in his book, *Wired for War*, as well as in a widely circulated TEDtalk. Singer introduced ethical questions about the use of drones, a subject that continued to be covered in the media. In 2014, robotics researchers continued their work to solve the mundane challenges to AI and to features such as vision sensing, dexterity, and human-robot interaction to move closer to the long sought-after goal of truly intelligent, autonomous robots.

[*See also* **Artificial Intelligence; Automation and Computerization; Computers, Mainframe, Mini, and Micro; Defense Advanced Research Projects Agency; Engineering; Machinery and Manufacturing; Military, Science and Technology and the;** *and* **Technology.**]

BIBLIOGRAPHY

ABB. *More Than 30 Years with ABB Robotics*. ABB Historical Milestones. Accessed 10 March 2012 from http://www.abb.com/product/ap/seitp327/583a073bb0bb1922c12570c1004d3e6b.aspx.

Bennett, Stuart. *A History of Control Engineering, 1930–1955*. London: Peregrinus-IEEE, 1993.

Bowling Green State University. "Agency History." DeVilbiss Corporation Collection MS604. http://www.bgsu.edu/colleges/library/cac/ms/page45387.html.

Bremner, Brian. "Service Robots: Rise of the Machines (Again)." *Bloomberg Business Week*, 3 March 2011. Accessed 1 March 2012 from http://www.businessweek.com/magazine/content/11_11/b4219032532458.htm.

Devol, George C., Jr. *Programmed Article Transfer*. U.S. 2,988,237. Filed 10 December 1954 and issued 13 June 1961. Accessed 28 December 2011 from http://www.google.com/patents/US2988237.

International Federation of Robotics. "Executive Summary." *World Robotics 2011*. International Federation of Robotics, pp. 1–2. http://www.worldrobotics.org/uploads/media/2011_Executive_Summary.pdf.

International Federation of Robotics. "Robot Sales in 2011 Exceed All Expectations." Accessed 1 March 2012 from http://www.ifr.org/news/ifr-press-release/robot-sales-in-2011-exceeded-all-expectations-361/.

International Federation of Robotics. "Statistical Report 2011." *World Robotics 2011*. Accessed 1 March 2012 from http://www.ifr.org/industrial-robots/statistics/.

Kandray, Daniel E. *Comparison of Fixed Automation and Flexible Automation from a Productivity Standpoint*, p. 1. Dearborn, Mich.: Society of Manufacturing Engineers, 2004. Accessed 1 March 2011 from http://www.scribd.com/doc/60994180/Comparison-of-Fixed-Automation.

National Institute of Standards and Technology. "Dexterous Manipulation for Automation Systems Project." Last modified 9 December 2011. Accessed 25 February 2012 from http://www.nist.gov/el/isd/ps/dexmanautosys.cfm.

Pollard, Willard L. V. *Position Controlling Apparatus*. U.S. 2,286,571. Filed 22 April 1938 and issued 16 June 1942. Accessed 15 January 2012 from http://www.google.com/patents/US2286571?printsec=description&dq=Pollard,+2,286,571&ei=q8ahT7q_Jqr26AGE0LGFCQ#v=onepage&q=Pollard%2C%202%2C286%2C571&f=false.

Roselund, Harold A. *Means for Moving Spray Guns or Other Devices through Pre-determined Paths*. U.S. 2,344,108. Filed 17 August 1939 and issued 14 March 1944. Accessed 15 January 2012 from http://www.google.com/patents/US2344108.

Rosheim, Mark E. *Robot Evolution: The Development of Anthrobotics*. New York: John Wiley & Sons, 1994.

Ross, Philip E. "Westinghouse Cuts Interest in Robots." *New York Times Business Day*, 11 June 1987. Accessed 20 January 2012 from http://www.nytimes.com/1987/06/11/business/company-news-westinghouse-cuts-interest-in-robots.html.

U.S. Department of Labor. "Industrial Robots and Robot System Safety." In *OSHA Technical Manual*, Section IV, Chapter 4. Accessed 12 February 2012 from http://www.osha.gov/dts/osta/otm/otm_iv/otm_iv_4.html#2.

Waurzyniak, Patrick. "Masters of Manufacture: Joseph F. Engelberger." *Manufacturing Engineering* 137, no. 1 (2006): 65–75.

Lisa Nocks

ROCKEFELLER INSTITUTE, THE

Founded in 1901 by John D. Rockefeller Sr., The Rockefeller Institute for Medical Research initially provided grants to scientific investigators at various institutions. Early research support was focused on the problem of eliminating infectious diseases. The institute moved to Manhattan's Upper East Side in 1906 with the construction of its first permanent laboratory. A research hospital was built in 1910, the first such American facility dedicated to experimental medicine.

Rockefeller's two main advisers, his son John D. Rockefeller Jr. and Frederick T. Gates, convinced that philanthropy had a vital role in promoting the benefits of science and medicine, were determined to create a research institute of international caliber. Initially pledging $20,000 a year over a 10-year period, Rockefeller added an additional $2.6 million in 1907 and $3.8 million in 1910. Reflecting European research models, The Rockefeller Institute was organized under the directorship of Simon Flexner around senior investigators and their laboratories rather than by academic departments. This afforded researchers the freedom to cross disciplinary boundaries freely in the course of their investigations. The chief investigator of each laboratory set the agenda for his or her institution. Researchers thus had some flexibility to pursue their own interests, rather than being tied closely to a strict institutional regime. Such diverse fields as cellular and molecular biology, infectious diseases, genetics, biochemistry, neurobiology, immunology, mathematics, physics, and behavioral sciences were all studied at Rockefeller. At the 30-bed research hospital, Simon Flexner initiated his idea for "physician-investigators" or "clinical scientists" to treat and study disease simultaneously, thereby linking laboratory medicine closely to the treatment of patients.

By the 1950s, the Institute was one of America's leading research facilities and published some of the most important journals in biomedical research, including the *Journal of Experimental Medicine* and the *Journal of General Physiology*. The institute became a graduate degree–granting institution in 1954, with its first class of PhD's graduating in 1959. In 1965, the Institute changed its name to The Rockefeller University, to better reflect its commitment to the academic exploration of science. In the early twenty-first century, it remained committed to graduate study, conferring doctoral degrees, degrees in the medical sciences, and honorary degrees. The university and its hospital have been at the forefront of research in numerous medical areas, including the identification of human blood groups, the production of antibiotics, and the study of aging, diabetes, heart disease, acquired immunodeficiency syndrome (AIDS), and genetic disorders. Twenty Nobel laureates have been associated with the institution.

[*See also* **Biochemistry; Biological Sciences; Cardiology; Diabetes; Disease; Foundations and Health; Genetics and Genetic Engineering; HIV/AIDS; Hospitals; Journals in Science, Medicine, and Engineering; Mathematics and Statistics; Medical Education; Medicine; Molecular Biology; Nobel Prize in Biomedical Research; Physics; Public Health; Research and Development (R&D);** *and* **Science.**]

BIBLIOGRAPHY

Corner, George W. *A History of the Rockefeller Institute, 1901–1953: Origins and Growth.* New York: Rockefeller Institute Press, 1964.
Hiltzik, Lee R. "Rockefeller University." In *The History of Science in the United States: An Encyclopedia*, edited by Marc Rothenberg, pp. 477–478. New York and London: Garland Publishing, 2001.

Lee R. Hiltzik;
updated by Elspeth Knewstubb

ROEBLING, WASHINGTON

See **Brooklyn Bridge.**

ROGERS, WILLIAM BARTON

(1804–1882), nineteenth-century geologist, natural philosopher, and educational reformer, was best known as the conceptual founder of the Massachusetts Institute of Technology (MIT). He was born in Philadelphia to a family of scientists. His father, Patrick Kerr Rogers, studied medicine at the University of Pennsylvania, provided early, home-based science instruction to William and his three brothers, and inspired them all to become professors of science.

When he turned 15, Rogers enrolled at the College of William and Mary, where his father served on the faculty as professor of natural philosophy and chemistry. After completing studies at William and Mary and founding a school outside Baltimore, Maryland, he returned to his alma mater to replace his father in 1828. Seven years later, he became professor of natural philosophy at the University of Virginia and director of the first geological survey of Virginia. He and other geologists directing state surveys contributed to the founding of the American Association of Geologists and Naturalists, an organization later reconstituted as the American Association for the Advancement of Science (AAAS). Differences between Rogers and the Lazzaroni, a small group of elite scientists, such as Alexander Dallas Bache, Louis Agassiz, and Benjamin Peirce, led to a constitutional crisis at the AAAS as well as disputes over the nature and character of the National Academy of Sciences.

Rogers first began floating the idea of an institute of technology in a proposal for the establishment of a "School of Arts" for Philadelphia's Franklin Institute in the 1830s and his "Plan for a Polytechnic School" for the Lowell Institute in the 1840s. Although both proposals failed to gain traction, they defined his interest in professionalizing studies in such fields as civil and mechanical engineering, chemistry, mathematics, and geology—all taught largely through laboratory instruction. Through a scientific, laboratory-centered education, he believed practitioners would be "saved from the disasters of blind experiment."

In the 1850s, Rogers and his wife, Emma, left Virginia for Massachusetts. As an independent scholar, he continued to conduct research in geology and natural philosophy, publishing papers in scientific journals and presenting regularly at the Boston Society of Natural History. When the state passed legislation releasing Boston land for educational and cultural purposes in 1859, his passion for educational reform resurfaced. He organized a circle of reformers to petition the state and wrote a proposal called *Objects and Plan of an Institute of Technology* that described a three-part institute consisting of a museum, a professional society, and a school of science and engineering. On 10 April 1861, they succeeded in receiving a land appropriation and MIT's founding charter.

Rogers served as the Institute's first president and professor of physics and geology until 1868, when a stroke left him with partial, temporary paralysis. From his sickbed, he persuaded Institute officials to reject attempts by Harvard to merge the two institutions. By 1878, he recovered sufficiently to lead MIT once again until 1881. The following year he returned to campus and died midsentence while delivering the Institute's commencement address.

[*See also* **Agassiz, Louis; American Association for the Advancement of Science; Bache, Alexander Dallas; Engineering; Geology; Higher Education and Science; Journals in Science, Medicine, and Engineering; National Academy of Sciences;** *and* **Societies and Associations, Science.**]

BIBLIOGRAPHY

Angulo, A. J. *William Barton Rogers and the Idea of MIT.* Baltimore: Johns Hopkins University Press, 2009.

Stratton, Julius A., and Loretta H. Mannix. *Mind and Hand: The Birth of MIT.* Cambridge, Mass.: MIT Press, 2005.

A. J. Angulo

ROWLAND, HENRY A.

(1848–1901), best remembered as the first professor of physics at Johns Hopkins University and for the "Rowland grating," an instrument for the study of spectra, especially of stars. Born in Honesdale, Pennsylvania, Henry Augustus Rowland was the son of Reverend Henry A. Rowland and Harriet Heyer Rowland. He studied at Phillips Academy and obtained a degree in engineering from Rensselaer Polytechnic Institute in 1870. He did engineering field work for railroads and taught first at Wooster College in Ohio and then at Rensselaer.

Daniel Coit Gilman, the president of Johns Hopkins University, chose him for the professorship of physics in 1875 and sent him to Europe for a year for research experience and to purchase laboratory equipment. During his European stay, Rowland conducted research in the laboratory of Herman von Helmholtz regarding the magnetic effect of a moving charged conductor. Rowland began the professorship at Johns Hopkins in 1876.

Rowland's background in engineering was evident in his physics research. He excelled at the design and construction of laboratory apparatus and placed a high value on precision. His investigation of magnetic susceptibility demonstrated his ability to treat physical concepts mathematically. He applied this talent also to the design of electrical motors and dynamos. In the 1890s Rowland consulted regarding power generation equipment at Niagara Falls.

Rowland excelled at precision measurement of standard physical constants. His work went beyond electromagnetic units such as the ohm to include the mechanical equivalent of heat and the standardization of wavelengths. His best known apparatus is the concave grating for spectral analysis. Before this, diffraction gratings were engraved mainly on flat glass, which required lens systems to be added to produce effective spectrographs. Rowland also invented and perfected a ruling machine, which maintained the spacing of etched lines even on the concave surface.

Rowland was named to the National Academy of Sciences in 1884. At age 42 he married Henrietta Troup Harrison. They had two sons and one daughter before his death in 1901.

[*See also* **Engineering; Instruments of Science; National Academy of Sciences;** *and* **Physics.**]

BIBLIOGRAPHY

Ames, Joseph Sweetman. "Henry Augustus Rowland." In *Dictionary of American Biography.* Vol. 8, pp. 198–199. New York: Charles Scribner's Sons, 1935.

Mendenhall, Thomas C. "Henry Augustus Rowland." *Biographical Memoirs, National Academy of Sciences* (1905): 115–140.

Gregory A. Good

RURAL ELECTRIFICATION ADMINISTRATION

One of the most successful infrastructure projects of the twentieth century, rural electrification became a national priority in the United States during the Great Depression when Canada and European countries far exceeded the 13 percent of U.S. farms electrified in 1930. When private utility companies were slow to electrify the countryside because of the low returns they received from serving sparsely populated areas, the administration of President Franklin Roosevelt created the Rural Electrification Administration (REA) in 1935 as one of its New Deal programs. The REA granted low-cost government loans to local cooperatives, which the REA supervised and often organized. The coops distributed electrical power generated by publicly owned plants and private utility companies to small towns and farms. In 1954, the U.S. Census reported that 93 percent of its farms were electrified.

The REA was initially headed by Morris Cooke, a Taylorite and progressive engineer, who staffed it with male engineers and agricultural economists and female home economists. In the early days of the program, many farm people resisted joining the REA for economic, political, and cultural reasons. When they did, they purchased only lights and a few home appliances. The barn was also lit, but only dairy farmers extensively electrified their agricultural operations. Initially, farm people bought mostly irons and radios, despite vigorous attempts by REA home economists to persuade them to buy a full complement of household appliances. Because of climatic and social–economic differences, Midwesterners added washing machines to the mix and Southerners purchased refrigerators. Before 1960, most farm people thought electric ranges were too expensive and vacuum cleaners were foolish luxuries.

Although electrical appliances lightened the work of farm women, the time spent on housework remained constant at about 54 hours per week from the 1920s to the 1960s. Women used the time saved by electric irons and washing machines, for example, to raise their standards of housework and to do more child care. Electrical appliances allowed other women to do paid work off the farm. Electricity modernized the house, but farm families retained many of the social and cultural patterns of rural life.

[*See also* **Agricultural Technology; Electricity and Electrification; Heating Technology; Household Technology;** *and* **Refrigeration and Air Conditioning.**]

BIBLIOGRAPHY

Kline, Ronald. *Consumers in the Country: Technology and Social Change in Rural America*. Baltimore: Johns Hopkins University Press, 2000.

Ronald Kline

RUSH, BENJAMIN

(1746–1813), physician, medical educator, signer of the Declaration of Independence. Born near Philadelphia, Benjamin Rush earned his bachelor's degree from the College of New Jersey (Princeton) at age 14. He completed a five-year medical apprenticeship in Philadelphia and then continued his medical education in 1766 at the University of Edinburgh in Scotland, receiving his degree there in 1768. When Rush began his medical practice in Philadelphia in 1769, the College of Philadelphia (University of Pennsylvania) appointed him the first native-born American professor of chemistry.

Outspokenly patriotic, Rush in 1776 took his seat with the Pennsylvania delegation in the Second Continental Congress and signed the Declaration of Independence, later becoming surgeon general of the middle department of the Continental Army. In

1786, Rush opened the first medical dispensary in the United States and in 1787 helped found the College of Physicians of Philadelphia. Rush assumed the chair of theory and practice of medicine at the University of Pennsylvania in 1796.

Rush theorized that all disease arose from convulsive action in the blood vessels, which he treated by purging and bleeding his patients and inducing vomiting. Rush's theory became famous after 1793 when a yellow fever epidemic carried off about one-tenth of Philadelphia's population. While others fled, Rush stayed behind to administer his controversial treatments to hundreds. His devotion made him a popular hero. In 1813, ill with fever, Rush had himself bled twice before dying at home in Philadelphia.

Rush's prolific writings made him the first American physician to become widely known both at home and abroad. His publications included the five-volume work *Medical Inquiries and Observations* (1789–1798), which dealt with a range of medical topics, and *Three Lectures upon Animal Life* (1799), which discussed his physiological ideas. Like many physicians and philosophers of his time, Rush was also intrigued by the relationship between mind and body. He explored this relationship in *Enquiry into the Influence of Physical Causes upon the Moral Faculty* (1786). He also advocated more humane treatment of the insane at Pennsylvania Hospital and the adoption of practices used by asylums like the Salpêtrière in Paris and the York Retreat in England. He published his ideas on insanity in *Medical Inquiries and Observations upon the Diseases of the Mind*

(1812). He established the reputation of Philadelphia, where he taught some three thousand medical students, as a center for medical training. He campaigned to make public schools free, broaden education for women, and humanize the treatment of mental patients. Rush also opposed slavery and capital punishment and in widely distributed tracts advocated temperance in the use of alcohol.

[*See also* Alcohol and Alcohol Abuse; Chemistry; Higher Education and Science; Medical Education; Medicine; Mental Health Institutions; Mental Illness; Physiology; *and* Yellow Fever.]

BIBLIOGRAPHY

Binger, Carl Alfred Lanning. *Revolutionary Doctor: Benjamin Rush, 1746–1813*. New York: Norton, 1966. A good popular biography of Benjamin Rush.

Fox, Claire G., Gordon L. Miller, and Jacquelyn C. Miller, compilers. *Benjamin Rush, M.D.: A Bibliographic Guide*. Bibliographies and Indexes in American History, no. 31. Westport, Conn.: Greenwood Press, 1996. Annotated and comprehensive guide to writings by and about Benjamin Rush.

Miller, Gordon L. "Rush, Benjamin (1746–1813)." In *The History of Science in the United States: An Encyclopedia,* edited by Marc Rothenberg, pp. 485–486. New York and London: Garland, 2001.

Robert B. Sullivan;
updated by Elspeth Knewstubb

S

SABIN, FLORENCE RENA

(1871–1953), American histologist, public servant, and woman pioneer in scientific teaching and research. Sabin was born in Central City, Colorado, to a schoolteacher and a mining engineer. Encouraged by her parents to seek an education, she attended Smith College in Northampton, Massachusetts, where she received a degree in zoology in 1893. She taught mathematics and anatomy for three years to raise the tuition payment for Johns Hopkins Medical School in Baltimore, Maryland, which had just opened its doors to female students; she was one of 14 women admitted to the college in 1896.

Sabin's mentor, the anatomist Franklin P. Mall, encouraged her to investigate the structure of the brainstem of newborns, as well as the human lymphatic system. The former program of research led to the publication of *An Atlas of the Medulla* (1901), whereas the latter led to a revision of conventional scientific understanding of the lymphatic system because Sabin proved that it developed from embryonic veins, not from other tissues, as previously believed. In 1902, Sabin began teaching anatomy and histology (the study of tissues) at the Johns Hopkins Medical School and was promoted to associate professor in 1905 and professor in 1917, making her the first woman to hold the latter rank at any American medical institution.

In 1924 Sabin was the first woman elected president of the American Association of Anatomists, and the following year she became the first woman elected into the National Academy of Sciences. Sabin remained at Johns Hopkins until accepting a position as head of the Department of Cellular Studies at The Rockefeller Institute in New York City, where for 13 years she studied the pathology of tuberculosis. During the course of her research, she perfected the technique of supravital staining for the study of living cells.

She retired in 1938, but left retirement in 1944 to embark on a new career in health advocacy, accepting Colorado Governor John Vivian's appointment to a subcommittee to overhaul the state's public-health system. The following year she became the Manager of Health and Charities in the city of Denver, donating her salary to medical research. Thanks to the passing of bills in the "Sabin Program," Coloradoans enjoyed improved sanitation and screening for tuberculosis and syphilis. In 1951, Sabin received the Lasker Foundation's Award for public service. She passed away on 3 December 1953.

[See also Anatomy and Human Dissection; Gender and Science; Medicine; National Academy of Sciences; Public Health; Sexually Transmitted Diseases; and Tuberculosis.]

BIBLIOGRAPHY

Florence Rena Sabin Papers. Sophia Smith Collection, Smith College. http://asteria.fivecolleges.edu/findaids/sophiasmith/mnsss110_bioghist.html (accessed 21 March 2012).
Florence R. Sabin Papers. Profiles in Science, National Library of Medicine http://profiles.nlm.nih.gov/ps/retrieve/Collection/CID/RR (accessed 21 March 2012).
Morantz-Sanchez, Regina. Sympathy and Science: Women Physicians in American Medicine. Chapel Hill: University of North Carolina Press, 2000.
Reynolds, Moira Davison. American Women Scientists: 23 Inspiring Biographies, 1900–2000. Jefferson, N.C.: McFarland and Company, 1999.

Julie Des Jardins

SAGAN, CARL

(1934–1996), astronomer, science popularizer. Born in Brooklyn, New York, the son of a clothing-factory worker, Sagan showed a precocious interest in science and earned a BA and PhD in astronomy and astrophysics from the University of Chicago. From an assistant professorship at Harvard he moved to Cornell in 1968, eventually becoming David Duncan Professor of Astronomy and Space Sciences and director of the Laboratory for Planetary Studies. His research findings, reported in numerous scientific papers, included the hypotheses, later borne out by space probes, that radio emissions from Venus were related to the planet's intense surface heat and dense atmosphere and that dust storms caused the seasonal changes in Mars's color. Sagan served as a science advisor for several National Aeronautics and Space Administration missions, including the Mars orbiter Mariner 9 (1971); Viking 2 (1975), which landed a camera-equipped research vehicle on Mars; and Voyager 1 and 2 (1977), which encountered Jupiter, Saturn, Uranus, and Neptune before leaving the solar system.

An early immersion in science fiction had awakened Sagan's fascination with the possibility of extraterrestrial intelligent life, and at his initiative, gold-plated copper disks were placed in the Voyager spacecrafts containing encoded information by which intelligent beings elsewhere might learn of life on the earth. A gifted communicator and prolific writer, Sagan increasingly turned to public advocacy on behalf of astronomy and science in general. He cofounded the Planetary Society to promote space research and probe for extraterrestrial intelligence. He published in Parade, a popular magazine inserted in Sunday newspapers, and appeared often on TV's popular "Tonight" show. His best known venture was the 13-part Cosmos series on public television (1980). Dramatically produced and suffused with Sagan's infectious enthusiasm, the series reached 400 million viewers in 60 countries. The accompanying book, also called Cosmos, became a best-seller. His more than 20 popular books promoting science and space research included The Dragons of Eden: Speculations on the Evolution of Human Intelligence (1977) and Pale Blue Dot: A Vision of the Human Future in Space (1994). His science-fiction novel Contact (1985) imagined an encounter with extraterrestrials while also commenting on U.S. politics in the early 1980s. Turning to public issues, Sagan supported the environmental and antinuclear movements, endorsing the "nuclear winter" hypothesis that a global thermonuclear war would render the earth uninhabitable. An agnostic, he opposed supernaturalist explanations for phenomena best approached through scientific inquiry. His last book, *The Demon-Haunted World: Science as a Candle in the Dark* (1995), elaborated on this theme. Sagan's third wife, Ann Druyan, who collaborated with him on the *Cosmos* series, on several of his books, and on the movie version of *Contact* (1997), aided his media career. He died at 62 of bone-marrow disease.

Although some disparaged Sagan as a publicity seeker or parodied his unabashed enthusiasm and distinctive speech patterns, his efforts were generally admired. At his death, Bruce Alberts, president of the National Academy of Sciences, said: "Carl Sagan, more than any contemporary scientist…, knew what it takes to stir passion within the public when it comes to the wonder and importance of science" (*New York Times,* 21 December 1996).

[*See also* **Astronomy and Astrophysics; National Aeronautics and Space Administration; Popularization of Science; Science; Science Fiction; Space Program;** *and* **Space Science.**]

BIBLIOGRAPHY

Cornell University. Press release, 20 December 1996. http://www.news.cornell.edu/releases/dec96/saganobit.ltb.html (accessed 21 March 2012).
Poundstone, William. *Carl Sagan: A Life in the Cosmos.* New York: Henry Holt, 1999.

Paul S. Boyer

SALK, JONAS

(1914–1995), virologist and developer of the first successful polio vaccine. Born in New York to immigrant parents, Jonas Salk was the oldest of three sons and the first in his family to attend college. He received his BA from the City College of New York in 1934 and his MD from New York University's College of Medicine in 1939. After graduation, Salk worked as a staff physician at the Mount Sinai Medical School before being appointed a research fellow at the University of Michigan School of Public Health in 1942.

Salk conducted virus research first at the University of Michigan and then, from 1947, at the University of Pittsburgh. He became an international hero at the age of 40 when he and his associates developed a vaccine against poliomyelitis, a viral disease that had paralyzed hundreds of thousands of victims, mostly children, in mysterious and terrifying epidemics that swept the industrialized world in the first half of the twentieth century. Traditional theory held that immunity to virus diseases came only from actual infection, but Salk showed that a vaccine made from killed-virus particles could spur immunity without danger. His inactivated-virus polio vaccine (IPV) was tested on 1.8 million school children in 1954 in a massive field trial sponsored by the National Foundation for Infantile Paralysis ("March of Dimes") and received a federal license the following year. Although an early batch of faulty vaccine caused several cases of paralysis, polio incidences dropped by 80 percent after two years in areas where Salk's vaccine was used. Still, many scientists dismissed his work as "cook-book biology," and Salk was never honored in any way by his peers.

After 1960, Salk's vaccine (but not his fame) was overshadowed by Albert Sabin's live-virus oral polio vaccine (OPV), which remained the preferred vaccine for areas in which wild virus was endemic or frequently imported. Since 1 January 2000, however, the U.S. Centers for Disease Control and Prevention recommended a return to the injected polio vaccine to avoid the small risk of vaccine-associated paralytic poliomyelitis from the live-virus vaccine, as have several other nations; the World Health Organization anticipates a global return to IPV (Salk) when the last pockets of endemic wild virus are eliminated. In 1963, Salk became founding director of the Salk Institute for Biological Studies at the University of California, San Diego. His later research sought vaccines to fight cancer and to boost immune system activity after HIV infection. He married twice and had three sons.

[*See also* **Biological Sciences; Cancer; Centers for Disease Control and Prevention; Disease; Germ Theory of Disease; HIV/AIDS; Medicine; Poliomyelitis; Public Health; Research** and Development (R&D); *and* World Health Organization.]

BIBLIOGRAPHY

Carter, Richard. *Breakthrough: The Saga of Jonas Salk*. New York: Trident Press, 1966.
Lawrence, Christopher. "Salk, Jonas." In *Dictionary of Medical Biography*, edited by W. F. Bynum and Helen Bynum, Vol. 5, p. 1101. Westport, Conn., and London: Greenwood Press, 2007.
Smith, Jane S. *Patenting the Sun: Polio and the Salk Vaccine*. New York: W. Morrow, 1990.
World Health Organization. Weekly epidemiological record, no. 23, 85, 213–228 (2 June 2010).

Jane S. Smith;
updated by Elspeth Knewstubb

SANGER, MARGARET

(1879–1966), birth control pioneer and sex reformer, founder of the international family-planning movement. Born Margaret Louisa Higgins, the middle child of a large Irish Catholic family, Sanger emerged on the American scene in the early years of the twentieth century, a follower of labor radicals, free thinkers, and bohemians. She studied nursing at White Plains Hospital from 1900 to 1902 and married William Sanger, an itinerant architect, in 1902. In 1910 they moved to New York City, where Margaret joined several political groups, including the Women's Committee of the New York Socialist Party. She also helped to support her three young children by working as a visiting nurse. This work directed her attention to women's sexual health. Following the death of a patient from an illegal abortion, she vowed to give all women ownership and control over their own bodies.

Sanger's socialist and feminist politics influenced her advocacy of contraception. She argued for reproductive choice as a way to liberate working-class women. In 1914, she coined the term "birth control" in *The Woman Rebel*, a feminist journal she published, as a simple way of talking about a still-clandestine and delicate subject. The first three issues of the journal were banned, and Sanger was indicted for violating the 1873 Comstock Law on obscene publications. She fled to England under a false name. In England she sought out British neo-Malthusians, whose theories led her to begin emphasizing economic and social justifications for birth control in her advocacy.

In 1915 Sanger returned to New York and one year later established the first U.S. family-planning clinic in Brooklyn, which distributed diaphragms and spermicidal jellies. The clinic was raided within a fortnight and Sanger was sent to jail for 30 days. But appeal of her conviction led to licensed medical prescription of contraception in many states and to the founding of what later became the Planned Parenthood Federation of America.

For more than half a century, Sanger battled religious and political opponents who identified birth control with moral and sexual license. At her death, contraception was publicly funded and constitutionally protected. The oral anovulant contraceptive pill had been developed privately with her assistance. In addition, a world population movement had emerged from her pioneering efforts.

But controversy remains over the extent to which Sanger's pragmatic alliances with middle-class reformers and social and professional elites, many of whom espoused eugenic arguments for limiting fertility, compromised her early idealism. Under the sanitized guise of family planning, has contraception primarily been a force for social reconstruction or a tool of social control?

[*See also* **Birth Control and Family Planning; Childbirth; Eugenics; Gender and Science; Midwifery; Nursing; Religion and Science; Sex and Sexuality; Sex Education;** *and* **Sexually Transmitted Diseases.**]

BIBLIOGRAPHY

Chesler, Ellen. *Woman of Valor: Margaret Sanger and the Birth Control Movement in America*. New York: Simon and Schuster, 2007. First published 1992. Definitive biography, reprinted with substantive new afterword considering how Sanger's life and work hold up in light of subsequent developments.

Coates, Patricia Walsh. *Margaret Sanger and the Origin of the Birth Control Movement, 1910–1930: The Concept of Women's Sexual Autonomy*. Lewiston, N.Y.: Edwin Mellen Press, 2008. Explores Sanger's early feminist philosophy, which led her to become an advocate for birth control.

Crozier, Ivan. "Sanger, Margaret." In *Dictionary of Medical Biography,* edited by W. F. Bynum and Helen Bynum, Vol. 5, pp. 1106–1107. Westport, Conn., and London: Greenwood Press, 2007.

Katz, Esther, ed., with assistance from Cathy Moran Hajo and Peter C. Engelman. *The Selected Papers of Margaret Sanger*. 3 vols. Urbana: University of Illinois Press, 2003–2010. Volume 1 covers 1900–1928, volume 2 covers 1928–1938, and volume 3 covers 1939–1966.

Reed, James. *The Birth Control Movement and American Society: From Private Vice to Public Virtue*. Princeton, N.J.: Princeton University Press, 1984. Originally published 1978. This edition includes a new preface. Analyzes how repressed Victorian sexual mores gave way to the growing public acceptance of birth control in twentieth-century America.

Ellen Chesler;
updated by Elspeth Knewstubb

SATELLITES, COMMUNICATIONS

Satellite communication was the only truly commercial space technology to be developed in the first 40 years or so after the beginning of the space age in 1957. Perhaps the first person to evaluate the technical and financial aspects of satellite communications was John R. Pierce of AT&T's Bell Telephone Laboratories, who in the mid-1950s outlined the utility of a communications "mirror" in space, estimating that such a satellite would be worth a billion dollars. Under Pierce's leadership, AT&T in 1960 petitioned the Federal Communications Commission (FCC) for permission to launch an experimental communications satellite with a view toward implementing an operational system. Caught off guard, the government scrambled to develop a policy to regulate this new medium of communication.

The John F. Kennedy administration opposed allowing AT&T a monopoly of satellite communications because it already enjoyed one on Earth. Accordingly, in 1961, to offset AT&T's lead in technological development, the National Aeronautics and Space Administration awarded contracts to RCA and Hughes Aircraft to build communication satellites, *Relay* and *Syncom*. By 1964, two AT&T *Telstars*, two *Relays*, and two *Syncoms* had been successfully launched, and technological know-how had been transferred to companies other than AT&T. Live television broadcasts from the 1964 Tokyo Olympics provided a glimpse of the dawning age of instantaneous global communications.

The Kennedy administration also sponsored legislation in 1962 that created the Communications Satellite Corporation (COMSAT), with ownership divided evenly between the public and telecommunications corporations such as AT&T, ITT, RCA, and Western Union, to lead the U.S. effort in global satellite communications. Later, COMSAT became the American component of an emerging global system known as the International Telecommunications Satellite Consortium (INTELSAT), formed in August 1964. On 6 April 1965, COMSAT's first satellite, *Early Bird*, was launched from Cape Canaveral, Florida. Global satellite communications had begun.

Although COMSAT and the initial launch vehicles and satellites were American, other countries had been involved from the beginning. By the time *Early Bird* was launched, the United Kingdom, France, Germany, Italy, Brazil, and Japan had established communications ground stations. From a few hundred telephone circuits and a handful of members in 1965, the INTELSAT system grew to embrace more members than the United Nations and to possess the technical capability to provide millions of telephone circuits.

Other companies expanded this system as the last two decades of the twentieth century progressed. Cost to carriers per circuit, and to individual customers, declined dramatically as the system matured. By the end of the century, orbiting satellites were generating billions of dollars annually in sales of products and services and had transformed global communication by facilitating commercial broadcasting, business and scientific exchanges, and telephone and Internet communication among individuals worldwide.

[*See also* **Bell Laboratories; Electronic Communication Devices, Mobile; Internet and World Wide Web; Military, Science and Technology and the; National Aeronautics and Space Administration; Space Program; Space Science; Technology;** *and* **Telephone.**]

BIBLIOGRAPHY

Butrica, Andrew J., ed. *Beyond the Ionosphere: Fifty Years of Satellite Communication.* Washington, D.C.: National Aeronautics and Space Administration, 1997.
Hudson, Heather E. *Communications Satellites: Their Development and Impact.* New York: Free Press, 1990.
Martin, Donald H. *Communication Satellites, 1958–1992.* El Segundo, Calif.: Aerospace Corporation, 1991.
Whalen, David H. *The Origins of Satellite Communications, 1945–1965.* Washington, D.C.: Smithsonian Institution Press, 2002.

Roger D. Launius

SATELLITES, GLOBAL POSITIONING

See Space Program.

SATELLITES, RECONNAISSANCE

See Military, Science and Technology and.

SAY, THOMAS

(1787–1834), early naturalist, was born in Philadelphia and died in New Harmony, Indiana. Of Quaker background, related to the eminent botanist-nurseryman John Bartram (great-grandfather) and the natural historian William Bartram (great-uncle), Say was intensely focused on the world of nature from his youth and, self-taught, became an outstanding biologist. His approach entailed the accurate description and classification of living things, dedicated to the task of creating a catalog of all the plants and animals in the vast, unknown, new Republic. He was trained as an apothecary and was one of the founders of the Academy of Natural Sciences of Philadelphia in 1812. As curator, for want of resources, he lived frugally in the Academy's small museum.

Say gathered extensive information about the plants and animals he encountered in his field trips, including one to northern Florida, and in the Long expeditions to the Rocky Mountains (1819–1820) and the Midwest (1823). Considered the "father" of American entomology, he characterized over 1,400 species of insect, belonging to many orders, some economically important. In his careful taxonomic work he described several new species of birds, mammals, snakes, reptiles, amphibians, and crustacea.

In 1825 he accompanied his patron, William Maclure, geologist and president of the Academy of Natural Sciences of Philadelphia, to New Harmony, Indiana, a settlement where a new, progressive form of education was taught, believed to be able to liberate the masses and alleviate society's problems by imparting useful skills and knowledge required for everyday living, as opposed to the inadequacies of a classical, elitist education. On the trip down the Ohio River to New Harmony with several other naturalists, Say met his future wife, Lucy W. Sistaire, who became the illustrator of his publications. Despite the difficulties endured by Say at New Harmony as Maclure's trusted assistant, required to serve as an editor of the New Harmony Press, to teach, administrate, and perform manual labor, he was still able to continue his investigations, which resulted in the completion and publication of his two classics, *American Entomology* (Vol. 3, 1924–1928) and *American Conchology* (1830–1834), as well as several other works. An unassertive man dedicated to science to the neglect of his own welfare, he was, arguably, the very best American naturalist of his day.

[*See also* **Academy of Natural Sciences of Philadelphia; Biological Sciences; Botany; Entomology; Science;** *and* **Zoology.**]

BIBLIOGRAPHY

Stroud, Patricia T. *Thomas Say, New World Naturalist.* Philadelphia: University of Pennsylvania Press, 1992.

Weiss, Harry B., and Grace M. Zeigler. *Thomas Say, Early American Naturalist.* Springfield, Ill.: C. C. Thomas, 1931.

Leonard Warren

SCIENCE

This entry has five subentries: Overview; Colonial Era; Revolutionary War to World War I; From 1914 to 1945; *and* Since 1945.

OVERVIEW

Before the early nineteenth century, "science" referred to organized knowledge generally. The few Americans who systematically studied nature spoke of doing "philosophy"; thus they called the first permanent scientific society, established in Philadelphia in 1769, the American Philosophical Society. By the 1830s, however, science increasingly designated knowledge of the natural world. Between the Revolutionary War and the Civil War, the number of Americans earning a living by doing science swelled from fewer than 25 to an estimated 1,500, most of them working for government agencies or educational institutions. By World War I, the United States had reached parity with the leading science-producing nations and was supporting over 14,000 scientists, perhaps 400 of whom did original research.

In the post–Civil War decades, as the popularity of science soared because of its association with medical and technological wonders, science increasingly came to represent "another name

for truth." By the early twentieth century, philanthropists were underwriting such scientific centers as New York City's Rockefeller Institute for Medical Research and the Carnegie Institution of Washington, whereas corporations, led by General Electric, were opening the first industrial research laboratories. Science's contributions to the two world wars elevated it to the status of a valuable national resource. During World War II the federal government emerged as the nation's primary patron of basic science, and this lavish support continued during the Cold War and beyond, swelling from roughly $1 billion in 1950 to about $70 billion as the century closed. By the year 2000 the United States was funding nearly half of the world's total expenditures on science and technology.

[*See also* **American Philosophical Society; Rockefeller Institute, The;** *and* **Technology.**]

Ronald L. Numbers

COLONIAL ERA

Early Spanish missionaries and explorers employed an Aristotelian cosmology; most early reports also used Pliny's *Natural History* as a guide to describing the fauna and flora of the Americas. Throughout the seventeenth century, Renaissance and Scholastic thought dominated American understandings of the natural world and even persisted into the eighteenth century. Throughout the Colonial Era, astrology figured prominently in almanacs and herbals, especially in discussions of medicine, agriculture, and meteorology. Alchemy was conspicuous in the science curriculum at colonial colleges; several Harvard theses on the philosophers' stone were accepted during the eighteenth century. Both astrology and alchemy were taught at Yale and the College of William and Mary, but Renaissance science received its most comprehensive treatment at Harvard, where Charles Morton's *Compendium Physicae* was used until the 1720s.

The eventual triumph of Newtonian science and the acceptance of Enlightenment thought in the eighteenth century coincided with the appearance of small communities of savants throughout the colonies. For many Americans, the Royal Society of London provided inspiration, books, patronage, and scientific instruments; around 50 Americans in the colonial period were elected Fellows of the Royal Society and many more published scientific communications in the society's *Philosophical Transactions.* Bostonians organized a philosophical society as early as 1683 to converse on natural history, astronomy, and natural philosophy, but it survived only five years. New Englanders, whether Puritan ministers or college tutors, were disproportionately influential in colonial scientific circles until the 1730s. Among their most notable publications were Cotton Mather's *The Christian Philosopher: A Collection of the Best Discoveries in Nature* (1721) and Isaac Greenwood's *A Philosophical Discourse Concerning the Mutability and Changes of the Material World* (1731).

During the eighteenth century, science was promoted most comprehensively and effectively by the colonial colleges. In 1711 the College of William and Mary named a professor of natural philosophy and mathematics, the first such appointment at an American college. At Yale, a gift in 1714 of several hundred books, including Isaac Newton's 1687 work *Principia Mathematica,* from Jeremiah Dummer, Connecticut's colonial agent in London, transformed the teaching of science at the college, most notably through the introduction of advanced algebra. Harvard established the Hollis professorship of mathematics and natural philosophy in 1727, appointing Isaac Greenwood as the first incumbent. His successor, John Winthrop, who taught at Harvard from 1738 until his death in 1779, introduced modern textbooks, conducted research, established a large private scientific library, and rebuilt Harvard's collection of scientific instruments after fire destroyed Harvard Hall in 1764.

Mathematics and natural philosophy were introduced at Princeton (then the College of New-Jersey) during the 1760s and at Brown (Rhode-Island College) during the 1770s and 1780s, but science at both colleges depended more on the efforts of individual tutors than on initiatives of college administrators. At the end of the Colonial Era, science was especially prominent at the University of Pennsylvania (College of Philadelphia) and Columbia University (King's College). Both institutions established medical schools before the Revolutionary War (in 1765 and 1767, respectively), thus inaugurating the systematic teaching of botany, chemistry, and anatomy in the American colonies. Both colleges, moreover, were led by men who emphasized the importance of science in the undergraduate curriculum. William Smith, appointed provost at Penn in 1756 by Benjamin Franklin, not only introduced a full program of algebra, geometry, surveying, navigation, natural philosophy, and agricultural science but also provided apparatus for experimental demonstrations. Science accounted for approximately 40 percent of classroom time. Although Samuel Johnson, president of Columbia from 1753 to 1763, promoted the teaching of mathematics, natural philosophy, and natural history, the scientific curriculum remained modest for many years. Nevertheless, Columbia, like Penn and William and Mary, offered science instruction in all four years of college.

The commercial and demographic growth of Philadelphia and New York City triggered the appearance of scientific, cultural, and educational institutions in each city. After moving to Philadelphia from Boston in 1723, Benjamin Franklin helped organize, *inter alia,* the Library Company of Philadelphia, Pennsylvania Hospital, the American Philosophical Society (APS), and the University of Pennsylvania. He won international acclaim for his research in electricity, published in 1751 as *Experiments and Observations on Electricity*; the Royal Society awarded him the Copley Medal in 1753 and elected him a Fellow in 1756. Although Franklin's American Philosophical Society, founded in 1743, survived only two years, a second attempt in 1769 resulted in a permanent society. Society members observed the transit of Venus across the face of the sun in 1769 and published the first volume of *Transactions* in 1771. John Adams, as American minister to France, was sufficiently impressed with the APS's reputation among the intellectuals of Paris to establish, in 1780, a similar organization in Boston: the American Academy of Arts and Sciences. With these institutions, science in America achieved a critical mass; in subsequent decades, American scientists would build on and extend the achievements of the Colonial Era.

[*See also* American Association for the Advancement of Science; American Philosophical Society; Anatomy and Human Dissection; Bartram, John and William; Biological Sciences; Botany; Chemistry; Colden, Cadwallader and Jane; Electricity and Electrification; Franklin, Benjamin; Higher Education and Science; Jefferson, Thomas; Mathematics and Statistics; Medicine; Meteorology and Climatology; Physics; *and* Religion and Science.]

BIBLIOGRAPHY

Burns, William E. *Science and Technology in Colonial America.* Westport, Conn.: Greenwood Press, 2005.

Chaplin, Joyce. *The First Scientific American: Benjamin Franklin and the Pursuit of Genius.* New York: Basic Books, 2007.

Cohen, I. Bernard. *Benjamin Franklin's Science.* Cambridge, Mass.: Harvard University Press, 1990.

Delbourgo, James. *A Most Amazing Scene of Wonders: Electricity and Enlightenment in Early America.* Cambridge, Mass.: Harvard University Press, 2006.

Hindle, Brooke. *The Pursuit of Science in Revolutionary America, 1735–1789.* Chapel Hill: University of North Carolina Press, 1956.

Hornberger, Theodore. *Scientific Thought in the American Colleges, 1638–1800.* Austin: University of Texas Press, 1946.

Leventhal, Herbert. *In the Shadow of the Enlightenment: Occultism and Renaissance Science in Eighteenth Century America.* New York: New York University Press, 1976.

May, Henry F. *The Enlightenment in America.* New York: Oxford University Press, 1976.

Newman, William R. *Gehennical Fire: The Lives of George Starkey, an American Alchemist in the Scientific Revolution.* Cambridge, Mass.: Harvard University Press, 1994.

Parrish, Susan Scott. *American Curiosity: Cultures of Natural History in the Colonial British Atlantic World.* Chapel Hill: University of North Carolina Press, 2006.

Stearns, Raymond Phineas. *Science in the British Colonies in America.* Urbana: University of Illinois Press, 1970.

Simon Baatz

REVOLUTIONARY WAR TO WORLD WAR I

When Henry Adams wrote in his autobiography, "the American boy of 1854 stood nearer the year 1 than to the year 1900," he was invoking the enormous upheavals—intellectual, social, cultural, and national—of the second half of the nineteenth century. He was also alluding to his favorite thesis: that the pace of history was accelerating, in large part owing to developments in science and technology. Indeed, the era between the Revolutionary War and World War I saw exponential growth in the organizations, journals, and amount of patronage devoted to science. As the U.S. population and economy expanded, so, too, did the industrial infrastructure and the capacity to produce precision instruments. Educational opportunities improved, and career paths, primarily for men, opened up in scientific research and engineering. Religious conservatives' resistance to such scientific theories as geological chronology and biological evolution had no lasting negative impact on science. Most notably, the federal government and a reformed university system became major players in the establishment of a national infrastructure supporting science in America.

Early National and Antebellum Eras.

In 1782 the new nation could boast of one scientist of international repute (Benjamin Franklin, whose 1751 *Experiments and Observations on Electricity* was widely translated and reprinted) and two scholarly societies (the American Philosophical Society, based in Philadelphia, and the American Academy of Arts and Sciences, in Boston). Although the Revolutionary War stimulated domestic manufactures, science itself played no role in the struggle for independence other than to enhance Franklin's reputation as a diplomat. Franklin's colleague, Thomas Jefferson, however, both promoted American science and symbolized American respect for science. Indeed, many of the Founding Fathers employed scientific metaphors in designing and justifying the American "experiment" in government.

Throughout the early Republic and Antebellum eras, most scientists—or men of science, as they were commonly called—were either self-educated or trained at eastern liberal arts colleges such as Harvard and Yale. Many had earned a BA degree and some an MD A few had spent a postgraduate year in Europe studying, touring, and purchasing books and apparatuses; still fewer had received PhD's at European universities. Most scientists identified their special interests in either natural history (botany, zoology, and geology) or medicine and agriculture. Research in antebellum America was typically conducted by individual scientists with very limited resources. Much research was done "out of doors" by specimen collectors, weather observers, and explorers. The naturalist William Bartram (whose father, John Bartram, had established America's first botanical garden in Philadelphia in 1728) explored the Southeast in the 1770s, recording plants, wildlife, and 215 species of native birds. Some government funding existed, particularly for geographical and geological exploration. The Lewis and Clark Expedition (1803–1806) gathered geologic, mineralogical, and natural-history data. The U.S. Coast Survey mapped and improved the nation's harbors; the Army Medical Department conducted a continent-wide survey of medical geography. The Wilkes Expedition (1838–1842), a six-ship U.S. naval mission led by Lieutenant Charles Wilkes, explored coastal South America, the South Pacific, Hawai'i, and the Pacific Northwest and produced 20 volumes of scientific reports.

Individual scientists of note whose careers began in the Antebellum Era include the zoologist Louis Agassiz and the botanist Asa Gray, both of Harvard; the chemist Benjamin Silliman, appointed professor at Yale in 1802, who did important work on carbon vaporization and also trained a notable group of geologists, including Edward Hitchcock (1793–1864) of Amherst College; the physicist Joseph Henry, who published pathbreaking studies in electromagnetism while a professor at the College of New Jersey, later becoming the first secretary of the Smithsonian Institution in 1846; and the chemist John William Draper (1811–1882) of the University of the City of New York, a pioneer in spectrum analysis and human physiology, and, in 1839, using the new daguerreotype process, the first to photograph the moon.

But with a few exceptions, such as the Harvard mathematician Benjamin Peirce (1809–1880), American scientists had little mathematical sophistication, and few possessed well-equipped laboratories. Those who conducted research generally did so in more than one field; for example, Elias Loomis was both an astronomer and a meteorologist. The theoretical foundations and boundaries of physics, chemistry, and biology remained ill-defined. Scientific papers on all subjects appeared in unspecialized journals such as Silliman's *American Journal of Science and Arts*, the *Journal of the Franklin Institute*, and the *Proceedings of the American Philosophical Society*.

The Gilded Age. The situation changed dramatically as the nineteenth century wore on. The Civil War was the first major conflict affected by the industrial revolution. Although it drew on existing technology rather than generating much that was new, the Union's organizational and administrative accomplishments introduced new national networks—railroads, banking, telegraph lines—and infused new technologies into American society. The earth and agricultural sciences continued to receive the greatest share of federal patronage during and after the Civil War, as they had earlier. In 1862, President Abraham Lincoln established the Department of Agriculture and signed the Morrill Land Grant Act for the support of agricultural and mechanical colleges. A national weather service was established by the Army Signal Corps in 1870. The Hatch Act (1887) provided for basic research at state agricultural experiment stations.

Despite the existence of a National Academy of Sciences (1863), centralization of effort proved elusive. By 1886, the federal government had spent an estimated $68 million on various, often overlapping, surveys of the West. The overarching concern motivating most of these government efforts was the central role of western settlement. Scientists who could connect their research to that nationalizing agenda, whether by extending telegraph wires into Indian Territory, mapping mineral deposits, or developing arid-land agricultural techniques, were first in line for government support.

Liberal arts colleges and the new research universities such as Johns Hopkins (incorporated in 1869), Clark (1889), and Chicago (1892) became major patrons of science in the late nineteenth century. Some of the older colleges began offering degrees in science and engineering. The new Massachusetts Institute of Technology (1861) and the post-1862 land-grant colleges supported applied sciences and engineering. Between 1870 and 1900, the number of bachelor's degrees granted by colleges and universities more than tripled, from about 10 thousand to almost 30 thousand. During the same period the number of American PhD's awarded soared from 1 in 1870 to 382 in 1900.

Specialization and professionalization loomed large as advanced training became a prerequisite for a career in science. Institutional support structures—associations, specialized journals, laboratories, and professional standards—grew up around the new divisions of knowledge established by the universities. As early as 1874, the American Association for the Advancement of Science reorganized itself into special-interest sections. The first scientific society based on a single discipline was the American Chemical Society, established in New York in 1876. A flurry of professional organizations followed a decade or two later. The American Physiological Society (1887), the Association of American Anatomists (1888), the American Society of Zoologists (1890), the Botanical Society of America (1894), the American Mathematical Society (1894), the American Astronomical Society (1897), the American Society for Microbiology (1899), and the American Physical Society (1899) shared the common goals of raising disciplinary standards and insulating their community of discourse from nonspecialists.

The Early Twentieth Century. In the first decade of the twentieth century, after this era of dramatic disciplinary and professional growth, developments in the corporate board room, in the laboratory, and in scientific theory and practice all prefigured the coming of a new order in American science. In 1901, the General Electric Company opened an industrial research laboratory and the federal government established the National Bureau of Standards; in 1902, the Carnegie Institution of Washington, D.C., began funding scientific research with an initial bequest of $10 million; in 1903, Wilbur and Orville Wright flew their airplane at Kitty Hawk, North Carolina; in 1904, George Ellery Hale established the Mount Wilson Observatory; and before World War I, Americans won the nation's first two Nobel Prizes in science: A. A. Michelson for his spectroscopic studies and measurements of light (1907) and Theodore Richards for his study of atomic weights (1914). Intellectuals and the general public alike were coming to believe that the key to progress lay in the increased application of the knowledge and methods of science and technology to all spheres of human activity. Science, it was widely believed, was the mother of technology; technology, the worker of wonders. Throughout the Progressive Era an optimistic nation remained convinced that the great engine of progress would operate ever more efficiently thanks to the forces of science and technology. Charles Sanders Peirce (son of the Harvard mathematician Benjamin Peirce), John Dewey, Walter Lippman, and other pre–World War I social thinkers all saw the methods and values of science—or an idealized version of those methods and ideals—as a model for society as a whole.

America's brief involvement in World War I reinforced this trend. Although the contributions of scientists did little to affect the outcome directly, the National Research Council, founded in 1916 to coordinate research for national security and welfare, made clear to both scientists and the general public that a new era of cooperation between science and government had dawned.

[*See also* **Agassiz, Louis; Agricultural Experiment Stations; Agricultural Technology; Agriculture, U.S. Department of; Airplanes and Air Transport; American Association for the Advancement of Science; American Philosophical Society; Astronomy and Astrophysics; Bartram, John and William; Biological Sciences; Botanical Gardens; Botany; Chemistry; Engineering; Evolution, Theory of; Franklin, Benjamin; Gender and Science;**

Geological Surveys; Geology; Gray, Asa; Hale, George Ellery; Henry, Joseph; Higher Education and Science; Hitchcock, Edward; Instruments of Science; Jefferson, Thomas; Journals in Science, Medicine, and Engineering; Lewis and Clark Expedition; Literature and Science; Mathematics and Statistics; Meteorology and Climatology; Military, Science and Technology and the; Morrill Land Grant Act; Museums of Science and Natural History; National Academy of Sciences; Nobel Prize in Biomedical Research; Physics; Physiology; Railroads; Religion and Science; Research and Development (R&D); Silliman, Benjamin, Sr.; Smithsonian Institution; Societies and Associations, Science; Technology; Telegraph; Wilkes Expedition; Wright, Wilbur and Orville; *and* Zoology.]

BIBLIOGRAPHY

Bruce, Robert V. *The Launching of Modern American Science, 1846–1876.* Ithaca, N.Y.: Cornell University Press, 1987.

Dupree, Hunter. *Science in the Federal Government: A History of Policies and Activities to 1940.* Cambridge, Mass.: Belknap Press of Harvard University Press, 1957.

Elliott, Clark A. *History of Science in the United States: A Chronology and Research Guide.* New York: Garland, 1996.

Fleming, James Rodger. *Meteorology in America, 1800–1870.* Baltimore: Johns Hopkins University Press, 1990.

Kohlstedt, Sally Gregory, and Margaret W. Rossiter, eds. *Historical Writing on American Science, Osiris* 2d ser., 1 (1985).

Numbers, Ronald L., and Charles E. Rosenberg, eds. *The Scientific Enterprise in America: Readings from Isis.* Chicago: University of Chicago Press, 1996.

Oleson, Alexandra, and John Voss, eds. *The Organization of Knowledge in Modern America, 1860–1920.* Baltimore: Johns Hopkins University Press, 1979.

Pauly, Philip J. *Biologists and the Promise of American Life: From Meriwether Lewis to Alfred Kinsey.* Princeton, N.J.: Princeton University Press, 2000.

Reingold, Nathan, ed. *Science in Nineteenth-Century America: A Documentary History.* New York: Hill and Wang, 1964.

Rossiter, Margaret. *Women Scientists in America: Struggles and Strategies to 1940.* Baltimore: Johns Hopkins University Press, 1982.

Rothenberg, Marc. *The History of Science and Technology in the United States: A Critical and Selective Bibliography.* 2 vols. New York: Garland, 1982–1993.

Slotten, Hugh Richard. *Patronage, Practice, and the Culture of American Science: Alexander Dallas Bache and the United States Coast Survey.* New York: Cambridge University Press, 1994.

James Rodger Fleming

FROM 1914 TO 1945

In 1916, two years after war erupted in Europe but before America's declaration of war, the astronomer George Ellery Hale began to organize and recruit scientists in universities and industrial laboratories across the nation to work on military problems. His plans for an organization to support such work, operating under the auspices of the National Academy of Sciences (NAS), culminated in the creation of the National Research Council (NRC). As a wartime science advisory board, the council dealt with problems ranging from the manufacture of nitrogen compounds for the production of explosives to the building and testing of submarine-detection devices and the physiology of battlefield shock. With the help of two coworkers, the chemist Arthur A. Noyes and the physicist Robert A. Millikan, Hale, who saw World War I as a great opportunity to promote the advancement of science in America, then orchestrated the transformation of the NRC into a permanent arm of the NAS. Reorganized on a peacetime basis in 1919, Hale's NRC now included a postdoctoral fellowship program for research in physics and chemistry, with the Rockefeller Foundation putting up the money and the council selecting the fellows and administering the program. The program, which later encompassed other disciplines, reinforced the role of universities as the traditional seats of American research. By the end of World War II, universities had emerged as the strongest and largest centers of scientific research in the United States. The number of PhD degrees in science and mathematics awarded by American universities rose from 525 in 1920 to more than 6,000 in 1950.

Scientific Research. The period 1920–1940 saw the rapid development of many scientific fields and the expansion of the scientific research establishment in the United States. Although some government agencies carried out research with the help of government funds, the American scientific community relied largely on private patronage and philanthropy, especially from the Rockefeller, Carnegie, and Guggenheim foundations, to pay for research.

The research ranged from *Drosophila* (fruit fly) genetics and the biochemistry of *Neurospora crassa* (bread mold) in biology to the development of particle accelerators and cosmic rays in physics. Geographically, scientific research spanned the nation; indeed, three of the important early developments in nuclear physics—Carl Anderson's discovery of the positron, Harold C. Urey's discovery of deuterium, and Ernest O. Lawrence's invention of the cyclotron—took place in California. In astronomy, Edwin Hubble's discovery of the expansion of the universe and the construction of the two-hundred-inch telescope, the world's largest optical telescope, paved the way for a revolution in cosmology. The theory of turbulence and airplane wing design in aeronautics opened new vistas in the applied sciences. Linus Pauling's application of quantum mechanics to molecular structure provided a deeper understanding of the nature of chemical bonding. Glenn Seaborg's research on the chemistry of the transuranium elements, starting with the discovery of neptunium in 1941, played a crucial role in the Manhattan Project's plutonium project and the development of the atomic bomb.

Mathematics. Pure mathematics was among the most successful scientific fields in the United States during the early twentieth century. The initial stimulus came from the contact of Eliakin Hastings Moore, Norbert Wiener, Griffith Evans, and other aspiring mathematicians with particular German, English, and Italian mathematical schools. As a result, American mathematicians were able, within a short time, to play prominent roles in developing research groups in academic settings in the areas of analysis, number theory, and the new fields of topology and mathematical logic. The leading centers of mathematical research and graduate education included the University of Chicago, Harvard University, the University of California at Berkeley, Princeton University, and the nearby Institute for Advanced Study.

Although American mathematicians tackled problems in pure mathematics, applied mathematics was at first largely ignored. The subject first emerged as an independent discipline in the United States during World War II. European-born scientists played an important role in closing this particular scientific gap in the United States. Theodore von Kármán, a Hungarian-born engineer and applied scientist and the first director of the Graduate School of Aeronautics at the California Institute of Technology (Caltech), was among those who campaigned vigorously before the war to make applied mathematics respectable to engineers and mathematicians. In 1941, Brown University's R. G. D. Richardson inaugurated the nation's first program in applied mathematics. Later, New York University's Richard Courant, who immigrated to the United States in 1934, established its program. The head of the Rockefeller Foundation's Natural Science Division, Warren Weaver, was also instrumental in advancing and expanding the academic base for applied mathematics in the United States in the 1930s. During World War II, Richard Courant served as a member of Weaver's Applied Mathematics Panel of the Office of Scientific Research and Development.

European Scientists. The arrival of émigré scientists from Europe, which coincided with the Great Depression of the 1930s, brought out the best and the worst in university deans, college presidents, and other representatives of American higher education. Relatively few institutions opened their doors to these displaced scientists, many of whom were Jewish. Latent anti-Semitism, a resistance in many physics departments to theoretical physics (a specialty of many of these refugees), antipathy in some quarters to foreigners, and a concern for young, unemployed, American-born scientists all exacerbated the problem.

Nevertheless, several hundred central European refugee physicists, mathematicians, and physical chemists, dismissed from academic positions on racial grounds following the Nazi rise to power in Germany and other countries after 1933, eventually found new employment in American universities and colleges, industry, and research institutions. Albert Einstein, fleeing Europe in 1933, accepted an appointment at Princeton's Institute for Advanced Study. Later on, many of the émigré theoretical physicists, including Hans Bethe, Enrico Fermi, Emilio Segrè, Edward Teller, and Victor Weisskopf, were recruited to work on the Manhattan Project. Despite their technical status as enemy aliens, these physicists proved essential to the atomic-bomb enterprise. Ironically, fascist dictators overseas helped level the playing field in science. In physics, especially, the émigré scientists contributed substantially to a marked shift of the centers of excellence from Europe to America.

Science after World War II.   Between the two world wars, the American geological community resisted the theory of continental drift and the notion of plate tectonics, subjects popular in Europe. Seismologists, however, at such universities as University of California at Berkeley, Caltech, and St. Louis University, turned their research into a powerful tool for exploring the earth's interior. Although interdisciplinary fields such as geochemistry and planetary science took off after World War II, war-related research, which brought together nuclear physicists and chemists, provided the intellectual spark.

The roots of molecular genetics, too, go back to two revolutionary World War II discoveries. By the early 1940s, Stanford University professors George Beadle and Edward Tatum had shown that the absence (or presence) of an enzyme was inherited as a single-gene trait. Their *Neurospora* genetics research cemented the idea that genes

control enzymes (the one-gene, one-enzyme theory), the chemical stuff of life, and led to the rise of a discipline that cut across conventional boundaries—biochemical genetics. In 1944, Oswald T. Avery, Colin M. MacLeod, and Maclyn McCarty at The Rockefeller Institute produced the first experimental evidence that genes are made of deoxyribonucleic acid (DNA). Their discovery that DNA alone was the carrier of genetic information greatly influenced the later work of James D. Watson and Francis Crick on the structure of DNA.

The growing strength of science in the United States in the interwar years was signaled by a substantial number of Nobel prizes awarded to Americans in the 1914–1945 era. These included, in physics, Robert A. Millikan, Arthur H. Compton, Isidor Isaac Rabi, Otto Stern, Ernest O. Lawrence, and Carl D. Anderson, and, in chemistry, Theodore W. Richards, Irving Langmuir, and Harold C. Urey.

In July 1945, Vannevar Bush, the director of the wartime Office of Scientific Research and Development, sent President Harry S. Truman an influential report, *Science: The Endless Frontier*, laying out a program for postwar scientific research. Insisting on the federal government's duty to support scientific research and scientific education, Bush argued eloquently that economic progress, the health and well-being of Americans, and national security depended on advances in science. He recommended the creation of a federal agency to carry out these activities. The National Science Foundation, established in 1950 in fulfillment of Bush's vision, would play a crucial role in the further development of science in America.

[*See also* **Astronomy and Astrophysics; Bethe, Hans; Biochemistry; Biological Sciences; Bush, Vannevar; Chemistry; Compton, Arthur H.; DNA Sequencing; Einstein, Albert; Engineering; Fermi, Enrico; Genetics and Genetic Engineering; Hale, George Ellery; High Schools, Science Education in; Higher Education and Science; Hubble, Edwin Powell; Hubble Space Telescope; Instruments of Science; Langmuir, Irving; Lawrence, Ernest O.; Manhattan**

Project; Mathematics and Statistics; Medicine; Military, Science and Technology and the; Millikan, Robert A.; Museums of Science and Natural History; National Academy of Sciences; Nobel Prize in Biomedical Research; Noyes, Arthur Amos; Nuclear Weapons; Office of Scientific Research and Development; Pauling, Linus; Physics; Plate Tectonics, Theory of; Quantum Theory; Rabi, Isidor I.; Religion and Science; Rockefeller Institute, The; Seaborg, Glenn T.; Social Sciences; Technology; Teller, Edward; Urey, Harold C.; Watson, James D.; *and* Wiener, Norbert.]

BIBLIOGRAPHY

Goodstein, Judith R. *Millikan's School: A History of the California Institute of Technology.* New York: W. W. Norton, 1991.

Hoch, Paul S. "The Reception of Central European Refugee Physicists of the 1930s: U.S.S.R., U.K., U.S.A." *Annals of Science* 40 (1983): 217–246.

Kevles, Daniel J. *The Physicists: The History of a Scientific Community in Modern America.* Cambridge, Mass.: Harvard University Press, 1977.

Kohler, Robert E. *Partners in Science: Foundations and Natural Scientists, 1900–1945.* Chicago: University of Chicago Press, 1991.

Lankford, John. *American Astronomy: Community, Careers, and Power, 1859–1940.* Chicago: University of Chicago Press, 1997.

McCarty, Maclyn. *The Transforming Principle.* New York: W. W. Norton, 1985.

Rader, Karen. *Making Mice: Standardizing Animals for American Biomedical Research, 1900–1955.* Princeton, N.J.: Princeton University Press, 2004.

Reingold, Nathan. *Science, American Style.* New Brunswick, N.J.: Rutgers University Press, 1991.

Reingold, Nathan, and Ida H. Reingold. *Science in America: A Documentary History, 1900–1939.* Chicago: University of Chicago Press, 1981.

Rhodes, Richard. *The Making of the Atomic Bomb.* New York: Simon and Schuster, 1986.

Servos, John W. *Physical Chemistry from Ostwald to Pauling: The Making of a Science in America.* Princeton, N.J.: Princeton University Press, 1990.

Judith R. Goodstein

SINCE 1945

World War II transformed American science. Before the war, the private foundations—Rockefeller, Carnegie, Macy, Guggenheim, and others—were the dominant patrons of university-based research in the natural and social sciences. Beginning with the mobilization of science for war in 1940, the federal government, especially the armed services, assumed this role, dwarfing prewar philanthropy while transforming both the political economy of science and the content of technical knowledge. Understanding this profound transformation lies at the center of much recent scholarship in the history of American science and technology.

Science and the Military in Cold War America.

At war's end, the leaders of the wartime research and development effort—including Vannevar Bush, James B. Conant, and Karl T. Compton (1887–1954)—attempted to craft the postwar relationship of science and the federal government through Bush's landmark 1945 report, *Science: The Endless Frontier*. Bush sought to insulate federal patronage of the natural sciences from political interference while arguing that only basic research guided and performed by academic scientists would produce the knowledge necessary both to fuel the nation's economy and to protect national security. Bush proposed a National Research Foundation to support research in the physical and biomedical sciences, leaving out the social sciences. Although Congress established a National Science Foundation in 1950, the foundation envisioned by Bush and his colleagues never materialized. Instead, between 1945 and 1950, the American military became the patron of choice on American campuses. Bush tried to manage this dominance through his chairmanship of the national military establishment's Joint Research and Development Board, but this effort, like many to follow, failed to control the military's appetite for science and technology.

Military support of academic research rested on an assumption derived from wartime research: given enough money, one could build any weapon.

For example, the Manhattan Project, with $2 billion of federal funding, took a rare laboratory-bound phenomenon, nuclear fission, and transformed it into an awesome new bomb. For the military, this suggested that scientists could deliver almost anything with enough funds. Believing this, the U.S. Air Force and Navy assumed that a massive research investment would produce the ballistic missile, a weapon (the V-2) that the Nazis had developed during the war. Although millions of dollars flowed into countless guided-missile projects, the United States did not have a successful and operational ballistic weapon until the late 1950s.

Weapons research was not isolated or secluded. Instead, such work took place in academic and corporate laboratories under various labels. For example, researchers at a variety of institutions used captured German V-2 rockets to investigate the upper atmosphere. The knowledge gained was not only of academic interest but of value to missile design. Basic research in the physical sciences was deemed essential to national security. Researchers might claim that they were using the military to fund "pure science," but such claims erroneously assumed that military patrons were easily duped. In fact, an important by-product of the war was the development of a technological intelligentsia within the military. University laboratories became sites for the education of a new kind of military officer, as familiar with calculus as the carbine. Members of this new class, possessing master's and doctoral degrees, understood the complexity of the technologies under development as well as the science behind them.

The ballistic-missile and continental-defense programs dominated the physical sciences in Cold War America. These massive projects had significant consequences at both the institutional and the intellectual levels. New institutions, including the Defense Advanced Research Projects Agency (DARPA), now famous for its funding of the ARPANET, a forerunner of the Internet, were created. Others, such as the Lincoln Laboratories of the Massachusetts Institute of Technology or the MITRE Corporation, became important actors in national security research and development. The digital computer and mass-produced semiconductor owe their existence to the military's ability to fund research that produced expensive and rare technologies. Military production experience allowed for semiconductor manufacturers, including Fairchild Semiconductor and Texas Instruments, to learn the art of growing silicon wafers and writing on them. Although the computer industry has been portrayed as an example of laissez-faire capitalism at work, in truth, the capital fueling research at California's Silicon Valley and Boston's Route 128 was as much a product of government contracts as of private investment. The massive government-funded projects often produced unexpected results. The ballistic-missile program yielded the Atlas booster that launched John Glenn into orbit and other feats of the early space program. The IBM Corporation repackaged software developed at government expense (SAGE) to produce the automated airline-reservation system (SABRE).

An emphasis on utilitarian projects turned American physical science into a large-scale development effort in which the crafting and manufacture of new technologies became more important than the work conducted with the apparatus. The industrial mindset directly affected laboratory life and practice, especially in so-called "big science." Before the war, successful laboratory instruments were often cannibalized for new investigations. In high-energy physics, for example, accelerators quickly became obsolete and new ones were constructed. The built-in obsolescence of mass production entered the physical sciences. Old accelerators might lose their cutting-edge research function, but they were easily turned to other purposes, such as medical research or the production of radioactive isotopes, atomic physics' most commercial product. Skills once essential for research changed. Prewar scientists had been forced to build apparatus from scratch: their postwar successors simply modified preexisting hardware and software to perform research and purchased lab equipment and instruments from catalogs.

Military patronage also affected the social sciences. A key element of military social science, operations research (OR), illustrates this point. OR's origins lay in the application of mathematical techniques to strategic and logistical problems.

Two campaigns secured OR's fame: the wartime antisubmarine effort in the North Atlantic, in which physicists, economists, mathematicians, and others developed new means of searching for submarines under various conditions and constraints, and the mining of the Sea of Japan. These successes generated support for continuing military investment in this new field, both at American universities and at new research institutions such as the RAND Corporation of Santa Monica, California, and the Johns Hopkins University Operations Research Office. OR became the leading edge of mathematical thinking in the social sciences, a trend that included the development of game theory, systems thinking, rational-choice theory, and econometrics. The spread of this quantitative approach to military strategy allowed for the rice paddies and villages of Vietnam to become laboratories for social science.

The Biomedical Disciplines. The other great federal patron of science after World War II, the National Institutes of Health (NIH), concentrated on the biomedical disciplines. A multimillion-dollar enterprise with ever-increasing budgets, the NIH set the tone of U.S. biomedical research. Only with the arrival of the Howard Hughes Medical Institute's grants program in 1987 did a private institution rival NIH in support of biomedical research. At the same time, NIH research was increasingly directed by Congress toward particular diseases. Although President Richard M. Nixon declared war on cancer in 1970, members of Congress were always eager to support disease-directed research for constituents, partly to compensate for their failure to establish national health insurance.

Two landmarks greatly affected the biomedical disciplines in the postwar era. First, the HIV/AIDS epidemic provided NIH with a disease that required research at multiple levels, from etiology through treatment. In turn, government-funded research catalyzed work in the pharmaceutical industry and other corporate settings. AIDS activists brought the military's assumption that "with enough money we can do anything" to the biomedical disciplines, as did those suffering from other diseases, such as breast cancer. Second, the

Human Genome Project (HGP), which mapped and sequenced the genetic blueprint for *Homo sapiens*, profoundly altered conceptions of illness and causality. Wielding computers and drawing on molecular biology and medical science, the HGP promised to alter the biomedical disciplines in ways previously unimagined. By the end of the century, big science, once the physicists' domain, had invaded the biomedical disciplines, with an important twist. For the physical sciences, big science was about location: a single accelerator or telescope served as the focus of research by individuals at an array of institutions. The HGP form of big science was decentralized, with multiple laboratories, public and private, sequencing genes and circulating this information on the Internet. Given the HGP's commercial potential, issues of intellectual property and government ownership arose in unprecedented ways, although the U.S. government preferred to see the genome remain in the public domain. At the same time, HGP threatened to become the biomedical equivalent of the Internet, that is, a foundational technology with standards set by the federal government that served as the base for a massive commercial enterprise. After 1945, science in America became a ward of the state; it remained so as the post–Cold War marketplace increasingly directed the aims and goals of federal funding.

[*See also* **Biochemistry; Biological Sciences; Biotechnology; Bush, Vannevar; Cancer; Chemistry; Compton, Karl Taylor; Computer Science; Conant, James B.; Defense Advanced Research Projects Agency; Diplomacy (post-1945), Science and Technology and; Engineering; Gender and Science; Genetics and Genetic Engineering; High Schools, Science Education in; Higher Education and Science; HIV/AIDS; Human Genome Project; Internet and World Wide Web; Manhattan Project; Mathematics and Statistics; Medicine; Military, Science and Technology and the; Missiles and Rockets; Molecular Biology; Museums of Science and Natural History; National Institutes of Health; National Laboratories; National Science Foundation; Nobel Prize in Biomedical Research; Nuclear Weapons; Physics; Research and**

Development (R&D); Rockefeller Institute, The; Social Sciences; Space Program; Space Science; *and* Technology.]

BIBLIOGRAPHY

Forman, Paul. "Behind Quantum Electronics: National Security as Basis for Physical Research in the United States, 1940–1960." *Historical Studies in the Physical Sciences* 18 (1987): 149–229.

Greenberg, Daniel S. *The Politics of Pure Science*, revised ed. Chicago: University of Chicago Press, 1999.

Kaiser, David. *How the Hippies Saved Physics: Science, Counterculture, and the Quantum Revival.* New York: W. W. Norton, 2011.

Krige, John. *American Hegemony and the Postwar Reconstruction of Science in Europe.* Cambridge, Mass.: MIT Press, 2006.

Leslie, Stuart W. *The Cold War and American Science: The Military–Industrial–Academic Complex at MIT and Stanford.* New York: Columbia University Press, 1993.

Rudolph, John L. *Scientists in the Classroom: The Cold War Reconstruction of American Science Education.* New York: Palgrave, 2002.

Strickland, Stephen P. *Politics, Science, and Dread Disease: A Short History of United States Medical Research Policy.* Cambridge, Mass.: Harvard University Press, 1972.

Wang, Jessica. *American Science in an Age of Anxiety: Scientists, Anticommunism, and the Cold War.* Chapel Hill: University of North Carolina Press, 1999.

Wang, Zuoyue. *In Sputnik's Shadow: The President's Science Advisory Committee and Cold War America.* New Brunswick, N.J.: Rutgers University Press, 2009.

Westwick, Peter J. *The National Labs: Science in an American System, 1947–1974.* Cambridge, Mass.: Harvard University Press, 2003.

Michael Aaron Dennis

SCIENCE FICTION

Modern science fiction was largely born in Europe, with books like Thomas More's *Utopia* (1516), Mary Shelley's *Frankenstein* (1818), and the novels of Jules Verne and H. G. Wells commonly cited as early examples of the genre, broadly defined. The popularization of science fiction in the United States, however, can largely be credited to one man: Hugo Gernsback. Earlier examples of American science fiction can certainly be found—time-travel stories like Edward Bellamy's *Looking Backward* (1888) and Mark Twain's *A Connecticut Yankee at King Arthur's Court* (1889) and sociopolitical tracts like Jack London's *The Iron Heel* (1907) and Charlotte Perkins Gilman's *Herland* (1915)—but it was Gernsback's works as a publisher that formalized science fiction into a truly recognizable genre. Indeed, he is credited with coining the term "science fiction." In April 1926, publisher Gernsback, who had written some science fiction of his own and published the work of others alongside nonfiction articles in his science magazines, launched the first periodical devoted exclusively to science fiction, *Amazing Stories*. Although more devoted to popular science and formula plots than to works of literary merit, *Amazing Stories* was an immediate success and spawned numerous imitations. Gernsback left the magazine in 1929, but it continued, under various publishers and editors, with shifting editorial approach until 2005. That Gernsback's own writing, as well as much of what had been published under his auspices, has since come under intense criticism as politically backward (even proto-fascist) and aesthetically clumsy does not diminish his influence, whether seen as positive or negative. In fact, the criticisms serve as an effective illustration of the primary struggle of the genre throughout the rest of the twentieth century and into the twenty-first: a struggle between science fiction as a serious genre for exploring questions of society and scientific advancement and science fiction as a purely escapist literary form.

Perhaps *Amazing*'s most prestigious imitator was *Astounding Science Fiction*, begun in 1929 and still published today under the name *Analog*, edited by John W. Campbell. These and other magazines introduced many major names in the genre, Robert Heinlein, Isaac Asimov, Ray Bradbury, and L. Ron Hubbard among them. Campbell's work as an editor helped to take science fiction to the next level of sophistication. Moving away (or, arguably, building upon) Gernsback's pulpy notions of technophiliac action/adventure, Campbell encouraged varied approaches to science fiction. Although he insisted on scientific accuracy, he encouraged the examination not only of the hard sciences, but also of social sciences. Perhaps more importantly, he saw science fiction as serving a moral and educative role and as being less about technology and more about the human ramifications of science. Although Gernsback certainly served as an early pioneer, the approach associated with Campbell, as well as the rapid proliferation of magazines, led to what has often been identified as the first golden age of American science fiction, roughly from 1940 to 1960.

In the 1960s and 1970s, science fiction continued to explore new approaches. Formally, American science fiction tended to be a bit more conventional than a "New Wave" of British (and generally European) fiction that was finding its way to the United States in the 1960s. However, political and sociological concerns intensified, resulting in some of the most startling and significant examples of American science fiction: Robert Heinlein's *Stranger in a Strange Land* (1961), Philip K. Dick's *Man in the High Castle* (1962) and *Do Androids Dream of Electric Sheep?* (1968), Frank Herbert's *Dune* (1965), Samuel R. Delaney's *Babel-17* (1966), Ursula K. LeGuin's *The Left Hand of Darkness* (1969), and others.

Beginning in the 1960s, an increased interest in science fiction themes could be found in the work of writers who were not considered purely science fiction practitioners. Kurt Vonnegut's early work was, indeed, published as science fiction, but by his third novel, *Mother Night* (1962), it was clear that he had moved beyond any kind of strict definition. *Cat's Cradle* (1963) and *Slaughterhouse-Five* (1969) represent the pinnacle of Vonnegut's blending of science fiction and what would come to be known as postmodernism. Other postmodern writers followed suit, most notably Thomas Pynchon, whose *Gravity's Rainbow* (1973) would prove a major influence on later breeds of science fiction.

Semiorganized science fiction "fandom" began in the 1950s, but reached a peak in these later decades. Nevertheless, the genre remained a niche interest throughout the 1960s and early 1970s. However, in 1977 science fiction exploded into mainstream American culture, not so much because of the printed material as because of two major motion pictures. *Star Wars* and *Close Encounters of the Third Kind*, although certainly not the first science fiction movies, achieved massive popular success. Some science fiction aficionados scorned these films as peeling back the complexity that the print genre had worked for years developing, reverting instead to traditional space fantasy and semimystical alien abduction narrative, respectively. But there is no question that the films proved that science fiction could be popular and profitable beyond its previous niche success. In cinema, these were followed by blockbusters like *Superman* (1978), *Aliens* (1979), *Blade Runner* (1982), and *E.T.—The Extraterrestrial* (1982), as well as several *Star Wars* sequels. Publishing in the post–*Star Wars* era was rather of two minds. As some cashed in on the success of space opera and alien abductions, others continued to push the genre in new directions.

The 1980s saw yet another influential subgenre arise. Although certainly building on the work of previous writers, including Thomas Pynchon, William Gibson's *Neuromancer* (1984) is often cited as the first major cyberpunk novel. Cyberpunk tended to focus on a near future earth, overrun by technology and globalized corporations. Typical characteristics included stylistic experimentation, a kind of *film-noir* atmosphere, and the use of virtual reality as a cipher for decoding the technocorporate machinations of the world. Key figures associated with cyberpunk include Bruce Sterling, Rudy Rucker, and Neal Stephenson.

Today, science fiction continues to exist as a vibrant and diverse genre. Previous approaches to the genre—from space fantasy to cyberpunk—continue to flourish, even as new writers continue to come into the field with fresh, timely themes—terrorism, ecology, biotechnology, and the like—and new aesthetic concerns.

[*See also* **Literature and Science; Popularization of Science; Sagan, Carl; Science; Social Sciences;** *and* **Technology.**]

BIBLIOGRAPHY

James, Edward. *Science Fiction in the 20th Century.* Oxford: Oxford University Press, 1994.

James, Edward, and Farah Mendlesohn, eds. *The Cambridge Companion to Science Fiction.* Cambridge, U.K.: Cambridge University Press, 2003.

Luckhurst, Roger. *Science Fiction.* Cambridge, U.K.: Polity, 2005.

Marc Oxoby

SCIENCE JOURNALISM

The character of science and medical journalism has reflected the evolution of both media industries and the scientific establishment in the United States. From its start, American journalism included reporting on science and medicine. *Publick Occurrences*, which on 25 September 1690 became the first American newspaper, included two paragraphs describing a smallpox outbreak in Boston.

Early science journalism was descriptive rather than interpretive or investigative. With the advent of the penny press in the 1830s, newspaper journalists treated science and medicine as a spectacle that could be leveraged to attract readers and advertisers. In 1832, for example, the *New York Sun* created a major stir with a hoax story reporting the discovery of winged creatures on the moon. By contrast, economic growth often was emphasized in coverage of technological advances such as the intercontinental railroad and inventions by Thomas Edison. Coverage of scientific journals and conferences was largely limited to reprinting excerpts from texts of papers and lectures.

World War I, with its reliance on military technology such as chemical warfare and radio communications, spurred a new interest by both the public and journalists in science reporting. Early in the twentieth century, scientific organizations began to organize efforts to disseminate science news to journalists and, through them, to the public. Most notable was the formation in 1921 of Science Service, a news service backed by the American Association for the Advancement of Science, the National Academy of Science, and the National Research Council and financially supported by newspaper magnate E. W. Scripps. Science Service provided much of the science coverage of the era. (Science Service now is named the Society for Science and the Public.)

The emerging professionalization of science journalism—and the growing number of full-time science journalists at newspapers—was underscored in 1934 when a dozen newspaper journalists met in New York City to create the National Association of Science Writers. The organization evolved to include public relations officials, broadcast journalists, and online journalists. Initially, the association had two classes of membership, with journalists controlling the organization and public relations practitioners relegated to having less influence. By 1998, public relations practitioners had grown to four-fifths of the membership, and the distinction was abolished. By 2013, it had grown to 2,279 members and 300 student members.

World War II, with its reliance on military technology such as nuclear weaponry and radar, fed renewed journalistic interest in journalism on science and technology in the postwar era. Scientific leaders also decided that more effective science communication was vital for producing a citizenry better informed about and more supportive of the priorities of the scientific community.

By the 1960s, skepticism began to creep into science reporting, with the nascent environmental movement fueled by Rachel Carson's 1962 book *Silent Spring*. Later, controversies over the safety of nuclear power and genetic engineering forced science journalists to address the social and political implications of science and technology. The U.S. space program also created a sense of camaraderie among science journalists.

The 1980s saw a general boom in science coverage, both in print and in broadcast. This was particularly evidenced in an increasing number of newspaper sections devoted to science and medicine. Most notable was the *New York Times*'s Science Times section, which debuted in 1978. However, the boom was short lived: the number of newspaper sections dedicated to science peaked at 95 in 1989 and dropped to 47 by 1992. New science magazines such as *Omni, Science Digest,*

Discover, and *Science 80* also sought to capitalize on the interest in science news during this era, although most of these folded after attracting lackluster advertising and circulation.

Nevertheless, journalists covering science-related topics continued to proliferate. The Society of Environmental Journalists was founded in 1990, and the Association of Health Care Journalists was founded in 1997.

Recognizing the media's influence over public attitudes toward science and technology, scientific institutions have long tried to influence science journalists. In the 1920s or 1930s Morris Fishbein, the politically powerful editor of the *Journal of the American Medical Association,* began giving journalists advance access to journal articles in an arrangement called an embargo that persists today. In 1969, Franz Ingelfinger, the editor of the *New England Journal of Medicine,* enunciated the Ingelfinger Rule, which states that the journal would not publish an article that previously has been covered by lay news media. The rule, adopted by many scientific and medical journals, has shaped many interactions between scientists and journalists. Scientific associations and institutions also have created a variety of awards and fellowship programs designed to promote science and medical journalism.

The advent of the Internet transformed science journalism. Cyberspace has expanded journalists' access to information about science around the globe, and it has enabled the development of new forms of science journalism. An increasing number of science journalist and media organizations operate blogs and produce podcasts such as WNYC's Radiolab. Online technology also has enabled scientists to bypass journalists and communicate directly with the public; the National Aeronautics and Space Administration, for example, has reached out to members of the public using Twitter. Meanwhile, online information undermined the business models of traditional news organizations, leading to cutbacks in the number of science journalists they employ. In 2008, for example, CNN eliminated its entire science, technology, and environment news staff.

[*See also* **Popularization of Science.**]

BIBLIOGRAPHY

Krieghbaum, Hillier. "American Newspaper Reporting of Science News." *Kansas State College Bulletin* 25, no. 5 (1941).

Lewenstein, Bruce V. "The Meaning of 'Public Understanding of Science' in the United States after World War II." *Public Understanding of Science* 1 (1992): 45–68.

Lewenstein, Bruce V. "Was There Really a Popular Science Boom?" *Science, Technology & Human Values* 12, no. 2 (1987): 29–41.

Nelkin, D. *Selling Science: How the Press Covers Science and Technology.* New York: W. H. Freeman, 1995.

Thurs, Daniel Patrick. *Science Talk: Changing Notions of Science in American Popular Culture.* New Brunswick, N.J.: Rutgers University Press, 2007.

Vincent Kiernan

SCIENTIFIC MANAGEMENT

The term "scientific management" was coined in 1910 to describe the system of industrial management created and promoted by Frederick W. Taylor (1856–1915) and his followers. Although Taylor, a native of Philadelphia, had used the term informally to describe his contributions to factory management, his associates, particularly Morris L. Cooke, deliberately chose the label scientific management to dramatize the novelty and significance of their work. This strategy worked brilliantly and the term came to be applied to managerial practices based on clear-cut responsibilities, rational organization, close attention to detail, and the centralized direction of work.

Scientific management arose from what historians have termed "systematic management," a wide-ranging late-nineteenth-century effort to improve factory performance through cost accounting, inventory and production controls, incentive wage plans, and other modern management techniques. Working at Midvale Steel, Bethlehem Steel, and other plants in the 1880s and 1890s, Taylor refined these managerial practices, added innovations such as stopwatch time study, and combined the disparate features into a single comprehensive management package. After his retirement in 1901, he and a group of associates effectively promoted his managerial system to manufacturers. Only after the publication of Taylor's *The Principles of Scientific Management* (1911), mostly written by Cooke, however, did their work become well known outside engineering circles, contributing to a Progressive Era "efficiency" vogue. The impact of scientific management on industry is harder to assess. Taylor's full system was too rigorous for most manufacturers; they adopted bits and pieces according to their needs. By the 1930s most American and European and many Asian factories had introduced isolated features of scientific management, but apparently no plant had introduced and maintained every feature of Taylor's original, carefully prescribed system. The intellectual currents Taylor set in motion, however, proved more profound. By the 1920s, "Taylorism" had disciples in virtually every industrialized nation, and they succeeded in publicizing the value of the precise, systematic management of economic resources, from machinery to national economies.

In the 1930s, American social scientists rediscovered Taylor's writings and began to stigmatize scientific management or Taylorism as a shorthand designation for an oppressive industrial system. In particular, Taylor and scientific management became straw men for theorists and consultants who advocated more humanistic approaches to industrial organization. Both the criticism and the application of Taylor's principles continued as the twentieth century ended. Scientific management has thus proven to be a highly malleable and ambiguous term defined by diverse, conflicting constituencies.

[*See also* **Machinery and Manufacturing.**]

BIBLIOGRAPHY

Kanigel, Robert. *The One Best Way*. New York: Viking Press, 1997.
Nelson, Daniel, ed. *A Mental Revolution: Scientific Management since Taylor*. Columbus: Ohio State University Press, 1992.

Daniel Nelson

SCOPES TRIAL

Celebrated 1925 case involving the teaching of evolution in public schools. By 1920, Protestant fundamentalism had coalesced from various conservative religious traditions into an organized movement fighting the spread of religious modernism and cultural secularism. Fundamentalist leaders viewed evolutionary naturalism, propounded by Charles Darwin in *The Origin of Species* (1859), as a root cause of both developments. Joined by William Jennings Bryan, they launched a national crusade against Darwinism. Their first major legal victory came in 1925, when Tennessee outlawed teaching about human evolution in public schools. The American Civil Liberties Union invited local teachers to challenge the law. John Scopes, a young science teacher in Dayton, Tennessee, accepted the challenge at the urging of local school and civic leaders, who sought to promote their town.

The case resulted in a highly publicized clash of ideas rather than a serious prosecution of Scopes, who was never threatened with jail or loss of job. Bryan joined the prosecution, which vigorously asserted popular and parental control over public education. Clarence Darrow, a famed Chicago lawyer, led a team of prominent attorneys and scientists in defense of Scopes and the concept of academic freedom. H. L. Mencken and many other journalists covered the trial, which was also carried live on a Chicago radio station.

Throughout the eight-day trial (10–21 July 1925), Bryan and Darrow sparred over the validity of evolutionary science and revealed religion. The jury convicted Scopes, but not before Darrow exposed Bryan to ridicule as an "expert witness" on the Bible. Bryan died a week later, and the religious crusade against Darwinism turned inward, focusing on building anti-evolution institutions within conservative Protestant churches before emerging nationally in a late-twentieth-century push for including creationist ideas in the public-school science curriculum. In 1927, the Tennessee Supreme Court reversed Scopes's conviction on a technicality but upheld the law. Several southern states adopted similar restrictions, although none was enforced in court.

Although the Scopes trial had little impact on popular religious or scientific beliefs, it passed into folklore as an object lesson in the danger of intolerance in a democratic society. The defense theory of individual freedom and strict separation of church and state was later adopted by the U.S. Supreme Court in a series of decisions, most notably *McCollum v. Board of Education* (1948), barring public-school religious instruction; *Abington Township School District v. Schempp* (1963), against officially sponsored prayer in public schools; and *Epperson v. Arkansas* (1968), overturning a state statute based on the Tennessee antievolution law.

[*See also* **Creationism; Evolution, Theory of; High Schools, Science Education in; Law and Science; Religion and Science;** *and* **Science.**]

BIBLIOGRAPHY

Larson, Edward J. *Summer of the Gods.* New York: Basic Books, 1997.
Larson, Edward J. *Trial and Error: The American Controversy over Creation and Evolution.* 3d ed. New York: Oxford University Press, 2003.
Numbers, Ronald L. *Darwinism Comes to America.* Cambridge, Mass.: Harvard University Press, 1998.

Edward J. Larson

SCRIPPS INSTITUTION OF OCEANOGRAPHY

Scripps Institution of Oceanography (SIO) is the first U.S. oceanographic institution, founded originally as a marine biology station in San Diego by William Emerson Ritter in 1903. As was traditional, the institute offered introductory courses in the marine sciences until Ritter obtained funding from the Scripps family to focus on "marine exploration…of the larger problems of the life of the sea" (Ritter, 1912). This did not include oceanography, however, as Ritter made clear: "while we are greatly interested in oceano-

graphic problems as such, we must not…let these rise to the place of primary importance. Biology is our main interest" (Ritter, 1908). In 1912, the station was transferred to the University of California, Berkeley, and named Scripps Institution of Biological Research. Over the next decade, independent investigators, University of California faculty members, and staff in La Jolla produced over 130 publications, ranging from descriptions of fauna and flora, fertilization studies, hydrography, plankton dynamics, and physiology of the cell surface.

Oceanography at Scripps dates from the appointment of T. Wayland Vaughan in 1924 as director and the subsequent renaming of the institution as Scripps Institution of Oceanography. After World War I, oceanography gained national prominence for its application to marine warfare and Vaughan turned his scientific interests toward the sea through his activity at the Pan-Pacific Science Congress and on the Committee on Physical and Chemical Oceanography of the Pacific. By 1927, he called for establishing "oceanographic stations" along the Pacific, the same year the National Academy of Sciences (NAS) appointed its influential Committee on Oceanography, on which he served. In 1930, when the Rockefeller Foundation announced recipients of support for oceanographic research, Scripps received substantial funds.

Under Vaughan, oceanography diverged from marine biology and established its separate sphere of investigation by the early 1930s. The new field benefited from several patrons, including philanthropic, federal, and military sources, and the important addition of research vessels, beginning with R/V Scripps in 1925. Given the proximity of naval operations in San Diego, developments in marine acoustics and related aspects of physical oceanography that applied to submarine warfare received particular attention. Sophisticated sonar devices, improvements of the Nansen bottle, creation of the bathythermograph (BT), and the invention of hydrophones for deep-sea sound detection were all features of Scripps. Geological oceanographers explored shallow oceanic basins for oil, notably in southern California and in the Gulf of Mexico. Meteorological research, pioneered originally by George McEwen, probed the relationship among pelagic currents, oceanic wind patterns, and continental weather.

Vaughan also added graduate education to his oceanographic institution, which had at least two major impacts. First, it required additional resources for the La Jolla facility, thus expanding the Scripps institution. Second, Scripps became the influential leader for newly emerging oceanographic centers. Thus, when Rockefeller funds created two new oceanographic centers (Woods Hole and Seattle), they were modeled after Scripps. This ensured that graduate education would continue as an integral part of American oceanography.

Scripps was also a pioneer in developing oceanography's interdisciplinary character, both in education and in research. This became explicit with the work of Harald Sverdrup in the early 1940s, especially in the coauthored "bible" of oceanography, *The Oceans*. Sverdrup was among the first to suggest that spatial–temporal patterns of sea surface water conditions mapped oceanic productivity, a clear argument to integrate the disciplines of physical and biological oceanography.

The century's World War II underscored oceanography's centrality to the American war effort, especially in terms of submarine warfare. When the war ended, the federal government established the Office of Naval Research (ONR) to ensure postwar funding for oceanography. In addition, surplus navy vessels provided a surfeit of research platforms for oceanographers; both money and ships were critical for continued growth and expansion at Scripps.

Later concerns during the Cold War continued the flow of patronage from the navy for oceanographic research. The presence at Scripps of several former submarine officers, including Fred Speiss and Walter Munk, led to new research directions. Although physical factors of the seas continued to interest the navy, it also became interested in deep ocean basins, which involved building an extensive hydrophone system to monitor the movement of Soviet submarines. Coincidentally, these same regions attracted attention from oceanographers in the late 1950s and 1960s as ideas of seafloor spreading and continental drift emerged. Mid-ocean ridges and deep-sea trenches

gave these notions added credence, but also called for new technological tools. Better measuring devices led to the discovery of deep-sea warm-water currents, suggesting the presence of hydrothermal activity. Other investigations of oceanic currents began to erode the age-old notion of separate oceans and led to ideas of a general and global oceanic circulation. Increasingly, this type of research at Scripps became more expensive, multidisciplinary, and technological, requiring greater financial resources, larger groups of collaborating researchers, and international cooperation.

With the continued growth of oceanography at Scripps, especially under the leadership of Roger Revelle, the institution became the centerpiece for the expansion of the University of California system when its San Diego campus opened in the 1960s. Revelle played a pivotal role in these developments, as well as providing the intellectual leadership for research at Scripps during its most expansive and productive phases. For example, during the 1970s, Charles Keeling initiated his career-long study of the ocean as an indicator of global warming and climate change. Other colleagues continued to pursue deep-ocean research, helping to develop a new technological device, the deep-sea submersible.

Although the navy developed submersibles earlier, by the 1970s it had pressed modified versions into basic oceanographic research. Returning to the question of seafloor spreading and hydrothermal vents, oceanographers soon discovered sea vents adjacent to oceanic ridges, work in which Scripps figured prominently. Even more dramatic were the faunal forms inhabiting these vents. For the first time, researchers described luxuriant "gardens" of deep-sea animals, all new to science. Plate tectonics was not just confirmed; the physical, chemical, and biological aspects of the vents opened a new era for oceanographic research. By the close of the century, new ideas concerning the origin of life, conditions for the emergence of life, sources for the chemical composition of seawater, and deep-ocean sources for thermal conductivity created fresh perspectives for oceanographic work. Coupled with exciting extensions of the century-long work to study open-ocean currents, including work on the longitudinal oscillations of large masses of warm and cold water in the central gyres of the oceans that affect the earth's climate, oceanography at the beginning of the twenty-first century promised to maintain its prominent role in scientific research.

[*See also* Biological Sciences; Global Warming; Meteorology and Climatology; Military, Science and Technology and the; National Academy of Sciences; Oceanography; Plate Tectonics, Theory of; *and* Rockefeller Institute, The.]

BIBLIOGRAPHY

Raitt, Helen, and Beatrice Moulton. *Scripps Institution of Oceanography: First Fifty Years*. Los Angeles: Ritchie Press; 1967.
Shor, Elizabeth, Deborah Day, Kevin Hardy, and Dora Dalton. "Scripps Time Line." *Oceanography* 16 (2003): 109–119.

Keith R. Benson

SEABORG, GLENN T.

(1912–1999), nuclear chemist, discoverer of atomic elements, university administrator, and long-time government advisor. Born in Ishpeming, Michigan, Seaborg grew up around Los Angeles, obtaining a bachelor's degree in chemistry in 1933 from the University of California, Los Angeles. As a PhD student at the University of California, Berkeley, Seaborg found his scientific vocation: the creation of new chemical isotopes and elements. In early 1941, as a young professor of chemistry at Berkeley, Seaborg and his associates were the first to isolate element 94, plutonium (just the second heavier-than-uranium—or transuranic—element ever observed), by bombarding uranium with deuterons produced in E. O. Lawrence's famed cyclotron. When Seaborg's group found that a heavier isotope of plutonium was highly fissionable, it became a promising candidate as weapons material to be used for the atomic bomb. Working at the University of Chicago's Metallurgical Laboratory as part of the wartime Manhattan Project, Seaborg led efforts to expand plutonium production to an industrial scale.

Government advising increasingly occupied Seaborg after the war, beginning in 1947 with a three-year appointment to the General Advisory Committee of the newly formed Atomic Energy Commission (AEC). He sat on the President's Science Advisory Committee for two years beginning in 1959 and in 1961 was called by John F. Kennedy to serve as chairman of the AEC, a post Seaborg held under three presidents, until 1971. During his time atop the AEC, Seaborg vigorously promoted civilian nuclear power and took a prominent role in nuclear arms–control negotiations, leading up to the Limited-Test-Ban Treaty of 1963 and the Nuclear Non-Proliferation Treaty of 1968—experiences recounted in two well-received books he published in the 1980s.

Seaborg would identify eight further transuranic elements (95 through 102), sharing the 1951 Nobel Prize in Chemistry with colleague Edwin McMillan. He held several administrative posts at Berkeley, including associate director of the Berkeley Radiation Laboratory during the 1950s and university chancellor from 1958 to 1961. He was a literate and engaged scientist, writing and speaking on a wide range of issues at the intersection of science and society throughout his career. Among his many honors was the naming of element 106—seaborgium—in 1997.

[*See also* Atomic Energy Commission; Chemistry; Lawrence, Ernest O.; Manhattan Project; Military, Science and Technology and the; Nobel Prize in Biomedical Research; Nuclear Weapons; Oppenheimer, J. Robert; Physics; *and* President's Science Advisory Committee.]

BIBLIOGRAPHY

Seaborg, Glenn T., with Eric Seaborg. *Adventures in the Atomic Age: From Watts to Washington*. New York: Farrar, Straus and Giroux, 2001.

Benjamin Wilson

SEWAGE TREATMENT AND SYSTEM

Only since the nineteenth century has waste been transported through sewers to designated sites. Earlier, individuals buried fecal waste, threw household debris onto the streets to be consumed by roving animals, and dumped industrial wastes at sites beyond the city limits. However, since colonial times, open channels or bored-out logs conveyed storm water to nearby waterways. Property owners built and paid for these sewers on an individual basis with little interest in coordinating or integrating them with one another, thus limiting their effectiveness. Moreover, although the wealthiest realized better drainage, the poor wallowed in wetness.

By the middle of the nineteenth century, most health professionals accepted the miasmic theory, which claimed that stagnant pools of water emitted vapors that caused disease. In response, lay reformers, physicians, and engineers lobbied for cities to assume a more active role in municipal sanitation, but only reluctantly did cities comply. City leadership was seldom centralized and few civic leaders had the authority or the technical ability to authorize or coordinate citywide sanitation policy. Furthermore, existing power brokers resisted relinquishing their own authority to empower appropriate mechanisms for infrastructure development. In the 1850s this began to change when Chicago and Brooklyn authorized engineers to devise and implement comprehensive sewerage plans to remove wastewater. Other cities followed suit. The engineers sewered the cities with modern brick, concrete, and clay pipes; however, problems continued to plague the systems. Repairing past haphazard construction practices proved difficult and an ever-increasing volume of wastewater, resulting from increased water supplies, exceeded the capacity of even the newest sewers. Nevertheless, by the end of the nineteenth century, most cities had sewers that dumped wastewater into nearby waterways, and there it went "out of sight and out of mind."

This changed in the 1880s and 1890s as the germ theory replaced the miasmic theory and raised questions over drinking water quality inasmuch as sewers often discharged wastewater into bodies that provided household water. For the next 30 years debates raged over the relative merits of treating sewage before releasing it or purifying the water before consuming it. By the 1920s, most agreed that preliminary screening of suspended solids facilitated purification of the sewage. Thereafter, secondary treatment settled the dangerous impurities in the sewage. By the early twentieth century research indicated that oxidation by filtration and disinfection with chlorine further purified the water.

After World War II, new developments strained city sewerage. Although initially builders installed septic tanks to alleviate the wastewater problems in postwar suburbia, the rate of suburban growth overpowered the septic tanks, compromising the quality of groundwater. Seeking alternative disposal practices, local leaders turned to neighboring city infrastructure and struck deals with the nearby municipalities to convey suburban sewage to city sewers. This increased the volume being transported, thus stressing the conduits. In addition, the aging city infrastructure showed signs of wear, leading to breakage that flooded the underground, backing up sewage and collapsing roadways.

After World War II, state and federal government became players in sanitary policy. They set standards for water quality and sewage treatment. Although the federal government at times provided modest assistance for cities to comply, the resources often proved inadequate and cities often fell short of implementing federal and state guidelines and realizing their goals.

The history of sewerage and sewer treatment in the United States is complex because it involves changing ideas of disease, evolving notions of municipal responsibility, and unclear lines of responsibility. The individual responsibility for their sanitary needs during the colonial period reluctantly changed during the nineteenth century as cities assumed charge over sanitary policy. During the last half of the twentieth century, state and federal governments viewed clean air and clean water as an American right and they too weighed in on standards of sanitation.

[*See also* Chemistry; Disease; Engineering; Environmentalism; Germ Theory of Disease; Household Technology; Hygiene, Personal; *and* Public Health.]

BIBLIOGRAPHY

Goldman, Joanne Abel. *Building New York's Sewers: Developing Mechanisms of Urban Management.* West Lafayette, Ind.: Purdue University Press, 1997. Goldman's emphasis is on changing social, political, and intellectual expectations of New York's city government with regard to public works during the first two-thirds of the nineteenth century.

Melosi, Martin V. *The Sanitary City: Environmental Services in Urban America from Colonial Times to the Present.* Abridged ed. Pittsburgh, Pa.: Pittsburgh University Press, 2008. Melosi's emphasis is on the history of sanitation, including water supply and the disposal of wastewater and solid wastes, for all of American history.

Tarr, Joel A. "The Separate vs. Combined Sewer Problem: A Case Study in Urban Technology Design Choice." *Journal of Urban History* 5 (May 1979): 308–339. One of the premier scholars of public works history, Tarr's emphasis is on the debate over whether to build separate or combined sewerage and its impact on the last 40 years of the nineteenth century.

Joanne Abel Goldman

SEX AND SEXUALITY

Scholars interested in the history of sexuality in America owe a great debt to John D'Emilio and Estelle Freedman, whose 1988 volume *Intimate Matters: A History of Sexuality in America* offered the first synthetic narrative on the topic. During the first half of the twentieth century, medical specialists and social scientists (such as Freud and Kinsey), not historians, assumed the rights to the field. Sexuality first appeared as a legitimate category of historical analysis in the 1970s, a result of a new interest in social history and a response to the women's and gay liberation movements. Feminist historians in particular "helped to spark a mod-erate explosion" of research into the history of sexuality (D'Emilio and Freedman, 1988, p. xii). Scrutinizing court cases, demographics, prostitutes, popular magazines, and language, scholars focused on particular themes, regions, and time periods in this early phase. D'Emilio and Freedman then offered a framework with which to place the meaning and regulation of sexuality in American society. Sexuality in America, they argued, does not represent a linear tale of progress. The assumed trajectory of sexual repression to sexual freedom, from the Puritans to the hippies, vastly oversimplifies and, indeed, mischaracterizes the nature of sexuality in America. Instead, sexuality has been "continually reshaped by the changing nature of the economy, the family, and politics" (D'Emilio and Freedman, 1988, p. xii). Sexuality means different things in varied times and places; thus, even defining "sexuality" in different contexts represents something of a challenge. D'Emilio and Freedman offer three approaches to addressing the history of sexuality: sexual meaning (how has sexuality been defined in different times and places?), sexual regulation (how does society channel sexuality into "acceptable social institutions"?), and sexual conflict (tensions between sexual meaning and sexual regulation).

Although this framework is far more complex than one of repression and liberation, it has invited increasingly sophisticated and useful analyses of sex and sexuality in American history. Since 1988, studies of sexual meaning, regulation, and conflict over the past four centuries continue to enhance our understanding of sexual negotiation, contestation, and practice. Many studies focus on the vibrancy of same-sex cultures and communities in American history, despite institutionalized repression. Starting with precontact Native American cultures and continuing into the late twentieth century, Leila Rupp's *A Desired Past: A Short History of Same-Sex Love in America* reveals the existence of sexual desire and behavior across the centuries. Well before sexologists had coined the term "homosexual," individuals engaged in same-sex behavior, although the meaning and experience varied in different contexts. George Chauncey's *Gay New York* documents the existence of a vibrant gay male culture in urban centers well before the sexual revolutions of the 1960s. In the late nineteenth and early twentieth centuries, both "homosexuality" and "heterosexuality" were categories in flux, far from the rigid boundaries that would come to divide and polarize Americans by the 1950s. Disease represents another area of study that has attracted scholarly attention, particularly in light of the AIDS epidemic. Cultural anxieties surrounding sexually transmitted diseases led to increasingly stringent forms of sexual regulation and public-health campaigns in the twentieth century.

Sexuality in the Eighteenth and Nineteenth Centuries. Since the 1970s, social historians such as Edmund Morgan, John Demos, and Laurel Thatcher Ulrich have added complexity and nuance to our understanding of Puritan behavior and society. Building on this scholarship, historians of sexuality have painted a much more colorful portrait of sexual meaning and practice in early America than previously documented. For example, Richard Godbeer's *Sexual Revolution in Early America* (2004) presents a comprehensive account of the conflict between sexual regulation and practice in the British colonies. In the early modern world, sex was something individuals did, not something that defined who they were. And in the Anglo-American world of the colonies, it was influenced by (and frequently distinguished from) what was perceived as the more permissive sexual practices of Native Americans.

Recent research has also shed light over the role of sexuality in Victorian America, an era fraught with contradictory messages regarding human sexuality. For example, historian Helen Horowitz begins *Rereading Sex: Battles over Sexual Knowledge and Suppression in Nineteenth-Century America* with the seemingly simple question: How did nineteenth-century Americans feel about sex? *Rereading Sex* challenges assumptions about the repressive nature of Victorian sexuality, offering a far richer and dynamic narrative of our sexual past. One of Horowitz's motives for researching this book was to understand why there has been such a dearth of understanding about

nineteenth-century sexual culture. Censorship and suppression succeeded in silencing this conversation, causing historians to mistakenly simplify the practices of late-nineteenth-century Americans. Skill and determination led her to fascinating discoveries of commercial erotica and its authors, printers, and sellers. Fear of prosecution meant that many of these images were never copyrighted, making them all the more difficult for historians to track. They make their first appearances as historical documents in this volume and attest to the widespread appeal of prurient material in the nineteenth century.

In many ways, the cultural fascination with sexual knowledge and repression in the nineteenth century stems from a wider shift in sexual meaning and practice between colonial and modern times. Generally speaking, sexuality in early America was associated with reproduction, whereas in modern America, it became associated with pleasure and intimacy. Beginning in the nineteenth century, reproductive technology and changing sexual mores allowed for increased practice of birth control, thereby allowing for the separation of sex from procreation.

The term "birth control" was coined by Margaret Sanger, the leading activist for contraceptive prevention in the twentieth-century United States. Specializing in obstetrics, she witnessed women struggling to deliver and raise baby after baby under crowded urban conditions with little money or power. She recalls the number of women who begged her to tell them the "secret" to preventing conception. All she could recommend, however, were condoms or withdrawal, both of which required the cooperation of the male partner. She vowed to make this her lifelong crusade—making birth control accessible to all women. She began publishing *The Woman Rebel* in 1914, a magazine intended for working women to educate them about sexuality and contraception. She also used it to challenge the Comstock Law, in effect since 1873, which prohibited the importation and mailing of contraceptive information and devices in the United States.

Sexuality in the Twentieth Century. Although sexuality and birth control were not openly discussed in public in the early twentieth century, there was plenty of evidence they were already in practice, at least within certain socioeconomic groups. College-educated middle-class white women demonstrated that they were practicing some form of birth control in the 1920s by a dramatic drop in fertility. Katharine Bement Davis's massive 10 year study (published in 1929), *Factors in the Sex Life of Twenty-two Hundred Women,* revealed the extent to which certain women were familiar with forms of birth control. Seventy-four percent of one thousand college-educated women queried admitted to using some form of contraception, although information on birth control had virtually been driven underground. Many middle-class social reformers couched their concern in eugenic terms, fearing that the Anglo-Saxon population would soon be overcome by immigrants and African Americans. Over the course of the century, the white middle-class birthrate had dropped by nearly half, from seven to just over three children. While Teddy Roosevelt and others had sparked a widespread concern about "race suicide" at the turn of the century, the white middle-class birthrate dropped even lower in the 1920s. The rate of childlessness reached a record high in the 1920s and 1930s, and the birth rate would not actually begin to increase until the postwar era.

Although the declining birthrate demonstrated that many (predominantly in the middle and upper classes) still managed to gain access to birth control, it was not widely talked about in public. Most professionals, including physicians and even feminists, avoided such a controversial topic, which they believed might undermine their credibility. Physicians, concerned about the declining birth rate and the change in sexual mores, often perceived contraceptives as both morally and physically dangerous.

Yet whether they liked it or not, sexual behavior and meaning were clearly changing in the early twentieth century. Women's historians such as Kathy Peiss and Beth Bailey link the emergence of consumer culture in the twentieth century with a change in courtship and dating patterns. The commodification of leisure led to a more elaborate style of social exchange. The dress, makeup, and behavior previously identified as working class blurred into the middle class as well, as dance halls, movie theaters, and amusement parks celebrated a more intimate heterosocial interaction. Yet rigidly defined gender roles continued to dictate sexual mores throughout much of the century; women (especially) were expected to remain virgins until marriage, whereas men were encouraged to play the field.

Although most people attribute the shift toward more modern gender roles and sexual behavior to the sexual revolution of the 1960s, in reality, this transformation occurred much more gradually. In 1948, sexologist Alfred Kinsey published the first volume of his massive study on human sexual behavior, based on over 17,000 frank interviews with American men and women. *Sexual Behavior of the Human Male* was a best seller, selling over 200,000 copies in its first year. Unlike Freudian assumptions that sexuality had psychosocial origins, Kinsey viewed it as primarily biological. One of his most radical assumptions, based on his findings, was that human sexuality, rather than being a fixed identity, existed on a continuum from exclusive heterosexuality to exclusive homosexuality. Based on his interviews, he believed that 10 percent of American males were exclusively homosexual. When Kinsey published *Sexual Behavior of the Human Female* five years later, he was immediately denounced by the popular press for trampling on the honor of American women. His argument that male and female sexual desire was more similar than different upset what social conservatives believed to be the innate virtue of American women.

The 1950s is frequently viewed as a decade that celebrated marriage, domesticity, and traditional gender roles for men and women. Yet it was also a time of unprecedented support for a new singles culture. Men's magazines such as *Playboy* celebrated bachelorhood as a desirable pursuit for men looking to escape the constraints of marriage and a family. Hugh Hefner published the first issue of *Playboy* in 1953, establishing the practice of positioning a glossy photograph of a nude young woman in the center of the magazine. Recent scholarship suggests that women also sometimes turned to the media and popular culture as a form of resistance to what they believed to be old-fashioned standards. In 1962, Helen Gurley Brown published *Sex and the Single Girl*, which sold 2 million copies in just three weeks. In 13 chapters, Brown shelled out advice for the unwed working woman. Rather than search for a husband, she stressed, women should celebrate their independence and their sexuality. The idea that women could engage in—and *enjoy*—sex outside of marriage was practically unheard of in 1962.

When Brown took over as chief editor of *Cosmopolitan* magazine in 1965, she further celebrated the world of the working single woman. Unlike traditional service magazines such as *Good Housekeeping* and *Ladies' Home Journal*, which focused on the domestic and family obligations of married women, *Cosmopolitan* (under Brown's leadership) celebrated female sexual independence. In Brown's inaugural issue, a sexy cover photo hinted at the newly sought-after readership, while blurbs guaranteed that these readers would find information inside that they would not see elsewhere, including information about the birth control pill and frank discussions about female sexuality.

Thus, well before the so-called "sexual revolution" of the 1960s, which celebrated a new sexual permissiveness among young unmarried men and women, facilitated by the increased availability of contraceptive methods, traditional sexual standards were beginning to unravel. Yet even as these new modern standards of sexual liberalism were coming into play, Christian conservatives were busy trying to restrict sexual language, in particular, sex education. It was this powerful movement that resulted in the dismissal of Surgeon General Joycelyn Elders for suggesting that masturbation was an appropriate aspect of sex education in 1994—and is the subject of sociologist Janice M. Irvine's *Talk about Sex: The Battles over Sex Education in the United States*. Irvine argues that the battle over sex education enabled the rise of the New Right. She describes this as a paradox; the very people who opposed sexual language "have themselves heavily relied on public talk about sex in order to build a movement and mobilize supporters" (Irvine, 2004, p. 3).

Sex education, of course, targets children, raising the question of how much children should know and when they should learn it. Since the debate over sex education began in the early twentieth century, the "phantasm of the innocent child being dangerously corrupted by sexual talk has provoked controversy" (Irvine, 2004, p. 13). Although a century later children have become increasingly sexualized in popular culture and have greater access to sexual language and material through the Internet, conservatives still attach a great deal of moral weight to the notion of childhood innocence. Fears of destroying this innocence were heightened by the strategic use of what Irvine calls "depravity narratives"—essentially, rumors that played on fears about what was taking place in the classroom. Like urban legends, tales of teachers disrobing or even having sex in front of the class traveled from town to town, provoking bitter disputes about the nature and content of sex education.

Ironically, in their crusade to silence sexual language in the classroom, conservatives themselves became marketers of sexuality. Irvine details the creation of an alternative sexuality industry, as conservatives positioned themselves as sex therapists, educators, and experts. By the early 1980s, they had created a powerful network (through marriage counseling centers, publications, and lecture circuits) enabling them to successfully dominate discussion of sex education with their proposed abstinence-only education. But by talking about sex, even in the interest of stifling sexual discourse, they also drew greater attention to the subject. The debate over sex education continues to dominate public discourse in the early twenty-first century.

[*See also* **Abortion Debates and Science; Birth Control and Family Planning; Kinsey, Alfred; Medicine; Psychiatry; Psychology; Public Health; Sanger, Margaret;** *and* **Sex Education.**]

BIBLIOGRAPHY

Bailey, Beth. *From Front Porch to Back Seat: Courtship in Twentieth-Century America*. Baltimore: Johns Hopkins University Press, 1989.
Bailey, Beth. *Sex in the Heartland*. Cambridge, Mass.: Harvard University Press, 2002.

Chauncey, George. *Gay New York: Gender, Urban Culture, and the Making of the Gay Male World, 1890–1940.* New York: Basic Books, 1995.

Chesler, Ellen. *Woman of Valor: Margaret Sanger and the Birth Control Movement in America.* New York: Doubleday, 1992.

D'Emilio, John, and Estelle Freedman. *Intimate Matters: A History of Sexuality in America.* New York: Harper & Row, 1988.

Demos, John. *A Little Commonwealth: Family Life in Plymouth Colony.* New York: Oxford University Press, 1970.

Fissell, Mary E. "Hairy Women and Naked Truths: Gender and the Politics of Knowledge in *Aristotle's Masterpiece.*" *The William and Mary Quarterly*, Third Series 60, no. 1 (2003): 43–74.

Gerhard, Jane. *Desiring Revolution: Second-Wave Feminism and the Rewriting of American Sexual Thought, 1920–1982.* New York: Columbia University Press, 2001.

Godbeer, Richard. *Sexual Revolution in Early America.* Baltimore: Johns Hopkins University Press, 2004.

Gordon, Linda. *Woman's Body, Woman's Right: Birth Control in America.* New York: Penguin Books, 1990.

Horowitz, Helen. *Rereading Sex: Battles over Sexual Knowledge and Suppression in Nineteenth-Century America.* New York: Alfred A. Knopf, 2002.

Irvine, Janice. *Talk about Sex: The Battles over Sex Education in the United States.* Berkeley: University of California Press, 2004.

Kline, Wendy. *Bodies of Knowledge: Sexuality, Reproduction, and Women's Health in the Second Wave.* Chicago: University of Chicago Press, 2010.

Kline, Wendy. *Building a Better Race: Gender, Sexuality, and Eugenics from the Turn of the Century to the Baby Boom.* Berkeley: University of California Press, 2001.

Luker, Kristin. *When Sex Goes to School: Warring Views on Sex—and Sex Education—since the Sixties.* New York: W. W. Norton, 2006.

May, Elaine Tyler. *Barren in the Promised Land: Childless Americans and the Pursuit of Happiness.* Cambridge, Mass.: Harvard University Press, 1997.

McCann, Carole. *Birth Control Politics in the United States, 1916–1945.* Ithaca, N.Y.: Cornell University Press, 1994.

Morgan, Edmund. *The Puritan Dilemma: The Story of John Winthrop.* New York: Pearson, 2006.

Numbers, Ronald L. "Sex, Science, and Salvation: The Sexual Advice of Ellen G. White and John Harvey Kellogg." In *Right Living: An Anglo-American Tradition of Self-Help Medicine and Hygiene*, edited by Charles E. Rosenberg, pp. 206–226. Baltimore: Johns Hopkins University Press, 2003.

Peiss, Kathy. *Cheap Amusements: Working Women and Leisure in Turn-of-the-Century New York.* Philadelphia: Temple University Press, 1986.

Rupp, Leila. *A Desired Past: A Short History of Same-Sex Love in America.* Chicago: University of Chicago Press, 2002.

Scanlon, Jennifer. *Bad Girls Go Everywhere: The Life of Helen Gurley Brown.* New York: Oxford University Press, 2009.

Tone, Andrea. *Devices and Desires: A History of Contraceptives in America.* New York: Hill and Wang, 2001.

Ulrich, Laurel Thatcher. *Good Wives: Image and Reality in the Lives of Women in Northern New England, 1650–1750.* New York: Vintage Books, 1991.

Wendy Kline

SEX EDUCATION

Before the twentieth century, sex education took the form primarily of personal observation and informal talks, but a handful of books such as *Aristotle's Masterpiece* (first published in English around 1684) and the Reverend John Todd's moralistic *Student's Manual* (1837) also conveyed rudimentary information about sexual functions. In the 1880s and 1890s, the Woman's Christian Temperance Union called for students to take a vague pledge of premarital sexual abstinence as part of its White Cross Movement for personal purity. Countless religious writers and moralists issued veiled but dire warnings against prostitution, masturbation, and all forms of sexual activity outside the bonds of matrimony.

The modern movement to place sex education in the public schools grew out of a broader Progressive-Era crusade against prostitution and venereal diseases that came to be known as the social-hygiene movement. *Social Diseases and Marriage* (1904) by Dr. Prince A. Morrow

(1846–1913), a New York dermatologist, became the central document for the American Social Hygiene Association, a union of public-health physicians, educators, religious leaders, and antiprostitution activists funded by John D. Rockefeller Jr. From its founding in 1914 to its decline and withdrawal from the field in the early 1960s, this organization led the fight for sex education. Prompted as much by fears of moral breakdown as by medical concern, Morrow and others insisted that almost all venereal diseases were transmitted through prostitution and that the social-hygiene movement must therefore attack both problems simultaneously. Despite what they perceived as a "conspiracy of silence" surrounding sexual matters, social hygienists argued that sex education was essential to dispel the ignorance about sex, disease, and immorality that made prostitution and other misbehavior possible. After experimenting with public lectures to adult audiences, sex educators by 1914 turned decisively toward the public schools to teach young people a mixture of medical and moral lessons about anatomy; proper thoughts; and Protestant, middle-class morality. It was a wise choice for a time in which mandatory schooling laws were greatly increasing attendance and Americans increasingly looked to public education for social improvement. However, sex education in the public schools also met strong opposition, particularly from the Catholic Church, and so implementation was halting at best.

Sex education in universities and public schools expanded significantly during World War I with funding from the Chamberlain–Kahn Act (1918), so that by 1920 at least 25 percent of public high schools offered some form of sex education through biology and social-studies classes, poster exhibits, or lectures by physicians. Despite attempts by sex educators to ally with the progressive-education and mental-hygiene movements, sex education drew most of its funding and energy from public-health officials in individual cities and states. Midcentury sex educators took a similarly sober and conservative approach, employing many of the same arguments as their predecessors but

leavening them with psychological and sociological concepts that seemed more therapeutic and less condemnatory.

In the mid-1960s, the U.S. Sex Information Education Council and its leader, Mary Steichen Calderone, reacted against the "sexual revolution" of the counterculture with a more frank and value-neutral approach they labeled "sexuality education," with a broader focus on individual clarification of sexual values and a critical inquiry into gender roles, as well as more explicit representations of sexual bodies and behaviors. Beginning in California, this allegedly "radical" approach sparked conservative opposition that soon grew into an important component of the new Christian Right of the 1970s.

At the same time, the federal government became more involved in sex education. Increasing concern over an "epidemic" of teenage pregnancy in the 1970s led Congress to pass the Adolescent Health Services and Prevention and Care Act of 1978, followed by a series of related measures. The HIV/AIDS crisis that began in the 1980s prompted the development of curricula that paid greater attention to contraception and homosexuality, spurring conservatives to propose an alternative approach, labeled abstinence education. These lessons dwelled upon the dangers of sexual activity outside of marriage and suggested that condoms, in particular, failed to protect against AIDS and pregnancy. Congress and President Bill Clinton enshrined abstinence education in the 1996 Welfare Reform Act, and since that time sex education became a struggle between supporters of abstinence education and sexuality education proponents who support more "medically accurate" programs.

Central questions dating from the earliest days of the sex education movement persisted nearly a century later: Is sex education's mission primarily moral or medical? Is sex education the school's or the parents' responsibility? Is sexual information by itself sufficient to alter sexual behavior at all?

[*See also* **Birth Control and Family Planning; Childbirth; Disease; Gender and Science; High Schools, Science Education in; HIV/**

AIDS; Hygiene, Personal; Kinsey, Alfred; Medicine; Midwifery; Public Health; Religion and Science; Rockefeller Institute, The; Sanger, Margaret; Sex and Sexuality; Sexually Transmitted Diseases; *and* Social Sciences.]

BIBLIOGRAPHY

Luker, Kristin. *When Sex Goes to School: Warring Views on Sex—and Sex Education—since the Sixties.* New York: W. W. Norton, 2006.

Moran, Jeffrey P. *Teaching Sex: The Shaping of Adolescence in the Twentieth Century.* Cambridge, Mass.: Harvard University Press, 2000.

Jeffrey P. Moran

SEXUALLY TRANSMITTED DISEASES

Although gonorrhea, syphilis, and other sexually transmitted diseases existed in colonial America, considerable confusion surrounded the distinctions among them, their causes, and their effects. Sexual activity itself was often blamed for symptoms now recognized as third-stage syphilis. The Revolutionary-era physician Benjamin Rush popularized such causal explanations, focusing especially on masturbation. The linking of masturbation and venereal disease continued through the nineteenth century. Medical knowledge about these diseases gradually increased, however. In *A Practical Treatise on Venereal Diseases* (1842), the American-born French researcher Philippe Ricord identified the three stages of syphilis and the tertiary stage's devastating effects.

Increasingly, researchers focused on prostitution as a means of transmission. In *History of Prostitution: Its Extent, Causes, and Effects throughout the World* (1858), the New York City physician William W. Sanger estimated that at least 40 percent of the prostitutes he interviewed in New York's Indigent and Convict Hospital in the mid-1850s had syphilis or gonorrhea. At New York Hospital, the city's preeminent nineteenth-century medical institution, syphilis and gonorrhea were the most often treated diseases. This connection gave rise in the late nineteenth and early twentieth centuries to a concentrated attack on prostitution, or "the social evil." The influential American Medical Association actively supported this campaign. The New York City dermatologist Prince A. Morrow (1846–1914), a prominent figure in the venereal-disease field in the later part of his life, worked to dispel the silence surrounding these diseases and their spread. Only the elimination of prostitution, not just its regulation, Morrow insisted, would suffice. Because of the reformers' emphasis on sexual self-control, the U.S. Army during World War I resisted issuing prophylactics to the troops, a decision that resulted in such rapid spread of venereal disease among U.S. soldiers in France that American military officers at the front were forced to ignore the government's policy.

Despite the public education efforts of Morrow and others, venereal disease remained a generally taboo subject until the later 1930s, when the U.S. Surgeon General, Thomas Parran, mounted a campaign to increase awareness of how these infections spread and how they could be prevented. The result was a dramatic decrease in venereal disease in the United States, even during World War II, when the government required that all cases be reported and assigned investigative teams to trace the source. The postwar development of penicillin, tetracycline, and other antibiotics provided powerful new weapons against venereal diseases, although some strains proved resistant. Nevertheless, infection rates began to rise in the 1950s, especially among teenagers and young people, with changing patterns of sexual behavior. The public paid little attention until the early 1980s, however, when the advent of acquired immunodeficiency syndrome reinvigorated the campaign to eradicate these ancient scourges, now renamed sexually transmitted diseases. Deaths from the acquired immunodeficiency syndrome epidemic peaked in the mid-1990s, when the annual number reached more than 40 thousand. During the three decades since the early 1980s nearly 2 million Americans contracted the disease.

[See also **Disease; HIV/AIDS; Medicine; Public Health; Race and Medicine;** *and* **Tuskegee Syphilis Study.**]

BIBLIOGRAPHY

Brandt, Allan M. *No Magic Bullet; A Social History of Venereal Disease in the United States since 1880*, expanded ed. New York: Oxford University Press, 1987.

Harden, Victoria A. *AIDS at 30: A History*. Washington, D.C.: Potomac Books, 2012.

Lord, Alexandra M. *Condom Nation: The U.S. Government's Sex Education Campaign from World War I to the Internet*. Baltimore: Johns Hopkins University Press, 2010.

Parascandola, John. *Sex, Sin, and Science: A History of Syphilis in America*. Westport, Conn.: Praeger, 2008.

Vern L. Bullough;
updated by Ronald L. Numbers

SHIPBUILDING

Shipbuilding in North America predated permanent settlement by English-speaking peoples and is generally traced back to the pinnace *Virginia* built by homesick settlers in what is now Maine in 1607. Shipbuilding, promoted by the abundance of shipbuilding timber and British mercantilist policies, provided English colonists with their most profitable export manufacturing industry. By the time of the Revolution, colonial shipyards, especially those in New England where construction costs were 30 to 50 percent lower than in Britain, had built about one-third of the registered commercial tonnage in the British Empire.

After the Revolution and through the Civil War, commercial shipbuilding boomed. Vast forests, cheap labor, and high demand by a rapidly growing U.S. commercial fleet were supported by federal laws that demanded U.S.-flagged ships be American built. In 1855 American shipbuilding peaked, with more than two thousand vessels of all types launched by American shipyards. American ship designers proved highly innovative, building sailing vessels known for their speed such as Chesapeake pilot schooners and extreme clippers, as well as the first steam boats and the unique western river steamboats that supported westward expansion. American antebellum shipbuilding also developed from a highly conservative

craft tradition to one driven by mathematical and scientific principles in this period as professional naval architects arose in response to the complex problems of scale, mechanical propulsion, and iron frames and hulls. However, commercial shipyards seldom built naval craft in this period, denying an effective transfer of ideas between the two. This changed somewhat during the Civil War, with innovative vessels like USS *Monitor* built in commercial shipyards.

The American shipbuilding industry did not thrive after the Civil War. Eastern shipyards found it more difficult to procure appropriate timber, and cheaper and technologically superior British iron and later steel ships drove American shipping from blue-water trades. Government policy also failed to support innovative blue-water American shipbuilding, and the few competitive shipyards that built iron vessels were located near Philadelphia. On the other hand, shipbuilding on the Great Lakes was highly innovative and featured highly efficient bulk carriers, mostly to carry iron ore for the burgeoning steel industry. Construction of the "New Navy" in the 1880s stimulated a revival of interest in designing innovative ships, and formal academic programs in naval architecture commenced at the Massachusetts Institute of Technology (MIT), Webb Institute, and the University of Michigan and a professional group, the Society for Naval Architects and Marine Engineers (SNAME), was founded in 1893. The prime customer was the U.S. Navy, and most of its ships in the "pre-dreadnought" era were built in privately held shipyards.

World War I found the United States lacking the tonnage to build a "bridge of ships" across the Atlantic to win the war. A massive government shipbuilding program produced thousands of cargo vessels such as the "Hog Islanders" built near Philadelphia, but virtually all of them were launched only after the November 1918 armistice and at huge expense to taxpayers. A postwar oversupply of ships, coupled with naval arms limitation treaties, severely restricted demand for new shipping tonnage. By 1928 there were a mere eight commercial shipyards building ocean-going ships, with a total of 60 building ways, of which only 10 were occupied (Harvard, 1945, p. 170). Some shipyards remained open by specializing in repair work, whereas others specialized in a particular type of ship, such as Sun Shipbuilding just outside of Philadelphia, which built oil tankers. Government contracts, policy, and subsidies saved the shipbuilding industry from extinction. The Merchant Marine Act of 1928 resulted in the construction of 64 commercial ships, and the small amount of naval construction was divided evenly between commercial and naval shipyards (Kilmarx, 1979, pp. 160–161). President Roosevelt's "New Deal" programs during the Depression subsidized more commercial shipbuilding after 1936, including standardized freighters like the C-2, oil tankers, and even the luxury ocean liner SS *America*, which went into service in 1940. Demand for shipping increased as Europe went to war in 1939, and by the end of 1940 American shipbuilding had recovered from its slump and was opening new shipyards on all four coasts.

World War II saw American shipbuilding reach its zenith in terms of ships produced, innovation, and social consequence. Shipbuilders produced almost six thousand combatant vessels, cargo ships, tankers, and minor types of vessels during the conflict, utilizing new welding technology and modular construction. With men off fighting at the front, shipyards hired women in large numbers, creating "Rosie the Riveter," an early American feminist icon, as well as the nation's first health maintenance organization (HMO) at the Kaiser Permanente shipyards in Oakland, California.

Following World War II, American shipyards slowly succumbed to foreign competition, which increasingly came from the Far East, which could build ships more cheaply and utilize labor more efficiently. There was some innovation such as the nuclear-powered ship *Savannah*, and a notable increase in the size of ships built as economies of scale became a major factor in shipping, but subsidies slowly eroded, and once again government contracts for civil and military tonnage dominated the industry. The Nixon administration's Merchant Marine Act of 1970 attempted to reverse this trend, but when the Ronald Reagan administration abolished the decades-old Construction Differential Subsidy (CDS) program in the 1980s, dozens of shipyards closed, and the naval buildup

in the 1980s benefited but few. In the early twenty-first century, the American shipbuilding industry was completely eviscerated and has all but disappeared from the American industrial landscape.

[*See also* **Canals and Waterways; Dams and Hydraulic Engineering; Forestry Technology and Lumbering; Gender and Technology; Health Maintenance Organizations; Iron and Steel Production and Products; Machinery and Manufacturing; Maritime Transport; Mathematics and Statistics; Military, Science and Technology and the; Nuclear Power; Oceanography; Science; Steam Power;** *and* **Technology.**]

BIBLIOGRAPHY

Harvard University, Graduate School of Business Administration. *The Use and Disposition of Ships and Shipyards at the End of World War II.* Washington, D.C.: U.S. Government Printing Office, 1945.

Kilmarx, Robert A., ed. *America's Maritime Legacy: A History of the U.S. Merchant Marine and Shipbuilding Industry since Colonial Times.* Boulder, Colo.: Westview Press, 1979.

Lindberg, Michael, and Daniel Todd. *Anglo-American Shipbuilding in World War II: A Geographical Perspective.* Westport, Conn.: Greenwood Publishing, 2004.

Thiesen, William H. *Industrializing American Shipbuilding: The Transformation of Ship Design and Construction, 1820–1920.* Gainesville: University Press of Florida, 2006.

Whitehurst, Clinton, Jr. *The U.S. Shipbuilding Industry: Past, Present, and Future.* Annapolis, Md.: Naval Institute Press, 1986.

Joshua M. Smith

SHOCKLEY, WILLIAM

(1910–1989), inventor of the transistor. Shockley was the leader of an AT&T Bell Telephone Laboratories research team, which included John Bardeen and Walter H. Brattain, credited with inventing the transistor, one of the fundamental technologies of modern information and communications industries. Shockley was a prolific researcher and was awarded over 50 U.S. patents for his work. He also created one of the founding companies in California's Silicon Valley.

Shockley was born in London, England, to American parents and moved with his family to Palo Alto, California, in 1913. He received a BS in physics from the California Institute of Technology in 1932 and a PhD in physics four years later from the Massachusetts Institute of Technology. After completing his degrees, he joined Bell Laboratories and worked in the company's research units in Whippany, New Jersey, and New York City. During World War II, Shockley directed the antisubmarine warfare department at the Columbia University Division of War Research in Washington, D.C.

After the war, he returned to Bell Laboratories as head of the solid-state physics division, where he concentrated on building a better alternative amplifier to the vacuum tube, which was the common technology of the time. In 1947, following an effort that required both trial-and-error research and fundamental insights into solid-state physics, Shockley and his fellow researchers found that a mixture of silicon and germanium behaved as a semiconductor and amplified an electrical signal. For this achievement, Shockley, along with Bardeen and Brattain, was awarded the 1956 Nobel Prize in Physics.

In 1955, Shockley left Bell Laboratories to exploit his invention commercially. He moved to Palo Alto, California, and formed Shockley Semiconductor Laboratory with funding from Beckman Instruments, Inc. He was able to recruit several leading researchers to join him in this venture, which helped to establish the region around Stanford University as one of the centers of technological industry. In 1957, the company lost eight of its key engineers, who departed to form their own semiconductor company. The company subsequently went into decline, and Shockley sold the firm in 1960.

Shockley was appointed to a named professorship at Stanford in 1963, where he served until his retirement in 1975. During this period, he wrote and lectured extensively, often expounding controversial opinions on genetics, race, and intelligence.

[*See also* **Bardeen, John; Bell Laboratories; Electronic Communication Devices, Mobile; Genetics and Genetic Engineering; Intelligence, Concepts of; Military, Science and Technology and the; Nobel Prize in Biomedical Research; Physics; Race Theories, Scientific; Radio; Satellites, Communications; Silicon Valley;** *and* **Solid-State Electronics.**]

BIBLIOGRAPHY

Bondyopadhyay, P. K. "W. Shockley, the Transistor Pioneer—Portrait of an Inventive Genius." *Proceedings of the IEEE* 86 (January 1998): 191–217. http://ieeexplore.ieee.org.proxygw.wrlc.org/stamp/stamp.jsp?tp=&arnumber=658771&isnumber=14340 (accessed 28 March 2012). Concentrates on Shockley's patents and contributions to science and contains reference to much existing literature.

Saxon, Wolfgang. "William B. Shockley, 79, Creator of Transistor and Theory on Race." *New York Times* 14 August 1989, p. D9.

"William B. Shockley—Biography." Nobelprize.org. http://www.nobelprize.org/nobel_prizes/physics/laureates/1956/shockley-bio.html (accessed 28 March 2012).

Eric Rouge and David Alan Grier

SICKLE-CELL DISEASE

Sickle-cell disease (SCD) comprises a group of genetically transmitted blood diseases found in the United States primarily in persons of African ancestry and worldwide in persons with roots in west and central Africa, India, eastern Saudi Arabia, and the Mediterranean. In early-twenty-first-century America an estimated 70,000 to 100,000 persons had SCD and approximately 8 percent of the African American population carried the sickle-cell genetic trait.

The medical history of SCD in America is intertwined with the country's racial history. In 1910 Chicago physician James B. Herrick published an article describing the case of a 20 year-old dental student from Grenada, West Indies (identified in 1989 as Walter Clement Noel), whose red blood cells were "elongated and sickle-shaped." This was the first fully documented description of SCD. The condition, which has existed for centuries in Africa and elsewhere, was carried by enslaved blacks to North and South America. Sickle-cell genes were thus present among people of color in seventeenth-, eighteenth-, and nineteenth-century America, where white planters and physicians noted that blacks often appeared immune to certain common fevers. Racial theories regarding medical differences between whites and blacks arose around such observations and became incorporated into the proslavery arguments of the antebellum South. (Today it is known that people carrying at least one sickle-cell gene are resistant to the most virulent form of malaria.)

In 1917, American anatomist Victor Emmel developed a blood test for SCD by sealing off a drop of blood on a slide and noting whether the blood sickled. If it did, that person, although healthy and with no signs of anemia, was considered to have SCD. Other case reports followed Herrick's, and by the late 1920s medical investigators had labeled SCD as genetic and unique to people of black African ancestry despite several case reports to the contrary. Any "white" person with SCD or a positive Emmel test was now assumed to have some "Negro blood" from past generations and could pass the disease on to offspring. In the 1940s, white Americans justified racial segregation and antimiscegenation laws as a protection of the white race. Healthy African American industrial workers with positive Emmel tests were sometimes barred or removed from jobs because of the belief that they could suddenly develop SCD and become unable to perform their jobs.

In the late 1940s, the introduction of a second screening method—blood electrophoresis—showed SCD to be a molecular disease of hemoglobin, an alteration in the structure of the hemoglobin molecule. Scientists found a variety of abnormal hemoglobins and also recognized that to inherit SCD one had to receive genes from both parents, not just one. The Emmel test, they said, showed the presence of asymptomatic sickle-cell *trait* in otherwise normal healthy people—not sickle-cell *disease*.

Until the civil rights movement of the 1960s and 1970s, neither physicians nor community health leaders paid much attention to SCD, although SCD was occasionally used as a reason for segregating blood supplies or as a test for racial "whiteness." Government funding for testing and research remained low. One bright spot was passage of the National Sickle Cell Anemia Control Act of 1972, which provided funds for research, screening and counseling, and public education. Ten comprehensive sickle-cell centers were established across the country. However, when public-health officials attempted to institute genetic screening for sickle-cell carriers in the early 1970s, many in the black community saw it as a way to restrict reproductive freedom and even as a form of attempted genocide against African Americans. Another social consequence of wider recognition of SCD built on an already existing negative association between African Americans and drug abuse. Severe pain episodes called "crises" are hallmarks of SCD. Relieving sickle-cell pain crises requires strong pain medicines, including addictive drugs. Drug-seeking behavior of SCD patients thus reinforced a stereotype of African Americans.

In the early twenty-first century, research into cures continued. No widely available cure was available, although blood and marrow stem-cell transplants cured some young SCD patients. Gene therapy was also being investigated. Other treatments included blood transfusion, red cell exchange, hydroxyurea, and antibiotics for infection. Most states required sickle-cell screening of all newborns. Mandatory screening of NCAA Division I athletes for SCD/trait became an area of controversy in 2010.

[*See also* **Disease; Genetics and Genetic Engineering; Malaria; Medicine; Pharmacology and Drug Therapy; Race and Medicine; Race Theories, Scientific;** *and* **Stem-Cell Research.**]

BIBLIOGRAPHY

Savitt, Todd L. *Race and Medicine in Nineteenth- and Early-Twentieth-Century America*. Kent, Ohio: Kent State University Press, 2007.

Wailoo, Keith. *Dying in the City of the Blues: Sickle Cell Anemia and the Politics of Race and Health*. Chapel Hill: University of North Carolina Press, 2001.

Todd L. Savitt

SIERRA CLUB

The Sierra Club of California was founded in May 1892 by San Francisco Bay–area businessmen and university professors concerned especially about the uncontrolled destruction of nature: "To explore, enjoy, and render accessible the mountain regions of the Pacific Coast; to publish authentic information concerning them; and to enlist the support and cooperation of the people and the government in preserving the forests and other natural features of the Sierra Nevada Mountains." Under the founding president, the Scottish-born John Muir, the Sierra Club acted as a protective association for Yosemite National Park during the controversy over a reservoir proposed in Hetch Hetchy Valley by wealthy San Francisco businessman James Phelan in the first decade of the twentieth century. The Sierra Club lost the effort to block the reservoir in 1913, when the bill to dam Hetch Hetchy passed Congress. The dam was completed in 1923.

Following World War II, the Sierra Club expanded its mission nationwide and grew meteorically. Its first paid executive director, David Brower, enlisted a large membership, engaged in national campaigns against hydroelectric dams in Dinosaur National Monument and the Grand Canyon, lobbied for the Wilderness Act (1964), and promoted national parks in the North Cascades (1968) and California's redwood groves (1968). Bower and the Sierra Club lobbied federal bureaus like the Forest Service to open their planning processes to public comment. They also pushed to institutionalize this public comment process. Publishing, lobbying, and grassroots political activities made the Sierra Club the most powerful environmental organization in the United States in the years preceding the first Earth Day (22 April 1970).

By the end of the twentieth century, with some 580,000 members and an annual budget of $52 million, the San Francisco–based Sierra Club once again enlarged its mission, now launching a global effort to "protect the wild places of the earth; to practice and promote the responsible use of the earth's ecosystems, and resources; and to educate and enlist humanity to protect and restore the quality of the natural and human environment." In the early twenty-first century, the Sierra Club, with over 1.4 million members, remained the largest and most influential grassroots environmental organization in America. The Club sought to reduce reliance on fossil fuels, protect the country's waters, and respond to climate change by creating resilient habitats for plants, animals, and people.

[*See also* **Carson, Rachel; Conservation Movement; Dams and Hydraulic Engineering; Ecology; Environmentalism; Environmental Protection Agency; Forest Service, U.S.; Global Warming; Hydroelectric Power; Muir, John;** *and* **National Park System.**]

BIBLIOGRAPHY

Cohen, Michael P. *The History of the Sierra Club: 1892–1970*. San Francisco: Sierra Club Books, 1988.

"Sierra Club." http://www.sierraclub.org/ (accessed 15 January 2013).

Worster, Donald. *A Passion for Nature: The Life of John Muir*. New York: Oxford University Press, 2008.

Michael P. Cohen

SILICON VALLEY

"Silicon Valley" is a region at the southern end of San Francisco Bay, stretching roughly from San

Mateo through San Jose, which is dominated by firms that design, manufacture, research, and market products for the information and telecommunications industry. It was developed through a collaboration of industry, universities, and the federal government.

The center of the region is Stanford University. During the 1920s and 1930s, the school educated radio engineers, who provided the expertise for a budding electronic component industry. Many of these firms created the technology for short-wave radios. The U.S. Navy, one of the major customers for such radios, created an airbase, Moffett Field, at the southern end of San Francisco Bay and began contracting with local firms for electronic products. During World War II, Moffett Field became one of the major development centers for the navy, which further expanded the local electronics industry.

After the war, the dean of engineering at Stanford, Frederick Terman, began exploring ways to expand the region's industrial base through collaborations between his university and industry. He encouraged businesses to locate near the university and hire university graduates. One of his students, Bill Hewlett, partnered with another Stanford graduate, Dave Packard, in an early success. Hewlett and Packard formed an electrical instrument firm that bore their names. In 1951, Terman institutionalized his efforts by creating the Stanford Industrial Research Park adjacent to the University.

The Cold War brought new demands for electronic technology. The region became a center for the development of microwave radar, which had a greater range than conventional radar and hence could give the military a longer warning of bombers approaching the country. The region began to shift from vacuum tube technology to solid-state devices in 1955, when William Shockley, one of the inventors of the transistor, located his company near the Stanford campus. Shockley's firm quickly failed. All accounts suggest that he was a difficult manager. Shockley's senior engineers left the company to join a second company, Fairchild, and later left Fairchild to form other firms such as Intel. In all, at least 65 firms claim some connection to Shockley's company.

The region began producing computing technology in the 1950s, when IBM opened a research laboratory in San Jose. Computing technology started to dominate the area with the rise of the integrated circuit, the "chip," first heavily used in the early 1960s as part of the guidance computer for the Minuteman Missile. By the end of the decade, the Intel Corporation could put an entire computer processor on a single chip. In 1971, an industrial trade journal first identified the region as "Silicon Valley."

The integrated circuit initiated the growth of the personal-computer industry, which was quickly followed by the rise of the software industry. Apple Computer was founded in 1977 and five years later Adobe Systems followed, whose software was a key element of the Apple Macintosh. The growth of the area has followed the fortunes of electronics, computer, and software industries. Although the area suffered in the economic recessions of 1992 and 2002, in 2012 it was one of the wealthiest and most productive parts of the country. Other nations and regions have attempted to duplicate its combination of university research, government support, and private industry but few have been as successful.

[*See also* **Computer Science; Computers; Mainframe, Mini, and Micro; Electronic Communication Devices, Mobile; Engineering; Higher Education and Science; Military, Science and Technology and the; Missiles and Rockets; Radio; Research and Development (R&D); Satellites, Communications; Shockley, William; Software; Solid-State Electronics; Technology;** *and* **Terman, Frederick E.**]

BIBLIOGRAPHY

Lecuyer, Christophe. *Making Silicon Valley: Innovation and the Growth of High Tech, 1930–1970.* Cambridge, Mass.: MIT Press, 2007.

Markoff, John. "Searching for Silicon Valley." *NYTimes.com.* 16 April 2009.

Stanford University. "History of Stanford." http://stanford.edu/about/history/ (accessed 12 January 2012).

Erin Dian Dumbacher and
David Alan Grier

SILLIMAN, BENJAMIN, SR.

(1779–1864), educator, editor, scientist. Silliman was born in Trumbull, Connecticut, to a family of modest means. His father was a general during the Revolutionary War. Continuing a family tradition, Silliman studied law in New Haven after his graduation from Yale College in 1796. Although he was admitted to the bar in 1802, the course of his life was radically altered that year when Yale's president offered Silliman the new professorship of chemistry and natural history. Silliman accepted the post, but spent the next four years in various American and European cities learning the sciences he was to teach.

Silliman taught at Yale until his retirement in 1853. By the end of his active teaching career, Silliman was widely acknowledged as the patriarch of American science. He achieved this status not through his own largely descriptive work in chemistry, mineralogy, and geology, but through the achievements of his many students and through the *American Journal of Science,* which he established in 1818. He was the journal's sole editor for the next 20 years. The *American Journal of Science,* commonly referred to as *Silliman's Journal,* the nation's first general scientific periodical, offered a venue where Americans could read about the experiments and observations of their countrymen and publish their own work. Silliman used the journal to call for further support for science and scientific projects and to present his own views on scientific disputes. His students included Amos Eaton, Edward Hitchcock, James Dwight Dana, Benjamin Silliman Jr., Oliver P. Hubbard, and Charles Upham Shepard. Silliman was president of the Association of American Geologists in 1841 and a founding member of the American Association for the Advancement of Science in 1848. He served as the hub of a wide system of correspondence that linked Americans interested in science to one another and to kindred spirits in Europe.

Originally chosen for the Yale faculty primarily on the strength of his Christian character, Silliman actively promoted the union of faith and science in his teaching and in the appendices he attached to his American editions of Robert Bakewell's *Introduction to Geology.* Silliman began to give public lectures in 1808, and his characteristic blend of Genesis and geology made Silliman one of the most popular public lecturers of the Antebellum Era. Under Silliman's influence, Yale became a center for chemistry, geology, and mineralogy. His public lecturing opened his subjects to wider audiences and spread the perception of science as a valuable pursuit.

[*See also* American Association for the Advancement of Science; Chemistry; Dana, James Dwight; Geology; Journals in Science, Medicine, and Engineering; Printing and Publishing; Religion and Science; *and* Science.]

BIBLIOGRAPHY

Brown, Chandos Michael. *Benjamin Silliman: A Life in the Young Republic.* Princeton, N.J.: Princeton University Press, 1989.

Fulton, John F., and Elizabeth H. Thomson. *Benjamin Silliman, 1779–1864: Pathfinder in American Science.* New York: H. Schuman, 1947.

Greene, John C. "Silliman, Benjamin." In *Complete Dictionary of Scientific Biography.* Vol. 12, pp. 432–434. Detroit: Charles Scribner's Sons, 2008.

Julie R. Newell;
updated by Elspeth Knewstubb

SIMPSON, GEORGE GAYLORD

(1902–1984), paleontologist. Simpson dominated American paleontology for some five decades spanning the middle of the twentieth century. This dominance was both quantitative and qualitative because not only did Simpson publish hundreds of articles, monographs, and books (his bibliography includes more than 750 entries), but also his work had a major impact on contemporary views of the origin, evolution, and classification of mammals; the concepts of historical biogeography; the principles of taxonomy and systematics; biostatistical methods; and especially the formulation of the "modern evolutionary synthesis."

His book *Tempo and Mode in Evolution* (1944) applied the concepts and conclusions of the new discoveries in genetics to the large body of fossil evidence from life's long history, claiming that the "microevolution" of the geneticist could indeed be extrapolated to explain adequately the "macroevolution" as evidenced by paleontology.

George Gaylord Simpson was born in Chicago on 16 June 1902. He was the third and last child of Helen J. (Kinney) and Joseph A. Simpson. Simpson attended Denver grammar and high schools, and in the fall of 1918 he entered the University of Colorado at Boulder, soon transferring to Yale, where he continued for his doctoral degree, awarded in 1926. The following year Simpson joined the scientific staff of the American Museum of Natural History as assistant curator of fossil vertebrates. After service in military inteligence during World World II, Simpson returned to the museum, where he became chairman of the Department of Geology and Paleontology until 1958, when he was appointed to an Alexander Agassiz professorship at the Museum of Comparative Zoology, Harvard University.

The special place that Simpson enjoyed in the revolution of the modern evolutionary synthesis was visible beyond his contribution of learned treatises. After the war he helped organize the Society for the Study of Evolution, becoming the society's first president. In 1967, Simpson retired to the University of Arizona, where he continued his extensive research and writing until 1984, when he died of pneumonia.

Professional honors and awards that acknowledge his many scientific contributions include election to the National Academy of Sciences and the American Philosophical Society, the National Medal of Science of the United States, and presidencies of the American Society of Mammalogists, American Society of Zoologists, Society of Vertebrate Paleontology, and the Society for the Study of Evolution.

[*See also* **American Museum of Natural History; American Philosophical Society; Biological Sciences; Evolution, Theory of; Genetics and Genetic Engineering; Geology; Mathematics and Statistics; Military, Science and Technology and the; Museums of Science and Natural History; National Academy of Sciences; Paleontology;** *and* **Zoology.**]

BIBLIOGRAPHY

Laporte, Léo F. *George Gaylord Simpson, Paleontologist and Evolutionist.* New York: Columbia University Press, 2000.
Simpson, George Gaylord. *Tempo and Mode in Evolution.* New York: Columbia University Press, 1944.

Léo F. Laporte

SKINNER, B. F.

(1904–1990), behavioral psychologist. Born in Susquehanna, Pennsylvania, Burrhus Frederic Skinner attended Hamilton College, received a Harvard PhD in psychology in 1931, and remained for several years of postdoctoral research on methods of modifying pigeon and rat behavior through positive and negative reenforcement. Behaviorism, anticipated in the work of Hobbes, Condorcet, and other European thinkers and by Progressive-Era intellectuals who saw modification of the urban environment as a key to benign social control, found its champion in the American psychologist John B. Watson (1878–1958), who contended in a seminal 1913 essay that only through the methodological rigor provided by quantifiable measurements of observable behavior could psychology gain scientific credibility.

Embracing Watson's vision, Skinner taught at the universities of Minnesota (1937–1945) and Indiana (1945–1948), and during World War II he worked for the U.S. Office of Scientific Research and Development. A 1945 *Ladies Home Journal* article, "Baby in a Box," described a glass-enclosed, thermostatically controlled "air crib" he had designed for his infant daughter. Critics later falsely claimed that he had caged her for experimental purposes and that as an adult she became psychotic and committed suicide.

In 1948 Skinner returned to Harvard, where he remained as a professor of psychology until his

1974 retirement. Here he pursued research demonstrating that laboratory animals' behavior could be modified by such strategies as delivering or withholding food pellets. The device he employed in these experiments, the operant conditioning chamber, or "Skinner Box," became a popular icon of behavioral psychology. He reported his findings in *Science and Human Behavior* (1953) and other books. His fascination with human social engineering emerged in *Walden Two* (1948, 1976), *The Technology of Teaching* (1968), and *Beyond Freedom and Dignity* (1971). *Walden Two*, a utopian (some said dystopian) novel, portrayed a small community of harmonious, cooperative, productive members whose behavior is shaped by the positive-reenforcement techniques of the Planners, a cadre of benevolent Skinnerian psychologists. A best-seller in the 1970s, *Walden Two* inspired some experimental communities seeking to transform its vision into reality.

Skinner's influence waned in the later twentieth century, with the rise of cognitive psychology, neuropsychology, and psycholinguistics and the influence of alternative theoretical models, notably Gestalt psychology, founded by Kurt Koffka, Wolfgang Köhler, and Max Wertheimer and humanistic or "positive" psychology associated with Carl Rogers, Abraham Maslow, and Martin Seligman. Advances in genetics research, new means of measuring neural activity through brain scans, and the use of pharmacological therapies for treating depression, addiction, and other conditions further eroded Skinner's influence. Critics attacked his lack of interest in consciousness (which he dismissed as "mentalism") and his simplistic model of environmental conditioning. His approach, they charged, chopped up what William James had called "the stream of consciousness" into a series of involuntary responses to altered environmental factors, leaving no place for the autonomous self, willed action, or moral responsibility. From the left, Noam Chomsky and others dismissed Skinner's social vision as totalitarian.

Nevertheless, Skinner's work influenced advertising practices, counseling techniques, business-management strategies, and educational theories, particularly as computer-based programmed instruction gained favor. Quantifiable empirical research, another legacy of behaviorism, remains normative within academic psychology, even for those who do not accept Skinner's radical behavioralist assumptions.

[*See also* **Behaviorism; Genetics and Genetic Engineering; Mental Illness; Military, Science and Technology and the; Office of Scientific Research and Development; Pharmacology and Drug Therapy; Psychology;** *and* **Social Sciences.**]

BIBLIOGRAPHY

Bjork, Daniel W. *B. F. Skinner: A Life*. New York: Basic Books, 1993.
Rutherford, Alexandra. *Beyond the Box: B. F. Skinner's Technology of Behavior from Laboratory to Life, 1950s–1970s*. Toronto: University of Toronto Press, 2007.

Paul S. Boyer

SKYSCRAPERS

The term "skyscraper" first appeared in Chicago in the 1880s to denote structures taller than the 10-story "elevator buildings" erected in New York City and elsewhere after 1870. First built in Chicago and New York, skyscrapers eventually spread worldwide. Initially they were dedicated to a single function—commercial, residential, service, or industrial—but as they grew taller, multi-use skyscrapers emerged.

No "first" skyscraper can be singled out, because elements of the type appeared in many European and American buildings. New York's five-story Haughwout Store (1856) installed the first safety passenger elevators. Changes in foundation technology in the early 1880s liberated cellar areas for ancillary services. The first non-load-bearing curtain walls were hung on the iron frame of a Liverpool, England, office building in 1864. Chicago's Home Insurance Building (1883) was long considered the world's first skyscraper.

However, it had an incomplete wrought- and cast-iron frame and used steel beams only for part of the upper floor framing. Chicago's Rand McNally Building (1890) boasted the first all-steel frame strong enough to resist wind forces on its own. Other notable early skyscrapers included Louis Sullivan's Wainwright Building in St. Louis (1890–1891) and New York's Flatiron Building (Daniel H. Burnham, 1902), the Metropolitan Life Insurance Tower (1909), and the 60-story Woolworth Building (Cass Gilbert, 1913). Manhattan's 102-story Empire State Building (1930–1931), a tourist mecca, long ranked as the world's tallest building.

Skyscrapers continued to evolve after World War II. Ludwig Mies van der Rohe's functionalist Seagram Building in Manhattan (1956–1958) employed reflecting glass to dramatic effect. Frame columns arranged in tubes along the exterior surfaces, introduced in Chicago's Dewitt-Chestnut Building (1964), provided unencumbered interior floor space. Chicago's Sears Tower (1974), at 110 stories, was the world's highest skyscraper until it was surpassed in 1996 by the Petronas Towers in Kuala Lumpur. The Burj Khalifa in Dubai became the tallest skyscraper in the world in 2010. Although the tallest buildings existed outside of the United States in the late twentieth and early twenty-first centuries, American architects and engineers continued to play important roles in building some of the tallest skyscrapers during this period. The Chicago firm of Skidmore, Owings & Merrill executed the architecture and engineering for the Burj Khalifa.

[*See also* **Building Technology; Empire State Building;** *and* **Iron and Steel Production and Products.**]

BIBLIOGRAPHY

Flowers, Benjamin. *Skyscraper: The Politics and Power of Building New York City in the Twentieth Century*. Philadelphia: University of Pennsylvania Press, 2009.
Goldberger, Paul. *The Skyscraper*. New York: Alfred A. Knopf, 1981.
Landau, Sarah Bradford, and Carl W. Condit. *Rise of the New York Skyscraper, 1865–1913*. New Haven, Conn.: Yale University Press, 1996.

Tom F. Peters;
updated by Hugh Richard Slotten

SLATER, SAMUEL

(1768–1835), key figure in the early U.S. textile industry, was born into a farm family in Belper, Derbyshire, England, a center of England's burgeoning cotton-milling industry. At the age of 10 he apprenticed in a Belper mill owned by Jedidiah Strutt, an associate of Richard Arkwright (1732–1793), a seminal figure, along with James Hargreaves, Edmund Cartwright, and others, in developing the mechanized cotton loom and related textile machinery. Seeking to protect its monopoly, the British government at this time forbade the immigration of textile workers and the export of textile machinery and even drawings of such machines. To circumvent these barriers and to promote American textile production, still a cottage industry dependent on household hand looms, several state legislatures in the newly independent United States offered bounties to immigrants with knowledge of the industry and even sent agents to England to recruit experienced mill workers.

Drawn by such inducements, Slater carefully studied and committed to memory the workings of the machinery in the Strutt mill. In 1789, in disguise and under an assumed name, he immigrated to New York. In America, he soon formed a business relationship, and later a partnership, with the wealthy Rhode Island merchant and would-be mill owner Moses Brown, who operated with a cousin and son-in-law under the name Almy & Brown. With Brown's financing, Slater designed and constructed a mechanized cotton mill by the Blackstone River in Pawtucket, Rhode Island, incorporating state-of-the-art water-powered machinery replicating those Slater had operated in England. Beginning operation in 1790 under Slater's supervision, this mill ranks as the first U.S. factory and a landmark in America's Industrial Revolution.

In 1798 Slater founded his own firm, Samuel Slater & Co., which over the years operated five mills along rivers in Rhode Island, Massachusetts, Connecticut, and New Hampshire. As trade disruptions related to the Napoleonic Wars and the War of 1812 choked off the importation of British textiles, the demand for American-made goods increased. Initially manufacturing cloth from cotton supplied by southern slave plantations, Slater in 1815 added woolen fabrics to his output. The mill workers, including children, were recruited from nearby farms. Building on Slater's foundations, Boston's Francis Cabot Lowell and his associates opened a mill at Waltham, Massachusetts, in 1814 and a larger one at Lowell, Massachusetts, on the Merrimack River in 1822, innovating new modes of corporate finance, a larger labor force, and fully integrated production, from raw cotton to finished, dyed fabric, in a single factory.

Samuel Slater's audacious industrial espionage, coupled with his mechanical genius and entrepreneurial energy, advanced U.S. textile technology and production capacity; provided new sources of income for hard-pressed New England farm families, although often under exhausting and paternalistic labor conditions; and established powerful economic bonds between the plantation South and the industrializing North—linking what abolitionists would soon call "the lords of the lash and the lords of the loom." When Slater died in 1835, a very wealthy man, his company operated 13 mills across New England. His original Pawtucket mill became a museum, dedicated to preserving this facet of early U.S. industrial history.

[*See also* **Cotton Gin; Lowell Textile Mills; Machinery and Manufacturing; Rivers as Technological Systems; Technology;** *and* **Whitney, Eli.**]

BIBLIOGRAPHY

Jeremy, David J. *Transatlantic Industrial Revolution: The Diffusion of Textile Technologies between Britain and America, 1790–1830s.* Cambridge, Mass.: MIT Press, 1981.

Tucker, Barbara M. *Samuel Slater and the Origins of the American Textile Industry.* Ithaca, N.Y.: Cornell University Press, 1984.

Paul S. Boyer

SMALLPOX

Smallpox, a highly contagious, often fatal viral disease marked by high fever and skin eruptions that leave survivors severely disfigured, was one of the most deadly diseases that Europeans unwittingly brought to the Americas. Native Americans, lacking both immunity and experience with its ravages, succumbed quickly when it swept through Mexico and Central America in the 1520s. The first pandemic established a pattern of devastation that persisted into the twentieth century. From New England to the Pacific, smallpox routinely killed at least 30 percent of the Native Americans exposed to it. Epidemics wiped out villages, uprooted tribes, and undermined resistance to European territorial incursions. In the 1760s, during Pontiac's Rebellion, the British military commander in America, Sir Jeffrey Amherst, advocated efforts to deliberately spread smallpox among the Indians.

Smallpox epidemics also severely affected English colonists in the eighteenth century, forcing them to develop rules of notification, isolation, and quarantine—the first systems of organized public-health law in America. Colonists also sought to minimize the virulence of smallpox through the practice of inoculation, a method of inducing mild smallpox that usually left patients alive, unscathed, and immune to further attacks. In 1721, the minister Cotton Mather and the physician Zabdiel Boylston (1679–1766) introduced inoculation in Boston, but controversy greeted their experiment. Townspeople reasonably feared that uncontrolled inoculation could start epidemics. Further refining their health regulations, most towns allowed inoculation only after an epidemic was already under way. By the late eighteenth century, widespread inoculation had greatly reduced smallpox mortality.

In 1798, the English physician Edward Jenner (1749–1823) announced that vaccination (inoculation with cowpox virus) could prevent smallpox altogether. Benjamin Waterhouse (1754–1846), a professor of physic (a branch of medicine) at Harvard, performed the first American vaccination in 1800. American physicians soon were vaccinating routinely. Smallpox did not disappear, however, and vaccination was not risk free. Vaccine purity and technique varied widely and vaccination occasionally led to infection or even death. These hazards convinced some people—antivaccinationists—to avoid it at all cost.

As epidemics periodically erupted throughout the nineteenth century, many cities instituted compulsory vaccination laws. Antivaccinationists refused to comply, arguing that these laws abridged their civil liberties and endangered their health. Although they won repeal in some states and routed health departments in Milwaukee, Wisconsin, and New York City in the 1890s, they lost in the Supreme Court. In *Jacobson v. Massachusetts* (1905), Justice John Marshall Harlan's majority opinion declared compulsory-vaccination statutes constitutional, providing the legal foundation for sweeping twentieth-century state authority over individuals to protect public health. Health departments realized, however, that persuasion was more effective than compulsion. By the early twentieth century, cities, states, and the federal government were addressing objections against vaccination by ensuring its safety. The Biologics Control Act of 1902 set production and quality standards for vaccines that became a model for the world. By 1947, confidence in vaccination was such that more than 6 million citizens avidly sought it when an epidemic threatened New York City. Smallpox last appeared in the United States in 1949, but the World Health Organization did not declare it eradicated globally until 1980. The Centers for Disease Control and Prevention in Atlanta and the Russian State Research Center of Virology and Biotechnology in Siberia kept samples of the virus. Although the World Health Organization slated these samples for destruction on 30 June 1999, both the American and the Russian governments postponed it to conduct research on defenses against the disease should it ever be used as a weapon of bioterrorism.

After the 2001 World Trade Center attack, growing fears that terrorists might acquire smallpox virus prompted President George W. Bush to announce in late 2002 a three-phase vaccination program to immunize nearly 500,000 health-care workers and first responders within 30 days, then over 10 million medical personnel in the months following, and eventually the rest of the population. The plan provoked controversy, skepticism, and confusion. Fewer than 10 percent of those targeted got vaccinated, and the Centers for Disease Control and Prevention quietly retired the effort.

[*See also* **Biological Sciences; Columbian Exchange; Disease; Life Expectancy; Medicine; Public Health; Public Health Service, U.S.;** *and* **Race and Medicine.**]

BIBLIOGRAPHY

Blake, John B. *Public Health in the Town of Boston 1630–1822.* New York and Oxford: Oxford University Press, 1959.

Colgrove, James. *State of Immunity: The Politics of Vaccination in Twentieth-Century America.* Berkeley and Los Angeles: University of California Press, 2006.

Davidovitch, Nadav. "Negotiation Dissent: Homeopathy and Anti-Vaccinationism at the Turn of the Twentieth Century." In *The Politics of Healing: Histories of Alternative Medicine in Twentieth-Century North America,* edited by Robert D. Johnston, pp. 11–28. New York: Routledge, 2003.

Fenn, Elizabeth A. *Pox Americana: The Great Smallpox Epidemic of 1775–82.* New York: Hill and Wang, 2001.

Johnston, Robert D. "A Populism of the Body: The Rationality and Radicalism of Antivaccinationism." In *The Radical Middle Class: Populist Democracy and the Question of Capitalism in Progressive Era Portland, Oregon,* pp. 177–220. Princeton, N.J.: Princeton University Press, 2003.

Leavitt, Judith W. "'Be Safe. Be Sure': New York City's Experience with Epidemic Smallpox." In *Hives of Sickness: Public Health and Epidemics in New York City,* edited by David Rosner, pp. 95–114. New York: Museum of the City of New York, 1995.

Willrich, Michael. *Pox: An American History.* New York: Penguin Press, 2011.

Karen Walloch

SMITHSONIAN INSTITUTION

Chartered by Congress in 1846 to promote "the increase & diffusion of knowledge." Established after more than a decade of debate in Congress about the appropriate disposition of a bequest to the nation from the Englishman James Smithson, the Smithsonian's museums and less-visible research facilities would ultimately dominate the central Mall west of the Capitol in Washington, D.C. With funding from Smithson's endowment, private gifts, and federal appropriations, the Smithsonian Institution operates, in fact, as the national museum of science, history, and art. It is governed by 14 trustees who include (ex officio) the U.S. vice president and the chief justice of the Supreme Court.

Under the first secretary, the physicist Joseph Henry, who served from 1846 until his death in 1878, the Smithsonian promoted research and publication with emphasis on the sciences. In 1848, for example, Henry published a pioneering archaeological study, *Ancient Monuments of the Mississippi*, launching a monograph series that ran until 1916. He and his staff offered a public lecture series, coordinated meteorological data gathered from around the country, and developed an international exchange that distributed publications from American learned societies worldwide. Henry's successor, the zoologist Spencer F. Baird, used a cadre of explorers and naturalists to build a substantial natural-history collection that, coupled with the specimens and artifacts acquired from other countries after the Philadelphia Centennial Exposition of 1876, led to the creation of the U.S. National Museum. Under the third secretary, the astrophysicist Samuel Pierpont Langley, the Smithsonian established a research branch, the Astrophysical Laboratory (1890), in Cambridge, Massachusetts, and a National Zoological Park (1891) in Washington, D.C.

The Smithsonian continued to grow in the twentieth century, despite some setbacks, including a failed effort to form a museum of science and industry in the 1920s. The Freer Gallery of Art (1923) became a center for the study and display of Oriental art. What some observers called the "nation's attic" added research branches, new museums on the Mall, and branch museums in Washington and New York City. Secretary S. Dillon Ripley (1963–1983) provided energy and vision that generated new museum buildings and provided for upgraded older facilities that included more visitor-oriented shops. The National Museum of History and Technology (1965, since transformed into the National Museum of American History) became the preeminent center for research on artifacts and the history of science and technology. The National Collection of Fine Arts (with holdings dating from 1846) joined the collections of the National Portrait Gallery and has been housed in the Old Patent Office Building since 1968. The National Air and Space Museum, whose new building opened in 1976, soon became the world's most visited museum. A few facilities, such as the Joseph H. Hirshhorn Museum and Sculpture Garden (1974), are under the Smithsonian's aegis but administered by separate boards of trustees. Together these agencies continued the tradition of encouraging research and, in most cases, furthered the diffusion of knowledge through their publications, public exhibitions, audiovisual materials, educational programs on and off site, and collaboration with other museums. The *Smithsonian* magazine, launched in 1970, and the Smithsonian Channel television network, launched in 2007, provided other popular ways to carry out the institution's mandate.

[*See also* **Baird, Spencer Fullerton; Henry, Joseph; Journals in Science, Medicine, and Engineering; Museums of Science and Natural History; Research and Development (R&D);** *and* **Science.**]

BIBLIOGRAPHY

Goode, G. Brown. *The Smithsonian Institution, 1846–1896: The History of Its First Half Century.* Washington, D.C.: Smithsonian Institution, 1897.

Oehser, Paul H. *Sons of Science: The Story of the Smithsonian Institution and Its Leaders.* New York: H. Schuman, 1949.

Sally Gregory Kohlstedt

SOCIAL SCIENCE RESEARCH COUNCIL

After holding its first meeting in 1923 in New York City, the Social Science Research Council (SSRC) became incorporated as an independent, non-profit organization in 1924. Dedicated to the advancement of the social sciences, the Council's leaders included representatives from the major national professional scholarly societies for anthropology, economics, history, political science, psychology, sociology, and statistics. Somewhat later, additional at-large members represented law, geography, psychiatry, and medicine.

The SSRC championed the notion that disinterested knowledge produced through empirical research should inform policy-making decisions, which, in turn, would promote social progress. The Council also advocated interdisciplinary studies to counteract disciplinary specialization and to provide knowledge relevant to real-world problems. Operating through a flexible system of committees, the SSRC assessed emerging opportunities and provided funding to stimulate the development of particular fields of study, tools of investigation such as mathematical techniques and survey research, and skilled researchers. The Council also sought to strengthen the scientific status of the social sciences within the academic community and wider society and to stimulate greater public support for social-science research.

Financing for the Council's general operations and specific committees came mainly from the Laura Spelman Rockefeller Memorial during the 1920s; the Rockefeller Foundation starting in the 1920s and continuing throughout the rest of the century; the Ford Foundation, the most important funding source from the 1950s to 1970s; and the Andrew W. Mellon Foundation and MacArthur Foundation in the late twentieth century.

Sometimes the SSRC worked closely with government as well. During the 1930s and 1940s, the Council had good relations with the Roosevelt administration, and the Council's Committee on Social Security contributed to the creation of the nation's social security system. During World War II, the Council served as a bridge between wartime agencies and the social sciences. During and after the war the Council also promoted social research on world regions deemed critical to expanding national interests and scholarly ambitions. Thus, in 1942, the Council and the American Council of Learned Societies (ACLS) created a joint Committee on Latin American Studies.

For the next 50 years the SSRC concentrated on promoting area-studies programs and research through the work of additional joint committees for Africa, China, Eastern Europe, Japan, Korea, Muslim societies, South Asia, Southeast Asia, the Near and Middle East, the Soviet Union, and Western Europe. By stimulating area-studies scholarship, which involved social scientists trained in established disciplines and in the departments of newer university area studies, as well as researchers from other relevant disciplines such as history and linguistics, the Council played a key role in the dramatic expansion of American scholarly expertise beyond national perspectives since the 1940s. In a related development, the Council's leadership and funding contributed to the flourishing of development studies and modernization theory. Through this work, scholars from the social-science disciplines and area-studies departments provided explanatory accounts of the transition from traditional to modern societies. Such work, in turn, contributed to American foreign-policy initiatives designed to lead so-called underdeveloped, developing, or third-world nations along the path toward modernity in ways compatible with U.S. interests in the context of the Cold War struggle for resources and allies. However, in 1996, the SSRC and ACLS closed their area-studies committees. In their place, the Council created a new international research program that emphasized thematic issues, cross-regional studies, and cross-cultural investigations, rather than national and regional contexts.

Many other SSRC committees also became influential in their respective fields of research. These included its Committee on Economic Growth (f. 1949), chaired by Economic Nobel Prize winner Simon Kuznets, and its Committee on Comparative Politics (f. 1954), which became central to the rise of behavioralism in political science. In 1972, the SSRC also opened a Washington, D.C., office, whose Center for Coordination of Research on Social Indicators worked with scholars, government agencies, and private organizations to advance the scientific foundations and policy relevance of social indicators. These are only a few of the many cases in which the SSRC acquired a major presence in the development of the social sciences.

[*See also* **Anthropology; Behaviorism; Geography; Mathematics and Statistics; Medicine; Nobel Prize in Biomedical Research; Psychiatry; Psychology; Rockefeller Institute, The; Social Sciences;** *and* **Societies and Associations, Science.**]

BIBLIOGRAPHY

Fisher, Donald. *Fundamental Development of the Social Sciences: Rockefeller Philanthropy and the United States Social Science Research Council.* Ann Arbor: University of Michigan Press, 1993.
Worcester, Kenton W. *Social Science Research Council, 1923–1998.* New York: Social Science Research Council, 2001.

Mark Solovey

SOCIAL SCIENCES

This entry has two subentries: Before 1945; *and* Post-World War II.

BEFORE 1945

The history of social science and the American republic are roughly coterminous. Both had their origins in the Enlightenment with its faith in progress and belief in the existence of natural laws. Scientific thinking about society required the decline of feudalism and the development of individualism. By the eighteenth century, figures such as Adam Smith and the Marquis de Condorcet were using the scientific method and factual data to discover new allegedly verifiable truths. They perceived social sciences as instruments that could provide guides to the construction of good societies.

In the United States, various versions of social science emerged in the first half of the nineteenth century. College professors of moral economy perceived existent social and economic conditions as synonymous with harmony and morality.

In the South, apologists for slavery such as George Fitzhugh (1806–1881) saw their society as reflecting Auguste Comte's emphasis on social stability. Finally, social statisticians sought to tabulate social ills like pauperism and crime to provide exact knowledge for reformers.

Stability was an even greater goal for Americans after the Civil War. Waves of immigrants and massive industrialization caused many intellectuals to see an empirically valid science of society as increasingly necessary. In 1865, a group of elite northeastern reformers formed the American Social Science Association. It declared its twin goals to be the discovery of what is and the promotion of what should be. As certain interest groups turned toward professionalization in the mid-1870s, they broke away and formed the present-day social science associations.

These nascent disciplines shared an emphasis on empirical quantification and practicality, an insistence on scholarly objectivity, and a belief in American exceptionalism. Like physicians and lawyers of the time, social scientists sought to win approval through professionalization achieved through a regulative code of ethics, common training, and community sanction. An alliance with the emerging universities and acceptance of the viewpoint of conservative boards of trustees further solidified their positions.

By the early twentieth century, empirical work became a reality rather than mere advocacy. In economics young German-trained scholars like Richard Ely (1854–1943) emphasized developing institutions rather than neoclassical theory. Historians embraced Leopold von Ranke's motto "Geschicte wie es eigentlich gewesen" (history as it really happened), with J. Franklin Jameson (1858–1937), the founder of *the American Historical Review,* calling for discrete small-scale studies without concern for overall synthesis. Although a few political scientists followed the British model of Idealism, most followed the lead of the University of Chicago's Charles Merriam

(1874–1953), who laid out detailed plans for empirical, quantitative research. In anthropology, Franz Boas (1858–1942) and his students replaced the evolutionary ranking of people and cultures with detailed ethnographic case studies of specific cultures. Psychology shifted from an introspective study of consciousness akin to philosophy to a concern with individual behavior. Sociology retained both its theoretical and its reformist orientations later than the other disciplines, but by the 1920s the University of Chicago School led by Robert Park (1864–1944), with its careful and often quantitative analysis of cities and their inhabitants, was completely dominant.

World War I had seemed to validate this approach. When the United States entered the war, historians, sociologists, and political scientists staffed the Committee on Public Information and economists and statisticians ran the essential War Industries Board. Their success in these areas led to corporate support for numerous research institutes. Emulation of the natural and physical sciences became the mantra with one prominent sociologist calling for indistinguishable journals of sociology and physics.

The relatively new development of quantitative social surveys in the 1920s reflected both practical and empirical turns. Descended from Charles Booth's 1889 study of London, these new surveys, beginning with Robert and Helen Lynd's Middletown studies, sought the representation of average/typical American cities. By the 1940s polling organizations of George Gallup (1901–1984) and Elmo Roper (1900–1970) used sophisticated polling techniques and probability approaches to capture the so-called average American. Unlike the Booth and Lynd surveys, Gallup and Roper's served business and government interests.

The history of women social scientists deviated from the mainstream. Only anthropology of all the disciplines admitted equal numbers of women. Topics of interest to women such as women's suffrage and women's wages were relegated to marginal fields like home economics and labor economics. Even the tolerant University of Chicago placed their two most productive women social scientists, Sophonisba Breckinridge (1866–1948) and Edith Abbott (1876–1957), in the School of Social Science Administration and denied them full professorships. Denied positions in academia, most women social scientists turned to social settlement work, social work, and administration of government agencies. Ironically, Progressive reformers and even municipal bosses preferred the advice of women social scientists because of their practical turn.

African Americans too occupied a marginal position in American social science. Little research on racial topics was done in the universities and was classified as a purely Southern issue. The philanthropic foundations that sponsored racial research and provided occasional graduate fellowships were conservative and in favor of "liberal" segregation. Almost all African American social scientists, such as Charles S. Johnson (1893–1956), had to win the support of Southern sympathizers such as Park and Gunnar Myrdal (1898–1987). No positions existed for black women. Only in the 1930s were a few African Americans such as E. Franklin Frazier (1894–1962) able to transcend the race-based hypotheses of both white and black social scientists, note the economic basis for continuing racial hatred, and advocate interracial class-based cooperation.

American social science before World War II emphasized empiricism and practicality. Indeed, social scientists perceived empirical and especially quantitative research as preferable because of their applicability to social problems. Practicality was a different issue. Did it represent, as most twentieth-century university social scientists maintained, an acceptance of the status quo and gradual progressive modification toward a better society? Or was true practicality, according to the founders of the American Social Science Association and most women and African American social scientists, a recognition of the need for a moral vision of a fundamentally different society and the creation of institutions and viewpoints that could achieve those goals?

[See also **Anthropology; Archaeology; High Schools, Science Education in; Higher Education and Science; Intelligence, Concepts of; Law and Science; Military, Science and Technology and the; Pseudoscience and Quackery;**

Psychological and Intelligence Testing; Psychology; Public Health; Race Theories, Scientific; Science; *and* Social Sciences: Post–World War II.]

BIBLIOGRAPHY

Bannister, Robert C. *Sociology and Scientism: The American Quest for Objectivity.* Chapel Hill: University of North Carolina Press, 1987.

Haskell, Thomas. *The Emergence of Professional Social Science: The American Social Science Association and the Nineteenth-Century Crisis of Authority.* Baltimore: Johns Hopkins University Press, 1977.

Herman, Ellen. *The Romance of American Psychology: Political Culture in the Age of Experts.* Berkeley and Los Angeles: University of California, 1995.

Novick, Peter. *That Noble Dream: The "Objectivity Question" and the American Historical Profession.* Cambridge, U.K.: Cambridge University Press, 1988.

Ross, Dorothy. *The Origins of American Social Science.* Cambridge, U.K.: Cambridge University Press, 1991.

Smith, Mark C. *Social Science in the Crucible: The American Debate over Objectivity and Purpose, 1918–1941.* Durham, NC: Duke University Press, 1994.

Mark C. Smith

POST–WORLD WAR II

After World War II, the field of social science grew in the professional arena, adopted scientific approaches to its research and practice, incorporated international perspectives, and developed ideological fragmentations.

Professional Expansion and Rising International Stature.

From the mid-1940s through the late 1960s, the U.S. social science enterprise grew dramatically. Membership figures for professional disciplinary associations indicate the sheer magnitude of this expansion. The American Sociological Association (ASA) had about 1,000 members in 1920, 1,500 members in 1930, and then 1,000 members again in 1940. But following World War II rapid growth ensued, as ASA membership rose to 3,200 in 1950, 6,900 in 1960, and 14,200 in 1970 (McAdam, 2007, p. 414). Between 1947 and 1967 total membership soared in other scholarly associations as well: in the American Political Science Association from 4,600 to 14,700; in the American Economic Association from 7,500 to 23,300; in the American Anthropological Association from 1,700 to 6,600; and in the American Psychological Association from 4,600 to 25,800 (all membership rounded to the nearest hundred) (Crowther-Heyck, 2005, p. 336). In addition, following broader expansionary trends in American higher education and science, the amount of social research undertaken, the quantity of scholarly publications, and the size and number of academic graduate and undergraduate programs all ballooned.

The United States also became a world leader in the social sciences. In the late nineteenth and early twentieth centuries, professional social science established firm roots. In certain cases, American scholarly contributions, such as business cycle research led by the economist Wesley Mitchell, acquired recognition from European scholars. But more typically, Europeans did not look to America for leadership, whereas many ambitious American scholars considered the work of European thinkers of central importance. During the 1930s and early 1940s, however, the scourges of Nazism and war profoundly undermined the international status and intellectual vigor of European social science. Furthermore, a large contingent of émigré scholars fleeing Nazi persecution and wartime misery greatly strengthened American academic life. Because of the enormous postwar presence on the world stage of the United States, which was the self-proclaimed leader of the "Free World" in the Cold War struggle against Communism, social scientists in the United States also acquired special opportunities to exercise international leadership, especially in Western Europe and in the so-called developing world.

Scientific Status, Practical Relevance, and Extra-University Funding.

As American social science grew, scholars engaged in extensive discussions about the scientific character of their work. Certainly, the general problem of showing how it was possible to create a legitimate science of human nature and society had been central ever since the rise of the modern social sciences during the seventeenth and eighteenth centuries. During the early Cold War decades, scholars in the United States often adopted a unity-of-science stance, which, in turn, typically supposed that the natural sciences represented the gold standard in scientific inquiry. Proponents of this view then argued that social science inquiry achieved scientific maturity as it assumed the characteristics of natural science inquiry.

In support of this rather general position, scholars regularly advanced more specific claims that could distinguish scientific social research from other forms of social inquiry and other spheres of social action that did not merit the scientific label. These claims included the notion that scientific social inquiry aimed to produce value-neutral knowledge; the premise that such research yields trustworthy knowledge that has instrumental uses, but such knowledge does not by itself favor any particular course of social action or political agenda; and the point that such knowledge was fundamentally different from dogma, ideology, and mere opinion. Sociologists, psychologists, economists, and the like also commonly pointed to methodological advances as a crucial source of scientific progress, especially statistical methods and other quantitative techniques of inquiry that became central in such important fields as social survey research, public opinion polling, and econometric analysis. A sense of across-the-board social science progress was also bolstered by widespread enthusiasm for interdisciplinary frameworks of inquiry, including a form of social system analysis championed by the prominent Harvard sociologist Talcott Parsons and rapid growth of interdisciplinary academic research centers, such as Harvard's Department of Social Relations, where Parsons played a starring role.

Pervasive claims about scientific maturation often went hand in hand with an instrumental viewpoint about the practical value of the social sciences, thereby explaining how supposedly value-neutral and objective knowledge became immensely important in the realization of particular social, economic, or political goals. One prominent theme that cut across a number of disciplines and more specific fields of research concerned the use of social science to facilitate what its proponents saw as beneficial forms of social control, a theme often discussed in the language of social engineering and systems thinking. The general idea suggested that scientific knowledge provided the basis for prediction and control, thereby enabling one to shape the course of events to produce desired outcomes. For example, advocates of Keynesian economics proposed that, based on their scientific knowledge of the economic system, government could manipulate fiscal and monetary policy to smooth out the business cycle, regulate the unemployment level, keep inflation in check, and ensure steady economic growth.

A second prominent theme, which also cut across a number of disciplines and fields of study, focused on placing decision-making processes at various key sites on a rational basis. Perhaps most famously—or infamously—scholars pursuing operations research, systems analysis, nuclear deterrence theory, and game theory sought to create a true "science of strategy," as the political scientist Bernard Brodie called it. Brodie and like-minded scholars argued that military common sense, intuitions, and experiences based on fighting past wars had little relevance in the nuclear age. Now, securing the national defense and avoiding a catastrophic nuclear war depended on new techniques of scientific analysis that would ensure the rationality of strategic decision making.

These scientific and instrumentalist commitments had roots in the pre–World War II decades and in the experiences of social researchers during World War II. The pervasive presence of those commitments following the war also owed much to the influence of powerful extra-university patrons, who expressed a special interest in supporting rigorously scientific forms of social research that promised to be useful in the sort of ways described above. These patrons included the American military and its individual branches—the U.S. Army, Navy, and Air Force—and also military-sponsored research organizations, the most famous of which was the RAND Corporation. RAND, which relied heavily on air force funding through the early 1960s, became a prominent center for quantitative forms of social research with strategic relevance. The military's Research and Development Board, the navy's

Office of Naval Research, the air force's Human Resources Research Institute, and the army's Special Operations Research Office all promoted significant research in fields such as psychological warfare, communications studies, counterinsurgency research, studies of motivation and morale, and human factors engineering. The Central Intelligence Agency relied heavily on social science expertise, for example, to analyze the Soviet Union's military and economic resources. The Central Intelligence Agency also sponsored widely controversial studies in mind control. A number of civilian agencies supported the social sciences as well, including the Department of Health, Education, and Welfare; the National Institute of Mental Health; the Department of Agriculture; and the National Science Foundation.

From the philanthropic sector, the Carnegie Corporation and the Rockefeller Foundation, which had been major sources of funding since the 1920s, remained important, for example, by providing crucial support for the post–World War II development of area studies programs in American universities, including the influential Soviet studies programs at Harvard and Columbia. Starting at midcentury, the Ford Foundation, which had recently emerged as the richest philanthropy in the world, took a strong interest in the social sciences and what Ford documents and personnel often referred to as the behavioral sciences. During the 1950s and 1960s, Ford became the single most important private patron in this area.

Cold War Entanglements.
American social science, as has already been suggested, also became entangled with the Cold War at many levels. Because gaining direct access to developments inside the Soviet Union was difficult if not impossible, political scientists, economists, sociologists, and historians acquired central roles in the rise of Soviet studies and the effort to know the enemy. Similarly, with coordination provided by joint committees operating through the Social Science Research Council and the American Council of Learned Societies, scholars from various social science disciplines became main participants in area studies programs centered on nations and regions enmeshed in the global struggle for influence be-

tween the two superpowers, including China, Korea, South Asia, Southeast Asia, Africa, Latin America, and the Near and Middle East.

A great deal of this social research addressed questions about development and modernization, with the aim of explicating how the United States could help guide the transition from a traditional society to a modern society in a manner friendly to American interests and ideals. Such work influenced U.S. foreign policy through the efforts of action-oriented scholars, such as Walt W. Rostow, a historical economist from the Massachusetts Institute of Technology who became national security advisor to presidents Kennedy and Johnson in the 1960s and who offered his vision of modernization theory as an explicit alternative to Marxist-inspired development programs in his classic 1960 book, *The Stages of Economic Growth: A Non-Communist Manifesto*. As anti-Communist sentiment and politics spread throughout American society, social scientists also found themselves under pressure to define their work in opposition to Marxism and other leftist programs of social, economic, and political transformation.

The Turbulent 1960s: Critiques and Challenges.
Amid the turbulence of the 1960s, discussions about the social sciences' scientific character, social relevance, and political uses spawned heated controversies and marked a major turning point for the social science enterprise. Social scientists, and especially economists, achieved a remarkable level of policy influence and public visibility, as evidenced by their roles in promoting Keynesian policies (under a program dubbed the New Economics); in shaping the nation's War on Poverty; in designing counterinsurgency strategies for the Vietnam War; and in promoting U.S.-supported modernization programs in Latin America, Southeast Asia, and other developing regions. But by the late 1960s, mounting critiques of these and other major federal initiatives, which came from both the left and the right, trained harsh scrutiny on the roles of social scientists.

A variety of disconcerted liberal and more committed leftist voices from both inside and outside the academy claimed that large segments of the social science enterprise had become tools of the establishment. According to such charges, all too often the work of social scientists, rather than advancing humanistic values and social welfare at home and abroad, helped to justify and enforce the nation's repressive domestic order, its imperialistic foreign policies, and its brutal military interventions around the world. An important focal point for debating the relationship of social science to the military patron and to the national-security state more generally was Project Camelot. This ambitious army-sponsored social research project had been designed to produce a social systems model of the revolutionary process, but it was canceled in mid-1965, following international and national concern about Camelot's anticipated political uses and ideological orientation. A complex controversy about the political meaning of social science research also erupted over *The Negro Family: The Case for National Action*, 1965— also known as the Moynihan Report. This government document, penned by the sociologist, assistant secretary of labor, and later U.S. senator Daniel P. Moynihan, claimed that the African American community suffered from a "tangle of pathology," which was rooted in African American family life, and then recommended governmental action to overcome the deep problems.

During the late 1960s and continuing in the following decades, an array of left-leaning perspectives made important contributions to the social sciences. Scholars from anthropology, economics, history, political science, psychology, sociology, and area studies programs developed new lines of inquiry with the aid of feminist insights, neo-Marxist analysis, critical race theory, and humanistic approaches. Historically minded researchers also documented the ways in which previous social science work had contributed to various forms of oppression, especially racism, sexism, economic exploitation, imperialism, and militarism. A number of influential writers also rejected, either explicitly or implicitly, the disinterested scientific stance and the notion of objectivity as neutrality. Instead, they called for researchers to cultivate reflexive analysis and awareness on how personal values, institutional environments, professional interests, political

ideology, and patron relations had shaped and continued to shape the production of knowledge and its uses.

Meanwhile, the social sciences faced pointed challenges from conservative quarters as well. Ever since the New Deal, conservative voices had argued that academic social science was, on balance, more supportive of liberal politics and social thought than conservative positions. During the 1940s and 1950s, conservative politicians, intellectuals, and academics had been among the strongest skeptics of social scientists' claims that they had achieved a strong measure of scientific objectivity and value neutrality. Not surprisingly, the contributions of action-oriented social scientists to the liberal agendas of the Kennedy and Johnson administrations, together with the subsequent flourishing of liberal and more radical forms of scholarship within the academy, inspired a vigorous response from a rapidly growing conservative movement.

During the 1970s and 1980s, conservative leaders and organizations, including an array of new or newly energized private foundations and think tanks, launched a concerted effort to expose the shortcoming in liberal ideas, including what they took to be the excessive and corrupting influence of the social sciences, or at least that large segment aligned with liberal and more radical causes. Religiously oriented criticism took special offense at the overwhelmingly secular orientation of the social sciences, which joined a wider spectrum of culturally oriented criticism that found the social sciences guilty of promoting insidious forms of relativism, including moral and cultural relativism. The conservative position against big government attracted firm support from various groups, including business interests who argued for the superiority of the free market and advocated government deregulation. The economic crises of the 1970s and the emergence of stagflation, when inflation and unemployment rose at the same time in a way that Keynesians could not explain, provided free-market advocates with a greater opportunity to make their case. As many conservatives saw it, beyond the specific case of excessive government intervention in economic affairs lay the more general problem of an inept, bloated, corrupt, and harmful system of government addicted to the false promises peddled by the social engineers.

Speaking broadly, for a good portion of the social sciences the last third of the twentieth century was filled with diminished scientific authority, chastened public confidence, and increasing professional divisions. A cloud of deep criticism enveloped the social science enterprise, pervaded particular disciplines, and rocked more specific fields of research. In the earlier post–World War II period social science leaders, as well as many of their patrons and supporters in the wider society, had expressed confidence in a rapidly advancing scientific maturity and a close kinship with the natural sciences. During the 1970s, 1980s, and 1990s, however, the notion of a unified scientific enterprise became more and more difficult to defend. Increasingly, scholarly discussions concentrated on examining various types of disunity, which separated the natural sciences from the social sciences, rendered the individual social science disciplines rather distinct from one another, and turned research specialties into distinct enclaves.

Furthermore, the period of tremendous expansion in academic social science leveled off by the early 1970s. Consider the case of sociology once again. After membership figures in the ASA soared from 3,200 to 14,200 between 1950 and 1970, as noted before, the peak came in 1972, with 14,900 members. Subsequent years saw a quick leveling off followed by a moderate decline and then a minor increase, such that in 2010 the number of ASA members was still slightly below the 1972 peak (http://www.asanet.org/about/Centennial_History_Index.cfm, Appendix 12). In a closely related development, the academic job market stopped expanding, making it much more difficult for recent PhDs to obtain desirable positions in university departments. On top of this, university scholars faced increasing competition from the burgeoning world of private research institutes and think tanks, a number of which supported a great deal of social science research.

Fragmentation: Troublesome or Healthy?
Yet in some other respects social science was flourishing, both inside and outside the universities. What seemed like hopeless fragmentation and divisive ideological conflict from one point of view could seem like a marvelously vigorous intellectual dynamism from another. Some scholars expected oppositional and divergent modes of thinking to produce greater insights and argued that different types of social inquiry needed to develop their own specialized ways of knowing.

Meanwhile, some new research orientations and programs aimed to place broad regions of inquiry on more robust scientific foundations. The Harvard biologist E. O. Wilson and other proponents of the new field he called sociobiology argued that widespread scientific progress in the social sciences required the establishment of a new paradigm founded upon the insights into human development and social behavior provided by evolutionary biology. The flourishing of evolutionary psychology toward the end of the century rested on a similar conviction, although its scholars focused less on social behavior and more on the biological roots of human cognitive, emotional, and behavioral repertoires. The new interdisciplinary field of cognitive science was also thriving, with contributions coming from artificial intelligence, computer science, linguistics, neuroscience, philosophy, and psychology.

In another major trend, advocates of rational-choice theory proposed that progress in the social sciences depended on the development of formal modeling, in which it was assumed that individuals acted in an instrumental fashion. Although this view had long been prominent in microeconomics, proponents such as the economist Gary Becker advocated its widespread adoption in other disciplines, such as political science and law.

Moreover, at the turn of the century, various areas of the social sciences had extensive influence in the wider society and in the political arena. Among other things, social research on the causes and means of combating poverty and welfare dependency contributed to the 1996 Personal Responsibility and Work Reconciliation Act, which, according to the rhetoric of the day, aimed to end "welfare as we know it." The tremendous expansion of evaluation research, supported by government agencies, private foundations, and university research centers, promised to provide sound evidence showing the extent to which various social programs were meeting their stated goals. Following the shocking attacks against the United States on 11 September 2001, various public and private organizations turned to social scientists for help in carrying out the war on terror.

Last but not least, the worldwide collapse of financial markets, starting in 2008, inspired extensive debate about whether the theories, models, and advice of professional economists had paved the way for this crisis. At the same time, major governments, banks, and corporations have continued to rely heavily on economists for guidance and policy advice.

[*See also* Anthropology; Archaeology; Behaviorism; Boas, Franz; High Schools, Science Education in; Higher Education and Science; Intelligence, Concepts of; Law and Science; Mead, Margaret; Military, Science and Technology and the; Pseudoscience and Quackery; Psychological and Intelligence Testing; Psychology; Public Health; Race Theories, Scientific; Science; Skinner, B. F.; Social Science Research Council; *and* Sociobiology and Evolutionary Psychology.]

BIBLIOGRAPHY

Amadae, Sonja M. *Rationalizing Capitalist Democracy: The Cold War Origins of Rational Choice Liberalism.* Chicago: University of Chicago Press, 2003. Emphasizes the crucial importance of RAND (the military think tank) in the development of rational-choice theory and then considers its spread into academia though a critical perspective.

Backhouse, Roger E., and Philippe Fontaine, eds. *The History of the Social Sciences since 1945.* New York: Cambridge University Press, 2010. Includes chapter histories by discipline (psychology, sociology, etc.), with a helpful concluding chapter that is more synthetic in nature.

Crowther-Heyck, Hunter. *Herbert Simon: The Bounds of Reason in Modern America.* Baltimore: Johns Hopkins University Press, 2005. Presents an intellectual, professional, and institutional biography

of one of the most important interdisciplinary scholars of the mid to late twentieth century.

Engerman, David. *Know Your Enemy: The Rise and Fall of America's Soviet Experts.* New York: Oxford University Press, 2009. Offers an extensive history of the field of Soviet Studies as it developed in the United States since World War II.

Gilman, Nils. *Mandarins of the Future: Modernization Theory in Cold War America.* Baltimore: Johns Hopkins University Press, 2003. Examines the impressive rise and then sharp critique of development studies and modernization theory, mainly from the 1940s to the 1970s.

Herman, Ellen. *The Romance of American Psychology: Political Culture in the Age of Experts.* Los Angeles: University of California Press, 1995. Offers a history of psychological experts and their influence in American society in a variety of areas from 1940 to 1970, including the military during World War II and the Cold War, the civil rights movement, and the women's movement.

Isaac, Joel. "The Human Sciences in Cold War America." *Historical Journal* 50 (2007): 725–746. A wide-ranging historiography analysis, delineating main themes, tensions, and limitations in the historical literature in this area.

McAdam, Doug. "From Relevance to Irrelevance: The Curious Impact of the Sixties on Public Sociology." In *Sociology in America: A History,* edited by Craig Calhoun. Chicago: University of Chicago Press, 2007.

O'Connor, Alice. *Poverty Knowledge: Social Science, Social Policy, and the Poor in Twentieth-Century U.S. History.* Princeton, N.J.: Princeton University Press, 2001. An intellectual, institutional, and political history of how social scientists studied the poor and contributed to antipoverty policies.

Solovey, Mark. *Shaky Foundations: The Politics-Patronage-Social Science Nexus in Cold War America.* New Brunswick, N.J.: Rutgers University Press, 2013. Analyzes the development of a largely new extra-university funding system for the social sciences in the early Cold War period, with the military, the Ford Foundation, and the National Science Foundation as key patrons.

Solovey, Mark, and Hamilton Cravens, eds. *Cold War Social Science: Knowledge Production, Liberal Democracy, and Human Nature.* New York: Palgrave Macmillan, 2012. Examines how the social sciences' Cold War entanglements shaped the production of social science knowledge and informed social science studies of liberal democracy and human nature.

Mark Solovey

SOCIETIES AND ASSOCIATIONS, SCIENCE

Voluntary associations were among the earliest American institutions related to science. In one form or another they have played a central role in the organization, advancement, and dissemination of scientific knowledge throughout the entire extent of U.S. history. Part of a long tradition of learned societies dating back centuries in Western culture, American societies were also products of their time and place. They took on traits and functions characteristic of the culture of science where they were established and when.

From the pre-Revolutionary period through the first decade or so of the nineteenth century, the most important societies were modeled on the great societies of Europe, especially the Royal Society and the Academie Française. Their founders sought to create exclusive, prestigious clubs formed of members who had already achieved a measure of distinction and national recognition—in science or some other endeavor. They managed to limit membership to elites, but they were typically local elites, with most members residing in or near the city where the society was established. Three of these early societies, the American Philosophical Society (founded in Philadelphia in 1743), the American Academy of Arts and Sciences (Boston, 1780), and the Connecticut Academy of Arts and Sciences (New Haven, 1799), still existed in the early twenty-first century.

Local Societies, Nineteenth Century.
Important as the elite societies have been, their influence on the development of scientific institutions in the United States has been relatively limited. In contrast, the Academy of Natural Sciences of Philadelphia (established 1812) and the Boston Society of Natural History (organized 1830) drew on a different organizational model from Europe, one that more fully addressed the needs and nurtured the growth of the scientifically active population in nineteenth-century America. Directly or indirectly, they provided the template or inspiration for literally hundreds of local and state societies.

For most of the nineteenth century, the American scientific community was a hierarchical but shifting and inclusive population. The leaders knew one another, but they interacted with a scientifically active population that was extremely diverse in terms of knowledge and commitment. Additionally, there was a strongly regional component to American science and scientists that counted for more, sometimes, than expertise. New Yorkers and Philadelphians, for example, saw themselves as distinct communities, often in competition, often at odds. Their scientific interests, residing largely in the taxonomic sciences and especially local natural history, had a regional flavor as well. Interest in science was widespread and abundant, whereas education, support, training, and texts were scarce commodities.

Local societies were founded in all parts of the country in numbers roughly proportional to the distribution of the scientifically active population. However, although scientifically active individuals might live in town or in the country, the societies were decidedly urban institutions. They could be founded in small towns, but in general larger communities (population over 10 thousand) were more likely to be able to support them over a period of years. Because of improvements in transportation, among other factors, the locations capable of supporting a society expanded and diversified over time.

Although the earliest societies were in the Northeast, successful societies began to appear in large cities throughout the country during the decades just prior to the Civil War, including Charleston, South Carolina (1853), New Orleans (1853), St. Louis (1856), and Chicago (1856). It was not until after the Civil War, however, that societies organized in smaller towns outside the Northeast began to flourish in significant numbers. Local academies were at the height of their popularity and importance—especially in the West and Middle West—in the 1870s and 1880s when they were founded in larger numbers and in more diverse locations than at any other time.

The history of each society is unique; some survived for decades or centuries, others merely weeks or months, and the quality of their activities was highly variable. Nevertheless, taken as a group, they were, until the closing decades of the nineteenth century, the primary sources of support for and dissemination of scientific research, as well as the principal providers of scientific education throughout much of the country.

These societies were a well-understood mechanism through which enthusiasts turned a private activity into a public one, a transformation that gave their members access to resources and support that had been previously out of reach. Typically, a new society declared its commitment to the advancement and diffusion of scientific knowledge, as well as its intent to found a natural history museum and to hold regular (usually monthly) meetings where original papers were to be read and subsequently published in the society's own transactions or proceedings. They received a measure of local support and goodwill because they were understood to be ornaments to the community—evidence of its sophistication and potential. In the world of science, the newly formed group entered into an international network of similar organizations and participated in a kind of commerce in which local knowledge (in the form of specimens or publications) was exported and international knowledge, generally in the form of society transactions, was imported. The exchange was often unequal, with newer societies receiving vastly more knowledge than they were able to export, leading to the establishment of scientific libraries and natural history collections throughout the country. There were clear hierarchies among scientific institutions during this period, just as there were among the scientifically active population.

National Societies, Mid- to Late Nineteenth Century. Two very different national societies were formed around midcentury; their success was a function of the progressive development and increased prominence of the scientific community in the United States. The American Association for the Advancement of Science (AAAS; established in 1848 on a foundation provided by the American Association of Geologists and Naturalists) reflected the emergence of a truly national scientific community. Such a community had not existed earlier in the century and even at this time was realized to a much greater extent among geologists than it was among other types of scientists. Modeled on the British Association for the Advancement of Science, the AAAS met annually, each year in a different location. The idea was to increase the visibility of science and encourage more widespread participation. At the same time, the society sought to promote the most advanced research. To this end, the society had two levels of membership. One was open to all interested individuals, men as well as women. The other, the "fellows," included select scientists, men and, more rarely, women who alone had a voice in the governance of the association. In practice, the costs associated with membership and attendance led members to self-select to a greater degree than was true of local societies, leading to a society that was diverse, but tended to include the more committed and experienced segment of the scientifically active population. Initially divided into just two sections, natural history and general physics, the society created many more subdivisions by the century's end, reflective of both growing numbers and the increasing specialization of American science.

The National Academy of Sciences established by an act of Congress in 1863 was fundamentally different in almost all respects. Created at the instigation of Alexander Dallas Bache and other politically connected scientific leaders, it was an elite, self-perpetuating organization composed of 50 leading scientists who alone had the power to fill vacancies as they occurred. It served thus to enhance both the prestige of American scientists and that of science in America because its function was to provide expert advice to the federal government.

State Societies, Mid- to Late Nineteenth Century. In many respects the state societies in the second half of the nineteenth century incorporated elements of both local and national organizations. The same infrastructure developments, especially railroad construction, which eased travel and made the AAAS possible, also meant that truly statewide scientific societies appeared around midcentury and grew in number throughout much of the country in the decades after the Civil War. Usually peripatetic, like the AAAS and state agricultural societies, they were based in the state capital, but held annual meetings in different parts of the state. They were generally most active in states that had dispersed populations and relatively few local societies. In these cases they provided the support and encouragement to interested individuals just as local societies did, but they met far less frequently and members were typically drawn from the core rather than the margins of the scientifically active population. Like the national societies, they saw themselves as fulfilling guiding and advisory functions, advocating for and frequently seeking to influence or direct such statewide scientific projects as geological and natural history surveys.

Professional Societies, End of the Nineteenth Century.

In the late nineteenth century, the rise of research universities with graduate programs, beginning with Johns Hopkins University, combined with and encouraged a profound shift in emphasis from observational to laboratory science. This shift in practice helped, in turn, to transform the structure of the American scientific community from an inclusive to an exclusive one, giving rise to fundamentally new kinds of organizations. The new national, professional societies that began to be formed at this time were organized around research interests, not geographic locale. These societies were created by and for specialized, frequently academic, scientists—professionals. From the outset, the research conducted by members of most of these new societies was beyond the means of individuals without formal training and institutional support. But unlike local societies, most professional groups were not themselves sites or direct supporters of research.

Of necessity and by intent, these organizations excluded nonprofessionals and (usually) women,

regardless of their qualifications. In their meetings and publications, experts presented and debated highly specialized research that was largely incomprehensible to outsiders.

It is important to note that professional societies of this type were being formed at this time across the academic disciplines, not just in the sciences. Thus, although they proved well suited to support laboratory science, they were less a response to changes in scientific practice than they were to developments in higher education generally.

Professional Societies, Twentieth Century.

Professional societies quickly became the dominant form of scientific association in the twentieth century, taking over that role from the local societies and sustaining it up to the present. That is not to say that these have been static organizations. To the contrary, their ongoing importance is evidence of their adaptability. Professional societies continually remade themselves, modifying their organizational structures, developing more elaborate and extensive governing bodies and bureaucracies, and merging and subdividing in response to fundamental and repeated shifts in the practice of science and its place in American culture and society throughout the twentieth century. The histories of many societies show that these transformations were often both highly contentious and lengthy as the organizations searched for a new role or, perhaps, to redefine their relationships to other societies.

It is important to understand what they did not do, as well as what they did. Most significantly, they did not become regulatory institutions conferring professional licenses in the manner of the American Medical Association or American Bar Association. Nor did they become principally advocates for their membership.

Instead, their focus began and has remained primarily focused on the subjects around which they are organized. Through a variety of mechanisms, including their journals and annual conferences, as well as subject-based bibliographic indexes (when they chose to develop them), these organizations established standards of research and professional conduct as well as the publishing conventions for the field. More than that, through these mechanisms, they established the cognitive parameters of the field itself. Through their year-in/year-out activities, these societies implicitly and occasionally explicitly set the boundaries for their fields. When research areas grew too large, a society might subdivide—either into sections or by spinning off affiliated societies or giving rise to independent new organizations. Equally, when different disciplines began to overlap, the result could be a new organization claiming that shared ground for itself and establishing an entirely new discipline.

Beyond their disciplinary concerns, societies, especially beginning in the 1960s and 1970s, struggled with how to respond to political and social issues as scientific organizations. A short list of these issues suggests the range of questions they tackled. Should they take a stand on the Vietnam War? Should they take active steps to increase the gender and racial diversity of their membership and their profession? Should they work to raise the quality of K–12 science education? Although these issues were difficult to ignore, some members believed that acknowledging them detracted from their organizational focus on research.

Local Societies, Twentieth Century.

The men and women whose scientific curiosity found expression in the local societies in the 1870s and 1880s were not succeeded by members of the generation that followed. Instead, would-be scientists were diverted onto a very different path, through college and graduate school and then to employment and involvement in professional associations. By century's end, few local societies could claim to be places for original research. Many societies failed at that time, but those that survived did so by redefining their function. In places like Davenport, Iowa, and Buffalo, New York, local societies turned from research to education. They kept their museum collections but transformed them into tools of elementary science education. They emphasized the dissemination of knowledge of local nature, encouraging their visitors to appreciate the world around them. In so doing, they helped to instill an interest in science that led many individuals to pursue careers

as scientists and also nurtured a public willing to support science through their tax dollars. Many local science museums active in the twenty-first century began as nineteenth-century societies.

State and National Societies in the Twentieth Century.

With the increased specialization of the sciences, the characteristic interdisciplinarity of state and national societies became one of their defining features. The state societies, in particular, function as places where specialists present their ideas formally to an informed audience outside of their own areas of specialization and where they can speculate freely about ideas that cross disciplinary boundaries. They support and publish some research (usually oriented toward their state) that might not otherwise be disseminated. Thus, they offer opportunities not available in the professional societies. State societies also provide some benefits of professional associations to scientists who are not employed at major research institutions and who cannot afford to travel to distant meetings. In addition, they have provided a means for some scientists to apply their expertise to matters of public policy regarding issues important to their state—including everything from a scientific understanding of race to the use and conservation of a state's natural resources.

In an analogous way, the AAAS, as it has evolved through the twentieth century, has come to focus on matters relating to science generally, rather than just to one or another specialized area—although it continues to support specialized sections. It tackles topics such as science education, the federal budget for scientific research, and international science policy that are generally seen as beyond the purview of a specialized society. The National Academy of Sciences has taken an ever more prominent role as the nation's scientific policy adviser. Over the course of the twentieth century it has greatly expanded its membership to well over two thousand scientists. It has also established associated organizations: the National Research Council in 1916, the National Academy of Engineering in 1964, and the Institute of Medicine in 1970. Collectively, these groups marshal the volunteer labor of leading scientists to address scientific and technological matters relevant to the public interest.

[*See also* Academy of Natural Sciences of Philadelphia; American Association for the Advancement of Science; American Association for the History of Medicine; American Institute of Physics; American Medical Association; American Philosophical Society; Bache, Alexander Dallas; Geological Surveys; High Schools, Science Education in; Higher Education and Science; History of Science Society; Museums of Science and Natural History; National Academy of Sciences; National Medical Association; Railroads; Science; Social Science Research Council; *and* Society for the History of Technology.]

BIBLIOGRAPHY

"About NAS History." *National Academy of Sciences.* http://www.nasonline.org/about-nas/history/overview-nas-history.html/ (accessed 12 April 2012).

Baatz, Simon. "Philadelphia Patronage: The Institutional Structure of Natural History in the New Republic, 1800–1833." *Journal of the Early Republic* 8 (1988): 111–138. An excellent analysis of the social context of the founding of the Academy of Natural Sciences of Philadelphia.

Bates, Ralph S. *Scientific Societies in the United States.* 3d ed. Cambridge, Mass.: MIT Press, 1965. The major chronological survey of the topic.

Benson, Keith R., and C. Edward Quinn. "The American Society of Zoologists, 1889–1989: A Century of Integrating the Biological Sciences." *American Zoologist* 30 (1990): 353–396. There are many histories written on the occasion of a society's hundredth anniversary. This one contextualizes and interprets the events it recounts.

Cain, Victoria E. M. "From Specimens to Steropticons: The Persistence of the Davenport Academy of Natural Sciences and the Emergence of Scientific Education." *Annals of Iowa* 3d ser., 68 (2009): 1–36. Uses the Davenport Academy to examine what happens to provincial societies after their heyday. Not simply a local history, its conceptual scope is broader than the title implies.

Ellsworth, Mary Ellen. "A History of the Connecticut Academy of Arts and Sciences, 1799–1999." *Transactions of the Connecticut Academy of Arts and Sciences* 55 (1999): 1–254.

Goldstein, Daniel. "Outposts of Science: The Knowledge Trade and the Expansion of Scientific Community in Post-Civil War America." *Isis* 99 (2008): 519–546. Considers societies as points in a network rather than as individual entities.

Hendrickson, Walter B. "Science and Culture in the American Middle West." *Isis* 64 (1973): 326–340. Hendrickson pioneered the study of the social history of local scientific societies. This essay is a synthesis of much of his previous work.

Kohlstedt, Sally Gregory. *The Formation of the American Scientific Community: The American Association for the Advancement of Science, 1848–1860.* Chicago: University of Illinois Press, 1976.

Lustig, Harry. "APS and the Wider World." *Physics Today* 52, no. 3 (1999): 27–33. A conversational piece reflecting on the American Physical Society's engagement in social and political issues.

Midgette, Nancy Smith. *To Foster the Spirit of Professionalism: Southern Scientists and State Academies of Science.* Tuscaloosa and London: University of Alabama Press, 1991. The broadest view of the accomplishments and social context of state academies available.

Oleson, Alexandra, and Sanborn C. Brown, eds. *The Pursuit of Knowledge in the Early American Republic: American Scientific and Learned Societies from Colonial Times to the Civil War.* Baltimore: Johns Hopkins University Press, 1976. The seminal collection of essays on early American learned societies, valuable both for historical content and for theoretical approaches.

Wolfle, Dael. *Renewing a Scientific Society: The American Association for the Advancement of Science from World War II to 1970.* Washington, D.C.: American Association for the Advancement of Science, 1989.

Daniel Goldstein

SOCIETY FOR THE HISTORY OF TECHNOLOGY

The Society for the History of Technology (SHOT) was chartered in June 1958 by Melvin Kranzberg (1917–1995), a professor at Case Institute of Technology in Cleveland. Kranzberg was an indefatigable institution builder—an "operator" in the best sense of the word—and he saw a future as the creator of a discipline aimed at studying "technology and its relations with society and culture." As a Harvard PhD in French history, his professional ties were mostly with other historians. But he was dedicated to the ideal of interdisciplinarity, and many of SHOT's most active and influential members have come from anthropology, sociology, economics, and other realms of social science and the humanities. Kranzberg took special care to encourage the participation of engineers, and museum professionals played a leading role in SHOT from the start. But always he urged his cohort to look beyond the engineering and design of devices and processes. The scholarly venue Kranzberg created was *Technology and Culture*, a quarterly journal he edited for its first 22 years, 1959 to 1981. What most needed study and analysis was *technology in history*—the relationship of technology to public policy, economics, science, the arts, human psychology, and the organization of production. As time went by, SHOT's scholars focused increasingly on technology's role in differentiating social status and the construction of gender and on "interpretive flexibility," the understanding that beliefs about whether a technology "works" are contingent on the needs, expectations, and ideologies of those who interact with it. Out of all this conceptual brew, Kranzberg coined an elegant aphorism, "*Technology is neither good, nor is it bad; nor is it neutral*," which lives on as Kranzberg's First Law.

Kranzberg's closest collaborator at the start was Lynn White Jr. (1907–1987), a scholar whose *Medieval Technology and Social Change* became SHOT's foundational text. Others of his initial cohort included Carl Condit (1914–1997), whose primary interest was the built environment; John Rae (1911–1988), an economic historian who became the premier analyst of automobility; and Robert Multhauf (1919–2004), a historian of science who, as director of the Smithsonian Institution's Museum of History and Technology in the 1960s, turned it into SHOT's foremost institutional ally in shaping a professional discipline. One of his successors as

director, Brooke Hindle (1918–2001), carried this collaboration forward. SHOT's first presidents included the sociologist William F. Ogburn; the bridge designer David Steinman; Cyril Stanley Smith, a central figure in the Manhattan Project who turned to analyzing the relationship of art and technology; and the famed management strategist Peter Drucker. Hindle was surely correct when he wrote that Kranzberg launched SHOT "with a motley crew of scholars who were but slightly conscious of their common interest in the history of technology."

Historians of technology understand that any invention is rooted in a specific historical ambience, but may also be contingent on the skill and enthusiasm of a particular individual. With SHOT, there was the Cold War, *Sputnik*, and the National Aeronautics and Space Administration (NASA). And there was Melvin Kranzberg. Upon finishing his presidential term in 1965, Drucker spoke from the heart when he told Kranzberg, "I am more than grateful to you for your willingness to do all the work and to make this venture such a success. All of us owe you more than anyone can express."

[*See also* **Anthropology; Engineering; Gender and Science; Gender and Technology; History of Science Society; Journals in Science, Medicine, and Engineering; Museums of Science and Natural History; National Aeronautics and Space Administration; Psychology; Research and Development (R&D); Smithsonian Institution; Social Sciences; Societies and Associations, Science;** *and* **Technology.**]

BIBLIOGRAPHY

Cutcliffe, Stephen H., and Robert C. Post, eds. *In Context: History and the History of Technology. Essays in Honor of Melvin Kranzberg*. Bethlehem, Pa.: Lehigh University Press, 1989.

Post, Robert C. "Back at the Start: History and Technology and Culture." *Technology and Culture* 51 (2010): 961–994.

Post, Robert C. "Chance and Contingency: Putting Mel Kranzberg in Context." *Technology and Culture* 50 (2009): 839–872.

Post, Robert C. "'A Very Special Relationship': SHOT and the Smithsonian's Museum of History and Technology." *Technology and Culture* 42 (2001): 401–435.

Seely, Bruce E. "SHOT, the History of Technology, and Engineering Education." *Technology and Culture* 36 (1995): 735–772.

Society for the History of Technology. http://www .historyoftechnology.org/ (accessed 29 March 2012).

Staudenmaier, John M. *Technology's Storytellers: Reweaving the Human Fabric.* Cambridge, Mass.: MIT Press, 1985.

Robert C. Post

SOCIOBIOLOGY AND EVOLUTIONARY PSYCHOLOGY

Sociobiology, as defined by Edward O. Wilson in 1975, is the study of the genetic basis of social behavior in social insects, animals, and human beings—behavior such as building hives, hunting in packs, and parental nurturing of young. Just as evolutionary biology holds that an organism's physical structure has changed over time in response to environmental pressures—those physical traits that contributed to the organism's survival and reproduction having been naturally selected—so sociobiology holds that those social behaviors that contributed to the survival of a group of organisms have also been naturally selected. Like evolutionary biology, sociobiology is concerned only with traits that are inherited—passed on mainly through genetic influence—because if they were not, and simply arose anew in each generation, natural selection could not act on them. Sociobiology also assumes that the social behaviors that persist among members of a species are adaptive: that they have helped their possessors cope with a changing environment and survive at least long enough to produce offspring (who inherit the genes giving rise to those successful behavioral adaptations).

Central to Wilson's development of sociobiology was William Hamilton's theory of inclusive fitness, or kin selection, published in 1964. According to the law of inclusive fitness, adaptive, hereditary social behaviors may not help the individual who possesses them to survive, but as long as they help the survival of enough close relatives who share genes with their possessor, those behaviors will persist in future generations. Hamilton's theory helped account for the persistence of behaviors that do not seem to carry adaptive value for their possessors, such as altruism. As long as the altruistic behavior (the squirrel that loudly warns its fellows of a predator's approach and thus draws the predator's attention to itself) helps the altruist's close relatives to survive and reproduce, that behavior, carried also on the relatives' genes, will be naturally selected and will continue to manifest in future generations.

Along with Hamilton, the mathematically inclined evolutionary biologists John Maynard Smith, George Williams, and George Price took a "gene's eye view" of evolution to explain the existence of altruistic behavior. From the perspective of the gene, any behavior that helped its vessels (the organisms that carried it) to survive, even if that behavior meant the self-sacrifice of one of them, would continue to appear in future generations because the genes for that behavior also existed in a group of related vessels. Hamilton believed that the theory of kin selection explained the evolution of altruism more successfully than the rival theory of group selection (developed by V. C. Wynne-Edwards), according to which groups of organisms of the same species, even if unrelated, would evolve behaviors (such as cooperation) that would aid the survival of the group. Hamilton's innovation, taken up by Wilson in *Sociobiology*, was to shift the level of evolutionary explanation from the group or the individual to the gene. In 1971, Robert Trivers proposed the idea of reciprocal altruism to explain how an altruistic act may, while aiding another, also bring benefits to the altruist and so maintain an adaptive advantage.

Wilson's monumental 1975 book, *Sociobiology: The New Synthesis*, drew on these theories to bring social behavior fully under the umbrella of evolutionary explanation, presenting sociobiological reasoning to practitioners in other branches of biology and popularizing it for general readers. The book dealt mostly with animals and insects (ants being Wilson's scientific specialization), discussing such behaviors as aggression, altruism, and nurturance, and devoted its last, admittedly speculative chapter to explaining the evolution of social behavior in human beings. In 1978 Wilson developed his views on human sociobiology in his Pulitzer Prize–winning book *On Human Nature*, where he gave adaptive explanations for human sexual behavior and gender differences in mate choice as well as for aggression, altruism, and religion.

Wilson's attempts to apply sociobiological reasoning to human behavior made him the target of criticisms from the biologists Stephen Jay Gould, Richard Lewontin, Ruth Hubbard, Jonathan Beckwith, and others, who formed the Sociobiology Study Group in Boston. Their critique centered on three main points. First, how could Wilson possibly know, given the immense diversity of human behavior, which traits were hereditary, and therefore required explanation as adaptations, and which were cultural overlays? Lewontin referred to this as the problem of "carving nature at the joints," and Gould argued that the genes must instead enable a range of possible behaviors, rather than determine specific traits. Second, the critics asked, how could Wilson be sure that the traits of interest were adaptive after all? Some traits could persist simply because they were by-products of functional, adaptive traits, just as the spandrels of San Marco cathedral (St. Mark's Basilica in Venice, Italy) served no architectural function, but simply filled in the space left by the arches of the dome. Wilson's adaptationist assumptions were nothing more than "just so stories," speculative exercises in reverse engineering. Finally, the critics argued that Wilson's sociobiology gave implicit sanction to the status quo. If behaviors like out-group enmity, male aggression, and female nurturance were encoded in the genes, then human nature stood as a roadblock to social change, and racism and sexism must be the orders of the day.

Evolutionary psychology, developed by the psychologist Leda Cosmides and the anthropologist John Tooby in 1992, further extended sociobiological reasoning to all aspects of human mentality. Just as human beings possess physical organs that have been shaped by evolution, so the mind is composed of "mental modules" that are products of natural selection. The modules are genetically based and can be discovered by stripping away the superficial differences between cultures. Evolutionary psychology seeks to discover the evolutionary history of such common human social characteristics as social hierarchy, xenophobia, sibling rivalry, romance, male aggressiveness, religious belief, selfishness, and self-sacrifice, traits that, according to Cosmides and Tooby, all cultures seem to share and that form a common human nature. Thus their argument is still vulnerable to the first two criticisms presented above. They attempt to evade the third point of critique by claiming that although this common heritage of mental modules was adaptive in the ancestral environment in which *Homo sapiens* evolved, it is not necessarily adaptive any longer in the modern world and so might need to be modified or countered in some way. Indeed, evolutionary psychologists believe that the mental modules are not unchangeable by environment; they are adjusted by context and experience. But the evolutionary psychologists' contention, still highly controversial, is that there are limits beyond which a human being cannot change—just as it is possible for a person to walk on her knees, but not very comfortably and not for very long.

[*See also* **Biological Sciences; Evolution, Theory of; Genetics and Genetic Engineering; Psychology;** *and* **Social Sciences: Post–World War II.**]

BIBLIOGRAPHY

Barkow, Ira, Leda Cosmides, and John Tooby. *The Adapted Mind: Evolutionary Psychology and the Generation of Culture*. New York: Oxford University Press, 1992.

Gould, Stephen Jay. "Biological Potentiality vs. Biological Determinism." In *Ever Since Darwin: Reflections in Natural History*, pp. 251–259. New York: W. W. Norton, 1977.

Gould, Stephen Jay, and Richard C. Lewontin. "The Spandrels of San Marco and the Panglossian Paradigm: A Critique of the Adaptationist Programme."

Proceedings of the Royal Society of London Series B 205 (1979): 581–598.

Harman, Oren. *The Price of Altruism: George Price and the Search for the Origins of Kindness.* New York: W. W. Norton, 2010.

Lewontin, Richard C., Steven Rose, and Leon Kamin. *Not In Our Genes: Biology, Ideology, and Human Nature.* New York: Pantheon Books, 1984.

Segerstråle, Ullica. *Defenders of the Truth: The Battle for Science in the Sociobiology Debate and Beyond.* Oxford: Oxford University Press, 2000.

Wilson, Edward O. *On Human Nature.* Cambridge, Mass.: Harvard University Press, 1978.

Wilson, Edward O. *Sociobiology: The New Synthesis.* Cambridge, Mass.: Harvard University Press, 1975.

Wright, Robert. *The Moral Animal: Evolutionary Psychology and Everyday Life.* New York: Vintage Books, 1994.

Nadine Weidman

SOFTWARE

Although the word "software" is today used as a synonym for "computer program," the history of software is not quite the same thing as the history of the computer program. Programming predated "software" by many years, and once the term did enter use it was often taken to encompass things other than programs or to include only certain kinds of programs. The history of software is treated here as the history of packaging and distributing programs.

Inventing Computer Programs. The identity of the "first computer" has been debated endlessly, and identification of the first program is even more subjective because programs were often written before the computer for which they were intended was finished. For example, Charles Babbage worked for decades during the mid-nineteenth century on his never-finished Analytical Engine, which would have run programs encoded on punched cards. Babbage's cousin, Ada Lovelace, has sometimes been claimed as the first computer programmer because in 1842–1843 she wrote detailed plans to apply the engine for a particular calculation.

The architecture of modern computers evolved from "First Draft of a Report on the EDVAC" circulated in 1945 under the name of mathematician John von Neumann. One of its key ideas was that programs should be loaded into the computer's memory, where they could be manipulated like other data. The handful of automatic digital computers designed previously had taken their instructions from switches, strips of paper tape, and the like. Historians of computing often refer not to the "computer" but to the "stored program computer" as the crucial innovation in computing. Stored programs are a kind of self-modifying text. They are usually read sequentially, but based on the results so far obtained the computer may repeat or skip a particular passage of instructions or modify the contents of a specified part of memory. Computers able to run such programs entered operation from 1948 onward.

Computers are often called "universal machines," in reference to the ideas of mathematician Alan Turing whose 1930s work on mathematical logic was fundamental to the development of theoretical computer science several decades later. Any computer can, given enough time and a sufficiently large memory, simulate the capabilities of any other computer and so, theoretically, run any program. Software and hardware are, in this sense, interchangeable. Software thus sets computers aside from other kinds of machines and turns a computer from a quasi-universal machine into one able to carry out a particular task. These theoretical issues were seldom mentioned in the 1940s, but pioneers were well aware of the practical advantages of what was then called a "general-purpose" computer. They quickly learned the challenges involved in programming such a machine.

Packaging Programs. Even in the early twenty-first century, it is common to speak of "software packages." This concept of packaging is fundamental to the history of software. In fact, the idea of packaging programs was well established several years before the term "software." Programs were packaged with other, related programs, but also with things such as documentation, standard machine configurations, and new practices that allowed them to be transferred from one site to another.

The first purpose-built stored program computer powerful enough to tackle useful programs entered use in 1949 at Cambridge University. This led almost immediately to the creation of a subroutine library. Subroutines were snippets of code needed repeatedly for different programs, for example, to read a number into memory or calculate a square root. Programs from this library filled much of the world's first textbook on computer programming, but because computers were then experimental one-off machines they could not be used elsewhere without modification.

The programs actually run by computers consist of a series of instructions represented as a sequence of numbers. A computer's coding scheme is called its "machine language." Writing a machine language program was tedious, and the programs were hard to debug. Work on what was then called "automatic coding" was therefore a major focus of computing research and development in the early 1950s. Programmers began to write computer instructions in the more convenient notation of "assembly language," which was then processed by an "assembler" program and automatically integrated with subroutine to produce the machine language.

By 1953 scientists and engineers at more than a dozen different sites were programming identical IBM computers. A group of Los Angeles–area firms began to collaborate on a common assembler system. This project grew into the SHARE user group, chartered formally in 1955, which pioneered the concept of a software library shared between computer installations. Programs within that library followed specific social and technical conventions so that they could be combined as needed. These included rewiring control panels in a particular way, standardizing operational procedures, adopting common programming tools, and establishing shared coding conventions. By 1958 SHARE participants had begun to refer to the programs they developed together as "packages."

Programming Languages. In 1957 IBM released its FORTRAN package. This relieved programmers of the need to specify computer operations at the lowest possible level of detail. FORTRAN code was much closer to a textual representation of mathematical formulae, including the manipulation of matrices. It rapidly became the lingua franca of scientific and technical application programming. The FORTRAN compiler, created by a small group of IBM staff programmers in collaboration with programmers on loan from United Aircraft and the Massachusetts Institute of Technology (MIT), automatically and efficiently translated this into machine language.

With FORTRAN, IBM set a new pattern for the physical distribution, documentation, support, and promotion of complex programming tools as a crucial part of the bundle of services provided with a computer. Hundreds of other programming languages followed, many aimed at specific tasks such as business administration or text processing.

The Concept of Software. In early usage, software was not always programs and programs were not always software. The first known usage of the word "software" in the computer field was by mathematician John W. Tukey in 1958 to describe automatic programming aids. It was not until 1960 that the term began to gain general favor, initially as a complement to hardware that was already established as a colloquial term for computer equipment. For much of the 1960s the most commonly accepted definition of software included only what would later be called "systems software." A Honeywell advertisement of early 1962 defined software as "the automatic programming aids that simplify the task of telling the computer 'hardware' to do its job" and explained that the "three basic categories of software" were assembly systems, compilers, and operating systems.

Sometimes software described, somewhat playfully, everything else provided by the computer manufacturer or independent company provided to accompany hardware—including services and other intangibles. Participants in the 1963 "RAND Symposium," an informal gathering of the computing elite organized by Fred Gruenberger, discovered that they lacked a common definition of software. One expert suggested that "many of us refer to software as programs to be used by programmers." Another, who had recently founded a software company, countered that software was "not only applications programming, but the writing of specification for programs, the giving of advice to people who might want to use computers, the installation manuals, etc." A third objected that "I don't believe that application packages are software," even if purchased from a specialist company (Haigh, 2002).

Multiple Models for Software Packages. In the mid-1950s computer manufacturers provided few programs of any kind with their machines, and companies using computers wrote, or at least heavily customized, the vast majority of the code run on them. This situation changed far more rapidly and completely for some kinds of programs than for others.

Operating systems were the most complex kind of software and the first to be standardized. SHARE's main early effort was the attempt to design a standard SHARE 709 System (SOS). When the SOS project disappointed, IBM took over primary responsibility for the design, implementation, and support of operating systems. Over the course of the 1960s computer hardware became much more complex and operating systems more ambitious. This exemplifies the trend over time of software systems toward greater complexity and abstraction. Most programs did not interact directly with hardware. Instead they exchanged data and requests with other programs, in an arrangement often visualized as a stack with many layers.

User companies started to take it for granted that computer manufacturers would supply operating systems and programming language compilers with their machines. Yet this pattern did not hold in all areas.

Businesses used computers primarily for administrative applications such as accounting, billing, payroll, and inventory management. Until the 1980s these "application programs" were usually written and maintained by in-house programming teams (sometimes with the aid of outside consultants). This work accounted for a large portion of the cost of running a computer center. In some cases, applications programs provided by computer vendors were widely used—notably IBM's '62 CFO (Consolidated Functions Ordinary) software package, which allowed many smaller insurance companies to computerize their operations with low-end IBM computers. By the late 1960s applications were usually written in COBOL, defined in 1959 to do for business programming what FORTRAN had done for scientific programming.

Computers were widely used for scientific modeling and engineering calculations. Each project involved writing new FORTRAN programs to perform the calculations. These programs themselves were sometimes shared; for example, derivatives of the NASTRAN structural analysis package developed for the National Aeronautics and Space Administration (NASA) in the 1960s are still widely used. More common, however, was the sharing of FORTRAN subroutines implementing mathematical methods useful for many different applications. These were packaged with tools and documentation to help programmers incorporate them into their own programs. New mathematical practices embedded in the subroutines were thus transported with the code from one site. In the twenty-first century, leading commercial mathematical (IMSL, NAG, Maple, Mathematica, and MATLAB) and statistical (SAS, SPSS) packages all have roots in university projects and maintained close ties with the mathematical research community.

Software Engineering and the Software Crisis. No topic in the history of software has received anything like the attention given by historians to the two international conferences on software engineering sponsored by the North Atlantic Treaty Organization (NATO) Science Committee in 1968 and 1969. They are remembered largely for the declaration by some influential participants of a "software crisis," evidenced by the great difficulties IBM and its competitors were having in producing the operating systems needed to power their most advanced computers. The conference was part of a push to establish software as an object of research in its own right, distinct from both hardware research and computing theory. Many participants had previously worked together on the widely influential Algol international computer language project. The new agenda mirrored the progression of their own careers, from virtuoso developers of compilers and operating systems to corporate or academic research positions. They went on to promote the application of mathematical rigor to the creation of software, giving rise to the "formal methods" approach to software engineering (itself a concept pushed into general awareness by the conference) and to the idea of "structured programming."

Unbundling and the Software Industry.

During the 1960s computer manufacturers gave away operating systems, compilers, utility programs, and even some application programs. IBM's famous 1969 decision to "unbundle" software (Grad, 2002) established software as an actual "ware" traded in the marketplace. IBM soon became the world's leading seller of software, a title it retained in the early twenty-first century even after surrendering its traditional position as the largest supplier of hardware.

Unbundling was just one milestone in a much longer journey, already begun with the successful introduction of commercial packages from independent software companies. The first commercially successful software packages tended to be utility programs that filled holes in software lineups provided by IBM. These included Applied Data Research's Autoflow (1965), which created flowcharts from program code; Pansophic's Panvalet (1970), which maintained source code files on disk; and Mark IV (1968) from Informatics General, which made it easy to manage data files and produce reports.

The commercial viability of packaged software relied on a legal framework in which the rights of producers were protected; on the acceptance of banks and investors that packaged software companies work in a profitable industry; on the willingness of accountants to value packages as assets on a software company's balance sheet; on the willingness of customers to purchase something that may contain bugs they are unable to fix; and on the creation of a set of shared cultural understandings governing concepts such as the difference between a bug fix (free) and an upgrade (usually paid for), the issuing of regular updates, and the period of free technical support to which a purchaser might be entitled. None of these was initially obvious, and each involved a process of collective learning and experimentation aided by formal and information social networks. The most important of these was the Software Industry Section of the Association of Data Processing Service Organizations (ADAPSO). Here company leaders shared new ideas, issued "position papers," and drew up model sales contracts. This helped to construct the software package as an artifact with a stable economic and legal basis for existence.

Personal Computer Software.

Mainframe packages were sold directly to institutional customers. Even a breakout hit would sell only a few thousand copies, each priced at tens of thousands of dollars. By 1970, annual sales of packaged software in the United States were already estimated at $250 million, according to figures quoted by Martin Campbell-Kelly (2003, p. 14). But the widespread use of mass-produced personal computers such as the Apple II, introduced in 1977, soon created a potential market of millions of individual computer users.

Early personal computer software was often written by individual programmers, sometimes in their spare time. The first publishers pursued a model similar to the music industry, where they would promote and distribute material produced largely independently. But as the complexity and expense of developing competitive programs expanded, the focus shifted to larger companies and salaried development teams. Many niches remained for the development of custom applications for businesses and production of software packages for niche markets such as Boy Scout troops or dairy farmers. Some programmers earned a good living writing "Shareware." Their programs could be copied and tested without charge, but contented users were asked to mail a payment to the author of the program.

Personal computer software was packed into new material forms, as disks and tapes were stuffed into plastic bags and cardboard boxes. Its producers, users, methods of distribution, function, and pricing were quite different from those of the established mainframe software industry. Pioneers again had to experiment with unfamiliar solutions before eventually evolving a workable model. Programs were sold through new networks of hobbyist magazines, distributors, stores, and user groups. Personal software producers formed their own associations, with licensing and piracy prevention as their main collective concerns.

Most personal computer software packages replicated in more limited and much more affordable form those already established for larger computers. Operating systems and programming languages mimicked existing models, as did popular database management, word processing, and accounting systems. Video games had originally been played on specialized coin-operated machines. Programmers created increasingly faithful copies of arcade favorites for personal computers and also explored the potential of more involved game genres such as text adventures, strategy games, and simulations.

Two important genres of software were unique to the personal computer. The first, invented in 1979 with VisiCalc, was the spreadsheet. This software exploited the low cost and interactivity of the personal computer to create financial and technical models quickly and without traditional programming. The second, pioneered in 1985 with Aldus PageMaker, was desktop publishing. The graphical interface of the newly available Apple Macintosh combined with the first reasonably affordable laser printer to make powerful page layout tools cheaper and easier to use than ever before.

Since the 1970s, an ever-increasing amount of software has been built into microprocessor-controlled products such as calculators, bank ATMs, microwaves, cars, fax machines, flat-screen televisions, and cell phones. The computers built into these products are known as "embedded systems" and their programs cannot usually be modified by users.

Industry Consolidation. The software market of the mid-1980s was highly fragmented. Most

successful software companies owed their fortune to one or two popular packages. In the 1990s this changed. By winning the contract to supply IBM with the operating system for its Personal Computer (1981), Microsoft had established MS-DOS as the standard personal computer operating system. As users shifted from text-based DOS to Microsoft Windows in large numbers from 1990 onward, they also tended to adopt Microsoft's Windows-based word processing and spreadsheet programs, Word and Excel, which the company began to bundle together and sell as Microsoft Office. In 1996 Microsoft displaced IBM as the world's largest computer company by market valuation.

By the end of the 1990s Microsoft had effective monopolies on both office applications and operating systems for personal computers, although not without engaging in sales practices that caused it to lose a landmark antitrust case. Over the next decade its main competition came from the open-source software movement. Open-source software is free to its users, and the source code is available to anyone who wants to read or modify it. The movement evolved from the GNU project, initiated by programmer Richard Stallman in 1984. Linux became the main competition to Windows as a network server operating system. OpenOffice, underwritten by Microsoft's competitor Sun Microsystems, was the leading alternative to Microsoft Office. Firefox gave the most serious competition to Microsoft's Internet Explorer Web browser. Open-source packages also dominated many behind-the-scenes aspects of the Internet, such as Web servers and e-mail delivery.

Large corporations have remained an important market for computer software. During the late twentieth and early twenty-first century, they increasingly shifted away from the internal coding of core administrative and operational systems toward the purchase and configuration of enormously complicated and expensive application software packages. These are known as "enterprise systems" and include modules to integrate almost every aspect of business. After a rash of takeovers, two giant software companies dominated the market for these packages: SAP and Oracle. However, many thousands of smaller companies thrived selling complementary programs and services to the users of their software.

Software and the Internet.

Following the introduction of the Netscape Navigator Web browser in 1994 and the rapid adoption of the Internet by home and business users over the next few years, network connections gradually replaced shrink-wrapped cartons as the standard method of software distribution. Large software companies adopted the Internet as a medium for the download of demonstration versions of programs and updates years before they began to sell programs for download. Features were built into software packages such as Microsoft's Windows XP operating system to automatically download and install minor updates and bug fixes. New features would suddenly appear many years after their initial release.

Apple's "App Store" was not the first online marketplace of the purchase and download of software, but by 2012 it was by far the most successful. Introduced in 2008 as an extension to the company's iTunes media store, the App Store was central to the spectacular success of Apple's iPhone and iPad tablet. As in the early days of personal computers, software for these new kinds of computer was written mostly by small companies and part-time developers. The App Store gave a convenient and trusted way for users to find and purchase programs from these developers. The success in 2010 of the game Angry Birds, sold for just $1, demonstrated the huge potential market.

The Internet also provided a new way to run software. As Internet connections became faster and Web browsers more powerful, they became a way of interacting with applications running on a distant server with no need to install or configure additional software. Successes in the "software as a service" area included Salesforce.com's software to support sales and customer management and Google Docs for collaborative access to word processing and other office applications. Such services may eventually replace the established model of purchasing and installing a program for most users. Other software systems, such as Facebook, offered services that could only exist online because of their inherently social nature. The distinction between packaged software and computer services, established in the 1960s and 1970s, was collapsing again.

[*See also* **Computer Science; Computers, Mainframe, Mini, and Micro; Engineering; ENIAC; Internet and World Wide Web; Mathematics and Statistics; Military, Science and Technology and the; National Aeronautics and Space Administration; Science; Technology;** *and* **Von Neumann, John.**]

BIBLIOGRAPHY

Akera, Atsushi. "Voluntarism and the Fruits of Collaboration." *Technology and Culture* 42, no. 4 (October 2001): 710–736. Documents the SHARE user group and its operating system development project of the late 1950s.

Auletta, Ken. *World War 3.0: Microsoft and Its Enemies*. New York: Random House, 2001. Journalistic treatment of Microsoft's antitrust woes and its response to the Internet.

Campbell-Kelly, Martin. *From Airline Reservations to Sonic the Hedgehog: A History of the Software Industry*. Cambridge, Mass.: MIT Press, 2003. The only book-length scholarly history of software, this provides a detailed and well-researched history of the U.S. software industry from the early days of contract programming services in the 1950s through to the personal computer software firms of the early 1990s.

Campbell-Kelly, Martin. "The History of the History of Software." *IEEE Annals of the History of Computing* 29, no. 4 (October–December 2007): 40–51.

Campbell-Kelly, Martin. "Programming the EDSAC: Early Programming Activity at the University of Cambridge." *IEEE Annals of the History of Computing* 2, no. 1 (October 1980): 7–36. From a series of articles by Campbell-Kelly exploring in great technical detail the programming practices of early computers.

Grad, Burton. "Software Unbundling: A Personal Perspective." *IEEE Annals of the History of Computing* 24, no. 1 (January–March 2002): 64–71. By a member of the IBM committee that recommended selling software separately from hardware.

Gruenberger, Fred. "Rand Symposium 6." In *RAND Symposia Collection (CBI 78), Charles Babbage*

Institute, University of Minnesota. Minneapolis: University of Minnesota, 1963.

Haigh, Thomas. "The History of Information Technology." *Annual Review of Information Science and Technology* 45 (2011): 431–487. Lengthy, recent review of the historical literature on computing including detailed coverage of software history.

Haigh, Thomas. "How Data Got Its Base: Generalized Information Storage Software in the 1950s and 60s." *IEEE Annals of the History of Computing* 31, no. 4 (October–December 2009): 6–25. Database management systems have been a crucial kind of software package since the 1960s. This traces their evolution from systems produced by computer users.

Haigh, Thomas. "Software in the 1960s as Concept, Service, and Product." *IEEE Annals of the History of Computing* 24, no. 1 (January–March 2002): 5–13. Explores the early history of software from the user-organization perspective.

Hashagen, Ulf, Reinhard Keil-Slawik, and Arthur L Norberg, eds. *Mapping the History of Computing: Software Issues.* New York: Springer-Verlag, 2002. The product of a conference intended to set an agenda for scholarly work on software history. Five main papers take perspectives such as "software as science" and "software as engineering."

Honeywell. "A Few Quick Facts on Software." *Business Automation* 7, no. 1 (January 1962): 16–17.

Mahoney, Michael S., and Thomas Haigh, eds. *Histories of Computing.* Cambridge, Mass.: Harvard University Press, 2011. Collects the papers of a leading historian of computing with a particular interest in the history of software.

Priestley, Mark. *A Science of Operations: Machines, Logic, and the Invention of Programming.* New York: Springer-Verlag, 2011. An ambitious and clearly written history of the coevolution of computer architectures, programming tools and techniques, and the mathematical theory of computation from Babbage to the 1970s.

von Neumann, John. *Papers of John von Neumann on Computers and Computing Theory.* Cambridge, Mass.: MIT Press, 1986. Includes a seminal series of early reports on "planning and coding" computers as well as the 1945 "First Draft of a Report on the EDVAC."

Yates, JoAnne. *Structuring the Information Age.* Baltimore: Johns Hopkins University Press, 2005. A study of the evolution of information technology use in the life insurance industry, including a section on IBM's early '62CFO package and its users.

Thomas Haigh

SOLAR ELECTRICITY

See Electricity and Electrification.

SOLID-STATE ELECTRONICS

The field of electronics deals with controlling the flow of electrons—storing, discharging, and amplifying electrical current—to process information in the form of electrical signals. Solid-state electronics, as its name suggests, refers to the control of electrical current within crystals (usually semiconductors, such as germanium or silicon), as opposed to vacuum or gaseous media. The first practical devices widely used in electronics utilized vacuum, such as the vacuum diode (invented by Sir John Ambrose Fleming in 1904) or the vacuum triode (invented by Lee de Forest in 1906). The vacuum devices had obvious disadvantages: they were fragile, consumed a large amount of power, and tended to overheat. Nevertheless, vacuum devices served as basic building blocks of electronics during the first half of the twentieth century in a wide array of electronic equipment.

The potential of solid-state devices, however, was known since the late nineteenth century and was gradually exploited alongside vacuum devices. As early as 1874, German physicist Ferdinand Braun discovered that mineral galena (lead sulfide) connected to a metal wire conducts electricity in one direction. In other words, Braun used galena to create a rectifier, or a diode. This came to be known as the "cat's whisker" diode and was widely used as a detector of wireless signals. Although the cat's whisker diode was too unstable to succeed as a commercial electronic device, its popularity grew especially among amateur radio enthusiasts and sparked the technical imaginations of many youngsters as they tried desperately to find the sweet spot with a metal wire.

With breakthroughs in solid-state physics during the interwar period, and with additional wartime research and development (R&D) efforts in semiconductor materials during World War II, scientists and engineers were able to develop a more stable solid-state electronic device. The primary aim during World War II was to develop radar, a device used to detect approaching enemy aircrafts. Much of the work was done at the Radiation Laboratory of the Massachusetts Institute of Technology (MIT). Research on the material properties of silicon and germanium was led by Karl Lark-Horovitz of Purdue University. Understandably, the radar project was extensively funded by the military, especially through the U.S. Army Signal Corps. The wartime R&D on crystal rectifiers served as a foundation for postwar developments in solid-state electronics, and its results were later published as part of the Rad Lab series titled *Crystal Rectifiers* (1948).

The Invention and Spread of the Transistor.
The transistor marked the beginning of a new era of solid-state electronics. On 16 December 1947, three physicists—William B. Shockley, John Bardeen, and Walter H. Brattain of the Bell Telephone Laboratories in Murray Hill, New Jersey—invented the point-contact transistor as a replacement for the bulky and unreliable vacuum tubes. Brattain was the experimental physicist who performed the first successful experiment using a plastic wedge covered in gold foil with a slit, sitting atop a piece of purified germanium crystal. The device exhibited the typical characteristics of the triode. In 1956, the three physicists were awarded the Nobel Prize for Physics for their work. The invention of the transistor was a product of a long tradition of basic research in the physical sciences at Bell Labs since the 1930s, as well as the accumulated experiences of wartime R&D.

Making one transistor was one thing; making them in mass quantities was quite another. When Bell Labs made the public announcement of the transistor in June 1948, it aroused considerable interest from other electronics manufacturers. By 1951, companies were flocking to Murray Hill and Allentown, Pennsylvania (where Western Electric, the manufacturing arm of the Bell System was located), to learn the emerging art of transistor manufacturing. Bell Labs organized several technical symposiums to provide basic lessons on transistor technology and allowed companies to license the basic transistor patents at a bargain rate of $25,000. This spurred a rapid spread of transistor technology in the 1950s, within and outside the United States.

The most popular version of the transistor manufactured in the 1950s was the alloy-junction transistor. The design of the point-contact transistor, with two narrowly spaced tungsten wires placed on top of a slab of germanium crystal, made the device subject to external shock. The researchers at General Electric (GE) and Radio Corporation of America (RCA) developed a method to create a semiconductor junction using the alloy process. The process involved fixing two "dots" of indium on either sides of the germanium pellet and heating them to an appropriate temperature, allowing germanium and indium to fuse into an alloy. This created regions of differing semiconductor properties within the crystal, allowing the device to function as an electronic switch or oscillator. Throughout the 1950s, the alloy-junction transistor served as the workhorse for a variety of electronic equipment, such as hearing aids and transistorized radios and televisions.

As the mass production of transistors stabilized in the early 1950s, the U.S. military began to show interest in utilizing the new electronic device with its communication gear and new weaponry. The major challenge in using transistors for military applications was what vice president of Bell Labs Jack A. Morton dubbed the "tyranny of numbers." The smaller size and superior heat characteristics of transistors allowed for a more complex circuitry than had been previously possible with vacuum devices. As the number of components in equipment grew, the number of interconnections between components increased even more quickly. The problem was that the interconnections were the weakest link, and the likelihood of equipment failure grew exponentially. Solving this problem emerged as an urgent technical problem within the context of the rising Cold War.

Microminiaturization and the Path to the Integrated Circuit.
In the late 1950s, there was no elegant solution to the interconnection

problem. The three branches of the military sought solutions through individual R&D contracts with major electronics manufacturers. The army partnered with RCA to develop the micromodule, which used standardized printed circuit boards stacked to form a cube-shape circuit. The Air Force provided an R&D contract to Westinghouse Electric to explore the ambitious technique of "molecular electronics." Inspired by MIT professor Arthur R. von Hippel's call for "molecular science and engineering," Westinghouse attempted to develop an entirely new method of materials processing to make full-blown circuit components directly from molten semiconductors. Although these attempts led to some promising results in terms of size reduction and increased reliability, they were largely abandoned when a more practical means to fabricate integrated circuits appeared in 1959.

In May 1959, Jack S. Kilby of Texas Instruments filed a patent for the "miniaturized self-contained circuit," later known as the solid circuit. If interconnections were responsible for the plummeting reliability of semiconductor devices, Kilby reasoned, why not eliminate them altogether? The solid circuit he created, however, failed to realize his intent. Kilby's model used flying gold wires to connect the components, which made it highly problematic as a practical device. A month later, Robert N. Noyce of Fairchild Semiconductor filed a patent for the planar integrated circuit (IC). Using photolithography techniques, Noyce proposed a method for fabricating semiconductor devices containing multiple components within a single piece of silicon. The planar process—developed by Fairchild cofounder Jean A. Hoerni—was, as one historian of technology noted, "arguably the most important innovation in twentieth-century technology" (Lécuyer, 2005, p. 297).

By 1965, the planar IC emerged as an industry standard for fabricating semiconductor devices. The significance of the planar IC was that it was "scalable"—meaning that one could continue to make progressively smaller devices with faster speeds at lower costs. This was what Fairchild cofounder Gordon E. Moore recognized when he published an article in the *Electronics* magazine entitled "Cramming More Components onto Integrated Circuits" (1965). When asked to make a

10 year forecast of semiconductor technologies, Moore predicted that the number of IC components with minimum manufacturing cost per unit would double every year. Following this logic, an economically fabricated IC in 1975 would have 65 thousand components within a single slab of silicon. When Moore's prediction was realized 10 years later, his prediction came to be widely known as "Moore's law." After almost 50 years, Moore's law still proved to be valid, albeit with some tweaks in the margins, leading to the popular phrase "doubling every *eighteen months*." In the early twenty-first century, some technologists raised concerns over the physical limits of Moore's law, especially those imposed by the wavelength of the light source used in photolithography equipment. These concerns led to an emerging interest in utilizing advanced nanotechnology to create a new technological platform to replace the planar IC.

The success of the planar IC platform led to a profound transformation of the semiconductor industry's structure. The availability of a standard platform allowed for the standardization of manufacturing equipment, which in turn created a niche for a new class of firms specializing in making semiconductor fabrication equipment. By 1970, there were enough of these specialty firms to form a trade association named Semiconductor Equipment and Materials Institute (SEMI). These comprised companies that focused on a specific piece of the overall manufacturing process, from photolithography equipment and ion implanters to diffusion furnaces and wire bonders. The emergence of this subsector reflected the increasing complexity of semiconductor manufacturing. These specialty manufacturers were active participants in the collective technological innovation that sustained Moore's law during the past 50 years.

International Competition and the Technology Roadmap. The U.S. solid-state electronics industry sustained its technological leadership for much of the twentieth century. Beginning in the late 1970s, however, it faced intense international competition, especially from Japan. In 1976, the Japanese Ministry of International Trade and Industry (MITI) began a national initiative to develop advanced semiconductor manufacturing technologies with the aim to leapfrog that of the United States. In response, the American semiconductor manufacturers banded together to maintain its leading edge. Much of the U.S. response was an explicit emulation of what was then perceived to be a Japanese model of industrial governance, including strong governmental leadership and cooperation among competitors. In 1986, the Semiconductor Industry Association (SIA), established in 1977 as a response to the Japanese challenge, solicited funds from the federal government to establish an industry cooperative to develop advanced semiconductor manufacturing techniques. As a result, Sematech was established in 1987 with funding from the U.S. Department of Defense.

One of the most important products of Sematech was the technology roadmap for semiconductors. The roadmapping activity began as a negotiation tool among various Sematech participants to determine the equipment required to set up an experimental lab at the new Sematech site in Austin, Texas. Within the context of the mid-1980s, however, the technology roadmap soon acquired a nationalistic rhetoric as a planning device for successfully fending off Japanese competition. In 1994, Sematech institutionalized the roadmap as an official publication entitled the *National Technology Roadmap for Semiconductors* (NTRS), which was to be updated every two years. The NTRS contained detailed technical requirements for the continued miniaturization of semiconductor devices, following a trajectory predicted by Moore's law.

As Japanese competition subsided in the 1990s, the nationalistic rhetoric of NTRS waned as well, leading to the internationalization of the roadmapping activity. By the end of the 1990s, the SIA began to invite foreign companies to participate in the planning process, renaming the exercise the *International Technology Roadmap for Semiconductors* (ITRS). In 2012, the ITRS was a fully internationalized activity with participants from the United States, Europe, Japan, South Korea, and Taiwan. What began as a tool to protect U.S. technological leadership metamorphosed into a mechanism for global industrial governance. The internationalization of the technology roadmapping activity reflected the globalization of the solid-state electronics industry. The early twenty-first century digital world was undergirded by a large number of industrial firms across many different nations coordinated through a complex planning process of the ITRS.

[*See also* Bardeen, John; Bell Laboratories; De Forest, Lee; Military, Science and Technology and the; Nobel Prize in Biomedical Research; Physics; Radio; Research and Development (R&D); Science; Shockley, William; *and* Television.]

BIBLIOGRAPHY

Braun, Ernst, and Stuart Macdonald. *Revolution in Miniature: The History and Impact of Semiconductor Electronics.* Cambridge, U.K.: Cambridge University Press, 1978. One of the seminal works in the history of semiconductor electronics.

Brock, David C., ed. *Understanding Moore's Law: Four Decades of Innovation.* Philadelphia: Chemical Heritage Foundation, 2006. A volume based on the 2005 symposium to celebrate the fortieth anniversary of Moore's law. Includes Moore's original texts, his retrospective, and other interpretive essays to illuminate the many aspects of Moore's law.

Browning, Larry D., and Judy C. Shetler. *Sematech: Saving the U.S. Semiconductor Industry.* College Station: Texas A&M University Press, 2000.

Choi, Hyungsub. "The Boundaries of Industrial Research: Making Transistors at RCA, 1948–1960." *Technology and Culture* 48, no. 3 (2007): 758–782.

Henriksen, Paul W. "Solid State Physics Research at Purdue." *Osiris* 2d ser., 3 (1987): 237–260.

Hoddeson, Lillian. "The Discovery of the Point-Contact Transistor." *Historical Studies in the Physical Sciences* 12, no. 1 (1981): 43–76.

Lécuyer, Christophe. *Making Silicon Valley: Innovation and the Growth of High Tech.* Cambridge, Mass.: MIT Press, 2005. Placing the Silicon Valley phenomenon within the context of the local history of northern California, Lécuyer skillfully weaves the story of Varian Associates, Eitel–McCullough, and Fairchild Semiconductor based on detailed documentations and interviews.

Riordan, Michael, and Lillian Hoddeson. *Crystal Fire: The Birth of the Information Age.* New York: W. W. Norton, 1997. Published in time for the fiftieth anniversary of the transistor's invention, this book provides a definitive account of the invention and spread of transistor technology.

Hyungsub Choi

SOUND TECHNOLOGY, RECORDED

The history of sound recording technology is part of the broad story of communications, culture, and consumerism in America. In terms of technological change over time, it can be roughly divided into three periods, the first from its invention to the end of World War II, the second from the postwar period to about 1980, and the third from about 1980 to the early twenty-first century.

Invention and Development. The physical nature of sound was being intensely studied during and after the mid-nineteenth century using a variety of instruments, and after 1856 it was possible to record a visible record of sound waves on a French invention called the phonautograph. The American inventor Thomas Edison was familiar with the device and may have been inspired by it because he was the first to demonstrate a workable device—he called it the "phonograph"—both to record and later to reproduce a sound. He first demonstrated his device in 1877 and later to great acclaim. The phonograph captured sound waves by embossing them into a groove on a soft medium (originally tin foil wrapped around a metal cylinder). A great deal of early scholarship focused on the details of the phonograph's invention, its improvement by Edison and others, and the ensuing patent battles and commercial rivalries. The phonograph (and its main American rival, a similar device called the graphophone) emerged commercially by the late 1880s primarily as a system for dictating and transcribing business correspondence, a response to the burgeoning U.S. market for office technologies. These systems later recorded on wax-compound cylinders, which were intended to be replayed once or twice

for transcription and then reused (Read and Welch, 1976).

Entertainment phonographs and recordings emerged almost simultaneously and took off commercially during the 1890s. Especially important among the many innovations made to improve sound recorders or perhaps avoid patent infringement was the introduction of the "gramophone" disc medium that replaced cylinders by about 1930. Consumers seemed more interested in playing music than making their own recordings, and factories churned out large numbers of recordings on more durable compounds of shellac or plastic that could be played numerous times. Sales of consumer phonographs and recordings peaked in 1929 and declined through the late 1930s, as many manufacturers failed or merged with their upstart competitors in radio and motion pictures.

Those two new industries became intense users of recording equipment, and each pushed the technology in different directions. After briefly using discs to provide sound, theaters showing the "talkies" of the 1930s universally switched to a new type of recording system, where the sound was captured photographically and the sound "track" was reproduced at the edge of the distribution copy of the film. Specialized optical recorders were used to create these sound tracks. Hollywood studios innovated the use of cut-and-splice editing techniques, the use of audio special effects, and the combining or "overdubbing" of multiple recordings into one and were early experimenters with stereophonic sound in the period after about 1930 (Gomery, 2005; Weis and Belton, 1985).

Diversification of the Technology. Americans failed to adopt the magnetic recording technologies developed in Europe in the 1930s and early 1940s, resulting in a temporary divergence. Magnetic recording on a steel wire (later a paper or plastic tape, coated with iron oxide) was announced first in the United States in 1888, but it was largely unsuccessful as a commercial product until adopted by the telephone and radio authorities in Europe beginning in the 1920s. It underwent rapid development in Germany beginning around 1930, emerging in the later 1930s as one of the standard pieces of equipment in many radio stations. The most successful of these new magnetic recorders was the magnetophon by the electrical firm AEG and the AGFA film subsidiary of the conglomerate I. G. Farben. The magnetophon used an oxide-coated plastic tape as its medium. Its sound quality could match the best discs, but its initial commercial advantage was the ability to make long-duration recordings (discs were only available for recordings of about 20 minutes). Tape recorders were used extensively during the Nazi period to distribute radio programs, broadcast propaganda from trucks, and make surveillance recordings (Morton, 2000).

In 1945, magnetophon technology was carried (literally in some cases) back to the United States by a number of military and civilian personnel. A number of firms enthusiastically advocated its commercialization for use in motion pictures, broadcasting, and consumer entertainment. As a consumer device, sales remained low compared to that of phonograph record players through the late 1960s. After reaching a nadir in the late 1930s, phonograph sales had exploded after the end of the war, and manufacturers offered several new technologies. The most important were the Columbia Record Company's Long Playing disc and the Radio Corporation of America's seven-inch disc (popularly known as the 45-rpm disc). The introduction of stereo discs in 1958–1959 helped fuel a record industry rebound and a fad for "high fidelity." Tape's commercial success was limited to the making of recordings. Studios rapidly adopted it as a low-cost way to make original recordings compared to the use of soft-wax "master" discs, which had to be converted to metal stampers and then commercially duplicated in plastic.

The Digital Era. The years since 1965 marked another sharp break with the past. Of particular interest was the consumer market for new types of audio devices and systems. Here, tape technology took the important U.S. market by storm with the introduction of the Lear/RCA Stereo Eight (or "eight track") tape in 1965. Conceived as a mobile system for automobiles, sales of recorded eight track tapes challenged discs by the early 1970s. The Philips Company's Compact Cassette system, which was even more portable and considered more convenient, gradually overtook sales of the eight-track in the late 1970s and, by the mid-1980s, the disc as well. The cassette became the dominant medium worldwide for some years, and a culture of re-recording commercial offerings from discs or other tapes emerged around it.

The second and more important development, one that cuts across all market segments and technical areas, was the introduction of digital recording. This method was not so much a new medium as a new method, converting sounds into tiny chunks or "samples" and storing them as binary numbers rather than as some analog of the original sound wave. In the studio, this meant that the problems of overdubbing, re-recording, or making copies of recordings would not result in a degradation of the sound. Consumers were sold on the notion of better "digital" sound, and sales of the Philips/Sony Compact Disc rose steadily after its introduction in 1982.

More significant was the fact that the digital process was the basis of a new means of distribution of recordings. It was independent of any particular medium, meaning that the same digital recording could exist on magnetic tape, on an optical Compact Disc, or even on a phonograph record. The importance of those differences became clear during the mid-1990s with the popularization of the Web, as the consumer redistribution of commercial recordings ran wild. Many of the changes in recording technology that became widespread during the early twenty-first century, such as digital "compression" techniques and the MP3 file format, owe their popularity to consumer-driven music distribution on the Internet. By the second decade of the twenty-first century, as the sellers of recorders and recordings mostly clung to the old media-centered model of business, both the makers and the consumers of recordings were using technology in a quite different direction.

[*See also* **Film Technology; Radio; Technology;** *and* **Television.**]

BIBLIOGRAPHY

Millard, Andre. *America on Record: A History of Recorded Sound.* Cambridge, U.K.: Cambridge University Press, 1995. A standard in the field, integrating the history of technology with a strong focus on cultural impact.

Gomery, Douglas. *The Coming of Sound: A History.* New York: Routledge, 2005. A good introduction to the introduction of sound in the U.S. motion picture industry.

Morton, David L., Jr. *Off the Record: The Technology and Culture of Sound Recording in America.* New Brunswick, N.J.: Rutgers University Press, 2000. The author's work, including chapters on nonentertainment recording technology.

Read, Oliver, and Walter L. Welch. *From Tin Foil to Stereo: Evolution of the Phonograph.* 2d ed. Indianapolis, Ind.: Howard W. Sams, 1976. The most detailed early history, first published in 1959 and updated to include events through the early 1970s. Although many details have emerged in the interim since publication, this book remains the best available reference for early phonograph history. Now out of print but readily available.

Weis, Elisabeth, and John Belton, eds. *Film Sound: Theory and Practice.* New York: Columbia University Press, 1985. Although not obvious from the title, much of the book is concerned with the history of sound recording in the motion picture industry.

David L. Morton Jr.

SPACE PROGRAM

Despite the almost universal reference to an "American Space program," in reality the United States has sponsored (and sponsors still in the early twenty-first century) not one space agency, but many. The U.S. Army, Navy, and Air Force—as well as the National Reconnaissance Office (NRO), an intelligence service—field independent space programs. The focus of this essay is the mainly civilian activities of the National Aeronautics and Space Administration (NASA) and its predecessor agency, the National Advisory Committee for Aeronautics (NACA). Unlike the military or intelligence agencies, which pursue parochial interests, NASA research occurs on a broad front, including aeronautics, human spaceflight, planetary observation, and exploration of the universe.

Origins. The foundation of America's national space program began long before the 1950s and the Space Race with the USSR. It started with a decision in 1915 to establish a laboratory for "the scientific study of the problems of flight, with a view to their practical solution, and to determine the problems which should be experimentally attacked" (Roland, 1985, Vol. 2, p. 394). Congress took this step because other countries recognized in the years before World War I that heavier-than-air flight might be consequential in battle and so initiated national laboratories devoted to air research. The United States lagged behind, and when Congress finally acted in 1915, it did so half-heartedly, authorizing a mere $5,000 to inaugurate NACA, added as an afterthought to the Naval Appropriations Act of that year. Through its five laboratories that opened gradually across the United States, NACA represented a consistent federal commitment to aeronautical research, concentrating especially (but not exclusively) on high-speed aerodynamics, of fundamental importance to spaceflight.

During the 1940s and 1950s, the engineers and scientists at NACA's Langley Memorial Aeronautical Laboratory in Hampton, Virginia, led the ascent on Mach 1, Mach 2, and hypersonic (Mach 5+) flight, in addition to conducting extensive rocket research at its Wallop's Island, Virginia, test facility. But despite its pioneering work, NACA lacked a national mandate to pursue a full-scale space program. This mandate eventually materialized, but not for NACA.

Space exploration sprang into global prominence during a competition announced by the planners of the International Geophysical Year (IGY) of 1957–1958. In proclaiming the IGY in 1954, the International Council of Scientific Unions invited nations to launch satellites to map the contours of the earth. This call set in motion a contest between the Soviet Union and the United States. The USSR won with *Sputnik 1* in October 1957; the U.S. Army deployed its *Explorer 1* satellite in January 1958. Russia's victory unleashed a torrent of recrimination in the United States, led by the mass media. Congress soon took up the call.

In the end, NACA assumed much of the blame, although it had been far-sighted in pursuing space-related research within the confines of its limited budget. Ultimately, President Eisenhower and Congress discontinued NACA, succeeding it on 1 October 1958 with NASA. But with the transfer of its headquarters and laboratories to NASA, NACA's spaceflight infrastructure, talent base, and ongoing research (on advanced projects like the X-15 hypersonic aircraft) continued intact. Perhaps the most enduring NACA legacy proved to be the Space Task Group (STG), a brain trust initiated by NACA director Hugh Dryden prior to NASA's inception. Led by Robert Gilruth, it guided early human spaceflight in the United States and stayed together to oversee future missions. Because of these and other pivotal NACA contributions, the new agency opened its doors poised and ready to contest the USSR.

Mercury and the Moon. Mindful of the importance of closing the gap with the Soviets quickly, the STG chose the name Mercury (the winged messenger of the Gods in Roman mythology) for the first American attempts at human spaceflight. The STG conceived a blunt-body, single-seat *Mercury* capsule and chose two missiles for launch vehicles—the Army's Redstone for the earlier flights and the Air Force's Atlas for the later ones. Gilruth supervised the selection of seven military test pilots, designated the *Mercury 7*, as the first astronaut class. Navy Commander Alan Shepard became the first American in space. Launched on 5 May 1961, he made a suborbital flight that lasted approximately 15 minutes and flew to an altitude of 116 miles.

But the U.S. candidate again crossed the finish line second. Soviet cosmonaut Yuri Gagarin not only became the first human being in space three weeks earlier (April 12), but also actually orbited the Earth. Far worse for the Kennedy administration, just days after the Soviet accomplishment, the U.S.-sponsored invasion of Cuba at the Bay of Pigs ended in disgrace. Eager for the United States

to regain the initiative, President Kennedy considered an expansive space initiative that leaped ahead of the USSR. He asked Vice President Johnson—an architect of NASA when he served in the Senate—to consult the experts. Sufficiently reassured, Kennedy addressed Congress on 25 May 1961, calling for a lunar landing by the end of the 1960s.

Congress accepted the challenge, but the president's offensive left NASA reeling. The space agency had launched just one suborbital flight so far, and only eight and a half years remained before the rendezvous with the Moon. Although in February 1962 astronaut John Glenn orbited the Earth three times and the final *Mercury* flight in May 1963 made 22 revolutions, by this date almost none of the essential technologies needed to voyage to the Moon and back had been fabricated or tested.

The Twins. As a consequence, Gilruth and the STG decided on an intermediate step between Mercury and the lunar trip. Because it required a two-seat capsule, they called it Gemini, after the mythological Greek twins Castor and Pollux, the guardians of mariners. Gemini acted as a proving ground for the upcoming Moon mission, testing whether astronauts could survive outside their spacecraft and whether capsules could rendezvous and dock with one another.

An early Gemini mission illustrates the uncharted technical waters in which NASA found itself. During *Gemini IV* in June 1965, a rendezvous with a Titan rocket second stage failed because NASA scientists had not yet mastered the finer points of orbital mechanics. On the same voyage, astronaut Edward White undertook America's first Extravehicular Activity (EVA). White floated in space for about 23 minutes, but he needed urgent help from mission commander James McDivitt to force open and then to force shut the egress hatch. Had McDivitt not encountered the same problem in training—a spring controlling the latches had failed to compress—the situation might have been dire.

A year and a half later, the last Gemini mission—number 12, crewed by James Lovell and Buzz Aldrin—succeeded not only in rendezvousing, but also in docking with an Agena target vehicle. Moreover, Aldrin made three EVAs lasting more than five hours in all, proving for the first time that astronauts could accomplish practical tasks during lengthy space walks.

The Apex. Although many of the technologies necessary for the Moon voyages still seemed far off when Gemini ended in November 1966, some obstacles had been cleared. After a contentious debate, NASA's leaders decided to land the astronauts on the Moon through a segmented process by which the spacecraft flew directly to, and then orbited, the Moon; detached a small lunar lander with a crew of two to touch down on the Moon; redocked with the lunar lander upon completion of its mission; and returned to Earth. In addition, NASA administrator James Webb enlisted a new method of project management (practiced effectively during the ballistic missile program) called concurrency. Rather than develop and test each system component sequentially—the standard practice—concurrency promised faster project completion by integrating many components first and then testing them as a unit.

Still, for Apollo to succeed, several high hurdles needed to be overcome. First, the immense *Saturn V* rocket had yet to prove itself; at the end of Gemini, not one had flown. Additionally, Grumman Aircraft's lunar module started late, fell behind schedule, and reported big cost overruns. Then, disaster struck. In January 1967, the *Apollo 1* capsule caught fire on the launch pad, killing astronauts Gus Grissom, Edward White, and Roger Chaffee. Months of investigation followed, delaying the Moon shot. Moreover, because the findings identified an obvious cause—the use of pure oxygen in the capsule—NASA's reputation suffered, particularly in Congress.

Despite these formidable setbacks, Apollo rebounded, in part because of sheer good fortune. To make up for lost time, the agency gambled in December 1968 with *Apollo 8*. Originally an orbital mission to test system hardware, the Apollo program directors decided instead to send it on a circumlunar voyage. The mission succeeded. Then, about five months before J.F.K.'s challenge expired, NASA launched *Apollo 11* to the Moon.

Events at first unfolded routinely. But on 20 July 1969, as Neil Armstrong and Buzz Aldrin orbited in the lunar module, they faced a crisis. First, the onboard computer froze. Then Armstrong, surprised by a landscape too rocky for a landing, took the controls from the autopilot. When he finally touched down, a mere 30 seconds of propellant remained in the lunar module's descent engine fuel tank—all that remained between Armstrong, Aldrin, and death.

Massive public outpourings greeted the *Apollo 11* crew when they returned. Paradoxically, the ill-fated *Apollo 13*—a dramatic mission in which the crew barely survived after an oxygen tank exploded, resulting in the loss of air and electrical power—attracted far more attention than the other remaining Apollo flights. Despite progressively longer space walks and the collection of increasing amounts of geological material, *Apollos 12, 14, 15, 16*, and *17* (November 1969 to December 1972) won less and less of the public's fascination.

In fact, the tide had been running out on the U.S. space program for some time. Beset by costly social programs and the Vietnam War, presidents Johnson and Nixon presided over a 10-year decline in NASA's appropriations, peaking at $5.18 billion in 1965 and falling to $3.23 billion in 1975 (Gorn, 2008, p. 149).

Robots, Not Astronauts. Even as budgets fell, NASA embarked on an ambitious set of missions to probe the cosmos. To begin with, Americans sent a series of probes to the lunar surface to gauge its composition and find locations for human landings. Like human spaceflight, many of the robotic voyages suffered serious setbacks. After nearly three years and six consecutive failures, the Jet Propulsion Laboratory (JPL) succeeded with *Ranger 7*, which in July 1964 returned 4,316 photos of the Moon before its planned crash landing. Then, five Lunar Orbiter spacecraft circled the Moon, mapping potential touchdown spots. Finally, the *Surveyor* spacecraft landed on the Moon in June 1966, eventually transmitting over 11,000 images and calming fears that the surface might be too powdery to support the lunar lander.

One of the longest series of planetary explorations began with the Mariner spacecraft. Although *Mariners 1, 3,* and *8* failed, *Mariner 2* flew past Venus in December 1962 and *Mariner 4* approached to within six thousand miles of Mars in July 1965, taking 21 photographs. *Mariner 5* also flew past Venus, and in July and August 1969 *Mariners 6* and *7* captured about two hundred images as they passed Mars. *Mariners 9* and *10* initiated a new era of sophistication in planetary research. Nearly four times the weight of *Mariner 4, Mariner 9* became the first probe to orbit another planet in November 1971, eventually mapping 85 percent of Mars's surface and unveiling a dynamic topography. Finally, *Mariner 10* flew by and photographed Venus and then, using the assistance of gravity, passed and observed Mercury three times, ending the mission in March 1975. NASA further burnished its robotic credentials with *Pioneers 10* and *11* (to Jupiter and Saturn), *Vikings 1* and *2* (to two Mars touchdowns), and *Voyagers 1* and *2* (to Jupiter, Saturn, Uranus, and Neptune; past many of their moons; and on to interstellar space).

A Shuttle and a Station. If the Kennedy presidency represented the heroic era of space travel, President Nixon's represented a new age of space pragmatism. After Apollo, Nixon felt that NASA should, above all, "devise less costly and less complicated ways of transporting payloads into space" (Launius, 1994, p. 219). Engineers at the space agency had been pursuing a similar line of reasoning since the 1960s. They conceived of a space system consisting of a reusable, winged space plane boosted into orbit by recoverable fuel tanks. This concept received strong support from NASA administrator Thomas Paine, who envisioned it as a supply vehicle, or tug, for an orbiting space station. The budget-conscious Nixon rejected the station, but approved the tug, known by then as the Space Shuttle.

After 10 years of design and fabrication, the shuttle—as big as an airliner and equipped with a 60 by 15 foot payload bay—made its initial voyage in April 1981. Five different shuttles flew 135 missions, the last in July 2011, and accomplished many things: launched civil and military satellites, conducted space-related experiments, tested human physiology in space, and repaired orbiting spacecraft (most famously, the Hubble space telescope). They also suffered two disasters: *Challenger* exploded shortly after launch in January 1986, ignited by a leaking solid rocket booster; and *Columbia* disintegrated on reentry in February 2003, caused by a gap in its external insulation created by flying external tank debris. In all, 14 astronauts died. Moreover, despite the original intentions, the Shuttle program proved to be expensive, costing close to $200 billion by one estimate (Hsu, 2011, p. 1).

Only in November 1998 did the shuttle participate in the mission its designers intended, when it lifted the first component of a massive space station. Over the next 13 years, it hoisted most of the station's trusses and modules. The process began under President Ronald Reagan, who gave the go-ahead in 1984, saying, "A space station will permit quantum leaps in our research in science, communications, in metals, and in lifesaving medicines which could be manufactured only in space" (Launius, 1994, p. 248). Despite the optimism, the station materialized at a snail's pace, stalled by heavy cost overruns, massive redesigns, and lengthy negotiations that in the end saved the project by forging an international partnership among the United States, Russia, Japan, Canada, and the European Space Agency. First occupied by a crew in 2000, by its completion in May 2011 it weighed almost 1 million pounds and measured the length of a football field. Called the International Space Station (ISS), it had hosted 30 expeditions by the early twenty-first century.

The Twenty-First Century. The American space program in the twenty-first century has suffered from the same post-Apollo malaise that has afflicted NASA since the 1970s. Having achieved its greatest success early, the space agency has been measured by that yardstick ever since and has often been found wanting.

Nonetheless, there have already been noteworthy achievements in the twenty-first century. The rovers *Spirit* and *Opportunity* landed on opposite sides of Mars in January 2004 and began to travel, photographing the landscape and sampling its rocks and soil. *Spirit* quit after covering almost five miles; *Opportunity* continues to roam, having traversed about 21 miles in the second decade of the twenty-first century. Both rovers detected geological features suggesting water.

Additionally, the prominent Earth telescopes found themselves equaled, if not eclipsed, by NASA's Great Observatories. In the early twenty-first century, the Chandra and Spitzer space telescopes joined the Hubble Space Telescope—repaired and modernized by no fewer than five shuttle missions, the last in 2009—in probing the farthest depths of the universe.

Meanwhile, two presidents have tried to reignite broad, long-range human exploration missions reminiscent of Apollo. In early 2004, George W. Bush unveiled a blueprint for a return to the Moon and ultimately voyages to Mars. Later called Constellation, it encountered headwinds. NASA received no additional funding for Constellation and to economize, its design borrowed liberally from the *Apollo* capsule, the *Saturn V* rocket, and the Space Shuttle.

The election of President Barack Obama resulted in a reconsideration of Constellation. The president canceled it in 2010 and directed NASA to pursue a more technologically advanced launch vehicle for possible future visits to asteroids and to Mars. The White House also asked NASA to offer incentives to private firms to develop smaller rockets for such orbital tasks as servicing the ISS.

Yet, despite these presidential initiatives, human spaceflight finds itself diminished in stature and opportunities. This impasse might suggest a historic change. During and since the Apollo program, two camps—human versus automated spaceflight—have waged an intense struggle inside NASA for budgets and prominence during the second decade of the twenty-first century. Generally, human spaceflight has won out. But more recently, robotics seems to be prevailing, in part because the severe economic recession that began in 2008 favors the lower cost of automated systems. Additionally, the reversal reflects the lack of a clear, compelling reason for astronaut-based space travel, as well as the fact that NASA's human exploration community faces an indeterminate wait before a heavy lift launch system succeeds the Space Shuttle. On the other hand, perhaps this situation represents a temporary hiatus, much like the long gap between the end of Apollo and the first shuttle launch.

In the meantime, the aging Hubble telescope is expected to be replaced in 2018 by the even more powerful James Webb Telescope, equipped with a primary mirror two and three-quarter times the diameter of Hubble's, orbiting almost 1 million miles from our planet. Realistically, the images from the distant Webb telescope may be the closest that Americans would come to the cosmos for some time.

[*See also* **Airplanes and Air Transport; Astronomy and Astrophysics; Hubble, Edwin Powell; Hubble Space Telescope; International Geophysical Year; Missiles and Rockets; National Aeronautics and Space Administration; Satellites, Communications;** *and* **Space Science.**]

BIBLIOGRAPHY

Bilstein, Roger E. *Testing Aircraft, Exploring Space: An Illustrated History of NACA and NASA.* Baltimore and London: Johns Hopkins University Press, 2003.

Dethloff, Henry C., and Ronald A. Schorn. *Voyager's Grand Tour: To the Outer Planets and Beyond.* Washington, D.C., and London: Smithsonian Institution Press, 2003.

Gorn, Michael H. *NASA: The Complete Illustrated History.* 2d ed. London and New York: Merrell Publishers, 2008.

Gorn, Michael H. *Superstructures in Space: From Satellites to Space Stations: A Guide to What's Out There.* London and New York: Merrell Publishers, 2008.

Hansen, James R. *Enchanted Rendezvous: John C. Houbolt and the Genesis of the Lunar-Orbit Rendezvous Concept.* Washington, D.C.: National Aeronautics and Space Administration, 1995.

Hansen, James R. *Engineer in Charge: A History of the Langley Aeronautical Laboratory, 1917–1958.* Washington, D.C.: National Aeronautics and Space Administration, 1987.

Hardesty, Von, and Gene Eisman. *Epic Rivalry: The Inside Story of the Soviet and American Space Race.* Washington, D.C.: National Geographic, 2007.

Hoff, Joan. "The Presidency, Congress, and the Deceleration of the U.S. Space Program in the 1970s." In *Spaceflight and the Myth of Presidential Leadership*, edited by Roger D. Launius and Howard E. McCurdy, pp. 92–132. Urbana and Chicago: University of Illinois Press, 1997.

Hsu, Jeremy. "End of Shuttle Era Opens Doors for Robotic Space Exploration." *Innovation News Daily* online, 1 July 2011. http://www.innovationnewsdaily.com/robotic-space-exploration-planets-2094/ (accessed 2 November 2011).

Hsu, Jeremy. "Total Cost of NASA's Space Shuttle Program: Nearly $200 Billion." space.com. 11 April 2011. http://www.space.com/11358-nasa-space-shuttle-program-cost-30-years.html (accessed 1 November 2011).

"International Space Station Expedition 30." National Aeronautics and Space Administration. http://www.nasa.gov/mission_pages/station/expeditions/expedition30/index.html (accessed 28 October 2011).

Johnson, Stephen B. *The Secret of Apollo: Systems Management in American and European Space Programs*. Baltimore and London: Johns Hopkins University Press, 2002.

"JWST [James Webb Space Telescope]." National Aeronautics and Space Administration. http://science.nasa.gov/missions/jwst/ (accessed 28 October 2011).

Launius, Roger D. *NASA: A History of the U.S. Civil Space Program*, Malabar, Fla.: Krieger Publishing, 1994.

Launius, Roger D., and Howard E. McCurdy. *Robots in Space: Technology, Evolution, and Interplanetary Travel*. Baltimore and London: Johns Hopkins University Press, 2008.

Logsdon, John. *John F. Kennedy and the Race to the Moon*. New York: Palgrave Macmillan, 2010.

Obama, Barack H. "President Obama's Speech at Kennedy [Space Center]." 15 April 2010. National Aeronautics and Space Administration. http://www.nasa.gov/about/obama_ksc_pod.html (accessed 28 October 2011).

Roland, Alex. *Model Research: The National Advisory Committee for Aeronautics, 1915–1958*. 2 vols. Washington, D.C.: National Aeronautics and Space Administration, 1985.

Siddiqi, Asif. *Challenge to Apollo: The Soviet Union and the Space Race, 1945–1974*. Washington, D.C.: National Aeronautics and Space Administration, 2000.

Michael H. Gorn

SPACE SCIENCE

Although commonly regarded as the product of Cold War rivalries, the space age actually originated with the pursuit of scientific knowledge. It began when the International Council of Scientific Unions (ICSU) designated July 1957 to December 1958 as the International Polar Year, dedicated to research on the most remote parts of the earth. Then, to incorporate findings obtained from recent sounding rocket payloads, the ICSU renamed it the International Geophysical Year (IGY). The ICSU further decided in October 1954 to invite participating countries to launch satellites capable of mapping the earth's contours. Because no artificial earth satellites existed at the time of the announcement, the United States and USSR—the world's two predominant powers—declared themselves contestants. Yet even in this gathering Cold War showdown, there remained a subtext of scientific discovery.

The United States fielded two candidate satellites. The army's Explorer program combined the efforts of the Wernher Von Braun rocket team at Huntsville, Alabama, with the Jet Propulsion Laboratory scientists in Pasadena, California, led by William Pickering. *Explorer 1* lifted off on 31 January 1958, but by then almost four months had passed since the USSR launched *Sputnik 1*, the first spacecraft to orbit the earth, on 4 October 1957. Although *Explorer* lost this contest, it won the contest for scientific value. University of Iowa physicist James A. Van Allen's Geiger counter instrument onboard *Explorer* detected two bands of cosmic rays encircling the earth, held in place by the planet's magnetic field. These phenomena became known as the Van Allen radiation belts, the first major scientific finding of the space age.

Meanwhile, the navy's Vanguard program took shape at the Naval Research Laboratory in Washington, D.C. Vanguard struggled technically, apparent for all to see in a disastrous launch pad failure on 6 December 1957. But after the Vanguard satellite took flight on 17 March 1958, it proved its value to IGY. Data from the spacecraft enabled scientists to confirm what had been suspected—that the earth has a pear, rather than a spherical, shape.

In the midst of these foundational developments, Congress authorized the National Aeronautics and Space Administration (NASA) on 1 October 1958. To a large extent, NASA grew out of and supplanted an earlier federal agency, the National Advisory Committee for Aeronautics (NACA). Founded in 1915, the NACA pursued aeronautical research in four laboratories that ranged from Virginia to California to Ohio. During the year between *Sputnik's* first flight and the creation of NASA, the NACA's Director, Hugh L. Dryden, took many steps to prepare for the emerging space age. Among them, he anticipated that the space science initiated by the IGY would become a pivotal part of the American space program. So, when the National Academy of Sciences decided to form a Space Science Board, Dryden joined the three-person organizing committee. The board met for the first time in June 1958 and immediately invited scientists from around the country to submit proposals for space science projects. The following month, the board winnowed the candidates down to six experiments worthy of spaceflight, but failed to specify which institution or institutions should sponsor them.

Into this bureaucratic breach stepped the fledgling NASA. Only four months after its founding, it assembled a cadre of space science policy makers to forge a home for this new discipline. In February 1959 they compiled a list of subjects that might profit from space science—atmospheres, ionospheres, energetic particles, electric and magnetic fields—and assigned specific projects to each. For instance, under atmospheres, the team suggested a study about the relationship between surface weather and the upper atmosphere. Surprisingly, little more than a year later (April 1960) the program planners had organized space science into a format familiar to this day, consisting of just a few encompassing categories: Sun–Earth relationships; the origin of the universe and the solar system; and the origin of life.

These quick steps by NASA to take command of the field did not meet with universal approval. Some scientific societies adapted quickly and well to the NASA paradigm, including the American Astronomical Society and the American Physical Society. But other organizations balked.

The National Academy of Sciences, which sponsored the Space Science Board in the first place, shadowed much of the early NASA program with a parallel one of its own and did not hesitate to criticize NASA for favoring narrowly defined projects over broader scientific pursuits. Although not always amicable, the relationship ultimately inclined NASA's space science program toward the needs of the broader scientific community. The space agency's program also brought it into conflict with some schools of higher learning. As sources of expertise and talent, academia contributed much to the NASA space science mission and NASA, in turn, provided support for an array of university-based space research. But the creation of space science units at the Jet Propulsion Laboratory (JPL), the Goddard Space Flight Center, and other NASA field organizations raised the institutional hackles of universities that feared they would have to compete for funding against these new, in-house entities. NASA countered by creating an office of university relations, designed to settle turf issues and define areas of collaboration.

From the beginning, then, NASA counted space science as one of its main mission areas, which the agency has since pursued in four categories: earth observation, astronaut research, exploration of the solar system, and exploration of the universe.

Earth Observation. America's first scientific study of the earth from space began with climate observations. NASA launched its initial U.S. weather satellites—Tiros-1 to -10—between 1960 and 1965. Each of the Tiros spacecraft weighed just 270 pounds. By its demise in 1967, Tiros-10's cameras and sensors captured four hundred images a day of weather patterns down to a two-mile resolution and covered an expanse of 640,000 square miles.

Nimbus-1 to -7 succeeded Tiros, serving from 1965 to 1994. Bigger (up to 2,176 pounds) and more complex (equipped with eight sensors) than Tiros, the Nimbus satellites broadened the range of weather data. Nimbus-7 undertook the most ambitious research to date, collecting information on the physical components of the atmosphere, the ocean, and the ocean–atmosphere interface.

Even as the Nimbus series continued to collect data, NASA and the National Oceanic and Atmospheric Administration (NOAA) joined forces to launch the transformative Geostationary Operational Environmental Satellites (GOES) in 1975. Among the first two GOES series (numbers 1 to 8 and 9 to 12), only GOES-12 (launched in July 2001) continued in service in 2012, operating at a fixed point over South America. The third series (GOES 13 to 15) became operational in May 2006, June 2009, and March 2010, respectively. GOES-13 surveys the eastern half of the United States, GOES-14 acts as an on-orbit backup, and GOES-15 observes the Pacific Ocean. These heavy (6,908 pounds apiece), big (almost 14 feet long and 6 feet wide) satellites processed two thousand bytes per second of data and enabled forecasters to assess the size, intensity, and direction of storms over 60 percent of the earth's surface. A new generation—beginning with GOES-16, scheduled to enter service in 2015—was expected to achieve almost twice the image clarity of previous GOES satellites.

Shortly after launching its early weather-related satellites, NASA focused on earth sensing. This initiative drew inspiration from the terrain photography on the Mercury, Gemini, and Apollo missions, which led the U.S. Geological Survey (USGS) to suggest in 1965 that NASA develop remote-sensing satellites to map the world's surface and resources. Seven years later, the space agency sent Landsat 1 into orbit. Its camera and multispectral scanner acquired more than 300,000 images. Six more Landsats followed, but only Landsats 5 and 7 remained in service in 2012. Landsat 7—14 feet long, 9 feet in diameter, and weighing 4,800 pounds—went into operation in April 1999. Because it recorded images of about one-fourth of the world's landmass every 16 days, it has produced a continuous archive of topographical change, monitoring such evolving landscapes as the urban sprawl of Washington, D.C., the Antarctic ice sheet, and the massive oil spill in the Gulf of Mexico in 2010. NASA and the USGS launched Landsat 8 on Feb 11, 2013.

With the activation of Landsat 7, the entire Landsat program transferred to one of NASA's biggest space science projects, known as the Earth Observing System (EOS). Started in the 1990s in response to environmental concerns, the EOS family of satellites monitored global change in an integrated manner, observing land, sea, and atmosphere in planetary terms, rather than as isolated phenomena. In addition to Landsat, EOS also included *Terra*, a spacecraft whose five instruments gauged biological processes (on land, snow, ice, the oceans, and in clouds), natural disasters (like volcanoes, fire, drought, and flood), and human-induced climate change (such as air pollution). EOS's third component, known as the Afternoon Constellation, or A-Train, consisted of six polar-orbiting satellites that made coordinated observations by flying in close formation. Designed to study climatic fluctuations, the A-Train's instruments concentrated on atmospheric chemistry (especially aerosols, ozone, and ice and water in clouds). By 2013, NASA planned for an A-Train suite consisting of Aqua, Aura, CALIPSO (Cloud-Aerosol Lidar and Infrared Pathfinder Satellite Observation), CloudSat, GCOM (Global Change Observation Mission–Water), and OCO (the Orbiting Carbon Observatory).

Astronaut Research. If earth observation represents perhaps the most programmed type of space science, astronaut-centered experiments represent the most free-form, owing to the vagaries of the human mind and body. At its most basic, this area involves the astronaut as subject. During the same year in which the first U.S. astronaut went into space (1961), Dr. Charles Berry—NASA's Director of Medical Operations during the Mercury, Gemini, and Apollo programs—coauthored a book entitled *Human Factors in Space and Jet Travel: A Medical–Psychological Analysis*. It pinpointed three main aspects of physiological research pertaining to spaceflight: life support, human performance, and the human–machine interface. In addition to these traditional factors, new ones have emerged as a result of missions aboard the Space Shuttle that lasted weeks and the International Space Station (ISS) that lasted for months. These involved microgravity effects, tight living quarters, poor sleep, loneliness, long-term human performance, and postflight adjustment, among others. Public awareness of these issues increased when 77 year-old senator (and former *Friendship 7* astronaut) John Glenn served as a mission specialist aboard Shuttle flight STS-95 in December 1998. By subjecting Glenn to microgravity, researchers hoped to differentiate between natural aging and the age-like symptoms induced by spaceflight.

In addition to their role as passive subjects of inquiry, the astronauts also made active contributions to scientific knowledge. Beginning in February 1962, when John Glenn carried a camera on board *Friendship 7*, the early astronauts photographed the earth. By the close of the Gemini program, 2,500 images had been made; Apollo added another 11,000 (of the earth and the moon). Astronauts aboard the four Skylab missions (1973–1974) took 2,400 pictures and automated cameras recorded 38,000 more. The Space Shuttle astronauts vastly expanded the catalog of earth-sensing imagery, taking a total of over 287,000 pictures, exceeded easily by the more than 1 million shot by crewmembers of the ISS as of August 2012. In fact, to maximize the value of the photographs, picture taking became an integral part of the astronauts' scheduled duties, augmented by training in geology, geography, and earth science. (The space agency makes this vast archive of pictures available on a searchable, online database called the Gateway to Astronaut Photography of Earth.)

More even than photographic representations of the earth, the hands-on pursuit of geological materials became the signature scientific activity of the Apollo program. Instructed by fellow astronaut and geologist Dr. Harrison Schmidt, crews from *Apollo 11, 12, 14, 15, 16,* and *17* carted home about 2,200 examples (842 pounds) of rock, pebbles, sand, and soil from the moon from six different sites. NASA technicians then compiled several guides to these items, such as the Lunar Sample Compendium, which cross-referenced each geological artifact by type (basalt, plutonic, core, and so on) and by Apollo mission (55 samples from *Apollo 11*; 210 from *Apollo 17*). The entry for *Apollo 17*'s object number 79,516, for instance, featured photographs, chemical analysis, and site location on the moon.

The Space Shuttle enabled more extended scientific inquiry. Its most noteworthy research component, known as *Spacelab*—a pressurized laboratory almost 23 feet long, installed in the Space Shuttle cargo bay and fabricated by the European Space Agency (ESA) during the 1970s— flew on 27 Shuttle missions between 1983 and 1998. NASA and ESA each nominated the scientific experiments that flew on *Spacelab*, although NASA crews actually operated the laboratory itself. Spacelab's missions concerned three main areas: life sciences, microgravity experiments, and materials research. On one mission (a nine-day flight aboard *Columbia* (STS-40) in June 1991) life sciences dominated the schedule. Rodents aboard *Spacelab* underwent exposure to microgravity, after which they experienced such physiological changes as lethargy, reduced muscle tone, and lower red and white blood cell counts.

As suggested by its long-duration missions (some over six months) and long-term presence in space (from 1998 to at least 2020), the ISS (sponsored chiefly by the United States, with four international partners) represented the most sophisticated space science facility ever built. It accommodated four research centers, all of which relied on the ISS crews for their care and monitoring. The American Destiny Laboratory arrived first, brought there by the Shuttle *Atlantis* in February 2001. This 28-foot, 32 thousand– pound pressurized module offers 13 racks (73 inches tall by 42 inches wide) for experiments conceived by a team of international scientists. It enables researchers to test the effects of microgravity on physical, biological, and physiological systems. ESA followed in February 2008 with its Columbus Laboratory, also flown to the ISS by *Atlantis*. Its presence added 15 telephone booth– size racks—10 for ESA (which sponsors the Biolab microgravity experiments, among others) and 5 for NASA. The Japanese Aerospace Exploration Agency contributed the Pressurized Research Module in June 2008, transported on board the Shuttle *Discovery*. The size of a sightseeing bus, its 10 experiment racks concentrated on microgravity, global warming, and ozone experiments. The 2012 NASA launch manifest anticipates the arrival of the fourth science component—the Russian Multipurpose Laboratory Module—in 2013.

Exploration of the Solar System.

Scientists wanted to learn more not only about the earth from space, but also about the sun and the solar system. This field of exploration began with Project Ranger, originated in 1961 at JPL to fly to the moon and chart landing sites for *Apollo*. At first, the project seemed ill-fated because *Rangers 1* to *6* all failed. The disappointment mounted in 1962 when the JPL engineers modified a Ranger spacecraft, called it *Mariner 1*, and launched it in the direction of Venus. It also failed. Under pressure from the Soviet planetary program as well as from the U.S. Congress, JPL finally achieved two successes: *Mariner 2* flew by Venus in December 1962 and sampled its atmosphere; and in July 1964, *Ranger 7* crash-landed (intentionally) on the lunar surface, taking 4,316 high-resolution photographs. Ranger underwent two more successful missions, but Project Mariner continued for some time. *Mariners 4, 6, 7,* and *9,* launched from 1964 to 1971, all flew close to Mars, sending home images and environmental data. *Mariner 9* holds a place of distinction among planetary exploration as the first probe to orbit another planet, eventually mapping 85 percent of Mars, revealing geographic features suggesting water erosion and hinting at past life.

Another series of spacecraft blazed an even wider trail in planetary and solar science. *Pioneers 5, 6, 7, 8,* and *9,* launched from 1960 to 1968, all orbited and observed the sun. *Pioneers 10* and *11* did even more. Despite the fact that no spacecraft had yet flown beyond Mars, these two left Earth in 1973 and passed Jupiter, Saturn (*Pioneer 10* only), and Neptune. Ultimately, both exited the solar system. *Pioneer 10* (the last to expire) sent back data until 1997. Meanwhile, acting on a rare gravity-assist alignment of the planets occurring between 1976 and 1979, JPL persuaded NASA to sponsor an exceptionally ambitious project called the Grand Tour. The two Grand Tour vehicles— *Voyager 1,* which approached Jupiter and Saturn; and *Voyager 2,* which made flybys of Jupiter, Saturn, Uranus, and Neptune, observing the moons of each at close range—left Earth in 1977. Once past Neptune, the pair departed the solar system, on their way to interstellar space. Plans called for their data to flow until 2020 or shortly thereafter, when their power sources will be spent and *Voyager 1* (the more distant) will be about 12.4 billion miles from the earth.

While these activities at the margins of the solar system unfolded, other space scientists continued to concentrate on Mars. Specialists at JPL realized that in August 2003 the earth and the Red Planet would come closer than they had been in thousands of years. Accordingly, they planned to send two mobile robots in that time frame, called the Mars Exploration Rovers. Golf-cart like, roughly five feet long and five feet tall, the first one (*Spirit*) landed on 4 January 2004; the second (*Opportunity*) touched down on 25 January. Traveling on opposite sides of the planet, these identical machines each carried a panoramic camera, a microscopic imager, and three spectrometers. *Spirit* journeyed a total of almost five miles, crossing over a range of hills and onto bedrock before going silent in March 2010. In 2012, *Opportunity* continued to advance, traversing more than 21 miles and exploring several craters. Both discovered geological evidence suggesting the former presence of water. Their successor— JPL's *Curiosity* rover, launched in November 2011—landed safely in August 2012. Five times as heavy and twice as long as its predecessors, *Curiosity* will search Mars for conditions conducive to life.

Exploration of the Universe.

Astronomical platforms in space have proven to be outstanding vantage points for observing the universe. Far above atmospheric interference, they offer unparalleled viewing and flexible targeting. Even as early as the 1940s and 1950s, scientists such as Lyman Spitzer and Fred Whipple propagated the idea of big space telescopes.

Ultimately, this concept reached fruition with the NASA Great Observatories program. Not only did these instruments herald a new maturity in space science, but also they offered the opportunity for coordinated operation, either to view the same phenomenon at different wavelengths or to combine two or more images into one.

This new way of seeing the universe relied mainly on two pairs of observatories. The initial telescopes originated at a time of relative prosperity in NASA's history and the second ones in a time of austerity.

The first became the most famous. Initiated in 1978, the Hubble Space Telescope (named for American astronomer Edwin P. Hubble) went into orbit in April 1990. A 43-foot-long behemoth weighing 24 thousand pounds, Hubble's 94-inch mirror operated in the visible light spectrum. Once launched, however, it proved to be defective; NASA discovered blurring on distant objects, caused by errors in the grinding of the mirror. More than three and a half years later (in December 1993), Shuttle astronauts aboard STS-61 returned and resolved the problem with corrective optics. Since then, Shuttle crews have visited in February 1997, December 1999, March 2002, and May 2009 to repair and replace much of the original equipment and to widen the telescope's viewing wavelengths by adding the ultraviolet and near-infrared ranges. Hubble has concentrated on the births, deaths, and massive explosions associated with galaxies and stars, captured in images seen by millions on Internet locations such as the HubbleSite Gallery.

Just a year after Hubble's launch, NASA added its second great telescope, the Compton Gamma-Ray Observatory (CGRO). It commemorated American physicist Arthur H. Compton. The four instruments aboard Compton detected bursts of gamma-ray high-energy radiation throughout the universe. One lasting contribution of the CGRO has been the Compton Telescope (COMPTEL) Gamma-Ray Source Catalog, a listing of all of the phenomena that the instrument encountered. Compton ended service in June 2000 with the failure of one of its three gyroscopes, after which NASA deorbited the 34-thousand-pound spacecraft. The space agency compensated in part for the loss in June 2008 when it launched the Gamma-Ray Large Area Space Telescope (GLAST), later called the Fermi Gamma-Ray Telescope (for Italian-born theoretical physicist Enrico Fermi).

The second pair of Great Observatories began with the Chandra X-ray Telescope, named for the Indian-born astrophysicist Subrahmanyan Chandrasekhar. First proposed in 1976, it represented one of the biggest and heaviest payloads ever carried by the Shuttle (45 feet long and 45,430 pounds with the inertial upper stage needed to boost it into high earth orbit). Before launching in July 1999, Chandra experienced cutbacks and redesign. During the 1990s, program managers reduced the original twelve telescope mirrors to eight and the six scientific instruments to four. Still, it surpassed previous X-ray spacecraft by offering 20 to 50 times greater sensitivity. Chandra proved most successful in black-hole observations and in uncovering clues about dark matter.

Finally, four years after Chandra, the last of the NASA Great Observatories—the Spitzer Space Telescope—rose in August 2003 from the launch pad at Cape Canaveral Air Force Station, Florida. It honored Lyman Spitzer Jr., an American astrophysicist. Like Chandra, it fell victim to reductions during its development period in the 1990s, when its original $2.2 billion budget declined to $500 million. Shorter and lighter than the other Great Observatories, its telescope, coupled with large-format arrays, operated in the infrared wavelengths. Unlike its three cohorts, Spitzer trailed, rather than orbited the earth to lessen the incidental infrared interference associated with our planet. Its telescope scanned the universe for planetary formation, penetrated cosmic dust to witness the birth of stars, and probed the creation of early and distant galaxies.

[*See also* **Astronomy and Astrophysics; Environmentalism; Fermi, Enrico; Geography; Geological Surveys; Geology; Global Warming; Hubble, Edwin Powell; Hubble Space Telescope; International Geophysical Year; National Academy of Sciences; National Aeronautics and Space Administration; Photography; Satellites, Communications; Science;** *and* **Space Program.**]

BIBLIOGRAPHY

"The Afternoon Constellation." 22 June 2011. http://atrain.nasa.gov/ (accessed 17 April 2012).

Bender, Karl. The NASA Armstrong Flight Research Center Library. http://www.nasa.gov/centers/armstrong/home/ (accessed 01 March 2014).

Campbell, Jon. "Landsat 5 Suspension of Operations Extended." 16 February 2012, USGS Newsroom. http://www.usgs.gov/newsroom/article.asp?ID=3109&from=rss (accessed 13 April 2012).

"CGRO Science Support Center: The CGRO Mission (1991–2000)." http://heasarc.gsfc.nasa.gov/docs/cgro (accessed 25 April 2012).

"Curation: Lunar Samples." 27 April 2011. http://curator.jsc.nasa.gov/lunar/index.cfm (accessed 19 April 2012).

DeVorkin, David H. Science with a Vengeance: How the Military Created the U.S. Space Sciences after World War II. New York: Springer-Verlag, 1992.

"First Image from GOES-14." 28 July 2009. http://www.nasa.gov/mission_pages/GOES-O/news/goes14_first_image.html (accessed 16 April 2012).

"The Gateway to Astronaut Photography of Earth: Earth Observation Team's Top Picks Today." 1 May 2012. http://eol.jsc.nasa.gov/ (accessed 29 August 2012).

"GOES-15 Satellite Is Activated and GOES-11 Deactivated after Nearly 12 Years in Orbit." 8 December 2011. http://www.nasa.gov/mission_pages/GOES-P/news/goes-15-active.html (accessed 11 May 2012).

Gorn, Michael H. NASA: The Complete Illustrated History. London and New York: Merrell, 2008.

Gorn, Michael H. Superstructures in Space: From Satellites to Space Stations—A Guide to What's Out There. London and New York: Merrell, 2008.

Hardesty, Von, and Gene Eisman. Epic Rivalry: The Inside Story of the Soviet and American Space Race. Washington, D.C.: National Geographic, 2007.

Harrington, J. D., et al. "NASA's GLAST Launch Successful." 11 June 2008. http://www.nasa.gov/home/hqnews/2008/jun/HQ_08141_GLAST_Launch.html (accessed 27 April 2012).

Harrison, Albert A., and Edna R. Fiedler. "Introduction: Psychology and the U.S. Space Program." In Psychology of Space Exploration: Contemporary Research in Historical Perspective, edited by Douglas A. Vakoch, pp. 1–14. Washington, D.C.: National Aeronautics and Space Administration, 2011.

Jenkins, Dennis R. Space Shuttle: The History of the National Space Transportation System. Cape Canaveral, Fla.: Dennis R. Jenkins, 2002.

Kennedy, Tom. "NASA's Voyager 1 in 'Cosmic Purgatory' on Verge of Entering Milky Way." 24 April 2012, The Telegraph (U.K.). http://www.telegraph.co.uk/science/space/8940350/Nasas-Voyager-1-in-cosmic-purgatory-on-verge-of-entering-Milky-Way.html (accessed 24 April 2012).

Kohut, Matthew. "Shaping the Space Age: The International Geophysical Year." NASA Ask Magazine 32 (Fall 2008). http://askmagazine.nasa.gov/issues/32/32i_shaping_the_space_age.html (accessed 12 April 2012).

"Landsat 5 History." 30 December 2010. http://landsat.usgs.gov/about_landsat5.php (accessed 13 April 2012).

"The Landsat Program: From the Beginning," and "Landsat 1." 11 April 2012. http://landsat.gsfc.nasa.gov/about/history.html and http://landsat.gsfc.nasa.gov/about/landsat1.html, respectively (accessed 13 April 2012).

"The Landsat Program: Landsat 7." 11 April 2012. http://landsat.gsfc.nasa.gov/about/landsat7.html (accessed 13 April 2012).

"Mars Science Laboratory." http://mars.jpl.nasa.gov/msl/mission/rover/ (accessed 24 April 2012).

"NASA's Consolidated Launch Schedule." http://www.nasa.gov/missions/highlights/schedule.html (accessed 31 August 2012).

Naugle, John E. First among Equals: The Selection of NASA Space Science Experiments. Washington, D.C.: National Aeronautics and Space Administration, 1991.

Newell, Homer E. Beyond the Atmosphere: Early Years of Space Science. Washington, D.C.: National Aeronautics and Space Administration, 1980.

Robinson, Julie A., et al. "Patterns in Crew-Initiated Photography of Earth from the ISS—Is Earth Observation a Salutogenic Experience?" In Psychology of Space Exploration: Contemporary Research in Historical Perspective, edited by Douglas A. Vakoch, pp. 79–100. Washington, D.C.: National Aeronautics and Space Administration, 2011.

"Spacelab." In Encyclopedia Astronautica. http://www.astronautix.com/craft/spacelab.htm (accessed 20 April 2012).

"Spacelab Life Sciences 1/STS-40." http://lis.arc.nasa.gov/lis2/Chapter4_Programs/SLS/SLS_1.html (accessed 20 April 2012).

"STS-95: American Space Pioneer Flies Again." 10 December 2003. http://spaceflight.nasa.gov/shuttle/archives/sts-95/ (accessed 18 April 2012).

"Team Hubble: Servicing Missions." http://hubblesite.org/the_telescope/team_hubble/servicing_missions.php#sm4 (accessed 25 April 2012).

"Update: Spirit and Opportunity." April 2012. http://marsrovers.jpl.nasa.gov/mission/status.html#spirit (accessed 24 April 2012).

"Vanguard Celebrates 50 Years in Space." 2008. http://www.nrl.navy.mil/vanguard50/legacy.php (accessed 12 April 2012).

"Weather Satellites." NASA History Program Office. http://history.nasa.gov/weathsat.html (accessed 16 April 2012).

Michael H. Gorn

SPOCK, BENJAMIN

See Baby and Child Care.

SPRINGFIELD ARMORY

In 1777, Revolutionary War generals George Washington and Henry Knox chose a bluff overlooking Springfield, Massachusetts, strategically located on the Connecticut River and near the route connecting Boston and Albany, as the site of a weapons storage depot. In 1794, President Washington designated the Springfield arsenal as a national armory to manufacture small arms for the U.S. Army. Beginning with muskets, production expanded to include an array of guns, projectiles, and shells. Through the nineteenth century and much of the twentieth, the Springfield Armory was the principal provider of U.S. military weaponry.

The Armory figured prominently in the American industrial revolution, along with New England's textile mills and Eli Whitney's arms factory near New Haven, Connecticut, where his machinery to manufacture interchangeable gun parts won him a government contract for 10,000 muskets in 1798. With a skilled workforce and innovative inventors and technicians, the Springfield Armory pioneered precision manufacturing. Thomas Blanchard's copying lathe for mass producing rifle stocks (1818) and machine for mass producing gun barrels (1822) proved particularly important. During the Civil War, the Springfield Armory produced more than 300,000 muskets for the Union Army. The Model 1903 clip-loading magazine rifle and the Enfield rifle of World War I, the semiautomatic M1 rifle of World War II, and machine guns and grenade launchers were all developed and manufactured here.

In 1968, reflecting a broader decline in New England manufacturing, the Department of Defense closed the Springfield Armory. In 1978, the facility reopened as a National Historic Site, administered by the National Park Service. Tours explain the Armory's military and technological significance and include a large exhibit of military firearms. Springfield Technical Community College, also on the grounds, carries on the Armory's links to technology.

The Springfield Armory also figures in the nation's social and cultural history. During Shays's Rebellion, the 1786–1787 uprising of debt-ridden western Massachusetts farmers, Captain Daniel Shays led a march on the facility (25 January 1787), intent on seizing its weapons. The defending militia fired on the attackers, killing four and effectively ending the uprising. In his 1845 poem "The Arsenal at Springfield," Henry Wadsworth Longfellow employed images of the Armory's massed rows of muskets ("From floor to ceiling / Like a huge organ, rise the burnished arms") to symbolize war's destructiveness. In 1968, controversy over the Armory's closing became caught up in the larger conflicts over U.S. involvement in the Vietnam War.

[*See also* American System of Manufactures; Machinery and Manufacturing; Military, Science and Technology and the; National Park System; Technology; *and* Whitney, Eli.]

BIBLIOGRAPHY

Hounshell, David. *From the American System to Mass Production, 1800–1935: The Development of*

Manufacturing Technologies in the United States. Baltimore: Johns Hopkins University Press, 1985.

U.S. National Park Service, Springfield Armory National Historic Site. http://www.nps.gov/spar/index.htm (accessed 30 March 2012).

Paul S. Boyer

STANLEY, WENDELL MEREDITH

(1904–1971), biochemist, virologist, science administrator, and Nobel laureate. Stanley was educated at Earham College, a small liberal arts college affiliated with the Religious Society of Friends (Quakers), and the University of Illinois, where he received a PhD in chemistry in 1929. During his career as a researcher and educator, he held positions at the Rockefeller Institute and the University of California at Berkeley.

Stanley became famous for using his training in organic chemistry to purify and crystallize tobacco mosaic virus (TMV) in 1935. By crystallizing a living agent, Stanley blurred the distinction between living and nonliving things and demonstrated the fruitfulness of a physical–chemical approach to the life sciences. This work was featured on the front page of the *New York Times* and he became a scientific celebrity. He and his collaborators' pioneering use of the ultracentrifuge, electrophoresis, and the electron microscope in virology would be widely adopted and become common tools in the emerging new field of molecular biology. At first Stanley thought of TMV as an autocatalytic self-reproducing protein. Although his early TMV work was newsworthy, British researchers F. C. Bawden and N. W. Pirie showed that Stanley failed to realize that TMV particles consisted of 6 percent RNA in addition to protein and J. D. Bernal and I. Fankuchen argued that the TMV "crystals" were not true three-dimensional crystals as Stanley imagined, but rather "liquid crystalline substances." Nonetheless, in 1946, Stanley received the Nobel Prize (with John Northrop and James Sumner) for his TMV work and it served as a model system for the study of other plant and animal viruses.

Two years after Stanley's Nobel Prize, he was recruited by the University of California to transform the biological sciences at Berkeley. He realized an interdisciplinary vision by bringing virology and biochemistry together—in particular, he raised funds to establish the Virus Laboratory and built what became Stanley Hall, a facility that housed both biochemists and virologists. Under his leadership, UC Berkeley became a world-class center for virus research. In the mid-1950s, researchers at the Virus Laboratory crystallized poliovirus and showed that RNA was the infectious part of TMV, among other things. In 1960, Stanley's group determined the complete amino acid sequence of the TMV protein. Wendell Meredith Stanley died suddenly in Spain at the age of 66. Eventually the research groups that Stanley assembled at Berkeley would become the Department of Molecular and Cell Biology. The original Stanley Hall was demolished in 2003 after it was rated seismically poor and in 2007 was replaced with a larger building, also called Stanley Hall.

[*See also* **Biochemistry; Biological Sciences; Chemistry; Instruments of Science; Molecular Biology; Nobel Prize in Biomedical Research Poliomyelitis; Rockefeller Institute, The;** *and* **Science.**]

BIBLIOGRAPHY

Creager, Angela N. H. *The Life of a Virus: Tobacco Mosaic Virus as an Experimental Model, 1930–1965.* Chicago: University of Chicago Press, 2002.

Creager, Angela N. H. "Wendell Stanley's Dream of a Free-Standing Biochemistry Department at the University of California, Berkeley." *Journal of the History of Biology* 29 (1996): 331–360.

Kay, L. E. "W. M. Stanley's Crystallization of the Tobacco Mosaic Virus, 1930–1940." *Isis* 77 (1986): 450–472.

Stanley, Wendell. "Isolation of a Crystalline Protein Possessing the Properties of Tobacco-Mosaic Virus." *Science* 81 (1935): 644–645.

Gregory J. Morgan

STEAM POWER

Thomas Newcomen constructed the first commercially useful steam engine in England around 1712 to pump water out of mines. During the 1720s, England exported a number of engines to continental Europe. American intellectuals such as John Adams and Thomas Jefferson knew of such engines, but not until 1753 was the first Newcomen engine brought to America, to pump water from the copper mine of Colonel John Schuyler, on New Jersey's Passaic River. It was accompanied by Joseph Hornblower, whose family had been installing Newcomen engines in Cornwall. Put into operation in 1755, Schuyler's steam engine burned in 1768 and remained out of commission until 1793. Between 1799 and 1801 the emigrant British engineer Benjamin Henry Latrobe designed and erected two massive engines for the new Philadelphia waterworks, built at the Soho Works in New Jersey.

These early engines were all used to pump water, a task adapted to their relatively slow reciprocating motion and small horsepower. By the time Robert Fulton (1765–1815) successfully launched his celebrated Hudson River steamboat *Clermont* in 1807 (using an English engine purchased from Boulton and Watt), a dozen other American inventors had already experimented with steamboats. With the exception of John Fitch's boat, which he operated on the Delaware River between Philadelphia and Burlington, New Jersey, during the summer of 1790, none of these worked well and all (including Fitch's) had engines designed by the makers themselves. Fulton's success, coupled with the appearance of boats designed specifically for the western waters by Oliver Evans (1755–1819) and others, launched a steamboat era that greatly improved the nation's transportation on both coasts and in the Mississippi River watershed. Fulton's Pittsburgh-built *New Orleans*, launched on the Mississippi in 1811, was only the first of a vast fleet that brought improved transportation and fostered industrialization throughout the interior.

Oliver Evans, whose high-pressure engine dominated the western fleet, built his first engine in 1801. The Newcomen engine had worked at atmospheric pressure (about 16 pounds per square inch [psi]), as had James Watt's improved design of 1763. In such engines, increased power could only be secured by increased size. Evans, a Delaware-born inventor and manufacturer, built his new "Columbian" engine at his Mars Iron Works in Philadelphia to operate on pressures as high as one hundred psi. Very powerful for their size, such engines quickly became standard on the western waters as well as in factories.

During the early nineteenth century steam engines gradually replaced water power as the favored source of power for manufacturing. As coal slowly replaced wood for fuel, new engine designs used steam expansively in more than one cylinder or in the form of turbines. With improved boilers, some of the new engines by the end of the century used steam at three hundred psi and produced thousands of horsepower. In this process, George H. Corliss of Providence and Charles T. Porter of Newark were particularly important innovators. Because steam engines were the first large machines made from iron, the spread of steam power stimulated the growth of the iron and machine trades. And by freeing manufacturers from reliance on water power, steam allowed factories to be built in cities, closer to transportation and a labor supply.

Steam was also applied to the operation of railroads. By the time Robert Stephenson's locomotive *Rocket* won the celebrated Rainhill trials in England in 1829, Americans were already investigating steam propulsion for land transport. In 1829–1830, Americans purchased the *John Bull* from Stephenson and *The Stourbridge Lion* from another English locomotive maker. The latter became the model for *The Best Friend of Charleston*, the first steam locomotive built in the United States for sale. In 1830, Peter Cooper's *Tom Thumb* raced a horse-drawn train on the new Baltimore and Ohio Railroad, which opened its first line that year. Soon such large manufacturers as Philadelphians William Norris and Matthias Baldwin dominated the American locomotive trade and sold large numbers of engines abroad as well. Steam remained the unchallenged source of power for railroads until 1925, when the Central

Railroad of New Jersey introduced the first diesel-electric locomotive. In 1934 the Burlington line used diesel-electric for its streamlined Zephyr passenger trains, and in 1941 the Santa Fe became the first railroad to use that power for freight service.

The use of steam power in American agriculture began late, proceeded slowly, and never became as widespread as in other sectors of the economy. A federal census of engines in 1838 reported several hundred at work at specialized tasks on farms, especially in grinding sugarcane on Louisiana plantations. The lack of power for fieldwork hampered nineteenth-century agriculture, although the replacement of oxen with horses improved the situation for most farmers. In 1849, however, portable steam engines that could be pulled by horses to a barn, woodlot, or wherever more power for belt work was needed became available. As the nation's wheat acreage doubled between 1866 and 1878, the demand for mechanically powered machines led to efforts to use these portable steam engines to power self-propelled vehicles that could be steered. The first such traction engines were produced in 1882, and in 1910 the horsepower produced by steam used in agriculture peaked. Some 10 thousand traction engines were in use on farms in 1913, but already gasoline-powered tractors were competing with them. By 1925 the manufacture of steam traction engines had largely been abandoned.

A few early automobiles were steam powered, including the Stanley Steamer, built in Massachusetts by the twin brothers Francis and Freelan Stanley from 1897 until 1918. But the gasoline-powered internal combustion engine soon supplanted the steam engine in automotive technology.

Steam power remained of some economic importance as the twenty-first century began. Steam turbines, for example, were widely used to generate electricity. Its ubiquity and dominance as a power source for transportation, manufactures, and agriculture, however, was largely confined to the nineteenth century, after which internal combustion engines burning petroleum products eliminated steam engines from most sectors of the American economy.

[*See also* **Agricultural Technology; Electricity and Electrification; Fulton, Robert; Internal Combustion Engine; Iron and Steel Production and Products; Latrobe, Benjamin; Machinery and Manufacturing; Maritime Transport; Motor Vehicles; Petroleum and Petrochemicals; Railroads;** *and* **Shipbuilding.**]

BIBLIOGRAPHY

Flexner, James Thomas. *Steamboats Come True.* New York: Viking Press, 1944. Traces the origin and development of early steamboats.

Hunter, Louis C. *A History of Industrial Power in the United States, 1780–1930.* Vol. 2. *Steam Power.* Charlottesville: University Press of Virginia, 1985.

Hunter, Louis C. *Steamboats on the Western Rivers: An Economic and Technological History.* Cambridge, Mass.: Harvard University Press, 1949. A classic text on the history of steamboats in America.

Lamb, J. Parker. *Perfecting the American Steam Locomotive.* Bloomington: Indiana University Press, 2003. Detailed account of the history of the steam locomotive in America.

Pursell, Carroll W., Jr. *Early Stationary Steam Engines in America: A Study in the Migration of a Technology.* Washington, D.C.: Smithsonian Institution Press, 1969. Deals with the technology and industrial uses of stationary steam engines.

White, John H., Jr. *American Locomotives: An Engineering History, 1830–1880*, revised ed. Baltimore: Johns Hopkins University Press, 1997. Traces the development of locomotive technology following its importation from Europe.

Carroll Pursell

STEINMETZ, CHARLES

(1865–1923), electrical engineer. Charles Proteus Steinmetz was born in Breslau, Germany, now Wrocław, Poland, on 9 April 1865 and died on 26 October 1923 in the United States at Schenectady, New York. Educated in mathematics and physics at the PhD level at the University of Breslau, where he studied synthetic geometry under Heinrich Schröter, and in engineering at the Swiss Federal Polytechnic Institute in Zurich, Steinmetz feared being arrested for his socialist activities as a student in Germany and immigrated to the United States in 1889. He became a leading industrial researcher in the areas of magnetic hysteresis and electrical power systems.

He is best known in science and engineering for stating an empirical "law" of magnetic hysteresis; for creating a method of solving steady-state alternating-current electrical-circuit problems using complex-quantity algebra, instead of differential equations, which became known as "Steinmetz's Method"; for creating equivalent-circuit theories of alternating-current machinery; and for deriving integrodifferential equations to express transient conditions in high-voltage transmission lines, equations that were not solved until the invention of analog computers in the 1930s. As chief consulting engineer of the General Electric Company, which he joined in 1893, Steinmetz trained a generation of engineers how to mathematically design electrical power systems, created an engineering research laboratory, and published several technical books that established his brand of "engineering science" while teaching part-time at Union College.

A dwarfed hunchback with a flair for publicity, Steinmetz gained a national reputation rivaling that of Thomas Edison in the early 1920s as an electrical wizard for creating lightning in the laboratory (to test GE's lightning arresters) and for running for New York State Engineer on the socialist ticket. In *America and the New Epoch* (1916), Steinmetz propounded a theory of corporate socialism, in which he saw the corporation as the model for a future technocratic society. In the American Institute of Electrical Engineers, of which he was president, Steinmetz promoted the social responsibility of engineers by helping to establish codes of ethics and technical standards as a compromise between corporate and professional interests.

[*See also* **Edison, Thomas; Electricity and Electrification; Engineering; Ethics and Professionalism in Engineering; Illumination; Mathematics and Statistics; Physics;** *and* **Research and Development (R&D)**]

BIBLIOGRAPHY

Kline, Ronald. *Steinmetz: Engineer and Socialist.* Baltimore: Johns Hopkins University Press, 1992.

Ronald Kline

STEM-CELL RESEARCH

The term "stem cell" refers to cells that have the capacity to self-renew and to give rise to differentiated daughter cells. Edmund Beecher Wilson first used the term in this way in 1896 (Maienschein, 2003). Stem cells fall into two categories: embryonic, which are derived from the early-stage embryo and are "pluripotent," that is, capable of producing all cell lineages in the adult organism; and adult, which exist within the body, include a variety of cell types, and maintain or repair tissues.

In 1961, James Till and Ernest McColloch first offered definitive evidence of the existence of a single hematopoietic (blood-forming) stem cell. Since then, a variety of other adult stem-cell types have been identified. Human adult stem-cell research is generally considered ethically uncontroversial.

Human embryonic stem-cell (hESC) research, however, has been a cause of significant controversy, because hESC derivation involves the destruction of human embryos. However, hESC research has also been seen as holding significant scientific and therapeutic promise.

Embryonic stem-cell research originated with *in vitro* culture of mammalian embryos. In the early 1960s, Robert Edwards experimented with culturing cells from rabbit embryos. He achieved the first successful *in vitro* fertilization (IVF) and culture of human embryos in 1969 and the birth of the first IVF baby, Louise Brown, in 1978. Edwards was awarded the 2010 Nobel Prize in

Physiology or Medicine for this work. In 1981, Martin Evans and Matthew Kaufman of Cambridge University and Gail Martin of the University of California, San Francisco, independently cultured embryonic stem cells from the inner cell mass of mouse embryos. In 1998, the University of Wisconsin's James Thompson first derived hESC lines from human IVF embryos.

Human embryos used in deriving hESC lines have primarily come from fertility treatment involving IVF. In contrast to many European countries, IVF practices in the United States have been largely unregulated. As a result, since the early 1980s IVF clinics have tended to produce excess embryos to increase the odds of pregnancy, thereby indirectly generating a reliable source of embryos for research.

U.S. federal law has not directly regulated research involving human embryos, but federal funding is restricted. Restrictions originated in the 1970s with federal regulations that required approval by an ethics advisory board for research involving human embryos and fetuses. A board was created in 1977, but dissolved in 1980, initiating a *de facto* moratorium on such research until the 1993 National Institutes of Health (NIH) Revitalization Act lifted the requirement for board approval. In 1994, an *ad hoc* committee that was convened to advise on the ethics of embryo research by NIH director Harold Varmus recommended permitting certain forms of research on excess IVF embryos, and, under compelling circumstances, allowing the creation of human embryos specifically for research. These recommendations precipitated substantial public controversy and a Congressional reaction. In 1995, Congress passed an appropriations bill rider, known as the Dickey–Wicker amendment, that banned federal funding for research that involved creating, destroying, or exposing human embryos to greater than minimal risk. The rider has been renewed each year.

In 1999, the Clinton administration interpreted Dickey–Wicker to permit hESC research, but not derivation, on the theory that utilizing an already established line did not harm an embryo. However, upon entering office, President George W. Bush halted funding; no federal dollars had yet flowed to research. On 9 August 2001, in the first televised address of his presidency, Bush announced a policy whereby only those hESC lines that had been established prior to his announcement would be eligible for federal funding, arguing that the restriction would allow research without encouraging production of additional lines and concomitant harm to embryos (Jasanoff, 2005).

This touched off a period of significant public controversy that pitted primarily religious and conservative critics of hESC research against primarily liberal advocates. It also led to a patchwork of state-level policies and funding sources, including a California ballot initiative that allocated $3 billion to hESC research in the state. The controversy extended to human cloning, which was seen as a potential technique for producing patient-matched embryonic stem cells. Congress extensively debated regulation of human cloning, but no legislation was enacted.

Public controversy around hESC research was significantly altered in 2007, when Shinya Yamanaka, a Japanese researcher, reprogrammed somatic cells, generating "induced pluripotent stem cells" (iPSCs). These cells are seen as ethically uncontroversial because derivation does not involve human embryos, although some ethical concerns do persist, for instance, with human–animal chimera produced using iPSCs. The focus of much hESC research has shifted to iPSCs. In 2012 Yamanaka was awarded the Nobel Prize in Physiology or Medicine for this discovery, jointly with John Gurdon.

In 2009, President Barack Obama issued a new policy making any hESC line eligible for federal funding, subject to certain restrictions. This policy, too, faced legal challenges.

[*See also* **Biological Sciences; Birth Control and Family Planning; Childbirth; Cloning; Ethics and Medicine; Law and Science; Medicine; Nobel Prize in Biomedical Research; Religion and Science; Research and Development (R&D); Science;** *and* **Wilson, Edmund Beecher.**]

BIBLIOGRAPHY

Jasanoff, Sheila. *Designs on Nature: Science and Democracy in Europe and the United States.* Princeton, N.J.: Princeton University Press, 2005.

Maienschein, Jane. *Whose View of Life? Embryos, Cloning, and Stem Cells.* Cambridge, Mass.: Harvard University Press, 2003.

J. Benjamin Hurlbut

STEVENS, NETTIE MARIA

(1861–1912), pioneer cytogeneticist, is best known for research that led her to conclude that sex is determined by a particular chromosome. During the last quarter of the nineteenth and first quarter of the twentieth century, investigators were exploring the relationship between chromosomes and heredity. By 1900 when Mendelism was rediscovered, cytologists had accumulated a vast amount of knowledge about the behavior of chromosomes during cell division and especially during the maturation of germ cells, but the fields of cytology and Mendelian genetics remained separate. In 1902, Walter Sutton (1877–1916) published an important paper indicating that chromosomes seemed to obey Mendel's laws, but he did not experimentally confirm that a specific trait in a parent was passed on to the offspring nor did he link a specific trait to a specific chromosome. When Stevens was doing her research there were hints that sex inheritance might be related to a morphologically distinct chromosome. If the inheritance of sex could be demonstrated to be a Mendelian characteristic, then a chromosomal theory of heredity could be supported. Both Stevens and Edmund Beecher Wilson (1856–1939) arrived at similar conclusions independently.

Stevens was born 7 July 1861 in Cavendish, Vermont, to Julia (Adams) and Ephraim Stevens. After the death of her mother, Stevens's father remarried and the family moved to Westford, Massachusetts, where she graduated from the Westford Academy in 1880. After teaching for three terms, she continued her education at Westfield (Massachusetts) Normal School, where she graduated with the highest scores in her class of 30. After being a schoolteacher and librarian in various Massachusetts towns from 1883 to 1896, she matriculated in 1896 as a special student at Stanford, was awarded regular freshman standing in January 1897, and attained advanced standing three months later. With bachelor's (1899) and master's (1900) degrees from Stanford, she returned to the East to study at Bryn Mawr College, where she was awarded a doctorate in 1903. She remained affiliated with Bryn Mawr throughout her life. The highest academic rank she attained was that of associate in experimental morphology (1905–1912). Although the trustees of Bryn Mawr eventually created a research professorship for her, she died of breast cancer in 1912 before she could occupy it.

Stevens published approximately 38 papers on many different subjects during her lifetime. The common mealworm, *Tenebrio molitor*, was the subject of her breakthrough paper on sex determination. Because of the variability of different species, Stevens hesitated to generalize unequivocally that chromosomes were the instruments of heredity, but her work was soon established as pivotal in the history of cytogenetics.

[*See also* **Gender and Science; Genetics and Genetic Engineering; Higher Education and Science;** *and* **Wilson, Edmund Beecher.**]

BIBLIOGRAPHY

Brush, Stephen G. "Nettie M. Stevens and the Discovery of Sex Determination by Chromosomes." *Isis* 59 (June 1978): 163–172.

Morgan, Thomas Hunt. "The Scientific Work of Miss N. M. Stevens." *Science* 36 (11 October 1912): 468–470.

Ogilvie, Marilyn Bailey, and Clifford J. Choquette. "Nettie Maria Stevens (1861–1912). Her Life and Contributions to Cytogenetics." *Proceedings of the American Philosophical Society* 125 (August 1981): 292–311.

Marilyn Bailey Ogilvie

STRATEGIC DEFENSE INITIATIVE

On 23 March 1983, President Ronald Reagan called for a missile defense system that would make nuclear weapons "impotent and obsolete." The president's Strategic Defense Initiative (SDI) was fiercely attacked by those who believed it scientifically impossible, fiscally irresponsible, and strategically dangerous because it threatened to upset the delicate balance of the nuclear age. It was supported by those who both believed in the limitless potential of American technology and had never accepted mutual nuclear-age vulnerability as inescapable.

Interest in ballistic missile defense began shortly after the end of World War II, with controversies over the development and deployment of an anti–ballistic missile (ABM) system, and continuing until the United States and the Soviet Union placed severe restrictions on such work in April 1972. Reagan revived interest in a high-tech shield at the urging of defense enthusiasts such as Edward Teller; General Daniel O. Graham (retired), former head of the Defense Intelligence Agency and founder of High Frontier, Inc., a missile defense advocacy group; members of the president's "kitchen cabinet"—brewer Joseph Coors, oilman William Wilson, and businessman Karl Bendetsen; and some members of Congress enthralled by Teller's vision of X-ray laser weapons or chemical lasers. At least one member of the Joint Chiefs of Staff pronounced missile defense morally superior to deterrence through mutual vulnerability to counterattack, arguing that it is better to save lives than avenge them.

Despite a lavish research budget, SDI—derided by its opponents as "Star Wars," after the 1977 science-fiction movie directed by George Lucas—did not come to fruition during the Reagan presidency. A drum fire of criticism continued, however, including warnings that such a system would violate the 1972 ABM Treaty. A more modest vision of missile defense endured, however, and in 1999, President Bill Clinton recommended further research into the possibility of defense against missiles from "rogue" nations, a recommendation that reawakened the contro-versy over the feasibility and strategic advisability of this approach.

[*See also* **Military, Science and Technology and the; Missiles and Rockets; Nuclear Weapons; Space Program;** *and* **Teller, Edward.**]

BIBLIOGRAPHY

Broad, William I. *Teller's War: The Top-Secret Story behind the Star Wars Deception.* New York: Simon and Schuster, 1992.
Linenthal, Edward Tabor. *Symbolic Defense: The Cultural Significance of the Strategic Defense Initiative.* Urbana: University of Illinois Press, 1989.
"Weapons in Space." *Daedalus* 1 and 2 (Spring and Summer 1985).

Edward Linenthal

SUBWAYS

American subways are the offspring of two parents: the elevated railroad and the electric streetcar. In 1870 investors began work on a steam railroad that would run above the crowded streets of New York City. Although it brought smoke, noise, and darkness to the streets below, the elevated railroad attracted passengers desperate to get from their downtown offices to residences in less crowded sections of Manhattan. Brooklyn and Chicago picked up on the idea, but other cities rejected it, in part because of concerns about noise, smoke, and shadow. London's steam-driven underground railroad, which opened in 1863, had similar problems with smoke and soot.

Meanwhile, other companies worked to replace horse-drawn streetcars with electric models that would draw power from overhead wires or, in some cases, conduits built between the rails. Could someone build a system that combined the best of both—the speed of the elevated railroad and the quiet and clean operation of the electric streetcar?

Bostonians were first, in 1897, opening a tunnel that allowed streetcars to burrow underneath the hopelessly congested Tremont Street

along the Boston Common. In 1901, those individual streetcars were joined in tunnels by longer
trains that also ran on elevated tracks. With its
trains composed of multiple cars (each with an
electric motor), high platforms that permitted
passengers to step directly on and off of cars, and
rights of way not shared with other traffic, this
combined underground and elevated system
would set the pattern for rapid transit in the
United States.

New York deployed these technologies on a far
larger scale. In 1899 the city contracted for a
system stretching from lower Manhattan to the
Bronx. As in Boston, the city financed the massive
capital expenses and then leased the subway to a
private operating company. The immediate popularity of these routes, which opened in 1904, led
to plans for extensions, including to Brooklyn.
Debates over the proper mix of public and private
capital—a reflection of the mixed nature of transit
itself—delayed major new contracts until a compromise deal in 1913. Once signed, however,
those contracts doubled the size of the New York
subway, allowing it to surpass London's as the largest in the world.

New York's example also inspired subway
dreams across the country, from Providence and
Washington to Detroit and St. Louis to San
Francisco and Seattle. But as automobiles became
cheaper, many Americans preferred to live in suburbs and drive to work, rather than remain in the
city and take any kind of rail. They now saw proposed subways as devices that would tax property
owners in outlying areas to subsidize greedy
transit companies and downtown business interests. Public opposition killed subway plans in
several cities. Cincinnati began a subway only to
abandon four miles of tunnel when funds ran out.

Not counting streetcar tunnels, only Philadelphia and Chicago opened full subways. Philadelphia's first line, opened in 1907, was built entirely
with private capital, but subsequent extensions
used public funds. A second, north–south line
opened in 1928. In Chicago, only the availability of
New Deal funds won a consensus among politicians and engineers, and the city broke ground on
its first subway lines in 1938 and 1939. One opened
in 1943; the second, delayed by war, opened in

1951. Both New York and Boston similarly used
New Deal programs to add lines to their systems.

After World War II, general prosperity and a
national commitment to highway construction
dampened enthusiasm for transit. In the 1940s,
city governments and public authorities took over
formerly private operations in Boston, Chicago,
and New York. Although Chicago and Cleveland
opened new rapid-transit lines, these were built at
ground level—in the median of a highway and
along an old railroad line—sparing the high costs
of tunneling. The nation's existing subways saw
their ridership drop enormously from mid-1940s
peaks, and diminished revenues meant poorer
service and dirtier trains and stations.

Then, starting in the 1960s, subways enjoyed
a surprising revival. In 1962, voters in the San
Francisco area approved plans for what would
become the Bay Area Rapid Transit system, or
BART. Although the system was planned to run
mainly above ground, it included a tunnel under
the bay and into downtown San Francisco. The
first trains ran in 1972, and the system was completed in 1974. Meanwhile, in 1964 Congress provided federal aid for new rapid-transit systems.
Eventually, such aid helped build systems in Atlanta, Miami, and Baltimore, as well as extensions
in Boston, Cleveland, and Chicago. Other cities
built less expensive light rail, which runs along
city streets.

The most ambitious postwar rail system serves
Washington, D.C., and its suburbs. Because of the
District of Columbia's special constitutional role
and the needs of federal workers, Congress authorized billions for Metro. The first section opened in
1976, and the originally planned system was completed in 2001. More reliant on expensive tunnels
than BART and Atlanta's MARTA, Metro also offered more extensive service, and in the 1980s it
overtook Chicago to become the nation's second
busiest rapid-transit system, after New York. In
2009, work began on a multi-billion-dollar extension to Dulles Airport.

Having rejected subways for decades, Los Angeles opened its first modern subway segment in
1993, and San Juan, Puerto Rico, began operation
of its Tren Urbano in 2004. In 2011, Honolulu
broke ground for an elevated rail system. The

Hawai'i Supreme Court halted construction for over a year for archaeological survey work, but by 2014 project managers hoped to complete the route in 2019.

The Honolulu lawsuits reflect the continuing controversy over rapid transit in an age of near-universal automobile ownership. Opponents of subways point to their massive cost and the relatively small numbers of Americans (outside of metropolitan New York) who choose transit. Proponents argue that building new freeways can be comparably expensive and that clustering development near rapid-transit stations can give commuters choices and reduce pollution. As in the 1890s, subway construction in the twenty-first century remained a high-stakes gamble, with high costs but potentially large payouts.

[*See also* **Bicycles and Bicycling; Electricity and Electrification; Environmentalism; Highway System; Motor Vehicles; Railroads;** *and* **Urban Mass Transit.**]

BIBLIOGRAPHY

Cudahy, Brian J. *A Century of Subways: Celebrating 100 Years of New York's Underground Railways.* 3d ed. New York: Fordham University Press, 2003.

Fogelson, Robert M. *Downtown: Its Rise and Fall, 1880–1950.* New Haven, Conn.: Yale University Press, 2001.

Hood, Clifton. *722 Miles: The Building of the Subways and How They Transformed New York.* New York: Simon and Schuster, 1993.

Middleton, William D. *Metropolitan Railways: Rapid Transit in America.* Bloomington: Indiana University Press, 2003.

Schrag, Zachary M. *The Great Society Subway: A History of the Washington Metro.* Baltimore: Johns Hopkins University Press, 2006.

Zachary M. Schrag

SURGERY

Chiros ourgos, the work of the hands, is the root of surgery. Surgery in America typically lagged behind that in Europe until after the Civil War. Education and practice improved after 1870, and by the early twentieth century and throughout it, American surgery was assuming a position of strength and leadership.

Early American Surgery. From the colonial period through the Civil War, professional boundaries between physicians and surgeons were missing; by necessity, physicians practiced surgery. Most were self trained or apprentice trained, and their level of surgical proficiency was low. Pain, infection, and blood loss created fear for surgeon and patient alike and limited the practice of surgery primarily to the surface of the body: amputating limbs, excising tumors, setting bones, repairing hernias, or cutting for the stone. For those who sought more than an apprenticeship before practice, European medical colleges beckoned. No American medical college offered instruction in surgery until 1805, when the University of Pennsylvania appointed Philip Syng Physick (1768–1837) as the nation's first professor of surgery.

American innovations were rare before the Civil War. In December 1809, Ephraim McDowell (1771–1830) performed the first successful ovariotomy. J. Marion Sims (1813–1883) reported in 1852 the first successful repair of a vesicovaginal fistula. In 1843, Oliver Wendell Holmes (1809–1894) asserted that to avoid spreading puerperal fever, physicians should not attend obstetric cases unless they had washed their hands in calcium chloride and changed their clothes. This advice went unheeded, and it was more than another 20 years before sustained efforts to control infectious diseases and wound infections began. On 16 October 1846, William T. G. Morton (1819–1868), a dentist, convinced Dr. John Collins Warren to give sulfuric ether to a patient undergoing surgery at the Massachusetts General Hospital for the removal of a tumor. The operation was quick, successful, and painless. The *Boston Medical and Surgical Journal* announced the feat, and soon anesthesia circled the globe. As novel or as impressive as these innovations were, they were empirical, not theoretical, successes. Surgery remained work for talented hands.

After the Civil War. In 1867, Joseph Lister (1827–1910), a British surgeon, published in the *Lancet* and the *British Medical Journal* an outline of a surgical procedure designed to eliminate wound infections: antisepsis. Many technical components comprised antisepsis, but its icon was carbolic acid sprayed over the operative field. Wound sepsis, Lister argued, could be stopped by killing bacteria floating in the air, an idea he took from the French chemist Louis Pasteur's (1822–1895) recently formulated germ theory of infectious diseases. Some American surgeons adopted Lister's method by the end of 1867, but unlike anesthesia's rapid acceptance, antiseptic surgery was not generally adopted for almost 20 years.

Its technique was tricky, exacting, and hard to master: the slightest lapse led to infection. Numerous surgeons considered it nothing but another new dressing among several new dressings. Commercially available antiseptic dressings or carbolic acid solutions were rare, so surgeons had to create their own antiseptic materials and that made it even harder to duplicate Lister's method.

Because Lister had explicitly based antisepsis on Pasteur's germ theory, the slow acceptance of the theory paralleled the slow acceptance of the technique. Surgeons relied not on germs but on miasma—bad smells—to explain infections. American hospitals, skeptics claimed, were cleaner and better ventilated than their British counterparts, so antisepsis was not needed in America. Not until Robert Koch (1843–1910), a pioneering German bacteriologist, confirmed Pasteur's theory in his 1878 paper on wound infection did surgeons admit that Lister's techniques were built on firm ground.

By the mid-1880s, however, an improved command of theory and technique guided surgeons such as Arpad Gerster (1848–1923) and William Halsted (1852–1922) to develop asepsis—a sterile operating theater was more important than a sterile operating field—that more efficiently removed the threat of surgical infections. Halsted, who became the first chief of surgery at the Johns Hopkins Hospital, is also credited with innovations such as gowns or rubber gloves that helped create the modern, aseptic operating room.

In professional and public opinion, the joining of theory to technique was a turning away from medicine's "empirical past" (*Journal of the American Medical Association* 2 (1884): 12–13). New or reformed medical schools such as the Johns Hopkins Medical School (founded in 1893) and its allied hospital believed in the ideal of science informing medical and surgical progress. The reforms that swept medical education between 1870 and 1920 elevated both medicine and surgery. Apprentice-trained surgeons disappeared, to be replaced by university-trained surgeons who were of higher social status and income than their pre–Civil War forbears. By then, surgery had become a profession distinct from medicine. The American Surgical Association was established in 1880 and its publication, *Transactions of the American Surgical Association* (now *Annals of Surgery*), appeared in 1883. Following the success of the first Clinical Congress of Surgeons held in 1910 in Chicago, the American College of Surgeons was organized in 1913.

As surgery became more technically proficient, it depended more on ancillary services, such as professional nursing and anesthesiologists, and technology, such as laboratories and X-rays. To meet these complicated demands, surgery consequently moved out of the patient's home and into the hospital.

Surgical Specialties Emerge. Anesthesia and asepsis spurred the growth of surgical practice and its organizational growth, but blood loss remained a barrier to further development. For centuries, surgeons hoped to replace lost blood to prevent shock, but every attempt failed. In 1910, Karl Landsteiner (1868–1943), who began his career in Austria but completed it at the Rockefeller Institute, defined blood groups; surgeons then understood that blood could be exchanged only among individuals of the same type. In 1905, George Washington Crile (1864–1963), a cofounder of the Cleveland Clinic, successfully transfused blood between patients. The collection and storage of blood was difficult, but by the 1940s it was discovered that adding sodium citrate prevented clotting and prolonged storage time.

After World War I, Crile, Alfred Blalock (1899–1964), Vivien T. Thomas (191–1985), and others recognized the physiological nature of shock. More than blood was required; overall cardiac functions, especially blood pressure, had to be monitored during operations. Reliable blood pressure measurements were an innovation introduced in the United States in 1901 by Harvey Cushing (1869–1939).

Although not the first American neurosurgeon, Cushing is commonly acclaimed as the founder of the specialty of neurosurgery. Educated at Yale College and Harvard Medical School, he learned surgery at the Massachusetts General Hospital and the Johns Hopkins Hospital, where he was deeply influenced by William Halsted's insistence on asepsis and attention to detail. To control surgical shock, by 1926 Cushing was using Scipione Riva-Rocci's (1863–1937) sphygmomanometer to monitor blood pressure continuously during operations and William Bovie's (1881–1958) electrocautery to stem bleeding. Cushing mastered the removal of brain tumors, and under his leadership, neurosurgical mortality fell drastically. The work on tumors led him to study pituitary endocrinology; he was also interested in medical history. Walter Dandy (1886–1946), who spent his career at the Johns Hopkins University, produced in 1918 clear X-ray images of the brain by injecting filtered air into the ventricles. Neurosurgery continued to benefit by advances in imaging technology, such as computed tomography scans, magnetic resonance imaging, or positron emission tomography scans.

Cardiac and thoracic operations were considered practically impossible for the first half of the twentieth century. Some nineteenth-century surgeons, such as the African American Daniel Dale Williams of Chicago, had performed pericardial surgery, but the heart itself remained untouchable. Wartime injuries, however, forced surgeons to repair the heart. Theory suggested that all such patients must die, but surgeons recorded sufficient successes that sporadic cardiac operations were done in the 1920s and 1930s. The specialty arose only after World War II. Elliott Carr Cutler (1888–1947) and Dwight Harken (1910–1993) pioneered open-heart surgery at Boston's Peter Bent

Brigham Hospital (now Brigham and Women's Hospital). Alfred Blalock, Vivien Thomas, and Helen Taussig (1898–1986), all at Johns Hopkins, created pediatric cardiac surgery with their operation for the Tetralogy of Fallot—blue babies—in 1944.

War injuries accelerated the expansion of plastic and reconstructive surgery. The American Society of Plastic and Reconstructive Surgeons was established in 1931 and gained board certification in 1941. By the 1950s, the field had expanded to include cosmetic surgery. The society changed its name in 1999 to the American Society of Plastic Surgeons.

Surgeons wanted to replace failing organs with healthy organs. Stories from antiquity onward told of attempted but failed organ transplants. In 1902, Alexis Carrel (1873–1944), a Nobel Prize–winning French surgeon who completed his scientific career at the Rockefeller Institute, first sutured severed veins without their subsequent clotting. He and Charles Guthrie (1880–1963) then transplanted animal organs and body parts. The recipients rejected the grafts, but their technical achievement showed that transplantation was possible. In 1954, at the Peter Bent Brigham Hospital, Joseph Murray (1919–2012) performed the first successful human-to-human organ transplant (kidneys) between identical twins. In December 1967, Christiaan Barnard (1922–2001), a South African surgeon who had trained in the United States, transplanted a human heart; the patient lived long enough to show the feasibility of this operation. These successes generated optimism and a demand for similar operations, but they failed. Murray's operation succeeded because the donor and recipient were genetically identical, but what if they weren't? Attempts to suppress immunity with radiation or with drugs continued to fail until the introduction of cyclosporine in the late 1970s. Once the immune response could be manipulated, the modern period of transplant surgery began.

Not every development in surgery succeeded. Between the 1930s and the 1950s, surgeons sought to cure psychiatric illnesses by severing the connections between the frontal lobes and the rest of the brain—the frontal lobotomy. Egas

Moniz (1874–1955), who pioneered the operation in Portugal in 1935, won the 1949 Nobel Prize for Medicine or Physiology; James Watts (1904–1994) and Walter Freeman (1895–1972) popularized it in America. Although initial results showed short-term promise, large-scale studies done by the Veterans Administration revealed that the procedure eventually harmed patients. When psychotropic drugs entered the market in the early 1950s, it was already falling into disuse and outlawed in several states.

Specialties Proliferate. A hallmark of the twentieth-century profession was the development of its specialties. At their start, the American Surgical Association and the American College of Surgeons served the needs of general surgeons, but as surgery branched into specialties, the specialists formed their own organizations and started their own journals.

In the 1920s and 1930s, specialists became concerned about the education and ethical conduct of their peers and the creation of barriers to professional entry. These concerns led to the foundation of the American Board of Medical Specialties, which aimed to certify by examination the competence of physicians and surgeons. The American College of Surgeons also governed fellowships and surgical specialties. Greater certification led to longer surgical education. Where an MD alone sufficed for practice in 1900, by 1930 surgeons needed internships, fellowships, and residencies.

The demand for certification of the new specialties accelerated during the twentieth century, and by the early years of the twenty-first century, there were not only at least two dozen specialty boards but also more than one hundred tertiary-care subspecialties.

Hospitals, medical schools, and state governments recognized the profession's autonomy to regulate its affairs with specialty certification, but these and other institutions such as insurance companies and the federal government by the 1970s and 1980s demanded greater financial accountability from surgeons. Medicare and Medicaid (as a proxy for an aging population in the early twenty-first century) increased demand and costs

began to soar. Technological advances in medical and surgical care also increased demand and costs. Consumers, once called patients, demanded input into their care. The complexity of surgical practice added to the weakness of the profession to organize its affairs beyond its own boundaries.

In the United States, surgeons were first physicians who, after being awarded the MD degree, specialized in surgery. The American medical and surgical professions were composed predominantly of white, Protestant males. Not until the 1970s did movements for civil rights and gender equality spur medical schools to remove the quotas that hindered many women, African Americans, Catholics, and Jews from gaining admission to the schools and entering the surgical profession. At the end of the twentieth century, more surgeons began specialty training earlier in their medical education. Consequently, the demography—the human face—of the surgical profession began to change from what it was in the 1970s.

Basic sciences such as immunology or genetics contributed to the profession's development, but new techniques, tools, and procedures remained the hallmarks of surgical progress. Increasingly, however, surgeons faced nonscientific and nontechnical challenges to their work. Mechanical ventilators, for example, raised ethical questions about defining the end of life. Organ transplants raised ethical questions about a market for organs where demand exceeds supply. How can the goods that surgery provided be distributed? Society, not only the profession, played an extensive role in the early twenty-first century in attempts to align the profession with societal needs and expectations. The profession, Rosemary Stevens noted, was "specialized, disorganized, expansionary, and flamboyant" (*American Medicine in the Public Interest*, updated ed., 1998, p. ix). Nonetheless, the arts, crafts, and sciences of surgery ranked among the most prominent achievements of the mind.

[*See also* **Anatomy and Human Dissection; Anesthesiology; Cardiology; Disease; Ethics and Medicine; Hospitals; Medical Education; Medical Specialization; Medicare and Medicaid; Medicine; Medicine and Technology;**

Nursing; Organ Transplantation; Public
Health; *and* War and Medicine.]

BIBLIOGRAPHY

Bliss, Michael. *Harvey Cushing: A Life in Surgery.* New York: Oxford University Press, 2005. The master biography of a surgical master.

Brieger, Gert H. "Surgery." In *The Education of American Physicians: Historical Essays,* edited by Ronald L. Numbers, pp. 175–204. Berkeley and Los Angeles: University of California Press, 1980.

Edmonson, James M. *American Surgical Instruments: The History of Their Manufacture and a Directory of Instrument Makers to 1990.* San Francisco: Norman, 1997.

Hamilton, David. *A History of Organ Transplantation: Ancient Legends to Modern Practice.* Pittsburgh, Pa.: University of Pittsburgh Press, 2012. Surgical advances depended on scientific advances and sometimes vice versa.

Hollingham, Richard. *Blood and Guts: A History of Surgery.* New York: Thomas Dunne Books, St. Martin's Press, 2008. Popular account based on a 2008 BBC documentary of the same name.

Journal of the American Medical Association 2 (1884): 12–13.

Lederer, Susan. *Flesh and Blood: Organ Transplantation and Blood Transfusion in Twentieth-Century America.* New York: Oxford University Press, 2008. Often not seen as such, blood transfusions are organ transplants; this excellent account examines racial stereotyping and blood typing, as well as religious hesitation and popular enthusiasm.

Miller, Franklin, and Robert D. Truog. *Death, Dying, and Organ Transplantation: Reconstructing Medical Ethics at the End of Life.* New York: Oxford University Press, 2012. Stark examination of ethical issues in end-of-life care.

Morantz-Sanchez, Regina. *Conduct Unbecoming a Woman: Medicine on Trial in Turn-of-the-Century Brooklyn.* New York: Oxford University Press, 2000.

Pernick, Martin S. *A Calculus of Suffering: Pain, Professionalism, and Anesthesia in Nineteenth-Century America.* New York: Columbia University Press, 1985. Serious account of a crucial technology.

Pressman, Jack D. *Last Resort: Psychosurgery and the Limits of Medicine.* Cambridge Studies in the History of Medicine. New York: Cambridge University Press, 1998. Studies an area that surgeons are eager to forget. Pressman's award-winning book examines the operation and its moral universe.

Stevens, Rosemary. *American Medicine and the Public Interest: A History of Specialization,* updated ed. with a new introduction. Berkeley: University of California Press, 1998. Best account of the engine that created modern medicine and surgery.

Thomas P. Gariepy

T

TATUM, EDWARD LAWRIE

See Lederberg, Joshua.

TAYLOR, FREDERICK W.

See Scientific Management.

TECHNOLOGICAL ENTHUSIASM

Henry Ford (1863–1947) was often asked what makes an invention successful. Success, he would answer, is contingent on the answer to three questions: Is it needed? Is it practical? Is it commercial? Nobody knew more about inventive success than Mr. Ford—at one point, half the automobiles in the world were Fords—and yet his answer failed to account for inventions to which momentum is imparted by quite a different question: Is it possible? For many inventions from around the turn of the twentieth century—the telephone, the airplane, new materials such as celluloid and aluminum—needs had to be *contrived*; invention was the mother of necessity. How could this be? Capitalist and Marxist ideologies both posit the dominance of economic motivation. Yet, a 1931 study titled *Industrial Creativity: The Psychology of the Inventor* told of inventors citing "love of inventing" as their primary motivation more often than either "financial gain" or "necessity or need." Historians of technology call love of inventing something else, "technological enthusiasm," and its power can scarcely be overestimated. If we fail to take full account of that power, said the historian Eugene Ferguson, "we will have missed a central motivating influence in technological development" (Ferguson, 1974, p. 21).

"When it became possible to make thread and cloth by machine," writes Brooke Hindle, another historian who stresses the power of technological enthusiasm, "they were so made; when boats, trains, or mills could be driven by steam, they were so driven" (Hindle, 1966, p. 24). The inventors responsible for these new technologies, men like Oliver Evans and William Norris, were driven by an obsession to fulfill new technological potentials simply because those potentials existed. About need and practicality they were uncertain. About commercialization (that is, profit) they had no idea. As it turned out, Evans' *Oruktor Amphibolos*, his self-powered land vehicle of 1805, was not practical at all. Norris's American Steam Carriage Company, on the other hand, would become the dominant producer of railroad locomotives for more than three decades. Technological enthusiasts who populate more recent sagas such as Tracy Kidder's *The Soul of a New Machine* likewise found commercial success, at least for a time. But consider inventions by some of their contemporaries. When it appeared possible that the earth could be circled nonstop, an airplane called *Voyager* was invented. When it appeared possible that a man might fly through the sky with only the power of his own muscles, the *Gossamer Condor* was invented. Sometimes there were prizes offered for such feats. But necessity, practicality, profit? Nothing of the sort.

Human conveyances have always been seductive to technological enthusiasts, with speed being a frequent ideal. The speed of a transatlantic packet or a high-wheeled express locomotive might confer commercial advantage, and such contrivances were central to a "technology of haste" that was linked, in historian Daniel Boorstin's words, "to rewards others might grab if you were not there before them" (Boorstin, 1965, p. 97). Yet speed was often idealized at the *expense* of commercial advantage, as with the Clipper ships of the 1840s and 1850s, whose design made carrying capacity so slight that they were profitable only in the best of times and were put out of business by a downturn before the Civil War. In the twentieth century, firms like Cunard and United States Lines were still chasing the "Blue Riband" for the fastest Atlantic crossing—to no practical purpose—even as their impending fate was foretold in the emergence of the jetliner, and aeronautical enthusiasts were eyeing the feasibility of flying passengers around at three times the speed of sound, even as denizens of the Society of Experimental Test Pilots were approaching speeds near *seven* times the speed of sound. Accomplishments of this sort speak to Henry Ford's "Is it practical?"—if one takes this to mean "Does it work?"—but they are light-years distant from an affirmative answer to his other two questions.

Why study technological enthusiasm? Historians live in a world of words on paper and often have little appreciation for technological pursuits, sometimes even contempt. But it is important to understand how fulfilling those pursuits can be to others, *all* technological pursuits, not just the essentially benign varieties mentioned here. Enthusiasm—the "Is it possible?" question—is in large measure what drove the development of a souped-up go-cart capable of covering a quarter mile in six seconds from a dead stop and also drove the development of much modern weaponry. (The availability of funding of course played a role, too.) The phenomenon of enthusiasm helps explain how all sorts of technologies gain momentum, including technologies of control, domination, and mass destruction, as well as extravagantly wasteful pursuits like the International Space Station whose funding from the public purse is rationalized on the basis of "national interest" or "cosmic destiny," when in truth the fundamental push may be nothing more than the human enthusiasm that an unfulfilled potential is bound to kindle.

[*See also* **Ford, Henry; Popularization of Science; Science;** *and* **Technology.**]

BIBLIOGRAPHY

Boorstin, Daniel J. *The Americans: The National Experience.* New York: Vintage Books, 1965.

Ferguson, Eugene S. "The American-ness of American Technology." *Technology and Culture* 20 (1979): 3–24.

Ferguson, Eugene S. "Toward a Discipline of the History of Technology." *Technology and Culture* 15 (1974): 13–30.

Hindle, Brooke. *The Technology in Early America: Needs and Opportunities for Study.* Chapel Hill: University of North Carolina Press, 1966.

Hughes, Thomas P. *American Genesis: A Century of Invention and Technological Enthusiasm*. New York: Viking Press, 1989.

Kidder, Tracy. *The Soul of a New Machine*. Boston: Back Bay Books, 2000. Reprint of a classic first published in 1981.

Post, Robert C. *High Performance: The Culture and Technology of Drag Racing, 1950–2000*, revised ed. Baltimore: Johns Hopkins University Press, 2001.

Wright, John L., ed. *Possible Dreams: Technological Enthusiasm in Twentieth Century America*. Dearborn, Mich.: Henry Ford Museum, 1992.

Robert C. Post

TECHNOLOGY

Few forces have more profoundly shaped the American experience than technology. This essay examines historians' shifting understanding of the term, traces the major eras of technological change, and explores some of the factors that have influenced the pace and direction of that change.

Defining the Term. The meaning of "technology" has undergone a revolution since the early nineteenth century. Although the term was familiar in German (Technologie) in the late Colonial Era, it came into limited use in English only as the American economy was beginning to industrialize. In 1829 Harvard professor Jacob Bigelow entitled his treatise "on the application of the sciences to the useful arts" *Elements of Technology* because he sought a "sufficiently expressive" word for his subject and "practical men" were employing it. Through 1900, however, its use was confined mainly to technical manuals or to the names of new institutes of technology. Most Americans favored the all-encompassing phrase "the useful arts" or the narrower "mechanical arts."

"Technology" came into currency in its modern sense in the early twentieth century. Popularized by Thorstein Veblen in the 1920s and in 1930s debates about technological unemployment, it was understood in an anthropological sense as "useful knowledge" but confined to the largely male preserves of industry and engineering. Veblen and others also stressed the machine-like, autonomous nature of the emerging "industrial system" (which they believed engineers were uniquely suited to head). As engineers strove to enhance their status, meanwhile, they embraced the term but defined it as "applied science," closely allied with "pure" or "basic" science. Although these conceptions continued to govern popular thought, a profoundly social understanding of technology took shape among scholars after the 1960s. Historians of technology, organized professionally in the 1950s, disputed the "applied science" definition, stressing instances where useful artifacts or processes were developed without a foundation of scientific understanding. This finding was reinforced by a federal study of weapons development (Project Hindsight, 1966). Also rejecting technological determinism and autonomy, historians explored the role of social choice and human agency in technological change and, inspired by gender and race studies, challenged the focus on white male–dominated industry and engineering that had characterized earlier conceptions of "technology."

The result was a broader view of technology as ways of "making and doing things" that, at its most expansive, encompasses all ways of shaping the real world—natural and social—to human ends. Technology so understood signifies a thoroughly social process that touches all human beings and whose history is inevitably bound up with questions of power and authority.

Overlapping Eras of Change. This definitional transformation reflected momentous changes in ways of shaping the real world, in the role of technology in American life, and in the nature of technological knowledge. Generalizing about these changes is risky, not least because some technologies, periods, and regions are better understood than others. Still, as a first approximation, the history of American technology may be divided into four broadly overlapping eras.

Colonial Era through the Early 1800s. The first era extends from the establishment of the British colonies through the early 1800s. Although conditions differed over this time span and from one colony to another, colonial technology shared certain characteristics. It was small in scale because most products, if not imported, were produced in limited quantities—in homes, on plantations or farms, or in village workshops—and used or consumed locally. Most work was done manually with simple tools rather than by machine. Direct personal relationships, accordingly, marked the social relations of technology: relations among producers, between producers and their work, and between producers and consumers. Furthermore, colonial technology was tied closely to nature and its rhythms. Wood, an abundant resource, provided fuel and construction material. Lighting as well as power (stationary and motive) came from natural sources (sun, wind, water, animals). The ebb and flow of daylight and the turning of the seasons shaped all technological activities. Great diversity also marked colonial technology because goods produced manually for local markets varied widely.

The workings of colonial technology had a certain transparency because its underlying principles, although seldom understood scientifically, were familiar. Transportation and communication still relied on age-old technologies (turnpikes and canals), as did even technically complex production sites such as iron "plantations" or water-powered gristmills. Skills passed from individual to individual, learned through hands-on experience rather than from books, reinforcing social intimacy.

Yet colonial technology was not static. Certainly, the technologies that transformed eighteenth-century British industry had little direct impact because British mercantilism encouraged the colonists to produce raw materials or semifinished goods (e.g., bar iron), not finished goods such as textiles or machinery. But conquest and settlement depended on the ability to adapt European technologies to a new environment; to develop crops such as rice (first grown successfully in South Carolina by slaves who probably brought the know-how from West Africa); and to adopt Indian techniques for cultivating maize and clearing forests. Indians, too, engaged in selective adaptation, favoring flintlock over matchlock guns, for example. Such accomplishments forged a distinctive American technology, although well within a preindustrial tradition.

But signs of a break with traditional practice gradually emerged. Adoption of the Constitution (1789) and a national patent law (1790) erected a political framework for a national market. Experimentation with steam engines and "automatic" flour milling (Oliver Evans, 1780s), erection of the first spinning mill, based on British know-know (Samuel Slater, 1790), and invention of the cotton gin (Eli Whitney, 1793) all signaled rising interest in mechanization. But the breakthrough came with the War of 1812, which stimulated the domestic market by cutting off imports and prompting tariff increases. As domestic manufacturing surged, Boston merchants built the nation's first large-scale cotton textile factory at Waltham, Massachusetts, in 1813. Integrating all steps of the manufacturing process, it applied water power even to weaving (a departure from British practice). Seeking more water power, the Boston merchants opened the Lowell mills in the 1820s. Wartime experience also heightened demand for improved transportation, stimulating the construction of steamboats, roads, canals, and, by the late 1820s, railroads. Under an 1815 congressional mandate, the War Department pursued "uniformity" in arms production, a project that ultimately led to the "American System" of interchangeable-parts manufacturing technology, a key to mass production.

The Later Nineteenth Century: The Industrial Age. As industrialization unfolded, technology took on very different qualities. Railroads and telegraphs opened regional and national markets. Labor-saving farm machinery freed labor for factory work and spurred urban growth. The scale of technology increased dramatically. Although many products continued to be produced by craft methods, others—from cigarettes to petroleum—were manufactured in vast quantities as mechanization and capital-intensive factory production soared after the Civil War. The social relations of technology grew correspondingly more complex. Production sites became removed from sites of consumption, as even preserved-food production moved out of the household or off the farm. As the division of labor increased and large firms employed more Americans, work relations took on a bureaucratic nature; with factory production and mechanization, control of the work process shifted from workers to managers (although not without resistance and seldom completely).

Industrial technology also altered ties to nature and diminished diversity. Railroads and telegraphs, it was said, "annihilated time and space." In both industry and agriculture, complex machines (sewing machines, machine tools, horse-drawn reapers) lessened dependence on manual skills. Although the shift to coal (for fuel) and iron or steel (for construction) proceeded slowly, by 1900 they had replaced wood as the material of choice. Meanwhile, gas illumination and, later, electrical lighting supplanted natural light, and steam slowly became the dominant source of stationary and motive power. Daily life was less closely linked to diurnal and seasonal rhythms, and new technologies altered the physical environment on an unprecedented scale. By the 1880s, coal smoke, lumber-mill sawdust, and wastewater from hydraulic mining and urban waterworks generated air and water pollution in many parts of the nation. With the spread of railroads, telegraphs, and mass production, diversity yielded to standardization—not only of products but also of time, news, work and travel schedules, and weights and measures.

Technological knowledge underwent equally dramatic changes. The principles underlying steam power, machine tools, and mass production were less familiar and hence less transparent. Invention by individuals remained the norm—indeed, the post–Civil War years marked the high point of independent inventors such as Thomas Edison— but was increasingly defined as machine-related and patentable. (The annual number of patents rose from six hundred in 1840 to some 26 thousand by 1900.) Further, invention was seen as the preserve of white males, despite efforts by African Americans and white women to defend a broader conception. With the rise of capital-intensive industry, moreover, the ability to profit from invention increasingly depended on access to capital, disadvantaging those without social connections, such as Granville T. Woods, a prolific African American inventor. Book-learning and systematic investigation also began to supplant traditional know-how. From a handful in the Antebellum Era (notably, Philadelphia's Franklin Institute and the U.S. Military Academy at West Point), institutions of engineering education multiplied (e.g., the Massachusetts Institute of Technology, 1861). As practitioners of the "mechanic arts" evolved into "engineers" distinguished by specialty (e.g., civil, mining, mechanical, or electrical), professional associations proliferated.

The Early Twentieth Century: Technological Systems Take Shape.   By 1900 a new era of "technological systems" had arisen. The electrical-power industry, for example, inaugurated by the opening of Edison's generating station in Manhattan (1882), grew from a fragmented collection of local lighting stations into an integrated system of regional power grids by the 1920s. Utility companies transmitted a standardized product (alternating current at 60 cycles per second) over a network of wires to one-third of American households. Electricity also powered streetcars (pioneered by Frank I. Sprague, 1888) and factory motors (after 1900). By the 1930s, the "system" included those who made and sold household devices such as radios and refrigerators, credit companies to finance their purchase, advertising to promote electrical use, and sophisticated techniques to manage demand. The two dominant companies, General Electric and Westinghouse, employed many engineers, and in 1901 General Electric opened the nation's first industrial research laboratory. An array of other system-like technologies emerged from 1880 to 1940: telephones, motor vehicles, and western irrigation projects as well as motion pictures, commercial broadcasting, and aviation.

The qualities that characterized industrial technology marked American life deeply in the early twentieth century: scale and standardization increased, the lines of mediation between production and (now largely female) consumption became more intricate, and nature grew more remote (although in a sense accessible by automobile). But the era of systems also introduced a new level of social interdependence. Technological systems comprise many interlocking parts—including people—that must function properly and predictably; disruption or change at any one point affects the whole. To be sure, personal interdependence had marked the Colonial Era, whereas railroads, telegraph companies, and mass producers had all grappled with organizational complexity in the Industrial Era, giving rise to managerial hierarchies and Frederick W. Taylor's scientific management methods in the 1880s. But technological systems brought new, industry-wide hierarchies of social interdependence that linked producers with distant consumers, in some cases shifting the production of services onto the consumer. By 1930 the housewife who drove an automobile and thus provided transportation for the household was embedded in a system that encompassed not only auto manufacturers such as Henry Ford and his assembly line but also steel, glass, rubber, and upholstery manufacturers, finance companies, gasoline producers and filling stations, garages and mechanics, roads, traffic lights, and self-service "supermarkets." Even farm households, once reliant on nature and neighbors, became dependent on complex systems for everything from gasoline-powered tractors and seed corn (from the 1930s) to entertainment.

Technological knowledge was systematized as well. In a transformation first perceptible in the electrical and chemical industries (in what some call the "second industrial revolution"), practical and scientific knowledge became interdependent. Technological knowledge became enmeshed in the corporations that spawned systems as independent inventors yielded to corporate engineers and industrial scientists. The workings of technology thus grew more opaque, more remote from everyday experience. Technological knowledge, concentrated in engineering schools and professional associations, also became further masculinized. As the percentage of doctoral degrees in science and engineering awarded to women declined from 1920 through the 1960s and as professional associations excluded women from full membership, the expertise and systems of male engineers came to symbolize "progress."

The 1930s to the Late Twentieth Century: Technology as "Second Nature."
In viewing the fourth era in the history of American technology, whose beginnings stretched back

to the 1930s, two trends stand out: the extension of ever larger technological systems into virtually every corner of American life and the reconstitution of nature itself through new technologies. From the 1930s on, technological systems expanded and multiplied, merging into an interlocking national, then global, infrastructure. New Deal–era programs promoted regional hydroelectric power systems and encouraged rural electrification, and the Rural Telephone Act (1949) brought telephone lines to American farms. Postwar agriculture became "agribusiness": capital, energy, and chemical intensive. In the 1950s and 1960s, the federal government built a nationwide interstate highway system. Airline passengers carried by a nascent civil aviation industry increased to nearly 13 million by 1947 and then multiplied as jets were introduced in the 1950s. The first radio network (National Broadcasting Company, 1926) linked two systems to create a third; partly owned by General Electric and Westinghouse, it distributed radio programs over leased telephone lines. Commercial television broadcasting, launched in 1939–1940, burgeoned after World War II. By 1959 Americans owned 50 million TV sets. The major networks dominated programming until the arrival of cable TV (also color television and videotape recorders) in the 1960s. The first major commercial communications satellite (Intelstat I) was launched in 1965; by the early 1970s virtually global satellite coverage had been achieved. By the twenty-first century, satellite transmissions, cable television, digital facsimiles, fiber optics, and the Internet put the vast majority of Americans within reach of a global network of technological systems.

World War II and the Cold War yielded other giant technological systems as well, including nuclear weapons, nuclear power, the space program, and the Internet, developed in the late 1950s chiefly through the Pentagon's Advanced Research Projects Agency (ARPA). At the heart of most systems in this era lay electronic devices. Electronic digital (i.e., binary) computers, developed for military purposes during World War II, became feasible for civilian use after transistors replaced vacuum tubes in the 1950s. Small electronic signal devices made of semiconductors (mainly silicon), transistors were soon integrated with other components into a single silicon chip—the integrated circuit (1960s)—then in large-scale circuits (microprocessors, 1971), and finally in very-large-scale integrated (VLSI) circuits (mid-1980s). These and related advances, most funded by the Pentagon, increased the power of computers dramatically and reduced their size from room-size mainframes to desktop (1980s) and palm-held (1990s) computers. Thanks to microprocessors, a host of consumer products as well as manufacturing and other business processes were computerized from the 1970s on. Linked in local-area networks (LAN) or through the Internet, microelectronic devices unleashed an "information revolution" that had touched the lives of virtually all Americans by the beginning of the twenty-first century. (Actual access remained uneven, however.)

Over the same years, other technologies offered sweeping powers to manipulate nature itself. One line of development centered on molecular manipulation in the manufacture of synthetic materials. An early, widely used plastic, Bakelite (ca. 1909), was the first in a series of synthetic materials constructed of complex molecules or "polymers." Technical advances during World War II included nylon (a linear polymer), alloys, and composites. The new postwar discipline of "materials science," emerging from chemistry, physics, and metallurgy, was funded after 1960 by the Pentagon's advanced research agency, which was interested in developing high-temperature, high-strength-to-weight materials for military purposes. This culminated in the 1990s in "nanotechnology," the precise positioning of atoms and molecules in what physicist Richard Feynman envisioned in 1959 as "bottom-up" manufacturing of materials and microscopic devices.

Another line of research, on the manipulation of reproduction, led from hybrid corn in the 1920s through discovery of the double helical structure of DNA (1952) to recombinant DNA techniques (gene cloning) in the 1970s. The 1980s and 1990s saw the development of genetically altered micro-organisms (declared patentable in 1980), plants (1977), and animals (1996), as well as gene therapies for human diseases (e.g., cystic fibrosis,

1993). Meanwhile, the birth control pill was approved for sale in 1960, and the first American in vitro fertilization was achieved in 1981. Amid debates about the ethics of human cloning, the federally funded Human Genome Project was launched in 1990 and successfully concluded a decade later as part of a global effort to identify the location and structure of every human gene. By the end of the twentieth century, in short, new technologies offered the possibility of constructing all kinds of matter from the bottom up.

These two trends combined to give American technology the qualities of "second nature" in the post–World War II years. For a time in the 1970s and 1980s, "quality management" techniques, computerization, flexible methods of production, and niche markets seemed to herald a reversal of the centralization and standardization that marked earlier technological systems. "Lean" production methods such as just-in-time inventory control and subcontracting eased the rigidities inherent in Fordist methods of mass production. The Internet, moreover, retained the decentralization designed into its military progenitor, ARPANET, to withstand a nuclear attack. But in practice, the hierarchies of interdependence expanded, as interlocking technological systems encompassed not only those who produced and consumed its products but also virtually all Americans. Standardization became pervasive, evident in the rapid spread of commodities (or computer viruses) around the world. Working in concert, systems such as electricity, automobiles, television, and the Internet ordered social life as nature once did. The "24/7 economy" of the late twentieth and early twenty-first centuries—operating 24 hours a day, 7 days a week—decoupled daily life from nature. Even environmental problems generated by twentieth-century technologies were addressed largely with new technologies (e.g., air pollution–control devices, genetically engineered micro-organisms to combat oil spills). Technology had become so deeply woven into American life as to be taken for granted. Nano- and biotechnologies, moreover, permitted nature itself to be constructed anew at the atomic and genetic level.

Technological knowledge became even more opaque and further removed from everyday life.

Technology's shift from the mechanical toward the scientific accelerated in these years with the growing importance of solid-state physics and molecular biology. The locus of technological knowledge moved from corporate research labs to a larger nexus composed of industry, the military, and universities—the "military–industrial complex" whose emergence President Dwight D. Eisenhower had discerned in 1961. During the Cold War—particularly in response to the Soviet atomic bomb (1949), the Korean War, and the Soviets' launching of *Sputnik 1* (1957)—federal funds poured into education (National Defense Education Act, 1958) and into industrial research and development (R&D), on the model that had proved so productive during World War II. By 1965, fully two-thirds of American R&D was funded by the federal government. As total R&D spending more than tripled thereafter, the government's share declined, but it still accounted for about one-third in the 1990s. In short, technological knowledge in the era of technology as second nature became increasingly scientific, highly institutionalized, and inflected by government priorities.

Understanding Technological Change.

Tracing the evolution of machines once seemed sufficient to explain technological change, but scholars now view it as a multilayered social process that has not followed a predetermined course. Sorting out the relevant historical forces involves distinguishing between the pace and the particular direction of technological change.

Two factors quickened the pace of change over the course of American history. Competition, both capitalist and nationalist, encouraged the search for improved technologies. The pursuit of profits and economic efficiency generated enormous increases in productivity. Farm productivity more than doubled between 1960 and 1996, for example, and nonfarm labor productivity nearly doubled. Likewise, international competition—economic as well as political—prompted government funding for specific technological advances. The pattern of support established after the War of 1812—the armories' work on interchangeable parts, the state governments' promotion of canals and railroads—grew more pronounced in the

twentieth century, particularly during World War II and the Cold War, when technological innovation appeared critical to national security. Federal funding supported virtually all post-1945 technological breakthroughs.

Technological "borrowing" also hastened the pace of change. Through the 1850s, the United States was a net borrower, adapting European textile and railroad technology to local circumstances, for example. By the Philadelphia Centennial Exhibition of 1876, however, American innovations enjoyed wide recognition in Europe. By 1900, American inventors were drawing from and contributing to an international pool of technical knowledge in the electrical, chemical, and other industries. Twentieth-century America became, on balance, a net technology exporter—for example, of mass-production techniques to Europe and the Soviet Union after World War I. Borrowing went on among industries as well. Innovations spread rapidly, for example, within the nineteenth-century machine-tool industry and the twentieth-century electronics industries. The "spinoff" of technologies from the military to the private sector further accelerated the process of technological change.

But the factors that help account for the pace of technological change do not necessarily explain its direction. At critical moments in American history, competing technologies seemed equally viable: canals, railroads, and steam carriages on common roads in the early 1830s; alternating and direct electric current or large-scale mass production and more flexible forms of production in the 1880s; numerical control and record-playback control in computerized manufacturing in the 1950s. Although Americans have been portrayed as naturally inventive, enthusiastic about mechanization, and prone to define "progress" in technological terms, throughout the nation's history critics have questioned the direction of technological change. Debates about the social utility of factory labor marked the 1830s and 1840s; intellectuals from Henry David Thoreau to Lewis Mumford questioned the movement toward technological systems; the Depression of the 1930s sparked debates about mass production's role in "technological unemployment"; and social protesters in the 1960s challenged technology's social and environmental consequences and launched an "alternative technology" movement. Why some voices or technologies, but not others, achieved dominance requires deeper analysis.

Among the factors that have influenced the direction of technological change, two stand out. The availability of resources created distinctive incentives expressed in relative prices. In the nineteenth century, natural resources such as wood and water were abundant, whereas capital and labor were comparatively scarce. Thus Americans relied longer on wood and water power than did the British. The relative costliness of labor encouraged labor-saving mechanization; the scarcity of capital made it worthwhile to build machines cheaply and use them intensively. But if relative costs biased the direction of technological change, they seldom determined specific technological choices because costs themselves change during the process of invention, development, and diffusion. Prior technological choices also generated inertia that constrained the direction of change. Existing technologies tended to absorb capital and inventive energy that would otherwise have been directed elsewhere and, once a set of supporting institutions and behaviors grew up around specific technologies such as the QWERTY keyboard layout or the internal-combustion automobile, fundamental change became more costly.

Within the parameters established by relative prices and existing technologies, other factors tipped the balance toward specific technological solutions. Sometimes the actions of individuals proved decisive (e.g., Thomas Edison's in the battle between alternating and direct current). Government funding was often critical, especially when it targeted specific technological solutions (e.g., machine tools and transistors better suited to military than to commercial needs). Although the effects of ideologies are difficult to gauge, they have also shaped the direction of technological change. Examples include the "command-and-control" ideology expressed in military support of computer research, gender or racial ideologies that influenced product design or use, and "progress" ideologies that privileged the use of iron or electricity. Consumers have also had

their say, putting technologies to unanticipated uses. The creators of both the telephone and the Internet's predecessor, ARPANET, intended them for business use; it was telephone callers and researchers who turned them into devices for social interaction. The answer to the question of which technology or whose voice prevails often lies immersed in the messy details of history.

[*See also* **Agricultural Technology; Airplanes and Air Transport; American Association for the Advancement of Science; American System of Manufactures; Animation Technology and Computer Graphics; Atomic Energy Commission; Automation and Computerization; Biotechnology; Birth Control and Family Planning; Blindness, Assistive Technologies and; Building Technology; Canals and Waterways; Chemistry; Computers, Mainframe, Mini, and Micro; Defense Advanced Research Projects Agency; Diplomacy (post-1945), Science and Technology and; DNA Sequencing; Edison, Thomas; Electricity and Electrification; Engineering; Environmentalism; Ethics and Professionalism in Engineering; Feynman, Richard; Film Technology; Ford, Henry; Forestry Technology and Lumbering; Gender and Technology; Genetics and Genetic Engineering; Heating Technology; Highway System; Household Technology; Human Genome Project; Hydroelectric Power; Internet and World Wide Web; Iron and Steel Production and Products; Lowell Textile Mills; Machinery and Manufacturing; Manhattan Project; Medicine and Technology; Military, Science and Technology and the; Mining Technology; Molecular Biology; Motor Vehicles; Mumford, Lewis; Nanotechnology; National Aeronautics and Space Administration; Nuclear Power; Nuclear Weapons; Nylon; Office of Science and Technology Policy; Office of Scientific Research and Development; Office of Technology Assessment, Congressional; Office Technology; Petroleum and Petrochemicals; Physics; Plastics; Radio; Railroads; Refrigeration and Air Conditioning; Research and**

Development (R&D); Roads and Turnpikes, Early; Rural Electrification Administration; Satellites, Communications; Science; Shipbuilding; Society for the History of Technology; Solid-State Electronics; Sound Technology, Recorded; Space Program; Steam Power; Technological Enthusiasm; Telegraph; Telephone; Television; Tennessee Valley Authority; and Whitney, Eli.]

BIBLIOGRAPHY

Cowan, Ruth Schwartz. *A Social History of Technology.* New York and Oxford: Oxford University Press, 1997.

Horowitz, Roger, and Arwen Mohun, eds. *His and Hers: Gender, Consumption, and Technology.* Charlottesville: University of Virginia Press, 1998.

Hounshell, David A. *From the American System to Mass Production, 1800–1932: The Development of Manufacturing Technology in the United States.* Baltimore: Johns Hopkins University Press, 1984.

Hughes, Thomas P. *American Genesis: A Century of Invention and Technological Enthusiasm.* Chicago: University of Chicago Press, 1989.

Leslie, Stuart W. *The Cold War and American Science: The Military–Industrial–Academic Complex at MIT and Stanford.* New York: Columbia University Press, 1993.

McGaw, Judith A., ed. *Early American Technology: Making and Doing Things from the Colonial Era to 1850.* Chapel Hill: University of North Carolina Press, 1994.

Noble, David F. *Forces of Production: A Social History of Industrial Automation.* New Brunswick, N.J.: Transaction Publishers, 1984.

Nye, David E. *Electrifying America: Social Meanings of a New Technology.* Cambridge, Mass.: MIT Press, 1990.

Nye, David E. *Technology Matters: Questions to Live With.* Cambridge, Mass.: MIT Press, 2006.

Oldenziel, Ruth. *Making Technology Masculine: Men, Women and Modern Machines in America, 1870–1945.* Amsterdam: Amsterdam University Press, 1999.

Pursell, Carroll. *The Machine in America: A Social History of Technology.* Baltimore: Johns Hopkins University Press, 1995.

Schatzberg, Eric. "Technik Comes to America: Changing Meanings of Technology before 1930." *Technology and Culture* 47 (July 2006): 486–512.

Schatzberg, Eric. *Wings of Wood, Wings of Metal: Culture and Technical Choice in American Airplane Materials, 1914–1945.* Princeton, N.J.: Princeton University Press, 1999.

Smith, Merritt Roe, and Gregory Clancy, eds. *Major Problems in the History of Technology: Documents and Essays.* Boston: Houghton Mifflin Company, 1998.

Winner, Langdon. *The Whale and the Reactor: A Search for Limits in an Age of High Technology.* Chicago: University of Chicago Press, 1986.

Colleen A. Dunlavy

TELEGRAPH

The telegraph was the outgrowth and application of advances in electrical science between about 1800 and 1840, particularly the invention of the electrical battery by Alessandro Volta around 1800 and research into electromagnetism by Hans Christian Oersted, Andre Marie Ampere, Joseph Henry, and Michael Faraday during the 1820s and 1830s. Telegraphy was the first technology to sever the connection between communication and transportation. Because of the telegraph's ability to transmit information almost instantly, it affected many aspects of society, culture, politics, and commerce after 1845. It helped to create an integrated national market, sped the dissemination of news, and spurred the federal government to develop telecommunications and technology policies.

In 1837 and 1838 Samuel F. B. Morse publicly demonstrated his electromagnetic recording telegraph to prominent scientists and government officials. Morse's system at this time comprised an alphabetic code of dots and dashes, a telegraph key to encode messages, and a receiving register that recorded signals onto a moving strip of paper. Morse believed that the federal government should own and operate his telegraph and tried to convince Congress to purchase his system. In 1843

Congress gave Morse $30,000 to build an experimental line between Washington and Baltimore. This line began operation in May 1844, but the government refused to fund an extension of the line northward to New York. In 1846 the government turned over the Washington–Baltimore line to private investors. Over the next 15 years, the telegraph network spread rapidly. By 1850 lines reached every important point east of the Mississippi River, and by 1861 a transcontinental line reached California. The major change to telegraph equipment in this period was the elimination of the recording register. Operators shifted to sound reception by deciphering the clicks of the receiving magnet. During the late 1840s and early 1850s a confusing welter of several dozen companies sprang up to build telegraph lines, many of them poorly organized and short-lived. During the late 1850s a cartel of six companies coalesced and provided stability to the industry.

The Civil War sparked a final wave of consolidation. Western Union emerged in 1866 as the country's dominant telegraph company. After 1866 Western Union would control at least 80 percent of the nation's telegraph traffic. Yet over the next decade, Western Union faced determined attempts at competition, creating a technological and entrepreneurial hothouse. In 1867 Edward A. Calahan invented the stock ticker, a telegraph receiver that printed the results of stock and commodity trades onto a paper tape. The ticker opened up new markets for the telegraph industry and modernized the nation's financial sector. In the mid-1870s, Thomas A. Edison (working for Western Union) invented the quadruplex, which allowed four messages to be transmitted simultaneously on a single telegraph wire. The quadruplex effectively quadrupled the bandwidth of telegraph circuits and permitted Western Union to lease circuits to bankers, brokers, and press associations. The telephone, simultaneously invented by Alexander Graham Bell and Elisha Gray (with key contributions by Edison), was an outgrowth of efforts to send more than four messages on a wire simultaneously.

After the mid-1870s, however, the telegraph industry entered a long period of stagnation. No major technical improvements occurred until after the turn of the century. Western Union's primary strategic goal in this period was to maintain enough control over the industry to allow it to behave as a monopolist. Between 1866 and 1909 Western Union faced two major challenges to its dominance. A vocal and vigorous movement arose to nationalize the telegraph and place it under postal administration, and Western Union officials spent much time and energy defending their private monopoly to the public and to Congress. The telephone was a more serious long-term challenge. After attempting to compete with Bell for about two years, Western Union withdrew from the telephone market in late 1879 in exchange for Bell's promise not to compete with Western Union's long-distance telegraph business. At that time, the telephone could carry intelligible conversations at a range of only a few dozen miles. However, by about 1890 telephone engineers expanded its range to a few hundred miles, culminating in the establishment of Bell's transcontinental telephone service in 1915. As Bell's long-distance network expanded and telephone rates dropped, the telephone steadily eroded the telegraph's share of the long-distance communications market.

Under the leadership of Theodore N. Vail, American Telephone and Telegraph (AT&T), Bell's parent company, was powerful enough to acquire working control of Western Union in 1909. AT&T's control of Western Union demonstrated that the telephone had eclipsed the telegraph as the nation's preferred long-distance communications medium. AT&T voluntarily relinquished its Western Union holdings in 1914 to forestall federal antitrust proceedings. Although short-lived, Vail's administration modernized Western Union's antiquated accounting and management structure and spurred the company to replace its Morse instruments with modern telegraph equipment.

After 1914, the telegraph's share of the long-distance communications market continued to decline because of competition from the telephone, government air mail service, and AT&T's teletype service inaugurated in the 1930s. During World War II the Federal Communications Commission forced Western Union to divest itself of its international cable network and to consolidate with its sole remaining competitor, the bankrupt Postal Telegraph Company, two moves that weakened Western Union's long-term financial position.

Following World War II, Western Union's managers attempted to modernize the company's physical plant and preserve a market niche for record communications. Between 1945 and 1980 the company undertook three major modernization programs, the development of analog facsimile technology, the construction of a microwave beam network to replace its wires and cables, and the launching of communications satellites. Although these systems were technologically successful, they failed to reverse Western Union's declining market share with respect to the telephone. By 1990 Western Union was defunct except for its money-transfer service. A reorganized Western Union sent the last telegram in 2006, although technologies like digital facsimile transmission and electronic mail continued to fulfill many of the same record-communication functions that the telegram once did.

[*See also* **Atlantic Cable; Bell, Alexander Graham; Bell Laboratories; Edison, Thomas; Electricity and Electrification; Henry, Joseph; Morse, Samuel F. B.; Postal Service, U.S.; Satellites, Communications; Technology;** *and* **Telephone.**]

BIBLIOGRAPHY

Blondheim, M. *News over the Wires: The Telegraph and the Flow of Public Information in America, 1844–1897.* Cambridge, Mass.: Harvard University Press, 1994.

Gabler, E. *The American Telegrapher: A Social History, 1860–1900.* New Brunswick, N.J.: Rutgers University Press, 1988.

Hochfelder, David. *The Telegraph in America: 1832–1920.* Baltimore: Johns Hopkins University Press, 2012.

Israel, P. *From Machine Shop to Industrial Laboratory: Telegraphy and the Changing Context of American Invention, 1830–1920.* Baltimore: Johns Hopkins University Press, 1992.

John, Richard R. *Network Nation: Inventing American Telecommunications.* Cambridge, Mass.: Belknap Press of Harvard University Press, 2010.

David Hochfelder

TELEPHONE

The telephone is a device for the two-way transmission of human speech. That definition has been muddied by the multiplication of new electronic gadgets. Many devices we do not call telephones can also transmit speech, and the smart phones of the early twenty-first century have been packed with many additional functions. Still, the two-way talking telephone has remained one of our most useful and ubiquitous appliances.

Bell and Gray.   Electrical telephones were invented in the 1870s, and people have argued about who invented them ever since. At least two men were on the verge of electrically transmitted speech by 1876. Alexander Graham Bell was a Scottish-born elocutionist working in Boston, Massachusetts, who became interested in speech transmission as an extension of his work teaching the deaf. On 14 February 1876, Bell's backer, Gardiner Greene Hubbard, applied on Bell's behalf for a patent on his work in what was then called "acoustic telegraphy." On the very same day, the Chicago-based inventor Elisha Gray also filed a caveat (a kind of provisional patent application) for his own similar work. Neither man had yet developed a working prototype. A few weeks later, on 10 March 1876, Bell succeeded in transmitting the words "Mr. Watson, come here, I want to see you," to his assistant in the next room.

There have always been questions about Bell and Gray's simultaneous patent claims, who was first and what each man knew of the other's work. The evidence seems good that Bell was the first to actually transmit speech by electrical means. But Gray's supporters charge that Bell had seen Gray's patent application and borrowed his ideas. Like many technologies, the telephone's paternity would not be decided by inventors but by lawyers. In 1877, Bell and Hubbard founded the Bell Telephone

Company and began leasing telephones in New England. Elisha Gray sold his invention to the Western Union Telegraph Company, which entered the telephone business in 1878. The telegraph giant would have been a formidable foe for the fledgling Bell Company had it not come under attack at just that moment by the financier Jay Gould. Western Union struck a deal with Bell Telephone, agreeing to forfeit Gray's claims and withdraw from the new industry in exchange for 20 percent of the earnings on Bell's telephone for the duration of its patent—about $7 million over the next 15 years. It was this out-of-court settlement, not the race to the patent office in 1876, which meant Alexander Graham Bell would be remembered as the inventor of the telephone.

Monopoly and Competition. Protected by its patents from 1878 to 1894, the Boston-based Bell Telephone leased its device to firms in different regions of the country, creating a patchwork of regional Bell monopolies. These Bell operating companies concentrated on large urban markets and often acted as a feeder network for Western Union's long-distance telegraph lines. Bell managers in the monopoly years set the price for service high, effectively restricting the telephone to large businesses and wealthy individuals. But they clashed with their customers and local regulators over high rates, poor service, and even the proper use and purpose of the telephone.

After the Bell patents expired in 1894, thousands of new telephone systems were established across the country. Many were in small towns and rural areas that the Bell operating companies did not serve. Others competed directly with Bell for its valuable urban markets. The price of service dropped and the number of telephones in the United States exploded from the thousands to the millions in just a few short years.

Bell's new competitors called themselves the independent telephone movement. They were a diverse and fractious bunch, ranging from tiny farmer's cooperatives connecting only half a dozen telephones to large commercial systems with thousands of subscribers. On the whole, the independents articulated a different vision of telephony than Bell's owners or promoters. The independents focused on small towns and rural markets instead of big cities. They emphasized local and regional telephone connections rather than building long-distance lines. And they embraced the social and even frivolous uses of the telephone, instead of regarding it as only a business tool.

Competition and political pressure drove the rapid growth of both Bell and independent systems. By 1907, there were more than 6 million telephones in the United States, with more than half of them operated by Bell's independent rivals. The Bell companies bounced back under the leadership of Theodore Vail, president of the American Telephone and Telegraph Company (AT&T) from 1907 to 1919. Vail centralized control of the Bell companies and promoted the idea of a single, national network, which he dubbed "the Bell System." He moved to ward off a government breakup or takeover of his company by loudly embracing an ethos of public service and consenting to government regulation. The federal government did nationalize the Bell System for one year during World War I, but the takeover was poorly handled, and the experience served to discredit government ownership. When control passed back to AT&T after the war, a regulatory structure was put in place that would protect the Bell System for the next 60 years.

"Ma Bell." From the 1920s through the 1960s, "Ma Bell" was the model monopoly, valued for the reliability of its service and the company's deep commitment to pure and applied research. Bell Laboratories, the research arm of the Bell System, won seven Nobel Prizes between 1937 and 2009 for work ranging from the transistor to conceptual advances in quantum physics. Yet critics have also charged that AT&T's corporate culture suppressed innovations that might have disrupted the Bell monopoly. In the 1930s, for example, AT&T ordered Bell Labs to abandon pioneering work on magnetic tape recording for fear that it could undermine the utility of the telephone.

Telephone technology has been continually refined and improved. The earliest instruments in common use were large, wall-mounted boxes containing hand-cranked magnetos or cumbersome wet-cell batteries. Common-battery systems introduced in the 1890s allowed one central battery to supply power to all the telephones in an exchange. The "French phone," which combined mouthpiece and earpiece into one handset, became popular in the 1930s. Push-button dialing replaced rotary dials after the 1960s, and cordless telephones appeared in the 1970s.

The evolution of the network behind each telephone was even more dramatic. The first telephone switchboard was installed in New Haven, Connecticut, in 1878, allowing an operator to connect calls between 20 or so subscribers. Automatic switching, in which customers dialed their own connections, was first promoted by the independents and then adopted by the Bell System in the 1920s and 1930s. As telephone traffic grew, the challenge of switching and connecting calls grew ever larger. The transistor, developed at Bell Labs in 1947, made it possible to shift from electromechanical to fully electronic switching. Subsequent advances in electronics greatly increased the traffic the system could bear. In the 1990s, the deregulation of the telephone industry and the growing integration of telephony and the Internet brought another significant shift in telephone switching as AT&T's hierarchical switching network gave way to decentralized packet-switching techniques.

Long-distance calling became possible in the early twentieth century with the development of vacuum tubes and loading coils to boost signal strength and reduce attenuation. The first transcontinental telephone line, from New York City to San Francisco, was inaugurated in 1915. Transatlantic service using radio began in the 1920s, although it was not widely used before World War II. In the late 1950s and 1960s, Bell Labs worked with the National Aeronautics and Space Administration to develop satellite communications. Telstar 1, the first active communications satellite, was launched into orbit in 1962.

By the 1970s, legal and technological cracks had appeared in the Bell monopoly. Firms like Motorola and Microwave Communications, Inc. (MCI), developed new technologies for mobile telephony and wireless long-distance transmission, and the Federal Communications Commission proved willing to allow competition in these emerging sectors of the industry. In 1974, the Department of Justice filed a federal antitrust suit against AT&T, which led to the breakup of the Bell System in 1984.

Cell Phones and Smart Phones. The second era of competition in American telephony, from the 1980s to the early 2000s, saw growth and change as dramatic as the first. Chief among these changes was the explosion of mobile or cellular telephony. Cellular telephones transmit to and from small radio towers, each tower serving a "cell" of perhaps a few miles' radius. Handheld mobile phones appeared in the 1970s and have become more powerful and popular every decade since. In 1987 there were 1 million cell phone subscribers in the United States; in 1999, there were 100 million.

By the early 2000s, the telephone industry had reconsolidated into the hands of a few large corporations, but growth and change continued at a rapid pace. By 2004, the number of mobile telephones in the United States surpassed the number of fixed or "land-line" phones. The move to mobile was even more dramatic in other parts of the world, especially in low-income countries where the traditional telephone network was less developed. By 2012, there were four times as many mobile telephones in the world as there were fixed phones and more telephone connections than human beings on the earth. Smart phones, little handheld computers that combine speech transmission with a host of other functions, were a growing part of that large number. As lines have blurred among telephones, computers, and other devices, telephony's identity as a distinct technology may have begun to disappear, but telephones have become more ubiquitous than ever before.

[*See also* **Bell, Alexander Graham; Bell Laboratories; Computer Science; Computers, Mainframe, Mini, and Micro; Electronic Communication Devices, Mobile; Internet and World Wide Web; National Aeronautics and Space Administration; Nobel Prize in Biomedical Research; Quantum Theory; Satellites, Communications; Technology;** *and* **Telegraph.**]

BIBLIOGRAPHY

Beauchamp, Christopher. "Who Invented the Telephone? Lawyers, Patents, and the Judgments of History." *Technology and Culture* 51 (2010): 854–878. The best single source on the controversy over the telephone's invention.

Brooks, John. *Telephone: The First Hundred Years.* New York: Harper & Row, 1976. Smart, deftly written, and still valuable, although written almost entirely from the AT&T archives and AT&T's point of view.

Fagen, M. D., ed. *A History of Engineering and Science in the Bell System.* 5 vols. New York: Bell Telephone Laboratories, 1975–1985. The authoritative in-house account of the Bell System's technological evolution and innovations.

Fischer, Claude. *America Calling: A Social History of the Telephone to 1940.* Berkeley: University of California Press, 1992. A social history of telephones in use, rather than the industry or the invention. Good on the social construction of telephony by ordinary users.

John, Richard R. *Network Nation: Inventing American Telecommunications.* Cambridge, Mass.: Belknap Press of Harvard University Press, 2010. An important and exhaustively researched history of both the telegraph and the telephone. Decenters AT&T to focus on Bell operating companies in cities like Chicago and New York.

MacDougall, Robert. *The People's Telephone: The Fight for the Network in the United States and Canada.* Philadelphia: University of Pennsylvania Press, 2013. A comparative history that takes the independent movement seriously and explores the role of politics in shaping technological systems and ideas.

Robert MacDougall

TELEVISION

Inventors first proposed specific plans to transmit images using radio waves after the 1873 discovery that the electrical resistance of selenium changed when exposed to light. They constructed selenium mosaics and found that light from an object would cause each cell in a mosaic to draw a current related to the brightness of the section of the image illuminating it. The first television systems operated mechanically. Light from an image was projected onto selenium cells after first passing through small holes arranged in a spiral pattern on the face of a thin spinning disk. The resulting multiple scanning lines yielded a complete scan of the image. Charles Francis Jenkins, the most important inventor of mechanical television in the United States, gave a public demonstration of a workable system in 1925. Major electronics manufacturers, including American Telephone and Telegraph and General Electric, conducted further experiments and demonstrated their improvements, especially to the press. Government regulators authorized licenses for experimental stations transmitting programming, and the public bought a number of television sets based on the mechanical technology. But this period in the history of television was largely over by 1933, partly because of the Depression but also because the quality of the broadcasts did not live up to public expectations shaped by experiences with the cinema.

During the 1930s, research shifted to all-electronic television using cathode-ray tubes. Experimenters had earlier observed that cathode-ray discharges created fluorescence on the walls of the tube. Inventors proposed creating a scanning device using electromagnets to direct the electrons onto a fluorescent screen. A system of sequential scanning would use electron-scanning beams in the camera and the receiver. The two inventors in the United States who made some of the most important contributions to all-electronic television were Vladimir Zworykin and Philo Farnsworth.

Zworykin immigrated to the United States in 1919 from Russia, where he had worked with Boris Rosing, an electrical engineer who had conducted important research exploring the use of the cathode-ray tube for television. Zworykin initially worked with the Westinghouse Electric Company on electronic television but made most of his significant contributions while employed by the Radio Corporation of America (RCA). David Sarnoff, the head of RCA, recognized the value of his work in electronic television and appointed him director of the RCA Victor Electronic Research Laboratory in Camden, New Jersey, in

1930. During 1931 he developed a type of cathode-ray camera he called an iconoscope and then combined this invention with his earlier development of a cathode-ray receiver (using his "kinescope" tube) to create a complete all-electronic television system. His team worked to improve the system during the 1930s. After two years of field tests, Sarnoff planned to start television service to the public at the opening of the 1939 New York World's Fair ("The World of Tomorrow").

Unlike Zworykin, Farnsworth was largely self-taught. He became interested in the development of electronic television when he was a teenager and managed to find financial backing for research beginning in 1926. He also participated in a partnership for a few years with one of RCA's main rivals, Philco Radio and Television Company. Farnsworth developed his own system and by the late 1930s was interested in pursuing commercial authorization. But he also was interested in funding further research through control of patents. This strategy paid off when RCA was forced to pay a license fee for the patent on his camera tube, known as the image dissector.

In April 1941, the Federal Communications Commission (FCC), which had authority over the regulation of television, decided to authorize commercial television service using a set of standards approved by a new technical advisory group it had established, the National Television System Committee. Technical standards for such issues as the number of lines per frame and the number of frames per second were crucial for synchronizing transmitters and receivers. Although a number of television stations had started commercial operations before the Japanese attack on Pearl Harbor, during the war the government severely limited the production of television equipment.

In the postwar period, consumer demand was initially slight but TV sales took off in 1948, soon after the beginning of regular network telecasts. In 1949, 2.3 percent of homes had televisions; by 1962, 90 percent did (Sterling and Kittross, 2002, p. 864). Despite the relatively high costs of the first sets, Americans purchased televisions regardless of income. And television quickly emerged as the most popular mass medium, with more Americans spending more time watching TV than consuming any other mass medium. Television's initial popularity owed much to its convenience. For the post–World War II family, television was cost-efficient entertainment compared to movie going; parents and children could be entertained at home, without traveling to a theater or buying tickets.

The 1950s: Rise of the Networks and Introduction of Color Television. Most TV stations—over 90 percent in the 1950s and early 1960s—signed exclusive "affiliation" agreements with networks. In exchange for compensation, an affiliate agreed to carry network programming at specified hours (usually in the evening). As a result, the networks determined evening viewing, when most Americans watched television.

Two networks, Columbia Broadcasting System (CBS) and the National Broadcasting Company (NBC), initially dominated. Their large lead in radio gave them clear advantages, including show-business expertise and goodwill with their radio affiliates, many of which acquired TV licenses. Then, too, the number of TV channels was limited to 12 on the very-high-frequency (VHF) transmitting band. The FCC encouraged rival commercial and noncommercial networks by awarding channels 14 through 81 in the ultra-high-frequency (UHF) band beginning in 1952. In most markets, however, UHF could not compete with VHF outlets. By early 1956, 60 of 159 UHF channels had left the air. UHF's stark disadvantages seriously undercut educational television as well as the third commercial network, the American Broadcasting Company (ABC), which disproportionately relied on UHF channels for affiliates.

Advertisers played a powerful role in early programming. With some advertisers holding back from entering television, the position of those who did was strengthened. Typically sponsoring entire programs, they often insisted on changes in individual productions. In one instance a tobacco company ordered that the Russian villains in a Cold War drama not be shown smoking cigarettes. Commercials were frequently integrated into shows. In the middle of a program, the leads would suddenly praise (or be shown using) the sponsor's product. Yet some of TV's earliest underwriters championed more diverse programming by sponsoring dramatic and news series targeting smaller, more educated audiences. As viewership increased and advertising rates rose in the late 1950s and early 1960s, however, advertisers abandoned sole sponsorships, preferring instead to spread their investment, and the networks asserted near total control over programming and scheduling.

The earliest programming appealed to a wide range of tastes. Because the first stations were established in the largest cities, popular shows tended to reflect a big-city sensibility. This included comedy variety hours, notably one starring Milton Berle, as well as original dramas. Nearly all were aired live. As television reached smaller communities in the South and West, however, the appeal of such shows faded. Viewers preferred filmed series with a regular cast of characters who were uniformly white, usually middle class, and living in smaller cities or towns. The dominant characters were almost always male.

The major technical innovation introduced after the war was color television. CBS had tried to introduce a color system immediately before World War II, partly as a response to RCA's control of the basic patents for monochrome television. The FCC rejected this early effort but did authorize CBS's field sequential color system in 1950. RCA had tried to introduce its own color system and had the support of most other manufacturers, but when the commission ruled in favor of CBS, RCA and the other manufacturers refused to cooperate. Although RCA lost in the Supreme Court when it took legal action against the commission, the resulting delay allowed monochrome television to become more firmly entrenched. CBS was also at a disadvantage because it was not a large conglomerate with a manufacturing division. The final problem for CBS was the decision by the government in 1951, during the Korean War, to forbid the manufacture of color television equipment.

RCA used these delays to further develop its own system. In December 1953, the FCC overturned its earlier decision and ruled in favor of RCA. Accepting defeat, CBS also supported the final FCC decision authorizing RCA's color system. RCA and other manufacturers promoted color television during the 1950s and 1960s but consumers were put off by the comparatively high cost. As late as 1965, less than 6 percent of all homes had color receivers. As prices fell, however, more families purchased color televisions, and by 1972 just over half of all households owned them (Sterling and Kittross, 2002, p. 864).

The 1960s and 1970s: New Technologies and New Challenges. By the late 1950s, network programming had been standardized. Most series were produced in Southern California in assembly-line fashion, by the old film studios or companies utilizing studio facilities and talent. Reruns of popular series, "syndicated" to TV stations across the country for fees, and later to cable channels, proved popular and immensely profitable.

The development of videotape in the late 1950s profoundly affected the industry. Until then, the networks had to telecast programs live, across four continental time zones, meaning that a dramatic program aired at 9 P.M. Eastern time was telecast at 6 P.M. on the West Coast. (Affiliates could carry poor-quality "kinescope" recordings, in which motion-picture cameras photographed the images on television picture tubes.) At first, the networks used videotaping largely for time shifting, to telecast programs later in the Mountain and Pacific time zones. Over time, however, most productions were taped to correct any flaws in a telecast and at the insistence of performers, most of whom preferred not to appear live. Videotape's greatest impact may have been on TV news. Film was expensive and could take hours to develop and edit. Videotape, by comparison, provided quick and cost-efficient TV reporting.

News programs appeared on TV from the beginning, but they had almost always lost money, and the networks offered them mainly to placate federal overseers. Resources normally went into 15-minute newscasts in the early and late evenings. Gradually, however, TV news gained respect and larger audiences. In 1963, CBS and NBC expanded their nightly newscasts to 30 minutes; ABC followed in 1967. In November

1963, the networks canceled all entertainment programming for four days to cover the assassination and funeral of President John F. Kennedy. By then most critics agreed that TV news had demonstrated its potential and maturity, and surveys suggested that, for the first time, Americans ranked TV as their main source of information. More important to the networks, advertising on the evening newscasts had become a vital revenue source. Debates between the major party presidential candidates, introduced in 1960, became a quadrennial ritual beginning in 1976.

Although economics normally shaped television broadcast fare, the FCC in the 1960s took modest steps to change the industry, promoting increased competition by improving UHF reception and fostering noncommercial, educational television stations, many of which were on the upper frequency. Empowered by Congress to set standards for TV receivers, the commission ruled that all TVs sold after 1 April 1964 must be able to receive both UHF and VHF signals. Over time, this greatly expanded the total audience for the upper-frequency channels. In 1967, with the Public Broadcasting Act, Congress created the Public Broadcasting System (PBS), which displaced the old educational television network. Although chronically underfunded, PBS provided alternatives in cultural and news programming that the commercial networks had largely abandoned.

In the 1960s and 1970s, most Americans most of the time watched network programming, and network TV became more diverse. African Americans began appearing and even starring in some programs. In series like *The Mary Tyler Moore Show* and *Charlie's Angels*, women played prominent roles. The main character in the most popular sitcom of the 1970s, *All in the Family*, was a working-class bigot.

Ever eager to fill their schedules, the networks in the late 1960s began producing made-for-TV movies. This partly reflected the growing sexual explicitness of theatrical releases as well as Hollywood's overattention to younger moviegoers. Although most made-for-TV movies were forgettable, some had enormous impact. ABC's *Roots* (1977), a panoramic history of an African American family, based on a book by Alex Haley,

helped to move the network for the first time into first-place in ratings and revenues. More often, TV movies consciously appealed to women viewers, who had gained more control over viewing, particularly in homes having second TVs.

The 1970s also brought important shifts in television news. Despite pressure from the Nixon administration, CBS aggressively reported on the Watergate scandals; NBC and ABC belatedly did so as well. CBS News also scored a ratings coup in the late 1970s and 1980s with its top-rated *60 Minutes*, an hour-long collection of features and interviews dubbed a TV "*news magazine.*" For the first time, a news program successfully competed for audiences in evening prime time. Only after many misfires did imitations by ABC and NBC enjoy comparable success with the news magazine, which was much less expensive to produce than the typical hour-long entertainment series. Meanwhile, early-morning news programs— NBC's *Today* and ABC's *Good Morning, America*—became immensely profitable.

The 1980s, 1990s, and Beyond: Fragmentation of Audience, Consolidation of Ownership, and Digital.

The three-network hold over television came undone in the 1980s. Nonnetwork or independent channels, often airing reruns of network shows, became serious competitors in many larger markets. Between 1979 and 1987, the proportion of stations affiliated with a network dropped from 86 to 61 percent (Sterling and Kittross, 2002, p. 835). The Fox network, founded in 1986, lured younger viewers and advertisers. Two more networks, WB and UPN, commenced operations in the early 1990s.

The spread of cable television further undermined the networks. First developed during the 1950s and often referred to as "community antenna television," cable improved reception for viewers in rural areas of the country, especially mountainous regions. Cable companies charged customers a fee for broadcasts transmitted over coaxial cables. Developed during the 1930s at American Telephone and Telegraph's Bell Laboratories, the coaxial cable could carry multiple signals and was also used to connect broadcast stations belonging to networks. Cable burgeoned in the late 1970s and 1980s as Americans started subscribing to increase their programming choices. In many areas, subscribing to cable meant access to as many as 32 channels. By the mid-1990s, just over 60 percent of all homes had cable (Sterling and Kittross, 2002, p. 871). Channels specializing in sports, the arts, religion, and other special-interest areas added to cable's allure, as did the programming on "superstations" like Atlanta's WTBS and Chicago's WGN. With so many choices, the networks' viewership fell. Between the 1976–1977 and 1996–1997 TV seasons, the combined network share of evening prime time had dropped by a third, from 93 percent of the audience to 62 percent.

As a new delivery system, satellite communications also supported the growth of cable television. Originally developed during the 1960s for general international communications, especially telephony, communication satellites made possible for the first time live international television broadcasts. The television networks, especially ABC and PBS, took an early interest in using satellites for program distribution but the pay-cable services, notably Home Box Office, pioneered their use for domestic broadcasting. Home Box Office first used a communication satellite in 1976 (*Satcom I*) and this led to an increased demand during the 1980s from pay-cable services as well as broadcast networks. The use of satellites able to broadcast directly to special receivers located at individual homes (direct broadcast satellites) also began to expand, especially during the late 1980s. By 1988 cable services transmitted over one hundred programs using 13 separate satellites (Slotten, 2000, p. 241).

The proliferation of cable prompted a number of responses from the networks. To hold viewers, they tolerated increased sexual explicitness and violence. Spurred by Fox's appeal to younger viewers, they paid more attention to the demographic composition of audiences. Series popular with older viewers were frequently dumped in favor of sitcoms targeting younger adults.

Meanwhile, the networks and many stations underwent changes in ownership. Stations owned by individuals all but vanished in favor of group ownership. This trend was hurried along by the relaxation of long-time FCC rules on multiple ownership. In 1985–1986, new proprietors acquired all three networks. A station group, Capital Cities, purchased ABC; General Electric purchased NBC's parent company, RCA; and Laurence Tisch assumed controlling interest in CBS. Two of the networks were purchased again in 1995, when Westinghouse secured CBS and Disney bought ABC. Four years later, Viacom bought CBS.

Despite such concentration in ownership, the larger development at the end of the twentieth century and the beginning of the twenty-first century was the fragmentation of the once gargantuan television audience. Although a few programs had high ratings, the audiences for most TV series dwindled drastically. The new world of choices, combined with greater Internet use, was fragmenting society and, by distracting citizens from informational programming, weakening civic bonds.

These new developments were also connected to the introduction of digital and high-definition television. Digital technology allowed streaming, interactive television, and convergence using single media platforms. Unlike satellites and cable, which were new delivery systems, digital television was based on a new set of technical standards synchronizing digital cameras, transmitters, and receivers. The effort to develop a new standard began in the late 1980s as American government officials and television manufacturers looked for ways to halt continued Japanese dominance in electronics. When it became clear that digital television was possible, the FCC directed the conversion of the entire television industry and mandated the use of new frequencies. By the beginning of the second decade of the twenty-first century, the conversion was complete and television receivers using a high-definition standard were also widely available.

[*See also* **Bell Laboratories; Computers, Main-frame, Mini, and Micro; Electronic Communication Devices, Mobile; Engineering; Farnsworth, Philo Taylor; Film Technology; Internet and World Wide Web; Radio; Research and Development (R&D); Satellites, Communications; Solid-State Electronics; Technological Enthusiasm; Technology; Telephone;** *and* Zworykin, **Vladimir Kosma.**]

538 · TELLER, EDWARD

Abramson, Albert. *The History of Television, 1880 to 1941*. Jefferson, N.C.: McFarland, 1987.
Abramson, Albert. *Zworykin, Pioneer of Television*. Urbana: University of Illinois Press, 1995.
Barnouw, Erik. *Tube of Plenty: The Evolution of American Television*. New York: Oxford University Press, 1975.
Baughman, James L. *Republic of Mass Culture: Journalism, Filmmaking and Broadcasting in America since 1941*. 3d ed. Baltimore: Johns Hopkins University Press, 2005.
Everson, George. *The Story of Television: The Life of Philo T. Farnsworth*. New York: Arno Press, 1974.
Hilmes, Michele. *Only Connect: A Cultural History of Broadcasting in the United States*. 4th ed. Boston: Cengage Learning, 2013.
Inglis, Andrew F. *Behind the Tube: A History of Broadcasting Technology and Business*. Boston: Focal Press, 1990.
Slotten, Hugh R. *Radio and Television Regulation: Broadcast Technology in the United States, 1920–1960*. Baltimore: Johns Hopkins University Press, 2000.
Sterling, Christopher H., and John Kittross. *Stay Tuned: A Concise History of American Broadcasting*. 3d ed. Mahwah, NJ: Lawrence Erlbaum, 2002.
Udelson, Joseph H. *The Great Television Race: A History of the American Television Industry, 1925–1941*. Tuscaloosa: University of Alabama Press, 1982.
Weinstein, David. *The Forgotten Network: DuMont and the Birth of American Television*. Philadelphia: Temple University Press, 2006.

Hugh Richard Slotten and
James L. Baughman

TELLER, EDWARD

(1908–2003), theoretical physicist, coinventor of the U.S. hydrogen bomb. Born in Budapest, Hungary, Teller studied physics at the University of Leipzig under Werner Heisenberg, receiving his doctorate in 1930. He then acted as Heisenberg's postdoctoral assistant for several months before becoming an assistant to a physical chemist in Göttingen. Fleeing Germany because of Nazi persecution, Teller and his wife traveled first to Co-

penhagen, where Teller worked in Niels Bohr's Institute for Theoretical Physics. In 1935 the couple immigrated to the United States, where Teller taught at George Washington University. He became an American citizen in 1941.

As early as 1941 Teller became interested in the idea of hydrogen weapons, quickly establishing himself as a leading campaigner for fusion weapons. In 1943, Teller joined the Manhattan Project at Los Alamos, New Mexico, where the atomic bomb was being developed under the direction of the physicist J. Robert Oppenheimer. At Los Alamos, Teller worked on the hydrogen bomb (H-bomb), an even more powerful weapon. His original concept proved unworkable.

After the war, the H-bomb became a near obsession for Teller, who joined a politically conservative coalition of government and military leaders to lobby for its development. After the Soviet Union tested an atomic bomb in August 1949, President Harry S. Truman gave a green light to the H-bomb project. In early 1951, Teller and the Los Alamos mathematician Stanislaw Ulam proposed a radically different design for the H-bomb, which broke the fusion process up into stages. The H-bomb was successfully tested the following year on Enewetak Atoll in the South Pacific. Also in 1952, Teller played an important role in establishing a second weapons-design laboratory, at Livermore, California. In 1954, Teller became a pariah to many in the nation's scientific community for his testimony against Oppenheimer at the latter's security hearing. Many thought that Teller was retaliating against Oppenheimer because of his refusal to fully support a fusion program. A number of Teller's former friends and colleagues refused to work with or even speak to him from then on.

Teller continued to have powerful allies in the military and the civilian government. As director of the Livermore laboratory from 1958 to 1960 and an outside advocate long after, Teller lobbied for causes he believed in. These included opposition to a nuclear test-ban treaty and support for the civilian nuclear-power industry. In 1983, as a member of the White House Science Council, Teller played a key role in President Ronald Reagan's Strategic Defense Initiative, which envisioned a space-based defense against missile attack.

[*See also* **Atomic Energy Commission; Manhattan Project; Military, Science and Technology and the; Nuclear Power; Nuclear Weapons; Oppenheimer, J. Robert; Physics; Science; Space Program;** *and* **Strategic Defense Initiative.**]

BIBLIOGRAPHY

Blumberg, Stanley A., and Louis G. Panos. *Edward Teller: Giant of the Golden Age of Physics.* New York: Charles Scribner's Sons, 1990.

Broad, William J. *Teller's War: The Top-Secret Story behind the Star Wars Deception.* New York: Simon and Schuster, 1992.

Goodchild, Peter. *Edward Teller: The Real Dr. Strangelove.* Cambridge, Mass.: Harvard University Press, 2004. Excellent biography provides insights into Teller and his peers as well as the intersection of science and technology with policy.

Mullet, Shawn. "Teller, Edward." In *Complete Dictionary of Scientific Biography.* Vol. 25, pp. 20–25. Detroit: Charles Scribner's Sons, 2008.

Gregg Herken;
updated by Elspeth Knewstubb

TENNESSEE VALLEY AUTHORITY

Established in May 1933 during the frenzied first one hundred days of the New Deal, the Tennessee Valley Authority (TVA) sought to revitalize one of America's poorest regions. At the time, the farms and small towns in the seven states that bordered the nearly impassable Tennessee River and its tributaries presented a bleak checkerboard of weather-beaten shacks lacking electricity, crumbling churches, and one-room schools.

President Franklin Delano Roosevelt was not the first public official who sought to harness the Tennessee River's power and address the valley's crippling poverty, but his vision surpassed anything previously imagined. Proposing the TVA to Congress, Roosevelt declared: "It is time [for] national planning for a complete river watershed involving many States and the future lives and welfare of millions." Under agency heads Arthur E. Morgan (1878–1976) and then the Chicago lawyer David

E. Lilienthal (1899–1981), the TVA built 16 dams to prevent spring floods and limit soil erosion, supplied the valley with cheap electricity and recreational facilities, provided farmers with inexpensive fertilizer, and established a model community of neatly placed modern homes. Like most TVA programs and, indeed, most New Deal programs, this model community was racially segregated. Indeed, the TVA's insistence on local control, or "grassroots democracy," meant that discriminatory political and social structures often remained in place, even while the agency fought to eradicate poverty.

For supporters and critics, TVA symbolized the best and worst of the New Deal. Roosevelt's opponents saw it as a frightening instance of government excess; some even denounced it as "creeping socialism." New Dealers, however, pointed to the project as a shining example of government action at its best. For the first time, thanks to TVA, recalled one enthusiast, "the poor and dispossessed of America could imagine a new kind of world, a life based on brotherhood and mutuality." A particularly strong supporter was Senator George W. Norris (1861–1944) of Nebraska, a long-time advocate of public power development. TVA's massive Norris Dam near Knoxville was named in his honor.

The TVA's legacy proved mixed. Within a decade the agency transformed an unpredictable river into a manageable waterway providing vast amounts of hydroelectric power to thousands of isolated rural homes. Malaria, once endemic in the area, was virtually eliminated. The TVA's accomplishments, moreover, eventually including nuclear power, laid the groundwork for industrial development and economic expansion in the Tennessee Valley. But that progress did not end economic inequities or racism or redistribute political power. The TVA survived into the twenty-first century, its spectacular dams a major tourist destination. But it survived simply as another big power company, no longer as a model of visionary government planning.

[*See also* **Agricultural Technology; Dams and Hydraulic Engineering; Electricity and Electrification; Hydroelectric Power; Malaria; Nuclear Power;** *and* **Rivers as Technological Systems.**]

BIBLIOGRAPHY

Hargrove, Erwin C., and Paul K. Conkin, eds. *TVA: Fifty Years of Grassroots Bureaucracy.* Urbana: University of Illinois Press, 1983.

Hubbard, Preston J. *Origins of the TVA: The Muscle Shoals Controversy, 1920–1932.* Tuscaloosa: University of Alabama Press, 2005.

McCraw, Thomas. *TVA and the Power Fight, 1933–1939.* Philadelphia: Lippincott, 1971.

Bryant Simon

TERMAN, FREDERICK E.

(1900–1982), electrical engineer, best known for his pioneering efforts to integrate technical industries with university research. As the dean of engineering at Stanford University, he was instrumental in making the university a model for successful university–industry relationships. He is also considered one of the founders of Silicon Valley.

Terman was born in Indiana but moved with his family at the age of 10 to Stanford, where his father, the creator of the Stanford–Binet IQ test, became a prominent professor of psychology. He studied under Vannevar Bush at MIT and received his doctorate in electrical engineering in 1924.

Terman began teaching at Stanford in 1925 and was influential in the career development of notable students including William Hewlett and David Packard, the founders of the Hewlett–Packard Company. He wrote what would become one of the basic texts in electrical engineering, *Radio Engineering,* which was noted for its attention to the practical needs of contemporary radio engineers, and published many other widely used textbooks. He was a founding member of the National Academy of Engineering and was awarded the Presidential Medal of Merit for his work during World War II in radar countermeasures, when he was the director of the Radio Research Laboratory at Harvard University.

Terman was appointed dean of engineering at Stanford after the war. Taking advantage of the many contacts he had developed through his prior wartime and academic work, he sought to bring the academic and industrial worlds closer together. To further this aim, he established the Stanford Industrial Park (later known as Stanford Research Park) in 1951, which allowed technology companies like Hewlett–Packard, General Electric, and Eastman Kodak to lease land next to the university. He also encouraged graduate students to find employment there and use these firms as a source of ideas for their research. After being appointed provost in 1955, Terman worked to develop the university's departments outside of the engineering school by encouraging links with government research agencies. He thus played a central role in bolstering Stanford's position as a premier research institution with close relationships to industry and government.

[*See also* **Bush, Vannevar; Engineering; Higher Education and Science; Military, Science and Technology and the; Research and Development (R&D);** *and* **Silicon Valley.**]

BIBLIOGRAPHY

"Frederick Terman." http://www.ieeeghn.org/wiki/index.php/Frederick_Terman (accessed 3 April 2012).

Saxon, Wolfgang. "Frederick Emmons Terman, Stanford Engineer, Dies at 82." *New York Times,* 21 December 1982, p. D23.

Villard, O. G. Jr. "Frederick Emmons Terman: June 7, 1900–December 19, 1982." http://www.smecc.org/frederick_terman.htm (accessed 3 April 2012).

Eric Rouge and David Alan Grier

TESLA, NIKOLA

(1856–1943), electrical engineer and inventor. Nikola Tesla was the eccentric inventor of the polyphase alternating-current (AC) motor and the polyphase AC power distribution system, as well as many other electricity, X-ray, radio, and radio-control devices. Tesla was born on 10 July 1856 to Serbian parents in the town of Smiljan, which was then part of the Austro-Hungarian Empire but is now part of Croatia. Tesla had a sickly childhood and a difficult relationship with his father, who negatively compared Tesla to his older brother, who was killed in an accident.

Tesla studied engineering in Graz and Prague, then worked at a telegraph office and later at an electrical component manufacturer in Budapest. While in Budapest in 1882, Tesla conceived of the idea of reversing the traditional motor design by placing the magnets on the rotor and the windings on the stator, creating the brushless-polyphase AC motor. Later the same year, Tesla accepted a position in Paris with a manufacturer of lighting systems under patent-license from Edison. Tesla's intelligence quickly brought him to the attention of Charles Batchelor, the manager of the company, who suggested that Tesla go to the United States to work at the Edison Machine Works in New York City. Tesla did this in 1884 but quit after only six months.

Remaining in the United States, Tesla teamed with two partners to patent Tesla's AC motor and power distribution system. The group received the patents in 1888. Tesla was a skillful inventor at this time, but unlike his contemporaries Thomas Edison, Elihu Thomson, and George Westinghouse, Tesla was not also a good entrepreneur, nor was he interested in being one. Instead, Tesla and his partners sold their patents in the same year they received them to George Westinghouse for $75,000, plus royalties.

In 1893, Tesla's two-phase AC motor was demonstrated in grandiose fashion at the World's Columbian Exposition in Chicago. In the same year, Tesla played a key role in getting his two-phase AC power distribution system selected for the Niagara Falls hydroelectric project. Both of these demonstrations were crucial to the selection of alternating current as today's standard for power distribution.

At this time, Tesla was at the height of his career and he enjoyed hobnobbing among Manhattan's high society, living at the Waldorf-Astoria Hotel, and holding court at Delmonico's Restaurant. In 1898, however, Tesla began making increasingly fantastic claims about his imminent inventions, yet he delivered few results, and his reputation in the technical community declined. In 1901, Tesla built a laboratory in Rhode Island called Wardenclyffe, where he tried to develop a system for wireless power distribution, which he believed would usher in a worldwide technological utopia. In 1905, with success eluding him, Tesla suffered a nervous breakdown.

Tesla lived the remainder of his life on two small pensions and the proceeds from a few remaining patents. He died in New York City on 7 January 1943. Tesla was awarded over one hundred U.S. patents, became a U.S. citizen in 1891, and received the Edison Medal in 1917. He never married. In 1960 the unit of magnetic flux density in the International System of Units was named the *Tesla*.

[*See also* **Electricity and Electrification; Physics;** *and* **Radio.**]

BIBLIOGRAPHY

Carlson, W. Bernard. *Tesla: Inventor of the Electrical Age*. Princeton, N.J.: Princeton University Press, 2013.

Martin, Thomas Commerford. *The Inventions, Researches, and Writings of Nikola Tesla*. 1894. Reprint, New York: Barnes & Noble, 1993.

Tesla, Nikola. *My Inventions*. 1919. Reprinted with editing and introduction by Ben Johnson. New York: Barnes & Noble, 1982.

Daniel M. Robert

THREE MILE ISLAND ACCIDENT

Accident at a nuclear power–generating station on the Susquehanna River near Harrisburg, Pennsylvania. Three Mile Island first attracted national attention—and precipitated a crisis for commercial nuclear power in the United States—on 28 March 1979, when a valve for regulating the flow of cooling water to a reactor closed. The malfunctioning of this valve led to a series of mechanical failures and human mistakes that threatened the surrounding area with radioactive contamination. Uncertain about how much radiation had been or would be released beyond the building, experts recommended that children and pregnant women leave the area. On 30 March, amid a glare of worldwide publicity, the governor of Pennsylvania ordered such an evacuation, although by that time engineers had stabilized the reactor. President Jimmy Carter, wearing protective garb, toured the plant.

The Three Mile Island accident jolted the nuclear-power industry. Utilities shelved plans to build new plants and shut down some already in operation. An anti–nuclear power movement, already under way, gained momentum. The Nuclear Regulatory Commission, the federal oversight body, moved aggressively to improve safety in all nuclear plants. The accident also affected research and scholarship. Earlier, engineering studies on reactor safety had typically sought to estimate the likelihood and health impact of specific mishaps. Subsequently, the research explored the interplay of multiple failures and the effect of procedures and training programs on operators' performance. More than a cataclysm for an industry, the Three Mile Island accident also illuminated larger issues on the technological, social, and ideological horizon.

[*See also* **Engineering; Nuclear Power; Nuclear Regulatory Commission;** *and* **Technology.**]

BIBLIOGRAPHY

Campbell, John L. *Collapse of an Industry: Nuclear Power and the Contradictions of U.S. Policy*. Ithaca, N.Y.: Cornell University Press, 1988.
Perrow, Charles. *Normal Accidents: Living with High-Risk Technologies*. New York: Basic Books, 1984.
Walker, J. Walter. *Three Mile Island: A Nuclear Crisis in Historical Perspective*. Berkeley: University of California Press, 2006.

Cora Bagley Marrett

TOWNES, CHARLES H.

(1915–), winner of the 1964 Nobel Prize for Physics and advocate for the convergence of science and religion, was born in Greenville, South Carolina. The fourth child of attorney Henry Keith Townes and Ellen (Hard) Townes, he grew up with two brothers and three sisters, attending a Baptist church. He married Frances H. Brown in 1941. They have four daughters.

Townes graduated summa cum laude from Furman College in 1935 with bachelor's degrees in modern languages and physics, receiving a master's degree in physics from Duke University the following year. He received a Ph.D. from California Institute of Technology in 1939, writing his dissertation under William R. Smythe. He then worked at Bell Labs rather than pursue an academic position during the Depression. Townes remained at Bell Labs through World War II working on radar bombing systems.

In 1948 Townes accepted a position at Columbia University, where he continued research developing the new field of quantum electronics and in particular seeking new methods for propagating shorter-millimeter waves. In what he describes as a "revelation" in 1951, Townes realized that microwaves could be propagated through stimulated emission in a stream of energized ammonia. This led to the invention of the ammonia maser by Townes, James P. Gordon, and Herbert J. Zeiger in 1953. In 1955 Townes and his brother-in-law, Arthur L. Schawlow, showed theoretically that masers or "lasers" could operate in optical and infrared regions. The 1964 Nobel Prize in Physics was awarded jointly to Townes and Russian scientists Nikolay Basov and Aleksandr Prokhorov for their contributions to the development of masers and lasers.

While at Columbia, Townes held a Guggenheim Fellowship and later a Fulbright Lectureship at the University of Paris and University of Tokyo in 1955 and 1956. He became vice president and director of research at the Institute for Defense Analysis in 1959 and moved from Columbia to the Massachusetts Institute of Technology (MIT) in 1961 and to the University of California, Berkeley, in 1967. There he has focused on applications of quantum electronics to astrophysics.

Describing himself as a progressive Protestant, Townes argued in several papers and interviews since 1966 that science and religion are on convergent paths; he received the 2005 Templeton Prize for his contributions to science and religion.

[*See also* **Astronomy and Astrophysics; Bell Laboratories; Military, Science and Technology** and the; Nobel Prize in Biomedical Research; Physics; Quantum Theory; *and* Religion and Science.]

BIBLIOGRAPHY

"Charles H. Townes." Interview by Finn Aaserud, Niels Bohr Library & Archives, College Park, Md., 20 and 21 May 1987. http://www.aip.org/history/ohilist/4918.html (accessed 3 April 2012).

Charles Hard Townes, a Life in Physics: Bell Telephone Laboratories and World War II, Columbia University and the Laser, MIT and Government Service, California and Research in Astrophysics. An oral history conducted in 1991–1992 by Suzanne B. Riess, Regional Oral History Office, Bancroft Library, University of California, Berkeley, 1994.

Overbye, Dennis. "Physicist Is Awarded the Templeton Prize in Spiritual Matters." *New York Times* 10 March 2005. http://www.nytimes.com/2005/03/10/science/10prize.html (accessed 3 April 2012).

Orville R. Butler

TRANSISTOR

See Solid-State Electronics.

TROLLEY AND TRAMS

See Urban Mass Transit.

TUBERCULOSIS

Tuberculosis (TB) is a highly contagious disease caused by several different mycobacteria, usually *Mycobacterium tuberculosis.* Tuberculosis, also called phthisis or consumption, has been described as a leading cause of death since ancient times. The bacterium usually infects the lungs, but can also affect any part of the body such as the kidney, spine, and brain. If not properly treated, the disease can be fatal.

Prior to the discovery of the TB bacillus in 1882, some medical experts suggested that the disease was hereditary since it seemed to run in families. Others argued that, because tuberculosis was most prevalent among the urban poor, the disease was caused by environmental conditions such as poor diet, pollution, and bad habits.

The TB mycobacterium was first identified and described in 1882 by the German physician Robert Koch, who won the Nobel Prize in Physiology or Medicine in 1905 for his work on this disease. Koch also argued that a glycerin extract of the bacillus, which he called tuberculin, could be used to cure the disease. Koch's claims proved incorrect but tuberculin was later used to diagnose latent forms of the disease in asymptomatic patients.

TB mortality declined dramatically during the nineteenth and early twentieth centuries as a result of a variety of public-health measures. During the period from 1900 to 1920, most of the prevention efforts focused on the poor, since epidemiologic evidence demonstrated that tuberculosis took a greater toll on this group because of inadequate food, housing, and health care. This focus on TB as an affliction of the downtrodden served to justify Progressive-Era social policies aimed at improving the living conditions of the poor and thereby enhancing their resistance to the disease.

The National Tuberculosis Association (NTA) was a leader in these Progressive-Era reform efforts. Founded in 1904 as the National Society for the Study and Prevention of Tuberculosis, it served to unite the various physicians, nurses, social workers, and local public-health organizations interested in containing the dread disease. The NTA mounted exhibitions, published pamphlets and journals for lay audiences, and helped establish dispensaries and visiting nurse services for the poor that were designed to detect and treat the disease in its early stages. The NTA also supported broader programs of social reform to alleviate conditions of the poor, such as malnutrition and crowded, badly ventilated tenement housing that allowed tuberculosis to spread and flourish.

Until the mid-twentieth century, tuberculosis was difficult to treat. Physicians in the late nineteenth and early twentieth centuries advocated the sanatorium treatment developed by Dr. Edward Livingston Trudeau at the Adirondack Cottage Sanatorium at Saranac Lake, New York, in 1884. This treatment regime consisted of a good diet, regular exercise, and long periods of bed rest in sleeping porches open to the fresh air. Physicians believed that these strict regulations of patient behavior would cause the disease to go into remission and restore the patient to health.

The idea that environment could help treat tuberculosis led to the construction of sanatoria throughout the country. These institutions became especially numerous in the southwest, which was believed to have an especially favorable climate for tuberculosis patients. Civic leaders in cities and towns throughout the region competed for patients seeking the cure by proclaiming the healthful benefits of year-round sunshine and clean air. I. M. Holt of San Bernardino County declared that Southern California was "Nature's Great Sanitarium." The journal *Land of Sunshine*, published by boosters in Los Angeles, billed the city as a health resort that was especially beneficial to those with "lung troubles." The first sanatoria in the region served affluent patients, but by the late nineteenth century, public-health officials argued that the poor also deserved the promise of health these institutions offered. Creating low- or no-cost sanatoria would also isolate tubercular individuals from the rest of the population and help stem the spread of the disease.

The French physicians Albert Calmette and Camille Guérin developed the first vaccine for TB in 1906 using an attenuated form of the bovine strain of the disease. The vaccine was first used in humans in France in 1921 and was soon adopted in countries around the world, except for the United States, where concerns about vaccine safety inhibited widespread use of the vaccine. Instead, campaigns against TB in the United States relied primarily on other public-health measures to prevent the disease. An especially popular strategy was the preventorium, which was designed to remove "at-risk" children from impoverished homes in the hopes that they could avoid developing the disease. Like other "child-saving"

reformers of this era, those who supported preventoria believed that removing sickly children from their families—especially poor, immigrant families—was the best way to restore them to health. By the late 1920s, there were 45 preventoria with 2,783 beds throughout the United States.

The removal of patients with active tuberculosis from the general population had a significant impact on mortality rates. The death rate fell from 1 of 4 individuals with the disease in the mid-nineteenth century to 121 per 100,000 by the early 1900s. Yet it was widely recognized that much work still needed to be done to control the disease. Illness and death still remained relatively high among women, the poor, and racial minorities, and the treatment options remained few.

Furthermore, during the early 1900s the work of Edward Livingston Trudeau and Clemens von Pirquet on the diagnostic utility of tuberculin revealed that individuals who were not clinically tubercular nevertheless could test positive for the disease. Pirquet found that up to 90 percent of the population tested positive by the age of 14; impoverished and minority communities showed the highest rates of infection, but a surprisingly large number of positive reactors were found among the middle class.

These findings created confusion among physicians and public-health workers. What was most confounding was the fact that although a high percentage of the population reacted positively to tuberculin, only a small portion of those infected actually became ill. Physicians used the metaphor of "seed and soil" to explain why some individuals developed the disease whereas others did not. Drawing on concepts of human heredity, they argued that certain individuals were genetically more likely to succumb to the TB "germ." Yet they also argued that proper diet, adequate rest, fresh air, and other environmental improvements would improve the constitution of the individual and provide a poor "soil" for the "seed" of tuberculosis to grow.

Public-health experts realized that the sanatorium was at best a limited strategy for combating the disease, since these institutions could accommodate only a small number of tubercular individuals. By the early twentieth century, cities like Los Angeles eventually found themselves overrun with large numbers of seriously ill tuberculosis patients, many of them destitute and too ill to hold down paying jobs. Eventually, the cost of running publicly funded sanatoria became prohibitive, especially during the economic crisis of the Great Depression. Instead of welcoming tuberculosis sufferers as a potential source of revenue, cities in the southwest passed laws that prohibited the migration of individuals with active cases of the disease to the state, especially if they were unable to support themselves. Because of racial prejudice that associated immigrants with dirt and disease, Mexican and Filipino immigrants were the prime targets for these policies of exclusion.

Tuberculosis prevention programs also included educating the public to avoid behaviors that spread the disease from person to person. The NTA focused many of its educational programs on children because they were easily accessible through the public schools. Immigrant children could also be used as agents of "Americanization," who would educate other members of their family in disease prevention. During the 1910s, the NTA began a program of health instruction in the public schools that enlisted children in a "modern health crusade" against tuberculosis. Children participated in the "battle" by buying and selling Easter Seals; by performing "health chores," such as brushing teeth, getting adequate sleep, and eating nourishing food; and by participating in health pageants that demonstrated the habits conducive to good health. The NTA designed instructional booklets with children's interests in mind, employing cartoon characters such as "Tommy Tubercle" and "Huber the Tuber" to engage their attention. This "crusade" spread quickly through the public schools, and by 1920 the NTA estimated that more than 3 million children were enrolled in the program.

Information about tuberculosis prevention was also disseminated through home economics programs in schools, colleges, settlement houses, and county extension services. Home economists argued that dust was a major source of TB infection and convinced middle-class women to eliminate heavy draperies, elaborately carved furniture, and other trappings of the Victorian home to reduce the accumulation of germ-laden dust. These concepts were also spread to lower-class, immigrant, and African American women, who were persuaded that by adopting middle-class standards of cleanliness, they could prevent disease and death.

There was no definitive cure for tuberculosis until the discovery of the antibiotic streptomycin, developed by Selman Waksman in 1943. Starting in the 1950s, combination treatment with the antibacterial agents isoniazid and para-aminosalicylic acid became the most common treatment for the disease in the United States.

The incidence of tuberculosis remained low until the 1980s, when the disease reemerged as a public-health threat in conjunction with the epidemic of acquired immunodeficiency syndrome. At the same time, multi-drug-resistant strains of tuberculosis have appeared, making the disease more difficult to treat. In 1993, the World Health Organization declared that TB was a global health emergency. According to the World Health Organization, in the early twenty-first century, there were 8 million new cases of tuberculosis each year and close to 2 million deaths. Because the disease is especially prevalent in the developing world, the resurgence of tuberculosis has reawakened social prejudices that equate immigrants with infection.

[*See also* Disease; Germ Theory of Disease; HIV/AIDS; Medicine; *and* Public Health.]

BIBLIOGRAPHY

Abel, Emily K. *Tuberculosis and the Politics of Exclusion: A History of Public Health and Migration to Los Angeles.* New Brunswick, N.J.: Rutgers University Press, 2007.

Bates, Barbara. *Bargaining for Life: A Social History of Tuberculosis, 1876–1938.* Philadelphia: University of Pennsylvania Press, 1992.

Connolly, Cynthia A. *Saving Sickly Children: The Tuberculosis Preventorium in American Life, 1909–1970.* New Brunswick, N.J.: Rutgers University Press, 2008.

Feldberg, Georgina D. *Disease and Class: Tuberculosis and the Shaping of Modern North American Society.* New Brunswick, N.J.: Rutgers University Press, 1995.

Lerner, Barron H. *Contagion and Confinement: Controlling Tuberculosis along the Skid Road.* Baltimore: Johns Hopkins University Press, 1998.

Ott, Katherine. *Fevered Lives: Tuberculosis in American Culture since 1870.* Cambridge, Mass.: Harvard University Press, 1996.

Rothman, Sheila M. *Living in the Shadow of Death: Tuberculosis and the Social Experience of Illness in America.* New York: Basic Books, 1994.

Shryock, Richard Harrison. *National Tuberculosis Association, 1904–1954: A Study of the Voluntary Health Movement in the United States.* New York: Arno Press, 1977.

Wilson, Leonard G. "The Rise and Fall of Tuberculosis in Minnesota: The Role of Infection." *Bulletin of the History of Medicine* 66 (1992): 16–52.

Heather Munro Prescott

TUSKEGEE SYPHILIS STUDY

From 1932 to 1972, the U.S. Public Health Service (PHS) sponsored and ran the nation's longest-running deceptive public-health experiment in and around Tuskegee, in Macon County, Alabama, in which hundreds of African American men were observed, but not intentionally treated, for their disease. The PHS did not give the men syphilis, as it is often rumored, but watched them over the decades and led them to believe they were being treated. The study was conducted with the cooperation of the Tuskegee Institute and the public-health departments of Macon County and the state of Alabama, but without the consent of the men who were told they were being treated. It ended only after a media exposé in 1972 prompted a national outcry. Controversy stemming from the experiment, known primarily as the Tuskegee Syphilis Study, prompted major reforms in medical research protections and a formal apology to the program's unwitting participants by President Bill Clinton in 1997.

Syphilis is primarily a sexually transmitted disease caused by a microscopic spirochete (a type of bacteria) that is transmitted through sexual contact or from mothers to children at birth. It is most infectious in its early stage, when sores called chancres appear. In the second stage, infected individuals often experience painful rashes, sores, and swellings. Left untreated, the disease goes into a third, usually not infectious, latent stage. Syphilis does not go away, but it can stay dormant for years or even decades. It can cause complications that can affect major organs, such as the heart or brain, in about two-thirds of cases. Debility, insanity, and death are often, but not always, the consequences.

When the study began, syphilis sufferers were usually treated with a combination of heavy metals, neo-arsephenamine, bismuth, and mercury, in individualized regimens that often lasted more than a year. Research conducted by physicians in urban clinics appeared to suggest differences in both the nature and the extent of the disease among whites and African Americans, although there was no biological basis for the differences. Many physicians assumed, inaccurately, that whites with syphilis were more likely to suffer from neurological symptoms and that blacks were more likely to suffer from cardiovascular complications, a conclusion based partly on faulty understandings of the disease process and a priori beliefs. Widely held assumptions regarding biological differences between blacks and whites also influenced the thinking of researchers during the Jim Crow era.

In 1929, with funding from the Julius Rosenwald Fund (a private philanthropic organization that had funded schools for African Americans throughout the South), the PHS began a project in six southern counties, including Macon County in Alabama, to survey and treat black men and women with syphilis. Using the somewhat inaccurate blood tests of the day, researchers in Macon County found a 39.8 percent infection rate among the 3,684 black men and women tested. Through a combination of philanthropic and public funds, nearly 1,400 of those people began treatment for their disease (Reverby, 2009, p. 36). Pleased by the results, the PHS now had both a model for studies of the prevalence of disease and a way to develop a rural treatment program. As the Great Depression deepened in early 1931, however, neither the PHS nor the Rosenwald Fund was able to continue funding.

A New Study Begins. These studies raised another question. The country's leading syphilis experts were puzzled as to why some patients did well with little or no treatment in the latent stages, whereas others did not. PHS officials expressed concerns about this phenomenon to public-health officials in Alabama, Macon County, and the Tuskegee Institute and outlined a short-term program of minimal treatment for a select group of black men who were assumed to be in the third, or latent, stage. PHS officials anticipated that the findings might indicate that treatment at certain stages of syphilis was unnecessary. PHS officers saw in this turn of events an opportunity for what is called a "study in nature" of untreated syphilis. That is, they assumed in this case that it would be "natural" for poor African Americans not to be treated.

The PHS selected only male subjects because it was easier for them to give a history of the visible sores and out of concern that pregnant women could possibly pass the disease on to their children. With the help of a Tuskegee Institute nurse, Eunice Rivers, officials set about finding subjects and controls (those without the disease) in Macon and surrounding counties. Advertisement by word of mouth, in churches, in schools, and through employers brought the men to be tested and then to the Tuskegee Institute's hospital and the county health department for further examinations. The study began, as had the Rosenwald program, with treatment. As the number of individuals showing up for treatment rose, however, costs began to skyrocket, putting the entire plan in jeopardy. In response, PHS physicians Taliferro Clark, Raymond Vonderlehr, and O. C. Wenger decided to shift their focus to a study of *untreated* syphilis, modeled on a retrospective study of white men in Oslo, Norway, done on early syphilis when mercury was the only treatment.

The PHS selected 427 men assumed to have the disease and 185 controls without it, plus 12 controls who were switched to the syphilitic arm when they tested positive for it, for a total of 624 participants (Reverby, 2009, p. 258). As was often typical for medical studies at the time, there was no informed consent. The men were led to believe that the rubs, tonics, and aspirins given them were treatments for their "bad blood," the general term used in many communities for syphilis. Even the painful spinal taps were explained, not as a diagnostic procedure (to check for neurological syphilis), but as a "back shot" and a form of treatment. PHS physicians realized that the best scientific data would come from autopsies showing how much damage the disease had done to the men's bodies, so they arranged for Rivers to offer $50 (funded by the Milbank Foundation) to participating families in exchange for autopsy agreements prior to burial. Local doctors were asked to withhold treatment from the men, although whether they always complied is uncertain. Rivers also provided food and clothing to the men and their families and referrals for medical care for other illnesses.

The Study Continues.   In the ensuing decades, the study took on a life of its own. Generations of PHS doctors came through Tuskegee to examine the men and participate in the study. The Alabama and Macon County health departments ignored the study's violations of state law requiring the reporting and treatment of syphilis as a sexually transmitted disease (then called a venereal disease, or VD). The men's medical records, now open to the public and available in the Southeast Regional National Archives in Morrow, Georgia, do not make it clear whether all the wives, children, and other sexual partners of the men were offered treatment. When the study ended, the government agreed to treat any of the wives and children who tested positive without determining how they became infected. In the end the government found 22 wives, 17 children, and 2 grandchildren who had syphilis (Reverby, 2009, p. 131).

The study was never really invisible. Between 1936 and 1973, researchers published 13 reports in medical journals, although sometimes the men were referred to as "volunteers." As more and more participants died, the statistics provided a clear message: untreated syphilis had shortened their lives and caused many, but not all, of their deaths. Even with such dramatic findings, the study continued.

During World War II, the PHS, with the help of Macon County health officer Dr. Murray Smith, made sure that none of the study's subjects was drafted. Had they been, their syphilis would have been detected and treated. When penicillin became widely available in the late 1940s as an effective cure for the disease, the PHS did not make this available nor individually assess whether the drug might help those already in the last stages of the disease. Physicians debated well into the 1950s whether penicillin would help those with the latent disease, and in some cases it could have proven harmful. The PHS, however, did not make individual assessments. Some men did receive penicillin from other health-care providers in the 1950s, probably to treat other illnesses. In the end, the study really became one of undertreated, rather than untreated, syphilis.

When PHS researchers published reports on the study or gave lectures at medical meetings, physicians occasionally questioned the ethics of the study. Their concerns were brushed away by the PHS doctors, who asserted that they were doing critical public-health work. Other concerns about the study expressed within the PHS were brushed aside. Even after knowledge of the Nazi war experiments on prisoners was denounced, the work in Tuskegee was seen as normative.

In 1966, Peter Buxtun, who was tracking sexually transmitted disease cases for the San Francisco Health Department, heard about the study from a colleague during a coffee break. Buxtun thought it was outrageous. He was trying to get people into treatment and the PHS was keeping others from it. He requested copies of the PHS reports and began a campaign, at first through government channels, to end the study. Stonewalled at every turn, Buxtun finally gave his information to Associated Press reporter Edith Lederer. Because Lederer was too junior at the time to write up what appeared to be a big story, her editor gave the information to veteran reporter Jean Heller. The report published first in the *Washington Star* on 26 July 1972 began to make news everywhere.

From History to Metaphor for Scientific Arrogance and Racism. The outcry that followed was international in scope. The story broke at a time when other deadly and unethical medical experiments were becoming more widely known, and it dropped a bombshell in the medical research world. Additionally, withholding treat-

ment from black men in such an important black community fueled the outrage that had come to a head in the recent civil rights struggle. Famed civil rights attorney Fred D. Gray of Tuskegee and Montgomery sued the PHS and Alabama on behalf of the men and their survivors in a case that settled out of court for $10 million and medical care for the families. A federal commission criticized the study, Senate hearings had Gray and four of the survivors testify, and extensive newspaper coverage led to widespread condemnation of the study. Reverberations from the outcry pushed forward the establishment of institutional review boards for the approval of research studies, with strict guidelines about informing participants about the purposes and potential consequences of taking part in such studies. No one was ever prosecuted for the crimes committed during the study of violating the Alabama state law on reporting disease or what might have been construed as intentionally causing deaths.

The study officially ended in 1973, the last man died in 2004, and the last of the men's wives died in 2009, but the impact continues. Tuskegee is often cited as the reason why many African Americans avoid medical care or refuse to participate in clinical trials, although it is clearly part of a long history of mistrust. More sophisticated research suggests it is not knowledge of the study that keeps African Americans from participation, but often access to and knowledge of clinical trials. The study is taught as a major example in bioethics of what not to do in research and was fictionalized in an HBO movie, "Miss Evers' Boys." An outcome of the federal apology in 1997 was the creation of a national bioethics center at Tuskegee University. The racism and scientific arrogance that underlay the study's rationale has continued to inform the use of human subjects in trials in the fields of health care and scientific investigation.

[*See also* **Ethics and Medicine; Gender and Science; Medicine; Penicillin; Pharmacology and Drug Therapy; Public Health; Public Health Service, U.S.; Race and Medicine; Research and Development (R&D);** *and* **Sexually Transmitted Diseases.**]

BIBLIOGRAPHY

Gray, Fred D. *The Tuskegee Syphilis Study*. Montgomery, Ala.: Black Belt Press, 1998.

Jones, James H. *Bad Blood*, revised ed. New York: Free Press, 1993.

Katz, Ralph, and Rueben Warren, eds. *The Search for the Legacy of the U.S. Public Health Service Syphilis Study at Tuskegee*. Lanham, Md.: Lexington Books, 2011.

Reverby, Susan M., ed. *Examining Tuskegee: The Infamous Syphilis Study and Its Legacy*. Chapel Hill: University of North Carolina Press, 2009.

Susan M. Reverby

TYPHOID FEVER

Typhoid fever is an infectious disease caused by the bacterium *Salmonella typhi* and spread by fecal contamination of food or water. When sanitary conditions are poor, insects may pick up the pathogen from open sewage and deposit it on food. Typhoid is characterized by fever, abdominal pain, diarrhea, and, in some patients, "rose spots" on the abdomen and chest. Untreated case mortality can be as high as 30 percent but in most outbreaks is considerably lower. With antibiotics, recovery may take as little as three or four days and the ultimate outcome is likely to be good. During the early twenty-first century, the Centers for Disease Control and Prevention encouraged U.S. residents to be vaccinated if they planned to travel to areas where typhoid is present. Immunization is not always completely effective and at-risk travelers are particularly advised to take care in what they eat and drink. Experimentation with an oral live vaccine was underway in 2011 and appeared promising. Typhoid has symptoms in common with other diseases, and only in the 1830s was it distinguished from typhus. Historians credit William Wood Gerhard of Philadelphia with having established typhoid as a specific disease in 1837.

The disease has probably been present in North America since the early seventeenth century, when an outbreak believed to be typhoid virtually depopulated Jamestown, Virginia. Nineteenth-century epidemiological studies in the United States consistently confirmed the 1859 British findings that typhoid is waterborne; and years before German bacteriologists identified the pathogen in the 1880s, the experience of American cities strongly suggested that water filtration reduced typhoid incidence.

Typhoid, Sanitary Reform, and the Healthy Carrier. Typhoid decimated army camps during the Civil War and posed serious problems to civilian populations during the war and the following decades. Between the 1870s and about 1920, large-scale public works and sanitary measures drastically reduced typhoid incidence and mortality. Businesses, notably railroads, acted to control typhoid through sanitary measures and vaccination.

In the 1890s, William Osler demonstrated how to differentiate between typhoid and malaria by clinical examination. Nonetheless, American doctors in the Spanish–American War frequently misdiagnosed typhoid and treated it with quinine (helpful in cases of malaria, but useless against typhoid). A commission headed by Walter Reed, Victor Vaughn, and Edward O. Shakespeare was charged with investigating the high mortality rate in camps and found that the cause was typhoid rather than malaria. The Reed–Vaughn–Shakespeare report recommended strict sanitary control of camps. This reform led to a significantly healthier army in World War I and inspired civilian sanitary campaigns as well.

In 1906, Mary Mallon, an immigrant Irish domestic servant, was identified as responsible for a typhoid outbreak in New York City. Dubbed "Typhoid Mary," Mallon eventually was incarcerated to prevent her from working in the food trades. Although the case of Mary Mallon demonstrated the importance of healthy carriers and tainted food in the transmission of typhoid, it also raised serious questions about potential conflicts between public health and civil liberties.

Continued high typhoid incidence, combined with the seriousness of the disease and its sequelae, led the U.S. Public Health Service (PHS) to undertake epidemiological studies of Washington, D.C., each year between 1906 and 1909. In response to a 1911 epidemic in Yakima, Washington,

PHS investigators recommended a municipal sanitary campaign to be coordinated by a reorganized city–county public-health department. Typhoid rates fell, and the success of the Yakima model inspired similar reforms in other small cities and their surrounding countryside. Public-health authorities came to see rural areas as presenting a dangerous reservoir of disease that could cause serious problems in the nation's growing cities. At the height of interest in public health in the United States, Yakima became a symbol of the need for comprehensive preventive measures for both urban and rural areas.

At the same time, Louis I. Dublin of the Metropolitan Life Insurance Company looked into the comparative long-term effects of scarlet fever and typhoid fever. He found that typhoid survivors were more likely to die sooner from specific sequelae of the disease. The studies were methodologically sophisticated, resembling those conducted three or four decades later.

By 1920, when almost all American municipal water supplies were filtered, public-health advocates pointed to the dramatic decline of typhoid as evidence that governmental action could reduce morbidity and mortality. More recent retrospective epidemiological studies suggested that the introduction of filtered and chlorinated water was responsible for almost half the mortality decline in American cities in the late nineteenth and early twentieth centuries. Much of that decline was caused by the decreased prevalence of typhoid.

The principal protection against typhoid remains a pure water supply and stringent enforcement of food-handling regulations. By the late twentieth century, almost all typhoid cases reported in the United States were contracted during visits to less-developed countries. During the early twenty-first century, about four hundred cases are reported in the United States each year. Those that were not brought in from overseas were caused by breakdowns in the separation of sewage from food and water.

[*See also* **Biological Sciences; Centers for Disease Control and Prevention; Disease; Food Processing; Germ Theory of Disease; Hygiene, Personal; Malaria; Medicine; Osler,** **William; Public Health; Public Health Service, U.S.; Railroads; Reed, Walter; Sewage Treatment and System; Typhus;** *and* **War and Medicine.**]

BIBLIOGRAPHY

Casner, Nicolas. "'Do It Now!' Yakima, Wash, and the Campaign against Rural Typhoid." *American Journal of Public Health* 91 (2001): 1768–1775. A detailed description of a notably successful public-health effort at the moment when popular support for public health was peaking.

Condran, Gretchen A., Henry Williams, and Rose Cheney. "The Decline in Mortality in Philadelphia from 1870 to 1930: The Role of Municipal Services." *Pennsylvania Magazine of History and Biography* 108 (1984): 153–178. Reprinted in *Sickness and Health in America*, edited by J. Leavitt and R. Numbers, pp. 422–436. Madison: University of Wisconsin Press, 1986.

Leavitt, Judith Walzer. *Typhoid Mary: Captive to the Public Health*. Boston: Beacon Press, 1996.

McCarthy, Michael P. *Typhoid and the Politics of Public Health in Nineteenth-Century Philadelphia*. Philadelphia: American Philosophical Society, 1987. A useful case study of a city that was relatively late to filter the entirety of its water supply.

National Center for Zoonotic, Vector-Borne, and Enteric Diseases. "Typhoid Fever." http://www.cdc.gov/nczved/divisions/dfbmd/diseases/typhoid_fever/ (accessed 17 October 2012). Brief overview of current knowledge about typhoid and its transmission.

Edward T. Morman

TYPHUS

The history of typhus fever in America offers a puzzle: immigrants repeatedly brought the disease, but it never became established north of the Rio Grande. Typhus fever includes a group of similar diseases caused by related bacteria of the Rickettsia genus. "Epidemic" typhus fever is the designation for the disease caused by *Rickettsia prowazekii*, a bacterium that moves from host to host through the vector of infected human body lice. The symptoms of typhus—fever, head and body aches, pink rash, sometimes death—are nonspecific, making the historian's task in identifying outbreaks in the historical record difficult. It does seem that the disease appeared in Europe in epidemic form after 1500 and that outbreaks of typhus were evident in the areas of Spanish conquest during their first three centuries in the Americas. It is tempting to argue that typhus traveled from Mexico to Europe with the Conquistadors, but this is just speculation. When the fever appeared in Europe, it went by names tied to its sites of eruption, such as jail fever, camp fever, or ship fever. Typhus favors situations of human crowding, misery, and poor sanitation—conditions that encourage the profusion of body lice.

Typhus was tied to ships and immigrants throughout most of its American career north of the Rio Grande. It struck during the American Revolution, when British surgeons discovered the familiar jail fever of England among American prisoners of war held on English ships. Typhus again appeared in the United States in the 1830s, when William Wood Gerhard, fresh from medical studies in England and France, identified the infection among Irish immigrants in Philadelphia. Using information gathered at autopsy, Gerhard distinguished this fever from the similar (and more common) typhoid fever by describing the distinctive appearance of the intestinal wall in the latter disease.

The most significant invasion of typhus into North America came with the massive influx of Irish immigrants following the potato famine in the 1840s. Thousands died of typhus and relapsing fever, either on the voyage across the Atlantic or under the slum conditions that immigrants occupied upon immediate arrival. Doctors in Boston, New York, Philadelphia, and New Orleans (as well as Canada) all commented on the arrival of the unfamiliar and mortal epidemic. Typhus continued to infect European immigrants into the 1880s, but it never seems to have become indigenous to the United States. One might have expected it to have erupted in Civil War prison camps such as Andersonville, given the likelihood of infection and the conditions of deprivation and

crowding, but contemporaries were surprised that the men were spared this particular evil. It may be that something in the North American environment is inimical to the host/parasite reproductive cycle.

Around the turn of the twentieth century typhus remained central to concerns about immigrants and the importation of dangerous infections. Russian Jewish immigrants were harshly quarantined in New York in 1892 because of a typhus panic. Mexicans were likewise seen as carriers of this infection, so the U.S. Public Health Service set up quarantine and disinfection stations at major crossing points along the Rio Grande. To cleanse the incoming workers of lice, they were doused with gasoline, until a nasty fire in 1916 that killed 26 detainees put a stop to the practice. Typhus did cross the southern border successfully in 1920, causing an epidemic among the Navajo that was quelled by antilouse measures.

Although typhus never again threatened U.S. citizens in a major way, twentieth-century American researchers were active in studying the etiology and control of typhus in Mexico and Europe. Howard Ricketts, who first identified the cause of Rocky Mountain Spotted Fever, contracted typhus while studying it and died in Mexico in 1910. (Colleagues subsequently gave his name to the newly identified genus.) After World War I, Harvard's S. Burt Wolbach led a team that investigated and controlled typhus outbreaks that followed the chaos of war; after World War II American teams used dichlorodiphenyltrichloroethane (DDT) to kill lice on refugees.

In the early twenty-first century, scientists recognized multiple diseases caused by closely similar organisms of the Rickettsia genus. In 1926 Kenneth Maxcy of the U.S. Public Health Service identified murine typhus in southern cities, a usually milder form of typhus spread by rodents and their fleas. This disease was controlled with the use of DDT after World War II, but about the turn of the twenty-first century it emerged in Southern California and Texas, where it caused severe disease. Flying squirrels continued to spread epidemic typhus in rare circumstances in the American

South. Other animals have rickettsia of their own; cat typhus has been spread to humans more than once in Mexico. Scientists have been using genomic studies to illuminate the relationships among these different typhus organisms, which may ultimately illuminate the peculiarities of the history of typhus in North America.

[*See also* Biological Sciences; Disease; Germ Theory of Disease; Hygiene, Personal; Medicine; Public Health; Public Health Service, U.S.; Typhoid Fever; *and* War and Medicine.]

BIBLIOGRAPHY

Humphreys, Margaret. "A Stranger to Our Camps: Typhus in American History." *Bulletin of the History of Medicine* 80 (2006): 269–290.

Markel, Howard. "Lice, Typhus, and Riots on the Texas-Mexico Border." In *When Germs Travel: Six Major Epidemics that Have Invaded America since 1900 and Fears They Have Unleashed*, pp. 111–140. New York: Pantheon Books, 2004.

Zinsser, Hans. *Rats, Lice and History: A Bacteriologist's Classic History of Mankind's Epic Struggle to Conquer the Scourge of Typhus*. Boston: Little, Brown, 1934.

Margaret Humphreys

U

URBAN MASS TRANSIT

The phrase, or the word *transit* alone, evokes a variety of images, from "rapid transit" in the largest cities, divorced from other traffic—usually called "the subway" or "metro"—to minibuses plying "flexible" routes where patronage is sparse, often called *paratransit*. Between rapid transit and paratransit there are many other kinds, including automated "people movers," often at airports; light rail, with modernistic equipment but usually running along with city traffic; and different types of buses, most with diesel engines, but some cleaner, even hybrids and electrics. Occasionally, transit is part of a for-profit business, as in theme parks, where visitors ride into the past aboard conveyances drawn by horses. But nearly all transit agencies are dependent on subsidies, direct financial aid via taxes, to cover operating costs. It is important to remember, however, that urban transit began as private enterprise and until World War I could generate immense profits.

That was then. Now, only a small minority of Americans ride transit regularly, most aboard buses, which are often imagined as sites of danger and, above all, as the province of men and women in "service" occupations who are too poor to drive. But it was a different urban panorama for most of the century between the 1850s and 1950s. Patrons came in vast numbers and from all walks of life, and the conveyances they rode ran on rails, powered by electric motors that picked up current from overhead wires. Streetcars they were called, or, in other countries, trams.

Although they became commonplace elsewhere, nowhere were these conveyances so crucial to the growth and development of cities as in North America. A small town might have just one streetcar line, connecting the train station to the civic center. But it was much different in big cities. From an office window overlooking Chicago's State Street, one could see 30 streetcars coming and going at the same time. To handle all the traffic on Canal Street in New Orleans and Market Street in San Francisco, there were four tracks.

To avoid congestion in Boston and Philadelphia, tracks dove underground. More than 70 lines fanned out from downtown Pittsburgh.

Technological Choices.

Mass transit was essential to urban development beyond what was called "the walking city." The initial conveyances were dubbed omnibuses, meaning transit "for all." They were drawn by horses and ran right on the pavement, such as it was. But the advent of steam railroads proved the inherent advantages of steel wheel on steel rail, diminished rolling resistance being only one of many. An omnibus on rails was called a horsecar, and the first of these were built in the 1830s by a New Yorker named John Stephenson (1809–1893). By the time of the Civil War, there were horsecars in every large northern city and a few in the south. Then, in the 1870s, a San Franciscan named Andrew Halladie (1836–1900) developed another sort of streetcar, one whose source of propulsion was not immediately evident. Power came from steam engines that could be miles away from the cars out on the line, with the engines pulling cable in conduits beneath the tracks that could be gripped or released by the operator, who was fittingly call a "gripman."

With their complex infrastructure, cable cars were not as numerous as horsecars. Still, they operated in every large American city except Boston, Detroit, and New Orleans. Their heyday was brief, however, and by the turn of the twentieth century they were fast disappearing. So were horsecars, as both types were superseded by a third kind of streetcar whose source of power was invisible. In the mid-1880s, several attempts were made to operate streetcars with electric motors, notably in Baltimore and Los Angeles, but not until 1888 was there a system that was reasonably trouble-free. It was located in the one-time capital of the Confederacy, Richmond, Virginia, and it was engineered by a graduate of the U.S. Naval Academy named Frank Sprague (1857–1934). Electrification soon caught on everywhere. Power was usually transmitted from generating stations at six hundred volts, which was potentially lethal, hence the necessity of designing streetcars to draw current from wires that were out of reach. In Washington and New York (as well as in many of the great cities of Europe) they were located in conduits beneath the rails, as with the cables for cable cars. But everywhere else they were overhead. The device that picked up current as a streetcar moved along reminded people of a fisherman trolling and was first called a "troller." Soon it became "trolley," the word becoming interchangeable with streetcar. In the movie *Meet Me in St. Louis*, Judy Garland sang "The Trolley Song." Tennessee Williams had Blanche Dubois say that "They told me to take a streetcar named Desire, and then transfer to one called Cemeteries."

Automobility Ascendant.

Rather than being impelled by something external, horses or cables, an electric streetcar gained traction through its own wheels and indeed the whole system was called *traction*. But the same thing—providing its own traction—was also true of another invention dating from the 1880s, the horseless carriage, or automobile. And when autos, or "cars," started becoming part of everyday life in the 1920s, people began to attach a different meaning to the word. Always before, the reference had been to cars that ran on a "street railway." Usually there were two sets of tracks in the center of the road, to accommodate streetcars running in each direction; often the surface of the rails was flush with the pavement so as not to impede other traffic. Streetcars were the complex technological device with which most people were most familiar. They spoke of the "car line," waited at the "car stop" and paid "carfare." The place for overnight storage was called a "carbarn."

Steetcars enabled people to "commute" to work from several miles away, or to ride out to the country, or just go downtown to shop or catch a show. But familiarity bred contempt. When monetary inflation greatly increased the cost of operating streetcars after World War I and profits melted away, people had no sympathy for any so-called traction magnate. As more and more Americans could afford to buy autos and treat them as everyday transportation, streetcar patronage began to decline, and it declined fastest wherever authorities permitted fares higher than the traditional five cents. Then came the Great Depression of the 1930s and widespread bankruptcy.

In small towns, streetcars were quickly superseded by buses, which needed no tracks, no overhead wires, no central powerplants—and could be operated by one man, unlike many streetcars, which had both a "motorman" and a "conductor" to collect fares. After a while, the idea of regaining profitability by substituting buses took hold among the owners of transit systems in bigger towns, then small cities, and then in just about every city, no matter how extensive and heavily traveled its system. (A conspiracy hatched by General Motors? There was none, only, as historian Matt Roth puts it, a noir fantasy that will live forever.) A gallant try to develop a high-tech (and quite elegant) streetcar design only delayed the inevitable. Just before World War I, there had been more than 70,000 streetcars, operating in 370 cities and towns nationwide. By the 1970s there were less than 1,200 streetcars, but urban transit firms were operating 50,000 buses, mostly diesels devoid of any device to control air pollution. People hated "stink-buggies," and yet clean electric streetcars remained in service in only seven cities: Boston, Philadelphia, Pittsburgh, Cleveland, San Francisco, Newark, and New Orleans, none with more than a handful of lines.

Looking Ahead.   Trams still thrived in parts of Europe, in Japan, and in Australia, but the one extensive system in North America was in Toronto. The only American cities with substantial transit ridership were those with subway networks, which enabled the expression "rapid transit" to be taken literally: New York in particular, but also Philadelphia, Boston, and Chicago. Mostly these systems had been built early in the twentieth century when costs were much lower. In the latter half of the century, it was possible to secure funding for only two new systems of any extent, in Washington, D.C., and San Francisco, although a few other cities acquired a single rapid-transit line as a token of urban modernity. In 2012, nearly two dozen cities now have light-rail lines, which imitate some characteristics of rapid transit but operate on "the surface" to avoid the enormous expense of excavating subways. Light-rail vehicles must pick up current from overhead wires and are often portrayed as romantic, fun, and exciting, just like Judy Garland's St.

Louis trolley. A handful of cities even developed "heritage lines," with equipment that *looked* old-fashioned, to foster a "desire called streetcar," both nostalgic and progressive. Still, wherever there are to be rails and wires, there are big costs, and taxpayers are rarely enthusiastic.

In the second decade of the twenty-first century, the percentage of men and women who ordinarily ride mass transit remained in the single digits, as had been true for decades. In 2012, the reality of global warming and the realization that there might never again be cheap gasoline was bound to bring transit more centrally into the lives of more Americans, eventually. But when this would occur remained a question unanswered.

[*See also* **Airplanes and Air Transport; Bicycles and Bicycling; Electricity and Electrification; Environmentalism; Global Warming; Iron and Steel Production and Products; Motor Vehicles; Railroads; Steam Power;** *and* **Subways.**]

BIBLIOGRAPHY

Bobrick, Benson. *Labyrinths of Iron: Subways in History, Myth, Art, Technology, and War.* New York: William Morrow, 1981.

Dalzell, Frederick. *Engineering Invention: Frank J. Sprague and the U.S. Electrical Industry.* Cambridge, Mass.: MIT Press, 2010.

Divall, Colin, and Winstan Bond, eds. *Suburbanizing the Masses: Public Transport and Urban Development in Historical Perspective.* Aldershot, U.K.: Ashgate, 2003.

Hilton, George W. *The Cable Car in America.* San Diego, Calif.: Howell–North Books, 1982.

Middleton, William D. *The Time of the Trolley: The Street Railway from Horsecar to Light Rail.* San Marino, Calif.: Golden West Books, 1987.

Middleton, William D., and William D. Middleton III. *Frank Julian Sprague: Electrical Inventor and Engineer.* Bloomington and Indianapolis: Indiana University Press, 2009.

Post, Robert C. "Images of the Pacific Electric: Why Memories Matter." *Railroad History* 179 (1998): 30–68.

Post, Robert C. *Urban Mass Transit: The Life Story of a Technology.* Baltimore: Johns Hopkins University Press, 2010.

Warner, Sam B., Jr. *Streetcar Suburbs: The Process of Growth in Boston, 1870–1900.* Cambridge, Mass.: Harvard University Press, 1962.

Robert C. Post

UREY, HAROLD C.

(1893–1981), chemist, Nobel laureate. Born in Walkerton, Indiana, Urey received his BA in zoology with a minor in chemistry from Montana State University (1917). After the United States entered World War I, Urey worked at an industrial chemical laboratory producing munitions. But he decided that he preferred academia and in 1921 began graduate work, earning his PhD in chemistry from the University of California, Berkeley, in 1923. His doctoral dissertation dealt with the rotational contributions to the heat capacities and entropies of gases. It revealed Urey's talent for both empirical and theoretical work. In 1923–1924 Urey studied atomic physics in Copenhagen with Niels Bohr as an American–Scandinavian Fellow at the Institute for Theoretical Physics. On his return to the United States, he taught first at Johns Hopkins (1925–1928) and then at Columbia University (1929–1945). He won the Nobel Prize in Chemistry in 1934 for his 1931 discovery of deuterium (the rare "heavy" isotope of hydrogen), the first isotope tracer used in biomedical research.

During World War II, Urey directed one of the groups involved in the Manhattan Project, which built the atomic bomb. This group was the Substitute Alloys Materials Laboratory at Columbia, which worked on the separation of uranium isotopes. In 1945 he joined the Fermi Institute for Nuclear Studies at the University of Chicago. There he organized several nuclear institutes and arranged for major corporate funding. Although he had assisted in the development of atomic weapons, Urey was raised in a church with a pacifist tradition (the Church of the Brethren). This helps explain why he opposed dropping the bomb on Japan, did not support a bill that would have placed the military in charge of atomic research, and decided to resign from the Atomic Energy Commission in 1950. Throughout his career he continued to promote the peaceful uses of atomic energy.

Following the war, while teaching at the University of Chicago (1945–1958) and the University of California, San Diego (1958–1981), he turned to the uses of isotopes in studying the geochemistry of terrestrial and extraterrestrial planetary materials. He developed a means of inferring marine paleotemperatures over geologic time by measuring the oxygen isotope ratios of carbonates in marine sediments. Urey's interest in the origins of life gave rise to a famous experiment in which electric discharges through a mixture of gases produced amino acids. An active supporter of the U.S. space program, he served on the Space Board of the National Academy of Sciences.

[*See also* **Atomic Energy Commission; Chemistry; Fermi, Enrico; Manhattan Project; Military, Science and Technology and the; National Academy of Sciences; Nobel Prize in Biomedical Research; Nuclear Power; Nuclear Weapons; Physics;** *and* **Science.**]

BIBLIOGRAPHY

Cohn, Mildred. "Harold Urey: A Personal Remembrance, Part I." *Chemical Heritage* 23, no. 4 (Winter 2005/2006): 8–48. Part II is in 24, no. 1 (Spring 2006): 8–13.

Tatarewicz, Joseph N. "Urey, Harold Clayton." In *Complete Dictionary of Scientific Biography.* Vol. 18, pp. 943–948. Detroit: Charles Scribner's Sons, 2008.

Urey, Harold. *The Planets: Their Origin and Development.* New Haven, Conn.: Yale University Press, 1952.

R. E. Taylor;
updated by Elspeth Knewstubb and
Hugh Richard Slotten

V

VAN ALLEN, JAMES A.

(1914–2006), physicist and space and planetary scientist. Born in Mount Pleasant, Iowa, Van Allen earned a BS from Iowa Wesleyan University in 1935 and a PhD in physics at the University of Iowa in 1939. During World War II, he worked at the Applied Physics Laboratory at Johns Hopkins University on the development of proximity fuzes, detonators used especially by the navy to increase the effectiveness of antiaircraft projectiles. He then received a commission as a naval officer assigned to instruct gunnery officers and commanders with the Pacific Fleet in the use of the fuzes.

After the war, Van Allen returned to the Applied Physics Laboratory to organize and supervise a research team pioneering upper-atmospheric research using captured German V2 rockets. He continued this work when he accepted a position in charge of the department of physics and astronomy at the University of Iowa in 1951. He re-tired from teaching at Iowa in 1985. Working with the U.S. Office of Naval Research, he perfected the use of rockets launched from balloons at very high altitudes ("rockoons") to investigate cosmic rays and magnetic fields existing at the outer reaches of the atmosphere.

Van Allen played an important role in planning the International Geophysical Year of 1957–1958. He encouraged the U.S. government to use rockets to launch scientific satellites as part of the International Geophysical Year, and his instruments were chosen to fly with the first American satellite, *Explorer I*, successfully launched in January 1958, after the Soviet Union's spectacular triumph with the first satellite, *Sputnik I*, in October 1957. The National Advisory Committee for Aeronautics had selected Van Allen to a special committee on space technology it established one month after *Sputnik* to help the government decide about space policy. Van Allen's instruments on *Explorer I* detected the radiation environment surrounding the earth, and his team's discoveries were confirmed by instruments on *Explorer III* and *IV* (launched in March and July 1958) and *Pioneer III* (launched in December 1958), which helped map the contours of the earth's magnetosphere. Because of his connection to the first American satellite and because of his discovery and mapping of the belts of radiation outside the earth's atmosphere (subsequently named the Van Allen belts), which became the first major scientific triumph of the space age, Van Allen gained status as one of the country's foremost space scientists. *Time* published his picture on the cover of one of its issues in May 1959.

Van Allen's team at the University of Iowa continued scientific work using other satellites and interplanetary spacecraft during the following decades. As a member of the Space Science Board and the Lunar and Planetary Mission Board, Van Allen strongly advocated exploratory missions to the outer planets. Instruments developed by his team and his former students and associates were included with the first missions to the planets Mars, Venus, Jupiter, Saturn, Uranus, and Neptune, including the Pioneer, Mariner, Voyager, and Galileo programs. He was well known for opposing manned flight in favor of robotic missions, which he considered more economical and much safer.

[*See also* **Astronomy and Astrophysics; Geophysics; Instruments of Science; Missiles and Rockets; Physics; Science; Space Program; Space Science;** *and* **Technology.**]

BIBLIOGRAPHY

DeVorkin, David. "Van Allen, James." In *New Dictionary of Scientific Biography*. Vol. 7. Detroit: Charles Scribner's Sons, 2008.

Foerstner, Abigail. *James Van Allen: The First Eight Billion Miles.* Iowa City: University of Iowa Press, 2007.

Hugh Richard Slotten

VENEREAL DISEASE

See **HIV/AIDS; Sexually Transmitted Diseases.**

VENTER, J. CRAIG

(1946–), pioneer of DNA sequencing strategies. Born in Salt Lake City, Utah, (John) Craig Venter grew up in Millbrae, California, where he was rebellious, a good surfer and sailor, and a poor student. In 1965 he was drafted and served in Vietnam. Returning in 1968, he finished college and went on for a PhD in pharmacology and physiology at the University of California, San Diego. He focused on adrenaline (epinephrine) physiology, publishing 12 papers before he received his doctorate in 1975. After a stint at the Roswell Park Cancer Institute in Buffalo, New York, in 1984 he moved to the National Institutes of Health (NIH).

Venter's research breakthrough came in 1991, when he published a paper describing "expressed sequence tagging," a method of finding genes by their partial DNA sequence without knowing their function. When the NIH attempted to patent more than two thousand expressed sequence taggings, a furious James Watson resigned under duress as head of the National Human Genome Research Institute and was replaced by Francis Collins. Venter, meanwhile, had left the NIH for The Institute for Genome Research (TIGR), a nonprofit research institute backed with $70 million in venture capital from HealthCare Ventures, with an agreement to turn over the first six months' discoveries. With the Nobel laureate Hamilton Smith on board, TIGR developed "shotgun sequencing," a novel, fast method that relied on new automated DNA sequencers and high-powered computers.

Competition, speed, efficiency, and cost became central concerns in Venter's work. In 1995, TIGR published the first complete genome sequence, that of *Haemophilus influenzae*. In 1998, Venter founded Celera, a for-profit genome-sequencing company. He went head to head with Collins and the publicly funded NIH genome effort. Relying on conventional genetic strategies, the NIH genome project was behind schedule and over budget. The much-publicized race with Celera accelerated the project, leading to a joint announcement of a "draft" sequence by Venter and Collins in a White House ceremony on 26 June 2000. Venter then raced Watson to be the first to sequence and publish one's own genome: Venter won in September 2007. The competition was credited with helping to lower the cost of personal genome sequencing. Another pioneering effort combined Venter's love of sailing and his passion for DNA: he sailed the world, surveying the oceans and sequencing the "genomes" of entire marine ecosystems. In 2006, Venter merged TIGR and several other "legacy" institutes into the J. Craig Venter Institute (JCVI), a private genome research institute with facilities in Rockville, Maryland, and San Diego, California. JCVI researchers synthesized a prokaryotic genome—*Mycoplasma genitalium*—and in May 2010, Venter published the sequence of what he called a new species, *Mycoplasma laboratorium*, a self-replicating bacterial cell with a synthetic genome that JCVI scientists "transplanted" into a bacterial cell—a process Venter referred to as "rebooting" the cell.

Venter's hallmark is to treat life as a computing problem. A pioneer of the integration of the late twentieth century's two great information sciences—computing and molecular genetics—his goal is their ultimate fusion: synthetic life with computer-generated, robot-synthesized DNA whose in vitro–executed algorithms will yield viable organisms with (he hopes) beneficial properties. For Venter, as for the physiologist Jacques Loeb a century before, the control of life "and nothing else is the aim of biology."

Venter is a member of the National Academy of Sciences and a recipient of the Paul Ehrlich and Ludwig Darmstädter Award (2001), the Gairdner Award (2002), and the National Medal of Science (2008).

[*See also* **Biological Sciences; DNA Sequencing; Genetics and Genetic Engineering; Human Genome Project;** *and* **Instruments of Science.**]

BIBLIOGRAPHY

Kay, Lily. *Who Wrote the Book of Life?* Stanford, Calif.: Stanford University Press, 2000. A history of the information metaphor in biology and how the genome became an "information system."

Shreeve, James. *The Genome War: How Craig Venter Tried to Capture the Code of Life and Save the World.* New York: Alfred A. Knopf, 2004. The tale of the NIH/Celera race to get the human genome, told from Venter's perspective.

Venter, J. Craig. *Life at the Speed of Light: From the Double Helix to the Dawn of Digital Life.* New York: Viking Press, 2013.

Venter, J. Craig. *A Life Decoded: My Genome, My Life.* New York: Viking Press, 2007. Venter's autobiography up to the creation of "*M. laboratorium.*"

Nathaniel Comfort

VETERINARY MEDICINE

Veterinarians provide health care for individual animals, manage the health of large populations of animals for agriculture, and provide expertise on food safety and the global surveillance of zoonotic diseases (diseases transmissible between animals and humans). Like physicians and surgeons, veterinarians undergo extensive scientific education, professional training, and state licensure in the United States. Professional veterinary medicine has developed over the past two centuries in conjunction with how Americans have valued animals—whether that value was economic, scientific, sentimental, or as a source of wholesome food. As the roles of animals have shifted over time, so has the shape of the veterinary profession.

Animal Healing. Although this essay focuses on the development of professional veterinary medicine, it is important to recognize that the profession is embedded in a broader history of human–animal interactions that predated its establishment on the North American continent. Native American peoples vested animals with a great deal of importance and cared for them accordingly: to the Cherokee, healers and spiritual guides assumed the identities of specific animals; the peoples of the Great Plains (Comanche and Kiowa, among others) collected imported Spanish horses and became masters of horse training, care, and warfare. To the early British colonists in New England and the Chesapeake, domesticated animals served as symbols of civilization and agents of empire (Anderson, 2004). All of these cultures included skilled animal healers and a lay population whose survival often depended on animals. Skills such as feeding, assisting with difficult births, and treating illnesses and injuries have remained widespread among those who work with animals. Thus, "folk" care of animals preceded and has overlapped the development of a formal profession of veterinary medicine in the United States.

Formalized education in animal healing was a product of the Enlightenment, with later influences from intellectual developments in science and the social regulation of the medical marketplace. The first veterinary schools in the modern period were established in France, Denmark, Germany, Britain, and the Netherlands between the 1780s and 1820 (Swabe, 1999, p. 90). With the dramatic growth of livestock populations in the early American Republic and the deaths of valuable production animals (cattle, sheep, etc.) in recurrent disease outbreaks, gentlemanly agricultural societies such as the Philadelphia and Massachusetts Societies for Promoting Agriculture called for the formal education of veterinarians and the establishment of a recognized profession in the United States. In addition to economic concerns over outbreaks of animal plagues, humane attitudes toward animals played a role in the formalization of animal healing. The eminent Philadelphia physician Benjamin Rush told his medical students in 1807 that they had a "duty" to study the diseases of animals on moral grounds. Humanitarianism and economic needs would shape American veterinary medicine as it developed during the second half of the nineteenth century (Jones, 2003).

Organized Veterinary Medicine. Like physicians, veterinarians were usually educated through apprenticeship in the eighteenth and nineteenth centuries. Organized veterinary education in the United States began in the mid-1800s with a few private veterinary schools, which were not subject to regulation or accreditation and relied on student fees to remain in business. The first such school, the "Veterinary College of America," established in Philadelphia by Robert Jennings in 1852, failed immediately. More successful early schools

in North America included the New York College of Veterinary Surgeons (chartered in 1857) and the Ontario Veterinary College in Canada (1862, the oldest extant school). Later, reflecting a shift westward, private practitioners founded schools such as the Chicago Veterinary College, McKillip Veterinary College (also in Chicago), and the Kansas City Veterinary College. Some of the private schools had a rigorous three-year curriculum. Schools in large urban centers (Washington, D.C., Boston, Philadelphia, New York, San Francisco) emphasized the care of horses and investigations of zoonotic diseases, such as bovine tuberculosis (Smithcors, 1963).

In forming their profession in the late 1800s, veterinarians established numerous local associations and the U.S. Veterinary Medical Association (founded 1863, renamed the American Veterinary Medical Association in 1898). Associations worked toward state licensure of veterinarians to define standards for veterinary practice, ensure professional self-regulation, and restrict economic veterinary practice to the duly licensed. New York veterinary practitioners, after much infighting and several delays, succeeded in becoming what one vet called "practical politicians and lobbyists" and secured a licensure law in 1886. Early state laws allowed licensure of older, apprentice- or self-educated practitioners, but eventually required examinations and formal education. The state of Pennsylvania, for example, first passed a general licensure act in 1889, which was revised to require passing an examination in 1895 (Smithcors, 1963). By 1900, most states had licensure laws based on some measure of competence, but these laws often did not require graduation from a veterinary school and thus did not provide incentives toward formal education. In rural areas of the United States, half of the licensed practitioners were nongraduates even into the 1920s; some were highly regarded and skilled, continuing to be an important part of the profession (even with reforms in licensure laws, education, and therapeutics in the World War II period; Stalheim, 1994).

Veterinarians communicated through published journals, such as the *American Veterinary Review* (renamed the *Journal of the American Veterinary Medical Association* in 1914–1915) and the

Journal of Comparative Medicine and Veterinary Archives (established 1880), which included translated excerpts of European journal articles. Land-grant universities began offering courses in veterinary subjects after Congress enacted the Morrill Land Grant Act of 1862: Cornell University had a professor of veterinary science from 1868; Iowa State University inaugurated a full veterinary curriculum in 1879 (Smithcors, 1963). Most veterinarians before the 1880s and most of the young profession's leaders had been trained in Europe. Early veterinary educators in the United States included James Law (1838–1921) of Edinburgh (professor at Cornell University); Alexandre Liautard (1835–1918, New York College of Veterinary Surgeons and American Veterinary College) and Rush Shippen Huidekoper (1854–1901, University of Pennsylvania), schooled in France; and Henry J. Detmers (1833–1906, Ohio State), trained in Berlin.

In Canada, Duncan McEachran (1841–1924, founder in 1866 of the Montreal Veterinary College) and William Osler (1849–1919) played crucial roles in educating North American veterinarians, who crossed the border freely for educational and occupational opportunities. McEachran, Osler, and other research-oriented leaders of the more rigorous urban veterinary schools stressed education on the medical model and encouraged cooperation with physicians and scientists (Teigen, 1984, 1988). Students' backgrounds varied, although most were young white men with some familial connection to medicine, veterinary medicine, or an animal industry (such as livestock raising or blacksmithing). Mignon Nicholson (1870?–1930?) was the first woman (McKillip Veterinary College, 1903) and Henry Stockton Lewis (1858–1922) the first African American (Harvard, 1889) to graduate from American veterinary schools (Jones, 2003).

Shifts in Scientific Ideas and the Animal Economy, 1880s–1930s.

Beginning in the 1880s, germ ideas and practices (especially related to bacteriology) were an important key to veterinarians' claims to special expertise and status in the medical marketplace. Reliance on bacteriology ensured a body of scientific knowledge unavailable to most lay "animal doctors" and students

who had been trained in the less laboratory-oriented private schools. Severe outbreaks of animal disease gave veterinarians the opportunity to use new scientific ideas and tools from the fields of microbiology and sanitary science. In this era of what William Osler called "one medicine," veterinarians, physicians, and natural scientists all contributed to the rapidly developing knowledge of micro-organisms and disease. Some of the most famous events included Louis Pasteur's development of vaccines for chicken cholera, rabies, and anthrax (1870s–1880s) and Robert Koch's publications on anthrax (1876) and tuberculosis (1882; Dunlop and Williams, 1996).

Veterinary professional leaders urged greater emphasis on the microscope in disease investigations and veterinary education, but it is also clear that veterinary control of epizootics (animal epidemics) continued to rely on traditional practices of sanitary science such as quarantines and slaughtering infected animals (Worboys, 2000). With the establishment of the U.S. Department of Agriculture's Bureau of Animal Industry (BAI) in 1884, American veterinarians achieved their first federally funded research institution (although the more mundane duties of meat inspection took up an increasing amount of the BAI's resources over time). BAI employees Fred L. Kilborne (1857–1936), Cooper Curtice (1856–1939), and Theobald Smith (1859–1934) first demonstrated the vector transmission of a disease, Texas cattle fever, in the early 1890s (a direct precedent to later studies of malaria). The BAI also coordinated efforts to control outbreaks of animal disease (such as bovine pleuropneumonia) and to certify export goods (such as meat) in an era of increasing global trade and transport (Jones, 2003, p. 30).

Between the 1880s and 1925, veterinarians and the shifting animal economy consolidated the profession, orienting it more toward agriculture. Graduate veterinarians worked to sponsor state laws that created boards of examination and set graduation and licensing requirements, thus permanently preventing most laypeople from practicing professional veterinary medicine. At the turn of the twentieth century, veterinary medicine was largely an urban profession focusing on horses that provided power and transportation. (Some enterprising veterinarians and urban veterinary schools also opened clinics and hospitals devoted to pets, especially dogs, which were popular subjects of animal welfare associations.) However, as the internal combustion engine replaced horse power in the 1910s and 1920s, horses disappeared from American cities and their economic value plummeted. Enrollment dropped precipitously at the large urban private schools that had trained their students to be "equine physicians." The BAI, the steadiest source of veterinary employment at this time, needed trained agricultural and meat inspectors and would only employ graduates of schools with appropriate training programs (usually affiliated with universities). In 1927, the last existing private veterinary school in the United States closed its doors, shifting the center of veterinary education to land-grant universities. This change signaled a closer alignment of the veterinary profession with the economic needs of agriculture, including less reliance on the medical model of urban veterinary education and more migration of graduate veterinarians to rural areas (Jones, 2003).

Mid-Twentieth Century Expansion of Veterinary Medicine. The veterinary workforce contracted through the 1930s (largely because of the Depression and the school closures), but this was reversed by the developments of the 1940s and 1950s: the establishment of new veterinary schools after World War II, the discovery of new therapeutics, and the rise of intensive animal production (also known as "factory farming"). Returning World War II veterans played a key role in demanding the establishment of new veterinary schools in state land-grant universities such as those in California, Georgia, Illinois, Michigan, Minnesota, Missouri, and Oklahoma and at the Tuskegee Institute (devoted to educating African Americans). This postwar expansion almost doubled the seats available to students (there had been only 10 veterinary schools in the United States in 1940, according to the American Veterinary Medical Association).

Wartime medical developments, such as the production of antibiotics and new techniques for managing shock, transformed veterinary practice (as they did human medicine and surgery). But as scientists discovered in the 1950s, antibiotics played another important role: when fed in small doses, they promoted the fast growth of animals being raised for food. The new medications also enabled animals to be raised in large numbers in close quarters with less fear of disease outbreaks. These discoveries contributed to the rapid rise of intensive animal production in the United States during the Cold War, a time when cheap and plentiful food had tremendous political importance as a key component of "defense production" (Jones, 2003, p. 107). An increasing number of veterinarians, including those working on disease surveillance and food production at the global level, specialized in the "herd health" of poultry, swine, cattle, and other animals in the second half of the twentieth century. Veterinarians worked with zoo and exotic animals, poultry, fish, and wildlife as well as on disease eradication campaigns.

Companion animals such as dogs and cats (which had always garnered some interest from veterinary practitioners) became the fastest growing sector of the American market for individual animal care. This transformation followed the growth of pet-oriented consumer culture. Companion-animal veterinarians founded the American Animal Hospital Association in 1933 and later developed specialties reflecting new technologies and clients' increasing willingness to pay for expensive treatments. Humane care for all animals remained elusive, however, as debates over the treatment of laboratory animals (largely unregulated until the 1970s), stray animals, and intensively farmed livestock illustrated. Since the 1970s, discussions of the human–animal bond and the importance of addressing animal pain have appeared regularly in veterinary journals—largely stimulated by the concerns of companion-animal owners (and animal advocacy groups). By the end of the twentieth century, the majority of veterinary practitioners in the United States treated companion animals, and Americans spent over $7 billion each year on veterinary care for their pets (Jones, 2003, p. 115).

New Challenges in Recent Decades. Several factors shaped the veterinary profession in the 1980s and 1990s: the unrestrained admission of women into U.S. veterinary schools, the changing distribution of the veterinary workforce, and new public-health concerns. Federal legislation in the early 1970s mandated gender-blind admissions policies and thus opened veterinary schools to women (who had been admitted under a quota system up to this point by most schools). The profession has become increasingly feminized ever since, with veterinary classes approaching 75 percent women in the early 2000s. The number of veterinarians willing to work with food-producing animals has been decreasing for decades because pet practice has offered higher monetary compensation and better working conditions.

Veterinary professional leaders are concerned that the United States now has plenty of "pet vets" but suffers a shortage of professionals trained to address concerns about food safety and public health. Many of these concerns date to historical events. For example, antibiotic growth promoters, once seen as a key to modern intensive animal production, are now suspected of selecting for antibiotic-resistant, highly lethal superbugs that attack animals and humans. Outbreaks of zoonotic emergent and re-emergent diseases in the 1990s and early 2000s—BSE/Creutzfeld–Jakob syndrome, severe acute respiratory syndrome (SARS), and influenza—have called into question the practices of the global economy in animals and animal products in the 1990s and early 2000s. New ways of using animals, such as genetically manipulating them to serve as organ donors for humans, will raise medical and ethical concerns. The American veterinary profession will help to shape the response to these and other events in the future—even as it is transformed by the dynamics of the animal economy.

[See also Agricultural Education and Extension; Agricultural Technology; Agriculture, U.S. Department of; Disease; Ethics and Medicine; Food and Diet; Food Processing; Gender and Science; Genetics and Genetic Engineering; Germ Theory of Disease; Higher Education and Science; Internal Combustion Engine; Journals in Science, Medicine, and Engineering; Malaria; Medical Education; Medicine; Morrill Land Grant Act; Osler, William; Penicillin; Pharmacology and Drug Therapy; Pure Food and Drug Act; Race and Medicine; Rush, Benjamin; Science; Societies and Associations, Science; Surgery; Tuberculosis; War and Medicine; and Zoology.]

BIBLIOGRAPHY

Anderson, Virginia DeJohn. *Creatures of Empire: How Domestic Animals Transformed Early America.* New York: Oxford University Press, 2004.

Bierer, Bert W. *American Veterinary History.* Madison, Wisc.: Carl Olson, 1980.

Bierer, Bert W. *A Short History of Veterinary Medicine in America.* East Lansing: Michigan State University Press, 1955.

Dunlop, Robert, and David M. Williams. *Veterinary Medicine: An Illustrated History.* St. Louis, Mo.: Mosby, 1996.

Jones, Susan D. *Valuing Animals: Veterinarians and Their Patients in Modern America.* Baltimore: Johns Hopkins University Press, 2003.

Smithcors, J. F. *The American Veterinary Profession— Its Background and Development.* Ames: Iowa State University Press, 1963.

Smithcors, J. F. *The Veterinarian in America, 1625– 1975.* Goleta, Calif.: American Veterinary Publications, 1975.

Stalheim, O. H. V. *The Winning of Animal Health: 100 Years of Veterinary Medicine.* Ames: Iowa State University Press, 1994.

Swabe, Joanna. *Animals, Disease and Human Society: Human–Animal Relations and the Rise of Veterinary Medicine.* London: Routledge, 1999.

Teigen, Philip M. "The Establishment of the Montreal Veterinary College, 1866/67–1874/75." *Canadian Veterinary Journal* 26 (1988): 185–189.

Teigen, Philip M. "William Osler and Comparative Medicine." *Canadian Veterinary Journal* 25 (1984): 400–405.

Worboys, Michael. "Veterinary Medicine, the Cattle Plague and Contagion, 1865–1890." In *Spreading Germs: Disease Theories and Medical Practice in Britain, 1865–1900,* chap. 2. Cambridge, U.K.: Cambridge University Press, 2000.

Susan D. Jones

VON BRAUN, WERNHER

(1912–1977), rocket engineer. Born in Wirsitz, Germany (now Wyrzysk, Poland), to parents of the minor Prussian nobility, von Braun graduated from the Technische Universität Berlin (Berlin Institute of Technology) in 1932 and received a PhD in physics from Berlin's Humboldt University in 1934, shortly after the Nazis' rise to power. A rocket enthusiast, he assisted the rocket pioneer Hermann Oberth in testing liquid-fueled rockets and in 1937, having joined the Nazi Party, became technical director of Germany's rocket program at Peenemünde on the Baltic Sea. In September 1944, the Peenemünde team launched the first V-2 rocket attack on London. As World War II ended, von Braun fled to Bavaria to surrender to the Americans rather than the Russians. Signing a contract with the U.S. Army, he was brought to the United States with other Peenemünde engineers to pursue rocketry research—a field pioneered in America by Robert H. Goddard (1882–1945). Working first at the White Sands Proving Grounds in New Mexico and at Fort Bliss, Texas, he was transferred in 1950 to the Redstone Arsenal in Huntsville, Alabama. Here, as head of rocket research at the height of the Cold War, he led the development of nuclear-armed intercontinental ballistic missiles (ICBMs), including the Redstone, Jupiter, and Atlas series. Modified ICBMs could also propel satellites into orbit, a program that gained urgency after the Soviet Union launched the *Sputnik* satellite in 1957. The first U.S. satellite, *Explorer 1*, was launched in 1958 by *Juno 1*, a booster rocket adapted from a Jupiter ICBM.

As he gained fame, von Braun faced critical scrutiny, including his wartime membership in the Nazi party and the Waffen S.S., the party's paramilitary unit; his knowledge of the use of slave labor at Peenemünde from a nearby concentration camp; and his apparent political opportunism and tunnel-vision preoccupation with technological challenges. The 1965 song "Wernher von Braun" by satirist Tom Lehrer included the line: "'Once the rockets are up, who cares where they come down? That's not my department,' says Wernher von Braun." Some suggest that "Dr. Strangelove," the character played by Peter Sellers in Stanley Kubrick's 1964 film of that title, may have been partially inspired by von Braun.

From 1960 on, von Braun focused on his first love, the use of rocketry for space travel, as director of the Marshall Space Flight Center at Huntsville, operated by the National Aeronautics and Space Administration (NASA). His crowning achievement, the massive *Saturn V* booster rocket, three hundred feet in height, delivering 7.5 million pounds of thrust, powered NASA's *Apollo 2* mission that on 20 July 1969 landed two U.S. astronauts on the moon. Handsome and charismatic, von Braun through speeches, books, magazine articles, and three Disney educational films celebrated the romance of space. He retired from NASA in 1972 as public enthusiasm waned, but continued to promote space exploration until his death.

[*See also* **Engineering; Goddard, Robert H.; Military, Science and Technology and the; Missiles and Rockets; National Aeronautics and Space Administration; Nuclear Weapons; Physics; Popularization of Science; Satellites, Communications; Space Program; Space Science;** *and* **Technological Enthusiasm.**]

BIBLIOGRAPHY

Biddle, Wayne. *Dark Side of the Moon: Wernher von Braun, the Third Reich, and the Space Race.* New York: W. W. Norton, 2009.
Bilstein, Roger E. *Stages to Saturn: A Technological History of the Apollo/Saturn Launch Vehicles.* Gainesville: University Press of Florida, 2003.
Neufeld, Michael. *Von Braun: Dreamer of Space, Engineer of War.* New York: Alfred A. Knopf, 2007.
                                        Paul S. Boyer

VON NEUMANN, JOHN

(1903–1957), computer pioneer, mathematician, government consultant. Born in Budapest, John von Neumann received his doctorate in mathematics with minors in experimental physics and chemistry from the University of Budapest in 1926. He lectured in Berlin from 1927 to 1929 and then in Hamburg from 1929 to 1930. In 1930, he went to Princeton University as a visiting lecturer. Three years later he was invited to become professor of mathematics at the new Institute for Advanced Study in Princeton. Active in government service, he worked at Los Alamos on the Manhattan Project from 1943 to 1945; consulted with the army's Ballistic Research Laboratory at Aberdeen, Maryland; and served on the Atomic Energy Commission from 1954 to 1957.

Von Neumann worked in both pure and applied mathematics. His work in pure mathematics took place mainly between 1925 and 1940. He published papers in the areas of logic and set theory, measure theory, spectral theory of operators in Hilbert space, lie groups, and rings of operators. Von Neumann's most important research in applied mathematics was in the axiomatization of quantum mechanics, which he started to work on in 1927. In 1932 he published *Mathematische Grundlagen der Quantenmechanik* (1932), which was translated and published in 1955 as *Mathematical Foundations of Quantum Mechanics*. His crucial work on the theory of games began with a 1926 paper. He developed a model that allowed the concept of strategy to be analyzed mathematically and also constructed a quantitative model for games of chance such as poker and bridge. This work had further applications, notably in economics. His groundbreaking *Theory of Games and Economic Behavior* (with Oskar Morgenstern) was published in 1944.

Von Neumann also participated in numerous discussions with the staff of the Electronic Numeric Integrator and Computer (ENIAC) project at the University of Pennsylvania, and in 1945 he drafted a report on this project defining the key elements of a digital computer and introducing the "stored-program" concept used by ENIAC's successor, the Electronic Discrete Variable Computer (EDVAC). Although not intended for distribution, this document circulated widely, touching off an early controversy in the fledgling computer-science field because it bore only von Neumann's name. A computer von Neumann built at the Institute for Advanced Study, called the Mathematical Analyzer, Numerical Integrator, and Computer (MANIAC), served as a prototype for many early computers and supplied computations crucial to the development of the hydrogen bomb. A brilliant theoretician, von Neumann also wrote two posthumously published works, *The Computer and the Brain* (1958) and, with Arthur Burks, *Theory of Self-Reproducing Automata* (1966).

[*See also* **Atomic Energy Commission; Chemistry; Computer Science; Computers, Mainframe, Mini, and Micro; ENIAC; Manhattan Project; Mathematics and Statistics; Military, Science and Technology and the; Nuclear Weapons; Physics; Quantum Theory;** *and* **Science.**]

BIBLIOGRAPHY

Aspray, William. *John von Neumann and the Origins of Modern Computing.* Cambridge, Mass.: MIT Press, 1990.

Dieudonné, J. "Von Neumann, Johann (or John)." In *Complete Dictionary of Scientific Biography.* Vol. 14, pp. 88–92. Detroit: Charles Scribner's Sons, 2008.

Israel, Giorgio, and Ana Millán Gasca. *The World as a Mathematical Game: John von Neumann and Twentieth Century Science.* Science Networks, Historical Studies, vol. 38. Translated by Ian McGilvray. Basel and Boston: Birkhäuser, 2009.

Taub, A. H., ed. *John von Neumann: Collected Works.* 6 vols. New York: Pergamon Press, 1960–1963.

Thomas J. Bergin;
updated by Elspeth Knewstubb and
Hugh Richard Slotten

W

WAR AND MEDICINE

The relationship between war and medicine is complex. In analyzing historical developments in America, this essay considers war as organized interstate violence and the social institutions constructed to support it and medicine as the biosocial well-being of individuals as well as society's efforts to restore and conserve that well-being. Since the eighteenth century both medicine and war have become more technologically mediated and socially complex. American medicine has achieved more social acceptance and prestige. War has changed its character as the domestic interests of the United States and the country's role in international events have interacted with broad socioeconomic and political changes. Although complex, the different aspects of the relationship between war and medicine in America can be organized into three broad categories: (1) the impact of disease, and increasingly of medical knowledge, on the prosecution of war; (2) "advances" or specific changes later accepted in practice in health and medical science that result from, or at least become more common after, war; and (3) the impact of the war experience on the institutional organization of medicine and the biosocial health of the nation.

The use of medical care to conserve and restore the human strength of military units for both military and humanitarian purposes is the military response to the recognized impact of disease on military operations. This basic objective of military medicine is therefore a subset of the first category discussed above. It developed from the mid-eighteenth-century observations that hospitals, naval ships, and military camps and garrisons were insalubrious places and that making them less so would conserve fighting strength. This preventive concept in military medicine emerged almost simultaneously in the writings of navy and army physicians in Europe and also influenced the views of eighteenth-century American physicians at the time of the Revolution. Military medicine's earlier emphasis on trauma care reflected a social commitment to those who put themselves in harm's way on behalf of society. Such social commitments led to the creation of a Hospital Department within weeks of the establishment of the Continental Army in 1775.

Colonial Era through the Mid-Nineteenth Century.

Historians have clearly established the role of infectious diseases in the destruction of the indigenous cultures and peoples of North America. Applying modern diagnostics to the epidemics that destroyed Native Americans is a historiographical hobby, but positive diagnosis is difficult unless tissues remain that paleopathologists can examine. Febrile diseases with spots, such as smallpox and measles, clearly played a major role in the deaths of Native Americans, but respiratory diseases were also occasionally to blame. Usually this devastation was inadvertent; new recruits from urban areas infected recruits from rural areas in European and North American military formations. But for the Native Americans the European childhood infections, even if inadvertent, were mortal epidemics, wiping out villages and eventually unlucky tribes.

As European medical knowledge advanced in the eighteenth century, the option of deliberately giving smallpox to indigenous peoples became available and was used. In the 1720s leading British medical thinkers adopted the practice of inoculation or variolation, deliberately giving smallpox to susceptible individuals for prophylactic purposes by introducing pox crusts into arm incisions. In a time of epidemic the practice of variolation made social sense (mortality from variolation was two in one hundred whereas natural smallpox was seventeen in one hundred). But the practice could and did spread smallpox the natural way if not carefully regulated and controlled, especially if the sick individual could not effectively be quarantined. Since this task was usually beyond the capacity of contemporary social organizations, variolation was controversial. However, if the crusts were a source of contagion then perhaps they could be used to spread the disease. Apparently, on at least one occasion, during the so-called Pontiac Rebellion in 1763, smallpox crusts were deliberately secreted in materials provided to Native Americans with the intention of spreading smallpox to them. There is considerable debate surrounding the events and the sequelae, largely because of the limitations of documents.

Less debatable was the role of medical knowledge in the British victory over the French in the French and Indian War. The writings on the health of sailors by James Lind, a British physician especially famous for demonstrating that oranges and limes could prevent scurvy on long sea voyages, supported the close blockade strategy used by the Royal Navy. Lind's recommendations helped the British successfully deliver unprecedentedly healthy soldiers to both Louisburg and the Plains of Abraham during the war with the French in North America. Nutrition would also remain an area of military medical research, with frequent benefits to civil society beginning in the mid-eighteenth century.

The medicine of the American Revolution was, as in any revolution, an ad hoc affair. The colonies had local militia units but no experience with division-level maneuvers nor continental organization; the medical service, called the Hospital Department, was constructed as the army was being organized. The local medical practitioner was usually the militia surgeon and came to the colors with his regiment. Like other aspects of the army, there was a strong desire for congressional resources but little enthusiasm for higher headquarter's control of activities. Congress funded general hospitals, but the leadership of the Hospital Department was just another area of political machination.

Training in the unique aspects of military medicine did not exist before the Revolutionary War. Although American academics quickly compiled texts from European sources, they had little impact on care. Medical supplies were scarce and expensive, and therapeutic interventions that were generally regarded as effective for most diseases did not exist. Mobilization of both the militia and the new regular Continental Army brought nonimmune individuals from isolated areas together in camps where diseases were easily shared. Not surprisingly, the spread of classic camp diseases led to high morbidity and mortality during the Revolution.

Elizabeth Fenn (2002) has called attention to the fact that smallpox recurrence was a major problem during the Revolutionary War, with the 1775–1776 invasion of Canada foundering on the morbidity and mortality of that dreaded disease. British forces may have tried to spread smallpox among the colonial armies, both in Boston in 1775 and during the Southern campaigns, especially in Virginia in 1781, but data are ambivalent. In 1775, General Washington forbade variolation because of the fluid nature of militia reporting and recruitment induction. To protect the Continental Line, General Washington did have the regular force inoculated for smallpox during the winters of 1776 and 1777, and smallpox was not as significant a problem for the regulars in the second half of the war. This was the first army that had an intervention for medical prevention done by command order, although some regimental commanders had done so previously in the British army. Some historians have followed Stanhope Bayne Jones (1968) in believing this experience made the medical profession and population of the young nation during the following decades more willing to accept smallpox prophylaxis, including the use of cowpox vaccination to prevent smallpox, but no careful studies have been done to prove this assertion.

The politics of the Revolutionary and early national periods shaped the early development of American health-care institutions. Conflicts between Tories and Loyalists contributed to both the founding and the destruction of medical schools, especially in New York and Philadelphia. Such tensions played a role in the slow development of philanthropy supporting the New York Hospital. Political opinion had an impact on epidemic control efforts in the postwar period, and war experience helped develop careers. One of the careers most significantly impacted was that of John Warren (1753–1815) of Boston, who had served as a militia surgeon before the war and was the surgeon in charge of a general hospital in Boston during much of the Revolution. Warren was concerned about the skills of some young surgeons working in the hospital during the war and started a course of instruction in extremity anatomy to improve the surgical skill of his juniors. The popularity of Warren's teaching led the Harvard Corporation to appoint him professor of anatomy in the fall of 1782; two other professors and a medical school would follow in the winter and spring. The military medical establishment, like the entire army, was reduced following the war and then recreated in 1812.

American military physicians during the War of 1812 faced the same professional, mobilization, and command and control issues that existed during the Revolution. After the war the commanding general, Jacob Brown, and the secretary of war, J. C. Calhoun, convinced Congress to establish as part of the reorganization of the army a permanent medical service. In 1818 the Army Medical Department was created and Joseph Lovell (1788–1836), who had served with General Brown and prepared an influential report on the medical needs of the army, was selected as the first surgeon general. Lovell and his successor, Thomas Lawson (1789–1861), pursued a campaign of professional development aimed at appointing carefully selected and tested physicians as commissioned military officers, who would collect data and make staff recommendations to improve the health of the force. The European and Revolutionary War tradition dictated that only combat arms personnel held commissions, an aristocratic outgrowth of feudal obligations; other personnel (surgeons, lawyers, pursers, etc.) held warrants and had a different rank structure. In the new democratic United States the possibility of real commissions, with the commensurate increase in access to planning and operations, was achieved, at least in law and regulation, during the 1840s in both the army and the navy. In practice, however, tensions remained between line and staff throughout the nineteenth century in both services.

The existence of a permanent medical establishment within the military led to federal support of medical research and development, albeit on an ad hoc basis. The best known case is the work on gastric physiology by William Beaumont (1785–1853), an army surgeon who joined the military for the War of 1812 and stayed in for the next 20 years. In June of 1822, on Mackinac Island, Michigan, a Canadian voyageur, Alexis St. Martin, was accidentally shot. Beaumont was called from the local fort as the attending physician; St. Martin survived but with a gastric fistula (a hole through his skin into his stomach). Beaumont employed St. Martin as an experimental subject, placing various pieces of food directly into his stomach and extracting gastric juice for chemical analysis. Beaumont reported his work to Surgeon General Lovell, who paid for the two to come east, arranged consultations with American academics, and even assisted in enlisting St. Martin in the army to make it easier to keep him available for experimentation. Beaumont's 1833 monograph, *Experiments and Observations on the Gastric Juice and the Physiology of Digestion*, is frequently considered the most important American contribution to biomedical science prior to the twentieth century.

The navy medical establishment developed under different influences, primarily the challenges of the expensive shore establishment needed to support a sailing navy—in medicine's case, the need for hospitals. The central organization, similar to the army's, emerged in the reorganization of 1842 with the establishment of the Bureau of Medicine and Surgery; its chief, later surgeon general of the navy, would serve as a focal point for developments in professionalism. Edward Squibb (1819–1900) was a naval surgeon concerned about the differential quality of pharmaceuticals he received onboard ship. In the early 1850s he was assigned to the Brooklyn Naval Yard and developed a process for making consistently high-quality ether (introduced as an anesthetic in 1846). He resigned from the navy in 1858 to open a pharmaceutical laboratory and supply house, where he continued high-quality drug development.

Beaumont, Squibb, and other nineteenth-century medical innovators in uniform were an outgrowth of the need for a professional military medical force in America's emerging professional military, but that military remained a small cadre that expanded in time of need. Expansion brought physicians and ideas into the service during war and disseminated the ideas and experiences after the war as the physicians and patients returned to civilian life. The Second Seminole War (1835–1842) provides the first clear-cut example of war's influence on the practice of medicine in American

history—the development of the effective dosage of quinine for malaria. French researchers had first isolated quinine from cinchona bark in 1820; a few civilian practitioners subsequently experimented with its use. The challenge of the new preparation was that no one agreed on its mechanism of action or proper use. During the war army doctors collaborated, partly by sharing their prewar experiences and information as well as new data they systematically collected, which were then published in government reports under the supervision of the army medical department hierarchy. After the war, civilian teachers and practitioners cited the collective experience as an example of the scientific use of the new medicine.

War was not necessary for scientific advance. Had there been no war, physicians would have still learned to use quinine effectively. The exchange of ideas might have taken longer, and the collection of a significant number of patients, treated under common direction, would certainly have taken longer. Publication of a multiyear, multisite experience would have taken longer to assemble, but it would have happened. This prototypical second category of war's influence on medicine, "advances," that is, war-time changes later accepted in practice in health and medical science, illustrates the parameters of the typology: work initiated but not fully understood prior to the war; a need for the work during the war; an organized military effort to solve the problem; and dissemination after the war by both participants and publications. The preexistence of the ideas and the temporary military role of physicians from civilian life during the war, as well as a strong antiwar sentiment, have led some historians, like Roger Cooter (1990), to argue that war has no influence on medical progress. At the same time, failure to give sufficient attention to the preexistence of the ideas and the complex interplay of the civilian and the military during war frequently has led to overstatements of the influence of war in advancing medicine, typified by Zachary Cope's "The Medical Balance Sheet of War" (1961). The war experience in medical science is probably best seen as a "hothouse"-like phenomenon, accelerating what would happen by other means; the factors that have influenced the acceleration, however, have varied from case to case.

The Civil War. The small army and its small medical department underwent radical expansion when President Abraham Lincoln issued successive calls for volunteers. Volunteer regiments from the states brought local doctors, variously trained, and the Medical Department recruited new physicians for general hospital service. Civilian relief organizations were created—the largest was the U.S. Sanitary Commission—to provide supplies and guidance to military practitioners. The surgeon general was replaced in 1862 with a politically well-connected former military surgeon, William Hammond. Hammond led a reorganization of the Army Medical Department, which established an Army Medical Museum, a cadet corps to bring medical students into service, publications to regularize practice, and a government-supported formulary restricted to regular allopathic practice. He later began to restrict allopathic drugs—for example, removing calomel from the formulary—in an effort to improve care based on scientific data. Hammond then sought to limit sectarian medicine in the Union Army (that is, homeopathic and botanic practitioners). (Beginning in the late eighteenth century a variety of theoretical medical systems or sects had emerged with very different ideas on pathology and therapy. "Best practice" during the antebellum period had questioned the efficacy of all of them, but they remained as rival protoprofessions in antebellum America.)

Hammond supported civilian assistance in hospitals, especially dedicated nurses, and encouraged operational innovation in support of the field armies. The most significant operational innovation was the Letterman System, introduced primarily by Jonathan Letterman in the Army of the Potomac between 1862 and 1864 and extended by law to the other field armies in 1864. The Letterman System called for systematic medical command and control for the evacuation of wounded by dedicated vehicles and through an echeloned system of care, with lifesaving care given immediately and more complex care being provided at higher-echelon facilities some distance from the field of battle. It envisioned a reduced initial supply load with a push re-supply system based on usage and need. The supply reports were part of a series of inspections and reports to monitor medical effectiveness and the health and fitness of the force. The Letterman System ended with demobilization, but was adopted and adapted by European armies in the late nineteenth century and then reintroduced to the U.S. Army in World War I.

The impact of the Civil War outside the military is complicated: the experience, particularly by Union physicians (and patients), with ambulances and hospitals probably accelerated adoption of these institutions in the years after the war. Recent studies of Civil War medicine by Bollett (2002) and Rutkow (2005) have begun to redress the appraisal of care, using mid-nineteenth-century standards rather than the twentieth-century standards used by earlier medical histories. Of great significance was the Union Army decision to bar sectarian practitioners from serving their country as physicians in the conflict, placing the "regular" profession in the enviable position of being patriotic in the postwar era—a position they exploited in the debates on health legislation of the late nineteenth century, especially in the areas of anatomy laws, licensure laws, and public-health practice. Because of poverty, demographics, and perhaps lack of leadership, these developments did not contribute as clearly to changes in the profession in the South. Southern licensure, public health, and education lagged behind that of the metropolitan North in the postwar years.

Shauna Devine (2014) has argued that the war played a much more profound role in the shaping of a professional identity than has previously been considered in the development of American medical scientific thought and practice. She argues that wartime experience shaped the development of American medicine along scientific lines. In particular, she contends that the war gave American physicians enormous opportunities to conduct specific work that previously only small numbers had been able to observe in European centers. Under the leadership of the Office of the Surgeon General, Union physicians were taught autopsy techniques and case reporting and used the unprecedented opportunities provided by observing and treating deaths and injuries in the field hospitals (away from family and friends). They further used the regulations, including the requirement to submit reports to the Army Medical Museum, to vastly strengthen the scientific analysis and collection of specimens and the study of disease through postmortem analysis and experimentation. The applications of new knowledge in preventive and other approaches to disease, and the dissemination of new knowledge through publications and other professional activities, were also attempted with varying degrees of success. By 1865, thousands of Union physicians returned home having conducted autopsies, contributed postmortem reports, and attempted to correlate signs and symptoms with histologic lesions. They had begun to appreciate the importance of careful diagnosis of the natural history of diseases for evaluating the effectiveness of therapy. Their adoption of a scientific ethos for their profession and hospital-based clinical innovations led to efforts to reorganize American medicine in the Gilded Age.

The Civil War medical experience also had a broad impact on American society in general. Humphreys (2013) has highlighted the perception of the war as a breeder of disease and disability, its influence on women's roles, and the failures of racial health equity despite political efforts. The role of war on veterans remains an important area of study; Dean's pioneering work (1999) on psychiatric sequelae needs expansion to other populations, and Courtwright's suggestion (1982) that the war was a major contributor to opiate addiction has not yet been researched in detail. Despite a century and a half of research, the impact of the Civil War on American medicine has remained a fruitful field of inquiry.

Gilded Age through World War I. From the Civil War through World War I, military medicine was the most rigorous professional community in the nation, having advanced laboratories, restricted and supervised practice, and developed a system of reporting disease experience that was unmatched in the world. In Washington, D.C., at the Medical Museum, Joseph Woodward and his colleagues engaged in scientific correspondence with the medical leaders of Europe; their publications brought American experience to the world

stage. In the Library of the Army Surgeon General's Office, John Shaw Billings made pioneering contributions to medical bibliography with the creation of *Index Medicus*. Military doctors on the frontier, both before and after the Civil War, contributed significantly to the development of American ethnology and the Smithsonian collections. George Miller Sternberg, an army doctor, wrote the first English-language textbook on bacteriology (1890).

The 1898 War with Spain was a medical disaster, despite both military and medical leaders repeatedly stating that they intended to avoid the disease disasters of the past. More soldiers died in training camps of the presumably preventable camp diseases, typhoid and malaria, than died of Spanish shot and shell. The Medical Department was unprepared for rapid expansion of the force; the line officers paid virtually no attention to medical advice on camp hygiene. The postwar Dodge Commission blamed all parties. The public, aware of germs and sanitation from press coverage and the efforts of public-health reformers, responded with doubts—if army medicine was the best, how could this happen? Although the story of the war experience, public outcry, and internal reforms has been told by Gillett (1995) and Cirillo (2003), little attention has been paid to how public concerns influenced practice patterns of returning medical volunteers.

After the War with Spain, medical officers in Cuba, Puerto Rico, the Philippines, and the Canal Zone made contributions to the study and control of yellow fever, dengue, hookworm infection, malaria, and other tropical diseases. American history scholars have only just begun to carefully analyze the impact of tropical medicine research and military public-health efforts on the subsequent histories of extracontinental territories. An army physician working in Washington, D.C., Frederick Russell (1870–1960), developed an effective vaccine against typhoid fever, building on the work of British military physicians. Medical officers were assigned to military schools to improve medical tactics and the care of troops, and the medical departments of both the army and the navy underwent professional expansion with the addition of nurses, dentists, and other new health professions. For nursing in particular, the sanction of the profession by the government, through the creation of a nurse-led nursing corps in each service, was especially important. Equally significant was the acceptance of the new profession's civilian educational and training standards.

Certainly the medical professions engaged the military as part of the preparedness movement in the second decade of the new century. The Red Cross worked closely with both the army and the navy to build registries of nurses for military hospital duty. The leadership of the American Medical Association and the new American College of Surgeons served important consulting roles in the development of the Medical Reserve Corps. Instead of adopting an approach to military augmentation modeled on the tradition of state militias, they developed a new federal model that served as a prototype for the future Army and Navy Reserves. The Medical Reserve Corps and the Red Cross collaborated with the Army Medical Department in recruiting and staffing urban, frequently academic, hospital groups as the core of a new deployable Base Hospital unit to provide rapid augmentation of state-of-the-art specialty care in the event of mobilization.

Despite efforts to avoid war, war came, in 1917, and mobilization of these medical forces, along with a host of draftees and volunteers, brought military medicine into most American homes again. The reservist-staffed Base Hospital Units were the first elements of the American Expeditionary Force to reach Europe in 1917. The American participation in the war certainly facilitated the spread of flu around the world as troop ships traveling to Europe moved both prodromal patients not yet exhibiting severe symptoms and convalescent carriers who had recovered from the symptoms of the disease but were still able to transmit it to others.

As with quinine therapy in the nineteenth century, the war mostly served as a social accelerator of ideas already under discussion in medical science and practice. Although railway spine (a condition involving back pain linked to railroad accidents) and other nonorganic pain (not associated with observable lesions) had been discussed before World War I, the widespread recognition

of "shell shock" during the war brought neuropsychiatric injury into the wider discussion of the profession, although the extent to which either the profession or the public exhibited a sustained interest is a topic of continuing historical interest (see, for example, Jones and Wessely, 2005). An important and undeveloped area of research in medical history has been the stigma attached to psychiatric diseases and their relationship to military medical support and veterans' health.

A second area where medical science and practice were probably accelerated by the war experience and press coverage was the use of blood transfusion. George Crile (1864–1943) had introduced the modern era of transfusions in the first decade of the new century, but the technique was employed infrequently before the war. Its use in civilian practice immediately after the war was significantly greater than before the war. More research is needed, however, to determine the exact influence of the war because blood transfusions became frequent only in the last months of the conflict.

The impact of the war on patterns of practice—specialization and group practice—is almost certainly significant, but the histories of both changes are still areas where we have only preliminary historical research. Specialization began to appear in some cities during the late nineteenth century and significant debates about membership on local hospital staffs occurred in the years before the war. The military had hoped to meet the need for specialists through the reserve program, but too few were available. As part of its preparation for continuing needs in Europe, the army decided to train specialists in academically organized short courses, which focused on such areas as fractures and traumatic wound infection; neurological wounds, especially neurosurgery; urology, especially sexually transmitted diseases; plastic and reconstructive surgery; and pulmonary diseases, especially pneumonia and tuberculosis. The courses trained personnel to use new diagnostic tools and innovations in medical science, including the scientific laboratory and the X-ray. Although scholars have not studied the impact of these courses in detail, they were outlined in the official history of the work of the Army Medical Department during the war. Since medical education reform had started but not extended very far in 1917, these courses may have done much to improve the skills of practitioners.

Practice in the war hospitals exposed general practitioners to working with specialists and to patient care where different physicians (and other members of the health-care team) had different responsibilities. This experience of working with a group of specialists seems to have influenced the growth of group practice. The best-known example is George Crile's postwar commitment to "practice as a unit" that underlay his effort to found a group practice in Cleveland that was also modeled on the Mayo Clinic. Less studied is the influence of the war on the de facto or informal groups consisting of practitioners in mutual consultation and referral patterns of practice. These groups seem to have developed from shared hospital staff positions in "Physicians & Surgeons" buildings, structured with offices in close proximity and frequently built near hospitals during the 1920s. Hospital staff and academic referral, as well as consultation arrangements, predated the war, as did a few multispecialty group practice arrangements, but these practice patterns accelerated after the war to such a degree that a role for army experience must be carefully examined.

Other health professions were also influenced by specialist involvement during World War I. The war facilitated the professionalization of nursing, for example, and the demand for dentistry increased as the public became more aware of dental issues and concerns about oral hygiene. "Reconstruction aides," who gained visibility during the war, formed the basis for the emergence of the professions of physical and occupational therapy. Like the Civil War, World War I left a huge number of veterans with prostheses, but now reconstructive surgeons adopted regimens to aid the damaged and disabled individuals using trained paraprofessional personnel who conducted the actual hands-on manipulative therapy. Another specialty dramatically influenced by World War I was aviation medicine. During the war, the military employed all the physicians in the country who were specially trained and educated to deal with the man-machine interface and the physiology of flight.

After the war, these practitioners sought to take advantage of the emerging civilian market for aviation by developing a new civilian specialty of aviation medicine as a subset of preventive medicine.

Finally, the study of draftees in the army during World War I raised significant concerns about the health status of the American male. Health education efforts followed in many state educational systems, and child health advocates used the data to improve public-health programs. The Selective Service medical reports were caught up in the ongoing immigration debates of early-twentieth-century America. Alan Kraut's *Silent Travelers* remains the gold standard for the study of health and immigration, including many of the issues raised by the draft. One area did develop anew, the psychological examination of recruits, and the military added psychologists to its community of health professions.

World War II. World War II, which left millions of veterans with service-related health issues, transformed health care in America to a degree rivaled only by the Civil War. It shaped crucial social questions, accelerated research, and expanded governmental commitment to medical progress.

The shifting patterns of practice and the emerging role of specialty care remained complex in the 1920s and 1930s. The need for both specialists and generalists was commonly conceded, but how to achieve (or even what constituted) the right balance was widely debated. Both the army and the navy recruited specialists into their medical reserve corps and planned to use them in the event of war. The new urban economy utilized hospitals and specialists, but the Depression had slowed industrial and urban transformation. Although the power of medical research was increasingly recognized in fiction and public-opinion periodicals, philanthropic and state support of medical research grew only slowly during this period. The development of hospital-based surgical care and the efforts to pay for it with voluntary health insurance also shaped practice patterns during the interwar years.

When President Franklin Roosevelt ordered mobilization in 1940, the Army Medical Department needed a way to select and credential large numbers of specialists for the dozens of general hospitals the war planners believed the country would need. With the advice of senior reserve specialists, the Army Medical Department decided to use the brand-new civilian system of specialty board certification to appoint medical officers as specialists. If a physician had "boards" he was a specialist; if not, he was a generalist. The system of specialty boards had been created in the 1930s to control specialization, but it had the virtue of being external to the military and generally approved by the leadership of the civilian medical profession. The recruitment of board-certified specialists went well because they were assigned to hospitals rather than field duty and enjoyed an extra grade or two of military rank.

When the war began in 1941, mobilization was not complete. The American Medical Association endorsed the use of boards to identify and recruit specialists as part of the effort to negotiate draft exemptions for physicians. The war required a huge number of doctors and the AMA encouraged its constituent county medical societies to collaborate with the draft boards to encourage the younger and fitter members of the profession to "volunteer"; county medical societies used sanctions to encourage those members slow to volunteer. As Stevens (1989) has pointed out, the military decision to commission specialists at a higher grade and so pay them more than general practitioners certainly made specialization more attractive to young physicians and those training during the war. For the generalist in the war itself, the contrast was even sharper. Specialists worked in the hospitals, well behind the lines, with warm food, sheets, and soft beds; generalists were often assigned as battalion surgeons, sleeping on the ground and within range of the enemy's guns. There is probably no definition of social worth so dramatic as distance from enemy bullets.

Largely unstudied, but probably of great significance, are the demographics of health-care access during the war. Whereas only about 8 percent of Americans served during the war, participation by American physicians was almost 40 percent. If almost 40 percent of all doctors are restricted to taking care of 8 percent of the potential patients, there is almost bound to be an impact on expecta-tion of care and access to care. Having received prompt access to care during the war, often including referral to specialists, military beneficiaries not surprisingly anticipated receiving similar benefits when they returned to civilian life. Although the war likely would have had an impact on medical care on the home front, there has been little study of the role that limited access during the war may have played on American health or in attitudes toward health-care consumption after the war.

The Servicemen's Readjustment Act of 1944 (the GI Bill) played an especially important role in the development of American health care after the war, as it did on other aspects of American life. The GI Bill provided tuition reimbursement (mainly college and technical school tuition) for the retraining of GIs to enter the civilian workforce; innovative hospital administrators argued that because residents were engaged in graduate medical education, the Veterans Administration (VA) should provide support for residency slots in hospitals. The VA agreed, and residency opportunities, especially surgical and surgical subspecialty residencies, expanded exponentially in the late 1940s. Another of the dramatic impacts of the GI Bill was the expansion of home ownership in ready-built suburban communities. The Hospital Survey and Construction Act of 1946 (the Hill-Burton Act) made available federal matching funds to build hospitals in these (or other) suburban areas. So, as military medical practice in the war created a demand for hospital-based specialty care, the GI Bill and other postwar acts of Congress capitalized the expansion of the supply.

Of great long-term significance was the creation of the VA Dean's Hospital, a VA hospital intimately tied to an Academic Health Center. The VA administrator responsible for this innovation, General Omar Bradley (1893–1981), and his medical director, Paul Hawley (1891–1965), who had served as Bradley's chief doctor in the Army's European Theater of Operations, were trying to expand the prewar VA hospital system to care for World War II veterans. The VA hospitals had a severe shortage of full-time doctors (fewer than one thousand) and a reputation for substandard medicine, largely because of their custodial and rural orientation after World War I. General Bradley received advice about measures he could take to solve these problems from a team of experts that included a respected orthopedic surgeon from Chicago, Paul B. Magnuson (1884–1968), and the cardiovascular surgeon Michael E. De-Bakey (1908–2008), who was retained on active duty as a consultant to help shape graduate medical education in the Army Medical Department. They proposed a novel idea—tie a new VA hospital with a medical school.

The new VA hospitals would operate as teaching hospitals with a medical school faculty in charge of medical care and a dean's committee overseeing each institution. It was a bold move that would forever change the face of the nation's health care. Doctors were paid part time, often 80 percent by the government and part time by the medical school (sometimes to greater than 100 percent of a federal approved salary), radically expanding the medical school faculty, especially in medical subspecialties. VA-supported faculty members headed most of the subspecialty training programs in medical subspecialties in the 1950s. In addition, VA hospitals opened hundreds of new residency training positions for potential specialists in many fields. The impact of the education and research done by VA physicians and hospitals on the American health-care system in the second half of twentieth century is difficult to overestimate. This secondary impact of World War II on American health care is especially significant, extending well into the 1960s and early 1970s.

World War II significantly changed the expectations and availability of health-care providers during the postwar period, but it also changed the ability of consumers to afford the specialty-oriented, hospital-based system of care. The voluntary, philanthropy-financed Commission on the Costs of Medical Care had recognized in 1932 that for American medicine to continue to expand access, health insurance coverage would need to grow substantially. But by 1940 only slightly more than 9 percent of Americans had health coverage. During World War II, to achieve stability in war production the federal government froze wages across much of the industrial sector of the economy; however, since industry still needed to attract workers, employers and unions expanded fringe benefits, especially health insurance. In 1950, with more than 53 percent of Americans having health insurance coverage, paying for specialized hospital care became practical.

The example of the impact of World War II on medicine most often cited is the medical research sponsored by the government during the war, especially the introduction of penicillin. Like quinine therapy and blood transfusions in earlier wars, antibiotic research antedates the war; antibiosis as a concept goes back to Pasteur and penicillin research back to Alexander Fleming (1881–1955) in the 1920s. In the immediate prewar years, a research group at Oxford University, headed by Howard Florey (1898–1968), had begun productive research on penicillin antibiotic therapy. The group had isolated the active ingredient from the mold and had performed limited, but highly suggestive, therapeutic trials. However, the British pharmaceutical industry did not have sufficient capacity to explore commercial development of the new drug as war came to Britain in 1939. Florey told his American friends about the research and urged them to explore the possibilities. Alfred Newton Richards (1876–1966) of the University of Pennsylvania, who was serving as chair of the new Committee on Medical Research of the Office of Scientific Research and Development, decided to work on the problem.

The Office of Scientific Research and Development was created as part of the prewar mobilization to ensure that academic research on scientific and medical problems related to national defense received adequate attention. For penicillin, two efforts would be required: the development of large-scale production and therapeutic trials on the effective uses of the new drug. Richards undertook the first effort himself, calling a meeting with the research directors of four drug companies (Merck, Squibb, Lilly, and Pfizer) and the representatives of various interested government departments, particularly the Department of Agriculture, to request a collaborative development effort in the interest of national defense. The companies laid aside their proprietary interests and agreed to cooperate, in large measure because of the national emergency, the 7 December 1941 bombing of Pearl Harbor, and the needs of war wounded, but also because they expected the natural fermentation process to be replaced by proprietary syntheses in the near future. Chester Keefer (1897–1972) of the Thorndike Laboratory in Boston was asked to coordinate the therapeutic trial effort. Keefer was rigorous, if not rigid, in his determination to only release penicillin to physicians who followed a carefully constructed clinical trial protocol. His authority was only enforceable because of the powers assumed by the federal government in the war effort.

The war brought many academic physicians into the military. Both the training camps and the conflict exposed a host of patients to infections ranging from childhood diseases to a variety of bacterial pathogens infecting traumatic injuries. Different trials studied groups of patients and determined the utility of penicillin across a broad spectrum of diseases. By late 1943, both the utilization of the drug and the supply problems were being resolved. As the historian Robert Bud has documented, many observers believed that because the war had accelerated the peacetime development of penicillin in such a dramatic way, it appeared that the conflict had essentially produced the discovery of the new and miraculous drug.

The development of antibiotics for bacterial infections was not the only focus of infectious disease research during World War II. Because of the prevalence of malaria in the Mediterranean, the South Pacific, and many regions in Asia where fighting took place, researchers also renewed efforts to combat parasitic tropical infections. Malaria had been a major problem in the United States before the first half of the twentieth century when a successful public-health effort aimed at draining the areas where mosquitos bred and encouraging economic development managed to confine the disease to the rural South. The German pharmaceutical industry had developed a synthetic antimalarial drug in the 1930s, Atabrine, but knowledge of its use was limited. In the American South mosquito-control techniques had been developed, but an effective adulticide was not available; researchers then focused their efforts on the use of DDT, which had been resynthesized in

1937. An interallied committee studied Atabrine prophylaxis and an army entomology lab in Florida studied pesticides.

Malaria was controlled in troops before the end of the war, and the use of new repellants and DDT became the basis for successful mosquito-control programs reducing insect-borne diseases after the war in the United States and around the world. The successes of the war effort helped inspire the United States and the World Health Organization to attempt to eradicate malaria during the postwar period, but the program foundered on political and ecological realities. During the second decade of the early twenty-first century, malaria remained the significant disease issue in the tropical world, and the American military research community continued antimalarial work as both a troop protection and a health diplomacy issue. The memory of influenza from the 1918 pandemic suggested another area of research for American military researchers during World War II. The army organized the Board for the Investigation and Control of Influenza and Other Epidemic Diseases, which represented a collaborative activity among serving regular officers, academics in the service for the duration of the war, and academics still in civilian life. The board formed a series of commissions to investigate various camp disease problems, starting with respiratory infections but soon including gastrointestinal infections and other diseases. At the end of the war, the organization was rechartered as the Army Epidemiological Board and then, in 1949, renamed the Armed Forces Epidemiological Board. The board served as a continuing and dynamic interface between military medical research and the civilian academic health centers of the nation into the 1970s. As late as the early twenty-first century, it continued to serve an important consulting role in national public-health policy.

Throughout the war a host of young, academically inclined physicians received opportunities that would have taken decades to acquire in peacetime. This was particularly true in surgical areas. For example, Dwight Harken (1910–1993), while assigned to an Army General Hospital in England, took care of dozens of soldiers with pieces of metal in and around their hearts. From this work, he acquired in 18 months more experience operating in the cardiac cavity than anyone else in the world. An accidental chemical munitions contamination of the waters off Bari, Italy, created patients with suppressed lymphoid tissue, leading Stewart Francis Alexander (1914–1991) to suggest, in an after-action report, that this might have implications for cancer therapy. Dr. Louis Goodman (1906–2000) had an army contract to study potential therapies for chemical attack victims and used the Alexander report as the basis for a clinical trial to treat lymphoma patients with a nitrogen mustard preparation. Limited as it was, Goodman's trial started the search for chemotherapeutic agents and shaped the subspecialty of oncology after the war. The navy initiated studies of blood in the Chelsea Naval Hospital with Edwin Cohn (1892–1953) of Harvard as a collaborator; blood fractionation and the continuing study of hematology in the postwar period were influenced by this work.

Although the unique opportunities incidental to war could not be replicated in the postwar world, federal support might be. As the war came to a close, leaders of the army and navy medical research programs planned to close the research grants and contracts driven by wartime concerns, but Thomas Parran (1892–1968), the Surgeon General of the United States and head of the U.S. Public Health Service, offered to assume the management of the programs using the grant-giving authority of the National Cancer Institute. Parran and his deputy, Rollo Dyer, asked Congress for an expansion of the program in the immediate postwar years and the National Institutes of Health extramural research program was born. The National Institutes of Health grant program shaped and supported the vast expansion of American academic medicine in the middle years of the twentieth century and, like VA hospitals and faculty members, should be viewed as a second-order impact of the military medical efforts during World War II.

A similar second-order impact, as recent studies have demonstrated, was that of American military medicine on occupied Japan; it was in many ways just as dramatic as the early-twentieth-century impact of military medicine in the tropical world (Aldous and Suzuki, 2012).

The Cold War—Korea and Vietnam. Research questions and health programs undertaken in World War II often continued into the Cold War era, and military medical research and funding was a significant component of American medicine. Famine has long been associated with war and World War II was no exception as German U-boats tried to starve Britain into submission. The Army Quartermaster had laboratories and contracts devoted to nutritional studies and the creation of field rations. Ancel Keys (1904–2004), a physiologist at the Mayo Clinic, undertook basic nutritional experiments during the war (the K ration) and from continued studies after the war, as Tucker (2008) has recently shown, laid the foundations for food diplomacy during the Cold War.

Interest in psychoactive drugs began with rumors about new drugs during World War II but took on new urgency, in 1947, when lysergic acid diethylamide (LSD) was introduced into the United States. Almost immediately, military and civilian agencies began experimenting with psychoactive pharmaceuticals. Their purposes varied—interrogation, weapons, and therapy were all researched at various times. The programs continued into the 1970s. The growth of civilian federal activities involved with national security, paradigmatically the Central Intelligence Agency, introduced a new set of research players in the Cold War era. Stevens (1987) and Moreno (2006) have analyzed the complex history of national defense issues and psychopharmaceuticals.

Three World War II research areas were particularly important for the Korean Conflict and remain largely unstudied: thermal injuries, cold injury prevention, and acceleration injury and safety. During World War II the study of burns, both in civilian settings like Massachusetts General Hospital following the Coconut Grove Nightclub fire (1942) and in the Surgical Research Unit at Halloran General Hospital on Staten Island, had demonstrated the significance of metabolism in surgical wound healing and the importance of maintaining an appropriate balance of fluids and electrolytes in patients to avoid shock. With the development of the atomic bomb and the early reports of the Atomic Bomb Commission after the war, the military redoubled its efforts to study thermal injury. As part of this effort, the Surgical Research Unit was moved to San Antonio in 1947 and, two years later, was specifically directed to study burns. Much of modern burn treatment relates to work done and surgeons trained in San Antonio.

During the 1944 campaigns in Italy and the Battle of the Bulge in the European Theater of Operations, the army lost a significant number of soldiers to injuries caused by cold weather. Although the losses partly resulted from command failure, the Army Medical Department, in collaboration with the Quartermaster Corps and the U.S. Marine Corps, thought better cold-weather clothing would help immeasurably. Researchers at the Natick, Massachusetts, Quartermaster laboratory and at the Pickle Meadow field-testing area in California studied the physiology of cold injury and developed innovative gear based on the new research. The military used the new equipment, which made creative use of insulating materials in layers, during the Korean Conflict and found that it served admirably to reduce cold injuries. These developments later served as a foundation for the commercial development of a new cold-weather clothing industry. The new gear not only prevented cold weather–related injuries but also made possible a vast expansion of winter sporting events.

Also during World War II, the newly independent Air Force Medical Service joined the navy in studying the rapid acceleration and deceleration needed to evacuate a pilot from a jet airplane in an emergency. (The pilot was literally dynamited out of the plane by an explosive charge when he needed to eject.) John Paul Stapp (1910–1999), with the U.S. Air Force, built a rocket slide and, with other volunteers, rode the sled to study the physiology and necessary design restraints that would allow the pilot to experience the required acceleration and deceleration safely. These restraints formed the basis for the introduction of new automobile seatbelts in the 1960s that helped prevent thousands of unnecessary automobile accident injuries and fatalities. When the Cold War heated up on the Korean peninsula, these activities were ongoing, along with research in other areas of military medical interest including orthopedics,

reconstructive medicine, infectious diseases, and psychiatry.

As had the two previous twentieth-century wars, the Korean Conflict focused attention on wounds, infections, and neuropsychiatric care. In the study of wound care, first-generation studies, often in the clinical literature, superficially ascribe much to the war experience. The most repeated story of the impact of the Korean War is the "introduction" of arterial repair. Although surgeons had been performing arterial repair for 40 years prior to the military effort in Korea, it had been uncommon and frequently unsuccessful. During the late 1940s, in academic surgical centers, arterial repair was becoming increasingly common and successful; it was in fact the Walter Reed General Hospital vascular surgery team that went to Korea to perform wartime vascular repair. Several memoirs have told of young surgeons, pulled from training, who either did or wanted to perform arterial repairs late in the Korean War. (Official policy did not allow it.) Like blood transfusion in World War I, the story of vascular surgery in the era of the Korean Conflict calls for detailed study.

Many of those involved also argued after the war that there was significant progress in the postoperative care of spinal trauma. Even if the results were better, the progress may not have resulted from new knowledge but from more resources. Historians must consider the health-care resources devoted to patients in the Korean War; there were both more doctors and more ancillary professionals per patient than in World War II. American manufacturing and medical supplies were not limited. Small wars during the Cold War tended to be resource rich because the nation could afford it. Resources impact health outcomes.

Research on infectious diseases during the Korean Conflict highlighted the emerging discipline of virology, with both the known Japanese B encephalitis and the unknown Korean hemorrhagic fever the focus of considerable military medical research. Albert Sabin (1906–1993), a University of Cincinnati researcher who had worked on Japanese B encephalitis during World War II, assisted the military as a consultant during the Korean Conflict with vaccine trials and improvements; both the army and the navy began sustained virus research programs in their permanent laboratories in the United States and abroad. The hemorrhagic fevers were not well understood and new models of patient care emerged, particularly the artificial kidney developed by Willem Johan Kolff (1911–2009). The use of renal dialysis with Korean hemorrhagic fever and postoperative acute renal failure proved lifesaving in Korea. The role of the war in the development and use of the artificial kidney is not well studied, but postoperative renal failure was a significant complication in civilian surgery so the military publications may have had a role to play in improved postoperative care.

The early months of the Korean War saw a significant number of neuropsychiatric casualties; however, the reintroduction of the division psychiatrist and the establishment of successful World War II treatment methods reduced the problem to customary levels. There may be a relationship between the management of combat reaction by psychiatrists in Korea and the development of group therapy during the 1950s. Historians must conduct careful studies to evaluate self-interested contemporary claims. More socially divisive was the experience of "brainwashing," a journalistic term for behavior modifications pioneered by the Chinese during the Communist Revolution of the 1940s. Researchers wanted to understand why a higher percentage of captured American prisoners during the Korean Conflict collaborated with the enemy compared to previous wars. Freudian psychologists looked to the failure of American mothers in child rearing; others looked at social factors involving the class and education of those in the Korean-era armed forces. Despite studies at the time and since, no careful history of the experience exists.

The largest impact of the Korean War was again social. The Cold War standing army was a new American military departure, and 1950 saw the introduction of the "Doctor Draft" to help staff the military health system for the Cold War Defense establishment. For the next 22 years every healthy male medical graduate was obligated for two years of military (or equivalent public) service. In 1954, the law was modified, at the suggestion of Frank Berry (1892–1976), the assistant secretary of defense (health and medical), to give medical graduates an option of deferring service to allow them to complete specialty training. The deferred physicians would owe three, or in some cases four, years of service. This "Berry Plan," by bringing academically inclined, recently certified specialists into military hospitals and laboratories where they could continue their academic work, improved military medical education and research and created the medical version of Eisenhower's "military-industrial complex." These young physicians moved comfortably between their positions with mentors in civilian life, positions in the military medical services with colleagues of their mentors, and their own civilian positions. Some served in the U.S. Public Health Service, including the so-called "yellow berets" of the 1960s who were crucial to the emergence of the National Institutes of Health as an intramural research force in American medicine. The role of the Doctor Draft that resulted in 10 to 15 percent of American physicians of a generation spending time in uniform, and particularly the Berry Plan subset, remains an area in need of detailed and careful study.

Two areas where the Doctor Draft and the Berry Plan had a clear positive influence were in the expansion of specialized burn centers across the nation and the development of subspecialty pathology. The Surgical Research Unit studying thermal injuries in San Antonio became the Institute of Surgical Research and staffed a special ward in the Brooke Army General Hospital for the experimental care of burn patients. The military used the domestic areomedical evacuation system to move badly burned patients to the Burn Center, and pioneering care attracted surgical trainees from across the nation. Not only did burn specialists at the center make major contributions to thermal injury research, but also both the regular officers who led the work and their short-term fellows left the San Antonio area to establish burn centers in virtually every major academic health center in the United States during the late 1950s and the 1960s.

The revolving door between civilian academic and military laboratories was especially robust at the Armed Forces Institute of Pathology (AFIP). Founded as the Army Medical Museum in 1862, the AFIP grew into a tri-service pathological consulting laboratory of international fame in the second half of the twentieth century. After they returned to civilian life, medical professionals supported by the Berry Plan used military graduate education courses developed in the 1950s to enhance civilian programs. The AFIP charged for these courses and published course materials on the various registries of pathological specimens and cases, mixing private and public monies with cavalier abandon despite laws to the contrary.

By 1975, the various AFIP courses and registries were crucial to many specialty education activities across the nation but were becoming an embarrassment to the Army Surgeon General, who had legal responsibility for the institute. Senator Edward Kennedy (1932–2009), with the assistance of Arthur M. Silverstein, a Johns Hopkins University immunologist serving a congressional fellowship, prepared a new law chartering the American Registry of Pathology as a not-for-profit private company and allowing the use of AFIP personnel for civilian educational and consulting work in collaboration with the American Registry of Pathology. By the 1990s, the crucial role of the AFIP had declined, in large part because it trained its own competition and academic subspecialty pathology had built its own training programs.

The Doctor Draft and the Berry Plan came to an end in 1973 with the creation of the all-volunteer military in the post-Vietnam era. In subsequent years, the intimate association of American civilian medicine with medicine in the military that had existed since 1940 rapidly declined. The decline may have been accelerated by a growing anti-military sentiment among academic physicians, which resulted from the politically divisive Vietnam War. The Vietnam War saw significant medical research but much of it was on diseases of the tropics, particularly malaria. In the late 1960s, malaria among returning servicemen was so common that the Department of Defense and the American Medical Association collaborated on continuing-education programs for physicians to get them to consider malaria in their differential diagnoses. Work on acute combat reaction, the immediate neuropsychiatric injury of intense combat, continued during Vietnam; but the post-Vietnam

recognition of posttraumatic stress disorders, especially in nurses who had not seen actual combat duty, opened a new dimension of neuroscience research.

Advances in injury care and surgical research also continued during the Vietnam War. Vascular surgeons moved on to reconstruction of venous injury, and surgeons developed new orthopedic and reconstructive techniques. The improvement of postoperative care, especially electronic monitoring of patients, which was intimately tied to civilian medicine and the emergence in various centers of critical care units, is an area that needs further exploration. Frozen blood was used but not found to be the answer to trauma management, especially in the resource-rich environment of America's involvement in the Vietnam War. Blood research continued, mostly under military medical–funded contracts.

The Vietnam War did have one obvious impact on American medical care: the helicopter evacuation system that became a fixture at seemingly every hospital. Helicopter evacuation had been used in Burma and the Philippines toward the end of World War II and had become common in the Korean War, but the helicopters were fragile and slow. By the mid-1960s a robust helicopter had been developed for the purpose of battlefield evacuation, and the "Dust-Off" system of evacuating soldiers from the place where they were wounded became commonplace in Vietnam. Pictures of helicopter evacuation on the evening news combined with two other social phenomena put helicopters in every hospital: the need for Emergency Medical Systems and the automobile accident epidemic often remembered as "death on the highways." The death on the highways period was probably a result of automobiles engineered to create more power but not engineered for more safety, combined with diverse roadway quality and inadequate driver-training programs; whatever the causes, the nation experienced a dramatic increase in automobile-related deaths during the late 1960s.

The recognition that medical intervention could save lives, particularly in traffic accidents and heart attacks, led to the building of systems of emergency care, including prehospital care based on "military medic" models. R. Adams Cowley (1917–1991) at the University of Maryland, while studying shock under an army contract, developed the idea of the "golden hour" in which surgical intervention could be effective. The concept has been much discussed and data in support and against are commonplace, but the idea had political appeal. Despite studies questioning whether helicopters could make a difference, the Military Assistance to Safety and Traffic program was launched in San Antonio and Denver, making military evacuation helicopters available to civilian hospitals for the transportation of accident victims. Maryland used state police helicopters and other jurisdictions followed suit with civilian systems.

In the second Reagan administration, Republican leaders began to legislate the idea of balanced federal budgets and automatic sequestration when targets were not met. They attempted to impose cuts and limits in an equal amount on both the national security budget and the domestic portion of the budget. In 1991 (Fiscal Year 1992) Congress authorized the Army Medical Research Command to undertake peer-reviewed breast cancer research and appropriated funds that could not be added to the National Cancer Institute budget because of the budget-balancing laws. During the next fiscal year, the funds were increased almost 1000 percent, and military medicine began to influence American medicine in a new way—a way, arguably, not related to war (a justification based on the expansion of the number of women in the military). The military medical research community developed an exceptionally well-regarded extramural research program.

Also during the 1980s, and perhaps related to the antimilitary sentiment among academics, activists tried to hold the military responsible for exposing soldiers to chemicals and other factors that might produce chronic diseases. The recognition of various risk factors associated with chronic diseases in the last third of the twentieth century and the fact that military life potentially exposed soldiers to risks not seen in civilian life led to compensation claims. Compensation was not new; gas in World War I and Agent Orange in Vietnam had led to legislative battles to gain compensation when data were ambivalent, at best. The National Acad-

emies of Science report *Veterans at Risk* began with the ahistorical assumption that human values and respect for others are timeless. (They should be but the data say they are not.) The conclusions had more to do with the belief that the military leaders should have known of the risk and that they secretly exposed personnel in a callous disregard for their future health. The Adventist Church and U.S. Army developed a joint program for the use of human subjects in biological warfare research, Operation Whitecoat, which illustrates the ambiguities of retrospective medical ethics discussions. The contributions of Susan Lederer, a professor of history of medicine at the University of Wisconsin, in her role as a member of the official advisory committee established in 1994 to investigate the government's involvement in human radiation experiments, illustrate the responsible use of history in these kind of studies (historical integrity while acknowledging Americans may have been damaged and deserve help). Because of the strong feelings of many previous commentators, retrospective risk studies associated with military service will always remain especially difficult to write.

End of the Cold War to the Early Twenty-First Century. With the "end of the Cold War" and the effort to reduce the Defense establishment as part of the so-called "peace dividend," the military provided less support for academic medical research; academics became even less involved in military medicine. Although military medicine met standards of civilian practice, by law military physicians were required for the first time in 1991 to have a state license to practice in military hospitals. Operation Desert Shield and Operation Desert Storm underscored the high cost of moving modern medicine to the far-flung battlefield. Even the support of antipiracy and antiterror activities required significant medical investment. Although the military made history with the development of new patient evacuation technologies used in support of Operation Iraqi Freedom and other conflicts in the early twenty-first century, how those technologies would be applied to civilian medicine has remained unclear.

The twenty-first-century wars, like their antecedents, have faced medical challenges, including infectious diseases, neuropsychiatric care, and trauma care and rehabilitation. The military medical departments have reopened some of the bridges to civilian research with new models of collaboration. The Armed Forces Institute of Regenerative Medicine is a multi-institutional, interdisciplinary network working to develop advanced treatment options for the country's severely wounded servicemen and women. Innovations in control of bleeding and pain management that have been part of twenty-first-century combat casualty care have followed the pattern of earlier conflicts by originating in civilian hospitals and laboratories during peacetime.

The public awareness of psychiatric problems and the discovery that at least some of the illnesses believed to be functional are partly organic and can be defined as forms of mild traumatic brain injury have begun to help modify the stigma attached to the problems associated with postdeployment reintegration. A potential relationship between sports medicine and military experience is probable but its shape has not yet been determined. If the appreciation of the soldier in the early twenty-first century results in changes in the culture of stigma for psychiatric care, it will initiate a major cultural shift in American health, but the early data remain ambivalent. The all-volunteer force and repeated deployments have reduced the impact of contemporary military experience on American life, but the role of physicians and surgeons with war experience or awareness of wartime practice has anecdotally improved care in such high-profile cases as the 2011 assassination attempt on Congresswoman Gabrielle Gifford and the Boston Marathon bombing of 2013.

War will always remain an unpleasant and dangerous experience; people will continue to be injured and public health disrupted. The long-term impacts will remain difficult to fully understand. As war has become more destructive and medicine has become more capable, expectations have risen; and as long as war is dangerous there will be room for improvement. The expectations extend beyond the care of soldiers and sailors; the steady growth of international law with respect to the treatment of civilians in a war zone is only one area illustrating such changing social expectations.

In American history the various relationships between war and medicine illustrate these changing expectations at both the individual and the social level. Not surprisingly, wars in which a high percentage of the practicing physicians were mobilized, for example, the Civil War and World War II, had profound impacts on American medicine; the Doctor Draft of the middle quarter of the twentieth century was perhaps a Cold War proxy of a high-mobilization war. That wars in which strong political divisions existed, for example, the Revolutionary War and the Vietnam Conflict, have sequelae in the postwar social policy debates, including health and medicine, is not surprising but seldom considered. Beginning with the National Security Strategy change in 2010, the U.S. Department of Defense acquired a mission much broader than its traditional combat roles; it was required to provide humanitarian assistance and stability operations in cooperation with the Department of State. Military medicine has had a long history of acute humanitarian responses, but the 2010 strategy has taken the future of health and the American military establishment into new and even more complex arenas.

[*See also* **Animal and Human Experimentation; Cardiology; Death and Dying; Dentistry; Ethics and Medicine; Forensic Pathology and Death Investigation; Group Practice; Influenza; Malaria; Mayo Clinic; Medical Specialization; Medicine; Medicine and Technology; National Institutes of Health; Nursing; Penicillin; Psychiatry; Public Health; Smallpox; Surgery;** *and* **Tuberculosis.**]

BIBLIOGRAPHY

Aldous, Christopher, and Akihito Suzuki. *Reforming Public Health in Occupied Japan, 1945–52,* London: Routledge, 2012.

Anderson, Fred. *The Crucible of War.* New York: Alfred A. Knopf, 2000. The author skillfully places letters by Lord Jeffrey Amherst dealing with smallpox and Indian warfare in their proper context. Letters can also be found at http://www.umass.edu/legal/derrico/amherst/lord_jeff.html

Barger, A. C., Benison, S., and Wolfe, E. L. "Walter B. Cannon and the Mystery of Shock: A Study of Anglo-American Co-operation in World War I." *Medical History* 35 (1991): 217–249.

Bayne Jones, Stanhope. *Preventive Medicine in the United States Army, 1607–1939*. Washington, D.C.: Army Medical Department, 1968.

Berry, F. F. "The Story of the 'Berry Plan.'" *Bulletin of the New York Academy of Medicine* 52, no. 3 (1976): 278–282.

Bollett, Alfred J. *Civil War Medicine: Challenges and Triumphs*. Tucson, Ariz.: Galen Press, 2002. Began a modern and more historically informed trend in the interpretation of medicine in the Civil War.

Brandt, Allan M. *No Magic Bullet: A Social History of Venereal Disease in the United States since 1880*. New York: Oxford University Press, 1985. An excellent introduction to the campaign to control sexually transmitted diseases in the United States and especially the role of war mobilization and the military in the campaign.

Bud, Robert. *Penicillin: Triumph and Tragedy*. Oxford and New York: Oxford University Press, 2007. Currently the best overview of the introduction of penicillin.

Burnham, John C. "The New Psychology: From Narcissism to Social Control." In *Change and Continuity in Twentieth Century America: The 1920s*, edited by J. Braeman, R. H. Brencher, and D. Brody pp. 351–398. Columbus: Ohio State University Press, 1968. Provides an excellent orientation to post–World War I developments in psychology.

Cirillo, Vincent. *Bullets and Bacilli: The Spanish-American War and Military Medicine*. New Brunswick, N.J.: Rutgers University Press, 2003.

Collingham, Lizzie. *The Taste of War: World War Two and the Battle for Food*. New York: Penguin Press, 2012.

Committee to Review the Department of Defense's Breast Cancer Research Program, Institute of Medicine. *A Review of the Department of Defense's Program for Breast Cancer Research*. Washington, D.C.: National Academies Press, 1997.

Cooter, Roger. "Medicine and the Goodness of War." *Canadian Bulletin of Medical History/ Bulletin canadien d'histoire de la médicine* 7 (1990): 147–159.

Cope, Zachary. "The Medical Balance Sheet of War." In *Some Famous General Practitioners and other Medical Historical Essays*, pp. 169–183. London: Pitman, 1961.

Courtwright, David. *Dark Paradise: A History of Opiate Addiction in America*. Cambridge, Mass.: Harvard University Press, 1982. A pioneering but still very useful work on the social history of addiction.

Cowdrey, Albert E. *Fighting for Life: American Military Medicine in World War II*. New York: Free Press, 1994.

Cowdrey, Albert E. "'Germ Warfare' and Public Health in the Korean Conflict." *Journal of the History of Medicine* 39 (1984): 153–172. A careful look by a careful scholar at the charges of germ warfare in the Korean War.

Dean, Eric. *Shook over Hell: Post Traumatic Stress in Vietnam and the Civil War*. Cambridge, Mass.: Harvard University Press, 1999.

Devine, Shauna. *Learning from the Wounded*. Chapel Hill: University of North Carolina Press, 2014.

Dorland, Peter, and James Nanney. *Dust Off: Army Aeromedical Evacuation in Vietnam*. Washington, D.C.: U.S. Government Printing Office, 1982.

Downs, Jim. *Sick from Freedom: African-American Illness and Suffering during the Civil War and Reconstruction*. New York: Oxford University Press, 2012.

Fenn, Elizabeth. *Pox Americana: The Great Smallpox Epidemic of 1775–82*. New York: Macmillan, 2002. An innovative look at the social and political role of epidemic smallpox in the Revolutionary era, students will mine this work for ideas for years to come.

Final Report of the Advisory Committee on Human Radiation Experiments. Washington, D.C.: U.S. Government Printing Office, 1995. In my judgment, the most historically informed of the retrospective looks at the military and human-use issues.

Foster, Gaines. *The Demands of Humanity: Army Medical Disaster Relief*. Washington, D.C.: Center for Military History, 1983.

Gillespie, R. D. *The Psychological Effects of War on Citizen and Soldier*. New York: W. W. Norton, 1942.

Gillett, Mary C. *History of the Army Medical Department, 1775–1818*. Washington, D.C.: U.S. Government Printing Office, 1981.

Gillett, Mary C. *History of the Army Medical Department, 1818–1865*. Washington, D.C.: U.S. Government Printing Office, 1987.

Gillett, Mary C. *History of the Army Medical Department, 1865–1917*. Washington, D.C.: U.S. Government Printing Office, 1995.

Gillett, Mary C. *History of the Army Medical Department, 1917–1941*. Washington, D.C.: U.S. Government Printing Office, 2009.

Gourley, E. J., Schreiber, M. A., Gerhardt, R. T., and Stewart, T. R. "Military Assistance to Safety and Traffic Services in El Paso: A Retrospective Analysis." *Military Medicine* 165 (2000): 870–874.

Gritzer, Glen, and Arnold Arluke. *The Making of Rehabilitation: A Political Economy of Medical Specialization, 1890–1980.* Berkeley: University of California Press, 1985.

Haller, John S. *Farmcarts to Fords: A History of the Military Ambulance, 1790–1925.* Springfield: Southern Illinois University Press, 1992. First careful look at the issues around the development of modern ambulance systems.

Hartcup, Guy. *The War of Invention: Scientific Developments, 1914–18.* London: Brassey's Defence Publishers, 1988.

Hays, Marguerite T. *VA Research, 1925–1980.* Bloomington, Ind.: Author House, 2010.

Healy, David. *Images of Trauma: From Hysteria to Post-Traumatic Stress Disorder.* London: Faber & Faber, 1993.

Henry, Robert S. *The Armed Forces Institute of Pathology: Its First Century, 1862–1962.* Washington, D.C.: U.S. Government Printing Office, 1964.

Herbert, James. "Psychology on the March: American Psychologists and World War II." Unpublished PhD thesis, University of Pennsylvania, 1986.

Howell, Joel D. *Technology in the Hospital: Transforming Patient Care in the Early Twentieth Century.* Baltimore: Johns Hopkins University Press, 1995. An early history of the modern American hospital that places the war experience in context.

Humphreys, Margaret. *Intensely Human: The Health of the Black Soldier in the American Civil War.* Baltimore: Johns Hopkins University Press, 2008.

Humphreys, Margaret. *Marrow of Tragedy.* Baltimore: Johns Hopkins University Press, 2013. A recent study by a distinguished historian of medicine during the Civil War that deliberately moves away from the military experience itself.

Interagency Study Group. *MAST (Military Assistance to Safety and Traffic): Report of the Test Program.* Washington, D.C.: Departments of Defense, Transportation and Health Education and Welfare, 1971.

Jones, Edgar, and Simon Wessely. *Shell Shock to PTSD: Military Psychiatry from 1900 to the Gulf War.* London: Psychology Press, 2005.

Kraut, Alan M. *Silent Traveler: Germs, Genes, and Immigrant Menace.* Baltimore: Johns Hopkins University Press, 1995.

Kutcher, Gerald. *Contested Medicine: Cancer Research and the Military.* Chicago and London: University of Chicago Press, 2009.

Langley, Harold. *A History of Medicine in the Early U.S. Navy.* Baltimore: Johns Hopkins University Press, 1995.

Lederer, Susan. *Flesh and Blood: Organ Transplantation and Blood Transfusion in 20th Century America.* Oxford and New York: Oxford University Press, 2008.

Lewer, Nick. *Physicians and the Peace Movement.* London: Frank Cass, 1992.

Lind, James. *Lind's Treatise on Scurvy. A Bicentenary Volume Containing a Reprint of the First Edition of A Treatise of the Scurvy, By James Lind,* edited by C. P. Stewart and Douglas Guthrie. Edinburgh: Edinburgh University Press, 1953. Stewart and Guthrie's original notes tell the story of the success in mid-eighteenth century and explain that the same would not be true in the American Revolution and that the failure to maintain a close blockade resulted in the presence of a French Fleet in North American waters and changed the course of the war in the Battle of the Chesapeake.

Lindee, M. Susan. *Suffering Made Real: American Science and the Survivors at Hiroshima.* Chicago: University of Chicago Press, 1994.

Linker, Beth. *War's Waste: Rehabilitation in World War I Medicine.* Chicago: University of Chicago Press, 2011.

Lloyd, C. C. "Victualling of the Fleet in the Eighteenth and Nineteenth Centuries." In *Starving Sailors: The Influence of Nutrition upon Naval and Maritime History,* edited by W. F. Bynum and E. J. Freeman, pp. 9–15. Greenwich: National Maritime Museum, 1981.

The Medical Department of the United States Army in the World War, 15 vols. Washington, D.C.: U.S. Government Printing Office, 1923–1929.

The Medical Department of the United States Army in the Second World War, 41 vols. Washington, D.C.: Office of the Surgeon General, 1952–1987.

Miles, Wyndham D. *A History of the National Library of Medicine: The Nation's Treasury of Medical Knowledge.* Washington, D.C.: U.S. Government Printing Office, 1992.

Moreno, Jonathan. *Mind Wars: Brain Research and National Defense.* New York: Dana Press, 2006.

Neushul, Peter. "Fighting Research: Army Participation in the Clinical Testing and Mass Production of Penicillin during the Second World War." In *War, Medicine, and Modernity,* edited by R. Cooter, M. Harrison, and S. Sturdy, pp. 203–224. Stroud: Sutton, 1998. A useful article in one of two collections by these British editors looking at war and medicine.

Neushul, Peter. "Science, Government and the Mass Production of Penicillin." *Journal of the History of Medicine and Allied Sciences* 38 (1993): 371–395.

Noble, David E. "Mental Material: The Militarization of Learning and Intelligence in US Education." In *Cyborg Worlds: The Military Information Society,* edited by Les Levidow and Kevin Robins. London: Free Association Books, 1989.

Pechura, Constance M., and David P. Rall, eds.; Committee on the Survey of the Health Effects of Mustard Gas and Lewisite, Institute of Medicine. *Veterans at Risk: The Health Effects of Mustard Gas and Lewisite* Washington, D.C.: National Academies Press, 1993.

Pittman, P. R., et al. "An Assessment of Health Status among Medical Research Volunteers Who Served in the Project Whitecoat Program at Fort Detrick, Maryland." *Military Medicine* 170, no. 3 (2005): 183–187.

Pols, Hans. "The Repression of War Trauma in American Psychiatry after World War II." In *Medicine and Modern Warfare,* edited by R. Cooter, M. Harrison and S. Sturdy, pp. 251–276. Amsterdam: Rodopi, 1996. One of the limited U.S. articles in this collection of interesting modern historical considerations.

Riley, James C. *The Eighteenth-Century Campaign to Avoid Disease.* London: Palgrave Macmillan, 1987. An early attempt to assess the role of smallpox inoculation, criticized for too great a reliance on hypothesis.

Rutkow, Ira. *Bleeding Blue and Gray: Civil War Surgery and the Evolution of American Medicine.* New York: Random House, 2005. A strongly suggestive work on the role of Civil War experience on the work of American surgeons in the postwar nation.

Skocpol, Theda. *Protecting Soldiers and Mothers: The Political Origins of Social Policy in the United States.* Cambridge, Mass.: Harvard University Press, 1992. A pathbreaking study of early American social policy, highlighting the post–Civil War Pension Bureau, with the obvious question of what happened to the Progressive Movement post World War I.

Slater, Leo. *War and Disease: Biomedical Research on Malaria in the Twentieth Century.* New Brunswick, N.J.: Rutgers University Press, 2009.

Smith, Dale C. "Military Medical History: The American Civil War." *Magazine of History* 19 (2005): 17–19.

Smith, Dale C. "Modern Surgery and the Development of Group Practice in the Midwest." *Caduceus* 2 (1986): 1–39.

Smith, Dale C. "Quinine and Fever: The Development of the Effective Dosage." *Journal of the History of Medicine* 31 (1976): 343–367.

Stevens, Jay. *Storming Heaven: LSD and the American Dream.* New York: Grove Press, 1987.

Stevens, Rosemary. *American Medicine and the Public Interest.* New Haven, Conn.: Yale University Press, 1971.

Stevens, Rosemary. *In Sickness and in Wealth: American Hospitals in the Twentieth Century.* New York: Basic Books, 1989. Together with her other work listed above, provides some of the greatest insights into the role of war, particularly World War II, on health policy in America.

Talbott, John. "Combat Trauma in the American Civil War." *History Today* 46, no. 3 (1996).

Tribble, William D. *Doctor Draft Justified? A Management Diagnosis.* San Antonio, Tex.: National Biomedical Laboratories, 1968.

Tucker, Todd. *The Great Starvation Experiment: Ancel Keys and the Men Who Starved for Science.* Minneapolis: University of Minnesota Press, 2008.

U.S. Senate. *Is Military Research Hazardous to Veterans' Health? Lessons Spanning Half a Century; A Staff Report.* Prepared for the Committee on Veterans' Affairs; U.S. Senate, 8 December 1994.

Woodward, Theodore E. *The Armed Forces Epidemiological Board: The First Fifty Years.* Washington, D.C.: Borden Institute, 1990.

Woodward, Theodore E. *The Histories of the Commissions.* Washington, D.C.: Borden Institute, 1994.

Zarafonetis, C. J. "The Society of Medical Consultants to the Armed Forces on Its Twenty-Fifth Anniversary." *Bulletin of the New York Academy of Medicine* 47, no. 3 (1971): 224–228.

Zweiback, Adam J. "The 21 Turncoat GIs: Nonrepatriations and the Political Culture of the Korean War." *The Historian* 60, no. 2 (1998): 345–362.

Dale Smith

WATSON, JAMES D.

(1928–), molecular biologist, geneticist, and zoologist. Born in Chicago, James Dewey Watson matriculated at the University of Chicago in 1943. He majored in zoology, with a special interest in ornithology, and graduated in 1947, at age 19.

Watson traced his interest in the gene to a 1944 essay called *What Is Life?*, by the physicist Erwin Schrödinger. A speculative treatise on the physical nature of the gene, the book featured the work of a young German physicist named Max Delbrück. Primed by Schrödinger, Watson enrolled in a course on physiological genetics, from which, he said, he became convinced that the material nature of the gene was the most important problem in biology—and he set out to solve it.

Indiana University offered Watson a fellowship to its PhD program in genetics. Salvador Luria, an Italian physician-turned-geneticist and collaborator of Delbrück's, offered Watson a place in his laboratory. During World War II, excluded from the draft, Luria and Delbrück had met up each summer at Cold Spring Harbor, on the north shore of New York's Long Island. There they worked out the genetics of viruses that infect bacteria—bacteriophage, or simply "phage."

Watson completed his PhD thesis in 1950 and then accepted a postdoctoral fellowship to work with the biochemist Herman Kalckar in Copenhagen. But after meeting Maurice Wilkins from King's College, Cambridge University, he decided to relocate to the Cavendish Laboratory at Cambridge. Wilkins was using X-ray crystallography to try to solve the atomic structure of DNA, and Watson planned to learn X-ray crystallography at the Cavendish Laboratory from Max Perutz, one of the leaders in the field.

Watson arrived in Cambridge in September 1951 and soon met the brilliant but struggling Francis Crick, who was also interested in DNA. But DNA was Wilkins's problem and it would be considered bad form to usurp it. The Wilkins issue was further complicated by Rosalind Franklin, a brilliant crystallographer recently brought in by laboratory head J. T. Randall. Franklin understood that DNA would be her project alone, whereas Wilkins believed that she was working beneath him.

Politics and personalities clashed, and DNA became a scientific soap opera. Watson and Crick finessed the question of intellectual turf by approaching the problem theoretically, building anatomically correct molecular models, the way the great physical chemist Linus Pauling did. This put them in a sort of gentlemanly competition with Wilkins, whereas Wilkins and Franklin, ostensibly collaborators, grew increasingly hostile. Perhaps to mask these rivalries, Watson constructed yet another scientific race, with Pauling himself. Pauling was indeed working on the structure of DNA—it was by this time an obvious scientific problem—but he was never close to the prize and was anyway unaware of any race. After numerous embarrassing missteps and aided by Franklin's beautiful and now notorious Photograph 51, which Wilkins gave to Watson without Franklin's knowledge, Watson and Crick produced their model of deoxyribonucleic acid. The central insight of the structure was that it suggested how DNA could be faithfully replicated at cell division: unzip the chains and each can serve as a template for a new double helix, identical to the first. Watson recalled Crick bursting into their favorite pub—the Eagle—and shouting, "We have found the secret of life!"

DNA became famous in 1962, when Watson, Crick, and Wilkins were awarded the Nobel Prize in Physiology or Medicine. The question of whether Franklin would share in the prize was made moot by her death from cancer in 1958. With the Nobel, DNA made Watson; after the Nobel, Watson invented DNA. As a Harvard professor, he recruited students to work on DNA, viruses, and cancer. He wrote the first textbook of DNA: *Molecular Biology of the Gene* (1965), like its author, blunt, brash, and innovative. He wrote his own, wildly successful *What Is Life?* and his 1968 memoir of the DNA discovery, *The Double Helix*. By the second decade of the twenty-first century, *The Double Helix* had sold more than 1 million copies. Even so, many readers have been upset by the author's sexist caricature of Franklin, a treatment that may or may not be more forgivable for the knowledge that, on that score, Watson was in the book Wilkins's mouthpiece.

Also in 1968, Watson became director of Cold Spring Harbor Laboratory. He transformed Cold Spring Harbor into a world-class cancer research center, focused on the genes and proteins involved in the cycle of DNA replication and cell division. In 1998, Cold Spring Harbor Laboratory became an accredited, PhD-granting university, capping its transition from unkempt scientific playground to prosperous biomedical powerhouse.

As director of the fledgling National Center for Human Genome Research (later the National Human Genome Research Institute) at the National Institutes of Health from 1988 to 1992, Watson set DNA policy for the National Institutes of Health, and by extension the United States and much of the world. In 2007, he became the second person to publish his own genome sequence and was removed as chancellor of Cold Spring Harbor for making public remarks about the intellectual inferiority of black people. Watson has thus been seen both as a major contributor to the establishment of personalized genetic medicine and as something of a throwback to discredited ideas about race, heredity, and intelligence.

[See also Biochemistry; Biological Sciences; Cancer; Chemistry; Genetics and Genetic Engineering; Human Genome Project; Medicine; Molecular Biology; National Institutes of Health; Nobel Prize in Biomedical Research; and Zoology.]

BIBLIOGRAPHY

Creager, Angela N. H., and Gregory J. Morgan. "After the Double Helix: Rosalind Franklin's Research on Tobacco Mosaic Virus." Isis 99, no. 2 (2008): 239–272.

de Chadarevian, Soraya. "Portrait of a Discovery: Watson, Crick, and the Double Helix." Isis 94 (2003): 90–105.

Holmes, Frederic L. Meselson, Stahl, and the Replication of DNA: The History of "The Most Beautiful Experiment in Biology." New Haven, Conn.: Yale University Press, 2001.

Maddox, Brenda. Rosalind Franklin: The Dark Lady of DNA. New York, HarperCollins, 2002.

McElheny, Victor K. Watson and DNA: Making a Scientific Revolution. Cambridge, Mass.: Perseus, 2003.

Olby, Robert C. The Path to the Double Helix: The Discovery of DNA. New York: Dover Publications, 1994.

Nathaniel Comfort

WATSON, THOMAS, Sr.

See Computers, Mainframe, Mini, and Micro.

WELCH, WILLIAM H.

(1850–1934), pathologist, bacteriologist, first dean of the Johns Hopkins University Medical School. Welch was born in Norfolk, Connecticut, to William Wickham Welch, a physician, and Emiline Collin. He graduated from Yale College in 1870. Failing to secure a teaching position in classics, he turned to medicine in 1871 and received his MD degree in 1875 from the College of Physicians and Surgeons in New York City (now part of Columbia University).

In 1876, he left the United States to study experimental pathology in Europe at the major medical centers of Strasbourg, Leipzig, Breslau, and Vienna. He returned to establish America's first pathology teaching laboratory, at Bellevue Hospital Medical College, in 1878. Welch supplemented his relatively small income by conducting autopsies and examining specimens for medical colleagues. He also taught classes, saw a few private patients, and wrote a new edition of Austin Flint's Principles and Practice of Medicine (1886). Because of this heavy workload, Welch was not able to complete any research. In 1884 he became chairman of the department of pathology at the Johns Hopkins University in Baltimore, the first American university to make scientific research central to its curriculum. Thanks to increased support for research at Johns Hopkins, including especially better laboratory facilities, he was able to finish several research projects. As the first dean of its school of medicine, which opened in 1893, he made the scientific laboratory essential to the training of physicians and helped create a medical school widely regarded as a model. Among the first Americans to introduce bacteriology into medicine, he identified Clostridium perfringens, the bacillus of gas gangrene, in 1892 and used the success of bacteriology to promote laboratory research nationwide. Welch founded the *Journal of Experimental Medicine* (1895); the Johns Hopkins School of Public Health (1918); and the Institute for the History of Medicine, which he headed after his retirement in 1925.

A man of diplomacy and charisma, Welch became the premier national spokesman for scientific medicine. He presided over numerous medical and scientific societies, including the American Medical Association (1910–1911) and the National Academy of Sciences (1913–1916). He influenced the funding of scientific research by serving on the boards of various philanthropic organizations, including several financed by the Rockefeller and Carnegie foundations.

[*See also* American Medical Association; Biological Sciences; Germ Theory of Disease; Hospitals; Journals in Science, Medicine, and Engineering; Medical Education; Medicine; National Academy of Sciences; Public Health; Research and Development (R&D); Rockefeller Institute, The; *and* Societies and Associations, Science.]

BIBLIOGRAPHY

Brieger, Gert H. "Welch, William Henry." In *Complete Dictionary of Scientific Biography*. Vol. 14, pp. 248–250. Detroit: Charles Scribner's Sons, 2008.

Fleming, Donald H. *William H. Welch and the Rise of Modern Medicine*. Baltimore: Johns Hopkins University Press, 1987. First published 1954. This reprint with a new afterword by the author.

Flexner, Simon, and James Thomas Flexner. *William Henry Welch and the Heroic Age of American Medicine*. Baltimore: Johns Hopkins University Press, 1993. First published 1941. Biography of Welch covering his varied career and achievements.

Patricia Peck Gossel;
updated by Elspeth Knewstubb and
Hugh Richard Slotten

WESTINGHOUSE, GEORGE

(1846–1914), inventor, industrialist. Born in Central Bridge, New York, Westinghouse worked as an apprentice in his father's machine shop. During the Civil War, he ran away from home to join the Union army. He later served as an engineering officer in the U.S. Navy. After the war, Westinghouse returned home and devoted himself to invention. He began to study engineering at Union College in Schenectady, New York, and developed a special interest in the safety and efficiency of trains. He invented and started manufacturing an improved apparatus for remounting derailed railway cars and, in 1869, patented the railroad air brake. Until then, brakemen stopped trains by manually applying brakes in each car. Collisions could occur when brakemen did not respond to the signal fast enough to brake. Westinghouse perfected a compressed air system; by operating a valve in the locomotive, the engineer could now brake all cars simultaneously. To manufacture and market this invention, Westinghouse moved to Pittsburgh where, over the next four decades, he became a major industrialist. Over several decades, Westinghouse established 60 companies, employing a total of approximately 50 thousand workers. This made him at one time the largest private employer in American industrial history (Wicks, 1996).

Westinghouse entered the electrical field in 1884. The electrical industry was dominated by Thomas Edison's direct-current (DC) system. DC required a high current to transmit a low voltage, resulting in large transmission losses. Westinghouse, therefore, focused on alternating current (AC), seeking more efficient transmission. Employing a transformer designed by William Stanley and a motor invented by the Croatian immigrant Nikola Tesla (1856–1943), the Westinghouse system enabled utilities to serve more customers over a wider area and hence lowered the cost of electricity. Threatened by AC, the Edison company attacked Westinghouse's system, claiming that high-voltage AC would electrocute people. Insisting that AC was safe, Westinghouse used it at the 1893 Chicago World's Fair to power 100,000 electric lights. AC ultimately prevailed when Westinghouse engineers employed it in 1896 to transmit power over a distance of 25 miles from Niagara Falls to Buffalo, New York. They thus proved that electric power did not have to be used where it was produced but could be transmitted to another region. Thanks to Westinghouse's vision, America enjoyed the benefits of low-cost electric power and he grew wealthy as the founder of one of the nation's great industrial corporations.

[*See also* Edison, Thomas; Electricity and Electrification; Engineering; Illumination; Machinery and Manufacturing; Railroads; *and* Tesla, Nikola.]

BIBLIOGRAPHY

Hughes, Thomas P. *Networks of Power: Electrification in Western Society, 1880–1930.* Baltimore: Johns Hopkins University Press, 1982. Offers a comparative history of the evolution of modern electrical systems.
Prout, Henry G. *A Life of George Westinghouse.* New York: Charles Scribner's Sons, 1922.
Wicks, Frank. "How George Westinghouse Changed the World." *Mechanical Engineering* 118, no. 10 (1996): 74–79.

W. Bernard Carlson;
updated by Elspeth Knewstubb and
Hugh Richard Slotten

WHITNEY, ELI

(1765–1825), inventor and arms manufacturer. Born in Westboro, Massachusetts, the eldest son of farmer Eli Whitney and Elizabeth Fay Whitney, Eli Whitney demonstrated mechanical talent earlier than scholarship, but belatedly graduated from Yale in 1792. Upon graduation, Whitney accepted a position as a tutor in Georgia, traveling with Yale alumnus Phineas Miller and Miller's employer, Catherine Greene, the widow of Revolutionary War general Nathanael Greene. When the expected tutorship fell through, Greene invited Whitney to remain at her plantation near Savannah.

There he learned of the urgent need for an improved cotton gin (short for "engine"). The grooved roller gin used for removing the black seeds from the bolls of the long-staple cotton grown in coastal Georgia failed to dislodge with equal ease the tenacious green seeds of the upland short-staple cotton. With Greene's encouragement, workshop, and materials, Whitney constructed a model in which a hook-studded rotating cylinder pulled cotton fiber through slots in a metal barrier, leaving seeds behind. Powered by horse or waterwheel, Whitney's gin could clean as much cotton as 50 people working by hand.

Backed by Greene, Phineas Miller and Eli Whitney formed a partnership to build and operate such gins. In 1793 Whitney obtained a patent and began gin production in New Haven, Connecticut. Southern plantations vastly expanded their acreages of cotton for export to England's textile factories. As cotton harvests outstripped Miller and Whitney's capacity to meet the demand for ginning, southern blacksmiths made gins without paying for the patent, embroiling Miller and Whitney in costly and prolonged lawsuits. Whitney's patent, although finally upheld in southern courts before expiring in 1807, garnered him small reward.

Meanwhile, deep in debt from the cotton-gin venture, Whitney won a contract from the U.S. government in 1798 to produce 10 thousand muskets in an incredibly short two years. Responding to the desire of French-influenced U.S. Ordnance officers for uniform military muskets, Whitney propounded the elusive goal of interchangeable parts. He built a water-powered factory outside New Haven and trained unskilled workers to specialize in using different "molds and patterns" to standardize filling and drilling. They produced quantities of individual parts before fitting them together into complete muskets. With contract extensions, they completed the 10 thousand muskets in 10 years. By modern standards, their parts were not interchangeable, nor were those made then at other armories.

Through technological exchange among private arms contractors and the federal armories, however, such methods spread, along with gauges intended to induce uniformity. With subsequent inventions such as Thomas Blanchard's gunstock lathe and the milling machines of Simeon North and John Hall, arms makers were producing standard military muskets with interchangeable parts by the late 1840s. Over the next half century, other manufacturers adapted armory methods for high-volume production of sewing machines, typewriters, watches, bicycles, and, in the early twentieth century, automobiles.

Eli Whitney married Henrietta Edwards in 1817 and began a family before prostate cancer ended his life at age 60. Posthumous heroic stories credited Whitney with inventing both the cotton gin and interchangeable parts. Historians of technology have debunked this oversimplification, which lingers even into the twenty-first century.

[*See also* **Agricultural Technology; American System of Manufactures; Cotton Gin; Machinery and Manufacturing;** *and* **Military, Science and Technology and the.**]

BIBLIOGRAPHY

Green, Constance McLaughlin. *Eli Whitney and the Birth of American Technology.* Boston: Little, Brown, 1956.
Lakwete, Angela. *Inventing the Cotton Gin: Machine and Myth in Antebellum America.* Baltimore: Johns Hopkins University Press, 2004.
Smith, Merritt Roe. *Harpers Ferry Armory and the New Technology.* Ithaca, N.Y.: Cornell University Press, 1977.

Carolyn C. Cooper

WIENER, NORBERT

(1894–1964), mathematician and computer theorist. Norbert Wiener's father, a professor of Slavonic languages at Harvard, supervised his early education. A child prodigy, Wiener began to read at 4, graduated from Tufts College at 14, entered Harvard, and received his PhD in mathematics at 18 with a dissertation supervised by Josiah Royce. During a Harvard-sponsored trip to England and Germany, he consulted with such eminent mathematicians as Bertrand Russell, David Hilbert, and G. H. Hardy. In 1918, as a mathematician at the U.S. Army's Aberdeen Proving Grounds, he worked on ballistics. In 1919, he became a mathematics instructor at the Massachusetts Institute of Technology, where he remained until he retired in 1960, having become one of MIT's best-known faculty members and the subject of many affectionate stories about his legendary absent-mindedness.

Wiener's professional work was primarily in pure mathematics. He made major contributions to a number of fields, including theory of Fourier integrals, Tauberian theorems, integration in function space, potential theory, and probability theory. He also collaborated with engineers on the theory of electrical devices. Wiener's World War II work on fire-control systems turned his attention to theories of man–machine communications. His *Cybernetics; or, Control and Communication in the Animal and Machine* (1948), discussing control and automation theory, ranks as a classic anticipation of the computer revolution. In *The Human Uses of Human Beings* (1950), directed to general readers, Wiener discussed both the promise and the potential hazards of automation—the application of computers to information processing. His essay "Some Moral and Technical Consequences of Automation" (*Science* 6 May 1960) conveyed his deepening pessimism about the computer's social implications.

Wiener received a number of major honors in both mathematics and science during his career. In 1933 the American Mathematical Society awarded him the Bocher Prize. MIT appointed him "Institute Professor" when he reached retirement age, honoring his cross-disciplinary interests. He also traveled extensively, becoming a visiting professor in Peiping, China (1935–1936), and lecturing at other times in India, Japan, Norway, Italy, and France. In 1964, shortly before his death, Wiener was awarded the National Medal of Science by President Lyndon B. Johnson. He wrote two autobiographies: *I Am a Mathematician* (1956) and *Ex-Prodigy: My Childhood and Youth* (1979).

[*See also* **Automation and Computerization; Computer Science; Computers, Mainframe, Mini, and Micro; Engineering; Mathematics and Statistics;** *and* **Military, Science and Technology and the.**]

BIBLIOGRAPHY

Conway, Flo, and Jim Siegelman. *Dark Hero of the Information Age: In Search of Norbert Wiener, the Father of Cybernetics*. New York: Basic Books, 2005. Biography of Wiener written for the general reader.

Heims, Joshua. "Wiener, Norbert (1894–1964)." In *The History of Science in the United States: An Encyclopedia*, edited by Marc Rothenberg, pp. 572–573. New York and London: Garland, 2001.

Masani, Pesi. *Norbert Wiener, 1894–1964*. Basel and Boston: Birkhäuser, 1992.

Wiener, Norbert. *Norbert Wiener: Collected Works*, edited by Pesi Masani. 4 vols. Cambridge, Mass.: MIT Press, 1976–1986.

Thomas J. Bergin

WIGNER, EUGENE

(1902–1995), theoretical physicist, mathematician, engineer, and Nobel laureate. Born in Budapest in 1902, Eugene Paul Wigner was one of a quartet of great Hungarian Jewish scientists of the same generation. The others were John von Neumann, Edward Teller, and Leó Szilárd. He won a Nobel Prize in 1963 and felt pride and a little chagrin that he was the only one of that quartet to win this high honor. Wigner received half of the physics Nobel Prize "for his contributions to the theory of the atomic nucleus and the elementary particles, particularly through the discovery and application of fundamental symmetry principles." The other half of the prize was shared between Maria Goeppert Mayer and J. Hans D. Jensen "for their discoveries concerning nuclear shell structure."

Eugene Wigner began thinking seriously about mathematics as an 11-year-old tuberculosis patient at a sanitarium in the Austrian mountains. For the rest of his life, he associated mathematics with peace and quiet and physics with the far more turbulent world of armies and nations. After high school, Wigner studied physics in Gottingen and in Berlin. In 1930, he moved to Princeton University and was made a visiting professor in 1935, but the university did not grasp his value and, in 1936, asked him to leave (Szanton, 1992, pp. 163–175). After a few years at the University of Wisconsin in Madison, where Wigner worked with his colleague Gregory Breit, he was asked to return to Princeton as professor of mathematical physics (Szanton, 1992, p. 178).

A deeply peaceful and philosophical man, Wigner's distaste for Adolf Hitler and the Nazis was such that, in his quiet way, he became a forceful advocate of military resistance to the Nazis. What is called the Einstein-Szilárd Letter to President Franklin Roosevelt, describing, in August 1939, the possibility of an atomic bomb, is partly because of Eugene Wigner, who introduced Szilárd to Einstein. Wigner was a key figure in the Manhattan Project, which created the world's first nuclear bombs. He worked with Enrico Fermi in Chicago. Wigner contributed to the theory of neutron chain reactions and designed the large nuclear reactor built secretly at Hanford, Washington. He never doubted that such bombs were needed in a world threatened by Adolf Hitler, but he regretted the bombs being used against Japan and said, "I was very sorry to see our country set a precedent for using atomic bombs as regular weapons of war" (Szanton, 1992, p. 250).

Wigner, whether considering ethical questions or the atomic nucleus, delighted in finding symmetry principles. As an old man, he said in his memoir: "I scarcely feel that I have understood life. But then human beings are hugely innocent" (Szanton, 1992, p. 318). That memoir traces an arc from a young man's eager quest to know all of physics to the mature man's acceptance of the limits of his own knowledge and finally an old man's pleasure and pride at being associated with a great mystery.

[*See also* **Chemistry; Manhattan Project; Mathematics and Statistics; Military, Science and Technology and the; Physics;** *and* **Quantum Theory.**]

BIBLIOGRAPHY

Szanton, Andrew. *The Recollections of Eugene P. Wigner: As Told to Andrew Szanton*. New York: Plenum Press, 1992.

Wigner, Eugene P. *The Collected Works of Eugene Paul Wigner*, 8 vols. Berlin, Heidelberg, and New York: Springer Verlag, 1993–1998.

Wigner, Eugene P. *Symmetries and Reflections: Scientific Essays of Eugene P. Wigner*. Bloomington and London: Indiana University Press, 1967.

Andrew Szanton;
updated by Gregory A. Good

WILKES EXPEDITION

Beginning in the 1820s, New England merchants seeking new regions in which to hunt seals and whales, as well as U.S. Navy officers hoping to extend the reach of American naval influence, joined American scientists to persuade Congress to authorize a naval exploration of the South Seas. In 1836 Congress appropriated funds for an expedition, known officially as the U.S. South Seas Exploring Expedition and informally as the Wilkes Expedition after its commanding officer, U.S. Navy lieutenant Charles Wilkes (1798–1877). Mandated to explore the Antarctic and Pacific to gain information that would aid commerce, the expedition was instructed to make hydrographic surveys and astronomical observations, chart navigational hazards, and collect natural history specimens. This, the U.S. Navy's first large-scale scientific exploring mission, served as a model for subsequent expeditions. The nine civilians on the expedition included two artists, two botanists, a conchologist, a geologist, two naturalists, and a philologist.

In 1838 six naval vessels—the largest of which was the sloop-of-war USS *Vincennes*, weighing only seven hundred tons—set out from Norfolk, Virginia. By the time the squadron returned in 1842, it had traversed 85,000 miles of ocean; surveyed 280 islands, including the Tuamotu, Society, Samoan, and Fiji islands; charted 800 miles of rivers and coastline in Oregon Territory and 1,500 miles of coastal Antarctica; and established that Antarctica is a continent. The ensuing 19 scientific reports, including Wilkes's own five-volume narrative, recording findings on the botany, crustacea, ethnography, geology, hydrography, meteorology, and zoophytes of the South Seas, enhanced the stature of the United States in the international scientific community. Among the major scientific contributions resulting from the expedition were James Dwight Dana's trenchant observations on volcanic island chains. The tens of thousands of natural history specimens and ethnographic objects collected by the expedition became the basis of the Smithsonian Institution's National Museum of the United States in 1858.

[*See also* Astronomy and Astrophysics; Botany; Cartography; Dana, James Dwight; Geological Surveys; Geology; Meteorology and Climatology; Military, Science and Technology and the; Oceanography; Science; Smithsonian Institution; Technology; *and* Zoology.]

BIBLIOGRAPHY

Joyce, Barry Alan. *The Shaping of American Ethnography: The Wilkes Exploring Expedition, 1838–1842*. Lincoln: University of Nebraska Press, 2001.

Stanton, William. *The Great United States Exploring Expedition of 1838–1842*. Berkeley: University of California Press, 1975.

Michael J. Crawford

WILLIAMS, DANIEL HALE

(1856–1931), surgical pioneer, medical educator, and hospital founder. Born on 18 January 1856 at Hollidaysburg, Pennsylvania, to an African American father (a barber and landowner) and a Scottish American mother (a homemaker), Williams was a "Negro" by law and custom and identified himself as such throughout his life. After moving to Maryland and Illinois, his family settled in Wisconsin, where the teenage Williams studied law for one year while working as a barber. He attracted the patronage of former Wisconsin Surgeon General Henry Palmer, who urged him to study medicine. After two years as Palmer's apprentice, Williams entered Chicago Medical College (now Northwestern University Medical School), graduating in 1883. His subsequent yearlong internship at Chicago's Mercy Hospital further distinguished him in an era in which few physicians of any race received postgraduate training. Williams entered practice as surgeon to the South Side Dispensary and the Protestant Orphan Asylum and was Demonstrator of Anatomy at his alma mater. In 1889, he was the first African American physician appointed to the Illinois State Board of Health. In 1891, he founded Chicago's Provident Hospital and Training School—the United States's first African American–controlled hospital—serving as attending surgeon until 1912 and remaining on staff until 1913. During these years, Williams was an early and enthusiastic proponent of antisepsis, performed the second successful open-heart surgery (his 1893 operation on the pericardium followed H. C. Dalton's by two years), served as attending surgeon at Chicago's Cook County Hospital (1903–1906), and was among the first African American fellows of the American College of Surgeons (1913). Preferring integrated institutions to exclusively African American ones but dedicated to training and supporting African American physicians, Williams served as surgeon in chief at Freedman's Hospital in Washington, D.C., from 1893 to 1898, cofounded the American Association of Colored Physicians and Surgeons (later the National Medical Association) in 1895, and made regular clinical instruction visits to Meharry Medical College in Nashville, Tennessee, from 1900 onward. In 1913, long-standing conflicts among practitioners on Provident's staff forced Williams's resignation. He served as associate attending surgeon at Chicago's St. Luke's Hospital until his death in 1931.

[*See also* **Anatomy and Human Dissection; Higher Education and Science; Hospitals; Medical Education; Medicine; National Medical Association; Race and Medicine;** *and* **Surgery.**]

BIBLIOGRAPHY

Buckler, Helen. *Daniel Hale Williams: Negro Surgeon.* 1954; New York: Pitman Publishing Company, 1968.

Dailey, U. G. "Daniel Hale Williams, M.D., LL.D., F.A.C.S. (Obituary)." *Journal of the National Medical Association* 23, no. 4 (1931): 173–175.

Gamble, Vanessa Northington. *Making a Place for Ourselves: The Black Hospital Movement, 1920–1945.* New York: Oxford University Press, 1995.

Dayle B. DeLancey

WILSON, EDMUND BEECHER

(1856–1939), cell biologist who developed the chromosomal sex-determination system. Born in Geneva, Illinois, Wilson was the second child of Isaac C. Wilson, lawyer and judge, and Caroline (Clarke). Wilson completed his undergraduate studies at Yale in 1878. He then accepted a fellowship at Johns Hopkins University and began his graduate studies, obtaining the PhD in 1881. At Hopkins, Wilson conducted observational studies on animal metamorphosis and morphology. He married Ann Maynard Kidder in 1904; they had one daughter.

After serving as chair of biology at Bryn Mawr College for six years (1885–1891), Wilson accepted a prominent post at Columbia University. At Columbia, Wilson's attention turned toward the domain of cell biology and experimental embryology. His 1892 paper on the cell lineage of Nereis challenged the leading hypothesis, commonly associated with Ernest Haeckel, that "ontogeny recapitulates phylogeny." His cytological researches convinced him that cells contained the key to understanding the mechanism of inheritance. Building on Boveri's findings—that the nucleus contains the agents of heredity—Wilson began his groundbreaking work on the role of chromosomes in sex determination. In 1905, Wilson was able to show that the X and Y chromosomes in sperm cells determined the gender of the offspring. In a series of papers published from 1905 to 1912, Wilson brilliantly established a correlation between nuclear chromosomes and development and greatly advanced the chromosomal theory of development.

Edmund Beecher Wilson received honorary degrees from Johns Hopkins, the University of Cambridge, the University of Leipzig, Harvard, the University of Lwòw, and Columbia University. He received the John J. Carty Medal and Award and the gold medal of the Linnean Society and was elected Fellow of the Royal Society of London. Wilson was awarded the Daniel Giraud Elliot Medal from the National Academy of Sciences for the third edition of *The Cell in Development and Inheritance*.

[*See also* Biological Sciences; Evolution, Theory of; Genetics and Genetic Engineering; Science; *and* Zoology.]

BIBLIOGRAPHY

Morgan, T. H. "Edmund Beecher Wilson." *Biographical Memoirs* 21(1940): 315–342. Biographical memoir written by Wilson's colleague and friend containing an extensive bibliography of Wilson's publications.

Mateo Muñoz

WILSON, EDWARD O.

(1929–), naturalist, evolutionary biologist, writer, and conservationist. Wilson has written widely on both the theoretical framework and the cultural implications of evolutionary theory. His main area of research is myrmecology (the study of ants), which formed the foundation for his thinking on the evolution of sociality in both humans and nonhuman animals. He was born in Birmingham, Alabama, and spent most of his youth in the countryside of Alabama and near Washington, D.C. His early interest in the natural world was encouraged by an education at the University of Alabama, and he later earned a PhD degree from Harvard University. Wilson spent his career as a professor at Harvard and in 2014 continued to hold the positions of Professor Emeritus and Honorary Curator in Entomology at that institution.

Much of Wilson's importance and fame as a scientist came from his formulation of sociobiology. His 1975 book *Sociobiology: The New Syn-thesis* extended the theoretical framework of the modern synthesis (which demonstrated that Mendelian genetics was consistent with the theory of natural selection) to the study of the evolution of behavior. Wilson's comments on the evolution of human society in the last chapter of the book became controversial and put him at odds with fellow Harvard professors Stephen Jay Gould and Richard Lewontin. Wilson advocated for the importance of studying the genetic basis and evolutionary history of human social behavior and continued to publish on this and related topics for the next several decades. His 1979 work *On Human Nature* gave more room to his arguments that contemporary human behaviors, including generosity, altruism, and religious feelings, were rooted in humanity's evolutionary past. And his 1998 work *Consilience: The Unity of Knowledge* argued that biological knowledge could serve as a framework for all human intellectual endeavors. More recently, Wilson has retracted some of his initial work in the area of kin selection as a defining concept for the evolution of sociality and altruism. Kin selection accounts for altruism by arguing that individuals are more likely to self-sacrifice for close relatives, thereby enabling an indirect passing on of their genes. Wilson collaborated with Martin Novak, a Harvard professor and mathematician, to argue that simple natural selection better accounts for eusociality (the highest level of social organization that involves collective care for offspring and a social division of labor) than does kin selection.

Another area in which Wilson has worked and written extensively is the conservation of planetary biodiversity. He has argued that humans evolved an innate affinity for other organisms, a phenomena he terms "biophilia." As an advocate for conservation, Wilson has published a number of books, including *The Diversity of Life* (1999), and participated in numerous *Nature*, *NOVA*, and *BBC* documentaries. This area has also served as the catalyst for Wilson's primary comments on the relationship between science and religion. His 2004 book *The Creation: An Appeal to Save Life on Earth* was written as a series of letters from Wilson to an imaginary Baptist pastor, calling for the setting aside of philosophical differences between evolutionary biology and Christianity to preserve the diversity of life. Generally Wilson has termed himself an evolutionary atheist or deist.

[See also **Biological Sciences; Conservation Movement; Entomology; Environmentalism; Evolution, Theory of; Popularization of Science; Religion and Science;** and **Sociobiology and Evolutionary Psychology.**]

BIBLIOGRAPHY

Ruse, Michael. *The Evolution Wars: A Guide to the Debates.* New Brunswick, N.J.: Rutgers University Press, 2001.

Segerstråle, Ullica. *Defenders of the Truth: The Battle for Science in the Sociobiology Debate and Beyond.* Oxford: Oxford University Press, 2000.

Wilson, Edward O. *Consilience: The Unity of Knowledge.* New York: Knopf, 1998.

Wilson, Edward O. *Naturalist.* Washington, D.C.: Shearwater Books, 1994.

Wilson, Edward O. *Sociobiology: The New Synthesis.* Cambridge, Mass.: Harvard University Press, 1975.

Myrna Perez Sheldon

WIND POWER

During the second half of the twentieth century, many energy experts dismissed wind power as unreliable and capricious. By the early twenty-first century, a new view had emerged. In 2012 approximately 3 percent of electrical energy capacity in the United States was produced by alternative sources, primarily the wind. In Texas, the largest state producer of wind energy, the figure was 6 percent. Experts predicted that these percentages would increase; wind energy was the fastest growing renewable source of energy in the country. In 2012, the total power produced in the United States using wind energy was approximately 45,000 megawatts. The average nuclear plant produced about 1,000 megawatts (but to compare wind energy with other power sources, it is important to recognize that wind energy produces capacity only about 25 percent of the time). Even taking into account

the vagaries of the wind, the impact of this new energy source in the early twenty-first century was significant.

In 1888, Charles Brush, an inventor who worked with electrical dynamos, erected the first large wind generator in the backyard of his Euclid Avenue property in Cleveland. With his "wind dynamo" and a large passel of batteries he powered over two hundred incandescent lights, several arc lights, and several electric motors. Wind turbines became very popular on farms in the Great Plains region during the 1920s and 1930s. There were many brands, but the "Wincharger" and Jacobs machines dominated the market. But outside of rural areas, the wind turbine was quickly forgotten as centralized electrical generating systems multiplied in American cities.

For a time it appeared that the United States might develop a two-tiered electrical system— one centralized and the other composed of multiple decentralized stand-alone systems. However, the Rural Electrification Act of 1935 encouraged the extension of power lines into sparsely settled areas. Lacking support, wind energy died; the last company closed its doors in 1956.

The Oil Embargo of 1973 revealed how vulnerable and dependent the nation was on imported oil. For the first time, the federal government sponsored research in wind energy and funded the building of a number of large (1- to 5-megawatt) turbines. This program failed, but a number of wind turbines from Denmark proved successful in California, which by 1985 produced 90 percent of the total wind energy in the world.

Supporters have argued that wind energy has environmental advantages. The turbines transform nature's energy to electricity in a gentle way: one in which the planet and its inhabitants are not endangered by heat, pollution, toxicity, or depletions of irreplaceable natural resources. Yet, there are critics who have argued that the turbines "industrialize" the landscape, destroy the silence of the night, and kill birds. Furthermore, wind energy is unreliable and it causes many problems for the grid system, which must transport the electricity to American homes and factories. We would be better served, according to critics, if we used more natural gas and built more nuclear power plants.

New federal programs introduced during the late twentieth century, especially tax credits and benefits, played an important role in the expansion of wind energy. The most important was the federal production tax credit (FPTC), initially introduced as part of the Energy Policy Act of 1992, which allowed a specific federal tax credit for every kilowatt-hour produced. Some large producers saved millions of dollars every year. This tax credit played an especially important role in protecting wind energy from dramatic changes in energy economics during the late twentieth and early twenty-first centuries.

[*See also* **Electricity and Electrification; Environmentalism; Nuclear Power; Rural Electrification Administration;** *and* **Steam Power.**]

BIBLIOGRAPHY

American Wind Energy Association. http://www .awea.com/ (accessed 3 April 2012).

Gipe, Paul. *Wind Energy Comes of Age*. New York: John Wiley & Sons, 1995.

Pasqualetti, Martin J., Paul Gipe, and Robert W. Righter, eds. *Wind Power in View: Energy Landscapes in a Crowded World*. San Diego, Calif.: Academic Press, 2002.

Righter, Robert W. *Windfall: Wind Energy in America Today*. Norman: University of Oklahoma Press, 2011.

Righter, Robert W. *Wind Power in America: A History*. Norman: University of Oklahoma Press, 1996.

Robert W. Righter

WOODS HOLE OCEANOGRAPHIC INSTITUTION

See Oceanography.

WORLD HEALTH ORGANIZATION

Specialized organization of the United Nations (UN). Headquartered in Geneva, the World Health Organization (WHO) was founded in 1948. Its constitution, adopted in 1946 by a UN-sponsored World Health Assembly, envisioned an ambitious effort to raise health standards worldwide. The WHO's antecedents included a series of international sanitary conferences beginning in 1851; an International Bureau of Public Hygiene created in Paris in 1907; and an International Health Organization established by the League of Nations in 1921. Governed by a World Health Assembly that meets annually and financed by assessments on member states, the WHO has focused on combating such diseases as poliomyelitis, cholera, leprosy, malaria, and tuberculosis. A global program to combat acquired immunodeficiency syndrome (AIDS) was launched in 1987.

From the beginning, U.S. diplomats and public-health experts played key roles in planning and implementing the WHO's program. The WHO subsumed tasks earlier performed by other international organizations, including the Washington-based Pan American Sanitary Bureau (PASB). With U.S. diplomatic support, the PASB joined the WHO, while preserving its own budget and other autonomous powers. Designated the WHO's "regional office in the Western Hemisphere" in 1949, the PASB was renamed the Pan American Health Organization (PAHO).

In the spirit of postwar internationalism, Congress in 1948 agreed to underwrite approximately 35 percent of the WHO's budget. The organization soon became enmeshed in Cold War politics, however. In 1955, President Dwight D. Eisenhower urged support for international health programs because disease contributed to "the spread of Communism." The Soviet Union, for its part, brought such contentious issues as the Vietnam War before the WHO. During intervals of détente, however, the superpowers cooperated on major WHO initiatives. A Soviet proposal for eradicating smallpox, for example, was brought to fruition by epidemiologists from the Centers for Disease Control and Prevention, and in 1979 a global commission declared smallpox eradicated. In the later twentieth century, U.S. policy toward the WHO remained ambivalent. Although supporting programs to eradicate diseases such as polio and to reduce infant mortality through immunization, nutritional supplements, and control of diarrheal diseases, Washington balked at diffuse and expensive efforts to transform global health through long-term infrastructural change. Although thousands of Americans have worked for the WHO and PAHO, an ambitious WHO program entitled *Health for All by the Year 2000* won little support in Washington. Under President Barack Obama, however, the United States and the WHO moved to increase cooperation. In September 2011, U.S. and WHO officials signed a formal "memorandum of understanding" that called for a pooling of resources to assist public-health efforts around the world.

[*See also* **Centers for Disease Control and Prevention; Cholera; Disease; Foundations and Health; HIV/AIDS; Malaria; Medicine; Poliomyelitis; Public Health; Smallpox;** *and* **Tuberculosis.**]

BIBLIOGRAPHY

Lee, Kelley. *The World Health Organization (WHO).* New York: Routledge, 2009.
Pan American Health Organization. *Pro Salute Novi Mundi: A History of the Pan American Health Organization.* Washington, D.C.: Pan American Health Organization, 1992.
Siddiqi, Javed. *World Health and World Politics: The WHO and the UN System.* Columbia: University of South Carolina Press, 1995.

Paul R. Greenough

WOZNIAK, STEPHEN

See **Computers, Mainframe, Mini, and Micro; Software.**

WRIGHT, SEWALL

(1889–1988), geneticist, evolutionary theorist. Sewall Wright helped found the field of mathematical population genetics (along with R. A. Fisher, J. B. S. Haldane, and Sergei Chetverikov) and was one of the foremost evolutionary theorists of the twentieth century. He invented the statistical method of "path analysis" while studying under William Castle at Harvard's Bussey Institute during the 1910s and subsequently applied it to animal genetics while employed at the U.S. Department of Agriculture (1916–1925) and the University of Chicago (1926–1954). Together with R. A. Fisher, Wright also invented the partitioning of squared standard deviation ("analysis of variance"), which he used to calculate his "path coefficients."

In animal husbandry, Wright's key achievement was his Mendelian theory of livestock breeding, adopted in the 1920s/1930s by such agricultural theorists as Russia's Alexander Serebrovsky and America's J. L. Lush. Wright's theory stood apart because of its unique endorsement of the positive effects of inbreeding in semi-isolated lines of stock, which, when combined with moderate selection pressure and occasional crosses with foundation stock, produced more robust animals. Wright's Chicago students Lianne Brauch (Russell) and William Russell later applied these principles to develop models for radiation genetics research at Oak Ridge National Laboratory after World War II.

Wright realized that "population structuring" (the splitting of animal populations into semi-isolated subgroups) was an important factor not only for controlled stock, but also for natural species populations. He authored two landmark papers (1931, 1932) demonstrating the role of *structure* in a hypothetical evolutionary process that he named the "shifting balance theory" of evolution (SBT). Wright's SBT stressed inbreeding (isolation), outbreeding (migration), gene mutation, random drift, and natural selection as the primary sources of *intragroup* differentiation, but emphasized that once *intergroup* differences arose, a higher level (population-wide) set of selective pressures would begin to modify a greater portion of the species, redefining the species itself.

Wright's SBT had a dramatic influence on American field zoologists, who were just beginning to understand the complex processes by which species modifications unfolded. His theory proved especially invaluable as the intellectual template for Theodosius Dobzhansky's classic work, *Genetics and the Origin of Species*, which re-invigorated scientific interest in Darwin's evolutionary theory during the 1930s. Wright later collaborated with Dobzhansky on the *Genetics of Natural Populations* series, attempting to substantiate SBT under real ecological conditions. He participated in both of the National Academy of Sciences Committees on the Biological Effects of Atomic Radiation (in 1956 and 1960).

[*See also* **Agriculture, U.S. Department of; Biological Sciences; Dobzhansky, Theodosius; Evolution, Theory of; Genetics and Genetic Engineering; National Academy of Sciences;** *and* **Zoology.**]

BIBLIOGRAPHY

Dobzhansky, Theodosius G. *Genetics and the Origin of Species.* New York: Columbia University Press, 1937, 1st ed.; 1941, 2nd ed.; 1951, 3rd ed.; reprint ed., 1982.
Provine, William B. *The Origin of Theoretical Population Genetics.* Chicago: University of Chicago Press, 1971; reprint ed., 2001.
Provine, William B. *Sewall Wright and Evolutionary Biology.* Chicago: University of Chicago Press, 1986.
                                        David M. Steffes

WRIGHT, WILBUR AND ORVILLE

(1867–1912) and (1871–1948), respectively, inventors of the airplane. The Wright brothers operated a bicycle shop in Dayton, Ohio, in the 1890s. As expert mechanics, they became avidly interested in the problem of human flight. They designed and flew three gliders in the years 1900–1902. In the course of these gliding experiments, they perfected (and in 1906 patented) the most efficient method of controlling an aircraft in the air. In 1903, using data derived from a series of model airfoil tests in their bicycle-shop wind tunnel, they constructed a propeller-driven flying machine, powered by a homemade motor.

In this machine, the Wright brothers made the world's first man-carrying airplane flights on 17 December 1903, above the sands of the Outer Banks near Kitty Hawk, North Carolina.

They continued experimenting in relative secrecy until October 1905, when their long, circling flights over a pasture near Dayton attracted attention. Afraid that others might copy their invention, they dismantled their flying machine and spent two years trying to interest the governments of the United States, England, France, and Germany in purchasing a Wright airplane.

In February 1908, the U.S. War Department finally agreed to consider a purchase. In March, the Wrights signed a contract with the French. By that summer, French aviators were making flights of up to 20 minutes. Europe seemed poised to take the lead in aviation development, but when Wilbur made his first flights in France in August 1908, they created a sensation. Wilbur's smooth, banked turns convinced the world that the Wrights were far ahead of their competitors. In September, Orville astounded Americans with flights of more than an hour near Washington, D.C.

In November 1909, the brothers established the Wright Company and went into business. They could now afford to sue infringers of their basic 1906 patent, which was not for the airplane itself, but for the means of controlling an airplane—any airplane—in flight. They therefore felt justified in suing anyone who manufactured or flew airplanes for profit and refused to pay royalties to the Wright Company. Warned that the patent suits were hampering the development of aviation, they protested that they merely sought a fair return for having spent their own money and risked their lives while inventing the airplane and learning to fly it.

Wilbur died in 1912. In 1914, Orville locked horns with the Smithsonian Institution over former Smithsonian Secretary Samuel Langley's unflyable airplane, the *Aerodome*, which had crashed into the Potomac River on 8 December 1903. The new secretary authorized the rebuilding of the *Aerodome* with many modifications. After the plane made a few brief hops, the Smithsonian claimed that had it been properly launched in 1903, it would have flown, nine days before the Wrights' airplane, the *Kitty Hawk*. The *Aerodome* was later displayed in the Smithsonian's National Museum as the first airplane "capable of sustained free flight." Orville retaliated by exiling the *Kitty Hawk* to England for display in London's Science Museum. The feud was settled in 1942, but not until December 1948—11 months after Orville's death—was the *Kitty Hawk* installed as the National Museum's prized centerpiece.

[*See also* **Airplanes and Air Transport; Military, Science and Technology and the;** *and* **Smithsonian Institution.**]

BIBLIOGRAPHY

Couch, Tom D. *The Bishop's Boys: A Life of Wilbur and Orville Wright*. New York: W. W. Norton, 1989.
Howard, Fred. *Wilbur and Orville: A Biography of the Wright Brothers*. New York: Alfred A. Knopf, 1987.

Fred Howard

WU, CHIEN-SHIUNG

(Wu Jianxiong in pinyin, 1912–1997), a prominent Chinese American physicist renowned for her many major contributions in nuclear physics and internationally celebrated as a pioneering woman scientist who advocated for equal opportunities for women in science.

Born in Shanghai, China, Wu pursued academic studies with the encouragement of her father, Wu Zhongyi, who instilled in her both a strong sense of Chinese nationalism and a belief in equality for women. In 1930, Wu enrolled in the elite National Central University in Nanjing where she studied physics, drawing inspiration from the example of the famous Marie Curie. After graduation in 1934, Wu worked as an assistant at Zhejiang University in Hangzhou and later at the Academia Sinica in Shanghai. Encouraged by Gu Jinghui, her supervisor in Shanghai who had received her PhD from the University of Michigan, Wu came to the United States to pursue graduate studies in physics in 1936.

Enrolling at the University of California, Berkeley, Wu studied under Ernest Lawrence but also worked closely with J. Robert Oppenheimer and Emilio Segrè. For her thesis she conducted experiments on two important topics in nuclear physics: beta decay, when electrons are emitted by the atomic nuclei, and nuclear fission, when the nuclei are split by neutrons. After receiving her PhD in 1940, Wu stayed for two years as a research fellow in Lawrence's lab. She married Luke Chia-Liu Yuan, a fellow Chinese American physicist, in May 1942. They then moved to the East Coast where Yuan worked on radar in Princeton, New Jersey, and Wu taught at Smith College and Princeton University before moving to Columbia University in 1944 to conduct research for the Manhattan Project.

Following the war, Wu stayed at Columbia as a research scientist instead of returning home to China, as she and her husband had originally planned. This was mainly because of the political instability in China during this period. They naturalized as U.S. citizens in 1954.

Wu's research in this period provided experimental proof for the Italian-American Enrico Fermi's theory on beta decay and brought her promotion to associate professor with tenure in 1952 at Columbia. Four years later Wu returned to beta decay when a conversation with Tsung-Dao Lee, her Chinese American colleague at Columbia, led her to design an experiment in beta decay to check the validity of a radical theory proposed by Lee and Chen Ning Yang, another Chinese American physicist then at Princeton. The theory predicted that in the case of weak nuclear interactions such as beta decay, particles would not follow the law of left–right parity as previously presumed. Working with scientists at the National Bureau of Standards in Washington, D.C., and overcoming many obstacles, Wu carried out the intricate experiment that proved Lee and Yang's theory to be right.

The breaking of parity was a turning point in modern physics but the Nobel Prize for Physics for 1957 went only to Lee and Yang, not Wu. Over the years, however, Wu received just about every other prize for a scientist, including the National Medal of Science from President Gerald Ford in 1975. The same year she was elected president of the American Physical Society, the first woman and Asian American to hold the position. In the last years of her life she promoted scientific exchange between the United States, mainland China, and Taiwan, and inspired many young people, especially girls, to pursue a scientific career.

[*See also* **Fermi, Enrico; Gender and Science; Lawrence, Ernest O.; Lee, Tsung-Dao; Manhattan Project; Nobel Prize in Biomedical Research; Nuclear Power; Nuclear Weapons; Oppenheimer, J. Robert; Physics; Research and Development (R&D);** *and* **Yang, Chen Ning.**]

BIBLIOGRAPHY

Jiang, Caijian. *Wu Jianxiong: Wu li ke xue de di yi fu ren* (Chieng-Shiung Wu: The First Lady of the Physical Sciences). Taipei, Taiwan: Shibao Wenhua, 1996.

Wang, Zuoyue. "Wu Chien-Shiung." In *New Dictionary of Scientific Biography*, edited by Noretta Koertge, Vol. 7, pp. 363–368. Detroit: Charles Scribner's Sons, 2008.

Wu, Chien-Shiung. "One Researcher's Personal Account." *Adventures in Experimental Physics* γ (1973): 101–123.

Zhu, Yuelin. "Chien-Shiung Wu: An Intellectual Biography." PhD diss. Harvard University, 2001.

Zuoyue Wang

XEROGRAPHY

See **Photocopying.**

X-RAY IMAGING

See **Radiology.**

Y

YANG, CHEN NING

(Yang Zhenning in pinyin, 1922–), a prominent Chinese American physicist and one of the most influential theoretical physicists in the world in the second half of the twentieth century. He also played an active role in U.S.–China scientific relations.

Born in Hefei, China, Yang grew up on the campus of Tsinghua (Qinghua) University in Beijing where his father, Yang Wuzhi, was a professor of mathematics. He was an excellent student but his sheltered environment collapsed with the Japanese invasion in 1937. He fled with his family to southern China and studied physics in the elite Southwestern Associated University in Kunming. After receiving his BS in 1942 and MS in 1944, he taught in a middle school for one year, where he met his future wife, Du Zhili.

In 1945, Yang won a Boxer fellowship and came to the University of Chicago to study with the great physicist Enrico Fermi and gave himself the nickname "Frank" in honor of Ben Franklin.

Although deeply influenced by Fermi's way of doing physics, Yang ended up taking his PhD in theoretical physics in 1947 with the physicist Edward Teller because Yang, as a foreigner, could not enter Argonne National Laboratory where Fermi conducted his experiments.

Yang taught at Chicago for one year before moving to the Institute for Advanced Study at Princeton, New Jersey, initially as a visitor but later as a permanent member at the invitation of its director J. Robert Oppenheimer. In the summer of 1954, when visiting the Brookhaven National Laboratory on Long Island, he devised, with the graduate student Robert Mills, the so-called Yang–Mills gauge field theory to describe patterns of interactions between elementary particles. It has since become one of the most fundamental theories in physics with far-reaching impact.

Yang's best-known contribution to physics came as a result of collaboration with T. D. Lee of Columbia University, a fellow Chinese American physicist whom he had met in Chicago when both studied under Fermi. Trying to solve the puzzles in the behaviors of subatomic particles, they proposed in 1956 the possibility that in the so-called "weak interactions" the commonly presumed law of left–right parity was violated. Initially received with much skepticism, they were soon, however, proven right in an experiment conducted by a third Chinese American physicist, Chien-Shiung Wu of Columbia, in collaboration with colleagues at the National Bureau of Standards. The news electrified the world of physics and Yang and Lee received the Nobel Prize in Physics in 1957.

Yang and Lee continued their collaboration until 1962 when personal friction developed between the two, in part over credit for their famous discovery. In 1966 Yang moved to the new Stony Brook campus of the State University of New York, where he stayed until retirement in 1999 and contributed much to the school's development. In this period he collaborated with Rodney J. Baxter and came up with the Yang–Baxter equation, another major breakthrough in physics with widespread applications and growing importance in physics and mathematics.

Yang spent much of his energy in his later years promoting U.S.–China scientific relations, with his first visit back to China in 1971. He became president of the National Association of Chinese Americans in 1977 and pushed for the successful renormalization of U.S.–China relations. Through public speeches and frequent visits, he has played an active role in promoting science and education in mainland China, Taiwan, Hong Kong, and the rest of East Asia. In 2003, Yang moved to China following the death of Du Zhili and then married Weng Fan, a graduate student in English in Guangzhou; and during the second decade of the twenty-first century, he split his time between Tsinghua and the Chinese University of Hong Kong.

[*See also* **Fermi, Enrico; Lee, Tsung-Dao; Nobel Prize in Biomedical Research; Oppenheimer, J. Robert; Physics; Teller, Edward;** *and* **Wu, Chien-Shiung.**]

BIBLIOGRAPHY

Bernstein, Jeremy. *A Comprehensible World.* New York: Random House, 1967. Contains a profile of Tsung-Dao Lee and Chen Ning Yang, "A Question of Parity," first published in *The New Yorker,* 12 May 1962, pp. 49–103.

Jiang, Caijian. *Guifan yu duicheng zhi mei: Yang Zhenning zhuan* (The Beauty of Gauge and Symmetry: A Biography of Chen Ning Yang). Taipei: Tianxia Press, 2002.

Yang, Chen Ning. *Selected Papers 1945–80 with Commentary.* San Francisco: W. H. Freeman, 1983.

Zuoyue Wang

YELLOW FEVER

Yellow fever was a major epidemic disease in the Atlantic world from the time of its importation via the West African slave trade in the seventeenth century to its effective control by the mid-twentieth. The disease is caused by a virus that is spread by mosquitoes of the *Aedes* genus, and it features dramatic symptoms of high fever, headache, jaundice, and a diffuse bleeding tendency. This last feature caused bleeding in the stomach, which, when forcibly ejected, generated the grisly symptom of black vomit that so distinguished the terrible infection. Case mortality rates could appear as high as 50 percent because the milder cases went unrecognized. Imported from West Africa, the first outbreaks struck the Caribbean in the mid-seventeenth century and reached the cities of Boston, New York, and Philadelphia in the 1690s. Throughout its history in North America, yellow fever remained largely an urban disease, traveling on the trade routes connecting American cities to tropical locales.

The disease flared dramatically in Philadelphia in 1793, when it disrupted the new federal government and caused the first major controversy over the causes of epidemic disease. One side argued that the disease arose spontaneously from the filth coating the streets and docks; others claimed that it was an imported pestilence. Arguments about public-health policy flowed from these theories, with one side promoting sanitation and the other quarantine. All segments of the population were affected, although the affluent found some protection in flight, and African Americans appeared to suffer less than others.

By the mid-nineteenth century, yellow fever had become principally a disease of southern ports, especially New Orleans, where multiple outbreaks in the 1850s led to the formation of a state board of health. Physicians noted that the disease favored recent immigrants, such as the large numbers of Irish who fled the potato famine. They dubbed it the "strangers' disease" and spoke of a necessary "seasoning" process that new arrivals to the city had to endure. The argument over transmission and prevention continued, but with a new twist. Southern physicians practicing in rural areas became increasingly convinced that yellow fever could be transported because they were able to tie rare outbreaks in their areas to contacts with epidemic centers. Physicians voiced a compromise "seed–soil" theory, which held that "seeds" of the disease had to be imported but only thrived in the sort of welcoming environment provided by poor sanitation. Hence, both quarantine *and* sanitation would help prevent yellow fever.

During the Civil War southerners happily predicted that yellow fever would join in the attack on the invading Yankees, but they were disappointed. More southerners died of yellow fever during the war than did northern troops. Although blockade-running vessels brought infection to a few port cities in southern hands, the limitation of trade led to a predictable decline in importation. After federal troops took New Orleans in the spring of 1862, local commander General Benjamin Butler enforced a rigid quarantine and put the armies of unemployed to work cleaning the streets. He succeeded in preventing a major yellow fever epidemic there during the war, and his efforts served as a model of how to prevent yellow fever—until the return of the city to southern control. Yellow fever reappeared in the city in 1867 and in full force in 1873. One curious footnote to the story of yellow fever in the war was the attempt of physician Luke Blackburn to deliberately spread yellow fever in Washington, D.C. (and, he hoped, to the White House itself). The plot failed.

Epidemic of 1878. Yellow fever was a panic disease. Even while physicians argued over whether it was contagious, members of the population who could flee a city in the midst of an epidemic did so. Refugees from infected cities were refused shelter at outlying towns, and locals tore up railroad tracks or refused a ship the right to dock to keep the infection away. Yellow fever accordingly had a major impact on commerce. The cities affected were, at least initially, port cities that brought in goods from the tropics; such trade could cease entirely when the fever struck. The disruption of rail traffic likewise caused heavy commercial losses, leading to strong pressure from businessmen or politicians to take action against the disease. These pressures came to a head in the worst yellow fever outbreak of the century, the epidemic of 1878.

Estimates vary on the number of cases, but somewhere in the range of 100,000 cases and 10,000 deaths from yellow fever occurred during the 1878 epidemic. Imported to New Orleans from Cuba, the epidemic spread as far north as Ohio on rail and steamship lines. Memphis was so badly affected that the state had to assume control of its government, which was in total disarray. Writings at the time suggest that this was not only a particularly widespread epidemic, but also perhaps a new strain of the fever, a strain that was both highly virulent and attacked natives as well as strangers. The heavy impact on trade led directly to the formation of the first federal public-health agency, the National Board of Health. This foray into national health policy ended in the early 1880s, but the standard was taken up again in the late 1880s by the Marine Hospital Service, which was called on to quell a yellow fever outbreak in Jacksonville, Florida, in 1888. This federal organization, previously charged with providing hospital care for sailors, assumed responsibility for yellow fever prevention after the 1888 epidemic and in the early twentieth century evolved into the U.S. Public Health Service (PHS).

Both state and federal authorities built disinfecting quarantine stations in the 1880s and 1890s to kill the suspected yellow fever "germ," although its identity eluded investigators. These stations pumped the holds of ships with sulfurous acid gas, washed decks with disinfectants, baked clothing and bedding in huge autoclaves, and watched passengers for signs of disease. These stations were effective guardians of the ports, even if they were killing mosquitoes in the holds rather than killing the long-sought-after germ. Many candidates for this germ were identified in the two decades following the 1878 epidemic, when researchers such as Robert Koch and Louis Pasteur were finding the bacterial causes of many common diseases, including tuberculosis and cholera. Some scientists were so sure of their yellow fever germs that they proceeded to create and distribute vaccines made from the organisms. But they were all wrong. Yellow fever was not caused by a bacterium and could not be seen with a light microscope.

Identifying and Eliminating Causes.

After the U.S. occupation of Cuba in the Spanish–American War, Surgeon General George Sternberg sent Walter Reed there as the head of a commission to study yellow fever. He and his colleagues first searched for a supposed bacterial agent suggested by yet another researcher, but quickly identified this agent as the cause of hog cholera, not yellow fever. Then they turned to a theory proposed by local physician Carlos Finlay, which held that mosquitoes spread the disease. Having established that the mosquito, and only the mosquito, was the vector, Reed's commission likewise suspected that the cause was one of the family of tiny organisms just beginning to be identified, now called viruses.

In 1905 the PHS used this knowledge to terminate the last U.S. yellow fever epidemic when it broke out in New Orleans. Mosquito larvae breed in water, and New Orleans had many large cisterns, which collected rain water for household drinking purposes. Public-health workers oiled the surface of such water receptacles, drained water where they could, and urged the screening of homes, all to avoid mosquito contact. They isolated known cases of the disease, burned insecticides to kill mosquitoes in the sickroom, and screened the sick space to prevent mosquito access. The PHS was able to claim victory over the epidemic using these methods, bolstering their public reputation as disease fighters. William Crawford Gorgas likewise used the mosquito theory to stamp out yellow fever in Havana, the frequent source of infections bound for the United States, and then, most famously, he controlled yellow fever and malaria in the Panama Canal Zone, which allowed the United States finally to complete that long-sought passage.

Researcher Max Theiler and his laboratory solved the final pieces of the puzzle. Working first at the Harvard Medical School and later at the Rockefeller Foundation laboratories in New York City, Theiler demonstrated that yellow fever was indeed spread by a virus, that the virus could be propagated in white mice, and finally that an effective vaccine could be formulated using the mice as a source. In the 1930s the yellow fever vaccine became available to protect those working in tropical regions where the disease persisted. During World War II the federal public-health service, worried that yellow fever might be imported yet again, began a program of spraying airplanes with insecticides upon landing. The fever did not slip through their protective measures. Yellow fever had been effectively eradicated from the United States.

[*See also* **Biological Sciences; Columbian Exchange; Disease; Entomology; Germ Theory of Disease; Life Expectancy; Medicine; Pesticides; Public Health; Public Health Service, U.S.; Race and Medicine; Reed, Walter,** *and* **Rockefeller Institute, The.**]

BIBLIOGRAPHY

Bell, Andrew McIlwaine. *Mosquito Soldiers: Malaria, Yellow Fever, and the Course of the American Civil War.* Baton Rouge: Louisiana State University Press, 2010. Reviews the importance of these two mosquito-borne diseases in the war and describes the military responses to them.

Carrigan, Jo Ann. *The Saffron Scourge: A History of Yellow Fever in Louisiana, 1795–1905.* Lafayette: Center for Louisiana Studies, 1994. Detailed history of yellow fever's visitation to Louisiana, which experienced the most severe and frequent yellow fever epidemics.

Ellis, John H. *Yellow Fever and Public Health in the New South.* Lexington: University Press of Kentucky, 1992. Describes the course of yellow fever in the United States after the Civil War, with a particularly detailed account of the 1878 epidemic.

Espinosa, Mariola. *Epidemic Invasions: Yellow Fever and the Limits of Cuban Independence, 1878–1930.* Chicago: University of Chicago Press, 2009. Examines the importance of yellow fever from a Cuban perspective.

Estes, J. Worth, and Smith, Billy G., eds. *A Melancholy Scene of Devastation: The Public Response to the 1793 Philadelphia Yellow Fever Epidemic.* Canton, Mass.: College of Physicians, 1997. Collected essays about the 1793 epidemic, including Martin Pernick's classic essay on the role of politics in managing the outbreak, and interesting demographic detail about the city and the epidemic.

Humphreys, Margaret. *Yellow Fever and the South.* New Brunswick, N.J.: Rutgers University Press, 1992. Monograph that details the role of debates over causation and prevention from the antebellum period to 1905; tracks the rise of southern state and federal public-health initiatives that built on the public panic engendered by yellow fever.

Margaret Humphreys

Z

ZAKRZEWSKA, MARIE

(1829–1902), midwife, physician, founder of the New England Hospital for Women and Children. Born in Berlin, Zakrzewska (pronounced Zak-shef'-ska) studied midwifery in Germany before coming to America in 1853 to pursue a medical education. Earning her MD from Western Reserve College in Cleveland, Ohio, in 1856, she first practiced at the New York Infirmary for Indigent Women and Children. In 1859, she moved to Boston to teach at the New England Female Medical College, but soon clashed with the college's founder, Samuel Gregory, over her desire to instruct students in such new scientific techniques as microscopy and thermometry. In 1862, with the support of several of Boston's leading liberal reformers, including Caroline Severance and William Lloyd Garrison, Zakrzewska founded the New England Hospital for Women and Children, where she worked until her retirement in 1899. This institution provided women an opportunity to receive clinical training at a time when most hospital positions were closed to them.

Zakrzewska's strong commitment to scientific medicine was unusual among her contemporaries. At a time when most women physicians justified their entry into the medical profession by emphasizing their caring and sympathetic natures, she insisted that women physicians, like their male counterparts, must develop their scientific investigative skills. Zakrzewska's battles to help women gain entry into the medical profession earned her a reputation as one of the leading women physicians of the nineteenth century.

[*See also* **Birth Control and Family Planning; Childbirth; Gender and Science; Higher Education and Science; Hospitals; Medical Education; Medical Specialization; Medicine;** *and* **Midwifery.**]

BIBLIOGRAPHY

Drachman, Virginia G. *Hospital with a Heart. Women Doctors and the Paradox of Separatism at the New*

England Hospital, 1862–1969. Ithaca, N.Y.: Cornell University Press, 1984.

Tuchman, Arleen Marcia. *Science Has No Sex. The Life of Marie Zakrzewska, MD*. Chapel Hill: University of North Carolina Press, 2006.

Vietor, Agnes. *A Woman's Quest: The Life of Marie E. Zakrzewska, M.D*. New York: D. Appleton, 1924, reprinted 1972.

Arleen Marcia Tuchman

ZOOLOGY

Broadly, zoology refers to the science of studying the animal kingdom. During the early history of the United States, zoology was considered a field of study within natural history (along with botany) and, beginning in the 1870s and 1880s, within biology. Throughout the nineteenth century, zoological activities in the United States evolved from the pursuit of self-trained enthusiasts to an academic discipline located in museums and universities. In the decades after 1900, as interest in traditional systematic zoology declined, research into animal life continued in increasingly specialized biological subfields.

Exploration. The earliest zoological work focusing on the United States was conducted by European-trained explorers such as the British naturalist Mark Catesby (1683–1749). Catesby traveled through the Atlantic coast and published his descriptions of native fauna in the *Natural History of Carolina, Florida, and the Bahama Islands* (1731). Increasingly, however, American gentlemen-naturalists published regional zoological investigations that underscored the scientific importance of New World animals. The third president of the United States, Thomas Jefferson, penned an account of American quadrupeds in *Notes on the State of Virginia* (1784–1785) to refute the French naturalist Count Georges-Louis Leclerc Buffon's theory of the degeneracy of American animals. Along with publishing accounts of the usefulness of local fauna, nationalistic interests in American zoology translated into initial efforts to organize

natural history museums. Founded in 1786, Charles Willson Peale's museum in Philadelphia displayed North American specimens, notably an American mastodon skeleton and an extensive collection of American birds. Ornithology was the most popular zoological tradition at this time, supported by networks of private collectors like Peale and the circulation of illustrated natural history works such as John James Audubon's *Birds of America* (1827–1838). Chiefly self-trained, many American naturalists remained in step with their European counterparts, using natural theology and the classificatory frameworks of the French zoologist Georges Cuvier to understand animal form and function.

During the early nineteenth century, the scientific culture of zoology developed as the federal government started to employ naturalists, dispatching them across the United States in exploring parties. These expeditions were seen as opportunities to gather information about the newly acquired territories in the American West and to amass collections of novel North American species. Sent by Thomas Jefferson in 1804, the Lewis and Clark Expedition traveled throughout the trans-Mississippi West, collecting and keeping records of regional fauna. Congressionally funded domestic and international surveys—such as the U.S. Exploring Expedition of 1838–1842 and the Pacific Railroad Surveys of 1853–1855—included a naturalist charged with collecting and preserving specimens. Shipped back to Washington, D.C., these specimens formed the basis of the Smithsonian Institution's natural history collection. Established by an act of Congress on 10 August 1846, the Smithsonian Institution led by Joseph Henry (1797–1878) and later the zoologist Spencer Fullerton Baird (1823–1887) took on the role of the national natural history museum.

Building Institutions. Along with the Smithsonian, a range of urban natural history institutions, such as the Academy of Natural Sciences in Philadelphia, the Boston Society of Natural History, and the American Museum of Natural History, facilitated specimen collection networks, the careers of a growing community of naturalists, and a growing popular fascination with zoology. In Cambridge, Massachusetts, the Swiss ichthyologist Louis Agassiz (1807–1873) was given a professorship by Harvard University in 1847 and transformed Harvard into a center for natural history research by founding the Museum of Comparative Zoology in 1859. Agassiz's museum was an important site for museum-based zoological research and for training a generation of advanced students. Crucial to Agassiz's vision of zoology was his 1857 "Essay on Classification," which underscored the immutability of species, a tenuous position he would hold throughout the nineteenth century despite the growing popularity of Darwin's theory of evolution. At the Smithsonian, Baird amassed a comprehensive collection of North American specimens to be used for assessing the distribution of American animals and plants; and as the director of the U.S. Fish Commission, he supported intensive studies of American fisheries with the goal of improving collapsed marine industries in New England. Along with the organization of urban natural history institutions, this period was marked by the founding of influential publications like the *American Naturalist* and disciplinary societies like the American Society of Zoologists (later the American Morphological Society).

Between 1870 and 1900, American universities reorganized their educational priorities and started to include undergraduate and advanced graduate work in biology, which included the physiology, comparative anatomy, and morphology of animals. What counted as biology in America at this time was often up for debate, influenced by research programs in Europe, especially in Germany, institutional priorities, and the scientific training of early instructors in the field. In 1876, Johns Hopkins University president Daniel Gilman hired the physiologist Henry Newell Martin to create a research-oriented biology program. As other universities followed in his footsteps, they often garnered support for zoology programs by linking them to medical school curriculum reforms. Marine stations also became important sites for zoological research, notably the Marine Biological Laboratory at Woods Hole in Massachusetts. Founded in 1888 and directed by the embryologist Charles O. Whitman (1842–1910), the Marine Biological Laboratory brought together a community of specialized practitioners to think through fundamental problems in American biology. It supported a generation of zoologists, including the cytologist Edmund Beecher Wilson, the embryologist Edwin Grant Conklin, and the geneticist Thomas Hunt Morgan. Through their work at the Marine Biological Laboratory, each became increasingly invested in experimental practices, evolution, and questions of heredity. During the next three decades, the professional network of zoologists extended across the country. They were hired to teach in medical schools and biology departments, as well as to do research and outreach for a range of state and federal applied science institutions.

Transformation and Legacy. The rediscovery of Gregor Mendel's theories of inheritance in 1900 invigorated the American biological community and accelerated research into the mechanisms of evolution. In the field of genetics, zoologists conducted breeding experiments with an array of organisms as a way of exploring the nature of variation and heredity. Large-scale animal breeding required extensive facilities, and in 1904 the Carnegie Institution funded Charles Benedict Davenport's Station for Experimental Evolution at Cold Spring Harbor, New York. At Columbia, genetic mapping of *Drosophila* mutants by Thomas Hunt Morgan and his students yielded not only a robust experimental organism but also the chromosome theory of Mendelian inheritance. Sites for conducting zoological research proliferated and diversified. Along with museums, universities, and marine stations, zoologists conducted research in inland field stations, such as the Rocky Mountain Biological Laboratory, and in agricultural experiment stations affiliated with land-grant colleges. At the same time, zoological investigations entered high school classrooms as part of a unified science of biology. Traces of traditional zoology as advocated by Louis Agassiz, namely analyses of animal structure and function through comparative anatomy, remained present in secondary school biology textbooks.

After the 1920s, the study of animal life in the biological sciences was folded into a range of professionalizing subfields from genetics, ecology, and population biology to cellular and molecular biology. Zoology remained present in named departments located in universities and museums, specialized taxonomic literature, and scientific societies such as the International Congress of Zoology, which met regularly until 1963. Crucial to the development of the life sciences was the modern, or "evolutionary," synthesis in the 1930s and 1940s, which strove to connect new findings in genetics with systematics under the aegis of evolutionary biology. World War II ushered in new structures for biological work in the United States, establishing different funding and research priorities and shifting interest toward molecular biology, genetics, and biomedical research.

[*See also* **Academy of Natural Sciences of Philadelphia; American Museum of Natural History; Anatomy and Human Dissection; Animal and Human Experimentation; Biochemistry; Biological Sciences; Botany; Columbian Exchange; Conservation Movement; Ecology; Entomology; Environmentalism; Evolution, Theory of; Fish and Wildlife Service, U.S.; Genetics and Genetic Engineering; Geography; Higher Education and Science; Lewis and Clark Expedition; Molecular Biology; Museums of Science and Natural History; Oceanography; Physiology; Science; Smithsonian Institution; Veterinary Medicine;** *and* **Zoos.**]

BIBLIOGRAPHY

Allen, Garland. *Life Science in the Twentieth Century*. 1975. Reprint, Cambridge, U.K.: Cambridge University Press, 1978. One of the first general studies of the life sciences in the history of science.

Kohler, Robert E. *All Creatures: Naturalists, Collectors, and Biodiversity, 1850–1950*. Princeton, N.J.: Princeton University Press, 2006. A revised

history of the life sciences that foregrounds the importance of systematic specimen-collecting practices.

Lurie, Edward. *Louis Agassiz: A Life in Science*. 1960. Reprint, Baltimore: Johns Hopkins University Press, 1988. Seminal, richly written biography of Louis Agassiz.

Maienschein, Jane. *Transforming Traditions in American Biology, 1880–1915*. Baltimore: Johns Hopkins University Press, 1991. Provides a fine-grained analysis of the intellectual commitments and career trajectories of the first generation of American-trained morphologists.

Pauly, Philip. *Biologists and the Promise of American Life: From Meriwether Lewis to Alfred Kinsey*. Princeton, N.J.: Princeton University Press, 2000. One of the most thoughtful synthetic accounts of American zoology since the early republic.

Winsor, Mary P. *Reading the Shape of Nature: Comparative Zoology at the Agassiz Museum*. Chicago: University of Chicago Press, 1991. Excellent analysis of the development of a natural history institution during the late nineteenth century.

Jenna Tonn

ZOOS

The word "zoo," short for zoological park or zoological garden, can refer to many things. Although most members of the public commonly think of a zoo as a publically or privately owned entity where keepers confine animals within enclosures for public viewing, a zoological garden can also be a place where highly trained professionals keep animals for scientific study, conservation, breeding, and care. In its broadest sense, people also use the term zoo to refer to unregulated animal collections owned by private individuals; petting zoos with domesticated animals; safari parks, such as Bush Gardens in Tampa, Florida; public aquaria; and theme parks that have animals onsite, for example, the several Sea World parks located throughout the United States.

This article focuses on the term "zoo" in the sense of civic zoological gardens. These are entities—owned either by a government body or by a zoological society—that the proprietors establish with the express purpose of giving the public a place to view animals, while also providing for the conservation, breeding, and care of animals. The Association of Zoos and Aquariums (formally the American Zoo Association), which regulates and accredits zoological gardens in seven countries, lists about 220 of these zoos in the United States.

European Origins. The zoos in America can trace their origins to the long-established European tradition of displaying wild animals in menageries. The first recorded menagerie (a collection of animals owned privately, normally by royalty or other social elites) dates to approximately 3500 BCE, when Egyptian pharaohs began to keep animals for their personal enjoyment. Historical records also show that King Solomon, of the Kingdom of Israel (ruled ca. 970 to 931 BCE), various kings of the Assyrian and Babylonia empires, and some of the leaders of the ancient Greek city-states also maintained collections of exotic animals.

The popularity of menageries spread throughout Europe as the Roman Empire developed during the final centuries BCE. Most often, the Roman menageries contained animals captured and traded throughout the Roman Empire, which included much of Europe, Northern Africa, and the Middle East. Whereas non-Roman elites developed their menageries as displays of both status and luxury—the animals' owners keeping them as exotic pets—the proprietors of Roman menageries often kept their animals for use within the gladiatorial arena. Their owners forced them to fight against other animals (for example, a pack of dogs against a rhinoceros), allowing gladiators to hunt them or putting wild animals into pits as a form of executing criminals (for example, a group of lions in the same pit as convicted thieves).

The practice of keeping menageries declined with the fall of the Roman Empire in the third century. Then, during the 1200s, menageries became favorable again, with the kings of England and the holy Roman emperors as their biggest supporters. Often royal menageries contained animals that nobles received as gifts from foreign diplomats. For example, King John (King of England from 1199 to 1216) kept a collection of animals, which

he received from other monarchs, in the Tower of London. His successors maintained this tradition, and, during the sixteenth century, the Tower menagerie opened to the public. When royal officials closed this menagerie in 1835, they transferred the animals to the London Zoo.

These menageries, kept by royal families across Europe, formed the foundations for the first European public zoos, which opened across the continent in the second half of the eighteenth century. The oldest still-existing zoological garden, in Vienna, Austria, opened in 1765. In 1775, a zoo opened in Madrid, Spain, and the citizens of Paris established a zoo in their city in 1795. By the mid-nineteenth century, zoological gardens were open in most of the major European capitals.

The First Zoos in America. Both the Philadelphia and the New York Central Park zoos claim to be the first public zoological gardens in the United States. In 1859, the Philadelphia Zoological Society designed the plan for the first public zoo in the United States; however, the American Civil War delayed the zoo's opening until 1874. In the meantime, Central Park opened its zoo in 1860, giving it the title of the first American zoological garden to open to the public.

These zoos illustrate the two main ways that American cities established the earliest zoological gardens in the United States. A charter, written by the Commonwealth of Pennsylvania, formally established the Philadelphia Zoo. The aim of the zoo was both to facilitate public recreation and to establish a place of scientific research. Because of its charter, zoo officials had the ability to plan the zoo before any animals arrived. Whereas most zoological societies, like the Philadelphia Zoo, formally established their zoos before they opened, others, such as the Central Park Zoo, came about by accident. The Central Park Zoo was never a part of the original design, which called for a public park mainly consisting of natural landscape; rather, it came into being after several gifts of exotic animals to Central Park; this meant that the zoo arose out an immediate need to house and care for the animals.

Like the Central Park Zoo, some zoological gardens came into being as private individuals gifted animals to cities, colleges, and other public institutions. In other cases, such as the original Detroit Zoo, the need to house animals seized from defunct circuses and private collections led to the establishing of public zoological gardens without much initial planning or funding. This meant that these zoos often lacked the scientific components of their formally established counterparts.

Along with public libraries and museums, the zoological garden became one of the central features of American city life by the early 1900s. During the period between 1880 and 1930, the opening of municipal funded zoos accelerated; by 1930, slightly less than one hundred cities in the United States had a public zoo. During the Great Depression (1929–1939), the federal government funded the creation of new zoos and the expansion of already existing zoos as a way of putting unemployed men to work. These public-works programs led to the building of 26 new zoos across the country. Although the United States did not see any new zoos opened during World War II (1941–1945), between the end of the war and the year 2000, public and private entities established another one hundred zoos in the United States.

Conservation and Education. Many of the early American zoological gardens did little to promote the conservation and welfare of animals. In many institutions, zookeepers kept animals in small cages and provided minimal professional care for the animals. Furthermore, these zoos often promoted themselves as places of amusement, with animal rides and chances for the public to feed the animals. As a result, the welfare of the animals on display was not a primary concern for zoo directors; rather, ensuring a steady stream of visitors to their zoos, to generate cash flow, was their primary goal. Often, meeting this goal meant harsh treatment of animals in an effort to get them to perform for the public.

In a few extreme cases, zoo directors also put foreign peoples on display in zoos. These displays, which modern scholars refer to as "human zoos," were very popular in the late 1800s and early 1900s. For instance, in 1906 the Bronx Zoo displayed Ota Benga, a Congolese Mbuti tribe member, within the same cage as the zoo's orangutan. The context of the display was that Ota and his tribe members were more like wild animals than the civilized patrons who visited the zoo to see him.

During the 1920s, the focus of some zoological societies began to shift gradually toward the promotion of animal welfare and conservation. For example, some zoos—such as the one in Detroit—built larger exhibits and used a series of ditches and moats instead of cages to contain the animals. Based on the design of the German animal distributor Carl Hagenbeck, this open-enclosure design promoted exhibits that better approximated the animals' natural habitats. Because of its popularity with the public, most zoos have adapted this design for many of their newer exhibits.

However, the creation of these open-air exhibits did not necessarily lead to better treatment of animals in zoos. During the 1960s, the growing environmentalist movement began to question the treatment of animals in zoological parks. By the late 1960s, animal rights groups were protesting the treatment of animals kept by zoos. Because of growing objection from animal rights groups, some zoos began to make animal preservation their primary mission. By the early 1980s, most major American zoos stopped having animals perform shows and the Association of Zoos and Aquariums made conservation its highest priority.

Although zoos have shifted their focus toward animal welfare, zoological gardens still have many critics who claim that the public should do away with zoos entirely. Animal rights groups and scholars, many of whom are in the field of animal studies, equate the keeping of animals in zoos to a form of slavery. In the face of these criticisms, zoos continue to evolve; for example, some zoological gardens have ceased keeping elephants because they cannot provide them with enough space to ensure the elephants' happiness.

In the second decade of the twenty-first century, most North American and European zoos emphasized conservation of endangered species as their primary mission. Because of this, breeding and researching endangered animals has become the primary focus of most zoological societies, with the entertainment of guests a secondary function. Furthermore, many zoos have developed specialized areas designed to educate the public about the environment, endangered animals, and the impact of humans on animal well-being.

[See also Biological Sciences; Popularization of Science; Science; and Zoology.]

BIBLIOGRAPHY

Baratay, Eric, and Elisabeth Hardouin-Fugier. *Zoo: A History of Zoological Gardens in the West.* London: Reaktion Books, 2002.

Blanchard, Pascal. *Human Zoos: Science and Spectacle in the Age of Colonial Empires.* Liverpool, U.K.: Liverpool University Press, 2008.

Blunt, Wilfrid. *The Ark in the Park: The Zoo in the Nineteenth Century.* London: Hamilton, 1976.

Donahue, Jesse C., and Erik K. Trump. *American Zoos during the Depression: A New Deal for Animals.* Amazon Kindle ed. Jefferson, N.C.: McFarland & Company, 2010.

Hahn, Daniel. *The Tower Menagerie: Being the Amazing True Story of the Royal Collection of Wild and Ferocious Beasts.* London: Simon & Schuster, 2003.

Hanson, Elizabeth. *Animal Attractions: Nature on Display in American Zoos.* Princeton, N.J.: Princeton University Press, 2002.

Kisling, Vernon N. *Zoo and Aquarium History: Ancient Animal Collections to Zoological Gardens.* Boca Raton, Fla.: CRC Press, 2001.

Rothfels, Nigel. *Savages and Beasts: The Birth of the Modern Zoo.* Baltimore: Johns Hopkins University Press, 2002.

Thomas S. Darragh

ZUCKERBERG, MARK

See Computers, Mainframe, Mini, and Micro; Internet and World Wide Web; Software.

ZWORYKIN, VLADIMIR KOSMA

(1888–1982), one of the most important American inventors of electronic television, was born in Mourom, Russia. Zworkykin studied electrical engineering at the St. Petersburg Institute of Technology and conducted early television research under Boris Rosing. After service in the Russian signal corps during World War I, he left Russia in 1918 and by 1920 was settled in the United States, working for Westinghouse in Pittsburgh.

Zworykin's first American television patents were applied for in late 1923 and 1925 and granted in 1928, 1931, and 1938. These included the iconoscope camera tube and the kinescope picture display tube that were central to the final system. In 1925, Zworykin applied for his first color television system patent and also built his first complete electronic television system. Based in part on these efforts, he earned a PhD from the University of Pittsburgh a year later. In 1928 he visited television researchers in Britain, France, and Germany and gained many valuable ideas. But Westinghouse officials seemed unimpressed with his television experimentation, and thus Zworykin was open to an invitation in 1929 to join the RCA Victor Company as director of its Electronic Research Group based in Camden, New Jersey.

Zworykin became infamous for his 1930 prediction that it might take $100,000 for RCA to develop a workable commercial television system—in fact, it took tens of millions of dollars over the next decade. That same year he visited the Philo Farnsworth labs in San Francisco at a time when it appeared the two men might work together for RCA, although that did not eventuate. Most of RCA's television research expense in the 1930s centered on continually improving the basic system and increasing its picture definition. By late in the decade, RCA's subsidiary, NBC, was conducting regular experimental broadcasts.

Zworykin's wartime research efforts from 1941 to 1945 included developing the first commercial electron microscope for industry, applications of television to military needs, and development of the image orthicon camera tube, which would become the backbone of postwar television. During his lifetime, he held more than 120 patents. Zworykin retired in 1954, but remained active in research and television policy within RCA for the next quarter century. He died in Princeton, New Jersey.

[*See also* **Electricity and Electrification; Engineering; Farnsworth, Philo Taylor; Military, Science and Technology and the; Research and Development (R&D);** *and* **Television.**]

BIBLIOGRAPHY

Abramson, Albert. *Zworykin: Pioneer of Television.* Urbana: University of Illinois Press, 1995.

Zworykin, Vladimir K. "The Early Days: Some Recollections." *Television Quarterly* 1, no. 4 (November 1962): 69–73.

Zworykin, Vladimir K., and George A. Morton. *Television: The Electronics of Image Transmission.* New York: John Wiley & Sons, 1940, revised 1952.

Christopher H. Sterling

TOPICAL OUTLINE
OF ENTRIES

This topical outline presents an overview of the encyclopedia, with entries listed under the following subject categories:

Agriculture, Fish, and Wildlife
Biological Sciences
Building and Household Technologies
Computer, Communication, and Information Technologies
Concepts, Research, and Theories
Diseases, Disabilities, and Disorders
Earth Sciences
Education and Fields of Study
Electricity and Electronics
Energy and Illumination
Engineering
Environment and Disasters
Ethics and Religion
Events
Gender, Sexuality, and Family Relations
Institutions and Organizations
Machinery and Manufacturing
Media and Literature
Medical Procedures and Technologies
Military and Diplomacy
Physical Sciences
Policy and Law
Public Health
Race
Social Sciences
Space Science and Technology
Transportation Technologies
Biographies

Some categories are not mutually exclusive; thus, entries may be listed in more than one category.

Agriculture, Fish, and Wildlife

Agricultural Education and Extension
Agricultural Experiment Stations
Agricultural Technology
Agriculture, U.S. Department of
Barbed Wire
Botanical Gardens
Botany
Columbian Exchange
Dust Bowl
Ecology
Entomology
Fish and Wildlife Service, U.S.
Fisheries and Fishing
Food and Diet
Food Processing
Forestry Technology and Lumbering
Forest Service, U.S.
4-H Club Movement
Hybrid Seeds
Morrill Land Grant Act
Pesticides
Rural Electrification Administration
Veterinary Medicine
Zoology
Zoos

Biological Sciences

Biochemistry
Biological Sciences
Botanical Gardens
Botany
Ecology
Entomology
Genetics and Genetic Engineering
Instruments of Science
Molecular Biology
Nobel Prize in Biomedical Research
Paleontology
Physiology
Sociobiology and Evolutionary Psychology
Veterinary Medicine
Zoology
Zoos

Building and Household Technologies

Brooklyn Bridge

Building Technology
Elevator
Empire State Building
Engineering
Heating Technology
Home Economics Movement
Hoover Dam
Household Technology
Panama Canal
Refrigeration and Air Conditioning
Skyscrapers
Technology

Computer, Communication, and Information Technologies

Animation Technology and Computer
  Graphics
Artificial Intelligence
Atlantic Cable
Automation and Computerization
Bell Laboratories
Cartography
Computer Science
Computers, Mainframe, Mini, and Macro
Electronic Communication Devices, Mobile
ENIAC
Film Technology
Internet and World Wide Web
Office Technology
Photocopying
Photography
Printing and Publishing
Radio
Satellites, Communications
Silicon Valley
Software
Sound Technology, Recorded
Technology
Telegraph
Telephone
Television

Concepts, Research, and Theories

American System of Manufactures
Animal and Human Experimentation
Cloning
Columbian Exchange

Creationism
DNA Sequencing
Eugenics
Evolution, Theory of
Genetics and Genetic Engineering
Germ Theory of Disease
Global Warming
Group Practice
Human Genome Project
Intelligence, Concepts of
International Geophysical Year
Nobel Prize in Biomedical Research
Plate Tectonics, Theory of
Quantum Theory
Research and Development (R&D)
Stem-Cell Research

Diseases, Disabilities, and Disorders

Alcohol and Alcohol Abuse
Alzheimer's Disease and Dementia
Anorexia Nervosa
Arthritis
Asthma and Allergy
Autism
Blindness, Assistive Technologies and
Cancer
Centers for Disease Control and Prevention
Cholera
Deafness
Diabetes
Diphtheria
Disabilities, Intellectual and Developmental
Disease
Epilepsy
Germ Theory of Disease
HIV/AIDS
Hospitals
Influenza
Malaria
Mental Illness
Obesity
Occupational Diseases
Poliomyelitis
Rabies
Sexually Transmitted Diseases
Sickle-Cell Disease
Smallpox

Tuberculosis
Typhoid Fever
Typhus
Yellow Fever

Earth Sciences

Cartography
Geography
Geological Surveys
Geology
Geophysics
Global Warming
Instruments of Science
Meteorology and Climatology
Oceanography
Plate Tectonics, Theory of

Education and Fields of Study

Anesthesiology
Anthropology
Archaeology
Astronomy and Astrophysics
Baby and Child Care
Biochemistry
Biological Sciences
Biotechnology
Botany
Cardiology
Cartography
Computer Science
Dentistry
Dinosaurs
Ecology
Engineering
Entomology
Ethics and Professionalism in Engineering
Flexner Report
Forensic Pathology and Death Investigation
Genetics and Genetic Engineering
Geography
Geology
Geophysics
Gerontology
Higher Education and Science
High Schools, Science Education in
Mathematics and Statistics
Medical Education

Ethics and Religion

Abortion Debates and Science
Animal and Human Experimentation
Creationism
Death and Dying
Ethics and Medicine
Ethics and Professionalism in Engineering
Eugenics
Evolution, Theory of
Missionaries and Science and Medicine
Pseudoscience and Quackery
Religion and Science

Events

Challenger Disaster
Deepwater Horizon Explosion and Oil Spill
Exxon Valdez Oil Spill
Lewis and Clark Expedition
Scopes Trial
Three Mile Island Accident
Tuskegee Syphilis Study
Wilkes Expedition

Gender, Sexuality, and Family Relations

Abortion Debates and Science
Baby and Child Care
Birth Control and Family Planning
Childbirth
Gender and Science
Gender and Technology
Home Economics Movement
Midwifery
Sex and Sexuality
Sex Education

Institutions and Organizations

Academy of Natural Sciences of Philadelphia
American Association for the Advancement
    of Science
American Association for the History of
    Medicine
American Institute of Physics
American Medical Association
American Museum of Natural History
American Philosophical Society
Army Corps of Engineers, U.S.
Atomic Energy Commission

Bell Laboratories
Botanical Gardens
Centers for Disease Control and Prevention
Defense Advanced Research Projects Agency
Environmental Protection Agency
Fish and Wildlife Service, U.S.
Foundations and Health
4-H Club Movement
Group Practice
Health Insurance
Health Maintenance Organizations
History of Science Society
Hospitals
Indian Health Service
Mayo Clinic
Mental Health Institutions
Museums of Science and Natural History
National Academy of Sciences
National Aeronautics and Space
    Administration
National Institutes of Health
National Laboratories
National Medical Association
National Park System
National Science Foundation
Nuclear Regulatory Commission
Office of Science and Technology Policy
Office of Scientific Research and Development
Office of Technology Assessment,
    Congressional
Postal Service, U.S.
President's Science Advisory
    Committee
Public Health Service, U.S.
Red Cross, American
Rockefeller Institute, The
Rural Electrification Administration
Scripps Institution of Oceanography
Smithsonian Institution
Social Science Research Council
Societies and Associations, Science
Society for the History of Technology
Tennessee Valley Authority
World Health Organization

Machinery and Manufacturing

Clocks and Clockmaking
Cotton Gin

Public Health
Public Health Service, U.S.
Sexually Transmitted Diseases

Race

Demography
Eugenics
Indian Health Service
National Medical Association
Native American Healers
Race and Medicine
Race Theories, Scientific
Tuskegee Syphilis Study

Social Sciences

Anthropology
Archaeology
Behaviorism
Demography
Geography
Linguistics
Social Sciences

Space Science and Technology

Astronomy and Astrophysics
Challenger Disaster
Hubble Space Telescope
Instruments of Science
Space Program
Space Science
Technology

Transportation Technologies

Airplanes and Air Transport
Bicycles and Bicycling
Canals and Waterways
Elevator
Erie Canal
Highway System
Internal Combustion Engine
Maritime Transport
Motor Vehicles
Panama Canal
Railroads
Rivers as Technological Systems
Roads and Turnpikes, Early
Shipbuilding

Subways
Technology
Urban Mass Transit

Biographies

Agassiz, Louis
Alvarez, Luis Walter
Andrews, Roy Chapman
Armstrong, Edwin Howard
Audubon, John James
Bache, Alexander Dallas
Baird, Spencer Fullerton
Bardeen, John
Bartram, John and William
Beaumont, William
Bell, Alexander Graham
Berkner, Lloyd
Bethe, Hans
Blackwell, Elizabeth
Blalock, Alfred
Boas, Franz
Bowditch, Nathaniel
Bridgman, Percy
Bush, Vannevar
Cannon, Walter Bradford
Carothers, Wallace Hume
Carson, Rachel
Carver, George Washington
Cattell, James McKeen
Colden, Cadwallader and Jane
Colt, Samuel
Compton, Arthur H.
Compton, Karl Taylor
Conant, James B.
Condon, Edward
Cope, Edward Drinker
Cori, Gerty and Carl
Dalton, John Call, Jr.
Dana, James Dwight
Davenport, Charles Benedict
DeBakey, Michael
De Forest, Lee
Delbrück, Max
Dobzhansky, Theodosius
Drew, Charles Richard
Dubos, René Jules
Du Pont, Pierre S.

DIRECTORY OF
CONTRIBUTORS

Duncan Agnew
Institute of Geophysics & Planetary Physics,
University of California, San Diego
    Plate Tectonics, Theory of

Stephen G. Alter
Department of History, Gordon College
    Linguistics

R. Joseph Anderson
American Institute of Physics
    American Institute of Physics

A. J. Angulo
Curriculum and Pedagogy, Winthrop University
    Rogers, William Barton

Rima D. Apple
Professor Emerita, University of
Wisconsin-Madison
    Home Economics Movement

Simon Baatz
Department of History, John Jay College of
Criminal Justice, City Unviersity of New York
    American Philosophical Society; Science:
    Colonial Era

Douglas Bacon
The School of Medicine, Wayne State University
    Anesthesiology

Jeffrey P. Baker
Department of Pediatrics, Division of
Pediatrics-Primary Care, Duke University
    Pediatrics

Jesse F. Ballenger
Science, Technology, and Society Program at
Pennsylvania State Unversity
    Alzheimer's Disease and Dementia

Jenny Bangham
Max-Planck-Institut für Wissenschaftsgeschichte
(Max Planck Institute for the History of
Science)
    Muller, Hermann J.

Robert C. Bannister
Professor Emeritus, Swarthmore College
   Parsons, Talcott

Mark V. Barrow Jr.
*Department of History, Virginia Polytechnic
Institute and State University*
   Audubon, John James; Fish and Wildlife
   Service, U.S.

Richard A. Bartlett
*Professor Emeritus of History, Florida State
University*
   Lewis and Clark Expedition

Ronald Bayer
*Center for the History and Ethics of Public
Health, Mailman School of Public Health,
Columbia University*
   HIV/AIDS

Catherine Nisbett Becker
Independent Scholar
   Pickering, Edward Charles

Trudy E. Bell
*Senior Writer, University of California High-
Performance Astro Computing Center;
Contributing Editor, Sky & Telescope Magazine*
   Astronomy and Astrophysics

John Belton
*Department of English, Rutgers University, The
State University of New Jersey, New Brunswick*
   Film Technology

Keith R. Benson
*Department of History, University of British
Columbia*
   Scripps Institution of Oceanography

Thomas J. Bergin
*Professor Emeritus of Computer Science,
American University*
   Von Neumann, John; Wiener, Norbert

Craig Biegel
Department of History, Florida State University
   Oceanography

Lindy Biggs
Department of History, Auburn University
   American System of Manufactures

Carla Bittel
*Department of History, Loyola Marymount
University*
   Jacobi, Mary Putnam

Michael Bliss
Department of History, University of Toronto
   Osler, William

Walter J. Bock
*Department of Biological Sciences, Columbia
University*
   Mayr, Ernst

Nicholas E. Bonneau
Department of History; University of Notre Dame
   Cholera

Hannah Borgeson
Independent Scholar
   Bicycles and Bicycling

Charlotte G. Borst
Dean of the Faculty, Whittier College
   Midwifery

Mary Ellen Bowden
*Senior Research Fellow, Chemical Heritage
Foundation*
   Priestley, Joseph

Paul S. Boyer [±]
*Merle Curti Professor of History Emeritus,
University of Wisconsin-Madison*
   American Museum of Natural History;
   Blalock, Alfred; Carver, George
   Washington; Colt, Samuel; Fulton, Robert;
   Hoover Dam; Mitchell, Maria; Nuclear
   Power; Office of Technology Assessment,
   Congressional; Printing and Publishing;
   Sagan, Carl; Skinner, B. F.; Slater, Samuel;
   Springfield Armory; Von Braun, Wernher

Susan Hanket Brandt
Department of History, Temple University
   Birth Control and Family Planning

Paul D. Brinkman
North Carolina Museum of Natural Sciences
   Academy of Natural Sciences of
   Philadelphia; Cope, Edward Drinker;
   Dinosaurs; Marsh, Othniel Charles;
   Paleontology

Loren A. Broc
Department of History, University of Rochester
Phrenology

David L. Browman
Department of Anthropology, Washington University in St. Louis
Archaeology

C. D. B. Bryan±
Independent Scholar
Mayo Clinic

Rex C. Buchanan
Kansas Geological Survey
Geological Surveys

Diana Kormos Buchwald
California Institute of Technology
Einstein, Albert

Kerry W. Buckley
Independent Scholar
Behaviorism; Hall, G. Stanley

Robert Bud
The Science Museum, London
Biotechnology; Penicillin

John D. Buenker
Professor Emeritus of History, University of Wisconsin-Parkside
Pure Food and Drug Act

Joshua Buhs
Independent Scholar
Entomology

Vern L. Bullough±
Distinguished Professor Emeritus in History and Sociology, State University of New York, Buffalo
Sexually Transmitted Diseases

Orville R. Butler
American Institute of Physics
Townes, Charles H.

Carol R. Byerly
Department of History, University of Colorado at Boulder
Influenza

Angelina Callahan
Naval Research Lab, Washington, D.C.
International Geophysical Year

David Cantor
National Institutes of Health
Cancer

James H. Capshew
Department of History and Philosophy of Science, Indiana University
Psychology

W. Bernard Carlson
Corcoran Department of History, University of Virginia
Westinghouse, George

John Carson
Department of History, University of Michigan
Intelligence, Concepts of

Fred V. Carstensen
Connecticut Center for Economic Analysis, University of Connecticut
McCormick, Cyrus Hall

Joyce E. Chaplin
Department of History, Harvard University
Franklin, Benjamin

Ellen Chesler
Roosevelt Institute
Sanger, Margaret

Hyungsub Choi
Department of Materials Science and Engineering, Seoul National University
Solid-State Electronics

Eric Howard Christianson
Department of History, University of Kentucky
Medicine: Colonial Era

Michael P. Cohen
Professor Emeritus of English, Southern Utah University
Sierra Club

Nathaniel Comfort
Department of History of Medicine, Johns Hopkins University
Venter, J. Craig; Watson, James D.

Jan Gregoire Coombs
Independent Scholar
Health Maintenance Organizations

Carolyn C. Cooper
Independent Scholar
Whitney, Eli

David Cortes
Independent Scholar
Blalock, Alfred

Ruth Schwartz Cowan
Department of History & Sociology of Science,
University of Pennsylvania
Amniocentesis

Thomas R. Cox
Emeritus Professor of History, San Diego State
University
Forestry Technology and Lumbering

Michael J. Crawford
Early History Branch, Naval Historical Center
Wilkes Expedition

Christopher Crenner
Department of History and Philosophy of
Medicine, University of Kansas School of Medicine
American Association for the History of
Medicine

Alfred W. Crosby
Professor Emeritus of History, Geography, and
American Studies, University of Texas at Austin
Columbian Exchange

Nathan Crowe
Center for Biology and Society, Arizona State
University
Cloning

Neil Dahlstrom
Independent Scholar
Barbed Wire; Cotton Gin; Hybrid Seeds

Patricia D'Antonio
School of Nursing, University of Pennsylvania
Nursing

Regna Darnell
Department of Anthropology, University of
Western Ontario
Anthropology

Thomas S. Darragh
Department of History, Central Michigan University
Zoos

Sheri I. David
Department of History, Northern Virginia
Community College
Medicare and Medicaid

Frederick R. Davis
Department of History, Florida State University
Pesticides

Soraya de Chadarevian
Department of History, University of California,
Los Angeles
Molecular Biology

Dayle B. DeLancey
Department of Medical History and Bioethics,
University of Wisconsin-Madison
Williams, Daniel Hale

Michael Aaron Dennis
Security Studies Program, Georgetown
University
Atoms for Peace; Bush, Vannevar; Defense
Advanced Research Projects Agency;
Military, Science and Technology and the;
Office of Scientific Research and
Development; Science: Since 1945

Alan Derickson
Department of Labor Studies and Employment
Relations, Pennsylvania State University
Occupational Diseases

Kenneth Allen DeVille
Brody School of Medicine
Medical Malpractice

Ronald E. Doel
Department of History, Florida State University
Geophysics

Thomas Dublin
Department of History, Binghamton University,
State University of New York
Lowell Textile Mills

Erin D. Dumbacher
Fulbright Alumni
Silicon Valley

Colleen A. Dunlavy
Department of History, University of
Wisconsin-Madison
Technology

Ellen Dwyer
*Department of History, Indiana University
Bloomington*
  Epilepsy; Mental Health Institutions

H. Frederick Dylla
American Institute of Physics
  American Institute of Physics

Diane D. Edwards
Independent Scholar
  Optometry

J. Nicholas Entrikin
*Associate Provost for Internationalization,
University of Notre Dame*
  Park, Robert

Elizabeth W. Etheridge
*Professor Emerita of History, Longwood
University*
  Centers for Disease Control and Prevention

Gil Eyal
Department of Sociology, Columbia University
  Autism

Price V. Fishback
Department of Economics, University of Arizona
  Mining Technology

James Rodger Fleming
Science, Technology, and Society, Colby College
  Science: Revolutionary War to World
  War I

Daniel M. Fox
President Emeritus, Milbank Memorial Fund
  Dentistry

Stephen Fox
*Department of Chemistry, University of New
England*
  Muir, John

Libbie J. Freed
*Department of History, State University of
New York, Potsdam*
  Heating Technology

Joshua B. Freeman
*Urban Studies Program, Queens College, City
University of New York*
  Brooklyn Bridge

W. Bruce Fye
College of Medicine, Mayo Clinic
  Cardiology; Dalton, John Call, Jr.; DeBakey,
  Michael

Thomas P. Gariepy
*Department of Healthcare Administration,
Stonehill College*
  Surgery

Roger L. Geiger
*Department of Education Policy Studies,
Pennsylvania State University*
  Higher Education and Science; Morrill
  Land Grant Act

Tal Golan
*Department of History, University of California,
San Diego*
  Law and Science

Joanne Abel Goldman
*Department of History, University of Northern
Iowa*
  Sewage Treatment and System

Daniel Goldstein
Shields Library, University of California, Davis
  Journals in Science, Medicine, and
  Engineering; Owen, David Dale; Societies
  and Associations, Science

Gregory A. Good
*Center for History of Physics, American Institute
of Physics*
  Kármán, Theodore von; Rowland, Henry
  A.; Wigner, Eugene

Judith R. Goodstein
*Department of History, California Institute of
Technology*
  Millikan, Robert A.; Science: From 1914 to 1945

Hugh S. Gorman
*Department of Social Sciences, Michigan Tech
University*
  Petroleum and Petrochemicals

Melinda Gormley
*Reilly Center for Science, Technology & Values,
University of Notre Dame*
  Dobzhansky, Theodosius; Genetics and
  Genetic Engineering

Michael H. Gorn
Smithsonian Institution, National Air and Space Museum
  Space Program; Space Science

Patricia Peck Gossel±
History of Science Society
  Welch, William H.

William Graebner
Department of History, State University of New York, Fredonia
  Baby and Child Care

Jeremy A. Greene
Department of the History of Science, Harvard University
  Pharmacology and Drug Therapy

Paul R. Greenough
Department of History, University of Iowa
  World Health Organization

David Alan Grier
Elliott School of International Affairs, George Washington University
  Artificial Intelligence; Automation and Computerization; Computer Science; Computers, Mainframe, Mini, and Micro; ENIAC; Shockley, William; Silicon Valley; Terman, Frederick E.

Gerald N. Grob
Institute for Health, Health Care Policy & Aging Research, Rutgers University, State University of New Jersey
  Disease

Sara Stidstone Gronim
Department of History, C. W. Post Campus, Long Island University
  Colden, Cadwallader and Jane

Cai Guise-Richardson
Chemical Heritage Foundation
  Goodyear, Charles; Psychopharmaceutical Drugs

Carole Haber
Dean, School of Liberal Arts; Department of History, Tulane University
  Gerontology

Barton C. Hacker
Curator, National Museum of American History
  Nuclear Weapons

Joel B. Hagen
Department of Biology, Radford University
  Ecology; Odum, Eugene and Howard

Thomas Hager
Independent Scholar
  Pauling, Linus

Thomas Haigh
School of Information Studies, University of Wisconsin-Milwaukee
  Internet and World Wide Web; Software

Michael R. Haines
Department of Economics, Colgate University
  Life Expectancy

Michael R. Hall
Department of History, Armstrong Atlantic State University
  Columbian Exchange

Richard P. Hallion
Alfred Verville Fellow in Aeronautics, Smithsonian Institution
  Airplanes and Air Transport

Christopher Hamlin
Department of History, University of Notre Dame
  Cholera

Bert Hansen
Department of History, Baruch College of the City University of New York
  Rabies

Victoria A. Harden
Director Emeritus, Office of History, National Institutes of Health
  National Institutes of Health

Kristine C. Harper
Department of History, Florida State University
  Global Warming; Meteorology and Climatology

Brendan Hart
Department of Sociomedical Sciences, Columbia University
  Autism

Sidney Hart
Department of History, Smithsonian, National Portrait Gallery
Peale, Charles Willson

Stephen Haycox
Department of History, University of Alaska-Anchorage
Deepwater Horizon Explosion and Oil Spill; *Exxon Valdez* Oil Spill

Pamela M. Henson
Smithsonian Instiution, Institutional History Division
Baird, Spencer Fullerton

Gregg Herken
Professor Emeritus, University of California, Merced
Teller, Edward

David Herzberg
Department of History, SUNY University at Buffalo
Advertising, Medical

Lee R. Hiltzik
Assistant Director, The Rockefeller Archive Center
Rockefeller Institute, The

Laura Hirshbein
Department of Psychiatry, University of Michigan
Mental Illness; Psychiatry

David Hochfelder
Department of History, University at Albany, State University of New York
Bell, Alexander Graham; Telegraph

Sheldon Hochheiser
Archivist and Institutional Historian, IEEE History Center
Bell Laboratories

Lillian Hoddeson
Professor Emerita of History, University of Illinois at Urbana-Champaign
Bardeen, John; Manhattan Project

Sylvia D. Hoffert
Department of History, Texas A&M University
Childbirth

Ellen Jane Hollingsworth
Senior Scientist Emerita, Department of Sociology, University of Wisconsin-Madison
Nobel Prize in Biomedical Research

J. Rogers Hollingsworth
Departments of History and Sociology, University of Wisconsin-Madison
Nobel Prize in Biomedical Research

Reginald Horsman
Professor Emeritus of History, University of Wisconsin-Milwaukee
Beaumont, William

Fred Howard
Co-editor, The Papers of Wilbur and Orville Wright
Wright, Wilbur and Orville

Suellen Hoy
Independent Scholar
Hygiene, Personal

Margaret Humphreys
Department of History, Duke University
Malaria; Typhus; Yellow Fever

J. D. Hunley
Independent Scholar
Goddard, Robert H.; Missiles and Rockets

Bruce J. Hunt
Department of History, University of Texas, Austin
Michelson, Albert Abraham

J. Benjamin Hurlbut
School of Life Sciences, Arizona State University
Stem-Cell Research

John F. Hutchinson[±]
Department of History, Simon Fraser University
Red Cross, American

Paul Israel
Thomas A. Edison Papers, Rutgers University, State University of New Jersey, New Brunswick
Atlantic Cable; Edison, Thomas; Morse, Samuel F. B.

Donald C. Jackson
Department of History, Lafayette College
Dams and Hydraulic Engineering; Hydroelectric Power

Peter L. Jakab
Chief Curator, Smithsonian National Air and Space Museum
Lindbergh, Charles

Julie Des Jardins
Department of History, Baruch College
Sabin, Florence Rena

Reese V. Jenkins
Professor Emeritus, Department of History, Rutgers University, State University of New Jersey, New Brunswick
Photography

Jeffrey M. Jentzen
Department of Pathology, University of Michigan
Death and Dying; Forensic Pathology and Death Investigation

Carole Joffe
Advancing New Standards in Reproductive Health (ANSIRH) OB/GYN, University of California, San Francisco
Abortion Debates and Science

Ann Johnson
Department of History, University of South Carolina
Engineering

Johnson, Karen E.
Department of Physics, St. Lawrence University
Mayer, Maria Goeppert

Russell L. Johnson
Department of History & Art History, University of Otago
Deafness

David S. Jones
Department of Global Health and Social Medicine, Department of the History of Science, Harvard University
Indian Health Service

James H. Jones
Department of Anthropology, Stanford University
Kinsey, Alfred

Susan D. Jones
Department of Ecology, Evolution & Behavior and Program in the History of Science and Technology, University of Minnesota
Veterinary Medicine

David Kaiser
Program in Science, Technology, and Society, Massachusetts Institute of Technology
Feynman, Richard; Physics

George B. Kauffman
Department of Chemistry, California State University, Fresno
Langmuir, Irving; Remsen, Ira

Gwen Kay
Department of History, State University of New York, Oswego
Richards, Ellen Swallow

Carla C. Keirns
Departments of Preventive Medicine, Medicine, and History, Stony Brook University, State University of New York
Arthritis; Asthma and Allergy

Evelyn Fox Keller
Professor Emerita of History, Massachusetts Institute of Technology
McClintock, Barbara

Bettyann Holtzmann Kevles
Department of History, Yale University
Radiology

Daniel J. Kevles
Department of History, Yale University
Carson, Rachel

Richard B. Kielbowicz
Department of Communication, University of Washington, Seattle
Postal Service, U.S.

Vincent Kiernan
School of Continuing Studies, Georgetown University
Science Journalism

Barbara A. Kimmelman
Department of History, Philadelphia University
Agricultural Experiment Stations

Daniel Lee Kleinman
Department of Sociology, University of Wisconsin-Madison
National Academy of Sciences; National Science Foundation

Kim Kleinmann
Webster University
  Botanical Gardens

Ronald Kline
Department of Science and Technology Studies,
Cornell University
  Rural Electrification Administration;
  Steinmetz, Charles

Wendy Kline
Department of History, University of Cincinnati
  Eugenics; Sex and Sexuality

Elspeth Knewstubb
Department of History & Art History, University
of Otago
  Agassiz, Louis; Bartram, John and William;
  Beaumont, William; Blackwell, Elizabeth;
  Botany; Carson, Rachel; Compton, Arthur
  H.; Gibbs, Josiah Willard; Gray, Asa; Hall,
  G. Stanley; Halsted, William; Henry,
  Joseph; Kinsey, Alfred; McClintock,
  Barbara; McCormick, Cyrus Hall; Mead,
  Margaret; Menninger, Karl and William;
  Mitchell, Maria; Morgan, Lewis Henry;
  Morse, Samuel F. B.; Mumford, Lewis;
  Newcomb, Simon; Oppenheimer, J.
  Robert; Osler, William; Park, Robert;
  Parsons, Talcott; Pauling, Linus; Powell,
  John Wesley; Rabi, Isidor I.; Reed, Walter;
  Rockefeller Institute, The; Rush, Benjamin;
  Salk, Jonas; Sanger, Margaret; Silliman,
  Benjamin; Teller, Edward; Urey, Harold C.;
  Von Neumann, John; Welch, William H.;
  Westinghouse, George

Sally Gregory Kohlstedt
History of Science, Technology, & Medicine,
University of Minnesota
  American Association for the Advancement
  of Science; Smithsonian Institution

Jennifer Koslow
Department of History, Florida State University
  Public Health

Helge Kragh
Department of Science Studies, Aarhus
University, Denmark
  Quantum Theory

John Krige
School of History, Technology, and Society,
Georgia Institute of Technology
  Diplomacy (post-1945), Science and
  Technology and

Peter J. Kuznick
Department of History, American University
  Conant, James B.

M. S. Laas
Department of the History of Science, University
of Wisconsin-Madison
  Physiology

Marcel Chotkowski LaFollette
Research Associate, Smithsonian Institution
Archives
  Popularization of Science

Léo F. Laporte
Department of Earth and Planetary Sciences,
University of California, Santa Cruz
  Simpson, George Gaylord

Edward J. Larson
Department of History, Pepperdine University
  Scopes Trial

Thomas C. Lassman
Division of Space History, National Air and
Space Museum, Smithsonian Institution
  Condon, Edward

Roger D. Launius
Associate Director, National Air and Space
Museum
  National Aeronautics and Space
  Administration; Satellites, Communications

Susan C. Lawrence
Department of History, The Ohio State
University
  Anatomy and Human Dissection

Susan E. Lederer
Department of Medical History & Bioethics,
School of Medicine and Public Health, University
of Wisconsin-Madison
  Animal and Human Experimentation;
  Ethics and Medicine; Obesity; Organ
  Transplantation; Reed, Walter

Thomas M. Leonard
Professor Emeritus of History, University of North Florida
    Panama Canal

Thomas Leslie
Pickard Chilton Professor, Department of Architecture, Iowa State University
    Building Technology

Harvey Levenstein
Professor Emeritus of History, McMaster University
    Food and Diet

James G. Lewis
Forest History Society
    Forest Service, U.S.

Susan Lindee
History & Sociology of Science, University of Pennsylvania
    Human Genome Project

Edward Linenthal
Department of History, Indiana University Bloomington
    Strategic Defense Initiative

Tulley Long
History of Medicine, University of Minnesota
    Cannon, Walter Bradford; Cori, Gerty and Carl; Pincus, Gregory Goodwin

Spencie Love
Independent Scholar
    Drew, Charles Richard

Henry E. Lowood
History of Science and Technology Collections, Stanford University
    Animation Technology and Computer Graphics

Paul Lucier
History, Philosophy, and the Social Sciences, Rhode Island School of Design
    Dana, James Dwight; Geology

Robert MacDougall
Department of History, University of Western Ontario
    Telephone

Daniele Macuglia
Morris Fishbein Center for the History of Science and Medicine, University of Chicago
    Margulis, Lynn; Menard, Henry William

John Majewski
Department of History, University of California, Santa Barbara
    Roads and Turnpikes, Early

Robert J. Malone
Executive Director, History of Science Society, University of Notre Dame
    History of Science Society

Theresa M. Maresca
Department of Family Medicine, University of Washington School of Medicine
    Native American Healers

Harry M. Marks ±
Institute of the History of Medicine, Johns Hopkins University
    Medicine: From 1776 to the 1870s;
    Medicine: From the 1870s to 1945;
    Medicine: Since 1945

Michael F. Marmor
Department of Ophthalmology, Stanford University
    Ophthalmology

Cora Bagley Marrett
National Science Foundation
    Three Mile Island Accident

Jessica Martucci
Department of History, Mississippi State University
    Childbirth

Seymour Mauskopf
Professor Emeritus, Focus Interdisciplinary Programs, Duke University
    Parapsychology

Bernadette McCauley
Department of History, Hunter College, City University of New York
    Hospitals

Michael McGeary
Institute of Medicine of the National Academies
    Public Health Service, U.S.

Daniel J. McKaughan
Department of Philosophy, Boston College
    Delbrück, Max

Shelley McKellar
*Hannah Chair in the History of Medicine,
Department of History, Department of Surgery,
Schulich School of Medicine and Dentistry,
University of Western Ontario*
    Medicine and Technology

Matthew McKenzie
Department of History, University of Connecticut
    Fisheries and Fishing

Clay McShane
*Professor Emeritus of History, Department of
History, Northeastern University*
    Motor Vehicles

Jeffrey L. Meikle
*Department of American Studies, University of
Texas at Austin*
    Plastics

Curt Meine
Senior Fellow, The Aldo Leopold Foundation
    Leopold, Aldo

David Meshoulam
*Department of Curriculum and Instruction,
University of Wisconsin-Madison*
    High Schools, Science Education in

Donald L. Miller
Department of History, Lafayette College
    Mumford, Lewis

Carol L. Moberg
*Ralph Steinman Laboratory, The Rockefeller
University*
    Dubos, René Jules

Cyrus C. M. Mody
Department of History, Rice University
    Nanotechnology

Arwen P. Mohun
Department of History, University of Delaware
    Gender and Technology

Jeffrey P. Moran
Department of History, University of Kansas
    Sex Education

Gregory J. Morgan
*College of Arts and Letters, Stevens Institute of
Technology*
    Stanley, Wendell Meredith

Edward T. Morman
Community College of Baltimore County
    Blindness, Assistive Technologies and;
    Diphtheria; Keller, Helen; Typhoid Fever

David L. Morton Jr.
*School of Industrial Design, College of
Architecture, Georgia Tech*
    Sound Technology, Recorded

Albert E. Moyer [±]
*Department of History, Virginia Polytechnic
Institute and State University*
    Newcomb, Simon

Mateo Muñoz
History of Science, Harvard University
    Pearl, Raymond; Wilson, Edmund Beecher

Daniel Nelson
Professor Emeritus of History, University of Akron
    Scientific Management

G. Blair Nelson
Core Humanities, Benedictine University
    Race Theories, Scientific

Julie R. Newell
*Social and International Studies Department,
Southern Polytechnic State University*
    Silliman, Benjamin

Lisa Nocks
*Federated Department of History, New Jersey
Institute of Technology*
    Robots

Sherwin B. Nuland [±]
Yale University School of Medicine
    Halsted, William

Ronald L. Numbers
*Department of Medical History and Bioethics,
University of Wisconsin-Madison*
    Creationism; Evolution, Theory of;
    Graham, Sylvester; Gray, Asa; Guyot,
    Arnold Henry; Health Insurance; Jefferson,
    Thomas; Medical Education; Medicine:

Overview; Pseudoscience and Quakery; Religion and Science; Science: Overview; Sexually Transmitted Diseases

David E. Nye
Center for American Studies, University of Southern Denmark
Electricity and Electrification; Illumination

Marilyn Bailey Ogilvie
History of Science Department, University of Oklahoma
Stevens, Nettie Maria

Alan L. Olmstead
Department of Economics, University of California, Davis
Agricultural Technology

Todd M. Olszewski
Health Policy and Management Program, Providence College
Biochemistry

Gerald M. Oppenheimer
School of Public Health, City University of New York and Department of Sociomedical Sciences, Mailman School of Public Health, Columbia University
HIV/AIDS

Marc Oxoby
Core Humanities Program, University of Nevada, Reno
Science Fiction

Michelle Lee Park
Independent Scholar
National Park System

Karen Hunger Parshall
Departments of History and Mathematics, University of Virginia
Mathematics and Statistics

Philip J. Pauly±
Department of History, Rutgers University, State University of New Jersey, New Brunswick
Biological Sciences

James Lal Penick Jr.
Professor Emeritus, University of Alabama at Birmingham
Conservation Movement

Myrna Perez Sheldon
Department of the History of Science, Harvard University
Wilson, Edward O.

Tom F. Peters
Professor Emeritus of Architecture and History, Lehigh University
Skyscrapers

Gabriella M. Petrick
Department of History and Art History, Department of Nutrition and Food Studies, George Mason University
Food Processing

Sarah K. A. Pfatteicher
Civil and Environmental Engineering, University of Wisconsin-Madison
Challenger Disaster; Ethics and Professionalism in Engineering

Robert C. Post
The Smithsonian Institution
Society for the History of Technology; Technological Enthusiasm; Urban Mass Transit

Heather Munro Prescott
Department of History, Central Connecticut State University
Anorexia Nervosa; Tuberculosis

Patricia Princehouse
Institute for the Science of Origins, Case Western Reserve University
Gould, Stephen Jay

Carroll Pursell
Department of History, Australian National University
Steam Power

Karen A. Rader
Department of History, Virginia Commonwealth University
Andrews, Roy Chapman; Biological Sciences; Museums of Science and Natural History

James Ravin
Department of Surgery, Division of Ophthalmology, University of Toledo
Ophthalmology

Jonathan Rees
Department of History, Colorado State University, Pueblo
  Iron and Steel Production and Products; Refrigeration and Air Conditioning

Martin Reuss
Senior Historian, Civil Works, U.S. Army Corps of Engineers (Retired)
  Rivers as Technological Systems

Susan M. Reverby
Department of Women's and Gender Studies, Wellesley College
  Tuskegee Syphilis Study

Paul W. Rhode
Department of Economics, Population Studies Center, University of Michigan
  Agricultural Technology

John S. Rigden
American Institute of Physics
  Gell-Mann, Murray; Rabi, Isidor I.

Robert W. Righter
Department of History, Southern Methodist University
  Wind Power

Daniel M. Robert
Department of History, University of California, Berkeley
  Tesla, Nikola

Jon H. Roberts
Department of History, Boston University
  Psychotherapy

Mark Robinson
Department of Anthropology, Princeton University
  Just, Ernest Everett

Naomi Rogers
Program in the History of Science and Medicine, Yale University
  Medicine: Alternative Medicine; Poliomyelitis

Marc Rothenberg
Historian, National Science Foundation
  Bartram, John and William; Bowditch, Nathaniel; Henry, Joseph

William G. Rothstein
Department of Sociology and Anthropology, University of Maryland Baltimore County
  Flexner Report

Eric Rouge
Center for International Science and Technology Policy, George Washington University
  ENIAC; Shockley, William; Terman, Frederick E.

John Rudolph
Department of Curriculum and Instruction, University of Wisconsin-Madison
  High Schools, Science Education in

Nancy A. Sahli
Independent Scholar
  Blackwell, Elizabeth

Todd L. Savitt
Department of Bioethics and Interdisciplinary Studies, Brody School of Medicine, East Carolina University
  National Medical Association; Sickle-Cell Disease

Richard C. Sawyer
Independent Scholar
  Agriculture, U.S. Department of

Londa Schiebinger
Department of History, Stanford University
  Gender and Science

Rennie B. Schoepflin
Department of History, California State University, Los Angeles
  Health and Fitness

Zachary M. Schrag
Department of History and Art History, George Mason University
  Subways

Susan Schulten
Department of History, University of Denver
  Cartography; Geography

Silvan S. Schweber
Department of Physics, Professor Emeritus, Brandeis University
  Bethe, Hans

Roy V. Scott
Professor Emeritus of History,
Mississippi State University
    Agricultural Education and Extension

Bruce E. Seely
Department of History, Michigan Technological
University
    Highway System

Robert W. Seidel
Program in History of Science, Technology, and
Medicine, University of Minnesota
    Fermi, Enrico; Lawrence, Ernest O.;
    National Laboratories

Christopher Sellers
Department of History, Stony Brook University,
State University of New York
    Environmental Protection Agency

Todd A. Shallat
Center for Idaho History & Politics, Boise State
University
    Army Corps of Engineers, U.S.; Canals and
    Waterways

Leslie N. Sharp
Associate Vice Provost, Georgia Institute of
Technology
    Elevator; Ladd-Franklin, Christine

Ronald E. Shaw±
Professor Emeritus of History, Miami University
    Erie Canal

Martin J. Sherwin
Department of History, George Mason University
    Oppenheimer, J. Robert

Ana Simões
Centro Interuniversitário de História das Ciências
e Tecnologia, Universidade de Lisboa, Faculdade
de Ciências
    Mulliken, Robert S.

Bryant Simon
Department of History, Temple University
    Tennessee Valley Authority

Nancy G. Slack
Department of Biology, The Sage Colleges
    Hutchinson, G. Evelyn

Hugh Richard Slotten
Department of Media, Film, and Communication,
University of Otago
    American Philosophical Society; Atlantic
    Cable; Berkner, Lloyd; Bowditch, Nathaniel;
    Conant, James, B.; Eastman, George; Erie
    Canal; Gibbs, Josiah Willard; Gray, Asa; Hale,
    George Ellery; Human Genome Project;
    Lewis and Clark Expedition; Maury,
    Matthew Fontaine; McCormick, Cyrus Hall;
    Menninger, Karl and William; Mitchell,
    Maria; Morgan, Lewis Henry; Morse, Samuel
    F. B.; Mumford, Lewis; National Academy of
    Sciences; National Institutes of Health;
    Newcomb, Simon; Nuclear Power; Osler,
    William; Pauling, Linus; Rittenhouse, David;
    Skyscrapers; Television; Urey, Harold C.; Van
    Allen, James A.; Von Neumann, John; Welch,
    William H.; Westinghouse, George

Dale Smith
Department of Medical History, Uniformed
Services University of the Health Sciences
    Group Practice; War and Medicine

Daniel Scott Smith±
Department of History, University of Illinois at Chicago
    Demography

Jane S. Smith
Department of History, Northwestern University
    Salk, Jonas

John Kenly Smith Jr.
Department of History, Lehigh University
    Carothers, Wallace Hume; Du Pont, Pierre S.;
    Nylon; Photocopying

Joshua M. Smith
U.S. Department of Transportation, Maritime
Administration, U.S. Merchant Marine Academy
    Maritime Transport; Shipbuilding

Mark C. Smith
Department of American Studies, University of
Texas at Austin
    Social Sciences: Before 1945

Robert W. Smith
Department of History and Classics, University of
Alberta
    Hubble, Edwin Powell; Hubble Space Telescope

Michael M. Sokal
Worcester Polytechnic Institute, Emeritus
  Cattell, James McKeen; Psychological and Intelligence Testing

Mark Solovey
Institute for the History and Philosophy of Science and Technology, University of Toronto
  Social Science Research Council; Social Sciences: Post–World War II

Darwin H. Stapleton
Department of History, University of Massachusetts Boston
  Latrobe, Benjamin

John M. Staudenmaier, S. J.
University of Detroit, Mercy
  Ford, Henry

David M. Steffes
Global Institute of Sustainability, Arizona State University
  Wright, Sewall

John Stenhouse
Department of History, University of Otago
  Missionaries and Science and Medicine

Carlene E. Stephens
National Museum of American History, Smithsonian Institution
  Clocks and Clockmaking

Christopher H. Sterling
Emeritus Professor of Media and Public Affairs, George Washington University
  Armstrong, Edwin Howard; De Forest, Lee; Electronic Communication Devices, Mobile; Farnsworth, Philo Taylor; Zworykin, Vladimir Kosma

Rodney L. Stiling
History Department, Seattle Pacific University
  Hitchcock, Edward

Anthony N. Stranges
Department of History, Texas A&M University
  Chemistry

Sharon Hartman Strom
Department of History, University of Rhode Island
  Office Technology

Roger H. Stuewer
Professor Emeritus of Physics, University of Minnesota
  Compton, Arthur H.

Robert B. Sullivan
Independent Scholar
  Rush, Benjamin

William C. Summers
History of Science & Medicine, Yale University
  Lederberg, Joshua

John Suval
Department of History, University of Wisconsin-Madison
  King, Clarence Rivers

Andrew Szanton
Independent Scholar
  Wigner, Eugene

John Tauranac
Independent Scholar
  Empire State Building

R. E. Taylor
Professor Emeritus of Anthropology, University of California, Riverside
  Urey, Harold C.

Karen Kruse Thomas
Johns Hopkins Bloomberg School of Public Health
  Race and Medicine

Ross Thomson
Department of Economics, University of Vermont
  Machinery and Manufacturing

Phillip S. Thurtle
Comparative History of Ideas, University of Washington
  Jordan, David Starr

Nancy Tomes
Department of History, Stony Brook University, State University of New York
  Germ Theory of Disease

David A. Tomlin
Independent Scholar
  Gibbs, Josiah Willard

Jenna Tonn
Department of the History of Science, Harvard University
Zoology

Elizabeth Toon
Department of Life Sciences, University of Manchester
American Medical Association

Sarah W. Tracy
Honors College, University of Oklahoma
Alcohol and Alcohol Abuse

Thomas Trautmann
Department of History, University of Michigan
Morgan, Lewis Henry

James W. Trent Jr.
Department of Sociology & Social Work, Gordon College
Disabilities, Intellectual and Developmental

Arleen Marcia Tuchman
Department of History, Vanderbilt University
Diabetes; Zakrzewska, Marie

Steven W. Usselman
School of History, Technology, & Society, Georgia Institute of Technology
Railroads; Research and Development (R&D)

Marga Vicedo
Institute for the History and Philosophy of Science and Technology, University of Toronto
Davenport, Charles Benedict; Morgan, Thomas Hunt

Priscilla Wald
Department of English, Duke University
Literature and Science

J. Samuel Walker
Independent Scholar
Atomic Energy Commission; Nuclear Power; Nuclear Regulatory Commission

Karen Walloch
Medical History & Bioethics, University of Wisconsin-Madison
Smallpox

Maila L. Walter
Independent Scholar
Bridgman, Percy

Kevin A. Walters
Department of History, University of Wisconsin-Madison
Foundations and Health

Zuoyue Wang
California State University, Pomona
Killian, James Rhyne, Jr.; Lee, Tsung-Dao; Office of Science and Technology Policy; President's Science Advisory Committee; Wu, Chien-Shiung; Yang, Chen Ning

Deborah J. Warner
Curator, Division of Medicine and Science, National Museum of American History, Smithsonian Institution
Instruments of Science

John Harley Warner
Program in the History of Science and Medicine, Yale University
Medicine: From 1776 to the 1870s

Leonard Warren
The Wistar Institute, University of Pennsylvania
Leidy, Joseph; Rafinesque, Constantine Samuel; Say, Thomas

Nadine Weidman
Department of History of Science, Harvard University; Department of Psychology, Boston College
Sociobiology and Evolutionary Psychology

Stephen J. Weininger
Department of Chemistry, Worcester Polytechnic Institute
Noyes, Arthur Amos

George Weisz
Department of Social Studies of Medicine, McGill University
Medical Specialization

Tracy A. Weitz
Advancing New Standards in Reproductive Health (ANSIRH) OB/GYN, University of California, San Francisco
Abortion Debates and Science

Christopher W. Wells
Department of Environmental Studies,
Macalester College
Household Technology; Internal
Combustion Engine; Motor Vehicles

Marilyn Wessel
Museum of the Rockies
4-H Club Movement

Thomas Wessel
Professor Emeritus of History, Montana State
University
4-H Club Movement

Mark I. West
Department of English, University of North
Carolina at Charlotte
Menninger, Karl and William

Catherine Westfall
Lyman Briggs College, Michigan State University
Alvarez, Luis Walter; Compton,
Karl Taylor

Vernon J. Williams Jr.
Department of African American & African
Diaspora Studies
Boas, Franz

Benjamin Wilson
Doctoral Program in History, Anthropology,
and Science, Technology, and Society

(HASTS), Massachusetts Institute of
Technology
Physics; Seaborg, Glenn T.

Mary Pickard Winsor
Institute for the History & Philosophy of Science
& Technology, University of Toronto
Agassiz, Louis

Donald Worster
Department of History, University of Kansas
Dust Bowl

Virginia Yans
Department of History, Rutgers University,
State University of New Jersey, New
Brunswick
Mead, Margaret

Doogab Yi
Korea Institute for Advanced Studies
DNA Sequencing

Christian C. Young
Department of Biology, Alverno College
Environmentalism

John J. Zernel
Independent Scholar
Powell, John Wesley

James L. Baughman
School of Journalism and Mass Communication
Television

± (*deceased*)

INDEX

ethics and medicine (*continued*)
  Percival, Thomas, and, **1**:332
  Potter, Van Rensselaer, and, **1**:338
  pre-AMA's Code of Ethics, **1**:332–334
ethics and professionalism in engineering, **1**:343–352
  age of autonomy, **1**:345
  commonalities across specialties, **1**:346
  corporate engineering, **1**:346–347
  education for a new era, **1**:351
  engineer, defined/described, **1**:343–344
  engineers and society, **1**:348–349
  first ethics codes, **1**:347–348
  new leadership, **1**:345–346
  point of no return, **1**:348
  professional differences, **1**:350
  public safety, **1**:351–352
  recent activities, **1**:352
  The Revolt of the Engineers (Layton), **1**:344
  subordination, **1**:349–350
  technological criticism, **1**:350–351
eugenics, **1**:354–355. *See also* race theories, scientific
  biological sciences and, **1**:129–130
  biotechnology and, **1**:135–136
  birth control and, **1**:129–130, 141, 355, 440
  Buck v. Bell (1927), decision, **1**:141–142
  Davenport, Charles Benedict, and, **1**:129–130, 228–113
  Deaf community and, **1**:230
  Dobzhansky, Theodosious, and, **1**:279
  early 20th century advocacy for, **1**:581
  epilepsy and, **1**:141
  "feeble-mindedness" and, **1**:268
  Galton's naming of, **1**:354
  genetics and, **1**:440, 443
  Gilman, Charles Perkins, and, **1**:354–355
  Human Genome Project and, **1**:558
  Jordan, David Starr, and, **1**:598
  Oxford Handbook of the History of Eugenics, **1**:354
  race, medicine, and, **2**:325–326
  Sanger, Margaret, and, **1**:142, 354–355
  temperance movement and, **1**:38
Eugenics (Davenport), **1**:228–229
Eugenics Committee of the American Breeders Association, **1**:598
Eugenics Record Office (ERO), **1**:129–130, 228, 440, 441–442
European Atomic Energy Community (Euratom), **1**:258–259
European Center for Nuclear Research (CERN), **2**:148–149
European Recovery Program, **1**:261–262
European Space Agency (ESA), **1**:557, 574–575, **2**:495, 500
European Union
  appliance efficiency ratings, **1**:296–297
  ban on GMOs, **1**:560–561
  support for women in science, **1**:428
Evangelical Christianity, **2**:364
Evans, Dale, **1**:64

Evans, Griffith, **2**:429
Evans, Herbert, **1**:129
Evans, John, **1**:341
Evans, Martin, **2**:508–509
Evans, Oliver, **1**:307, 414–415, **2**:2–3, 128–129, 506, 519–520, 522
Evans, Warren Felt, **1**:481
Everson, George, **1**:359
evolution, "shifting balance theory" (Wright), **2**:598
evolution, theory of, **1**:356–357. *See also* Darwin, Charles; Jordan, David Starr; *The Origin of Species* (Darwin)
Evolution and the Bible (Brown), **1**:221
Evolution journal, **2**:33
Evolution of Physics (Einstein and Infeld), **1**:292
evolutionary biology, **2**:478
Evolutionary Ecology (Pianka), **1**:288–289
Ewen, Harold I., **1**:93
Ewing, W. Maurice, **1**:458, **2**:194–195
exobiology, **1**:627
Expedia, **1**:589
Experimental Embryology (Morgan), **2**:126
experimental psychology, **1**:184–185
Experiments and Observations on Electricity (Franklin), **1**:293, 413–414, **2**:424, 425
Experiments and Observations on the Gastric Juice and the Physiology of Digestion (Beaumont), **1**:115, **2**:256–257, 569–570
An Explication of the First Causes of Action in Matter; and the Cause of Gravitation (Colden), **2**:246
Exploratorium (San Francisco), **2**:138, 278
Explorer I satellite (U.S.), **1**:93, **2**:492–493
Explorer's Club (NY), **1**:57
Exploring Expedition. *See* Wilkes Expedition
Ex-Prodigy: My Childhood and Youth (Wiener), **2**:591
Extra-Sensory Perception after Sixty Years: A Critical Appraisal of the Research in Extra-Sensory Perception (Rhine), **2**:219, 220
Extravehicular Activity (EVA), **2**:493–494
Exxon Valdez oil spill, **1**:358, **2**:23. *See also* Deepwater Horizon explosion and oil spill
Eyal, Gil, *as contributor*, **1**:105
Eysenck, Hans, **2**:306

Faber, Sandra M., **1**:92
Facebook, **1**:589
Fackler, John, **1**:192
Factors in the Sex Life of Twenty-two Hundred Women (Davis), **2**:444–445
Faifchild Semiconductor, **2**:488
"fair balance" standard (of the FDA), **1**:13
Fair Science (Cole), **1**:420
Fairchild, David, **1**:30
Fairchild Semiconductor, **2**:432, 488
Fairchild Tropical botanical garden, **1**:149
Fairfield, George, **2**:11
falciparum malaria, **2**:16–17, 324
Falk, I. S., **2**:56

Infantile Autism (Rimland), **1**:103
infantile paralysis. *See* poliomyelitis
Infeld, Leopold, **1**:292
infliximab, **1**:80–81
influenza, **1:569–572**
    colonial era, **2**:58
    epidemics/pandemics, **1**:462, 546–547, 569–570,
        2:63, 190, 577
    eradication efforts, limits, **1**:276, 403
    germ theory of disease and, **1**:461
    global surveillance, **1**:570–572
    H1N1/H2N2 virus strains, **1**:571
    Honk Kong flu, **1**:571
    Langmuir, Alexander, and, **1**:185
    obesity epidemic comparison, **2**:187
    Old World origins, **1**:206
    penicillin and, **2**:232
    religion and, **2**:361
    Stanley, Wendell, and, **1**:129
    treatment discoveries, **2**:58
    vaccine development, **1**:570–572
    veterinary medicine and, **2**:563
    World Influenza Center, **1**:571
Informal Coordinating Committee on Oceanography,
        2:196
Information International, Inc. (III), computer graphics
        company, **1**:64
Infrared Astronomical Satellite, **1**:575
infrared astronomy, **1**:93
Ingelfinger, Franz, **2**:437
in-patient hospital facilities, **1**:547
*Inquiry into the Effects of Ardent Spirits upon the Human
        Body and Mind* (Rush), **1**:37
insecticides, **1**:20, 180, 320, **2**:18–19, 233, 375, 606
inshore fishing, **1**:370
instant messaging, **1**:589
Institute for Advanced Study (Princeton University),
        1:211, 292, 498, 578–579, 628, **2**:28–29, 90,
        208, 429, 430, 564–565, 603
Institute for Cancer Research, **1**:202
Institute for Creation Research (ICR), **1**:223
The Institute for Genome Research (TIGR), **2**:558–559
Institute for Nuclear Studies (University of Chicago),
        2:31–32
Institute for Radio Engineers (IRE), **1**:209
Institute for Sex Research (Indiana University),
        1:609–610
Institute for the History of Medicine (Johns Hopkins
        University), **1**:46
Institute of Electrical and Electronic Engineers (IEEE),
        1:210, 344
Institute of Mathematical Statistics (IMS), **2**:28
Institute of Medicine (IOM), **2**:144, 475–476
Institute of Society, Ethics, and the Life Sciences,
        1:338–339
Institute on Religion in an Age of Science, **2**:364
instruments of science, **1:572–579**

astronomy, **1**:574–575
atomic clocks, **1**:579
biology, **1**:578
chemistry, **1**:577
computers, **1**:578–579
geodesy, **1**:573
geophysics, **1**:573–574
industry, **1**:577
meteorology, **1**:574
microscopes, and other instruments, **1**:577
particle accelerators, detectors, **1**:579
pedagogy, **1**:579
physics, **1**:575–577
psychology, physiology, anatomy, **1**:578
surveying, **1**:572–573
insulin, **1**:246, **2**:75, 83, 228. *See also* diabetes
insulin-dependent diabetes mellitus (IDDM), **1**:247.
        See also diabetes
integrated circuit. *See* solid-state electronics
intelligence, concepts of, **1:579–581**. *See also*
        psychological and intelligence testing
    Binet, Alfred, and, **1**:580–581
    eugenics and, **1**:355
    evolution and, **1**:128, 580
    feeble-mindedness, **1**:268
    gender and, **1**:418
    Hall, Stanley G., and, **1**:479
    heredity and, **1**:129–130, 228–229
    "Innate Intelligence" concept, **2**:71, 291
    IQ testing, WW II era origins, **2**:98–99
    military interests in, **2**:105, 220–221
    race and, **1**:581, **2**:291, 334, 336
    Simon, Théodore, and, **1**:580–581
Intelligence Quotient (IQ), **1**:580–581, **2**:98–99,
        296–297, 336
intelligent design, **1**:223
INTELSAT (International Telecommunications Satellite
        Consortium), **2**:421
intensive-care unit development, **1**:548–549
Interagency Committee on Oceanography, **2**:196
internal combustion engine, **1**:311, 394, **582–583**,
        614–615, **2**:129, 561–562
International Association of Gerontology, **1**:463
International Astronomical Union, **1**:478
International Bureau of Public Hygiene, **2**:597
International Business Machines, Inc. (IBM), **1**:210,
        2:204, 455
    '62 CFO software package, **2**:482
    701 mainframe computer, **1**:211–212
    development of CAD, **1**:63–64
    FORTRAN programming language, **1**:209, **2**:481, 482
    microcomputers, **1**:213
    System/360 mainframe computer, **1**:212
    "unbundling" of software, **2**:483
International Childbirth Education Association, **1**:196
International Conference on the Peaceful Uses of Atomic
        Energy (1955), **2**:323–324

Nelson, Daniel, *as contributor*, **2**:438
Nelson, G. Blair, *as contributor*, **2**:337
neo-Darwinism, **2**:21
neo-Freudian movement, **2**:304
neomycin, **2**:67
neoprene synthetic rubber, **1**:179
"Neptunist" theory (of Werner), **1**:450
Nernst, Walther, **1**:612, **2**:164
Netflix, **1**:589
Netherlands
    biotechnology industry, **1**:136
    electrifciation of, **1**:565
    electrification history, **1**:565
    genetics research, **1**:439
    Nobel Prize winners, **2**:157
    veterinary schools, **2**:560
Netscape, **1**:589
Neuhaus, Ann Kristin, **1**:7–8
Neuromancer (Gibson), **2**:435
Neurospora crassa (bread mold) study, **1**:129, 627, **2**:123, 429, 430
New Age movement, **1**:483
New American Practical Navigator (Bowditch), **1**:153
The New American Practical Navigator (Bowditch), **1**:87–88
The New Astronomy (Langley), **1**:89
New England Congregationalists, **2**:116–117
New England Female Medical College (Boston), **2**:42
New England Hospital for Women and Children, **2**:609
New England Journal of Medicine, **1**:599, **2**:437
    abortion study publication, **1**:4
    Beecher's exposé of ethical violations, **1**:340
    HIV/AIDs editorial, **1**:528–529, 532–533
New England Kitchen, **2**:387
New Guide to Health (Thomson), **2**:60
New Horizons spacecraft, **1**:94
New London Eye Infirmary, **2**:205
New Museum Ida, **2**:137
New Nutrition. *See* food and diet
New Orleans, steamboat, **1**:414–415, **2**:506
New Panama Canal treaties, **2**:219
New Perspectives in Archaeology (Binford), **1**:76
"new" psychology, rise of, **2**:295–296
New Theory of the Earth (Whiston), **2**:357
New Thought movement, **1**:481, **2**:304
New York Athletic Games, **1**:121
New York Babies' Hospital, **2**:226–227
New York Botanical Garden, **1**:149
New York College of Veterinary Surgeons, **2**:560–561
New York Homeopathic Medical School, **2**:368
New York Infirmary for Women and Children (NYC), **1**:144, 595
New York Institute of Technology, **1**:64–65
New York Medical College, **2**:226
New York Museum of Science and Industry, **2**:137
New York Society for the Suppression of Vice, **2**:288–289

New York State Study of Malignant Diseases, **1**:218
New York Sun, hoax story, **2**:436
New York Times, Science Times section, **2**:436–437
New York University Medical School, **2**:123–124, 419
New York Women's Hospital (NYC), **1**:540
New Zealand
    environmental research, **1**:325
    lighting blackouts, **1**:567
    missionaries and health, **2**:120
Newcomb, Simon, **1**:88–89, **2**:26, 28, **155**
Newcomen, Thomas, **1**:414–415
Newcomen engines, **2**:2–3, 506
Newell, Julie R., *as contributor*, **2**:456
Newell, Norman, **2**:217
Newton, Isaac, **1**:29, 413, **2**:356–357, 423–424
    fluxional calculus, **2**:25
    Principia Mathematica, **1**:86, **2**:246, 424
    theories of light and color, **1**:490
    theories of physics, **1**:489–490
Neyman, Jerzy, **2**:28–29
Nichols, Herbert, **2**:299–300
Nichols, Mary Gove, **1**:481
Nicholson, Mignon, **2**:561
Nicholson, Seth Barnes, **1**:575
Nida, Eugene, **2**:120–121
Nier, Alfred, **1**:576
A Night at the Museum presentation (AMNH), **1**:50
night satellite photography, **1**:296
Nightingale, Florence, **1**:541–542, 543, **2**:187–188
Nimbus-1 to -7 spacecraft, **2**:498–499
Nine Mile Point Nuclear Station, **2**:408
Nirenberg, Marshall W., **1**:136–137, 278, 442–443, **2**:123–124, 158–159
Nissenbaum, Stephen, **1**:471
nitroglycerin, **1**:173
nitrous oxide ("laughing gas"), **1**:58, 242
Nixon, Richard, **1**:264
    dissolution of the PSAC, **1**:607
    EPA establishment, **1**:328
    funding for family planning, **1**:142
    Merchant Marine Act, **2**:23–24
    National Cancer Act, **2**:124
    National Research Act, **1**:62, 340
    support for HMOs, **2**:68
    war on cancer by, **1**:167, **2**:433
No Child Left Behind Act (2001), **1**:519
Nobel Prize in Biomedical Research, **2:156–171**
    biomedical sciences research environment, **2**:157–160
    characteristics of research, **2**:160
        California Institute of Technology, **2**:163–166
        institutional environments, **2**:160–161
        Johns Hopkins Medical School, **2**:166–167
        research organizations, **2**:161–162
        Rockefeller Institute/University, **2**:162–163
        University of Chicago, **2**:167
    Gilbert, Walter, **1**:137
    laboratory environments, **2**:170–171

public health role, **2:**311
smallpox eradication efforts, **2:**461
tuberculosis emergency declaration, **2:**545
U.S. diabetes data, **1:**248
World Influenza Center, **1:**571
World Influenza Center, **1:**571
The World Is Flat (Friedman), **1:**519–520
The World is Yours (Smithsonian Institution), **2:**273
World Medical Association, **1:**337
World Peace Foundation, **1:**598
World Robotics journal, **2:**408
World Trade Center, **1:**344
World Trade Organization, **2:**239
World Wide Fund for Nature, **1:**325
World Wide Web. *See* Internet and World Wide Web
World Wildlife Fund, **1:**325
Worster, Donald, *as contributor,* **1:**283
Worthington, Henry, **2:**6
Wozniak, Stephen. *See* computers, mainframe, mini, and
    micro; software
Wright, Benjamin, **1:**309, 331
Wright, Gavin, **1:**403–404
Wright, Sewall, **2:598–599**
Wright, Wilbur and Orville, **1:**30–31, 35, **2:**11, 427,
    599–600
Wu, Chien-Shiung, **1:**628, **2:600–601,** 603–604
Wundt, Wilhelm, **2:**296, 299
Würdemann, William, **1:**573
Wynne-Edwards, V. C., **2:**478

X-15 hypersonic aircraft, **2:**493
Xavier, Marie François, **1:**45
xerography. *See* photocopying
Xerox Corporation, **2:**240
Xerox Parc Laboratories, **1:**213
XI International AIDS Conference (Canada), **1:**532
XM radio, **2:**339
X-ray crystallography, **1:**124, **2:**21–22, 161, 587
X-ray imaging. *See* radiology
X-ray photography, **2:**243
X-ray radiation studies, **2:**133
X-ray scattering, **1:**207, **2:**318
X-ray technology, **1:**546, 547, 615, **2:**74–75, 340

Yaghi, Omar, **1:**192
Yale Center of Alcohol Studies, **1:**39
Yale Scientific School, **1:**493
Yalow, Rosalyn, **2:**157, 170
Yamanaka, Shinya, **2:**509
Yang, Chen Ning, **1:**628, **2:**600, **603–604**
Yang-Mills gauge field theory, **2:**603
Yans, Virginia, *as contributor,* **2:**36
Yekl (Cahan), **1:**644
yellow fever, **2:604–606**
    African American immunity to, **2:**324
    animal experimentation on, **1:**61
    Chapin, Charles, V., and, **2:**63

deaths caused by, **1:**197–198, 271, 272, 632, **2:**308
1878 epidemic, **2:**605–606
Gorgas, Crawford, and, **2:**17
hospitals and, **1:**538
identifying/eliminating causes, **2:**606
Koch, Robert, and, **1:**461
Marine Hospital Service and, **2:**313
medical geography of, **1:**445
minority susceptibility, **2:**307
mosquito eradication program, **2:**218
NIH and, **2:**146
Old World origins, **1:**206
in port cities, **1:**271–272
preventive measures, **2:**61
Reed, Walter, and, **2:**353–354, 606
religion and, **2:**361
Rush, Benjamin, and, **2:**415
1793 epidemic, **1:**538
in southern U.S., **1:**127–128, 273
Yellowstone National Park, **1:**322–323, **2:**151
Yerkes, Charles, **1:**496
Yerkes, Robert, **1:**578, **2:**98–99, 294
Yerkes Observatory (Wisconsin), **1:**88, 556, 627–628
Yersin, Alexandre, **1:**251
Yi, Doogab, *as contributor,* **1:**279
Yogic diets, **1:**483
Yorktown, Battle of, **1:**78
Yosemite Grant (1864), **2:**151
Yosemite National Park, **1:**226–227, 322–323, **2:**133,
    454. *See also* Hetch Hetchy Valley controversy
Youmans, Edward Livingston, **2:**270
Young, Charles A., **1:**89–90
Young, Christian C., *as contributor,* **1:**327
Young Men's Christian Association (YMCA), **1:**482
Your Health radio series (AMA), **2:**273–274
YouTube, **1:**589
Yu Xie, **1:**421
Yurok Brush Dance, **2:**154

Zacharias, Jerrold, **1:**513, 579
Zajac, Edward E., **1:**64
Zakrzewska, Marie, **2:609**
Zeidler, Othmar, **2:**233
Zeiger, Herbert J., **2:**542
zenith sectors, **2:**388
Zentmayer, Joseph, **1:**577
Zernel, John J., *as contributor,* **2:**285
Zewail, Ahmed, **1:**191, **2:**165–166
Zimmer, Karl, **1:**239
Zoo Parade tv series, **2:**277
zooarchaeology, **1:**76
zoology, **2:610–612**
    Agassiz, Louis, and, **1:**14, 127, 506, **2:**426, 457, 610–611
    American Society of Zoologists, **1:**603–604, **2:**427
    AMNH Central Asiatic exhibitions, **1:**57
    Audubon, James, and, **1:**101–102, **2:**610
    Bickmore, Albert Smith, and, **1:**49–50

zoology (*continued*)
  Buffon, Georges-Louis Leclerc, and, **2:**610
  Bussey Institution and, **1:**128
  Cannon, Walter Bradford, and, **1:**171
  Catesby, Mark, and, **2:**610
  Cope, Edward Drinker, and, **1:**217
  Copeia journal, **1:**217–218
  Dana/Exploring Expedition, **1:**227
  Davenport, Charles Benedict, and, **1:**228–229
  Dobzhansky, Theodosius, and, **1:**279
  exploration, **2:**610
  forensic sciences and, **1:**615
  gender and science in, **1:**426
  high school science education and, **1:**504–505, 510, 514
  higher education and, **1:**491
  Hutchinson, G. Evelyn, studies of, **1:**558–559
  Huxley, Thomas Henry, and, **1:**508
  institutions, **2:**610–611
  Jefferson, Thomas, and, **2:**610
  Just, Ernest Everett, and, **1:**603–604
  Marsh, Othniel Charles, and, **2:**24
  Martin, Henry Newell, and, **2:**258, 611
  Morgan, Thomas Hunt, and, **2:**126
  Museum of Comparative Zoology, **1:**14, 50, **2:**33, 457, 610–611
  National Zoological Park, **1:**111–112, **2:**462
  Pearl, Raymond, and, **2:**225
  protozoology, **1:**629
  religion and, **1:**505, **2:**360–361
  Ritter, William E., and, **2:**271–272
  Simpson, George Gaylord, and, **2:**457
  transformation and legacy, **2:**611–612
  Wright, Sewall, and, **2:**598–599
  zooarchaeology, **1:**76
zoonotic (animal-transmitted) diseases, **1:**270–271
zoos, **2:612–615**
  American zoos, **2:**613–614
  Association of Zoos and Aquariums, **2:**612–613
  conservation and education, **2:**614
  European origins, **1:**95, **2:**613
  Galaxy Zoo (Britain), **1:**95
  Lincoln Park Zoo (Chicago), **2:**269
  Perkins, Marlin, and, **2:**277
  veterinary medicine, and, **2:**562
Zuckerberg, Mark. *See* computers, mainframe, mini, and micro; Internet and World Wide Web; software
Zuckerman, Michael, **1:**109–110
Zulu grammar and ethnography, **2:**116–117
Zunz, Olivier, **1:**399
Zweig, George, **1:**418
Zwicky, Fritz, **1:**92
Zworykin, Vladimir Kosma, **1:**359, 577, **2:**533–534, **615–616**